STUDENT'S SOLUTIONS MANUAL

BOB DAHL
Minnesota State University, Mankato

RANDY KRIEGER
Concordia University

TERRY A. KRIEGER
Winona State University

to accompany

BEGINNING AND INTERMEDIATE ALGEBRA WITH APPLICATIONS & VISUALIZATION

Gary K. Rockswold
Minnesota State University, Mankato

Terry A. Krieger
Winona State University

PEARSON
Addison Wesley

D1400006

Boston San Francisco New York
London Toronto Sydney Tokyo Singapore Madrid
Mexico City Munich Paris Cape Town Hong Kong Montreal

Reproduced by Pearson Addison-Wesley from electronic files supplied by the author.

Copyright © 2005 Pearson Education, Inc.
Publishing as Pearson Addison-Wesley, 75 Arlington Street, Boston, MA 02116

All rights reserved. No part of this publication may be reproduced, stored in a retrieval system, or transmitted, in any form or by any means, electronic, mechanical, photocopying, recording, or otherwise, without the prior written permission of the publisher. Printed in the United States of America.

ISBN 0-321-20601-0

5 6 BRG 08 07 06

PEARSON
Addison
Wesley

Table of Contents

Preface

This solutions manual is written as an aid for students studying the text *Beginning and Intermediate Algebra with Applications and Visualization* by Rockswold and Krieger. It contains answers and solutions to the odd-numbered exercises from each section as well as all solutions to the Checking Basic Concepts, Chapter Review and Chapter Test, Cumulative Review, and Extended and Discovery exercises.

This manual is consistent with the text and gives solutions that are accessible to beginning and intermediate algebra students. The solutions are written in a clear format with hundreds of graphs and tables to help with the learning process. Solutions frequently include not only symbolic solutions but also graphical and numerical solutions to help students understand the problem completely. It is recommended that you make a genuine attempt to solve a problem before looking in this solutions manual for help. Regular class attendance is also recommended. Following these suggestions will promote insight and understanding of beginning and intermediate algebra.

It is the author's hope that you will find this manual helpful when studying the text *Beginning and Intermediate Algebra with Applications and Visualization*. Please email any comments or questions to tkrieger@mcleodusa.net. Your opinion is important. Best wishes for an enjoyable and successful beginning and intermediate algebra course.

Terry A. Krieger

Chapter 1: Introduction to Algebra

1.1: Numbers, Variables and Expressions

Concepts

1. counting
3. 1
5. prime
7. factors
9. variable

Prime Numbers and Composite Numbers

11. The number 4 is a composite number because it has factors other than itself and 1; $4 = 2 \times 2$
13. The number 1 is neither a prime or a composite number.
15. The number 29 is a prime number because it's only factors are itself and 1.
17. The number 92 is a composite number because it has factors other than itself and 1; $92 = 2 \times 2 \times 23$
19. The number 225 is a composite number because it has factors other than itself and 1; $225 = 3 \times 3 \times 5 \times 5$
21. The number 149 is a prime number because it's only factors are itself and 1.
23. $6 = 2 \times 3$
25. $12 = 2 \times 2 \times 3$
27. $32 = 2 \times 2 \times 2 \times 2 \times 2$
29. $294 = 2 \times 3 \times 7 \times 7$
31. $300 = 2 \times 2 \times 3 \times 5 \times 5$
33. Yes, the population of a country could be described by the whole numbers because we cannot have a fraction of a person.
35. No, a student's grade point average could not be described by the whole numbers because a grade point average usually contains a decimal point.
37. Yes, the number of bytes stored on a computer's hard drive could be described by the whole numbers because computer bytes do not contain a fraction or a decimal point.
39. Yes, the number of students in a class could be described by the whole numbers because we cannot have a fraction of a person.

Algebraic Expressions, Formulas and Equations

41. The value of the expression $2x$, when $x = 5$, is $2x = 2(5) = 10$.
43. The value of the expression $8 - x$, when $x = 1$, is $8 - x = 8 - 1 = 7$.
45. The value of the expression $\frac{x}{8}$, when $x = 32$, is $\frac{x}{8} = \frac{32}{8} = 4$.

47. The value of the expression $3(x + 1)$, when $x = 5$, is $3(x + 1) = 3(5 + 1) = (3)(6) = 18$.

49. The value of the expression $\frac{x}{2} + 1$, when $x = 6$, is $\frac{x}{2} + 1 = \frac{6}{2} + 1 = 3 + 1 = 4$.

51. When $x = 5$ and $y = 4$, $x + y = 5 + 4 = 9$.

53. When $x = 8$ and $y = 4$, $4 \cdot \frac{x}{y} = 4 \cdot \frac{8}{4} = 4 \cdot 2 = 8$.

55. When $x = 5$ and $y = 7$, $y(x - 3) = 7(5 - 3) = (7)(2) = 14$.

57. When $x = 0$, $y = x + 1 = 0 + 1 = 1$.

59. When $x = 7$, $y = 4x = 4 \cdot 7 = 28$.

61. When $z = 12$, $F = z - 5 = 12 - 5 = 7$.

63. When $z = 6$, $F = \frac{30}{z} = \frac{30}{6} = 5$.

65. When $x = 3$ and $z = 15$, $y = x + z = 3 + 15 = 18$.

67. When $x = 9$ and $z = 3$, $y = \frac{x}{z} = \frac{9}{3} = 3$.

Translating Words to Symbols

69. If s is the cost of a soda, then three times this cost is $3s$.

71. If x is the number, $x + 5$ is five more than the number.

73. If n is the number, $3n$ is triple the number.

75. If p is the population of a town, $p - 200$ is two hundred less than the population.

77. If z is the number, $\frac{z}{6}$ is the number divided by 6.

79. If x is one number and y is another number, $\frac{x + 7}{y}$ is a number plus 7, all divided by another number.

Applications

81. See Figure 81. $F = 3y$ because there are three feet in one yard.

Yards (y)	1	2	3	4	5	6	7
Feet (F)	3	6	9	12	15	18	21

Figure 81

83. $P = 100D$ because there are one hundred pennies in one dollar.

85. $M = 50H$; M is miles and H is hours. If $H = 3$, then $M = 50H = 50(3) = 150$ mi.

87. $B = 70x$. If $x = 60$, then $B = 70x = 70(60) = 4200$ beats.

89. Each CD costs \$12. Thus, $C = 12x$ where C is cost and x is number of CD's.

91. Since the area of a rectangle equals its length times its width, 22 ft. × 9 ft. = 198 square feet.

1.2: Fractions

Concepts

1. The person ate $\frac{3}{4}$ of the pie. $\frac{1}{4}$ of the pie remains.

3. The variable b cannot equal 0.

5. numerators

7. $\frac{a}{b} \cdot \frac{c}{d} = \frac{ac}{bd}$

9. The fractional part of half of a half is $\frac{1}{4}$.

11. $\frac{a}{b} \div \frac{c}{d} = \frac{a}{b} \cdot \frac{d}{c} = \frac{ad}{bc}$.

13. $\frac{a}{b} - \frac{c}{b} = \frac{a-c}{b}$.

15. The greatest common factor of 4 and 6 is 2 because 2 is the largest number that divides into both 4 and 6.

Lowest Terms

17. The largest number that divides into 4 and 12 is 4, so the GCF is 4.

19. The largest number that divides into 50 and 75 is 25, so the GCF is 25.

21. The largest number that divides into 100, 60 and 70 is 10, so the GCF is 10.

23. $\frac{3 \cdot 4}{5 \cdot 4} = \frac{3}{5} \cdot \frac{4}{4} = \frac{3}{5} \cdot 1 = \frac{3}{5}$

25. $\frac{3 \cdot 8}{8 \cdot 5} = \frac{3 \cdot 8}{5 \cdot 8} = \frac{3}{5} \cdot \frac{8}{8} = \frac{3}{5} \cdot 1 = \frac{3}{5}$

27. $\frac{4}{8} = \frac{1 \cdot 4}{2 \cdot 4} = \frac{1}{2} \cdot \frac{4}{4} = \frac{1}{2} \cdot 1 = \frac{1}{2}$

29. $\frac{5}{15} = \frac{1 \cdot 5}{3 \cdot 5} = \frac{1}{3} \cdot \frac{5}{5} = \frac{1}{3} \cdot 1 = \frac{1}{3}$

31. $\frac{10}{25} = \frac{2 \cdot 5}{5 \cdot 5} = \frac{2}{5} \cdot \frac{5}{5} = \frac{2}{5} \cdot 1 = \frac{2}{5}$

33. $\frac{12}{36} = \frac{1 \cdot 12}{3 \cdot 12} = \frac{1}{3} \cdot \frac{12}{12} = \frac{1}{3} \cdot 1 = \frac{1}{3}$

35. $\frac{12}{30} = \frac{2 \cdot 6}{5 \cdot 6} = \frac{2}{5} \cdot \frac{6}{6} = \frac{2}{5} \cdot 1 = \frac{2}{5}$

37. $\frac{19}{76} = \frac{1 \cdot 19}{4 \cdot 19} = \frac{1}{4} \cdot \frac{19}{19} = \frac{1}{4} \cdot 1 = \frac{1}{4}$

Multiplication and Division of Fractions

39. $\frac{1}{2} \cdot \frac{1}{3} = \frac{1 \cdot 1}{2 \cdot 3} = \frac{1}{6}$

41. $\frac{3}{4} \cdot \frac{1}{5} = \frac{3 \cdot 1}{4 \cdot 5} = \frac{3}{20}$

43. $\frac{5}{3} \cdot \frac{3}{5} = \frac{5 \cdot 3}{3 \cdot 5} = \frac{15}{15} = 1$

45. $\frac{5}{6} \cdot \frac{18}{25} = \frac{5 \cdot 18}{6 \cdot 25} = \frac{90}{150} = \frac{3 \cdot 30}{5 \cdot 30} = \frac{3}{5} \cdot \frac{30}{30} = \frac{3}{5} \cdot 1 = \frac{3}{5}$

47. $\frac{4}{1} \cdot \frac{3}{5} = \frac{4 \cdot 3}{1 \cdot 5} = \frac{12}{5}$

49. $\frac{2}{1} \cdot \frac{3}{8} = \frac{2 \cdot 3}{1 \cdot 8} = \frac{6}{8} = \frac{3 \cdot 2}{4 \cdot 2} = \frac{3}{4} \cdot \frac{2}{2} = \frac{3}{4} \cdot 1 = \frac{3}{4}$

51. $\frac{x}{y} \cdot \frac{y}{x} = \frac{xy}{yx} = \frac{xy}{xy} = \frac{x}{x} \cdot \frac{y}{y} = \frac{x}{x} \cdot 1 = \frac{x}{x} = 1$

53. $\frac{a}{b} \cdot \frac{3}{2} = \frac{a \cdot 3}{b \cdot 2} = \frac{3a}{2b}$

55. $\frac{1}{4} \cdot \frac{3}{4} = \frac{1 \cdot 3}{4 \cdot 4} = \frac{3}{16}$

57. $\frac{2}{3} \cdot \frac{6}{1} = \frac{2 \cdot 6}{3 \cdot 1} = \frac{12}{3} = \frac{4 \cdot 3}{1 \cdot 3} = \frac{4}{1} \cdot \frac{3}{3} = \frac{4}{1} \cdot 1 = 4$

59. $\frac{1}{2} \cdot \frac{2}{3} = \frac{1 \cdot 2}{2 \cdot 3} = \frac{2}{6} = \frac{1 \cdot 2}{3 \cdot 2} = \frac{1}{3} \cdot \frac{2}{2} = \frac{1}{3} \cdot 1 = \frac{1}{3}$

61. (a) $\frac{1}{5}$

(b) $\frac{1}{7}$

(c) $\frac{7}{4}$

(d) $\frac{8}{9}$

63. (a) $\frac{2}{1}$

(b) $\frac{9}{1}$

(c) $\frac{101}{12}$

(d) $\frac{17}{31}$

65. $\frac{1}{2} \div \frac{1}{3} = \frac{1}{2} \cdot \frac{3}{1} = \frac{1 \cdot 3}{2 \cdot 1} = \frac{3}{2}$

67. $\frac{3}{4} \div \frac{1}{2} = \frac{3}{4} \cdot \frac{2}{1} = \frac{3 \cdot 2}{4 \cdot 1} = \frac{6}{4} = \frac{3 \cdot 2}{2 \cdot 2} = \frac{3}{2} \cdot \frac{2}{2} = \frac{3}{2} \cdot 1 = \frac{3}{2}$

69. $\frac{4}{3} \div \frac{1}{6} = \frac{4}{3} \cdot \frac{6}{1} = \frac{4 \cdot 6}{3 \cdot 1} = \frac{24}{3} = \frac{8 \cdot 3}{1 \cdot 3} = \frac{8}{1} \cdot \frac{3}{3} = \frac{8}{1} \cdot 1 = 8$

71. $\frac{32}{27} \div \frac{8}{9} = \frac{32}{27} \cdot \frac{9}{8} = \frac{32 \cdot 9}{27 \cdot 8} = \frac{288}{216} = \frac{4 \cdot 72}{3 \cdot 72} = \frac{4}{3} \cdot \frac{72}{72} = \frac{4}{3} \cdot 1 = \frac{4}{3}$

73. $\frac{9}{1} \div \frac{8}{7} = \frac{9}{1} \cdot \frac{7}{8} = \frac{9 \cdot 7}{1 \cdot 8} = \frac{63}{8}$

75. $\frac{10}{1} \div \frac{5}{6} = \frac{10}{1} \cdot \frac{6}{5} = \frac{10 \cdot 6}{1 \cdot 5} = \frac{60}{5} = \frac{12 \cdot 5}{1 \cdot 5} = \frac{12}{1} \cdot \frac{5}{5} = \frac{12}{1} \cdot 1 = 12$

77. $\frac{9}{10} \div \frac{3}{1} = \frac{9}{10} \cdot \frac{1}{3} = \frac{9 \cdot 1}{10 \cdot 3} = \frac{9}{30} = \frac{3 \cdot 3}{10 \cdot 3} = \frac{3}{10} \cdot \frac{3}{3} = \frac{3}{10} \cdot 1 = \frac{3}{10}$

79. $\frac{a}{b} \div \frac{2}{b} = \frac{a}{b} \cdot \frac{b}{2} = \frac{ab}{2b} = \frac{a}{2} \cdot \frac{b}{b} = \frac{a}{2} \cdot 1 = \frac{a}{2}$

81. $\frac{x}{y} \div \frac{x}{y} = \frac{x}{y} \cdot \frac{y}{x} = \frac{xy}{xy} = 1$

Addition and Subtraction of Fractions

83. (a) $\frac{2}{3} + \frac{1}{3} = \frac{2+1}{3} = \frac{3}{3} = 1$

(b) $\frac{2}{3} - \frac{1}{3} = \frac{2-1}{3} = \frac{1}{3}$

85. (a) $\frac{3}{2} + \frac{1}{2} = \frac{3+1}{2} = \frac{4}{2} = 2$

(b) $\frac{3}{2} - \frac{1}{2} = \frac{3-1}{2} = \frac{2}{2} = 1$

87. (a) $\frac{5}{33} + \frac{2}{33} = \frac{5+2}{33} = \frac{7}{33}$

(b) $\frac{5}{33} - \frac{2}{33} = \frac{5-2}{33} = \frac{3}{33} = \frac{1 \cdot 3}{11 \cdot 3} = \frac{1}{11} \cdot \frac{3}{3} = \frac{1}{11} \cdot 1 = \frac{1}{11}$

89. Prime factorizations are 5 and $10 = 5 \times 2$. The LCD is $5 \times 2 = 10$.

91. Prime factorizations are $9 = 3 \times 3$ and $15 = 3 \times 5$. The LCD is $3 \times 3 \times 5 = 45$.

93. Prime factorizations are 5 and $15 = 5 \times 3$. The LCD is $5 \times 3 = 15$.

95. Prime factorizations are $6 = 2 \times 3$ and $8 = 2 \times 2 \times 2$. The LCD is $2 \times 2 \times 2 \times 3 = 24$.

97. Prime factorizations are 2, 3 and $4 = 2 \times 2$. The LCD is $2 \times 2 \times 3 = 12$.

99. Prime factorizations are $4 = 2 \times 2$, $8 = 2 \times 2 \times 2$ and $12 = 2 \times 2 \times 3$. The LCD is $2 \times 2 \times 2 \times 3 = 24$.

101. $\frac{1}{2} + \frac{1}{3} = \frac{1}{2} \cdot \frac{3}{3} + \frac{1}{3} \cdot \frac{2}{2} = \frac{1 \cdot 3}{2 \cdot 3} + \frac{1 \cdot 2}{3 \cdot 2} = \frac{3}{6} + \frac{2}{6} = \frac{3+2}{6} = \frac{5}{6}$

103. $\frac{5}{8} + \frac{3}{16} = \frac{5}{8} \cdot \frac{2}{2} + \frac{3}{16} = \frac{5 \cdot 2}{8 \cdot 2} + \frac{3}{16} = \frac{10}{16} + \frac{3}{16} = \frac{10+3}{16} = \frac{13}{16}$

105. $\frac{1}{2} - \frac{1}{4} = \frac{1}{2} \cdot \frac{2}{2} - \frac{1}{4} = \frac{1 \cdot 2}{2 \cdot 2} - \frac{1}{4} = \frac{2}{4} - \frac{1}{4} = \frac{2-1}{4} = \frac{1}{4}$

107. $\frac{25}{24} - \frac{7}{8} = \frac{25}{24} - \frac{7}{8} \cdot \frac{3}{3} = \frac{25}{24} - \frac{7 \cdot 3}{8 \cdot 3} = \frac{25}{24} - \frac{21}{24} = \frac{4}{24} = \frac{1 \cdot 4}{6 \cdot 4} = \frac{1}{6} \cdot \frac{4}{4} = \frac{1}{6} \cdot 1 = \frac{1}{6}$

109. $\frac{11}{14} + \frac{2}{35} = \frac{11}{14} \cdot \frac{5}{5} + \frac{2}{35} \cdot \frac{2}{2} = \frac{11 \cdot 5}{14 \cdot 5} + \frac{2 \cdot 2}{35 \cdot 2} = \frac{55}{70} + \frac{4}{70} = \frac{55+4}{70} = \frac{59}{70}$

111. $\frac{5}{12} - \frac{1}{18} = \frac{5}{12} \cdot \frac{3}{3} - \frac{1}{18} \cdot \frac{2}{2} = \frac{5 \cdot 3}{12 \cdot 3} - \frac{1 \cdot 2}{18 \cdot 2} = \frac{15}{36} - \frac{2}{36} = \frac{15-2}{36} = \frac{13}{36}$

113. $\frac{3}{100} + \frac{1}{300} - \frac{1}{200} = \frac{3}{100} \cdot \frac{6}{6} + \frac{1}{300} \cdot \frac{2}{2} - \frac{1}{200} \cdot \frac{3}{3} = \frac{3 \cdot 6}{100 \cdot 6} + \frac{1 \cdot 2}{300 \cdot 2} - \frac{1 \cdot 3}{200 \cdot 3} =$

$\frac{18}{600} + \frac{2}{600} - \frac{3}{600} = \frac{18+2-3}{600} = \frac{17}{600}$

115. $\frac{7}{8} - \frac{1}{6} + \frac{5}{12} = \frac{7}{8} \cdot \frac{3}{3} - \frac{1}{6} \cdot \frac{4}{4} + \frac{5}{12} \cdot \frac{2}{2} = \frac{7 \cdot 3}{8 \cdot 3} - \frac{1 \cdot 4}{6 \cdot 4} + \frac{5 \cdot 2}{12 \cdot 2} =$

$\frac{21}{24} - \frac{4}{24} + \frac{10}{24} = \frac{21 - 4 + 10}{24} = \frac{27}{24} = \frac{9 \cdot 3}{8 \cdot 3} = \frac{9}{8} \cdot \frac{3}{3} = \frac{9}{8} \cdot 1 = \frac{9}{8}$

Applications

117. Find the sum of the motor vehicle deaths and the firearms deaths as a fraction of all accidental deaths.

$\frac{31}{42} + \frac{31}{1260} = \frac{31}{42} \cdot \frac{30}{30} + \frac{31}{1260}$. It follows that $\frac{31 \cdot 30}{42 \cdot 30} + \frac{31}{1260} = \frac{930}{1260} + \frac{31}{1260} = \frac{930 + 31}{1260} = \frac{961}{1260}$.

119. Find the value of one-half of $64\frac{5}{8}$. First convert $64\frac{5}{8}$ to $\frac{517}{8}$. $\frac{517}{8} \div 2 = \frac{517}{8} \cdot \frac{1}{2} = \frac{517}{16} = 32\frac{5}{16}$ in.

121. Increase the amount of flour used because there are more people. The ratio of people is $\frac{12}{8}$.

Convert $3\frac{1}{2}$ to $\frac{7}{2}$ and multiply by $\frac{12}{8}$. $\frac{7}{2} \cdot \frac{12}{8} = \frac{7 \cdot 12}{2 \cdot 8} = \frac{84}{16} = \frac{21 \cdot 4}{4 \cdot 4} = \frac{21}{4} \cdot \frac{4}{4} = \frac{21}{4} \cdot 1 = \frac{21}{4} = 5\frac{1}{4}$ cups.

123. Convert the base of the triangle from $1\frac{2}{3}$ to $\frac{5}{3}$.

$\frac{1}{2} \cdot \frac{5}{3} \cdot \frac{3}{4} = \frac{1 \cdot 5 \cdot 3}{2 \cdot 3 \cdot 4} = \frac{15}{24} = \frac{5 \cdot 3}{8 \cdot 3} = \frac{5}{8} \cdot \frac{3}{3} = \frac{5}{8} \cdot 1 = \frac{5}{8}$ square yards.

125. Add the distance from Smalltown to Middletown and Middletown to Bigtown.

$3\frac{1}{2} + 4\frac{3}{4} = \frac{7}{2} + \frac{19}{4} = \frac{7}{2} \cdot \frac{2}{2} + \frac{19}{4} = \frac{7 \cdot 2}{2 \cdot 2} + \frac{19}{4} = \frac{14}{4} + \frac{19}{4} = \frac{14 + 19}{4} = \frac{33}{4} = 8\frac{1}{4}$ miles.

127. Multiply the fraction of the adult population by the fraction of the people aged 18 to 24 who smoked in 1995 to find the fraction of the entire adult population who were aged 18 to 24 and who smoked in 1995.

$\frac{1}{4} \cdot \frac{7}{25} = \frac{1 \cdot 7}{4 \cdot 25} = \frac{7}{100}$.

Checking Basic Concepts for Sections 1.1 & 1.2

1. (a) prime

(b) composite; $28 = 2 \times 2 \times 7$

(c) neither

(d) composite; $180 = 2 \times 2 \times 3 \times 3 \times 5$

2. $\frac{10}{3 + 2} = \frac{10}{5} = 2$

3. $y = 6 \cdot 5 = 30$

4. $x + 5$

5. $\frac{17}{2} \cdot \frac{15}{1} = \frac{17 \cdot 15}{2 \cdot 1} = \frac{255}{2} = 127\frac{1}{2}$ square feet.

6. (a) $\frac{25}{35} = \frac{5 \cdot 5}{7 \cdot 5} = \frac{5}{7} \cdot \frac{5}{5} = \frac{5}{7} \cdot 1 = \frac{5}{7}$

(b) $\frac{26}{39} = \frac{2 \cdot 13}{3 \cdot 13} = \frac{2}{3} \cdot \frac{13}{13} = \frac{2}{3} \cdot 1 = \frac{2}{3}$

7. $\frac{3}{4}$

8. (a) $\frac{2}{3}\cdot\frac{3}{4}=\frac{2\cdot 3}{3\cdot 4}=\frac{6}{12}=\frac{1\cdot 6}{2\cdot 6}=\frac{1}{2}\cdot\frac{6}{6}=\frac{1}{2}\cdot 1=\frac{1}{2}$

   (b) $\frac{5}{6}\div\frac{10}{3}=\frac{5}{6}\cdot\frac{3}{10}=\frac{5\cdot 3}{6\cdot 10}=\frac{15}{60}=\frac{1\cdot 15}{4\cdot 15}=\frac{1}{4}\cdot\frac{15}{15}=\frac{1}{4}\cdot 1=\frac{1}{4}$

   (c) $\frac{3}{10}+\frac{1}{10}=\frac{3+1}{10}=\frac{4}{10}=\frac{2\cdot 2}{5\cdot 2}=\frac{2}{5}\cdot\frac{2}{2}=\frac{2}{5}\cdot 1=\frac{2}{5}$

   (d) $\frac{3}{4}-\frac{1}{6}=\frac{3}{4}\cdot\frac{3}{3}-\frac{1}{6}\cdot\frac{2}{2}=\frac{3\cdot 3}{4\cdot 3}-\frac{1\cdot 2}{6\cdot 2}=\frac{9}{12}-\frac{2}{12}=\frac{9-2}{12}=\frac{7}{12}$

9. Multiply $1\frac{2}{3}$ by 2. $\frac{5}{3}\cdot\frac{2}{1}=\frac{5\cdot 2}{3\cdot 1}=\frac{10}{3}=3\frac{1}{3}$ cups.

1.3: Exponents and Order of Operations

Concepts

1. add

3. a^6

5. 6^2

7. 17, multiplication; addition

9. 4; left; right

11. No; $2^3 = 8$, but $3^2 = 9$

Natural Number Exponents

13. 2^5

15. 3^4

17. $\left(\frac{1}{2}\right)^4$

19. a^5

21. (a) $2^4 = 2\cdot 2\cdot 2\cdot 2 = 16$

    (b) $4^2 = 4\cdot 4 = 16$

23. (a) $6^1 = 6$

    (b) $1^6 = 1$

25. (a) $2^5 = 2\cdot 2\cdot 2\cdot 2\cdot 2 = 32$

    (b) $10^3 = 10\cdot 10\cdot 10 = 1000$

27. (a) $\left(\frac{2}{3}\right)^2=\frac{2}{3}\cdot\frac{2}{3}=\frac{2\cdot 2}{3\cdot 3}=\frac{4}{9}$

    (b) $\left(\frac{1}{2}\right)^5=\frac{1}{2}\cdot\frac{1}{2}\cdot\frac{1}{2}\cdot\frac{1}{2}\cdot\frac{1}{2}=\frac{1\cdot 1\cdot 1\cdot 1\cdot 1}{2\cdot 2\cdot 2\cdot 2\cdot 2}=\frac{1}{32}$

29. (a) $\left(\frac{2}{5}\right)^3 = \frac{2}{5} \cdot \frac{2}{5} \cdot \frac{2}{5} = \frac{2 \cdot 2 \cdot 2}{5 \cdot 5 \cdot 5} = \frac{8}{125}$

(b) $\left(\frac{9}{7}\right)^2 = \frac{9}{7} \cdot \frac{9}{7} = \frac{9 \cdot 9}{7 \cdot 7} = \frac{81}{49}$

31. $8 = 2 \cdot 2 \cdot 2 = 2^3$

33. $25 = 5 \cdot 5 = 5^2$

35. $49 = 7 \cdot 7 = 7^2$

37. $1000 = 10 \cdot 10 \cdot 10 = 10^3$

39. $\frac{1}{16} = \frac{1}{2} \cdot \frac{1}{2} \cdot \frac{1}{2} \cdot \frac{1}{2} = \left(\frac{1}{2}\right)^4$

Order of Operations

41. Perform multiplication before addition: $5 + 4 \cdot 6 = 5 + 24 = 29$

43. Perform division before addition: $6 \div 3 + 2 = 2 + 2 = 4$

45. Perform division before subtraction: $100 - \frac{50}{5} = 100 - 10 = 90$

47. $10 - 6 - 1 = 3$

49. $20 \div 5 \div 2 = 4 \div 2 = 2$

51. $3 + 2^4 = 3 + 2 \cdot 2 \cdot 2 \cdot 2 = 3 + 16 = 19$

53. $4 \cdot 2^3 = 4 \cdot 2 \cdot 2 \cdot 2 = 4 \cdot 8 = 32$

55. $(3 + 2)^3 = 5^3 = 5 \cdot 5 \cdot 5 = 125$

57. $\frac{4 + 8}{1 + 3} = \frac{12}{4} = \frac{3 \cdot 4}{1 \cdot 4} = \frac{3}{1} \cdot \frac{4}{4} = \frac{3}{1} \cdot 1 = 3$

59. $\frac{2^3}{4 - 2} = \frac{2 \cdot 2 \cdot 2}{2} = \frac{8}{2} = 4$

61. $10^2 - (30 - 2 \cdot 5) = 10^2 - (30 - 10) = 10^2 - 20 = 10 \cdot 10 - 20 = 100 - 20 = 80$

63. $\left(\frac{1}{2}\right)^4 + \frac{5 + 4}{3} = \frac{1}{2} \cdot \frac{1}{2} \cdot \frac{1}{2} \cdot \frac{1}{2} + \frac{9}{3} = \frac{1}{16} + 3 = \frac{1}{16} + \frac{3}{1} \cdot \frac{16}{16} = \frac{1}{16} + \frac{48}{16} = \frac{1 + 48}{16} = \frac{49}{16}$

Translating Words to Symbols

65. $2^3 - 8 = 2 \cdot 2 \cdot 2 - 8 = 8 - 8 = 0$

67. $30 - 4 \cdot 3 = 30 - 12 = 18$

69. $\frac{4^2}{2^3} = \frac{4 \cdot 4}{2 \cdot 2 \cdot 2} = \frac{16}{8} = \frac{2 \cdot 8}{1 \cdot 8} = \frac{2}{1} \cdot \frac{8}{8} = \frac{2}{1} \cdot 1 = 2$

71. $\frac{40}{10} + 2 = \frac{4 \cdot 10}{1 \cdot 10} + 2 = \frac{4}{1} \cdot \frac{10}{10} + 2 = \frac{4}{1} \cdot 1 + 2 = 4 + 2 = 6$

73. $100(2 + 3) = 100 \cdot 5 = 500$

Applications

75. 1.44 MB $= 1.44 \cdot 2^{20}$ bytes $\approx$ 1,509,949 bytes

77. (a) $K = 10$

(b) Because $2^{10} = 1024$, $\dfrac{1024 \text{ weeks}}{52 \text{ weeks}} \approx 20$ years

1.4: Real Numbers and the Number Line

Concepts

1. $-b$

3. b

5. rational

7. irrational

9. $\sqrt{2}$ is one example; *Answers may vary.*

11. approximately equal

13. 0

15. origin

17. $>$

19. $=$

Signed Numbers

21. (a) The opposite of 9 is -9.

(b) The opposite of -9 is $-(-9) = 9$.

23. (a) The opposite of $\frac{2}{3}$ is $-\frac{2}{3}$.

(b) The opposite of $-\frac{2}{3}$ is $-\left(-\frac{2}{3}\right) = \frac{2}{3}$.

25. (a) $-(-8) = 8$, so the opposite of 8 is -8.

(b) $-(-(-8)) = -8$, so the opposite of -8 is $-(-8) = 8$.

27. (a) The opposite of a is $-a$.

(b) The opposite of $-a$ is $-(-a) = a$.

29. The additive inverse of t is $-t$. $-t = 6$

31. The additive inverse of $-b$ is $-(-b) = b$. $b = \frac{1}{2}$

Numbers and the Number Line

33. $\frac{1}{4} = 0.25$

35. $\frac{7}{8} = 0.875$

37. $\frac{3}{2} = 1.5$

39. $\frac{1}{20} = 0.05$

41. $\frac{2}{3} = 0.\overline{6}$

43. $\frac{7}{9} = 0.\overline{7}$

45. 8 is a natural, whole and rational number, and is an integer.

47. $\frac{16}{4} = 4$ is a natural, whole and rational number, and is an integer.

49. 0 is a whole and rational number, and is an integer.

51. $-4.5 = -4\frac{1}{2} = -\frac{9}{2}$ is a rational number.

53. $\sqrt{11}$ is an irrational number.

55. $\frac{8}{4} = 4$ is a natural and rational number, and is an integer.

57. $-\sqrt{3}$ is an irrational number.

59. 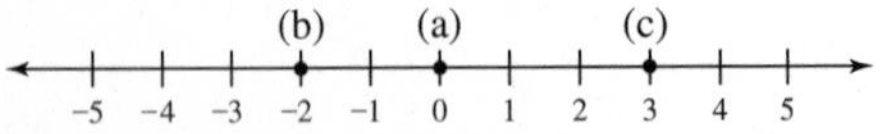

61. 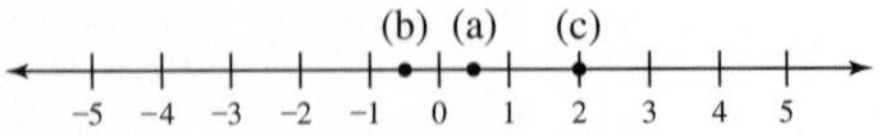

63. 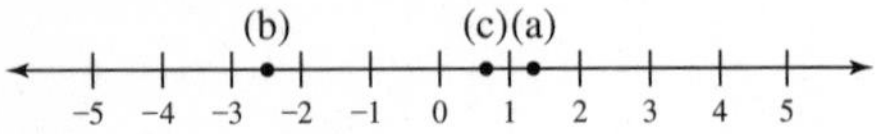

65. 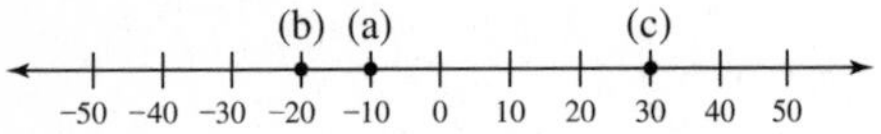

67. 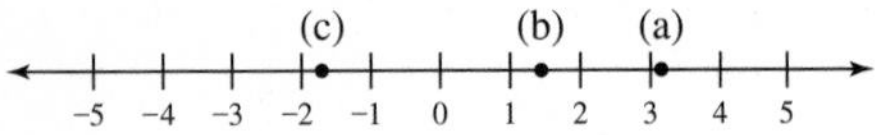

Absolute Values

69. $|5.23| = 5.23$

71. $|-7| = 7$

73. $\left|-\frac{1}{2}\right| = \frac{1}{2}$

75. $|\pi - 3| = \pi - 3$

77. $|b|$, if b is negative, $= -b$

79. $5 < 7$

81. $-5 > -7$

83. $-\frac{1}{3} > -\frac{2}{3}$

85. $-1.9 < -1.3$

87. $-9, -2^3, -3, 0, 1$

89. $-2, -\frac{3}{2}, \frac{1}{3}, \sqrt{5}, \pi$

91. $-4^2, -\frac{17}{28}, -\frac{4}{7}, \sqrt{2}, \sqrt{7}$

Applications

93. (a) The enrollment in 1998 was 14.6 million.

(b) *Answers may vary.*

(c) The average enrollment was $\frac{14.5 + 14.6 + 14.9 + 15.1}{4} = \frac{59.1}{4} = 14.775$ million.

Checking Basic Concepts for Sections 1.3 & 1.4

1. (a) $2^3 = 2 \cdot 2 \cdot 2 = 8$

(b) $10^4 = 10 \cdot 10 \cdot 10 \cdot 10 = 10{,}000$

(c) $\left(\frac{2}{3}\right)^3 = \frac{2}{3} \cdot \frac{2}{3} \cdot \frac{2}{3} = \frac{2 \cdot 2 \cdot 2}{3 \cdot 3 \cdot 3} = \frac{8}{27}$

(d) $-3^4 = -(3 \cdot 3 \cdot 3 \cdot 3) = -81$

2. (a) $6 + 5 \cdot 4 = 6 + 20 = 26$

(b) $6 + 6 \div 2 = 6 + 3 = 9$

(c) $5 - 2 - 1 = 2$

(d) $\frac{6 - 3}{2 + 4} = \frac{3}{6} = \frac{1 \cdot 3}{2 \cdot 3} = \frac{1}{2} \cdot \frac{3}{3} = \frac{1}{2} \cdot 1 = \frac{1}{2}$

(e) $12 \div (6 \div 2) = 12 \div 3 = 4$

(f) $2^3 - 2\left(2 + \frac{4}{2}\right) = 8 - 2(2 + 2) = 8 - 2(4) = 8 - 8 = 0$

3. $5^3 \div 3$, or $\frac{5^3}{3}$

4. (a) The opposite of -17 is $-(-17) = 17$.

(b) The opposite of a is $-a$.

5. (a) $\frac{10}{2} = 5$ is a natural and rational number, and is an integer.

(b) -5 is a rational number and is an integer.

(c) $\sqrt{5}$ is an irrational number.

(d) $-\frac{5}{6}$ is a rational number.

6. 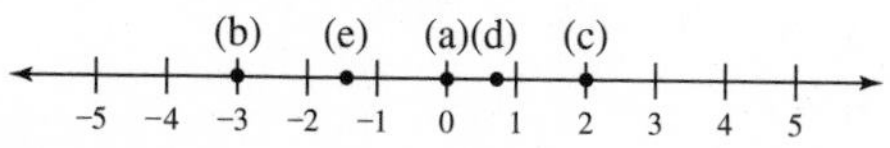

7. (a) $|-12| = -(-12) = 12$

   (b) $|-a|$, if $a > 0$, $= -(-a) = a$

8. $-7, -1.6, 0, \frac{1}{3}, \sqrt{3}, 3^2$

1.5: Addition and Subtraction of Real Numbers

Concepts

1. 0

3. addends

5. difference

7. negative

9. addition

Addition and Subtraction of Real Numbers

11. The opposite of 25 is -25. $25 + (-25) = 0$

13. The opposite of $-\sqrt{21}$ is $\sqrt{21}$. $-\sqrt{21} + \sqrt{21} = 0$

15. The opposite of 5.63 is -5.63. $5.63 + (-5.63) = 0$

17. 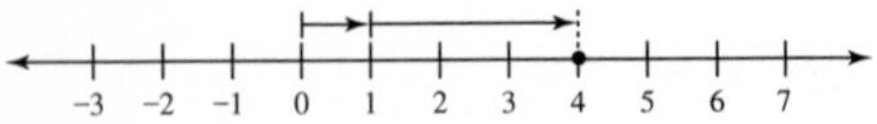

; $1 + 3 = 4$

19. 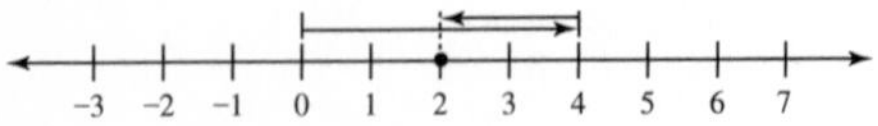

; $4 + (-2) = 2$

21. 

; $-1 + (-2) = -3$

23. 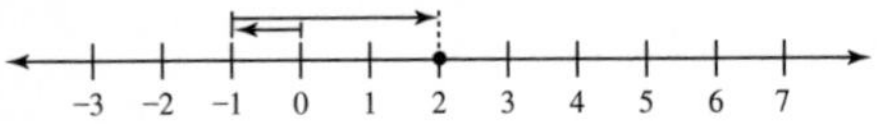

; $-1 + 3 = 2$

25. 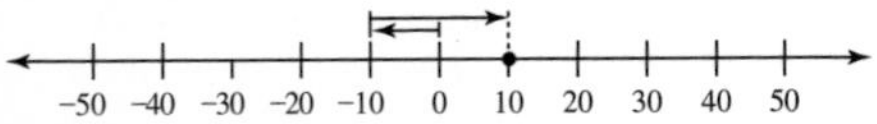

; $-10 + 20 = 10$

27. 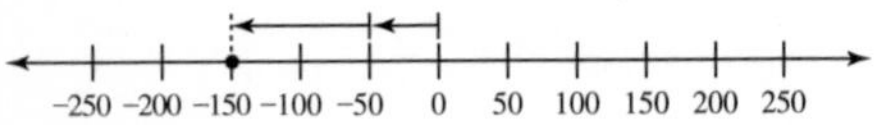

; $-50 + (-100) = -150$

29. $5 + (-4) = 5 - |-4| = 5 - 4 = 1$

31. $-1 + (-6) = -1 - |-6| = -1 - 6 = -7$

33. $\frac{3}{4} + \left(-\frac{1}{2}\right) = \frac{3}{4} - \left|-\frac{1}{2}\right| = \frac{3}{4} - \frac{1}{2} = \frac{3}{4} - \frac{1}{2} \cdot \frac{2}{2} = \frac{3}{4} - \frac{2}{4} = \frac{1}{4}$

35. $-\frac{6}{7} + \frac{3}{14} = \frac{3}{14} - \left|-\frac{6}{7}\right| = \frac{3}{14} - \frac{6}{7} = \frac{3}{14} - \frac{6}{7} \cdot \frac{2}{2} = \frac{3}{14} - \frac{12}{14} = -\frac{9}{14}$

37. $-\frac{1}{2} + \left(-\frac{3}{4}\right) = -\frac{1}{2} - \left|-\frac{3}{4}\right| = -\frac{1}{2} - \frac{3}{4} = -\frac{1}{2} \cdot \frac{2}{2} - \frac{3}{4} = -\frac{2}{4} - \frac{3}{4} = -\frac{5}{4}$

39. $0.6 + (-1.7) = 0.6 - |-1.7| = 0.6 - 1.7 = -1.1$

41. $-52 + 86 = 86 - |-52| = 86 - 52 = 34$

43. $8 + (-7) + (-2) = 8 - |-2| - |-7| = 8 - 2 - 7 = -1$

45. $\frac{1}{2} + \frac{3}{4} + \left(-\frac{1}{2}\right) + \left(-\frac{3}{4}\right) = \frac{1}{2} + \frac{3}{4} - \left|-\frac{1}{2}\right| - \left|-\frac{3}{4}\right| = \frac{1}{2} + \frac{3}{4} - \frac{1}{2} - \frac{3}{4} = \frac{1}{2} - \frac{1}{2} + \frac{3}{4} - \frac{3}{4} = 0 + 0 = 0$

47. $5 - 8 = 5 + (-8) = -3$

49. $-2 - (-9) = -2 + 9 = 7$

51. $\frac{1}{3} - \left(-\frac{2}{3}\right) = \frac{1}{3} + \frac{2}{3} = \frac{3}{3} = 1$

53. $\frac{6}{7} - \frac{13}{14} = \frac{12}{14} - \frac{13}{14} = \frac{12}{14} + \left(-\frac{13}{14}\right) = -\frac{1}{14}$

55. $-\frac{1}{10} - \left(-\frac{3}{5}\right) = -\frac{1}{10} + \left(-\frac{6}{10}\right) = -\frac{1}{10} + \frac{6}{10} = \frac{5}{10} = \frac{1}{2}$

57. $0.8 - (-2.1) = 0.8 + 2.1 = 2.9$

59. $-73 - 91 = -73 + (-91) = -164$

61. $-7 - (-6) - 10 = -7 + 6 - 10 = -11$

63. $10 - 19 = 10 + (-19) = -9$

65. $19 - (-22) + 1 = 19 + 22 + 1 = 42$

67. $-3 + 4 - 6 = -3 + 4 + (-6) = 4 - |-3| + (-6) = 4 - 3 + (-6) = -5$

69. $100 - 200 + 100 - (-50) = 100 + 100 - 200 + 50 = 200 - 200 + 50 = 50$

71. $1.5 - 2.3 + 9.6 = 1.5 + (-2.3) + 9.6 = 8.8$

73. $-\frac{1}{2} + \frac{1}{4} - \left(-\frac{3}{4}\right) = -\frac{2}{4} + \frac{1}{4} + \frac{3}{4} = \frac{2}{4} = \frac{1}{2}$

75. $|4 - 9| - |1 - 7| = |-5| - |-6| = 5 - 6 = -1$

77. $2 + (-5) = -3$

79. $-5 + 7 = 2$

81. $2^3 = 8$; the opposite of 8 is -8

83. $-6 - 7 = -6 + (-7) = -13$

85. $6 + (-10) - 5 = 6 + (-10) - 5 = 6 + (-10) + (-5) = -9$

Applications

87. Take the initial balance and then add to it the deposits and subtract from it the withdrawals.

$358 - 45 + 37 + 120 - 240 = 358 + 37 + 120 + (-45) + (-240) = \$230$

89. The word height is in reference to sea level, the height of Mount Everest is 29,029 feet and the height of the Mariana Trench is (−35,839).

To find the difference take $29{,}029 - (-35{,}839) = 29{,}029 + 35{,}839 = 64{,}868$ feet.

1.6: Multiplication and Division of Real Numbers

Concepts

1. factors
3. negative
5. quotient
7. $\frac{1}{a}$
9. reciprocal or multiplicative inverse
11. positive
13. $\frac{-4}{-2} = 2$

Multiplication and Division of Real Numbers

15. $-3 \cdot 4 = -12$
17. $6 \cdot (-3) = -18$
19. $0 \cdot (-2.13) = 0$
21. $-6 \cdot (-10) = 60$
23. $-\frac{1}{2} \cdot \left(-\frac{2}{4}\right) = \frac{2}{8} = \frac{1}{4}$
25. $-\frac{3}{7} \cdot \frac{7}{3} = -\frac{21}{21} = -1$
27. $-10 \cdot (-20) = 200$
29. $-50 \cdot 100 = -5000$
31. $-2 \cdot 3 \cdot (-4) \cdot 5 = -6 \cdot (-20) = 120$
33. $-6 \cdot \frac{1}{6} \cdot \frac{7}{9} \cdot \left(-\frac{9}{7}\right) \cdot \left(-\frac{3}{2}\right) = -\frac{6}{6} \cdot \left(-\frac{63}{63}\right) \cdot \left(-\frac{3}{2}\right) = -1 \cdot (-1) \cdot \left(-\frac{3}{2}\right) = 1 \cdot \left(-\frac{3}{2}\right) = -\frac{3}{2}$
35. $(-1) \cdot (-1) \cdot (-1) \cdot (-1) = 1 \cdot 1 = 1$
37. $-10 \div 5 = -\frac{10}{1} \cdot \frac{1}{5} = -\frac{10}{5} = -2$
39. $-20 \div (-2) = -\frac{20}{1} \cdot \left(-\frac{1}{2}\right) = \frac{20}{2} = 10$
41. $-\frac{12}{3} = -4$
43. $\frac{39}{-13} = -3$
45. $-16 \div \frac{1}{2} = -\frac{16}{1} \cdot \frac{2}{1} = -\frac{32}{1} = -32$
47. $\frac{1}{2} \div (-11) = \frac{1}{2} \cdot -\frac{1}{11} = -\frac{1}{22}$

49. $-\frac{4}{5} \div (-3) = -\frac{4}{5} \cdot \left(-\frac{1}{3}\right) = \frac{4}{15}$

51. $\frac{5}{6} \div \left(-\frac{8}{9}\right) = \frac{5}{6} \cdot \left(-\frac{9}{8}\right) = -\frac{45}{48} = -\frac{15}{16}$

53. $-\frac{1}{2} \div 0 =$ undefined, because division by 0 is not allowed.

55. $-0.5 \div \frac{1}{2} = -\frac{5}{10} \div \frac{1}{2} = -\frac{5}{10} \cdot \frac{2}{1} = -\frac{10}{10} = -1$

57. $-\frac{2}{3} \div 0.5 = -\frac{2}{3} \div \frac{5}{10} = -\frac{2}{3} \cdot \frac{10}{5} = -\frac{20}{15} = -\frac{4}{3}$

Converting Between Fractions and Decimals

59. $\frac{1}{2} = 0.5$

61. $\frac{3}{16} = 0.1875$

63. Because $1 \div 2 = 0.5$, $3\frac{1}{2} = 3.5$

65. Because $2 \div 3 = 0.\overline{6}$, $5\frac{2}{3} = 5.\overline{6}$

67. Because $7 \div 16 = 0.4375$, $1\frac{1}{16} = 1.4375$

69. $\frac{7}{8} = 7 \div 8 = 0.875$

71. $0.25 = \frac{25}{100} = \frac{1 \cdot 25}{4 \cdot 25} = \frac{1}{4}$

73. $0.16 = \frac{16}{100} = \frac{4 \cdot 4}{25 \cdot 4} = \frac{4}{25}$

75. $0.625 = \frac{625}{1000} = \frac{5 \cdot 125}{8 \cdot 125} = \frac{5}{8}$

77. $0.6875 = \frac{6875}{10{,}000} = \frac{11 \cdot 625}{16 \cdot 625} = \frac{11}{16}$

Applications

79. (a) 49.5 million tourists visited Spain in 2001.

(b) Add the number of tourists who visited each country, then divide this total by the number of countries;

$$\frac{33.2 + 39.1 + 44.5 + 49.5 + 76.5}{5} = \frac{242.8}{5} = 48.56 \text{ million.}$$

81. Add the down payment of 1497 to the product of 249 and 36. The best estimate is \$10,500.

83. (a) The number of subscribers is increasing.

(b) Notice that the trend is to increase the number of subscribers from year to year by about one million. An estimate based on the table would be 5.3 to 5.5 million subscribers in 2003.

Checking Basic Concepts for Sections 1.5 & 1.6

1. (a) $-4 + 4 = 0$

   (b) $-10 + (-12) + 3 = -22 + 3 = -19$

2. (a) $\frac{2}{3} - \left(-\frac{2}{9}\right) = \frac{2}{3} + \frac{2}{9} = \frac{6}{9} + \frac{2}{9} = \frac{8}{9}$

   (b) $-1.2 - 5.1 + 3.1 = -1.2 + (-5.1) + 3.1 = -6.3 + 3.1 = -3.2$

3. $98 - (-46) = 98 + 46 = 144°F$ is the difference between these two temperatures.

4. (a) $-5 \cdot (-7) = 35$

   (b) $-\frac{1}{2} \cdot \frac{2}{3} \cdot \left(-\frac{4}{5}\right) = -\frac{2}{6} \cdot \left(-\frac{4}{5}\right) = \frac{8}{30} = \frac{4}{15}$

5. (a) $-5 \div \frac{2}{3} = -\frac{5}{1} \cdot \frac{3}{2} = -\frac{15}{2}$

   (b) $-\frac{5}{8} \div \left(-\frac{4}{3}\right) = -\frac{5}{8} \cdot \left(-\frac{3}{4}\right) = \frac{15}{32}$

6. The reciprocal of $-\frac{7}{6}$ is $-\frac{6}{7}$.

7. (a) $\frac{-10}{2} = \frac{-5 \cdot 2}{1 \cdot 2} = \frac{-5}{1} = -5$

   (b) $\frac{10}{-2} = \frac{5 \cdot 2}{-1 \cdot (2)} = \frac{5}{-1} = -5$

   (c) $-\frac{10}{2} = -\frac{5 \cdot 2}{1 \cdot 2} = -\frac{5}{1} = -5$

   (d) $\frac{-10}{-2} = \frac{-5 \cdot 2}{-1 \cdot 2} = \frac{-5}{-1} = 5$

8. (a) $\frac{3}{5} = 0.6$

   (b) Because $\frac{7}{8} = 0.875$, $3\frac{7}{8} = 3.875$

9. (a) The incarceration rate is increasing.

   (b) From 1980 to 2000, the average increase each five-year period was 67.6 million. Since 2010 is two five-year periods away from 2000, we could find the sum of the incarceration rate in 2000 and the average increase of two five-year periods. Thus, $477 + 2 \cdot 67.6 = 612.2$ prisoners per 100,000 resident population, or an estimated amount of 539-596 prisoners. *Answers may vary.*

1.7: Properties of Real Numbers

Concepts

1. commutative; addition
3. associative; addition
5. distributive

7. identity; addition

9. $-a$

Properties of Real Numbers

11. $-6 + 10 = 10 + (-6)$

13. $-5 \cdot 6 = 6 \cdot (-5)$

15. $a + 10 = 10 + a$

17. $b \cdot 7 = 7 \cdot b$

19. $(1 + 2) + 3 = 1 + (2 + 3)$

21. $2 \cdot (3 \cdot 4) = (2 \cdot 3) \cdot 4$

23. $(a + 5) + c = a + (5 + c)$

25. $(x \cdot 3) \cdot 4 = x \cdot (3 \cdot 4)$

27. $4(3 + 2) = (4 \cdot 3) + (4 \cdot 2) = 12 + 8 = 20$

29. $a(b - 8) = ab - 8a$

31. $-1(t + z) = -1t - 1z = -t - z$

33. $-(5 - a) = -(1)(5) - 1(-a) = -5 + a$

35. $(a + 5)3 = 3a + (3)(5) = 3a + 15$

37. $(6 - z)(-3) = -18 + 3z = 3z - 18$

39. Commutative (multiplication)

41. Associative (addition)

43. Distributive

45. Distributive, Commutative (multiplication)

47. Distributive

49. Associative (multiplication)

51. Distributive

Identity and Inverse Properties

53. Identity (addition)

55. Identity (multiplication)

57. Identity (multiplication)

59. Inverse (multiplication)

61. Inverse (addition)

Mental Calculations

63. $(4 + 2) + (9 + 8) + (1 + 6) = 30$

65. $(45 + 43) + (5 + 7) = 100$

67. $129 + 49 = 178$

69. $379 + 98 = 477$

71. $178 - 99 = 79$

73. $6 \cdot 15 = 90$

75. $8 \cdot 102 = 816$

77. $\left(\frac{1}{2} \cdot \frac{1}{2} \cdot \frac{1}{2}\right) \cdot 2 \cdot 2 \cdot 2 = \left(\frac{1}{8}\right) \cdot 8 = 1$

79. $\left(\frac{7}{6} \cdot \frac{1}{2}\right) \cdot \left(\frac{1}{2} \cdot \frac{1}{2}\right) \cdot \frac{8}{7} = \left(\frac{7}{12} \cdot \frac{1}{4}\right) \cdot \frac{8}{7} = \frac{7}{48} \cdot \frac{8}{7} = \frac{56}{336} = \frac{1}{6}$

Multiplying and Dividing by Powers of 10 Mentally

81. (a) $10 \times 41 = 410$

(b) $10 \times 997 = 9970$

(c) $-630 \times 10 = -6300$

(d) $-14{,}000 \times 10 = -140{,}000$

83. (a) $1000 \times 19 = 19{,}000$

(b) $100 \times (-451) = -45{,}100$

(c) $10{,}000 \times 6 = 60{,}000$

(d) $-79 \times 100{,}000 = -7{,}900{,}000$

85. (a) $12.56 \div 10 = 1.256$

(b) $9.6 \div 10 = .96$

(c) $0.987 \div 10 = 0.0987$

(d) $-0.056 \div 10 = -0.0056$

(e) $1200 \div 10 = 120$

(f) $4578 \div 10 = 457.8$

Applications

87. Because $100 + 75 = 75 + 100$, this shows the commutative property of addition.

89. Because 1 gallon is $10 \div 10$ gallons, divide 198 by 10 to get 19.8 miles.

91. (a) Because of the commutative property of multiplication, $500 \cdot 400 = 400 \cdot 500$. Thus, the number of pixels in an image 400 pixels wide and 500 pixels high is $400 \cdot 500 = 200{,}000$ pixels.

(b) The commutative property of multiplication.

1.8: Simplifying and Writing Algebraic Expressions

Concepts

1. term
3. coefficient
5. like, unlike

Like Terms

7. The expression 91 is a term; it's coefficient is 91.
9. The expression $-6b$ is a term; it's coefficient is -6.
11. The expression $x + 10$ is not a term because it is the sum of two terms.
13. The expression x^2 is a term; it's coefficient is 1.
15. The expression $4x - 5$ is not a term because it is the difference of two terms.
17. The expression $-9xyz$ is a term; it's coefficient is -9.
19. The terms 6 and -8 are like because neither term contains a variable.
21. The terms $5x$ and $-22x$ are like because each term contains the same variable raised to the same power.
23. The terms $18x$ and $18y$ are unlike because the first term contains a different variable than the second term.
25. The terms x^2, $-15x^2$ and $6x^2$ are like because each term contains the same variable raised to the same power.
27. The terms xy, xz and $2xy$ are unlike because each term does not contain the same variables.
29. $3x + 5x = (3 + 5)x = 8x$
31. $19y - 5y = (19 - 5)y = 14y$
33. It is not possible to combine terms because the first term contains a different variable than the first term.
35. It is not possible to combine terms because the first term does not contain a variable and the second term does.
37. $5x^2 - 2x^2 = (5 - 2)x^2 = 3x^2$
39. $8xy - 10xy + xy = (8 - 10 + 1)xy = -1xy = -xy$

Simplifying and Writing Expressions

41. $5 + x - 3 + 2x = 5 - 3 + x + 2x = 5 - 3 + (1 + 2)x = 2 + 3x = 3x + 2$
43. $-\frac{3}{4} + z - 3z + \frac{5}{4} = z - 3z + \frac{5}{4} - \frac{3}{4} = (1 - 3)z + \frac{5}{4} - \frac{3}{4} = -2z + \frac{5}{4} - \frac{3}{4} = -2z + \frac{1}{2}$
45. $4y - y + 8y = (4 - 1 + 8)y = 11y$
47. $-3 + 6z + 2 - 2z = 6z - 2z - 3 + 2 = (6 - 2)z - 3 + 2 = 4z - 1$
49. $-2(3z - 6y) - z = -6z + 12y - z = -6z - z + 12y = (-6 - 1)z - 12y = -7z + 12y = 12y - 7z$
51. $2 - \frac{3}{4}(4x + 8) = 2 - \frac{3 \cdot 4}{4}x - \frac{3 \cdot 8}{4} = 2 - \frac{12}{4}x - \frac{24}{4} = 2 - 3x - 6 = 2 - 6 - 3x =$

    $-4 - 3x = -3x - 4$
53. $-x - (5x + 1) = -x - 5x - 1 = (-1 - 5)x - 1 = -6x - 1$

55. $1 - \frac{1}{3}(x + 1) = 1 - \frac{1}{3}x - \frac{1}{3} = -\frac{1}{3}x + 1 - \frac{1}{3} = -\frac{1}{3}x + \frac{3}{3} - \frac{1}{3} = -\frac{1}{3}x + \frac{2}{3}$

57. $\frac{3}{5}(x + y) - \frac{1}{5}(x - 1) = \frac{3}{5}x + \frac{3}{5}y - \frac{1}{5}x + \frac{1}{5} = \frac{3}{5}x - \frac{1}{5}x + \frac{3}{5}y + \frac{1}{5} = \left(\frac{3}{5} - \frac{1}{5}\right)x + \frac{3}{5}y + \frac{1}{5} =$
$\frac{2}{5}x + \frac{3}{5}y + \frac{1}{5}$

59. $0.2x^2 + 0.3x^2 - 0.1x^2 = (0.2 + 0.3 - 0.1)x^2 = 0.4x^2$

61. $2x^2 - 3x + 5x^2 - 4x = 2x^2 + 5x^2 - 3x - 4x = (2 + 5)x^2 - (3 + 4)x = 7x^2 - 7x$

63. $\frac{8x}{8} = \frac{8}{8} \cdot \frac{x}{1} = 1 \cdot \frac{x}{1} = 1 \cdot x = x$

65. $\frac{-3y}{-y} = \frac{-3}{1} \cdot \frac{y}{-y} = -3 \cdot (-1) = 3$

67. $\frac{-108z}{-108} = \frac{-108}{-108} \cdot \frac{z}{1} = 1 \cdot \frac{z}{1} = 1 \cdot z = z$

69. $5x + 6x = (5 + 6)x = 11x$

71. $x^2 + 2x^2 = (1 + 2)x^2 = 3x^2$

73. $6x - 4x = (6 - 4)x = 2x$

Applications

75. (a) Let w be the constant width of the street in feet. The area of each street section equals it's length times it's width. The total area of the street is $400w + 350w + 220w + 600w = (400 + 350 + 220 + 600)w = 1570w$.

(b) If the width $= 42$ feet, $w = 42$. Then, $1570w = 1570 \cdot 42 = 65{,}940\ \text{ft}^2$.

77. (a) Let x be the number of minutes. Then, $20x + 30x = 50x =$ the number of cubic feet of snow removed in x minutes.

(b) Let $x = 48$. Then, the total number of cubic feet of snow removed in 48 minutes is $50x = 50 \cdot 48 = 2400\ \text{ft}^3$.

(c) First, calculate how many cubic feet of snow the driveway contains. Volume equals length times width times height; thus, the driveway contains $30 \cdot 20 \cdot 2 = 1200\ \text{ft}^3$ of snow. If 50 cubic feet of snow is removed in 1 minute, then $\frac{1200}{50}$ cubic feet of snow is removed in 24 minutes.

Checking Basic Concepts for Sections 1.7 & 1.8

1. (a) $y \cdot 18 = 18y$

(b) $10 + x = x + 10$

2. $5 \cdot (y \cdot 4) = 5 \cdot (4y) = 20y$

3. (a) $10 - (5 + x) = 10 - 5 - x = 5 - x$

(b) $5(x - 7) = 5x - 35$

4. Because $5x + 3x = (5 + 3)x = 8x$, this equation illustrates the distributive property.

5. $-4xy + 4xy = (-4 + 4)xy = 0xy = 0$

6. (a) $32 + 17 + 8 + 3 = 60$

(b) $\frac{5}{6} \cdot \frac{7}{8} \cdot \frac{6}{5} \cdot 8 = \frac{5 \cdot 7}{6 \cdot 8} \cdot \frac{6 \cdot 8}{5 \cdot 1} = \frac{35}{48} \cdot \frac{48}{5} = \frac{35}{5} \cdot \frac{48}{48} = 7 \cdot 1 = 7$

(c) $567 - 199 = 368$

7. (a) $5z + 9z = (5 + 9)z = 14z$

(b) $5y - 4 - 8y + 7 = 5y - 8y - 4 + 7 = (5 - 8)y - 4 + 7 = -3y + 3$

8. (a) $2y - (5y + 3) = 2y - 5y - 3 - (2 - 5)y - 3 = -3y - 3$

(b) $-4(x + 3y) + 2(2x - y) = -4x - 12y + 4x - 2y = -4x + 4x - 12y - 2y =$

$(-4 + 4)x - (12 + 2)y = 0x - 14y = -14y$

(c) $\frac{20x}{20} = \frac{20}{20} \cdot x = 1 \cdot x = x$

(d) $\frac{35x^2}{x^2} = 35 \cdot \frac{x^2}{x^2} = 35 \cdot 1 = 35$

Chapter 1 Review Exercises

Section 1.1

1. The number 29 is prime it's only factors are itself and 1.
2. The number 27 is a composite number because it has factors other than itself; $27 = 3 \times 3 \times 3$.
3. The number 108 is a composite number because it has factors other than itself; $108 = 2 \times 2 \times 3 \times 3 \times 3$.
4. The number 91 is a composite number because it has factors other than itself; $91 = 7 \times 13$.
5. $2x - 5$, when $x = 4$, is $2 \cdot 4 - 5 = 8 - 5 = 3$
6. $7 - \frac{10}{x}$, when $x = 5$, is $7 - \frac{10}{5} = 7 - \frac{2 \cdot 5}{1 \cdot 5} = 7 - \frac{2}{1} \cdot \frac{5}{5} = 7 - 2 \cdot 1 = 7 - 2 = 5$
7. $9x - 2y$, when $x = 2$ and $y = 3$, is $9 \cdot 2 - 2 \cdot 3 = 18 - 6 = 12$
8. $\frac{2x}{x - y}$, when $x = 6$ and $y = 4$, is $\frac{2 \cdot 6}{6 - 4} = \frac{12}{2} = \frac{6 \cdot 2}{1 \cdot 2} = \frac{6}{1} \cdot \frac{2}{2} = 6 \cdot 1 = 6$
9. $y = x - 5$, when $x = 12$, is $y = 12 - 5 \Rightarrow y = 7$
10. $y = xz + 1$, when $x = 2$ and $z = 3$, is $y = 2 \cdot 3 + 1 \Rightarrow y = 6 + 1 \Rightarrow y = 7$
11. Let c be the cost of the CD. Then, five times the cost of the CD is $5 \cdot c = 5c$.
12. Let x be the number. Then, five less than the number is $x - 5$.
13. Three squared increased by five is $3^2 + 5$.
14. Two cubed divided by the quantity three plus one is $2^3 \div (3 + 1)$.

Section 1.2

15. (a) $\frac{5 \cdot 7}{8 \cdot 7} = \frac{5}{8} \cdot \frac{7}{7} = \frac{5}{8} \cdot 1 = \frac{5}{8}$

(b) $\frac{3a}{4a} = \frac{3}{4} \cdot \frac{a}{a} = \frac{3}{4} \cdot 1 = \frac{3}{4}$

16. (a) $\frac{9}{12} = \frac{3 \cdot 3}{4 \cdot 3} = \frac{3}{4} \cdot \frac{3}{3} = \frac{3}{4} \cdot 1 = \frac{3}{4}$

(b) $\frac{36}{60} = \frac{3 \cdot 12}{5 \cdot 12} = \frac{3}{5} \cdot \frac{12}{12} = \frac{3}{5} \cdot 1 = \frac{3}{5}$

17 $\frac{3}{4} \cdot \frac{5}{6} = \frac{3 \cdot 5}{4 \cdot 6} = \frac{15}{24} = \frac{5 \cdot 3}{8 \cdot 3} = \frac{5}{8} \cdot \frac{3}{3} = \frac{5}{8} \cdot 1 = \frac{5}{8}$

18. $\frac{1}{2} \cdot \frac{4}{9} = \frac{1 \cdot 4}{2 \cdot 9} = \frac{4}{18} = \frac{2 \cdot 2}{9 \cdot 2} = \frac{2}{9} \cdot \frac{2}{2} = \frac{2}{9} \cdot 1 = \frac{2}{9}$

19. $\frac{2}{3} \cdot \frac{5}{11} \cdot \frac{9}{10} = \frac{2 \cdot 5 \cdot 9}{3 \cdot 11 \cdot 10} = \frac{90}{330} = \frac{3 \cdot 30}{11 \cdot 30} = \frac{3}{11} \cdot \frac{30}{30} = \frac{3}{11} \cdot 1 = \frac{3}{11}$

20. $\frac{12}{11} \cdot \frac{22}{23} \cdot \frac{1}{2} = \frac{12 \cdot 22 \cdot 1}{11 \cdot 23 \cdot 2} = \frac{264}{506} = \frac{12 \cdot 22}{23 \cdot 22} = \frac{12}{23} \cdot \frac{22}{22} = \frac{12}{23} \cdot 1 = \frac{12}{23}$

21. One-fifth of three-sevenths equals $\frac{1}{5} \cdot \frac{3}{7} = \frac{1 \cdot 3}{5 \cdot 7} = \frac{3}{35}$.

22. (a) The reciprocal of 8 equals the reciprocal of $\frac{8}{1} = \frac{1}{8}$.

(b) The reciprocal of 1 equals the reciprocal of $\frac{1}{1} = \frac{1}{1}$.

(c) The reciprocal of $\frac{5}{19} = \frac{19}{5}$.

(d) The reciprocal of $\frac{3}{2} = \frac{2}{3}$.

23. $\frac{3}{2} \div \frac{1}{6} = \frac{3}{2} \cdot \frac{6}{1} = \frac{3 \cdot 6}{2 \cdot 1} = \frac{18}{2} = \frac{9 \cdot 2}{1 \cdot 2} = \frac{9}{1} \cdot \frac{2}{2} = 9 \cdot 1 = 9$

24. $\frac{9}{10} \div \frac{7}{5} = \frac{9}{10} \cdot \frac{5}{7} = \frac{9 \cdot 5}{10 \cdot 7} = \frac{45}{70} = \frac{9 \cdot 5}{14 \cdot 5} = \frac{9}{14} \cdot \frac{5}{5} = \frac{9}{14} \cdot 1 = \frac{9}{14}$

25. $8 \div \frac{2}{3} = \frac{8}{1} \cdot \frac{3}{2} = \frac{8 \cdot 3}{1 \cdot 2} = \frac{24}{2} = \frac{12 \cdot 2}{1 \cdot 2} = \frac{12}{1} \cdot \frac{2}{2} = 12 \cdot 1 = 12$

26. $\frac{3}{4} \div 6 = \frac{3}{4} \cdot \frac{1}{6} = \frac{3 \cdot 1}{4 \cdot 6} = \frac{3}{24} = \frac{1 \cdot 3}{8 \cdot 3} = \frac{1}{8} \cdot \frac{3}{3} = \frac{1}{8} \cdot 1 = \frac{1}{8}$

27. The least common denominator for the fractions $\frac{1}{8}$ and $\frac{5}{12}$ is 24, because 24 is the smallest number that both 8 and 12 divide into evenly.

28. The least common denominator for the fractions $\frac{2}{14}$ and $\frac{1}{21}$ is 42, because 42 is the smallest number that both 14 and 21 divide into evenly.

29. $\frac{2}{15} + \frac{3}{15} = \frac{2 + 3}{15} = \frac{5}{15} = \frac{1 \cdot 5}{3 \cdot 5} = \frac{1}{3}$

30. $\frac{5}{4} - \frac{3}{4} = \frac{5 - 3}{4} = \frac{2}{4} = \frac{1 \cdot 2}{2 \cdot 2} = \frac{1}{2}$

31. $\frac{11}{12} - \frac{1}{8} = \frac{11 \cdot 2}{12 \cdot 2} - \frac{1 \cdot 3}{8 \cdot 3} = \frac{22}{24} - \frac{3}{24} = \frac{22 - 3}{24} = \frac{19}{24}$

32. $\frac{6}{11} - \frac{3}{22} = \frac{6 \cdot 2}{11 \cdot 2} - \frac{3}{22} = \frac{12}{22} - \frac{3}{22} = \frac{12 - 3}{22} = \frac{9}{22}$

33. $\frac{2}{3} - \frac{1}{2} + \frac{1}{4} = \frac{2 \cdot 4}{3 \cdot 4} - \frac{1 \cdot 6}{2 \cdot 6} + \frac{1 \cdot 3}{4 \cdot 3} = \frac{8}{12} - \frac{6}{12} + \frac{3}{12} = \frac{8 - 6 + 3}{12} = \frac{5}{12}$

34. $\frac{1}{6} + \frac{2}{3} - \frac{1}{9} = \frac{1 \cdot 3}{6 \cdot 3} + \frac{2 \cdot 6}{3 \cdot 6} - \frac{1 \cdot 2}{9 \cdot 2} = \frac{3}{18} + \frac{12}{18} - \frac{2}{18} = \frac{3 + 12 - 2}{18} = \frac{13}{18}$

Section 1.3

35. $5 \cdot 5 \cdot 5 \cdot 5 \cdot 5 \cdot 5 = 5^6$

36. $\frac{7}{6} \cdot \frac{7}{6} \cdot \frac{7}{6} = \left(\frac{7}{6}\right)^3$

37. $3 \cdot 3 \cdot 3 \cdot 3 = 3^4$

38. $x \cdot x \cdot x \cdot x \cdot x = x^5$

39. (a) $4^3 = 4 \cdot 4 \cdot 4 = 64$

(b) $7^2 = 7 \cdot 7 = 49$

(c) $8^1 = 8$

40. $2^n = 32$; $2 \cdot 2 \cdot 2 \cdot 2 \cdot 2 = 32$, thus $2^5 = 32$ and $n = 5$

41. $7 + 3 \cdot 6 = 7 + 18 = 25$

42. $15 - 5 - 3 = (15 - 5) - 3 = 10 - 3 = 7$

43. $24 \div 4 \div 2 = (24 \div 4) \div 2 = 6 \div 2 = 3$

44. $30 - 15 \div 3 = 30 - (15 \div 3) = 30 - 5 = 25$

45. $18 \div 6 - 2 = (18 \div 6) - 2 = 3 - 2 = 1$

46. $\frac{18}{4 + 5} = \frac{18}{9} = \frac{2 \cdot 9}{1 \cdot 9} = \frac{2}{1} \cdot \frac{9}{9} = 2 \cdot 1 = 2$

47. $9 - 3^2 = 9 - 9 = 0$

48. $2^3 - 8 = 8 - 8 = 0$

49. $2^4 - 8 + \frac{4}{2} = (2 \cdot 2 \cdot 2 \cdot 2) - 8 + 2 = 16 - 8 + 2 = (16 - 8) + 2 = 8 + 2 = 10$

50. $3^2 - 4(5 - 3) = 3^2 - 4(2) = 9 - 8 = 1$

51. $7 - \frac{4 + 6}{2 + 3} = 7 - \frac{10}{5} = 7 - 2 = 5$

52. $3^3 - 2^3 = (3 \cdot 3 \cdot 3) - (2 \cdot 2 \cdot 2) = 27 - 8 = 19$

Section 1.4

53. The number 0 is a whole number and a rational number, and is an integer.

54. The number $-\frac{5}{6}$ is a rational number.

55. The number −7 is a rational number and is an integer.

56. The number $\sqrt{17}$ is an irrational number.

57. The number π is an irrational number.

58. The number 3.4 is a rational number.

59. 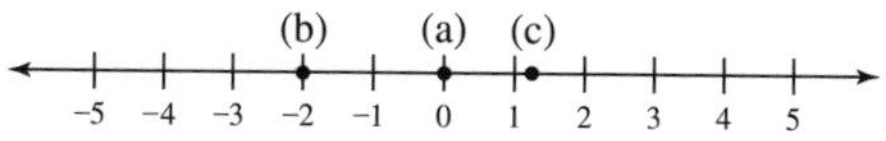

60. (a) $|-5| = 5$

(b) $|-\pi| = \pi$

(c) $|\sqrt{2} - 1| = \sqrt{2} - 1$

61. (a) $-5 < 4$

(b) $-\frac{1}{2} > -\frac{5}{2}$

62. $-3, -\frac{2}{3}, \sqrt{3}, \pi - 1, 3$

Sections 1.5 and 1.6

63. $-1 + 2 = 1$
64. $-2 + (-3) = -5$
65. $5 + (-4) = 1$
66. $-9 - (-7) = -9 + 7 = -2$
67. $11 \cdot (-4) = -44$
68. $-8 \cdot (-5) = 40$
69. $11 \div (-4) = -\frac{11}{4}$
70. $-4 \div \frac{4}{7} = -\frac{4}{1} \cdot \frac{7}{4} = -\frac{4 \cdot 7}{4} = -\frac{28}{4} = -\frac{7 \cdot 4}{1 \cdot 4} = -\frac{7}{1} \cdot \frac{4}{4} = -7 \cdot 1 = -7$
71. $-\frac{1}{2} + \left(-\frac{3}{4}\right) = -\frac{1 \cdot 2}{2 \cdot 2} + \left(-\frac{3}{4}\right) = -\frac{2}{4} + \left(-\frac{3}{4}\right) = -\frac{5}{4}$
72. $-\frac{5}{9} - \left(-\frac{1}{3}\right) = -\frac{5}{9} + \frac{1}{3} = -\frac{5}{9} + \frac{1 \cdot 3}{3 \cdot 3} = -\frac{5}{9} + \frac{3}{9} = -\frac{2}{9}$
73. $-\frac{1}{3} \cdot \left(-\frac{6}{7}\right) = \frac{1 \cdot 6}{3 \cdot 7} = \frac{6}{21} = \frac{2 \cdot 3}{7 \cdot 3} = \frac{2}{7} \cdot \frac{3}{3} = \frac{2}{7} \cdot 1 = \frac{2}{7}$
74. $\frac{\frac{4}{5}}{-7} = \frac{4}{5} \div (-7) = \frac{4}{5} \cdot \left(-\frac{1}{7}\right) = -\frac{4}{35}$
75. $-\frac{3}{2} \div \left(-\frac{3}{8}\right) = -\frac{3}{2} \cdot \left(-\frac{8}{3}\right) = \frac{24}{6} = 4$
76. $\frac{3}{8} \div (-0.5) = \frac{3}{8} \div \left(-\frac{1}{2}\right) = \frac{3}{8} \cdot \left(-\frac{2}{1}\right) = -\frac{6}{8} = -\frac{3 \cdot 2}{4 \cdot 2} = -\frac{3}{4} \cdot \frac{2}{2} = -\frac{3}{4} \cdot 1 = -\frac{3}{4}$
77. $3 + (-5) = -2$
78. $2 - (-4) = 2 + 4 = 6$
79. $\frac{7}{9} = 0.\overline{7}$
80. $2\frac{1}{5} = 2.2$
81. $0.6 = \frac{6}{10} = \frac{3 \cdot 2}{5 \cdot 2} = \frac{3}{5} \cdot \frac{2}{2} = \frac{3}{5} \cdot 1 = \frac{3}{5}$
82. $0.375 = \frac{375}{1000} = \frac{3 \cdot 125}{8 \cdot 125} = \frac{3}{8} \cdot \frac{125}{125} = \frac{3}{8} \cdot 1 = \frac{3}{8}$

Section 1.7

83. Commutative (multiplication)
84. Associative (addition)
85. Distributive

86. Commutative (addition)

87. Identity (multiplication)

88. Associative (multiplication)

89. Distributive

90. Identity (addition)

91. Inverse (addition)

92. Inverse (multiplication)

93. $7 + 9 + 12 + 8 + 1 + 3 = (7 + 9) + (12 + 8) + (1 + 3) = 16 + 20 + 4 = (16 + 20) + 4 = 36 + 4 = 40$

94. $500 - 199 = 500 + (-199) = 301$

95. $25 \cdot 99 = (5 \cdot 5) \cdot (33 \cdot 3) = (5 \cdot 5) \cdot (11 \cdot 3) \cdot 3 = 5 \cdot 5 \cdot 3 \cdot 3 \cdot 11 = 2475$

96. $4581 + 1999 = 6580$

97. $54.98 \times 10 = 549.8$ because we move the decimal point to the right one place.

98. $4356 \div 100 = 43.56$ because we move the decimal point to the left two places.

Section 1.8

99. $55x$ is a term; it's coefficient is 55.

100. $-xy$ is a term; it's coefficient is -1.

101. $9xy + 2z$ is not a term because it is the sum of two terms.

102. $x - 7$ is not a term because it is the difference of two terms.

103. $-10x + 4x = (-10 + 4)x = -6x$

104. $19z - 4z = (19 - 4)z = 15z$

105. $3x^2 + x^2 = (3 + 1)x^2 = 4x^2$

106. $7 + 2x - 6 + x = 7 - 6 + 2x + x = 7 - 6 + (2 + 1)x = 1 + 3x = 3x + 1$

107. $-\frac{1}{2} + \frac{3}{2}z - z + \frac{5}{2} = -\frac{1}{2} + \frac{5}{2} + \frac{3}{2}z - z = \frac{-1 + 5}{2} + \left(\frac{3}{2} - 1\right)z = \frac{4}{2} + \left(\frac{3}{2} - \frac{2}{2}\right)z = 2 + \frac{1}{2}z = \frac{1}{2}z + 2$

108. $5(x - 3) - (4x + 3) = 5x - 15 - 4x - 3 = 5x - 4x - 15 - 3 = (5 - 4)x - 15 - 3 = x - 18$

109. $\frac{35a}{7a} = \frac{35}{7} \cdot \frac{a}{a} = \frac{35}{7} \cdot 1 = 5 \cdot 1 = 5$

110. $\frac{0.5c}{0.5} = \frac{0.5}{0.5} \cdot c = 1 \cdot c = c$

Applications

111. (a) Let x be the number of minutes. The first person then paints $3 \cdot x$. or $3x$, square feet in x minutes. The second person paints $4 \cdot x$. or $4x$, square feet in x minutes. working together the two people paint $3x + 4x = (3 + 4)x = 7x$ square feet in x minutes.

(b) First convert hours to minutes; 1 hour = 60 minutes. Replace x with 60 to get $7x = 7 \cdot 60 = 420 \text{ ft}^2$.

(c) First find the number of square feet the wall contains. The area of the wall is width times height. The area $= 8 \cdot 21 = 168 \text{ ft}^2$. Because the two people paint 7 square feet in 1 minute, $168 \div 7 = 24$ minutes.

112. The area of a triangle is $\frac{1}{2} \cdot$ base $\cdot$ height. The base of the triangle is 8 and the height is 4. Thus,

$\frac{1}{2} \cdot 8 \cdot 4 = 16 \text{ ft}^2$.

113. See Figure 113. Since there are 8 pints in 1 gallon, $P = 8G$, where P = pints and G = gallons.

Gallons (G)	1	2	3	4	5	6
Pints (P)	8	16	24	32	40	48

Figure 113

114. Because each CD costs 25 cents, $C = 0.25x$, where C represents cost and x represents the number of CD's purchased.

115. Find the fraction of the population that will be over the age of 65 but under the age of 85. Thus,
$\frac{1}{5} - \frac{1}{20} = \frac{1 \cdot 4}{5 \cdot 4} - \frac{1}{20} = \frac{4}{20} - \frac{1}{20} = \frac{3}{20}$.

116. Find the length of each piece when the board is cut into five equal lengths. Because the board measures
$5\frac{3}{4} = \frac{23}{4}, \frac{23}{4} \div 5 = \frac{23}{4} \cdot \frac{1}{5} = \frac{23}{20} = 1\frac{3}{20}$ feet per piece.

117. Add the individual lengths to find the total distance. Thus, $3\frac{1}{8} + 4\frac{3}{8} + 6\frac{1}{4} + 1\frac{5}{8} = \frac{25}{8} + \frac{35}{8} + \frac{25}{4} + \frac{13}{8} =$

$\frac{25}{8} + \frac{35}{8} + \frac{50}{8} + \frac{13}{8} = \frac{25 + 35 + 50 + 13}{8} = \frac{123}{8} = 15\frac{3}{8}$ miles.

118. (a) Because in 1940 there were 1042 thousand federal employees, $1042 \cdot 1000 = 1{,}042{,}000$.

(b) One method of estimation is to add the 1940 number to the 1960 number and divide this sum by two. Thus,

$(1042 + 2399) \div 2 = 3441 \div 2 = \frac{3441}{1} \cdot \frac{1}{2} = \frac{3441}{2} = 1720.5 = 1720.5$ thousands $= 1720.5 \cdot 1000 =$

1,720,500 federal employees in 1960. *Answers may vary.*

119. Subtract the withdrawals and add the deposits to the initial balance.

Thus, $1652 - 78 - 91 + 256 - 638 = \$1101$.

120. The difference between the two temperatures is $108 - (-16) = 108 + 16 = 124°\text{F}$.

121. (a) The average rainfall in March was 3.2 inches.

(b) Add the average monthly amounts to get the yearly average rainfall.

Thus, $2.5 + 3.0 + 3.2 + 2.5 + 3.1 + 5.7 + 5.5 + 6.3 + 6.7 + 4.6 + 2.6 + 2.4 = 48.1$ inches.

Answers may vary.

122. Find the sum of the down payment and the monthly payments.

Thus, $2800 + 310 \cdot 20 = 2800 + 6200 = \$9000$. *Answers may vary.*

Chapter 1 Test

1. The number 56 is a composite number because it has factors other than itself and 1; $56 = 2 \times 2 \times 2 \times 7$.
2. $\frac{5x}{2x - 1}$, when $x = -3$, is $\frac{5 \cdot (-3)}{2 \cdot (-3) - 1} = \frac{-15}{-6 - 1} = \frac{-15}{-7} = \frac{15}{7}$

3. $4^2 - 3 = 16 - 3 = 13$

4. $\frac{24}{32} = \frac{3 \cdot 8}{4 \cdot 8} = \frac{3}{4}$

5. (a) $\frac{5}{8} + \frac{1}{8} = \frac{5+1}{8} = \frac{6}{8} = \frac{3 \cdot 2}{4 \cdot 2} = \frac{3}{4}$

   (b) $\frac{5}{9} - \frac{3}{15} = \frac{5 \cdot 5}{9 \cdot 5} - \frac{3 \cdot 3}{15 \cdot 3} = \frac{25}{45} - \frac{9}{45} = \frac{25-9}{45} = \frac{16}{45}$

   (c) $\frac{3}{5} \cdot \frac{10}{21} = \frac{3 \cdot 10}{5 \cdot 21} = \frac{30}{105} = \frac{2 \cdot 15}{7 \cdot 15} = \frac{2}{7}$

   (d) $6 \div \frac{8}{5} = \frac{6}{1} \cdot \frac{5}{8} = \frac{6 \cdot 5}{1 \cdot 8} = \frac{30}{8} = \frac{15 \cdot 2}{4 \cdot 2} = \frac{15}{4}$

6. (a) $6 + 10 \div 5 = 6 + 2 = 8$

   (b) $4^3 - (3 - 5 \cdot 2) = 64 - (3 - 10) = 64 - (-7) = 64 + 7 = 71$

   (c) $-6^2 - 6 + \frac{4}{2} = -36 - 6 + 2 = -40$

7. (a) Distributive

   (b) Associative (multiplication)

   (c) Commutative (addition)

8. (a) $5 - 5z + 7 + z = 5 + 7 - 5z + z = 12 + (-5 + 1)z = 12 + (-4)z = 12 - 4z$

   (b) $12x - (6 - 3x) = 12x - 6 + 3x = 12x + 3x - 6 = (12 + 3)x - 6 = 15x - 6$

   (c) $5 - 4(x + 6) + \frac{15x}{3} = 5 - 4x - 24 + \frac{15}{3}x = 5 - 4x - 24 + 5x = 5x - 4x + 5 - 24 =$

   $(5 - 4)x - 19 = 1x - 19 = x - 19$

9. (a) Let x be the number of hours. Then, the first person can mow $\frac{4}{3} \cdot x$ acres in x hours, and the second person can mow $\frac{1}{4} \cdot x$ acres in x hours. Thus, $\frac{4}{3}x + \frac{1}{4}x = \frac{16}{12}x + \frac{3}{12}x = \left(\frac{16}{12} + \frac{3}{12}\right) = \frac{19}{12}x$.

   (b) Let $x = 8$. Then, $\frac{19}{12} \cdot 8 = \frac{19 \cdot 8}{12} = \frac{152}{12} = \frac{38 \cdot 4}{3 \cdot 4} = \frac{38}{3} = 12\frac{2}{3}$ acres.

10. (a) Because $39 \div 3 = 13$, each ticket costs \$13.

    Then, let c = cost and x be the number of tickets to obtain $c = 13x$.

    (b) Let $x = 17$. Thus, $13 \cdot 17 = \$221$.

11. Find $7\frac{4}{5} \div 3$ to find the length of three equal parts.

    Because $7\frac{4}{5} = \frac{39}{5}, \frac{39}{5} \div 3 = \frac{39}{5} \cdot \frac{1}{3} = \frac{39}{15} = \frac{13 \cdot 3}{5 \cdot 3} = \frac{13}{5} = 2\frac{3}{5}$ feet.

12. Subtract the withdrawals from and add the deposits to the initial balance.

    Thus, $892 - 57 + 150 - 345 = \$640$.

Chapter 1 Extended and Discovery Exercises

1. $2 + 2 - 2 - 2 = 4 - 4 = 0$; $3 \cdot 3 + 3 \div 3 = 9 + 1 = 10$; $4 \div 4 + 4 - 4 = 1 + 0 = 1$;

   $6 \cdot 6 + 6 - 6 = 36 + 0 = 36$; $7 \cdot 7 + 7 + 7 = 49 + 14 = 63$ *Answers may vary.*

2.

16	2	3	13
5	11	10	8
9	7	6	12
4	14	15	1

Critical Thinking Solutions for Chapter 1

Section 1.1

- Because you can not find a fraction of a population, this is an example natural or whole number use.
- Because a prime number has as it's only factors itself and 1, the tree diagram will consist of a single dot.

Section 1.2

- Fractions are needed when baking a cake from scratch, because the measurements of cake ingredients are in fractions.

Section 1.3

- A gigabyte is $2^{30} = 1{,}073{,}741{,}824$ bytes, which is more than 1 billion bytes.

Section 1.4

- $-\pi + \pi = 0$

Section 1.5

- Change the problem to an addition problem. Then, if you are adding a negative number, you move left on the number line, and if adding a positive number you move right on the number line.

Section 1.6

- The estimate for 1995 would generally be more accurate because you are making an estimate based on known numbers.

Section 1.7

- Subtract 200 from 5283 to obtain 5083 and then add 2. The result is 5085.

Section 1.8

- Draw rectangles x by y and $2x$ by y. Their combined areas equal $3xy$.

Chapter 2: Linear Equations and Inequalities

2.1: Introduction to Equations

Concepts

1. equal
3. solution set
5. solutions
7. $b + c$
9. 1

The Addition Property of Equality

11. 22

13. $x + 5 = 0 \Rightarrow x + 5 - 5 = 0 - 5 \Rightarrow x + 0 = -5 \Rightarrow x = -5$; To check you answer, substitute -5 for x in the original equation, $-5 + 5 = 0$. This statement is true. Thus, the solution $x = -5$ is correct.

15. $x - 7 = 1 \Rightarrow x - 7 + 7 = 1 + 7 \Rightarrow x + 0 = 8 \Rightarrow x = 8$

17. $9 = y - 8 \Rightarrow 9 + 8 = y - 8 + 8 \Rightarrow 17 = y + 0 \Rightarrow 17 = y \Rightarrow y = 17$

19. $\frac{1}{2} = z - \frac{3}{2} \Rightarrow \frac{1}{2} + \frac{3}{2} = z - \frac{3}{2} + \frac{3}{2} \Rightarrow \frac{4}{2} = z + 0 \Rightarrow 2 = z \Rightarrow z = 2$

21. $t - 0.8 = 4.2 \Rightarrow t - 0.8 + 0.8 = 4.2 + 0.8 \Rightarrow t + 0 = 5 \Rightarrow t = 5$

23. $25 + x = 10 \Rightarrow 25 - 25 + x = 10 - 25 \Rightarrow 0 + x = -15 \Rightarrow x = -15$

25. $1989 = 26 + y \Rightarrow 1989 + (-26) = 26 + (-26) + y \Rightarrow 1963 = 0 + y \Rightarrow 1963 = y \Rightarrow y = 1963$

The Multiplication Property of Equality

27. 5

29. $5x = 15 \Rightarrow \frac{5x}{5} = \frac{15}{5} \Rightarrow x = 3$

31. $-7x = 0 \Rightarrow \frac{-7x}{-7} = \frac{0}{-7} \Rightarrow x = 0$

33. $\frac{1}{2}x = \frac{3}{2} \Rightarrow \frac{2}{1} \cdot \frac{1}{2}x = \frac{3}{2} \cdot \frac{2}{1} \Rightarrow x = 3$

35. $\frac{1}{2} = \frac{2}{5}z \Rightarrow \frac{5}{2} \cdot \frac{1}{2} = \frac{5}{2} \cdot \frac{2}{5}z \Rightarrow \frac{5}{4} = z \Rightarrow z = \frac{5}{4}$

37. $25 = 5z \Rightarrow \frac{25}{5} = \frac{5z}{5} \Rightarrow 5 = z \Rightarrow z = 5$

39. $0.5t = 3.5 \Rightarrow \frac{0.5t}{0.5} = \frac{3.5}{0.5} \Rightarrow t = 7$

41. $\frac{3}{8} = \frac{1}{4}y \Rightarrow \frac{3}{8} \cdot \frac{4}{1} = \frac{4}{1} \cdot \frac{1}{4}y \Rightarrow \frac{3}{2} = y \Rightarrow y = \frac{3}{2}$

Applications

43. (a) See Figure 43.

(b) Let R represent total rainfall and let x represent the number of hours past noon. Start with 3 inches of rain and then add $\frac{1}{2}$, or 0.5, inches per hour after noon, $3 + 0.5x = R$, or equivalently $R = 0.5x + 3$.

(c) At 3 pm, $x = 3$. Substituting x with 3 in the formula, $R = 0.5 \cdot 3 + 3 \Rightarrow R = 4.5$ inches. This answer agrees with the table from part (a).

(d) At 2:15 pm, $x = 2.25$. Substituting x with 2.25 in the formula, $R = 0.5 \cdot 2.25 + 3 \Rightarrow R = 4.125$ inches.

Hours (x)	0	1	2	3	4	5	6
Rainfall (R)	3	3.5	4	4.5	5	5.5	6

Figure 43

45. (a) Let L be the length of the football fields and x be the number of fields. Because each field x contains 300 feet, $L = 300x$.

(b) Substitute L with 870. Then $870 = 300x$.

(c) $870 = 300x \Rightarrow \frac{870}{300} = \frac{300x}{300} \Rightarrow x = \frac{870}{300} \Rightarrow x = 2.9$

47. Let x represent the total number of cubic miles that have melted and let y represent the number of years. Because the glaciers are melting at a rate of 24 cubic miles per year, $x = 24y$. Substitute x with 420. Then, $420 = 24y \Rightarrow \frac{420}{24} = \frac{24y}{24} \Rightarrow y = \frac{420}{24} \Rightarrow y = 17.5$. Thus, it takes 17.5 years for 420 cubic miles of the glacier to melt.

49. Let x represent the cost of the car to obtain the equation $0.07x = 1750$. Then the solution is $\frac{0.07x}{0.07} = \frac{1750}{0.07} \Rightarrow x = \frac{1750}{0.07} \Rightarrow x = 25{,}000$. Thus, the cost of the car is \$25,000.

2.2: Linear Equations

Concepts

1. $ax + b = 0$

3. addition, multiplication

5. LCD

7. Infinitely many

Identifying Linear Equations

9. $3x - 7$ is a linear equation. $a = 3$ and $b = -7$.

11. $\frac{1}{2}x = 0$ is a linear equation. $a = \frac{1}{2}$ and $b = 0$.

13. $4x^2 - 6 = 11$ is not a linear equation because in cannot be written in the form $ax + b = 0$. It has a non-zero term containing x^2.

15. $1.1x = 0.9$ is a linear equation. $1.1x = 0.9 \Rightarrow 1.1x - 0.9 = 0.9 - 0.9 \Rightarrow 1.1x - 0.9 = 0$.
$a = 1.1$ and $b = -0.9$.

17. $2(x - 3) = 0$ is a linear equation. Use the distributive property to obtain $2x - 6 = 0$. $a = 2$ and $b = -6$.

19. $6x - x^2 = 0$ is not a linear equation because in cannot be written in the form $ax + b = 0$. It has a non-zero term containing x^2.

21. For $x = 1$, substitute 1 for x and solve: $-4(1) + 8 = -4 + 8 = 4$.
For $x = 2$, substitute 2 for x and solve: $-4(2) + 8 = -8 + 8 = 0$.
For $x = 3$, substitute 3 for x and solve: $-4(3) + 8 = -12 + 8 = -4$.
For $x = 4$, substitute 4 for x and solve: $-4(4) + 8 = -16 + 8 = -8$.
For $x = 5$, substitute 5 for x and solve: $-4(5) + 8 = -20 + 8 = -12$.
See Figure 21. From the table, we see that the equation $-4x + 8 = 0$ is true when $x = 2$. Therefore, the solution to the equation $-4x + 8 = 0$ is $x = 2$.

x	1	2	3	4	5
$-4x + 8$	4	0	−4	−8	−12

Figure 21

x	−2	−1	0	1	2
$4 - 2x$	8	6	4	2	0

Figure 23

23. For $x = -2$, substitute -2 for x and solve: $4 - 2(-2) = 4 + 4 = 8$.
For $x = -1$, substitute -1 for x and solve: $4 - 2(-1) = 4 + 2 = 6$.
For $x = 0$, substitute 0 for x and solve: $4 - 2(0) = 4 + 0 = 4$.
For $x = 1$, substitute 1 for x and solve: $4 - 2(1) = 4 - 2 = 2$.
For $x = 2$, substitute 2 for x and solve: $4 - 2(2) = 4 - 4 = 0$.
See Figure 23. From the table, we see that the equation $4 - 2x = 6$ is true when $x = -1$. Therefore, the solution to the equation $4 - 2x = 6$ is $x = -1$.

Solving Linear Equations

25. $11x = 3 \Rightarrow \dfrac{11x}{11} = \dfrac{3}{11} \Rightarrow x = \dfrac{3}{11}$

27. $x - 18 = 5 \Rightarrow x - 18 + 18 = 5 + 18 \Rightarrow x = 23$

29. $2x - 1 = 13 \Rightarrow 2x - 1 + 1 = 13 + 1 \Rightarrow 2x = 14 \Rightarrow \dfrac{2x}{2} = \dfrac{14}{2} \Rightarrow x = 7$

31. $5x + 5 = -6 \Rightarrow 5x + 5 - 5 = -6 - 5 \Rightarrow 5x = -11 \Rightarrow \dfrac{5x}{5} = \dfrac{-11}{5} \Rightarrow x = -\dfrac{11}{5}$

33. $3z + 2 = z - 5 \Rightarrow 3z + 2 - 2 = z - 5 - 2 \Rightarrow 3z = z - 7 \Rightarrow 3z - z = z - z - 7 \Rightarrow 2z = -7 \Rightarrow$
$\dfrac{2z}{2} = \dfrac{-7}{2} \Rightarrow z = -\dfrac{7}{2}$

35. $12y - 6 = 33 - y \Rightarrow 12y - 6 + 6 = 33 + 6 - y \Rightarrow 12y = 39 - y \Rightarrow 12y + y = 39 - y + y \Rightarrow$
$13y = 39 \Rightarrow \dfrac{13y}{13} = \dfrac{39}{13} \Rightarrow y = 3$

37. $4(x - 1) = 5 \Rightarrow 4x - 4 = 5 \Rightarrow 4x - 4 + 4 = 5 + 4 \Rightarrow 4x = 9 \Rightarrow \dfrac{4x}{4} = \dfrac{9}{4} \Rightarrow x = \dfrac{9}{4}$

39. $1 - (3x + 1) = 5 - x \Rightarrow 1 - 3x - 1 = 5 - x \Rightarrow -3x = 5 - x \Rightarrow -3x + x = 5 - x + x \Rightarrow$
$-2x = 5 \Rightarrow \frac{-2x}{-2} = \frac{5}{-2} \Rightarrow x = -\frac{5}{2}$

41. $5t - 6 + 2(t + 1) = 0 \Rightarrow 5t - 6 + 2t + 2 = 0 \Rightarrow 7t - 4 = 0 \Rightarrow 7t - 4 + 4 = 0 + 4 \Rightarrow$
$7t = 4 \Rightarrow \frac{7t}{7} = \frac{4}{7} \Rightarrow t = \frac{4}{7}$

43. $3(4z - 1) - 2(z + 2) = 2(z + 1) \Rightarrow 12z - 3 - 2z - 4 = 2z + 2 \Rightarrow 10z - 7 = 2z + 2 \Rightarrow$
$10z - 7 - 2 = 2z + 2 - 2 \Rightarrow 10z - 9 = 2z \Rightarrow 10z - 9 + 9 = 2z + 9 \Rightarrow 10z = 2z + 9 \Rightarrow$
$10z - 2z = 2z - 2z + 9 \Rightarrow 8z = 9 \Rightarrow \frac{8z}{8} = \frac{9}{8} \Rightarrow z = \frac{9}{8}$

45. $7.3x - 1.7 = 5.6 \Rightarrow 7.3x - 1.7 + 1.7 = 5.6 + 1.7 \Rightarrow 7.3x = 7.3 \Rightarrow \frac{7.3x}{7.3} = \frac{7.3}{7.3} \Rightarrow x = 1$

47. $-9.5x - 0.05 = 10.5x + 1.05 \Rightarrow -9.5x - 10.5x - 0.05 = 10.5x - 10.5x + 1.05 \Rightarrow$
$-20x - 0.05 = 1.05 \Rightarrow -20x - 0.05 + 0.05 = 1.05 + 0.05 \Rightarrow -20x = 1.1 \Rightarrow \frac{-20x}{-20} = \frac{1.1}{-20} \Rightarrow$
$x = -0.055$

49. $\frac{1}{2}x - \frac{3}{2} = \frac{5}{2} \Rightarrow \frac{1}{2}x - \frac{3}{2} + \frac{3}{2} = \frac{5}{2} + \frac{3}{2} \Rightarrow \frac{1}{2}x = 4 \Rightarrow 2 \cdot \frac{1}{2}x = 4 \cdot 2 \Rightarrow x = 8$

51. $-\frac{3}{8}x + \frac{1}{4} = \frac{1}{2}x + \frac{1}{8} \Rightarrow -\frac{3}{8}x - \frac{1}{2}x + \frac{1}{4} = \frac{1}{2}x - \frac{1}{2}x + \frac{1}{8} \Rightarrow -\frac{7}{8}x + \frac{1}{4} = \frac{1}{8} \Rightarrow$
$-\frac{7}{8}x + \frac{1}{4} - \frac{1}{4} = \frac{1}{8} - \frac{1}{4} \Rightarrow -\frac{7}{8}x = -\frac{1}{8} \Rightarrow \left(-\frac{8}{7}\right)\left(-\frac{7}{8}\right)x = \left(-\frac{1}{8}\right)\left(-\frac{8}{7}\right) \Rightarrow x = \frac{8}{56} \Rightarrow x = \frac{1}{7}$

53. $4y - 2(y + 1) = 0 \Rightarrow 47 - 2y - 2 = 0 \Rightarrow 2y - 2 = 0 \Rightarrow 2y - 2 + 2 = 0 + 2 \Rightarrow 2y = 2 \Rightarrow$
$\frac{2y}{2} = \frac{2}{2} \Rightarrow y = 1$

55. $5x = 5x + 1 \Rightarrow 5x - 5x = 5x - 5x + 1 \Rightarrow 0 = 1$
Because the equation $0 = 1$ is always false, there are zero solutions.

57. $8x = 0 \Rightarrow \frac{8x}{8} = \frac{0}{8} \Rightarrow x = 0$ Thus, there is only one solution.

59. $4(x + 2) - 2(2x + 3) = 10 \Rightarrow 4x + 8 - 4x - 6 = 10 \Rightarrow 8 - 6 = 10 \Rightarrow 2 = 10$
Because the equation $2 = 10$ is always false, there are zero solutions.

61. $4x = 5(x + 3) - x \Rightarrow 4x = 5x + 15 - x \Rightarrow 4x = 4x + 15 \Rightarrow 43x - 4x = 4x - 4x + 15 \Rightarrow 0 = 15$
Because the equation $0 = 15$ is always false, there are zero solutions.

63. $2x - (x + 5) = x - 5 \Rightarrow 2x - x - 5 = x - 5 \Rightarrow x - 5 = x - 5 \Rightarrow x - x - 5 = x - x - 5 \Rightarrow$
$-5 = -5$ Since the equation $-5 = -5$ is always true, there are infinitely many solutions.

Applications

65. (a) See Figure 65.

(b) Let D represent the distance from home and x represent the number of hours. Then $D = 4 + 8x$.

(c) Substitute 3 for x. Then, $D = 4 + 8(3) = 28$ miles. This agrees with the value found in the table.

(d) Using the formula $D = 4 + 8x$, substitute 22 for D. Then, $22 = 4 + 8x$. Then, solving for x:
$22 - 4 = 4 - 4 + 8x \Rightarrow 18 = 8x \Rightarrow \frac{18}{8} = \frac{8x}{8} \Rightarrow \frac{9}{4} = x \Rightarrow x = 2.25$ miles. Thus, the bicyclist is 22 miles from home after 2 hours and 15 minutes.

Hours (x)	0	1	2	3	4
Distance (D)	4	12	20	28	36

Figure 65

x	3	3.5	4	4.5	5
$4x - 3$	9	11	13	15	17

Figure 1

67. Using the formula, substitute 815 for N and solve for x. $815 = 40x - 79{,}065 \Rightarrow$

$$815 + 79{,}065 = 40x - 79{,}065 + 79{,}065 \Rightarrow 79{,}880 = 40x \Rightarrow \frac{79{,}880}{40} = \frac{40x}{40} \Rightarrow 1997 = x \Rightarrow x = 1997$$

69. Using the formula, substitute 908 for N and solve for x. $908 = 70x - 138{,}532 \Rightarrow$

$$908 + 138{,}532 = 70x - 138{,}532 + 138{,}532 \Rightarrow 139{,}440 = 70x \Rightarrow \frac{139{,}440}{70} = \frac{70x}{70} \Rightarrow 1992 = x \Rightarrow$$

$x = 1992$

Checking Basic Concepts for Sections 2.1 & 2.2

1. For $x = 3$, substitute 3 for x and solve: $4(3) - 3 = 12 - 3 = 9$

   For $x = 3.5$, substitute 3.5 for x and solve: $4(3.5) - 3 = 14 - 3 = 11$

   For $x = 4$, substitute 4 for x and solve: $4(4) - 3 = 16 - 3 = 13$

   For $x = 4.5$, substitute 4.5 for x and solve: $4(4.5) - 3 = 18 - 3 = 15$

   For $x = 5$, substitute 5 for x and solve: $4(5) - 3 = 20 - 3 = 17$

   See Figure 1. To solve $4x - 3 = 13$, the table tells us that when $x = 4$, $4x - 3 = 13$.

2. (a) $x - 12 = 6 \Rightarrow x - 12 + 12 = 6 + 12 \Rightarrow x = 18$ To check the answer, substitute 18 for x in the original equation $x - 12 = 6$. $18 - 12 = 6 \Rightarrow 6 = 6$. Since this is true $x = 18$ is correct.

   (b) $\frac{3}{4}z = \frac{1}{8} \Rightarrow \frac{4}{3} \cdot \frac{3}{4}z = \frac{1}{8} \cdot \frac{4}{3} \Rightarrow z = \frac{4}{24} \Rightarrow z = \frac{1}{6}$

   (c) $0.6t + 0.4 = 2 \Rightarrow 0.6t + 0.4 - 0.4 = 2 - 0.4 \Rightarrow 0.6t = 1.6 \Rightarrow \frac{0.6t}{0.6} = \frac{1.6}{0.6} \Rightarrow t = 2.\overline{6}$

   (d) $5 - 2(x - 2) = 3(4 - x) \Rightarrow 5 - 2x + 4 = 12 - 3x \Rightarrow 9 - 2x = 12 - 3x \Rightarrow$

   $9 - 2x + 3x = 12 - 3x + 3x \Rightarrow 9 + x = 12 \Rightarrow 9 - 9 + x = 12 - 9 \Rightarrow x = 3$

3. (a) $x - 5 = 6x \Rightarrow x - x - 5 = 6x - x \Rightarrow -5 = 5x \Rightarrow \frac{-5}{5} = \frac{5x}{5} \Rightarrow -1 = x$. Thus, the equation has 1 solution.

   (b) $-2(x - 5) = 10 - 2x \Rightarrow -2x + 10 = 10 - 2x \Rightarrow -2x + 2x + 10 = 10 - 2x + 2x \Rightarrow 10 = 10$

   Since $10 = 10$ is always true, the equation has infinitely many solutions.

   (c) $-(x - 1) = -x - 1 \Rightarrow -x + 1 = -x - 1 \Rightarrow -x + x + 1 = -x + x - 1 \Rightarrow 1 = -1$

   Since this is never true, the equation has zero solutions.

4. (a) Let D represent distance from home and x represent hours driven. Note that the driver is initially 300 miles from home and that each hour driven the driver gets closer to home by 75 miles. Thus, the formula is $D = 300 - 75x$.

   (b) Since the distance from home, when the drive is home, is 0, use the formula and set D equal to 0. Thus, $0 = 300 - 75x$.

   (c) $0 = 300 - 75x \Rightarrow 0 + 75x = 300 - 75x + 75x \Rightarrow 75x = 300 \Rightarrow \frac{75x}{75} = \frac{300}{75} \Rightarrow x = 4$ hours.

2.3: Introduction to Problem Solving

Concepts

1. Check your solution

3. $\frac{x}{100}$

5. 50

7. $\frac{P_2 - P_1}{P_1} \times 100$

Number Problems

9. Let x represent the number. $2 + x = 12 \Rightarrow 2 - 2 + x = 12 - 2 \Rightarrow x = 10$

11. $\frac{x}{5} = x - 24 \Rightarrow \frac{x}{5} \cdot 5 = 5(x - 24) \Rightarrow x = 5x - 120 \Rightarrow x - 5x = 5x - 5x - 120 \Rightarrow -4x = -120 \Rightarrow$
$\frac{-4x}{-4} = \frac{-120}{-4} \Rightarrow x = 30$

13. $\frac{x + 5}{2} = 7 \Rightarrow \frac{x + 2}{2} \cdot 2 = 7 \cdot 2 \Rightarrow x + 5 = 14 \Rightarrow x + 5 - 5 = 14 - 5 \Rightarrow x = 9$

15. $\frac{x}{2} = 17 \Rightarrow \frac{x}{2} \cdot 2 = 17 \cdot 2 \Rightarrow x = 34$

17. Let the smallest natural number be represented by x. $x + (x + 1) + (x + 2) = 96 \Rightarrow 3x + 3 = 96 \Rightarrow$
$3x + 3 - 3 = 96 - 3 \Rightarrow 3x = 93 \Rightarrow \frac{3x}{3} = \frac{93}{3} \Rightarrow x = 31$ Thus, the numbers are 31, 32 and 33.

19. $3x = 102 \Rightarrow \frac{3x}{3} = \frac{102}{3} \Rightarrow x = 34$

21. $5x = 2x + 24 \Rightarrow 5x - 2x = 2x - 2x + 24 \Rightarrow 3x = 24 \Rightarrow \frac{3x}{3} = \frac{24}{3} \Rightarrow x = 8$

23. $\frac{6x}{7} = 18 \Rightarrow \frac{6x}{7} \cdot 7 = 18 \cdot 7 \Rightarrow 6x = 126 \Rightarrow \frac{6x}{6} = \frac{126}{6} \Rightarrow x = 21$

25. $4(x + 5) = 64 \Rightarrow 4x + 20 = 64 \Rightarrow 4x + 20 - 20 = 64 - 20 \Rightarrow 4x = 44 \Rightarrow \frac{4x}{4} = \frac{44}{4} \Rightarrow x = 11$

Percent Problems

27. $37\% = \frac{37}{100}$
$37\% = 37 \times 0.01 = 0.37$

29. $148\% = \frac{148}{100} = \frac{37 \cdot 4}{25 \cdot 4} = \frac{37}{25}$
$148\% = 148 \times 0.01 = 1.48$

31. $6.9\% = \frac{6.9}{100} = \frac{6.9}{100} \cdot \frac{10}{10} = \frac{69}{1000}$
$6.9\% = 6.9 \times 0.01 = 0.069$

33. $0.05\% = \frac{0.05}{100} = \frac{0.05}{100} \cdot \frac{100}{100} = \frac{5}{10{,}000} = \frac{1 \cdot 5}{2000 \cdot 5} = \frac{1}{2000}$
$0.05\% = 0.05 \times 0.01 = 0.0005$

35. $0.45 = 0.45 \times 100 = 45\%$

37. $1.8 = 1.8 \times 100 = 180\%$

39. $\frac{2}{5} = 0.4 = 0.4 \times 100 = 40\%$

41. $\frac{3}{4} = 0.75 = 0.75 \times 100 = 75\%$

43. $\frac{5}{6} = 0.83\overline{3} = 0.83\overline{3} \times 100 = 83.\overline{3}\%$

45. Let P_2 represent voters in 2000 and let P_1 represent voters in 1980. Then, the percent change in the number of voters is $\frac{P_2 - P_1}{P_1} = \frac{105.4 - 86.5}{86.5} = \frac{18.9}{86.5} \approx .218$ or about 21.8%.

47. Calculate the value of 4% of 950, then add the value to 950. Thus, 4% of 950 $= .04(950) = 38$. Then, $950 + 38 = \$988$ per credit.

49. Let x represent the number of returns in 1998. Then, $\frac{125 - x}{x} = 0.0162 \Rightarrow \frac{125 - x}{x} \cdot x = 0.0162 \cdot x \Rightarrow$ $125 - x = 0.0162x \Rightarrow 125 - x + x = 0.0162x + x \Rightarrow 125 = 1.0162x \Rightarrow \frac{125}{1.0162} = \frac{1.0162x}{1.0162} \Rightarrow$ $123 \approx x \Rightarrow x \approx 123$ Thus, about 123 million returns were processed in 1998.

51. Let x represent the number of AIDS deaths in 1995. Then, $0.345x = 17{,}047 \Rightarrow \frac{0.345x}{0.345} = \frac{17{,}047}{0.345} \Rightarrow$ $x \approx 49{,}412$ Thus, there were about 49,412 AIDS deaths in 1995.

53. To calculate the number of people participating in the survey, let x represent the unknown number and note that 480 is 32% of the unknown number. Then, $0.32x = 480 \Rightarrow \frac{0.32x}{0.32} = \frac{480}{0.32} \Rightarrow x = 1500$ Thus, 1500 people participated in the survey.

Distance Problems

55. $d = rt \Rightarrow d = 4 \cdot 2 \Rightarrow d = 8$ miles

57. $d = rt \Rightarrow 1000 = r \cdot 50 \Rightarrow \frac{1000}{50} = \frac{r \cdot 50}{50} \Rightarrow 20 = r \Rightarrow r = 20$ feet/second

59. $d = rt \Rightarrow 200 = 40t \Rightarrow \frac{200}{40} = \frac{40t}{40} \Rightarrow 5 = t \Rightarrow t = 5$ hours

61. Given that the distance traveled (d) is 255 and that the time spent traveling (t) is 4.25 hours, calculate the speed of the car (r). Then, $d = rt \Rightarrow 255 = r \cdot 4.25 \Rightarrow \frac{255}{4.25} = \frac{r \cdot 4.25}{4.25} \Rightarrow 60 = r \Rightarrow r = 60$ miles/hour.

63. Let the slower runner be standing still. Then, the faster runner will be traveling at $0 + 2$ mph. Then, this problem is equivalent to solving how long it takes the faster runner to travel $\frac{3}{4}$ of a mile. Using the $d = rt$ formula: $\frac{3}{4} = 2t \Rightarrow \frac{3}{4} \cdot \frac{1}{2} = \frac{2}{1} \cdot \frac{1}{2}t \Rightarrow \frac{3}{8} = t \Rightarrow t = \frac{3}{8}$. So, in $\frac{3}{8}$ hour the faster runner will be $\frac{3}{4}$ mile ahead of the slower runner.

65. Let x represent the amount of time spent running 5 mph. Since the total time spent running was 1.3 hours, let $1.3 - x$ represent the amount of time running at 6 mph. Using the $d = rt$ formula, the distance run will equal the sum of $5x$ and $6(1.3 - x)$. Thus, $7 = 5x + 6(1.3 - x) \Rightarrow 7 = 5x + 7.8 - 6x \Rightarrow 7 = 7.8 - x \Rightarrow$ $x + 7 = 7.8 - x + x \Rightarrow x + 7 = 7.8 \Rightarrow x + 7 - 7 = 7.8 - 7 \Rightarrow x = 0.8$. Therefore, the athlete ran at 5 mph for 0.8 hour and ran at 6 mph for $(1.3 - 0.8) = 0.5$ hour.

67. Since the plane is already 300 miles west of Chicago, it will have to fly $2175 - 300 = 1875$ miles to be 2175 miles west of Chicago. The plane is traveling at 500 mph. Then, $1875 = 500t \Rightarrow \frac{1875}{500} = \frac{500t}{500} \Rightarrow 3.75 = t \Rightarrow t = 3.75$. Therefore, it will take the plane 3.75 hours to be 2175 miles west of Chicago.

Other Types of Problems

69. Let x represent the amount of water that should be added. Note that there is no salt in pure water and that we will add the amount of pure water to the 3% salt solution to obtain a 1.2% solution. Therefore, set up the equation so that the amount of salt on both sides of the equation is equal. Thus, $x(0.00) + 20(0.03) = (x + 20)(0.012) \Rightarrow 0.00x + 0.6 = 0.012x + 0.24 \Rightarrow$ $0.6 - 0.24 = 0.012x + 0.24 - 0.24 \Rightarrow 0.36 = 0.012x \Rightarrow \frac{0.36}{0.012} = \frac{0.012x}{0.012} \Rightarrow 30 = x \Rightarrow x = 30$. Therefore, 30 ounces of water should be added.

71. Let x represent the amount of the loan at 6% and let $x + 1000$ represent the amount of the loan at 5%. The total interest for one year is \$215 and this is the sum of the interest paid on the two loans. Therefore: $0.06x + 0.05(x + 1000) = 215 \Rightarrow 0.06x + 0.05x + 50 = 215 \Rightarrow 0.11x + 50 - 50 = 215 - 50 \Rightarrow$ $0.11x = 165 \Rightarrow \frac{0.11x}{0.11} = \frac{165}{0.11} \Rightarrow x = 1500$. Therefore, the amount of the loan at 6% interest is \$1500 and the amount of the loan at 5% interest is $1500 + 1000 = \$2500$.

73. Let x represent the amount of 70% antifreeze. Then, the 45% antifreeze mixture is the sum of the 70% mixture and the 30% mixture. Therefore: $0.7x + 10(0.3) = (x + 10)(0.45) \Rightarrow 0.7x + 3 = 0.45x + 4.5 \Rightarrow$ $0.7x + 3 - 3 = 0.45x + 4.5 - 3 \Rightarrow 0.7x = 0.45x + 1.5 \Rightarrow 0.7x - 0.45x = 0.45x - 0.45x + 1.5 \Rightarrow$ $0.25x = 1.5 \Rightarrow \frac{0.25x}{0.25} = \frac{1.5}{0.25} \Rightarrow x = 6$. Therefore, 6 gallons of 70% antifreeze should be mixed with 10 gallons of 30% antifreeze to obtain the 45% mixture.

2.4: Formulas

Concepts

1. formula

3. $\frac{1}{2}bh$

5. 360

7. $2\pi r$

9. lwh

Formulas from Geometry

11. $A = lw$. Thus, $A = 6 \cdot 3 = 18 \text{ ft}^2$.

13. $A = \frac{1}{2}bh$. Thus, $A = \frac{1}{2} \cdot 6 \cdot 3 = 9 \text{ in}^2$.

15. $A = \pi r^2$. Thus, $A = \pi 4^2 \approx 50.3 \text{ ft}^2$.

17. $A = \frac{1}{2}(a + b)h$. Thus, $A = \frac{1}{2}(5 + 6)2 = \frac{1}{2}(11)2 = 11 \text{ ft}^2$.

19. $A = lw$. Thus, $A = 13 \cdot 7 = 91 \text{ in}^2$.

21. $A = \frac{1}{2}bh$. Thus, $A = \frac{1}{2} \cdot 12 \cdot 6 = 36 \text{ in}^2$.

23. $C = 2\pi r$. Because the circle has a diameter of 8 inches, the radius is $= \frac{8}{2} = 4$ inches. Thus, $C = 2\pi r = 2\pi 4 = 8\pi \approx 25.1$ inches.

25. The total area of the lot is the sum of the area of the square and the area of the triangle. The area of the square is $lw = 52 \cdot 52 = 2704 \text{ ft}^2$. The area of the triangle is $\frac{1}{2}bh = \frac{1}{2} \cdot 73 \cdot 52 = 1898 \text{ ft}^2$. Thus, the area of the lot is $1898 + 2704 = 4602 \text{ ft}^2$.

27. The sum of the angles of a triangle is 180°. Let the unknown angle be represented by x. Then, $x + 75 + 40 = 180 \Rightarrow x + 75 + 40 - 75 - 40 = 180 - 75 - 40 \Rightarrow x = 65$. Thus, the third angle is 65°.

29. The sum of the angles of a triangle is 180°. Let the unknown angle be represented by x. Then, $x + 23 + 76 = 180 \Rightarrow x + 23 + 76 - 23 - 76 = 180 - 23 - 76 \Rightarrow x = 81$. Thus, the third angle is 81°.

31. Because the sum of the angles of a triangle is 180, $x + 2x + 3x = 180 \Rightarrow 6x = 180 \Rightarrow \frac{6x}{6} = \frac{180}{6} \Rightarrow$ $x = 30$. Thus, the value of x is 30°.

33. Let x represent the largest angle. Then, $x + \frac{1}{3}x + \frac{1}{3}x = 180 \Rightarrow \frac{5}{3}x = 180 \Rightarrow \frac{3}{5} \cdot \frac{5}{3}x = \frac{180}{1} \cdot \frac{3}{5} \Rightarrow$ $x = \frac{540}{5} \Rightarrow x = 108$. Thus, the largest angle has a measure of 108° and the two small angles each have measure $\frac{1}{3} \cdot \frac{108}{1} = \frac{108}{3} = 36°$.

35. $C = 2\pi r$. Since the diameter of the circle is 12 inches, the radius is $\frac{12}{2} = 6$ inches. Then, $C = 2\pi 6 = 12\pi \approx 37.7$ inches. Then, $A = \pi r^2 = \pi 6^2 = 36\pi \approx 113.1 \text{ in}^2$.

37. $C = 2\pi r$. Then, set C equal to 2π and solve for r. $2\pi = 2\pi r \Rightarrow \frac{2\pi}{2\pi} = \frac{2\pi r}{2\pi} \Rightarrow 1 = r \Rightarrow r = 1$ inch. Then, $A = \pi r^2$. Because $r = 1$, substitute 1 for r and solve for A. $A = \pi(1)^2 = \pi$. Thus, the area is equal to π, which is approximately equal to 3.1 in^2.

39. $V = lwh$. Thus, $V = 22 \cdot 12 \cdot 10 = 2640 \text{ in}^3$. Surface area equals $2lw + 2lh + 2wh$. Thus, $S = 2 \cdot 22 \cdot 12 + 2 \cdot 22 \cdot 10 + 2 \cdot 12 \cdot 10 = 528 + 440 + 240 = 1208 \text{ in}^2$.

41. Convert yards to feet. Then, $\frac{2}{3}$ yard $= \frac{2}{3} \cdot 3 = 2$ feet. Then, $V = lwh = 2 \cdot \frac{2}{3} \cdot \frac{3}{2} = 2 \text{ ft}^3$. Surface area equals $2lw + 2lh + 2wh$. Thus, $S = 2 \cdot 2 \cdot \frac{2}{3} + 2 \cdot 2 \cdot \frac{3}{2} + 2 \cdot \frac{2}{3} \cdot \frac{3}{2} = \frac{8}{3} + 6 + 2 = 8\frac{8}{3} = 10\frac{2}{3} \text{ ft}^2$.

43. $V = \pi r^2 h$. Thus, $V = \pi 2^2 \cdot 5 = \pi \cdot 4 \cdot 5 = 20\pi \text{ in}^3$.

45. Convert feet to inches to obtain $h = 2$ feet $= 2 \cdot 12 = 24$ inches. Then, $V = \pi r^2 h$. Thus, $V = \pi 5^2 \cdot 24 = \pi \cdot 25 \cdot 24 = 600\pi \text{ in}^3$.

47. The volume formula for a cylindrical container is given by $V = \pi r^2 h$. Because the diameter of the barrel is $1\frac{3}{4} = \frac{7}{4}$ feet, the radius is $\left(\frac{1}{2}\right)\left(\frac{7}{4}\right) = \frac{7}{8}$ feet. Thus, $V = \pi r^2 h = \pi\left(\frac{7}{8}\right)^2(3) = \pi\left(\frac{49}{64}\right)(3) = \pi\left(\frac{147}{64}\right) = \frac{147}{64}\pi \approx 7.2 \text{ ft}^3$.

Solving for a Variable

49. The formula is given as $A = lw$. To solve for W, proceed as follows: $A = lw \Rightarrow \frac{A}{l} = \frac{lw}{l} \Rightarrow w = \frac{A}{l}$.

51. The formula is given as $V = \pi r^2 h$. To solve for h, proceed as follows: $V = \pi r^2 h \Rightarrow \frac{V}{\pi r^2} = \frac{\pi r^2 h}{\pi r^2} \Rightarrow h = \frac{V}{\pi r^2}$.

53. The formula is given as $\frac{1}{2}(a + b)h = A$. To solve for a, proceed as follows: $A = \frac{1}{2}(a + b)h \Rightarrow 2A = \frac{1}{2}(2)(a + b)h \Rightarrow 2A = (a + b)h \Rightarrow \frac{2A}{h} = \frac{(a + b)h}{h} \Rightarrow \frac{2A}{h} = a + b \Rightarrow \frac{2A}{h} - b = a + b - b \Rightarrow a = \frac{2A}{h} - b$.

55. The formula is given as $V = lwh$. To solve for W, proceed as follows: $V = lwh \Rightarrow \frac{V}{lh} = \frac{lwh}{lh} \Rightarrow w = \frac{V}{lh}$.

57. $s = \frac{a + b + c}{2} \Rightarrow 2s = \frac{a + b + c}{2} \cdot 2 \Rightarrow 2s = a + b + c \Rightarrow 2s - a - c = a + b + c - a - c \Rightarrow 2s - a - c = b \Rightarrow b = 2s - a - c$

59. $\frac{a}{b} - \frac{c}{b} = 1 \Rightarrow b\left(\frac{a}{b} - \frac{c}{b}\right) = 1(b) \Rightarrow a - c = b \Rightarrow b = a - c$

61. $ab = cd + ad \Rightarrow ab - ad = cd + ad - ad \Rightarrow ab - ad = cd \Rightarrow a(b - d) = cd \Rightarrow \frac{a(b - d)}{(b - d)} = \frac{cd}{(b - d)} \Rightarrow a = \frac{cd}{b - d}$

63. Because the perimeter equals the lengths of the four sides, $P = 2w + 2l$. Thus, $P = 2w + 2l \Rightarrow 40 = 2(5) + 2l \Rightarrow 40 = 10 + 2l \Rightarrow 40 - 10 = 10 + 2l - 10 \Rightarrow 2l = 30 \Rightarrow \frac{2l}{2} = \frac{30}{2} \Rightarrow l = 15$

Thus, the length of the rectangle is 15 inches.

Other Formulas and Applications

65. The formula for GPA is given by $\dfrac{4a + 3b + 2c + d}{a + b + c + d + f}$.

$$\frac{4(30) + 3(45) + 2(12) + 1(4)}{30 + 45 + 12 + 4 + 4} = \frac{120 + 135 + 24 + 4}{95} = \frac{283}{95} \approx 2.98.$$ Thus, the GPA is 2.98.

67. The formula for GPA is given by $\dfrac{4a + 3b + 2c + d}{a + b + c + d + f}$.

$$\frac{4(0) + 3(60) + 2(80) + 1(10)}{0 + 60 + 80 + 10 + 6} = \frac{0 + 180 + 160 + 10}{156} = \frac{350}{156} \approx 2.24.$$ Thus, the GPA is 2.24.

69. To convert Celsius to Fahrenheit temperature, the formula given is $\frac{9}{5}C + 32 = F$.

$$\frac{9}{5}(25) + 32 = F \Rightarrow \frac{225}{5} + \frac{160}{5} = F \Rightarrow \frac{385}{5} = F \Rightarrow F = 77°\text{F}.$$

71. To convert Celsius to Fahrenheit temperature, the formula given is $\frac{9}{5}C + 32 = F$.

$$\frac{9}{5}(-40) + 32 = F \Rightarrow \frac{-360}{5} + \frac{160}{5} = F \Rightarrow \frac{-200}{5} = F \Rightarrow F = -40°\text{F}.$$

73. To convert Fahrenheit to Celsius temperature, the formula given is $C = \frac{5}{9}(F - 32)$.

$$C = \frac{5}{9}(23 - 32) \Rightarrow C = \frac{5}{9}(-9) \Rightarrow C = \frac{-45}{9} \Rightarrow C = -5°\text{C}.$$

75. To convert Fahrenheit to Celsius temperature, the formula given is $C = \frac{5}{9}(F - 32)$.

$$C = \frac{5}{9}(-4 - 32) \Rightarrow C = \frac{5}{9}(-36) \Rightarrow C = \frac{-180}{9} \Rightarrow C = -20°\text{C}.$$

77. The formula given for calculating the delay between seeing lightning and hearing the thunder is $D = \frac{x}{5}$ where D represents the distance form the lightning and x represents the delay. Therefore, $D = \frac{x}{5} \Rightarrow D = \frac{12}{5} \Rightarrow$ $D = 2\frac{2}{5} = 2.4$ miles.

Checking Basic Concepts for Sections 2.3 & 2.4

1. (a) $3x = 36 \Rightarrow \frac{3x}{3} = \frac{36}{3} \Rightarrow x = 12$

   (b) $35 - x = 43 \Rightarrow 35 - 35 - x = 43 - 35 \Rightarrow -x = 8 \Rightarrow -1(x) = 8(-1) \Rightarrow x = -8$

2. $x + (x + 1) + (x + 2) = -93 \Rightarrow 3x + 3 = -93 \Rightarrow 3x + 3 - 3 = -93 - 3 \Rightarrow 3x = -96 \Rightarrow$ $\frac{3x}{3} = \frac{-96}{3} \Rightarrow x = -32$. The three consecutive integers are $-32, -31, -30$.

3. $9.5\% = 0.095$

4. $\frac{5}{4} = 1\frac{1}{4} = 1.25 = 125\%$

5. Convert 8% to the decimal 0.08 and let x represent the unknown rate. Therefore, $x - 0.08x = 3850$. Thus, $x - 0.08x = 3850 \Rightarrow 0.92x = 3850 \Rightarrow \frac{0.92x}{0.92} = \frac{3850}{0.92} \Rightarrow x \approx 4285$. Thus, the rate in 1998 was about 4185.

6. Use the formula $D = rt$, where D is distance, r is the speed and t is the time. Thus, $390 = 60t \Rightarrow$ $\frac{390}{60} = \frac{60t}{60} \Rightarrow 6.5 = t$. Thus, the travel time is 6.5 hours.

7. Let x represent the amount of the loan at 7% and $x + 2000$ represent the amount of the loan at 6%. Thus, $0.07x + 0.06(x + 2000) = 510 \Rightarrow 0.07x + 0.06x + 120 = 510 \Rightarrow 0.13x + 120 - 120 = 510 - 120 \Rightarrow$ $0.13x = 390 \Rightarrow \frac{0.13x}{0.13} = \frac{390}{0.13} \Rightarrow x = 3000$. Thus, the loan at 7% was \$3000 and the loan at 6% was \$5000.

8. The area of a triangle is given by $A = \frac{1}{2}bh$. Thus, $A = \frac{1}{2}bh \Rightarrow 36 = \frac{1}{2}(6)h \Rightarrow 36 = 3h \Rightarrow \frac{36}{3} = \frac{3h}{3} \Rightarrow$ $12 = h$. Thus, the height of the triangle is 12 inches.

9. The area of a circle is given by $A = \pi r^2$. Thus, $A = \pi r^2 \Rightarrow A = \pi(3)^2 \Rightarrow A = 9\pi \approx 28.3 \text{ ft}^2$.

   The circumference of a circle is given by $C = 2\pi r$. Thus, $C = 2\pi r \Rightarrow C = 2\pi 3 \Rightarrow C = 6\pi \approx 18.8$ feet.

10. Notice that the angle denoted by $3x$ is a right angle, that is, it is an angle measuring 90º. Thus, $3x = 90 \Rightarrow \frac{3x}{3} = \frac{90}{3} \Rightarrow x = 30$. Thus, the value of x is 30º.

11. $A = \pi r^2 + \pi rl \Rightarrow A - \pi r^2 = \pi r^2 - \pi r^2 + \pi rl \Rightarrow A - \pi r^2 = \pi rl \Rightarrow \frac{A - \pi r^2}{\pi r} = \frac{\pi rl}{\pi r} \Rightarrow l = \frac{A - \pi r^2}{\pi r}$

2.5: Linear Inequalities

Concepts

1. equals sign; $<$; $\leq$; $>$; $\geq$

3. one

5. number line

7. >

9. >

Solutions and Number Line Graphs

11. 

13. 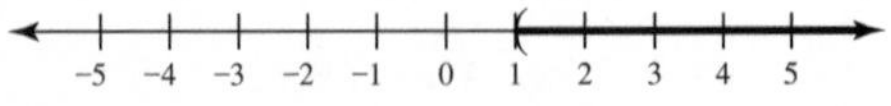

15. 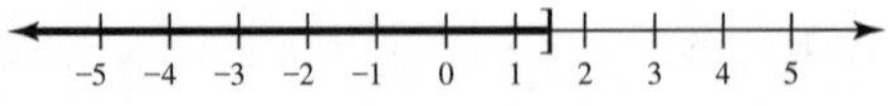

17. 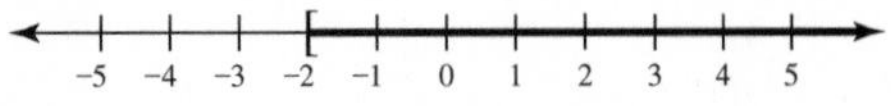

19. $x < 0$

21. $x \leq 3$

23. $x \geq 10$

25. Substitute x with 4 in order to test the inequality. Thus, $x + 5 > 5 \Rightarrow 4 + 5 > 5 \Rightarrow 9 > 5$. Because this inequality statement is true, $x = 4$ is a solution.

27. First, isolate x on one side of the statement. Thus, $5x \geq 25 \Rightarrow \frac{5x}{5} \geq \frac{25}{5} \Rightarrow x \geq 5$. Then substitute x with 5 in order to test the inequality. Thus, $x \geq 5 \Rightarrow 5 \geq 5$. Because this inequality statement is true, $x = 5$ is a solution.

29. First, isolate y on one side of the statement. Thus, $4y - 3 \leq 5 \Rightarrow 4y - 3 + 3 \leq 5 + 3 \Rightarrow 4y \leq 8 \Rightarrow \frac{4y}{4} \leq \frac{8}{4} \Rightarrow y \leq 2$. Then substitute y with -3 in order to test the inequality. Thus, $y \leq 2 \Rightarrow -3 \leq 2$. Because this inequality statement is true, $y = -3$ is a solution.

31. First, isolate z on one side of the statement. Thus, $5(z + 1) < 3z - 7 \Rightarrow 5z + 5 < 3z - 7 \Rightarrow 5z - 3z + 5 < 3z - 3z - 7 \Rightarrow 2z + 5 < -7 \Rightarrow 2z + 5 - 5 < -7 - 5 \Rightarrow 2z < -12 \Rightarrow \frac{2z}{2} < \frac{-12}{2} \Rightarrow z \leq -6$. Then substitute z with -7 in order to test the inequality. Thus, $z < -6 \Rightarrow -7 < -6$. Because this inequality statement is true, $z = -7$ is a solution.

33. First, isolate t on one side of the statement. Thus, $\frac{3}{2}t - \frac{1}{2} \geq 1 - t \Rightarrow \frac{3}{2}t + t - \frac{1}{2} \geq 1 - t + t \Rightarrow \frac{5}{2}t - \frac{1}{2} \geq 1 \Rightarrow \frac{5}{2}t - \frac{1}{2} + \frac{1}{2} \geq 1 + \frac{1}{2} \Rightarrow \frac{5}{2}t \geq \frac{3}{2} \Rightarrow \frac{2}{5} \cdot \frac{5}{2}t \geq \frac{3}{2} \cdot \frac{2}{5} \Rightarrow t \geq \frac{3}{5}$. Then substitute t with -2 in order to test the inequality. Thus, $t \geq \frac{3}{5} \Rightarrow -2 \geq \frac{3}{5}$. Because this inequality statement is not true, $t = -2$ is not a solution.

Tables and Linear Inequalities

35. $x > -2$

37. $x < 1$

39. To complete the table, insert the x value into $-2x + 6$ whenever there is a missing value in the table. Thus, $-2x + 6 \Rightarrow -2(2) + 6 \Rightarrow -4 + 6 = 2; -2x + 6 \Rightarrow -2(3) + 6 \Rightarrow -6 + 6 = 0;$ $-2x + 6 \Rightarrow -2(4) + 6 \Rightarrow -8 + 6 = -2$. Thus, the missing values in the table are 2, 0 and -2. See Figure 39. From the table, we see that $-2x + 6 \leq 0$ whenever $x \geq 3$. Thus, the solution to the inequality is $x \geq 3$.

x	1	2	3	4	5
$-2x + 6$	4	2	0	−2	−4

Figure 39

x	−3	−2	−1	0	1
$5 - x$	8	7	6	5	4
$x + 7$	4	5	6	7	8

Figure 41

41. To complete the table, insert the x value into $5 - x$ and $x + 7$ whenever there is a missing value in the table.
$5 - x \Rightarrow 5 - (-2) = 7; 5 - x \Rightarrow 5 - (-1) = 6; 5 - x \Rightarrow 5 - (0) = 5.$
Thus, the missing values in the table that correspond to $5 - x$ are 7, 6 and 5.
$x + 7 \Rightarrow (-2) + 7 = 5; x + 7 \Rightarrow (-1) + 7 = 6; x + 7 \Rightarrow (0) + 7 = 7.$
Thus, the missing values in the table that correspond to $x + 7$ are 5, 6 and 7. See Figure 41.
From the table, we see that $5 - x > x + 7$ whenever $x < -1$. Thus, the solution to the inequality is $x < -1$.

Solving Linear Inequalities

43. $x - 3 > 0 \Rightarrow x - 3 + 3 > 0 + 3 \Rightarrow x > 3$. See Figure 43.

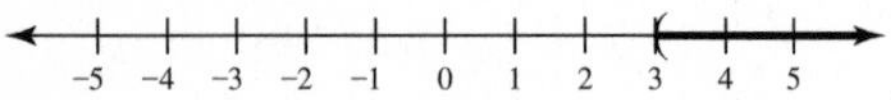

Figure 43

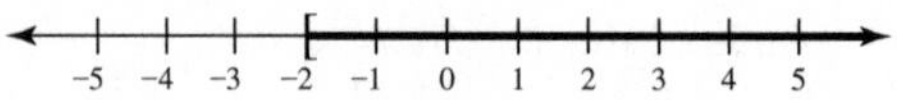

Figure 45

45. $3 - y \le 5 \Rightarrow 3 - 3 - y \le 5 - 3 \Rightarrow -y \le 2 \Rightarrow -1(-y) \ge 2(-1) \Rightarrow y \ge -2$. See Figure 45.

47. $12 < 4 + z \Rightarrow 12 - 4 < 4 - 4 + z \Rightarrow 8 < z \Rightarrow z > 8$. See Figure 47.

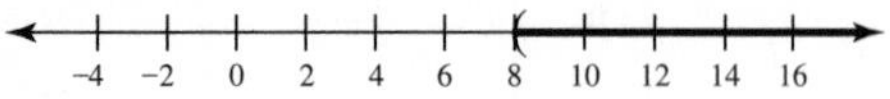

Figure 47

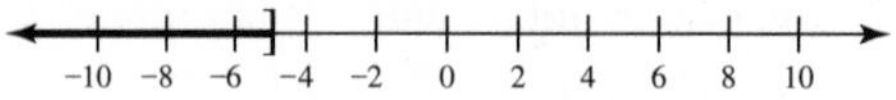

Figure 49

49. $5 - 2t \ge 10 - t \Rightarrow 5 - 2t + t \ge 10 - t + t \Rightarrow 5 - t \ge 10 \Rightarrow 5 - 5 - t \ge 10 - 5 \Rightarrow -t \ge 5 \Rightarrow$
$-1(-t) \le 5(-1) \Rightarrow t \le -5$. See Figure 49.

51. $2x < 10 \Rightarrow \frac{2x}{2} < \frac{10}{2} \Rightarrow x < 5$. See Figure 51.

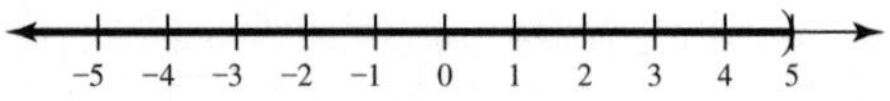

Figure 51

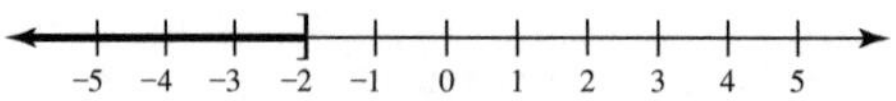

Figure 53

53. $-\frac{1}{2}t \ge 1 \Rightarrow \frac{-\frac{1}{2}t}{-\frac{1}{2}} \le \frac{1}{-\frac{1}{2}} \Rightarrow t \le -2$. See Figure 53.

55. $\frac{3}{4} > -5y \Rightarrow -5y < \frac{3}{4} \Rightarrow \frac{-5y}{-5} < \frac{\frac{3}{4}}{-5} \Rightarrow y < \frac{3}{4} \cdot \left(-\frac{1}{5}\right) \Rightarrow y > -\frac{3}{20}$. See Figure 55.

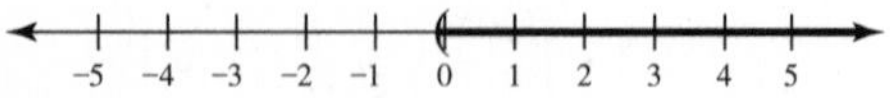

Figure 55

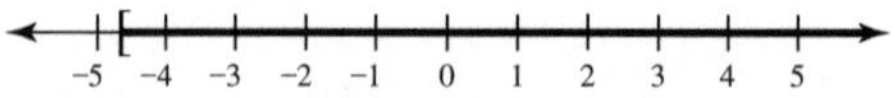

Figure 57

57. $-\frac{2}{3} \le \frac{1}{7}z \Rightarrow \frac{1}{7}z \ge -\frac{2}{3} \Rightarrow \frac{7}{1}\left(\frac{1}{7}z\right) \ge -\frac{2}{3}\left(\frac{7}{1}\right) \Rightarrow z \ge -\frac{14}{3}$. See Figure 57.

59. $3x + 1 < 22 \Rightarrow 3x + 1 - 1 < 22 - 1 \Rightarrow 3x < 21 \Rightarrow \frac{3x}{3} < \frac{21}{3} \Rightarrow x < 7 \Rightarrow \{x \mid x < 7\}$

61. $5 - \frac{3}{4}x \ge 6 \Rightarrow 5 - 5 - \frac{3}{4}x \ge 6 - 5 \Rightarrow -\frac{3}{4}x \ge 1 \Rightarrow -\frac{4}{3}\left(-\frac{3}{4}x\right) \le 1\left(-\frac{4}{3}\right) \Rightarrow x \le -\frac{4}{3} \Rightarrow \left\{x \,\middle|\, x \le -\frac{4}{3}\right\}$

63. $45 > 6 - 2x \Rightarrow 6 - 2x < 45 \Rightarrow 6 - 6 - 2x < 45 - 6 \Rightarrow -2x < 39 \Rightarrow \frac{-2x}{-2} > \frac{39}{-2} \Rightarrow x > -\frac{39}{2} \Rightarrow$
$\left\{x \,\middle|\, x > -\frac{39}{2}\right\}$

65. $5x - 2 \le 3x + 1 \Rightarrow 5x - 3x - 2 \le 3x - 3x + 1 \Rightarrow 2x - 2 \le 1 \Rightarrow 2x - 2 + 2 \le 1 + 2 \Rightarrow 2x \le 3 \Rightarrow$
$\frac{2x}{2} \le \frac{3}{2} \Rightarrow x \le \frac{3}{2} \Rightarrow \left\{x \,\middle|\, x \le \frac{3}{2}\right\}$

67. $-x + 24 < x + 23 \Rightarrow -x - x + 24 < x - x + 23 \Rightarrow -2x + 24 < 23 \Rightarrow -2x + 24 - 24 < 23 - 24 \Rightarrow$
$-2x < -1 \Rightarrow \frac{-2x}{-2} > \frac{-1}{-2} \Rightarrow x > \frac{1}{2} \Rightarrow \left\{x \,\middle|\, x > \frac{1}{2}\right\}$

69. $-(x+1) \geq 3(x-2) \Rightarrow -x-1 \geq 3x-6 \Rightarrow -x-3x-1 \geq 3x-3x-6 \Rightarrow -4x-1 \geq -6 \Rightarrow$
$-4x-1+1 \geq -6+1 \Rightarrow -4x \geq -5 \Rightarrow \dfrac{-4x}{-4} \leq \dfrac{-5}{-4} \Rightarrow x \leq \dfrac{5}{4} \Rightarrow \left\{x \,\middle|\, x \leq \dfrac{5}{4}\right\}$

71. $3(2x-1) > -(5-3x) \Rightarrow 6x+3 > -5+3x \Rightarrow 6x-3x+3 > -5+3x-3x \Rightarrow 3x+3 > -5 \Rightarrow$
$3x+3-3 > -5-3 \Rightarrow 3x > -8 \Rightarrow \dfrac{3x}{3} > \dfrac{-8}{3} \Rightarrow x > -\dfrac{8}{3} \Rightarrow \left\{x \,\middle|\, x > -\dfrac{8}{3}\right\}$

73. $-(7x+5)+1 \geq 3x-1 \Rightarrow -7x-5+1 \geq 3x-1 \Rightarrow -7x-4 \geq 3x-1 \Rightarrow$
$-7x-3x-4 \geq 3x-3x-1 \Rightarrow -10x-4 \geq -1 \Rightarrow -10x-4+4 \geq -1+4 \Rightarrow -10x \geq 3 \Rightarrow$
$\dfrac{-10x}{-10} \leq \dfrac{3}{-10} \Rightarrow x \leq -\dfrac{3}{10} \Rightarrow \left\{x \,\middle|\, x \leq -\dfrac{3}{10}\right\}$

75. $1.6x+0.4 \leq 0.4x \Rightarrow 1.6x-0.4x+0.4 \leq 0.4x-0.4x \Rightarrow 1.2x+0.4 \leq 0 \Rightarrow$
$1.2x+0.4-0.4 \leq 0-0.4 \Rightarrow 1.2x \leq -0.4 \Rightarrow \dfrac{1.2x}{1.2} \leq \dfrac{-0.4}{1.2} \Rightarrow x \leq -\dfrac{1}{3} \Rightarrow \left\{x \,\middle|\, x \leq -\dfrac{1}{3}\right\}$

77. $0.8x-0.5 < x+1-0.5x \Rightarrow 0.8x-0.5 < 0.5x+1 \Rightarrow 0.8x-0.5x-0.5 < 0.5x-0.5x+1 \Rightarrow$
$0.3x-0.5 < 1 \Rightarrow 0.3x-0.5+0.5 < 1+0.5 \Rightarrow 0.3x < 1.5 \Rightarrow \dfrac{0.3x}{0.3} < \dfrac{1.5}{0.3} \Rightarrow x < 5 \Rightarrow \{x \mid x < 5\}$

79. $-\dfrac{1}{2}\left(\dfrac{2}{3}x+4\right) \geq x \Rightarrow -\dfrac{1}{3}x-2 \geq x \Rightarrow -\dfrac{1}{3}x-x-2 \geq x-x \Rightarrow -\dfrac{4}{3}x-2 \geq 0 \Rightarrow$
$-\dfrac{4}{3}x-2+2 \geq 0+2 \Rightarrow -\dfrac{4}{3}x \geq 2 \Rightarrow -\dfrac{3}{4}\left(-\dfrac{4}{3}x\right) \leq 2\left(-\dfrac{3}{4}\right) \Rightarrow x \leq -\dfrac{3}{2} \Rightarrow \left\{x \,\middle|\, x \leq -\dfrac{3}{2}\right\}$

81. $\dfrac{3}{7}x+\dfrac{2}{7} > -\dfrac{1}{7}x-\dfrac{5}{14} \Rightarrow \dfrac{3}{7}x-\dfrac{1}{7}x+\dfrac{2}{7} > -\dfrac{1}{7}x+\dfrac{1}{7}x-\dfrac{5}{14} \Rightarrow \dfrac{4}{7}x+\dfrac{2}{7} > -\dfrac{5}{14} \Rightarrow$
$\dfrac{4}{7}x+\dfrac{2}{7}-\dfrac{2}{7} > -\dfrac{5}{14}-\dfrac{2}{7} \Rightarrow \dfrac{4}{7}x > -\dfrac{5}{14}-\dfrac{4}{14} \Rightarrow \dfrac{4}{7}x > -\dfrac{9}{14} \Rightarrow \dfrac{7}{4}\left(\dfrac{4}{7}x\right) > -\dfrac{9}{14}\left(\dfrac{7}{4}\right) \Rightarrow x > -\dfrac{63}{56} \Rightarrow$
$x > -\dfrac{9}{8} \Rightarrow \left\{x \,\middle|\, x > -\dfrac{9}{8}\right\}$

83. $\dfrac{x}{3}+\dfrac{5x}{6} \leq \dfrac{2}{3} \Rightarrow \dfrac{2x}{6}+\dfrac{5x}{6} \leq \dfrac{2}{3} \Rightarrow \dfrac{7x}{6} \leq \dfrac{2}{3} \Rightarrow 6\left(\dfrac{7x}{6}\right) \leq \dfrac{2}{3}(6) \Rightarrow 7x \leq 4 \Rightarrow \dfrac{7x}{7} \leq \dfrac{4}{7} \Rightarrow x \leq \dfrac{4}{7} \Rightarrow$
$\left\{x \,\middle|\, x \leq \dfrac{4}{7}\right\}$

85. $\dfrac{6x}{7} < \dfrac{1}{3}x+1 \Rightarrow \dfrac{6x}{7}-\dfrac{1}{3}x < \dfrac{1}{3}x-\dfrac{1}{3}x+1 \Rightarrow \dfrac{6x}{7}-\dfrac{x}{3} < 1 \Rightarrow \dfrac{18x}{21}-\dfrac{7x}{21} < 1 \Rightarrow \dfrac{11x}{21} < 1 \Rightarrow$
$21\left(\dfrac{11x}{21}\right) < 1(21) \Rightarrow 11x < 21 \Rightarrow \dfrac{11x}{11} < \dfrac{21}{11} \Rightarrow x < \dfrac{21}{11} \Rightarrow \left\{x \,\middle|\, x < \dfrac{21}{11}\right\}$

Translating Inequalities

87. $x > 60$

89. $x \geq 21$

91. $x > 40{,}000$

93. $x \leq 70$

Applications

95. $2(x + 5) + 2x < 50 \Rightarrow 2x + 10 + 2x < 50 \Rightarrow 4x + 10 < 50 \Rightarrow 4x + 10 - 10 < 50 - 10 \Rightarrow$
$4x < 40 \Rightarrow \frac{4x}{4} < \frac{40}{4} \Rightarrow x < 10$ feet.

97. The area of a triangle is $\frac{1}{2}bh$. Substitute 12 for h and solve. $\frac{1}{2}bh < 120 \Rightarrow \frac{1}{2}b(12) < 120 \Rightarrow$
$6b < 120 \Rightarrow \frac{6b}{6} < \frac{120}{6} \Rightarrow b < 20$. Thus, the base of the triangle must be less than 20 inches.

99. Let x represent the unknown test score. Then, $\frac{74 + x}{2} \geq 80 \Rightarrow 2\left(\frac{74 + x}{2}\right) \geq 80(2) \Rightarrow 74 + x \geq 160 \Rightarrow$
$74 - 74 + x \geq 160 - 74 \Rightarrow x \geq 86$. Thus, the student needs a score of 86 or more to maintain an average of at least 80.

101. Let x represent the number of hours. We see that there is a \$2.00 cost for the first half hour and \$1.25 cost for each hour after that. Therefore, $2 + 1.25x \leq 8 \Rightarrow 2 - 2 + 1.25x \leq 8 - 2 \Rightarrow 1.25x \leq 6 \Rightarrow$
$\frac{1.25x}{1.25} \leq \frac{6}{1.25} \Rightarrow x \leq 4.8$. This result would indicate that the student can park for as long as 4.8 hours for \$8.00. However, because a partial hour of parking is charged as a full hour, the longest amount of time that the student could park for \$8.00 is 4.5 hours.

103. Let x represent the number of days. Then, $25x + 0.20(90)x \leq 200 \Rightarrow 25x + 18x \leq 200 \Rightarrow 43x \leq 200 \Rightarrow$
$\frac{43x}{43} \leq \frac{200}{43} \Rightarrow x \leq 4.65$. Because the car can not be rented for a partial day, the person can rent the car for 4 days.

105. (a) $C = 1.5x + 2000$

(b) $R = 12x$

(c) $P = 12x - (1.5x + 2000) \Rightarrow P = 10.5x - 2000$

(d) To yield a positive profit, revenue must be greater than cost. Then, $12x > 1.5x + 2000 \Rightarrow$
$12x - 1.5x > 1.5x - 1.5x + 2000 \Rightarrow 10.5x > 2000 \Rightarrow \frac{10.5x}{10.5} > \frac{2000}{10.5} \Rightarrow x > 190.476$. Thus, 191 or more compact discs must be sold to yield a profit.

107. (a) Set the distances equal and then solve for x. Then, $70x = 60x + 35 \Rightarrow 70x - 60x = 60x - 60x + 35 \Rightarrow$
$10x = 35 \Rightarrow \frac{10x}{10} = \frac{35}{10} \Rightarrow x = 3.5$. Thus, at 3.5 hours the cars are the same distance from the rest stop.

(b) $70x > 60x + 35 \Rightarrow 70x - 60x > 60x - 60x + 35 \Rightarrow 10x > 35 \Rightarrow \frac{10x}{10} > \frac{35}{10} \Rightarrow x > 3.5$. Thus, after 3.5 hours, the first car is farther from the rest stop than the second car.

109. Because $T = 60 - 29x$, set an inequality statement with T equal to 2 and solve. Then,
$60 - 29x > 2 \Rightarrow 60 - 60 - 29x > 2 - 60 \Rightarrow -29x > -58 \Rightarrow \frac{-29x}{-29} < \frac{-58}{-29} \Rightarrow x < 2$. Thus, at altitudes less than 2 miles, the air temperature is greater than 2ºF.

111. $4.4(x - 1994) + 7 \leq 29 \Rightarrow 4.4x - 8773.6 + 7 \leq 29 \Rightarrow 4.4x - 8766.6 \leq 29 \Rightarrow$
$4.4x - 8766.6 + 8766.6 \leq 29 + 8766.6 \Rightarrow 4.4x \leq 8795.6 \Rightarrow \frac{4.4x}{4.4} \leq \frac{8795.6}{4.4} \Rightarrow x \leq 1999$. Thus, in year 1999 and earlier, funding as less than or equal to \$29 million.

Checking Basic Concepts for Section 2.5

1. 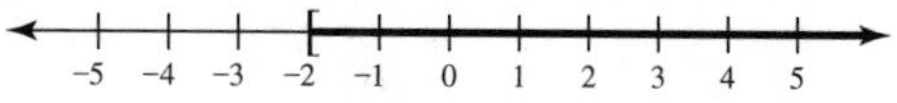

2. $x < 1$

3. When $x = -2$, then $5 - 2(-2) = 5 + 4 = 9$; When $x = -1$, then $5 - 2(-1) = 5 + 2 = 7$; When $x = 0$, then $5 - 2(0) = 5 - 0 = 5$; When $x = 1$, then $5 - 2(1) = 5 - 2 = 3$. Therefore, the numbers that complete the table are 9, 7, 5 and 3. See Figure 3.

x	−2	−1	0	1	2
$5 - 2x$	9	7	5	3	1

Figure 3

From the table, we see that $5 - 2x \le 7$ whenever $x \ge -1$. Thus, the solution to the inequality is $x \ge -1$.

4. (a) $x + 5 > 8 \Rightarrow x + 5 - 5 > 8 - 5 \Rightarrow x > 3 \Rightarrow \{x \mid x > 3\}$

(b) $-\frac{5}{7}x \le 25 \Rightarrow -\frac{7}{5}\left(-\frac{5}{7}x\right) \ge 25\left(-\frac{7}{5}\right) \Rightarrow x \ge -\frac{175}{5} \Rightarrow x \ge -35 \Rightarrow \{x \mid x \ge -35\}$

(c) $3x \ge -2(1 - 2x) + 3 \Rightarrow 3x \ge -2 + 4x + 3 \Rightarrow 3x \ge 1 + 4x \Rightarrow 3x - 4x \ge 1 + 4x - 4x \Rightarrow -x \ge 1 \Rightarrow -1(-x) \le -1(1) \Rightarrow x \le -1 \Rightarrow \{x \mid x \le -1\}$

5. Let l represent length and w represent width. Then, $l = 2w + 5$. Therefore, $2(2w + 5) + 2w > 88 \Rightarrow 4w + 10 + 2w > 88 \Rightarrow 6w + 10 > 88 \Rightarrow 6w + 10 - 10 > 88 - 10 \Rightarrow 6w > 78 \Rightarrow \frac{6w}{6} > \frac{78}{6} \Rightarrow w > 13$. Thus, the possible widths must be more than 13 inches.

Chapter 2 Review Exercises

Section 2.1

1. $x + 9 = 3 \Rightarrow x + 9 - 9 = 3 - 9 \Rightarrow x = -6$

2. $x - 4 = -2 \Rightarrow x - 4 + 4 = -2 + 4 \Rightarrow x = 2$

3. $x - \frac{3}{4} = \frac{3}{2} \Rightarrow x - \frac{3}{4} + \frac{3}{4} = \frac{3}{2} + \frac{3}{4} \Rightarrow x = \frac{6}{4} + \frac{3}{4} \Rightarrow x = \frac{9}{4}$

4. $x + 0.5 = 0 \Rightarrow x + 0.5 - 0.5 = 0 - 0.5 \Rightarrow x = -0.5 \Rightarrow x = -\frac{1}{2}$

5. $4x = 12 \Rightarrow \frac{4x}{4} = \frac{12}{4} \Rightarrow x = 3$

6. $3x = -7 \Rightarrow \frac{3x}{3} = \frac{-7}{3} \Rightarrow x = -\frac{7}{3}$

7. $-0.5x = 1.25 \Rightarrow \frac{-0.5x}{-0.5} = \frac{1.25}{-0.5} \Rightarrow x = -2.5$

8. $-\frac{1}{3}x = \frac{7}{6} \Rightarrow -\frac{3}{1}\left(-\frac{1}{3}x\right) = \frac{7}{6}\left(-\frac{3}{1}\right) \Rightarrow x = -\frac{21}{6} \Rightarrow x = -\frac{7}{2}$

Section 2.2

9. The equation $5x - 3 = 0$ is linear; $a = 5, b = -3$

10. The equation $-4x + 3 = 2$ is linear.

    $-4x + 3 = 2 \Rightarrow -4x + 3 - 2 = 2 - 2 \Rightarrow -4x + 1 = 0;\ a = -4, b = 1$

11. The equation $0.55x = 0.05$ is linear.

    $0.55x = 0.05 \Rightarrow 0.55x - 0.05 = 0.05 - 0.05 \Rightarrow 0.55x - 0.05 = 0;\ a = 0.55, b = -0.05$

12. The equation $\frac{3}{8}x^2 - x = \frac{1}{4}$ is not a linear equation because it cannot be written in the form $ax + b = 0$.

13. $4x - 5 = 3 \Rightarrow 4x - 5 + 5 = 3 + 5 \Rightarrow 4x = 8 \Rightarrow \frac{4x}{4} = \frac{8}{4} \Rightarrow x = 2$. To check the solution, substitute 2 for x in the original equation: $4x - 5 = 3 \Rightarrow 4(2) - 5 = 3 \Rightarrow 8 - 5 = 3$. Because this statement is true, the solution checks.

14. $7 - \frac{1}{2}x = -4 \Rightarrow 7 - 7 - \frac{1}{2}x = -4 - 7 \Rightarrow -\frac{1}{2}x = -11 \Rightarrow -\frac{2}{1}\left(-\frac{1}{2}x\right) = -\frac{11}{1}\left(-\frac{2}{1}\right) \Rightarrow x = 22$. To check the solution, substitute 22 for x in the original equation: $7 - \frac{1}{2}x = -4 \Rightarrow 7 - \frac{1}{2}(22) = -4 \Rightarrow 7 - 11 = -4$. Because this statement is true, the solution checks.

15. $5(x - 3) = 12 \Rightarrow 5x - 15 = 12 \Rightarrow 5x - 15 + 15 = 12 + 15 \Rightarrow 5x = 27 \Rightarrow \frac{5x}{5} = \frac{27}{5} \Rightarrow x = \frac{27}{5}$. To check the solution, substitute $\frac{27}{5}$ for x in the original equation: $5\left(\frac{27}{5} - 3\right) = 12 \Rightarrow 5\left(\frac{27}{5} - \frac{15}{5}\right) = 12 \Rightarrow$ $5\left(\frac{12}{5}\right) = 12 \Rightarrow \frac{60}{5} = 12$. Because this statement is true, the solution checks.

16. $1 - (x - 3) = 6 + 2x \Rightarrow 1 - x + 3 = 6 + 2x \Rightarrow 4 - x = 6 + 2x \Rightarrow 4 - x + x = 6 + 2x + x \Rightarrow$ $4 = 6 + 3x \Rightarrow 4 - 6 = 6 - 6 + 3x \Rightarrow -2 = 3x \Rightarrow \frac{-2}{3} = \frac{3x}{3} \Rightarrow -\frac{2}{3} = x \Rightarrow x = -\frac{2}{3}$. To check the solution, substitute $-\frac{2}{3}$ for x in the original equation: $1 - \left(-\frac{2}{3} - 3\right) = 6 + 2\left(-\frac{2}{3}\right) \Rightarrow$ $1 + \frac{2}{3} + 3 = 6 - \frac{4}{3} \Rightarrow 4\frac{2}{3} = 4\frac{2}{3}$. Because this statement is true, the solution checks.

17. $3.4x - 4 = 5 - 0.6x \Rightarrow 3.4x - 4 + 4 = 5 + 4 - 0.6x \Rightarrow 3.4x = 9 - 0.6x \Rightarrow$ $3.4x + 0.6x = 9 - 0.6x + 0.6x \Rightarrow 4x = 9 \Rightarrow \frac{4x}{4} = \frac{9}{4} \Rightarrow x = \frac{9}{4}$. To check the solution, substitute $\frac{9}{4}$ for x in the original equation: $3.4\left(\frac{9}{4}\right) - 4 = 5 - 0.6\left(\frac{9}{4}\right) \Rightarrow 3.4(2.25) - 4 = 5 - 0.6(2.25) \Rightarrow$ $7.65 - 4 = 5 - 1.35 \Rightarrow 3.65 = 3.65$. Because this statement is true, the solution checks.

18. $-\frac{1}{3}(3 - 6x) = -(x + 2) + 1 \Rightarrow -1 + 2x = -x - 2 + 1 \Rightarrow 2x - 1 = -x - 1 \Rightarrow$ $2x - 1 + 1 = -x - 1 + 1 \Rightarrow 2x = -x \Rightarrow 2x + x = -x + x \Rightarrow 3x = 0 \Rightarrow \frac{3x}{3} = \frac{0}{3} \Rightarrow x = 0$. To check the solution, substitute 0 for x in the original equation: $-\frac{1}{3}(3 - 6(0)) = -(0 + 2) + 1 \Rightarrow$ $-\frac{1}{3}(3) = -2 + 1 \Rightarrow -1 = -1$. Because this statement is true, the solution checks.

19. $\frac{2}{3}x - \frac{1}{6} = \frac{5}{12} \Rightarrow \frac{2}{3}x - \frac{1}{6} + \frac{1}{6} = \frac{5}{12} + \frac{1}{6} \Rightarrow \frac{2}{3}x = \frac{5}{12} + \frac{2}{12} \Rightarrow \frac{2}{3}x = \frac{7}{12} \Rightarrow \frac{3}{2}\left(\frac{2}{3}x\right) = \frac{7}{12}\left(\frac{3}{2}\right) \Rightarrow$

$x = \frac{21}{24} \Rightarrow x = \frac{7}{8}$. To check the solution, substitute $\frac{7}{8}$ for x in the original equation: $\frac{2}{3}\left(\frac{7}{8}\right) - \frac{1}{6} = \frac{5}{12} \Rightarrow$

$\frac{14}{24} - \frac{4}{24} = \frac{10}{24} \Rightarrow \frac{10}{24} = \frac{10}{24}$. Because this statement is true, the solution checks.

20. $2y - 3(2 - y) = 5 + y \Rightarrow 2y - 6 + 3y = 5 + y \Rightarrow 5y - 6 = 5 + y \Rightarrow 5y - y - 6 = 5 + y - y \Rightarrow$

$4y - 6 = 5 \Rightarrow 4y - 6 + 6 = 5 + 6 \Rightarrow 4y = 11 \Rightarrow \frac{4y}{4} = \frac{11}{4} \Rightarrow y = \frac{11}{4}$. To check the solution,

substitute $\frac{11}{4}$ for y in the original equation: $2\left(\frac{11}{4}\right) - 3\left(2 - \frac{11}{4}\right) = 5 + \frac{11}{4} \Rightarrow \frac{22}{4} - 6 + \frac{33}{4} = \frac{20}{4} + \frac{11}{4} \Rightarrow$

$\frac{22}{4} - \frac{24}{4} + \frac{33}{4} = \frac{20}{4} + \frac{11}{4} \Rightarrow \frac{31}{4} = \frac{31}{4}$. Because this statement is true, the solution checks.

21. First, solve for x: $4(3x - 2) = 2(6x + 5) \Rightarrow 12x - 8 = 12x + 10 \Rightarrow$

$12x - 12x - 8 = 12x - 12x + 10 \Rightarrow -8 = 10$. Because this statement is not true, the equation has zero solutions.

22. First, solve for x: $5(3x - 1) = 15x - 5 \Rightarrow 15x - 5 = 15x - 3$. Because this statement is true for any value of x, the equation has infinitely many solutions.

23. First, solve for x: $8x = 5x + 3x \Rightarrow 8x = 8x$. Because this statement is true for any value of x, the equation has infinitely many solutions.

24. First solve for x: $9x - 2 = 8x - 2 \Rightarrow 9x - 8x - 2 = 8x - 8x - 2 \Rightarrow x - 2 = -2 \Rightarrow$

$x - 2 + 2 = -2 + 2 \Rightarrow x = 0$. Thus, there is one solution to the equation.

25. When $x = 1.0$, then $-2(1.0) + 3 = -2 + 3 = 1$; When $x = 1.5$, then $-2(1.5) + 3 = -3 + 3 = 0$;

When $x = 2.0$, then $-2(2.0) + 3 = -4 + 3 = -1$; When $x = 2.5$, then $-2(2.5) + 3 = -5 + 3 = -2$;

Thus, the missing values in the table are 1, 0, −1 and −2. See Figure 25. From the table we see that when $x = 1.5$, the value of $-2x + 3$ is 0.

x	0.5	1.0	1.5	2.0	2.5
$-2x + 3$	2	1	0	−1	−2

Figure 25

x	−2	−1	0	1	2
$-(x + 1) + 3$	4	3	2	1	0

Figure 26

26. When $x = -2$, then $-(-2 + 1) + 3 = 2 - 1 + 3 = 4$; When $x = -1$, then $-(-1 + 1) + 3 = 1 - 1 + 3 = 3$;

When $x = 0$, then $-(0 + 1) + 3 = 0 - 1 + 3 = 2$; When $x = 1$, then $-(1 + 1) + 3 = -2 + 3 = 1$;

Thus, the missing values in the table are 4, 3, 2 and 1. See Figure 26. From the table we see that when $x = 0$, the value of $-(x + 1) + 3$ is 2.

Section 2.3

27. $6x = 72 \Rightarrow \frac{6x}{6} = \frac{72}{6} \Rightarrow x = 12$

28. $x + 18 = -23 \Rightarrow x + 18 - 18 = -23 - 18 \Rightarrow x = -41$

29. $2x - 5 = x + 4 \Rightarrow 2x - 5 + 5 = x + 4 + 5 \Rightarrow 2x = x + 9 \Rightarrow 2x - x = x - x + 9 \Rightarrow x = 9$

30. $x + 4 = 3x \Rightarrow x - 3x + 4 = 3x - 3x \Rightarrow -2x + 4 = 0 \Rightarrow -2x + 4 - 4 = 0 - 4 \Rightarrow -2x = -4 \Rightarrow$
$\frac{-2x}{-2} = \frac{-4}{-2} \Rightarrow x = 2$

31. $x + (x + 1) + (x + 2) + (x + 3) = 70 \Rightarrow 4x + 6 = 70 \Rightarrow 4x + 6 - 6 = 70 - 6 \Rightarrow 4x = 64 \Rightarrow$
$\frac{4x}{4} = \frac{64}{4} \Rightarrow x = 16$. The numbers are 16, 17, 18 and 19.

32. $x + (x + 1) + (x + 2) = -153 \Rightarrow 3x + 3 = -153 \Rightarrow 3x + 3 - 3 = -153 - 3 \Rightarrow 3x = -156 \Rightarrow$
$\frac{3x}{3} = \frac{-156}{3} \Rightarrow x = -52$. The numbers are -52, -51 and -50.

33. $85\% = \frac{85}{100} = \frac{17}{20}$; $85\% = 0.85$

34. $5.6\% = \frac{56}{1000} = \frac{7}{125}$; $5.6\% = 0.056$

35. $0.03\% = \frac{.03}{100} = \frac{3}{10{,}000}$; $0.03\% = 0.0003$

36. $342\% = \frac{342}{100} = \frac{171}{50}$; $342\% = 3.42$

37. $0.89 = 89\%$

38. $0.005 = 0.5\%$

39. $2.3 = 230\%$

40. $1 = 100\%$

Section 2.4

41. $d = rt \Rightarrow d = 8(3) \Rightarrow d = 24$ miles.

42. $d = rt \Rightarrow d = 70(55) \Rightarrow d = 3850$ feet.

43. $d = rt \Rightarrow 500 = r(20) \Rightarrow \frac{500}{20} = r\frac{20}{20} \Rightarrow \frac{500}{20} = r \Rightarrow r = 25$ yd/sec.

44. $d = rt \Rightarrow 125 = 15t \Rightarrow \frac{125}{15} = \frac{15t}{15} \Rightarrow \frac{125}{15} = t \Rightarrow t = \frac{25}{3}$ hours.

45. The area of a triangle is given as $\frac{1}{2}$(base)(height). Thus, $A = \frac{1}{2}(b)(h) = \frac{1}{2}(5)(3) = 7.5 \text{ m}^2$.

46. The area of a circle is given as πr^2 where r represents radius. Thus, $A = \pi r^2 = \pi(6^2) = 36\pi \approx 113.1 \text{ ft}^2$.

47. The area of a rectangle is given as length (l) times width (w). Thus, $A = lw = (36)(24) = 864 \text{ in}^2$ or 6 ft^2.

48. $A = \frac{1}{2}bh$, where A represents area, b represents the length of the base and h represents the height. Thus,
$A = \frac{1}{2}bh = \frac{1}{2}(13)(7) = \frac{1}{2}(91) = 45\frac{1}{2} = 45.5 \text{ in}^2$.

49. The circumference of a circle is given as $2\pi r$, where r represents radius. Thus, $r = \frac{1}{2}$(diameter) $= \frac{1}{2}(18) = 9$.
$C = 2\pi r = 2\pi(9) = 18\pi \approx 56.5$ feet.

50. $A = \pi r^2$, where A represents area and r represents radius. Thus, $A = \pi r^2 = \pi(5^2) = 25\pi \approx 78.5 \text{ in}^2$.

51. The angles in a triangle must add up to 180°. Let x represent the unknown angle. Thus,
$90 + 40 + x = 180 \Rightarrow 130 + x = 180 \Rightarrow 130 - 130 + x = 180 - 130 \Rightarrow x = 50°$.

52. The angles in a triangle must add up to 180°. Thus, $x + 3x + 4x = 180 \Rightarrow 8x = 180 \Rightarrow \frac{8x}{8} = \frac{180}{8} \Rightarrow$

$x = 22.5°$.

53. $V = \pi r^2 h = \pi(5^2)(25) = \pi(25)(25) = 625\pi \approx 1963.5 \text{ in}^3$.

54. First, convert height (h) and base (b) to inches. $h = 5$ feet $= 5(12) = 60$ inches and

$b = 3$ feet $= 3(12) = 36$ inches. Then, $A = \frac{1}{2}(a + b)h = \frac{1}{2}(36 + 18)60 = \frac{1}{2}(54)60 = (27)60 = 1620 \text{ in}^2$.

Or, convert the base in inches to feet. $b = 18$ inches $= \frac{18}{12} = 1.5$ feet. Then,

$A = \frac{1}{2}(a + b)h = \frac{1}{2}(3 + 1.5)5 = \frac{1}{2}(4.5)5 = (2.25)5 = 11.25 \text{ ft}^2$.

55. $a = x + y \Rightarrow a - y = x + y - y \Rightarrow a - y = x \Rightarrow x = a - y$

56. $P = 2x + 2y \Rightarrow P - 2y = 2x + 2y - 2y \Rightarrow P - 2y = 2x \Rightarrow \frac{P - 2y}{2} = \frac{2x}{2} \Rightarrow \frac{P - 2y}{2} = x \Rightarrow$

$x = \frac{P - 2y}{2}$

57. $z = 2xy \Rightarrow \frac{z}{2x} = \frac{2xy}{2x} \Rightarrow \frac{z}{2x} = y \Rightarrow y = \frac{z}{2x}$

58. $S = \frac{a + b + c}{3} \Rightarrow 3S = \frac{a + b + c}{3} \cdot 3 \Rightarrow 3S = a + b + c \Rightarrow 3S - a - c = a + b + c - a - c \Rightarrow$

$3S - a - c = b \Rightarrow b = 3S - a - c$

59. $T = \frac{a}{3} + \frac{b}{4} \Rightarrow \frac{12T}{12} = \frac{4a}{12} + \frac{3b}{12} \Rightarrow 12\left(\frac{12T}{12}\right) = 12\left(\frac{4a}{12}\right) + 12\left(\frac{3b}{12}\right) \Rightarrow 12T = 4a + 3b \Rightarrow$

$12T - 4a = 4a - 4a + 3b \Rightarrow 12T - 4a = 3b \Rightarrow \frac{12T - 4a}{3} = \frac{3b}{3} \Rightarrow \frac{12T - 4a}{3} = b \Rightarrow b = \frac{12T - 4a}{3}$

60. $cd = ab + bc \Rightarrow cd - bc = ab + bc - bc \Rightarrow cd - bc = ab \Rightarrow c(d - b) = ab \Rightarrow$

$\frac{c(d - b)}{(d - b)} = \frac{ab}{(d - b)} \Rightarrow c = \frac{ab}{d - b}$

Section 2.5

61. 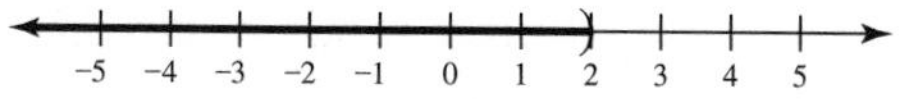

62. 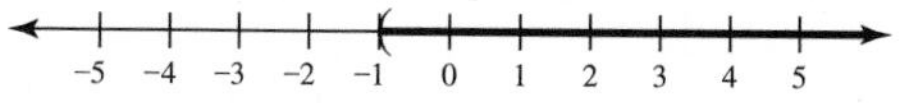

63. 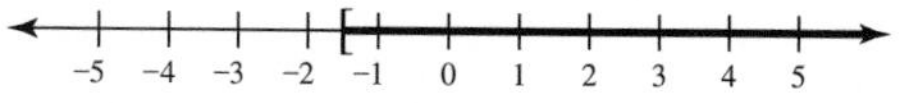

64. 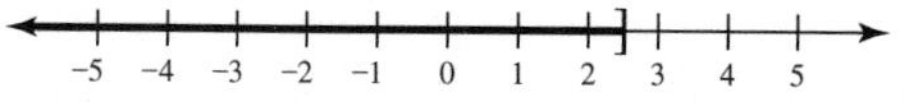

65. $x < 3$

66. $x \geq -1$

67. Substitute -3 for x and check for accuracy: $2x + 1 \leq 5 \Rightarrow 2(-3) + 1 \leq 5 \Rightarrow -6 + 1 \leq 5 \Rightarrow -5 \leq 5$.

Because this statement is true, $x = -3$ is a solution to the inequality.

68. Substitute 4 for x and check for accuracy: $5 - \frac{1}{2}(x) \geq -1 \Rightarrow 5 - \frac{1}{2}(4) \geq -1 \Rightarrow 5 - 2 \geq -1 \Rightarrow 3 \geq -1.$

Because this statement is true, $x = 4$ is a solution to the inequality.

69. Substitute -2 for x and check for accuracy: $1 - (x + 3) \geq x \Rightarrow 1 - (-2 + 3) \geq -2 \Rightarrow 1 - 1 \geq -2 \Rightarrow$ $0 \geq -2$. Because this statement is true, $x = -2$ is a solution to the inequality.

70. Substitute -1 for x and check for accuracy: $4(x + 1) < -(5 - x) \Rightarrow 4(-1 + 1) < -(5 - (-1)) \Rightarrow$ $4(0) < -(6) \Rightarrow 0 < -6$. Because this statement is not true, $x = -1$ is not a solution to the inequality.

71. When $x = 1$, then $5 - x = 5 - 1 = 4$; When $x = 2$, then $5 - x = 5 - 2 = 3$;

When $x = 3$, then $5 - x = 5 - 3 = 2$; When $x = 4$, then $5 - x = 5 - 4 = 1$;

Thus, the missing values in the table are 4, 3, 2 and 1. See Figure 71. From the table we see that $5 - x > 3$, when $x < 2$.

x	0	1	2	3	4
$5 - x$	5	4	3	2	1

Figure 71

x	1	1.5	2	2.5	3
$2x - 5$	-3	-2	-1	0	1

Figure 72

72. When $x = 1.5$, then $2x - 5 = 2(1.5) - 5 = 3 - 5 = -2$;

When $x = 2$, then $2x - 5 = 2(2) - 5 = 4 - 5 = -1$;

When $x = 2.5$, then $2x - 5 = 2(2.5) - 5 = 5 - 5 = 0$;

When $x = 3$, then $2x - 5 = 2(3) - 5 = 6 - 5 = 1$;

Thus, the missing values in the table are $-2, -1, 0$ and 1. See Figure 72. From the table we see that $2x - 5 \leq 0$ when $x \leq 2.5$.

73. $x - 3 > 0 \Rightarrow x - 3 + 3 > 0 + 3 \Rightarrow x > 3 \Rightarrow \{x \mid x > 3\}$

74. $-2x \leq 10 \Rightarrow \frac{-2x}{-2} \geq \frac{10}{-2} \Rightarrow x \geq -5 \Rightarrow \{x \mid x \geq -5\}$

75. $5 - 2x \geq 7 \Rightarrow 5 - 5 - 2x \geq 7 - 5 \Rightarrow -2x \geq 2 \Rightarrow \frac{-2x}{-2} \leq \frac{2}{-2} \Rightarrow x \leq -1 \Rightarrow \{x \mid x \leq -1\}$

76. $3(x - 1) < 20 \Rightarrow 3x - 3 < 20 \Rightarrow 3x - 3 + 3 < 20 + 3 \Rightarrow 3x < 23 \Rightarrow \frac{3x}{3} < \frac{23}{3} \Rightarrow x < \frac{23}{3} \Rightarrow$ $\left\{x \,\middle|\, x < \frac{23}{3}\right\}$

77. $5x \leq 3 - (4x + 2) \Rightarrow 5x \leq 3 - 4x - 2 \Rightarrow 5x + 4x \leq 3 - 4x + 4x - 2 \Rightarrow 9x \leq 1 \Rightarrow \frac{9x}{9} \leq \frac{1}{9} \Rightarrow$ $x \leq \frac{1}{9} \Rightarrow \left\{x \,\middle|\, x \leq \frac{1}{9}\right\}$

78. $3x - 2(4 - x) \geq x + 1 \Rightarrow 3x - 8 + 2x \geq x + 1 \Rightarrow 5x - 8 + 8 \geq x + 1 + 8 \Rightarrow 5x \geq x + 9 \Rightarrow$ $5x - x \geq x - x + 9 \Rightarrow 4x \geq 9 \Rightarrow \frac{4x}{4} \geq \frac{9}{4} \Rightarrow x \geq \frac{9}{4} \Rightarrow \left\{x \,\middle|\, x \geq \frac{9}{4}\right\}$

79. $x < 50$

80. $x \leq 45{,}000$

81. $x \geq 16$

82. $x < 1995$

Applications

83. (a) See Figure 83.

(b) $R = 2 + \frac{3}{4}x$

(c) At 5 PM, $x = 5$; $R = 2 + \frac{3}{4}(5) = 2 + \frac{15}{4} = \frac{23}{4} = 5\frac{3}{4}$ inches. This value does agree with the table.

(d) At 3:45 PM, $x = 3.75$; $R = 2 + \frac{3}{4}\left(3\frac{3}{4}\right) = 2 + \frac{3}{4}\left(\frac{15}{4}\right) = 2 + \frac{45}{16} = \frac{32}{16} + \frac{45}{16} = \frac{77}{16} = 4\frac{13}{16}$ inches.

Time	12:00	1:00	2:00	3:00	4:00	5:00
Rainfall (R)	2	2.75	3.5	4.25	5	5.75

Figure 83

Hours (x)	1	2	3	4	5
Distance (D)	40	30	20	10	0

Figure 85

84. Let x represent the cost of the laptop. $0.05x = 106.25 \Rightarrow \frac{0.05x}{0.05} = \frac{106.25}{0.05} \Rightarrow x = 2125$. Thus, the cost of the laptop is \$2125.

85. (a) See Figure 85.

(b) $D = 50 - 10x$

(c) $D = 50 - 10x = 50 - 10(3) = 50 - 30 = 20$ miles. This value does agree with the table.

(d) $D \geq 20$. Thus, $50 - 10x \geq 20 \Rightarrow 50 - 50 - 10x \geq 20 - 50 \Rightarrow -10x \geq -30 \Rightarrow \frac{-10x}{-10} \leq \frac{-30}{-10} \Rightarrow$ $x \leq 3$. Thus, the bicyclist was at least 20 miles from home when he had traveled for 3 or fewer hours, or from noon to 3 PM.

86. $N = \frac{1}{15}x - 130.4$. Substitute 2.8 for N and solve for x: $2.8 = \frac{1}{15}x - 130.4 \Rightarrow$ $2.8 + 130.4 = \frac{1}{15}x - 130.4 + 130.4 \Rightarrow 133.2 = \frac{1}{15}x \Rightarrow 133.2\left(\frac{15}{1}\right) = \frac{15}{1}\left(\frac{1}{15}x\right) \Rightarrow 1998 = x \Rightarrow$ $x = 1998$. Thus, in the year 1998, the number reached 2.8 million.

87. First, subtract the smaller number from the larger to obtain the difference between the: $419{,}401 - 230{,}500 = 188{,}901$. Then, determine what percentage 188,901 is of 230,500. Do this by dividing the smaller number by the larger: $\frac{188{,}901}{230{,}500} \approx 0.82$. Thus, there was about an 82% change in master's degrees received between 1971 and 1997.

88. Use the distance (d) = rate (r) $\times$ time (t) formula. Determine how long it takes the faster car to be 2 miles ahead of the slower car, let $(r + 12)$ be the rate of the faster car and r be the rate of the slower car. Thus, $d = rt \Rightarrow 2 = (r + 12 - r)t \Rightarrow 2 = 12t \Rightarrow \frac{2}{12} = \frac{12t}{12} \Rightarrow \frac{1}{6} = t \Rightarrow t = \frac{1}{6}$ hour, or 10 minutes.

89. Let x represent the amount of water. The amount of salt on one side of the equation must equal the amount of salt on the other side. Thus, $100(0.03) + x(0.00) = (100 + x)(0.02) \Rightarrow 3 + 0 = 2 + 0.02x \Rightarrow$ $3 - 2 = 2 - 2 + 0.02x \Rightarrow 1 = 0.02x \Rightarrow \frac{1}{0.02} = \frac{0.02x}{0.02} \Rightarrow 50 = x \Rightarrow x = 50$. Thus, 50 ml of water must be added.

90. Let x represent the higher interest rate. Then, $800(x) + 500(x - 0.02) = 55 \Rightarrow 800x + 500x - 10 = 55 \Rightarrow$

$1300x - 10 + 10 = 55 + 10 \Rightarrow 1300x = 65 \Rightarrow \dfrac{1300x}{1300} = \dfrac{65}{1300} \Rightarrow x = 0.05$. Thus, the interest rate on the

$800 loan is 5% and the interest rate on the $500 loan is 3%.

91. Perimeter $(P) = 2 \times$ width $(w) =$ length (l). Then, $w = l - 10 \Rightarrow 2(l - 10) + 2l = 112 \Rightarrow$

$2l - 20 + 2l = 112 \Rightarrow 2l - 20 + 20 + 2l = 112 + 20 \Rightarrow 4l = 132 \Rightarrow \dfrac{4l}{4} = \dfrac{132}{4} \Rightarrow l = 33$. Because

the length is 33, the width is $(l - 10) = 23$. Thus, the dimensions are 33 by 23 inches.

92. Area (A) of a triangle is $\frac{1}{2} \times$ base $(b) \times$ height (h). Thus, $A = \frac{1}{2}bh \Rightarrow \frac{1}{2}bh \le 100 \Rightarrow \frac{1}{2}b(8) \le 100 \Rightarrow$

$4b \le 100 \Rightarrow \dfrac{4b}{4} \le \dfrac{100}{4} \Rightarrow b \le 25$. Therefore, the base must be 25 inches or less.

93. Let x represent the unknown test score. Then, $\dfrac{75 + 91 + x}{3} = 80 \Rightarrow \dfrac{166 + x}{3} = 80 \Rightarrow$

$3\left(\dfrac{166 + x}{3}\right) = 3(80) \Rightarrow 166 + x = 240 \Rightarrow 166 - 166 + x = 240 - 166 \Rightarrow x = 74$. Thus, the student

must score 74 or more.

94. Let x represent the unknown number of hours. Then, $2.25 + 1.25x = 9 \Rightarrow$

$2.25 - 2.25 + 1.25x = 9 - 2.25 \Rightarrow 1.25x = 6.75 \Rightarrow \dfrac{1.25x}{1.25} = \dfrac{6.75}{1.25} \Rightarrow x = 5.4$. Because each partial hour

is charged as a full hour, the person can park for 6 hours.

95. (a) $C = 150{,}000 + 85x$

(b) $R = 225x$

(c) $P = 225x - (150{,}000 + 85x) \Rightarrow P = 140x - 150{,}000$

(d) $140x - 150{,}000 < 0 \Rightarrow 140x - 150{,}000 + 150{,}000 < 0 + 150{,}000 \Rightarrow 140x < 150{,}000 \Rightarrow$

$\dfrac{140x}{140} < \dfrac{150{,}000}{140} \Rightarrow x < 1071.43$. Therefore, if 1071 or fewer DVD players are sold, there will be a loss.

Chapter 2 Test

1. $9 = 3 - x \Rightarrow 9 - 3 = 3 - 3 - x \Rightarrow 6 = -x \Rightarrow 6(-1) = (-x)(-1) \Rightarrow -6 = x \Rightarrow x = -6$

To check the solution: $9 - 3 - (-6) \Rightarrow 9 = 9$. The solution checks.

2. $4x - 3 = 7 \Rightarrow 4x - 3 + 3 = 7 + 3 \Rightarrow 4x = 10 \Rightarrow \dfrac{4x}{4} = \dfrac{10}{4} \Rightarrow x = \dfrac{5}{2}$

To check the solution: $4\left(\dfrac{5}{2}\right) - 3 = 7 \Rightarrow \dfrac{20}{2} - \dfrac{6}{2} = 7 \Rightarrow \dfrac{14}{2} = 7 \Rightarrow 7 = 7$. The solution checks.

3. $4x - (2 - x) = -3(2x + 6) \Rightarrow 4x - 2 + x = -6x - 18 \Rightarrow 5x - 2 = -6x - 18 \Rightarrow$

$5x - 2 + 2 = -6x - 18 + 2 \Rightarrow 5x = -6x - 16 \Rightarrow 5x + 6x = -6x + 6x - 16 \Rightarrow 11x = -16 \Rightarrow$

$\frac{11x}{11} = \frac{-16}{11} \Rightarrow x = -\frac{16}{11}$. To check the solution: $4\left(-\frac{16}{11}\right) - \left(2 - \left(-\frac{16}{11}\right)\right) = -3\left(2\left(-\frac{16}{11}\right) + 6\right) \Rightarrow$

$-\frac{64}{11} - 2 - \frac{16}{11} = -6\left(-\frac{16}{11}\right) - 18 \Rightarrow -\frac{64}{11} - \frac{22}{11} - \frac{16}{11} = \frac{96}{11} - \frac{198}{11} \Rightarrow -\frac{102}{11} = -\frac{102}{11}$. The solution checks.

4. $\frac{1}{12}x - \frac{2}{3} = \frac{1}{2}\left(\frac{3}{4} - \frac{1}{3}x\right) \Rightarrow \frac{1}{12}x - \frac{2}{3} = \frac{3}{8} - \frac{1}{6}x \Rightarrow \frac{1}{12}x + \frac{1}{6}x - \frac{2}{3} = \frac{3}{8} - \frac{1}{6}x + \frac{1}{6}x \Rightarrow$

$\frac{3}{12}x - \frac{2}{3} + \frac{2}{3} = \frac{3}{8} + \frac{2}{3} \Rightarrow \frac{3}{12}x = \frac{9}{24} + \frac{16}{24} \Rightarrow \frac{3}{12}x = \frac{25}{24} \Rightarrow \frac{12}{3}\left(\frac{3}{12}x\right) = \frac{12}{3}\left(\frac{25}{24}\right) \Rightarrow x = \frac{300}{72} = \frac{25}{6}$.

To check the solution: $\frac{1}{12}\left(\frac{25}{6}\right) - \frac{2}{3} = \frac{1}{2}\left(\frac{3}{4} - \frac{1}{3}\left(\frac{25}{6}\right)\right) \Rightarrow \frac{25}{72} - \frac{48}{72} = \frac{1}{2}\left(\frac{27}{36} - \frac{50}{36}\right) \Rightarrow$

$-\frac{23}{72} = \frac{1}{2}\left(-\frac{23}{36}\right) \Rightarrow -\frac{23}{72} = -\frac{23}{72}$. The solution checks.

5. First, solve for x: $6(2x - 1) = -4(3 - 3x) \Rightarrow 12x - 6 = -12 + 12x \Rightarrow$

$12x - 12x - 6 = -12 + 12x - 12x \Rightarrow -6 = -12$. Because this statement is not true, there are no solutions.

6. When $x = 1$, then $6 - 2x = 6 - 2(1) = 4$; When $x = 2$, then $6 - 2x = 6 - 2(2) = 2$;

When $x = 3$, then $6 - 2x = 6 - 2(3) = 0$; When $x = 4$, then $6 - 2x = 6 - 2(4) = -2$;

Thus, the missing values in the table are 4, 2, 0 and −2. See Figure 6. From the table we see that

$6 - 2x = 0$, when $x = 3$.

x	0	1	2	3	4
$6 - 2x$	6	4	2	0	−2

Figure 6

7. $x + (-7) = 6 \Rightarrow x - 7 = 6 \Rightarrow x - 7 + 7 = 6 + 7 \Rightarrow x = 13$

8. $2x + 6 = x - 7 \Rightarrow 2x - x + 6 = x - x - 7 \Rightarrow x + 6 = -7 \Rightarrow x + 6 - 6 = -7 - 6 \Rightarrow x = -13$

9. $x + (x + 1) + (x + 2) = 336 \Rightarrow 3x + 3 = 336 \Rightarrow 3x + 3 - 3 = 336 - 3 \Rightarrow 3x = 333 \Rightarrow$

$\frac{3x}{3} = \frac{333}{3} \Rightarrow x = 111$. Thus, the three numbers are 111, 112 and 113.

10. $5.6\% = 0.056$; $5.6\% = \frac{56}{1000} = \frac{14}{250} = \frac{7}{125}$

11. $0.345 = 34.5\%$

12. Let x represent the unknown number. To find 7.5% of \$500, multiply 500 by 0.075. Then, $500(0.075) = x \Rightarrow$

$37.5 = x \Rightarrow x = 37.5$. Thus, 7.5% of \$500 is \$37.50.

13. $\frac{5280}{5} = \frac{5280}{5} \div \frac{5}{5} = 1056$ ft/sec.

14. Area $(A) = \frac{1}{2} \times$ base $(b) \times$ height (h). Thus, $A = \frac{1}{2}bh = \frac{1}{2}(5)(3) = 7.5\text{ in}^2$.

15. Circumference of a circle is given as $C = 2\pi r$. Then, $C = 2\pi r = 2\pi\left(\frac{30}{2}\right) = 2\pi(15) = 30\pi \approx 94.2$ inches.

Area of a circle is given as $A = \pi r^2$. Then, $A = \pi r^2 = \pi(15)^2 = 225\pi \approx 706.9$ in^2.

16. The angles in a triangle must add up to 180º.

Then, $x + 2x + 3x = 180 \Rightarrow 6x = 180 \Rightarrow \frac{6x}{6} = \frac{180}{6} \Rightarrow x = 30$. Thus, the angles are 30º, 60º and 90º.

17. $z = y - 3xy \Rightarrow z - y = y - y - 3xy \Rightarrow z - y = -3xy \Rightarrow \frac{z - y}{-3y} = \frac{-3xy}{-3y} \Rightarrow \frac{z - y}{-3y} = x \Rightarrow x = \frac{y - z}{3y}$

18. $3(6 - 5x) < 20 - x \Rightarrow 18 - 15x < 20 - x \Rightarrow 18 - 18 - 15x < 20 - 18 - x \Rightarrow -15x < 2 - x \Rightarrow$

$-15x + x < 2 - x + x \Rightarrow -14x < 2 \Rightarrow \frac{-14x}{-14} > \frac{2}{-14} \Rightarrow x > -\frac{1}{7} \Rightarrow \left\{x \middle| x > -\frac{1}{7}\right\}$

19. (a) $S = 5 + 2x$, where x represents hours past noon.

(b) $x = 8$. Thus, $S = 5 + 2(8) = 21$ inches.

(c) $x = 6.25$. Thus, $S = 5 + 2(6.25) = 17.5$ inches.

20. The amount of acid on the left side of the equation must equal the amount of acid on the right side of the equation. Let x represent the unknown amount of water. Then, $1000(0.45) + x(0) = (1000 + x)(0.15) \Rightarrow$

$450 = 150 + 0.15x \Rightarrow 450 - 150 = 150 - 150 + 0.15x \Rightarrow 300 = 0.15x \Rightarrow \frac{300}{0.15} = \frac{0.15x}{0.15} \Rightarrow$

$2000 = x \Rightarrow x = 2000$. Thus, 2000 ml. of water must be added.

21. Subtract the lesser amount from the larger amount and then calculate the percentage difference as compared to the smaller amount. Then, $32 - 8 = 24$; $\frac{24}{8} = 3 = 300\%$. Therefore, there was a 300% increase in premiums from 1998 to 2003.

Chapter 2 Extended and Discovery Exercises

1. For the first hour, the distance traveled was $d = rt$ such that $d = (50)(1) = 50$ miles. For the second hour, the distance traveled was $d = rt$ such that $d = (70)(1) = 70$ miles. Thus, for the two hours $r = \frac{d}{t}$ such that $r = \frac{70 + 50}{1 + 1} = \frac{120}{2} = 60$. Thus, the average speed of the car was 60 mph.

2. Uphill, $d = \frac{d}{r}$ such that $t = \frac{1}{5} = \frac{1}{5}$ of an hour. Downhill, $t = \frac{d}{r}$ such that $t = \frac{1}{10} = \frac{1}{10}$ of an hour. Thus, the average speed $r = \frac{d}{t}$ is $r = \frac{1 + 1}{\frac{1}{5} + \frac{1}{10}} = \frac{2}{\frac{3}{10}} = \frac{20}{3} = 6.\overline{6}$ mph.

3. For the first two miles, $t = \frac{d}{r}$ such that $t = \frac{2}{8} = \frac{1}{4}$ of an hour. For the third mile, $t = \frac{d}{t}$ such that $t = \frac{1}{10} = \frac{1}{10}$ of an hour. Thus, the average speed of the athlete is $r = \frac{d}{t} = \frac{3}{\frac{1}{4} + \frac{1}{10}} = \frac{3}{\frac{5}{20} + \frac{2}{20}} = \frac{3}{\frac{7}{20}} = \frac{60}{7} \approx 8.6$ mph.

4. Choose a distance of 400 miles as the distance between the two cities (the distance is arbitrary because any distance gives the same average speed). Then, the pilot flew at 200 mph for 1 hour and at 100 mph for 2 hours. Then, $r = \frac{d}{t} = \frac{400}{1 + 2} = \frac{400}{3} = 133.\overline{3}$. Thus, the average speed is $133.\overline{3}$ mph.

5. The lighter coin can be found in two weighings as follows: Place two coins on each pan of the balance and set three coins off to the side. Case 1: The pans balance and the lighter coin is one of the three coins that were set off to the side. Case 2: The pans do not balance and the lighter coin is one of the two coins on the higher pan. To find the lighter coin in Case 1, work only with the three remaining coins. Place one coin on each side of the balance and set one coin off to the side. If the pans do not balance, the lighter coin is the one on the higher pan. To find the lighter coin in Case 2, work with only the two coins from the higher pan. Place one coin on each side of the balance. The lighter coin is on the higher pan.

6. (a) Surface area $(A) = 4\pi r^2 = 4\pi(3960)^2 \approx 197{,}060{,}797$ mi^2.

   (b) $.71(197{,}060{,}797) \approx 139{,}913{,}166$ mi^2.

   (c) $\frac{680{,}000}{139{,}913{,}166} \approx 0.00486$ miles. To convert 0.00486 miles to feet: $0.00486(5280) \approx 25.7$ feet.

   (d) They would be flooded.

   (e) Divide the volume of the Antarctic ice cap by the surface area of the oceans: $\frac{6{,}300{,}000}{139{,}913{,}166} \approx 0.045$ miles. To convert 0.0045 miles to feet: $0.045(5280) \approx 237.7$ feet.

Critical Thinking Solutions for Chapter 2

Section 2.1

- If an error is made, the resulting equation may not be equivalent to the given equation.

Section 2.2

- Solve for x: $bx - 2 = dx + 7 \Rightarrow bx - 2 + 2 = dx + 7 + 2 \Rightarrow bx = dx + 9 \Rightarrow$ $bx - dx = dx - dx + 9 \Rightarrow bx - dx = 9 \Rightarrow x(b - d) = 9 \Rightarrow \frac{x(b - d)}{b - d} = \frac{9}{b - d} \Rightarrow x = \frac{9}{b - d}$. Thus, if $b = d$, then $x = \frac{9}{0}$. Because dividing by 0 is not allowed, there are no solutions. If $b \neq d$, then there is one solution.

Section 2.3

- Let x represent the lower salary. Then, $x + 2x$ equals the increased salary amount. Thus, because $x + 2x = 3x$, the lower salary increased by a factor of 3.

Section 2.4

- $C = 2\pi r = \pi 2r = \pi d;\ A = \pi r^2 = \pi\left(\frac{1}{2}d\right)^2 = \frac{1}{4}\pi d^2$
- Yes. Multiply one expression by 1 in the form $\frac{-1}{-1}$ to transform it to the other.

Section 2.5

- $-5 - 3x > -2x + 7 \Rightarrow -5 - 3x + 3x > -2x + 3x + 7 \Rightarrow -5 > x + 7 \Rightarrow -5 - 7 > x + 7 - 7 \Rightarrow$
  $-12 > x \Rightarrow x < -12$

Chapter 3: Graphing Equations

3.1: Introduction to Graphing

Concepts

1. xy plane
3. 4
5. III
7. scatterplot

Cartesian Coordinate Plane

9. $(-2, -2)$, $(-2, 2)$, $(0, 0)$, $(2, 2)$
11. $(-1, 0)$, $(0, -3)$, $(0, 2)$, $(2, 0)$
13. (a) Quadrant I
    (b) Quadrant III
15. (a) None, because the point is on the axis.
    (b) Quadrant I
17. (a) Quadrant II
    (b) Quadrant IV
19. See Figure 19.
21. See Figure 21.

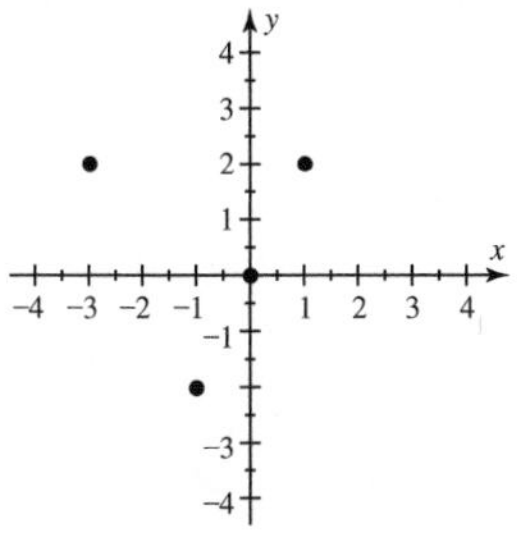

Figure 19

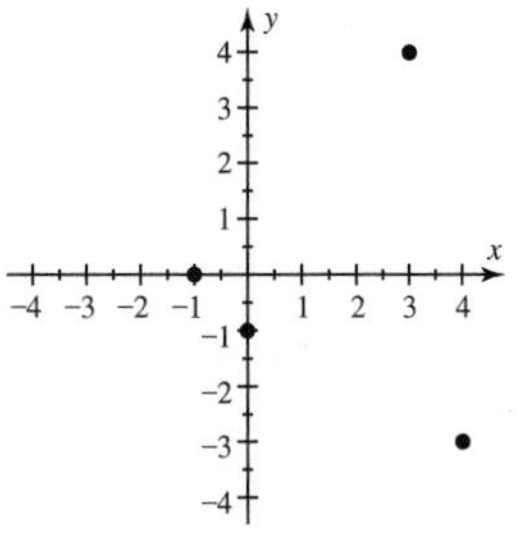

Figure 21

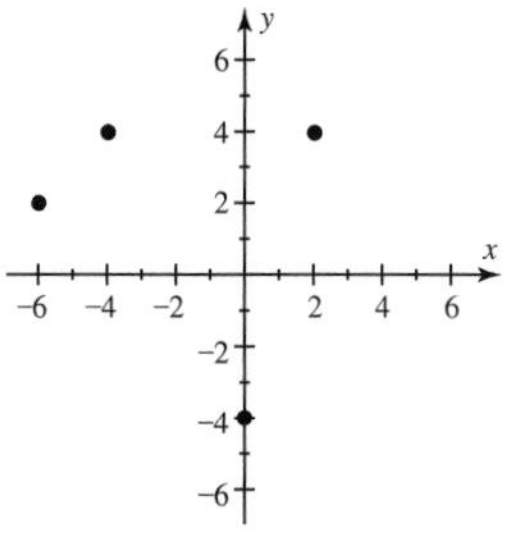

Figure 23

23. See Figure 23.
25. See Figure 25.

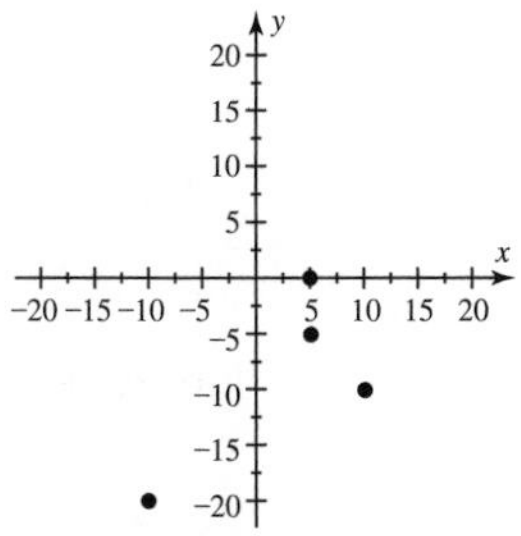

Figure 25

27. See Figure 27.

29. See Figure 29.

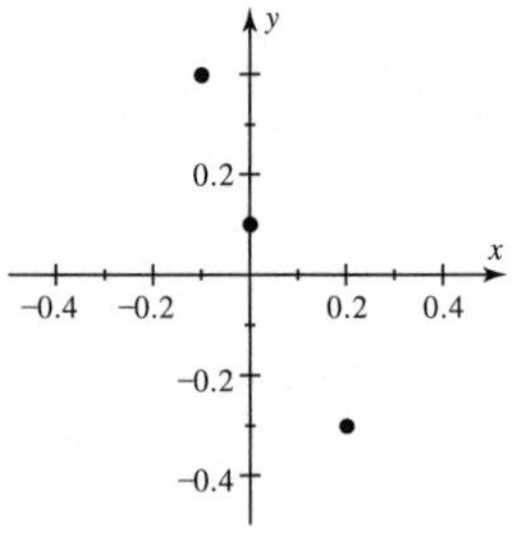

Figure 27

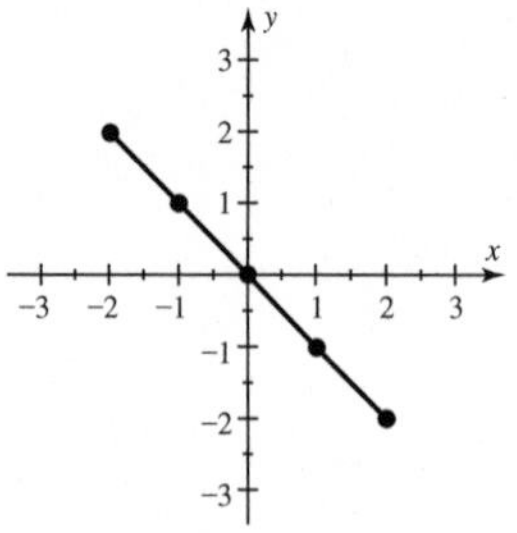

Figure 29

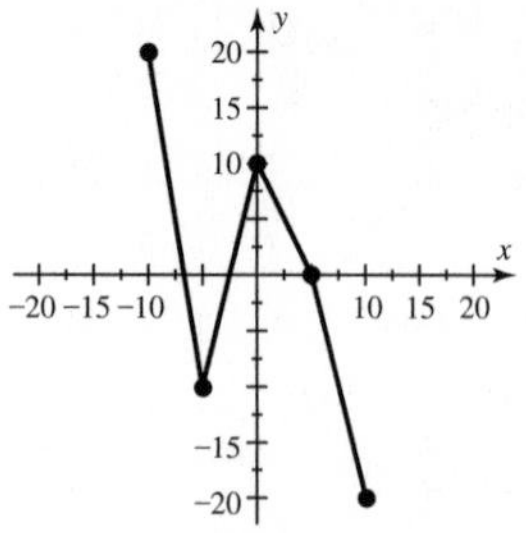

Figure 31

31. See Figure 31.

33. See Figure 33.

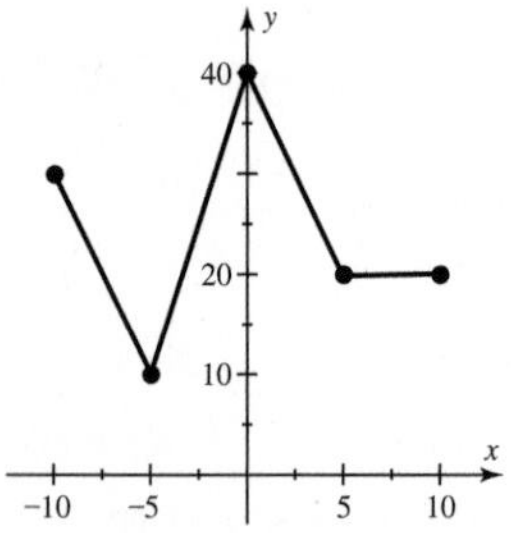

Figure 33

35. (1970, 29), (1980, 41), (1990, 79), (2000, 62); In 1970, the United States spent $29 billion on military personnel.

Graphing Real Data

37. (a) See Figure 37.

    (b) Head Start participation decreased and then increased.

39. (a) See Figure 39.

    (b) The number of welfare beneficiaries increased and then decreased.

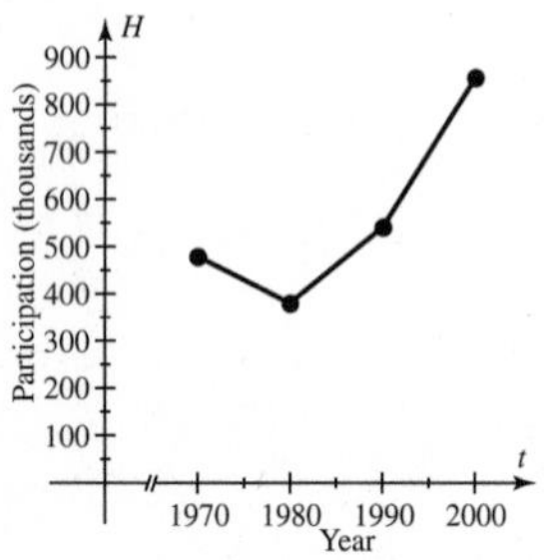

Figure 37

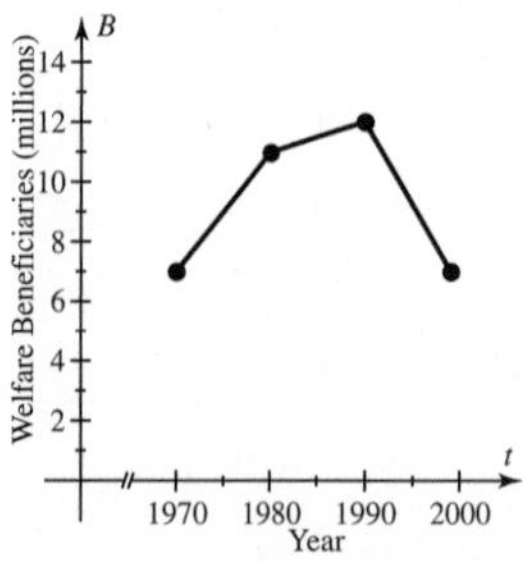

Figure 39

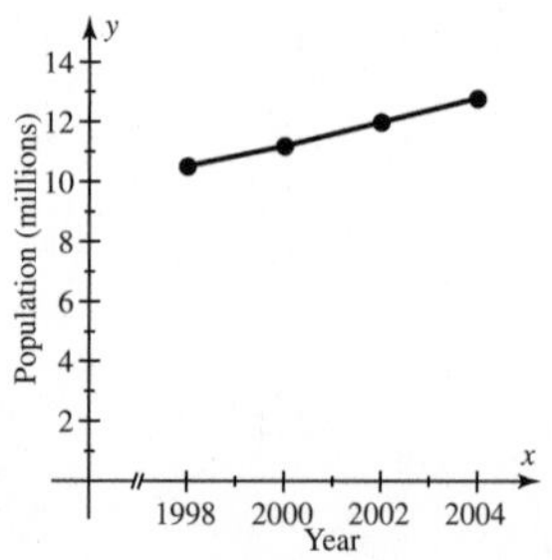

Figure 41

41. (a) See Figure 41.

    (b) The Asian-American population increased.

3.2: Linear Equations in Two Variables

Concepts

1. two
3. linear
5. graph

Solutions to Equations

7. Substitute 5 for x and 6 for y: $y = x + 1 \Rightarrow 6 = 5 + 1 \Rightarrow 6 = 6$. This is a true statement, so the ordered pair (5, 6) is a solution.
9. Substitute 2 for x and 13 for y: $y = 4x + 7 \Rightarrow 13 = 4(2) + 7 \Rightarrow 13 = 8 + 7 \Rightarrow 13 = 15$. This is not a true statement, so the ordered pair (2, 13) is not a solution.
11. Substitute -2 for x and 3 for y: $4x - y = -13 \Rightarrow 4(-2) - 3 = -13 \Rightarrow -8 - 3 = -13 \Rightarrow -11 = -13$. This is not a true statement, so the ordered pair $(-2, 3)$ is not a solution.
13. Substitute $\frac{1}{2}$ for x and 2 for y: $y - 6x = -1 \Rightarrow 2 - 6\left(\frac{1}{2}\right) = -1 \Rightarrow 2 - 3 = -1 \Rightarrow - = -1$. This is a true statement, so the ordered pair $\left(\frac{1}{2}, 2\right)$ is a solution.
15. Substitute 100 for x and 100 for y: $0.31x - 0.42y = -9 \Rightarrow 0.31(100) - 0.42(100) = -9 \Rightarrow$ $31 - 42 = -9 \Rightarrow -11 = -9$. This is not a true statement, so the ordered pair (100, 100) is not a solution.
17. When $x = -1$: $y = 4x \Rightarrow y = 4(-1) \Rightarrow y = -4$; when $x = 0$: $y = 4x \Rightarrow y = 4(0) \Rightarrow y = 0$; when $x = 1$: $y = 4x \Rightarrow y = 4(1) \Rightarrow y = 4$; when $x = 2$: $y = 4x \Rightarrow y = 4(2) \Rightarrow y = 8$. Thus, the missing values in the table are -4, 0, 4 and 8. See Figure 17.

x	−2	−1	0	1	2
y	−8	−4	0	4	8

Figure 17

x	−8	−4	0	4	8
y	−4	0	4	8	12

Figure 19

x	6	3	0	−3	−9
y	−2	0	2	4	8

Figure 21

19. When $y = 0$: $y = x + 4 \Rightarrow 0 = x + 4 \Rightarrow 0 - 4 = x + 4 - 4 \Rightarrow -4 = x \Rightarrow x = -4$;
when $y = 4$: $y = x + 4 \Rightarrow 4 = x + 4 \Rightarrow 4 - 4 = x + 4 - 4 \Rightarrow 0 = x \Rightarrow x = 0$;
when $y = 8$: $y = x + 4 \Rightarrow 8 = x + 4 \Rightarrow 8 - 4 = x + 4 - 4 \Rightarrow 4 = x \Rightarrow x = 4$;
when $y = 12$: $y = x + 4 \Rightarrow 12 = x + 4 \Rightarrow 12 - 4 = x + 4 - 4 \Rightarrow 8 = x \Rightarrow x = 8$.
Thus, the missing values in the table are -4, 0, 4 and 8. See Figure 19.
21. When $y = -2$: $3y + 2x = 6 \Rightarrow 3(-2) + 2x = 6 \Rightarrow -6 + 2x = 6 \Rightarrow -6 + 6 + 2x = 6 + 6 \Rightarrow$ $2x = 12 \Rightarrow \frac{2x}{2} = \frac{12}{2} \Rightarrow x = 6$; when $y = 0$: $3y + 2x = 6 \Rightarrow 3(0) + 2x = 6 \Rightarrow 2x = 6 \Rightarrow \frac{2x}{2} = \frac{6}{2} \Rightarrow$ $x = 3$; when $y = 2$: $3y + 2x = 6 \Rightarrow 3(2) + 2x = 6 \Rightarrow 6 + 2x = 6 \Rightarrow 6 - 6 + 2x = 6 - 6 \Rightarrow$ $2x = 0 \Rightarrow \frac{2x}{2} = \frac{0}{2} \Rightarrow x = 0$; when $y = 4$: $3y + 2x = 6 \Rightarrow 3(4) + 2x = 6 \Rightarrow 12 + 2x = 6 \Rightarrow$ $12 - 12 + 2x = 6 - 12 \Rightarrow 2x = -6 \Rightarrow \frac{2x}{2} = \frac{-6}{2} \Rightarrow x = -3$; when $y = 8$: $3y + 2x = 6 \Rightarrow$ $3(8) + 2x = 6 \Rightarrow 24 + 2x = 6 \Rightarrow 24 - 24 + 2x = 6 - 24 \Rightarrow 2x = -18 \Rightarrow \frac{2x}{2} = \frac{-18}{2} \Rightarrow x = -9$.
Thus, the missing values in the table are 6, 3, 0, -3 and -9. See Figure 21.

23. See Figure 23.

25. See Figure 25.

x	-3	0	3	6
y	-9	0	9	18

Figure 23

x	-8	-4	0	4
y	-2	0	2	4

Figure 25

x	8	6	4	2
y	-2	0	2	4

Figure 27

27. See Figure 27.

29. See Figure 29.

x	$-\frac{1}{2}$	$-\frac{1}{4}$	0	$\frac{1}{4}$
y	-2	-1	0	1

Figure 29

Graphing Equations

31. See Figure 31.

33. See Figure 33.

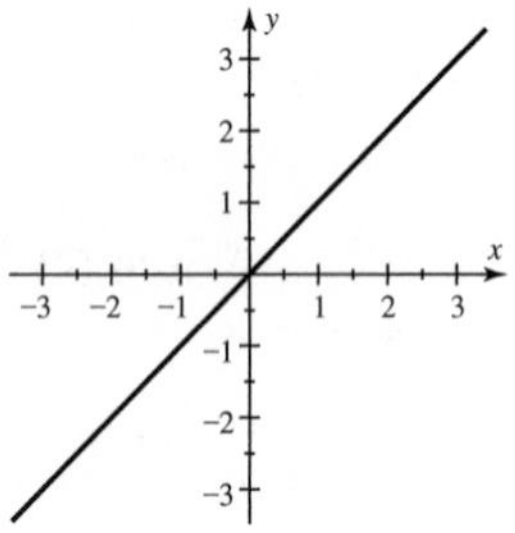

Figure 31

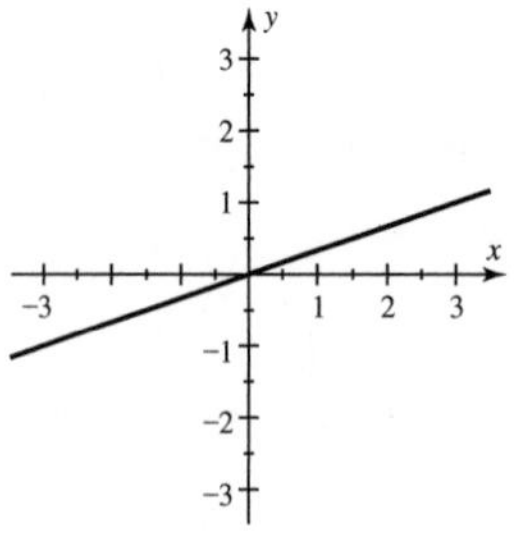

Figure 33

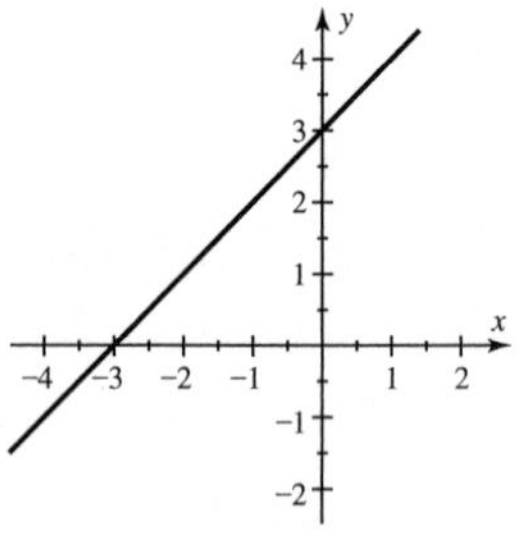

Figure 35

35. See Figure 35.

37. See Figure 37.

39. See Figure 39.

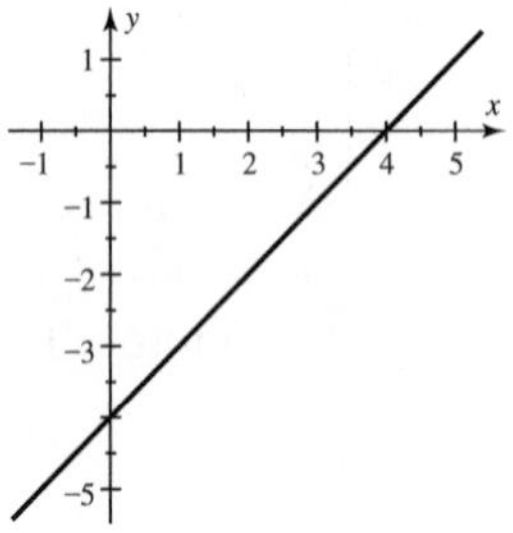

Figure 37

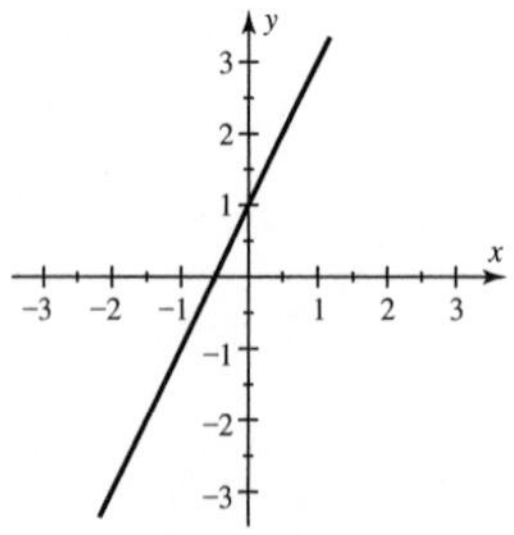

Figure 39

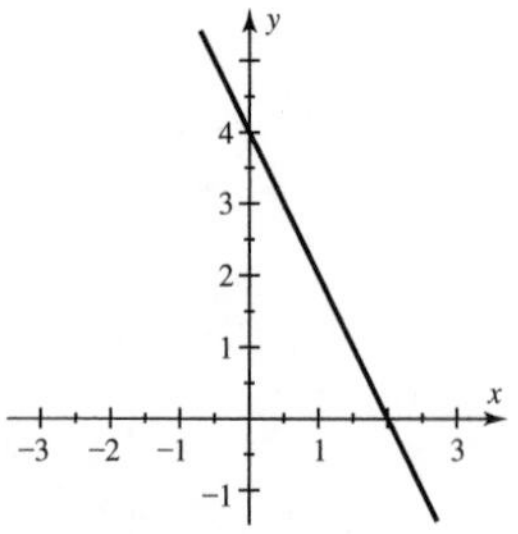

Figure 41

41. See Figure 41.

43. See Figure 43.

45. See Figure 45.

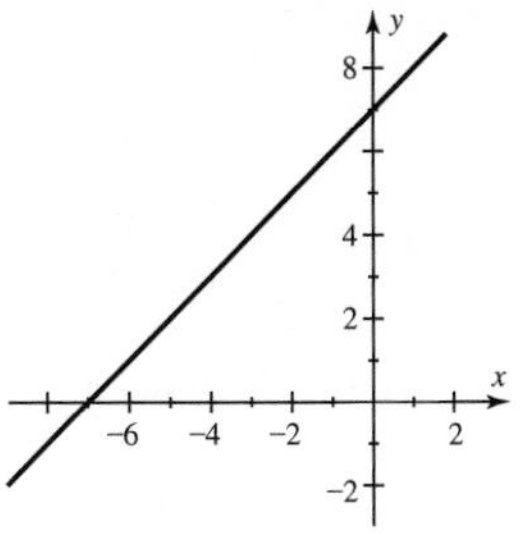

Figure 43

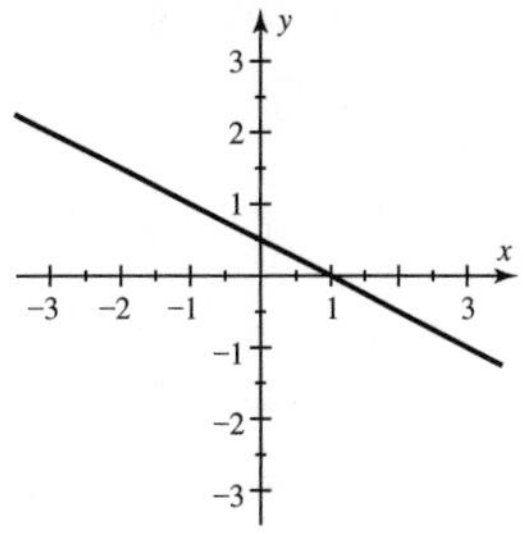

Figure 45

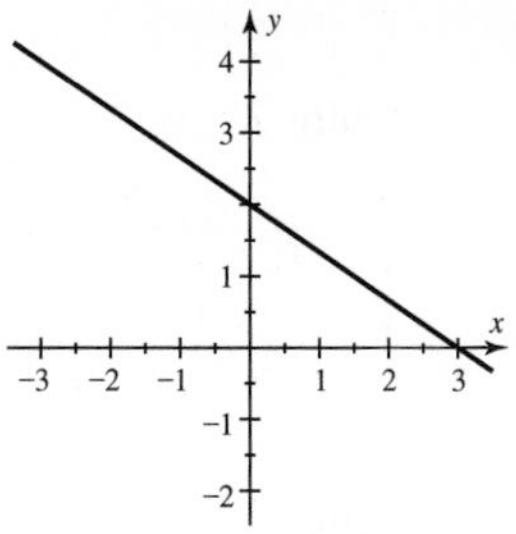

Figure 47

47. See Figure 47.

49. See Figure 49.

51. See Figure 51.

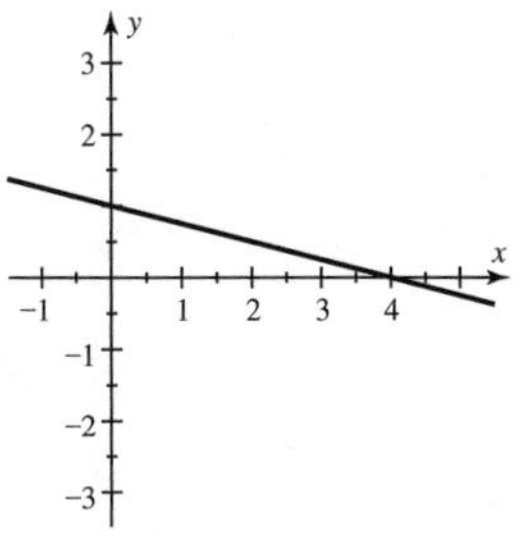

Figure 49

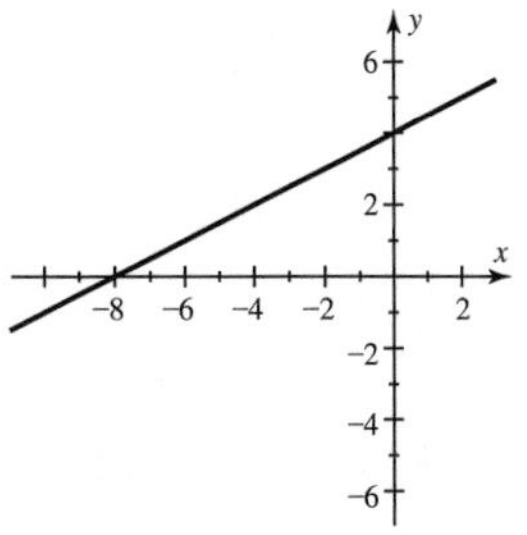

Figure 51

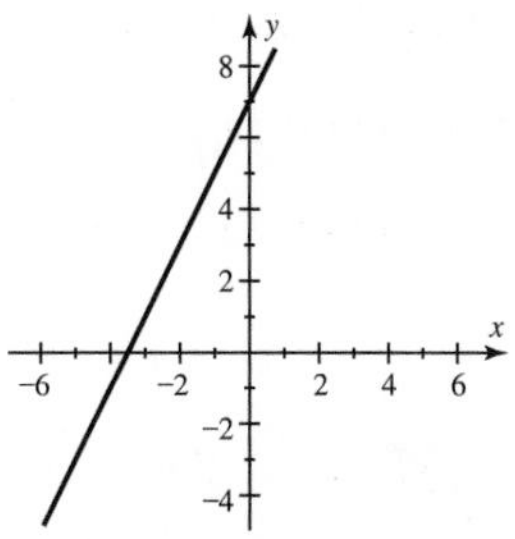

Figure 53

53. See Figure 53.

55. See Figure 55.

57. See Figure 57.

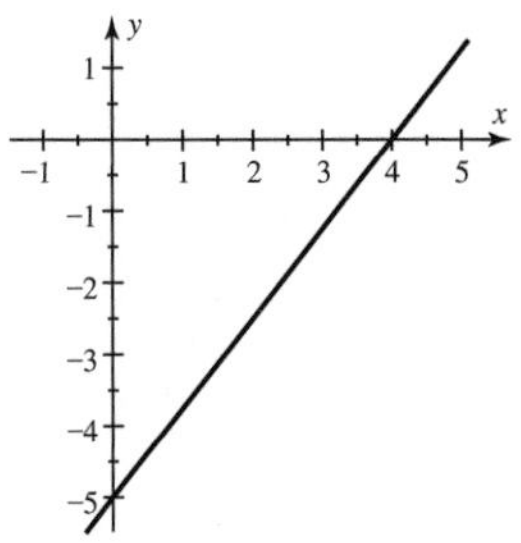

Figure 55

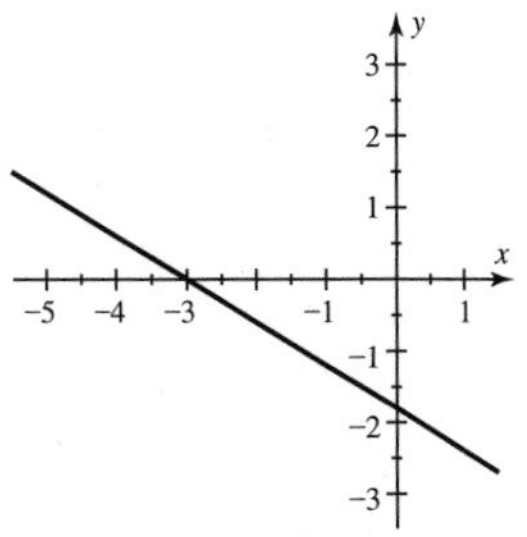

Figure 57

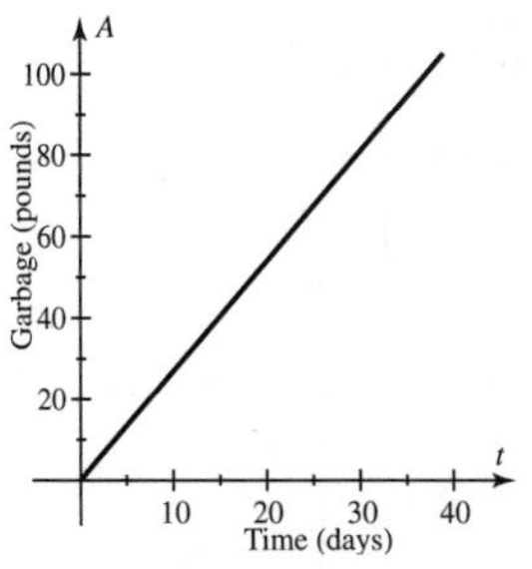

Figure 59

Applications

59. (a) See Figure 59.

(b) Set $A = 100$ and solve for t: $A = 2.7t \Rightarrow 100 = 2.7t \Rightarrow \dfrac{100}{2.7} = \dfrac{2.7t}{2.7} \Rightarrow t \approx 37$. Therefore, about 37 days.

61. (a) For year 1996, set $t = 1996$ and solve for P: $P = 5.5t - 10{,}911 = 5.5(1996) - 10{,}911 = 10{,}978 - 10{,}911 = 67$. Therefore, in year 1996 it was 67%.

For year 2000, set $t = 2000$ and solve for P: $P = 5.5t - 10{,}911 = 5.5(2000) - 10{,}911 = 11{,}000 - 10{,}911 = 89$. Therefore, in year 2000 it was 89%.

(b) See Figure 61.

(c) P was 83.5% in year 1999.

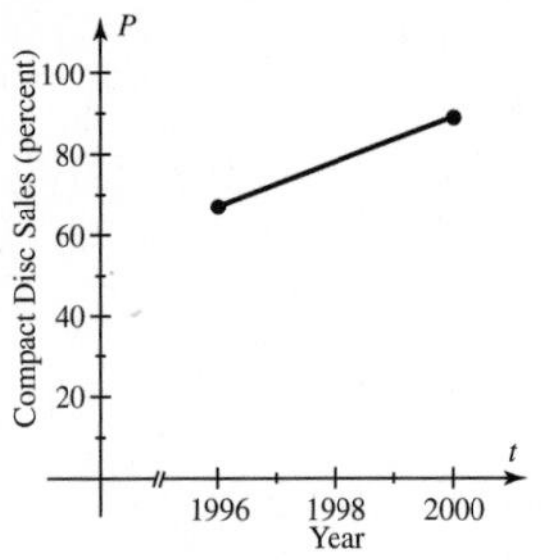

Figure 61

Checking Basic Concepts for Sections 3.1 & 3.2

1. $(-2,2)$, II; $(-1,-2)$, III; $(1,3)$, I; $(3,0)$, none.
2. See Figure 2.

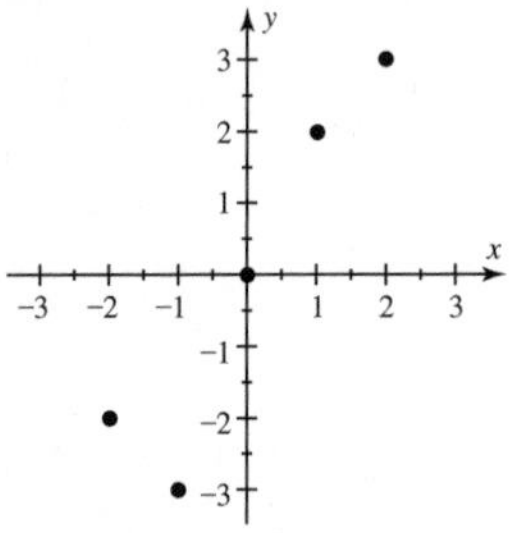

Figure 2

x	-2	-1	0	1	2
y	5	3	1	-1	-3

Figure 3

3. When $x = -1$: $Y = -2x + 1 = -2(-1) + 1 = 2 + 1 = 3$;

when $x = 0$: $Y = -2x + 1 = -2(0) + 1 = 1$;

when $x = 1$: $Y = -2x + 1 = -2(1) + 1 = -2 + 1 = -1$;

when $x = 2$: $Y = -2x + 1 = -2(2) + 1 = -4 + 1 = -3$.

Thus, the missing values in the table are $3, 1, -1, -3$. See Figure 3.

4. (a) $Y = 3 - x = 3 - (-2) = 3 + 2 = 5$

(b) $Y = \dfrac{4 + x}{3} = \dfrac{4 + 8}{3} = \dfrac{12}{3} = 4$

(c) $2x - 3y = 6 \Rightarrow 2(0) - 3y = 6 \Rightarrow -3y = 6 \Rightarrow \dfrac{-3y}{-3} = \dfrac{6}{-3} \Rightarrow y = -2$

5. (a) See Figure 5a.

 (b) See Figure 5b.

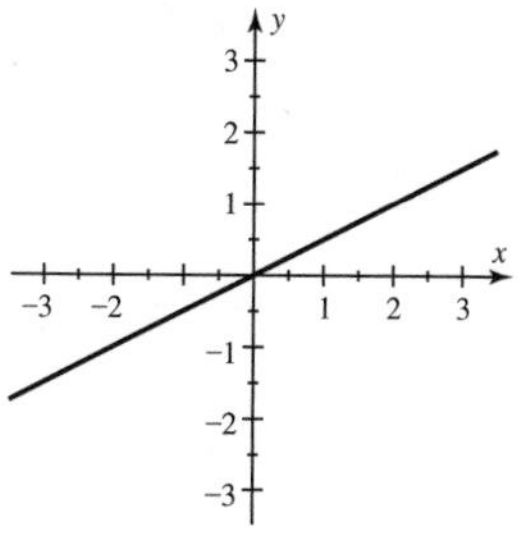

Figure 5a

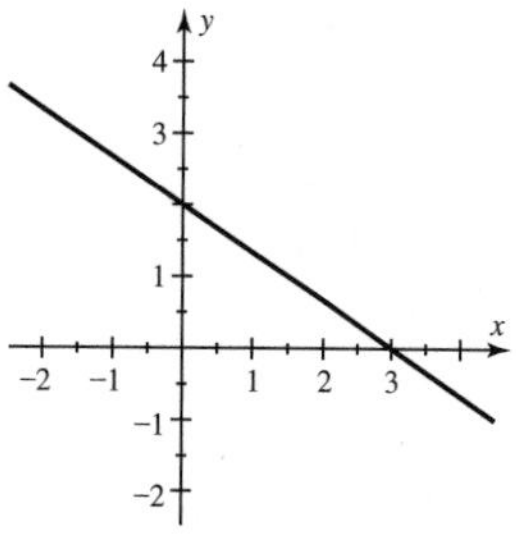

Figure 5b

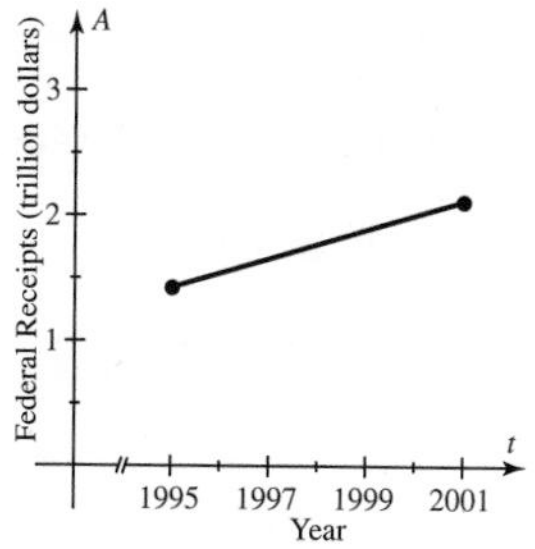

Figure 7

6. (1800,1), (1955, 3), (2000, 6); in 2000, the world population was 6 billion.

7. (a) Set $t = 1995$ and solve for A: $A = 0.115t - 228 = 0.115(1995) - 228 = 229.425 - 228 = 1.425$

 Set $t = 2001$ and solve for A: $A = 0.115t - 228 = 0.115(2001) - 228 = 230.115 - 228 = 2.115$

 In 1995, receipts were \$1.425 trillion; in 2001, receipts were \$2.115 trillion.

 (b) See Figure 7.

 (c) 1996

3.3: More Graphing of Lines

Concepts

1. Two

3. x-intercept

5. y-intercept

7. horizontal; 3

9. vertical; 3

Finding Intercepts

11. Because the graph crosses the x-axis at $x = 3$, $x = 3$ is the x-intercept.

 Because the graph crosses the y-axis at $y = -2$, $y = -2$ is the y-intercept.

13. Because the graph crosses the x-axis at $x = 0$, $x = 0$ is the x-intercept.

 Because the graph crosses the y-axis at $y = 0$, $y = 0$ is the y-intercept.

15. Because the graph crosses the x-axis at $x = -2$ and at $x = 2$, $x = -2$ and $x = 2$ are the x-intercepts.

 Because the graph crosses the y- axis at $y = 4$, $y = 4$ is the y-intercept.

17. Because the graph touches the x-axis at $x = 1$, $x = 1$ is the x-intercept.

 Because the graph crosses the y-axis at $y = 1$, $y = 1$ is the y-intercept.

19. When $x = -2$: $y = x + 2 = -2 + 2 = 0$; when $x = -1$: $y = x + 2 = -1 + 2 = 1$;

when $x = 0$: $y = x + 2 = 0 + 2 = 2$; when $x = 1$: $y = x + 2 = 1 + 2 = 3$;

when $x = 2$: $y = x + 2 = 2 + 2 = 4$. Therefore, the missing values in the table are 0, 1, 2, 3 and 4.

See Figure 19. The x-intercept is at $x = -2$, because at $x = -2$ the value of y is 0.

The y-intercept is at $y = 2$, because at $y = 2$ the value of x is 0.

x	−2	−1	0	1	2
y	0	1	2	3	4

Figure 19

x	−4	−2	0	2	4
y	−6	−4	−2	0	2

Figure 21

21. When $x = -4$: $-x + y = -2 \Rightarrow -(-4) + y = -2 \Rightarrow 4 + y = -2 \Rightarrow 4 - 4 + y = -2 - 4 \Rightarrow y = -6$;

when $x = -2$: $-x + y = -2 \Rightarrow -(-2) + y = -2 \Rightarrow 2 + y = -2 \Rightarrow 2 - 2 + y = -2 - 2 \Rightarrow y = -4$;

when $x = 0$: $-x + y = -2 \Rightarrow -(0) + y = -2 \Rightarrow y = -2$;

when $x = 2$: $-x + y = -2 \Rightarrow -(2) + y = -2 \Rightarrow -2 + y = -2 \Rightarrow -2 + 2 + y = -2 + 2 \Rightarrow y = 0$;

when $x = 4$: $-x + y = -2 \Rightarrow -(4) + y = -2 \Rightarrow -4 + y = -2 \Rightarrow -4 + 4 + y = -2 + 4 \Rightarrow y = 2$.

Therefore, the missing values in the table are −6, −4, −2, 0 and 2. See Figure 21.

The x-intercept is at $x = 2$, because at $x = 2$ the value of y is 0.

The y-intercept is at $y = -2$, because at $y = -2$ the value of x is 0.

23. To find the x-intercept, set $y = 0$ and solve for x: $-2x + 3y = -6 \Rightarrow -2x + 3(0) = -6 \Rightarrow$

$-2x = -6 \Rightarrow \dfrac{-2x}{-2} = \dfrac{-6}{-2} \Rightarrow x = 3$. Therefore, the x-intercept is at $x = 3$.

To find the y-intercept, set $x = 0$ and solve for y: $-2x + 3y = -6 \Rightarrow -2(0) + 3y = -6 \Rightarrow$

$3y = -6 \Rightarrow \dfrac{3y}{3} = \dfrac{-6}{3} \Rightarrow y = -2$. Therefore, the y-intercept is at $y = -2$. See Figure 23.

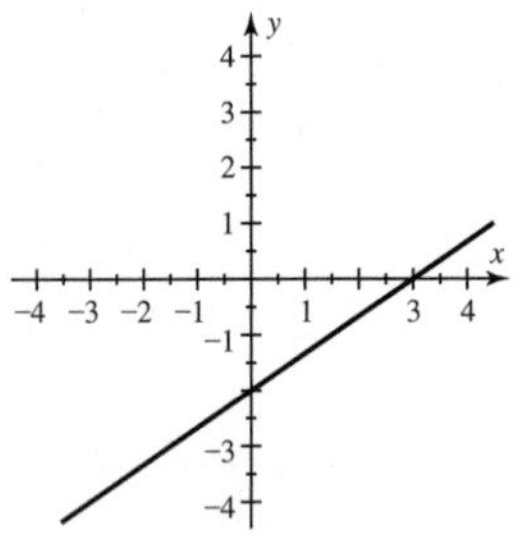

Figure 23

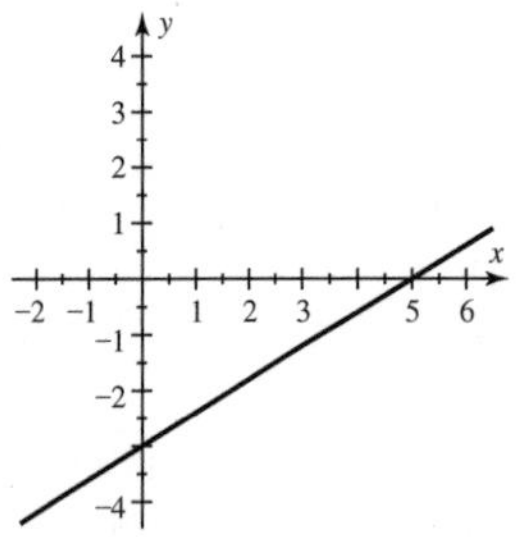

Figure 25

25. To find the x-intercept, set $y = 0$ and solve for x: $3x - 5y = 15 \Rightarrow 3x - 5(0) = 15 \Rightarrow$

$3x = 15 \Rightarrow \dfrac{3x}{3} = \dfrac{15}{3} \Rightarrow x = 5$. Therefore, the x-intercept is at $x = 5$.

To find the y-intercept, set $x = 0$ and solve for y: $3x - 5y = 15 \Rightarrow 3(0) - 5y = 15 \Rightarrow$

$-5y = 15 \Rightarrow \dfrac{-5y}{-5} = \dfrac{15}{-5} \Rightarrow y = -3$. Therefore, the y-intercept is at $y = -3$. See Figure 25.

27. To find the x-intercept, set $y = 0$ and solve for x: $x - 3y = 6 \Rightarrow x - 3(0) = 6 \Rightarrow x = 6$.

Therefore, the x-intercept is at $x = 6$.

To find the y-intercept, set $x = 0$ and solve for y: $x - 3y = 6 \Rightarrow 0 - 3y = 6 \Rightarrow$

$-3y = 6 \Rightarrow \frac{-3y}{-3} = \frac{6}{-3} \Rightarrow y = -2$. Therefore, the y-intercept is at $y = -2$. See Figure 27.

29. To find the x-intercept, set $y = 0$ and solve for x: $6x - y = -6 \Rightarrow 6x - 0 = -6 \Rightarrow$

$6x = -6 \Rightarrow \frac{6x}{6} = \frac{-6}{6} \Rightarrow x = -1$. Therefore, the x-intercept is at $x = -1$.

To find the y-intercept, set $x = 0$ and solve for y: $6x - y = -6 \Rightarrow 6(0) - y = -6 \Rightarrow -y = -6 \Rightarrow$

$-1(-y) = -1(-6) \Rightarrow y = 6$. Therefore, the y-intercept is at $y = 6$. See Figure 29.

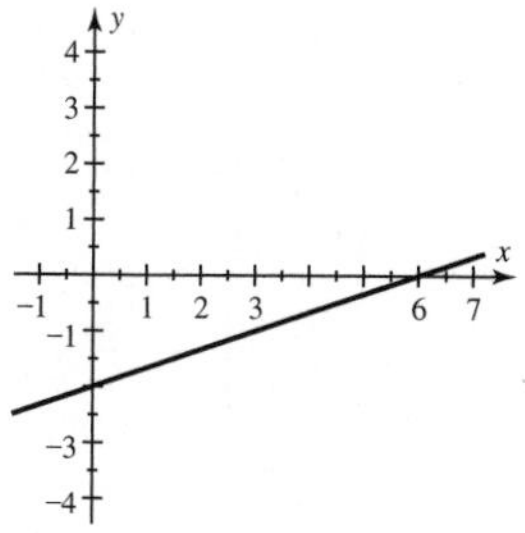

Figure 27

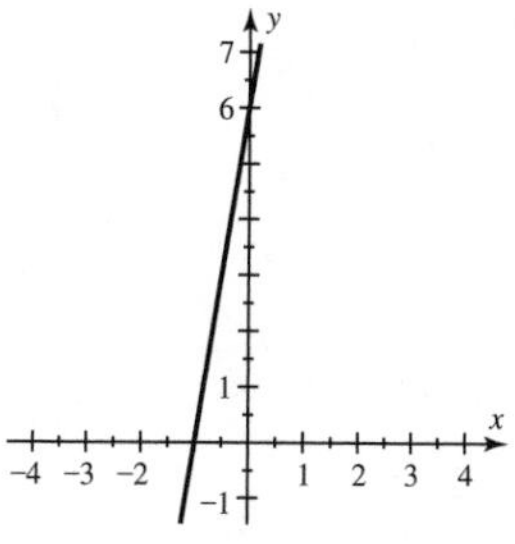

Figure 29

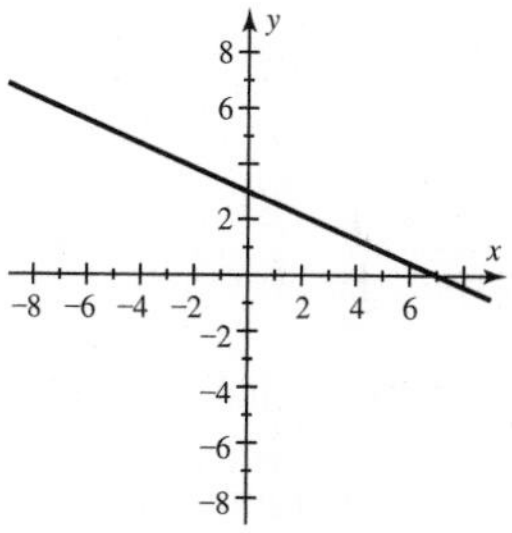

Figure 31

31. To find the x-intercept, set $y = 0$ and solve for x: $3x + 7y = 21 \Rightarrow 3x + 7(0) = 21 \Rightarrow$

$3x = 21 \Rightarrow \frac{3x}{3} = \frac{21}{3} \Rightarrow x = 7$. Therefore, the x-intercept is at $x = 7$.

To find the y-intercept, set $x = 0$ and solve for y: $3x + 7y = 21 \Rightarrow 3(0) + 7y = 21 \Rightarrow$

$7y = 21 \Rightarrow \frac{7y}{7} = \frac{21}{7} \Rightarrow y = 3$. Therefore, the y-intercept is at $y = 3$. See Figure 31.

33. To find the x-intercept, set $y = 0$ and solve for x: $40y - 30x = -120 \Rightarrow 40(0) - 30x = -120 \Rightarrow$

$-30x = -120 \Rightarrow \frac{-30x}{-30} = \frac{-120}{-30} \Rightarrow x = 4$. Therefore, the x-intercept is at $x = 4$.

To find the y-intercept, set $x = 0$ and solve for y: $40y - 30x = -120 \Rightarrow 40y - 30(0) = -120 \Rightarrow$

$40y = -120 \Rightarrow \frac{40y}{40} = \frac{-120}{40} \Rightarrow y = -3$. Therefore, the y-intercept is at $y = -3$. See Figure 33.

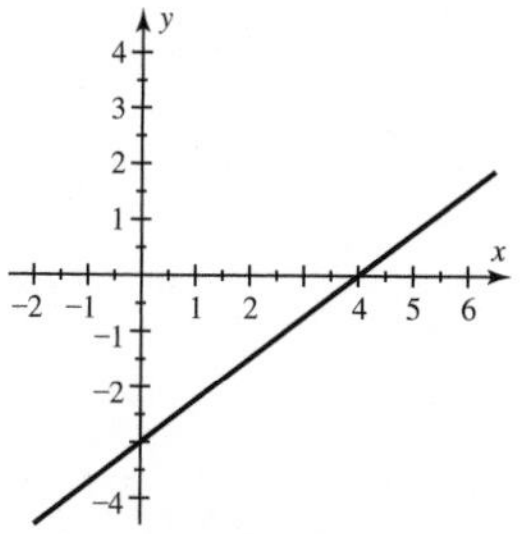

Figure 33

35. To find the x-intercept, set $y = 0$ and solve for x: $\frac{1}{2}x - y = 2 \Rightarrow \frac{1}{2}x - 0 = 2 \Rightarrow$
$\frac{1}{2}x = 2 \Rightarrow 2\left(\frac{1}{2}x\right) = 2(2) \Rightarrow x = 4$. Therefore, the x-intercept is at $x = 4$.
To find the y-intercept, set $x = 0$ and solve for y: $\frac{1}{2}x - y = 2 \Rightarrow \frac{1}{2}(0) - y = 2 \Rightarrow$
$-y = 2 \Rightarrow -1(-y) = 2(-1) \Rightarrow y = -2$. Therefore, the y-intercept is at $y = -2$. See Figure 35.

37. To find the x-intercept, set $y = 0$ and solve for x: $-\frac{x}{4} + \frac{y}{3} = 1 \Rightarrow -\frac{x}{4} + \frac{0}{3} = 1 \Rightarrow$
$-\frac{x}{4} = 1 \Rightarrow -4\left(-\frac{x}{4}\right) = 1(-4) \Rightarrow x = -4$. Therefore, the x-intercept is at $x = -4$.
To find the y-intercept, set $x = 0$ and solve for y: $-\frac{x}{4} + \frac{y}{3} = 1 \Rightarrow -\frac{0}{4} + \frac{y}{3} = 1 \Rightarrow$
$\frac{y}{3} = 1 \Rightarrow 3\left(\frac{y}{3}\right) = 3(1) \Rightarrow y = 3$. Therefore, the y-intercept is at $y = 3$. See Figure 37.

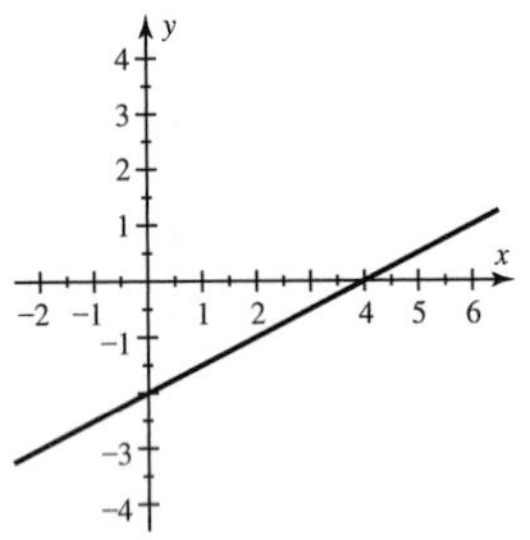

Figure 35

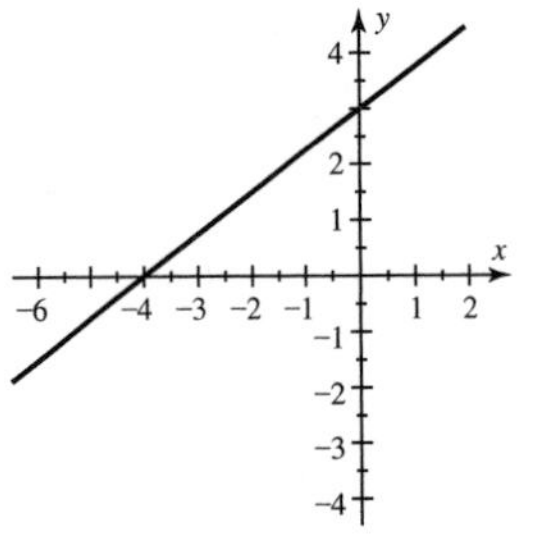

Figure 37

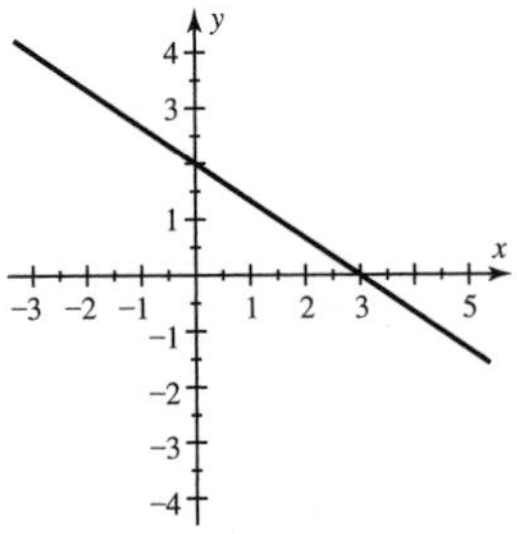

Figure 39

39. To find the x-intercept, set $y = 0$ and solve for x: $\frac{x}{3} + \frac{y}{2} = 1 \Rightarrow \frac{x}{3} + \frac{0}{2} = 1 \Rightarrow$
$\frac{x}{3} = 1 \Rightarrow 3\left(\frac{x}{3}\right) = 1(3) \Rightarrow x = 3$. Therefore, the x-intercept is at $x = 3$.
To find the y-intercept, set $x = 0$ and solve for y: $\frac{x}{3} + \frac{y}{2} = 1 \Rightarrow \frac{0}{3} + \frac{y}{2} = 1 \Rightarrow$
$\frac{y}{2} = 1 \Rightarrow 2\left(\frac{y}{2}\right) = 2(1) \Rightarrow y = 2$. Therefore, the y-intercept is at $y = 2$. See Figure 39.

41. To find the x-intercept, set $y = 0$ and solve for x: $0.6y - 1.5x = 3 \Rightarrow 0.6(0) - 1.5x = 3 \Rightarrow -1.5x = 3 \Rightarrow$
$\frac{-1.5x}{-1.5} = \frac{3}{-1.5} \Rightarrow x = -2$. Therefore, the x-intercept is at $x = -2$.
To find the y-intercept, set $x = 0$ and solve for y: $0.6y - 1.5x = 3 \Rightarrow 0.6y - 1.5(0) = 3 \Rightarrow 0.6y = 3 \Rightarrow$
$\frac{0.6y}{0.6} = \frac{3}{0.6} \Rightarrow y = 5$. Therefore, the y-intercept is at $y = 5$. See Figure 41.

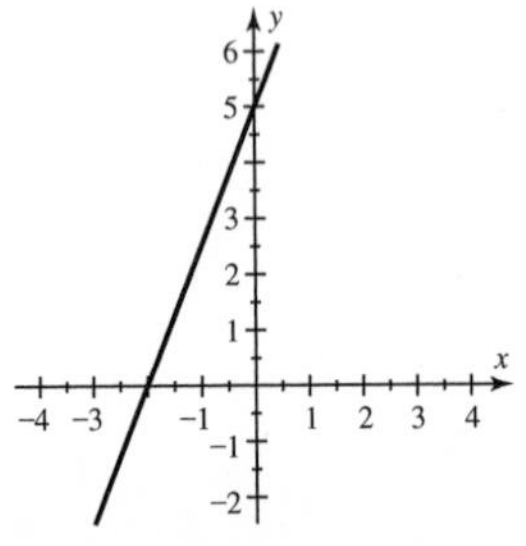

Figure 41

Horizontal and Vertical Lines

43. (a) See Figure 43a.

    (b) See Figure 43b.

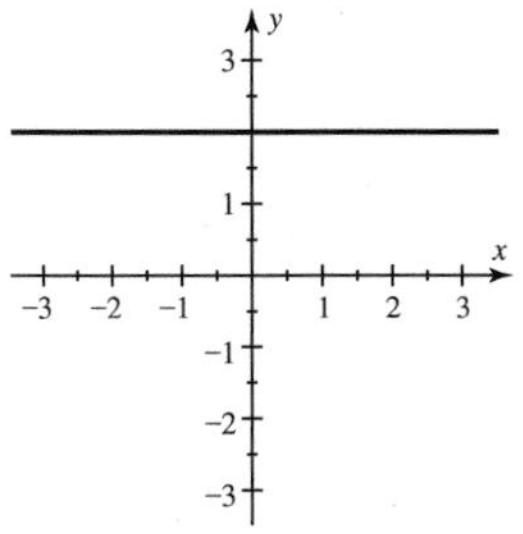

Figure 43a

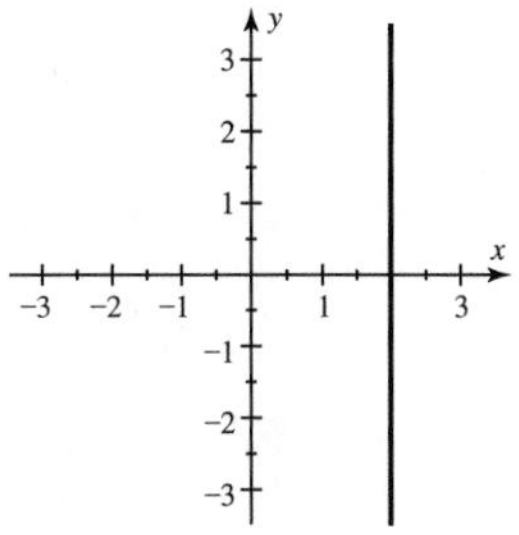

Figure 43b

45. (a) See Figure 45a.

    (b) See Figure 45b.

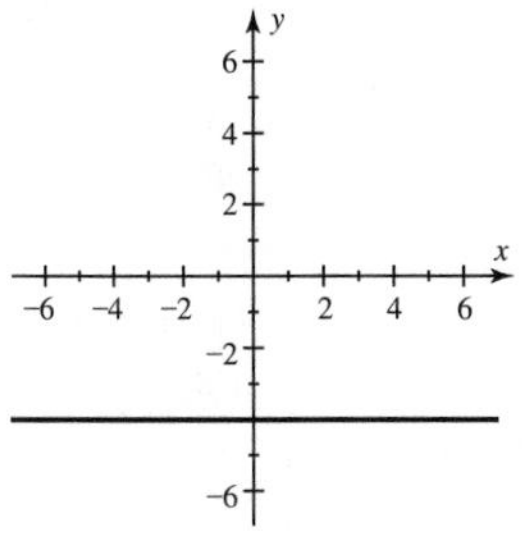

Figure 45a

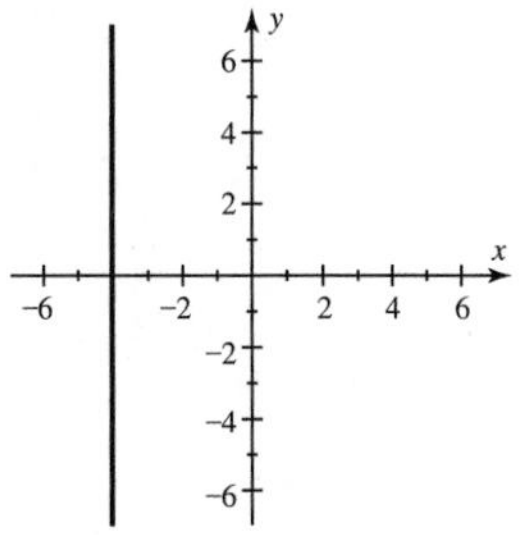

Figure 45b

47. (a) See Figure 47a.

    (b) See Figure 47b.

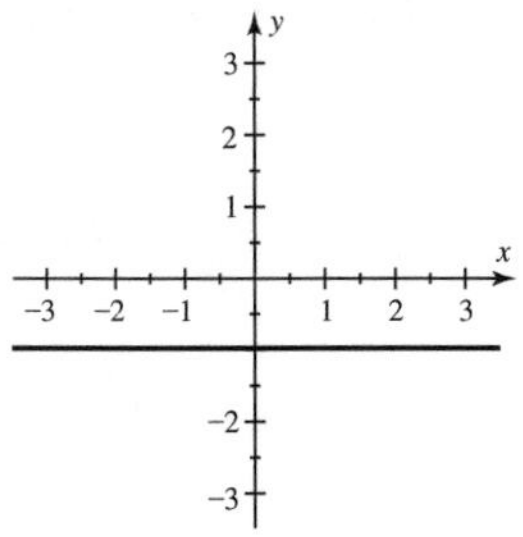

Figure 47a

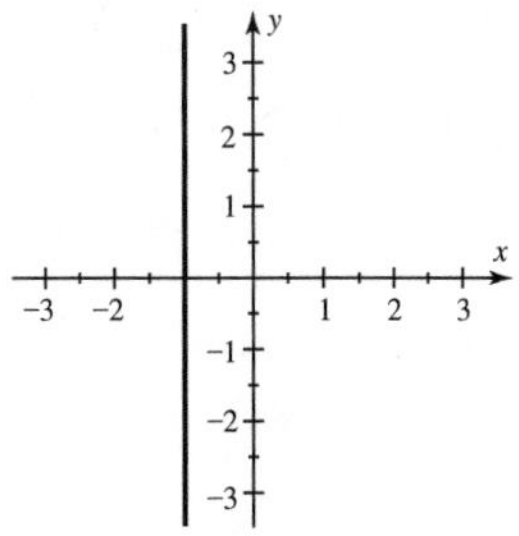

Figure 47b

49. (a) See Figure 49a.

(b) See Figure 49b.

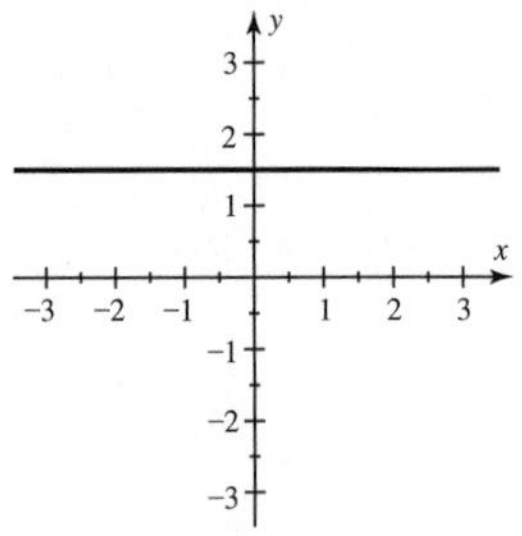

Figure 49a

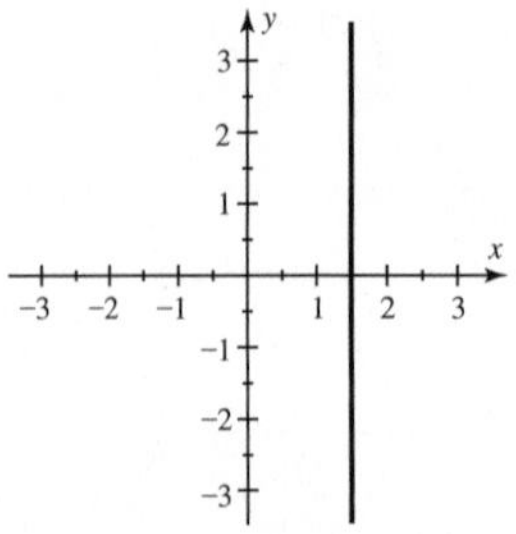

Figure 49b

51. $y = 4$

53. $x = -1$

55. $y = -6$

57. $x = 5$

59. Because $y = 1$ for every x-value, the graph is a horizontal line. The equation for the line is $y = 1$.

61. Because $x = -6$ for every y-value, the graph is a vertical line. The equation for the line is $x = -6$.

63. A horizontal line that passes through (1, 2) has a y-value of 2 for every x-value. Therefore, the equation for the horizontal line is $y = 2$.

A vertical line that passes through (1, 2) has an x-value of 1 for every y-value. Therefore, the equation for the vertical line is $x = 1$.

65. A horizontal line that passes through $(20, -45)$ has a y-value of -45 for every x-value. Therefore, the equation for the horizontal line is $y = -45$.

A vertical line that passes through $(20, -45)$ has an x-value of 20 for every y-value. Therefore, the equation for the vertical line is $x = 20$.

67. A horizontal line that passes through (0, 5) has a y-value of 5 for every x-value. Therefore, the equation for the horizontal line is $y = 5$.

A vertical line that passes through (0, 5) has an x-value of 0 for every y-value. Therefore, the equation for the vertical line is $x = 0$.

69. A vertical line that passes through $(-1, 6)$ has an x-value of -1 for every y-value. Therefore, the equation for the vertical line is $x = -1$.

71. A horizontal line that passes through $\left(\frac{3}{4}, -\frac{5}{6}\right)$ has a y-value of $-\frac{5}{6}$ for every x-value. Therefore, the equation for the horizontal line is $y = -\frac{5}{6}$.

73. Because $y = \frac{1}{2}$ is the equation of a horizontal line, a line perpendicular to $y = \frac{1}{2}$ is a vertical line. Therefore, the equation of the vertical line passing through $(4, -9)$ is $x = 4$.

75. Because $x = 4$ is the equation of a vertical line, a line parallel to $x = 4$ is also a vertical line. Therefore, the equation of the vertical line passing through $\left(-\frac{2}{3}, \frac{1}{2}\right)$ is $x = -\frac{2}{3}$.

Applications

77. (a) y-intercept, 200; x-intercept, 4.

(b) The driver was initially 200 mi from home; the driver arrived home after 4 hr.

79. (a) y-intercept, 2000; x-intercept, 4.

(b) The pool initially contained 2000 gal ; the pool was empty after 4 hr.

81. (a) To find the v-intercept, set $t = 0$ and solve for v: $v = 128 - 32t = 128 - 32(0) = 128$.

To find the t-intercept, set $v = 0$ and solve for t: $v = 128 - 32t \Rightarrow 0 = 128 - 32t \Rightarrow$

$0 + 32t = 128 - 32t + 32t \Rightarrow 32t = 128 \Rightarrow \frac{32t}{32} = \frac{128}{32} \Rightarrow t = 4$. See figure 81.

(b) The initial velocity was 128 ft/sec; the velocity after 4 seconds was 0.

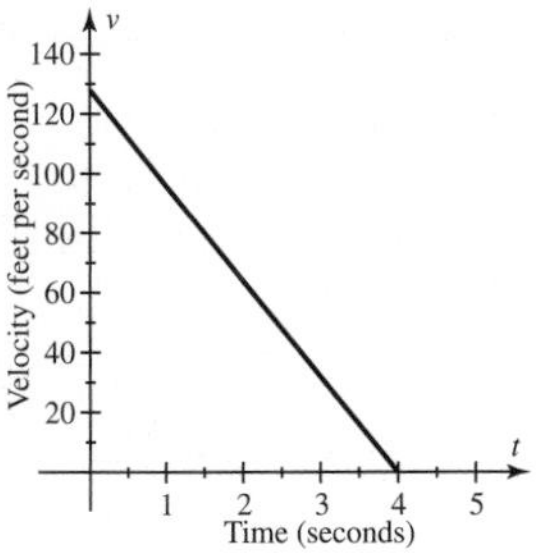

Figure 81

3.4: Slope and Rates of Change

Concepts

1. horizontal

3. rise; run

5. vertical

7. Because the graph of the line falls as it goes from left to right, the slope is negative.

9. Because the graph of the line neither falls or rises as it goes from left to right, the slope is zero.

11. Because the graph of the line falls as it goes from left to right, the slope is negative.

Finding Slopes of Lines

13. Because the graph is a horizontal line, the slope is 0. Thus, the rise always equals 0.

15. A point on the graph is $(0, -2)$ and another point is $(2, 0)$. Let $x_1 = 0$, $x_2 = 2$, $y_1 = -2$ and $y_2 = 0$. Then:

$m \text{ (slope)} = \frac{y_2 - y_1}{x_2 - x_1} = \frac{0 - (-2)}{2 - 0} = \frac{2}{2} = 1$. Thus, the slope is 1; the graph rises 1 unit for each unit of run.

17. A point on the graph is $(-1, -1)$ and another point is $(0, 1)$. Let $x_1 = -1, x_2 = 0, y_1 = -1$ and $y_2 = 1$. Then:

$$m\text{ (slope)} = \frac{y_2 - y_1}{x_2 - x_1} = \frac{1 - (-1)}{0 - (-1)} = \frac{2}{1} = 2.$$ Thus, the slope is 2; the graph rises 2 units for each unit of run.

19. Because the run always equals 0, the slope is undefined.

21. A point on the graph is $(0, -2)$ and another point is $(2, -1)$. Let $x_1 = 0, x_2 = 2, y_1 = -2$ and $y_2 = -1$. Then:

$$m\text{ (slope)} = \frac{y_2 - y_1}{x_2 - x_1} = \frac{-1 - (-2)}{2 - 0} = \frac{1}{2}.$$ Thus, the slope is $\frac{1}{2}$; the graph rises 1 unit for each 2 units of run.

23. A point on the graph is $(0, 4)$ and another point is $(4, 0)$. Let $x_1 = 0, x_2 = 4, y_1 = 4$ and $y_2 = 0$. Then:

$$m\text{ (slope)} = \frac{y_2 - y_1}{x_2 - x_1} = \frac{0 - 4}{4 - 0} = \frac{-4}{4} = -1.$$ Thus, the slope is -1; the graph falls 1 unit for each unit of run.

25. $m = \frac{y_2 - y_1}{x_2 - x_1} = \frac{4 - 2}{2 - 1} = \frac{2}{1} = 2$. Thus, the slope of the line is 2. See Figure 25.

27. $m = \frac{y_2 - y_1}{x_2 - x_1} = \frac{3 - 1}{-1 - 2} = \frac{2}{-3} = -\frac{2}{3}$. Thus, the slope of the line is $-\frac{2}{3}$. See Figure 27.

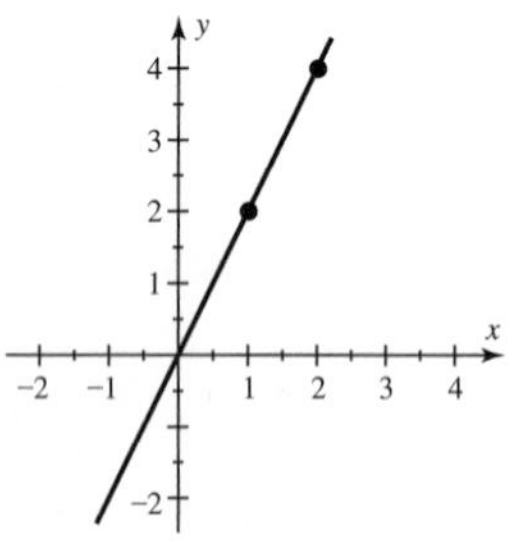

Figure 25

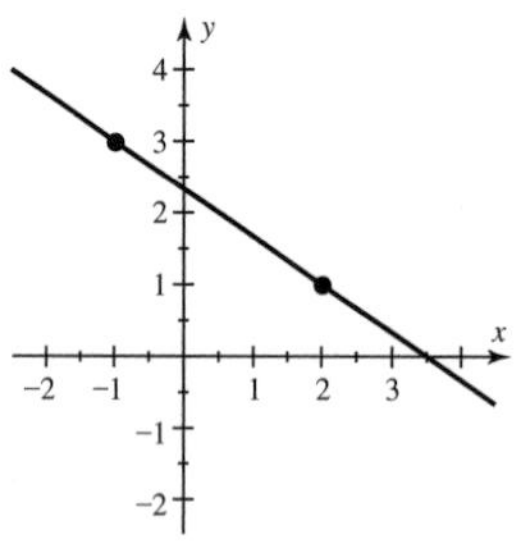

Figure 27

29. $m = \frac{y_2 - y_1}{x_2 - x_1} = \frac{-7 - (-2)}{-3 - 4} = \frac{-5}{-7} = \frac{5}{7}$. Thus, the slope of the line is $\frac{5}{7}$.

31. $m = \frac{y_2 - y_1}{x_2 - x_1} = \frac{-2 - 4}{4 - (-3)} = \frac{-6}{7} = -\frac{6}{7}$. Thus, the slope of the line is $-\frac{6}{7}$.

33. $m = \frac{y_2 - y_1}{x_2 - x_1} = \frac{6 - 6}{4 - (-3)} = \frac{0}{7} = 0$. Thus, the slope of the line is 0.

35. $m = \frac{y_2 - y_1}{x_2 - x_1} = \frac{-4 - 6}{-1 - (-1)} = \frac{-10}{0}$. Because the denominator is 0, the slope is undefined.

37. $m = \frac{y_2 - y_1}{x_2 - x_1} = \frac{18 - 5}{2000 - 1980} = \frac{13}{20}$. Thus, the slope of the line is $\frac{13}{20}$.

39. $m = \frac{y_2 - y_1}{x_2 - x_1} = \frac{10.6 - 6.1}{2000 - 1950} = \frac{4.5}{50} = \frac{9}{100}$. Thus, the slope of the line is $\frac{9}{100}$.

41. $m = \frac{y_2 - y_1}{x_2 - x_1} = \frac{\frac{3}{7} - (-\frac{2}{7})}{-\frac{2}{3} - \frac{1}{3}} = \frac{\frac{5}{7}}{-\frac{3}{3}} = -\frac{5}{7}$. Thus, the slope of the line is $-\frac{5}{7}$.

43. $m = \frac{y_2 - y_1}{x_2 - x_1} = \frac{64 - (-34)}{14 - 12} = \frac{98}{2} = 49$. Thus, the slope of the line is 49.

45. See Figure 45.

47. See Figure 47.

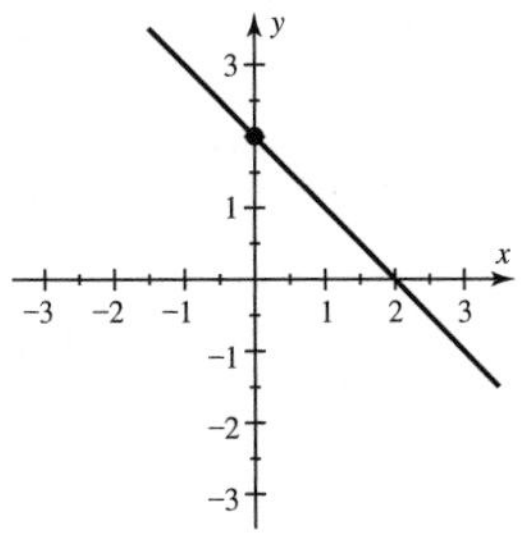

Figure 45

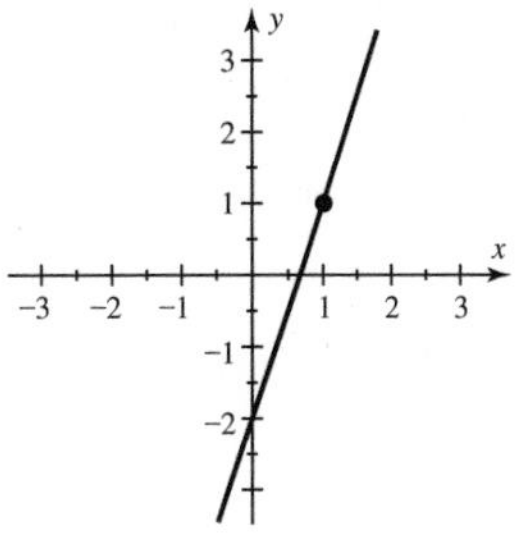

Figure 47

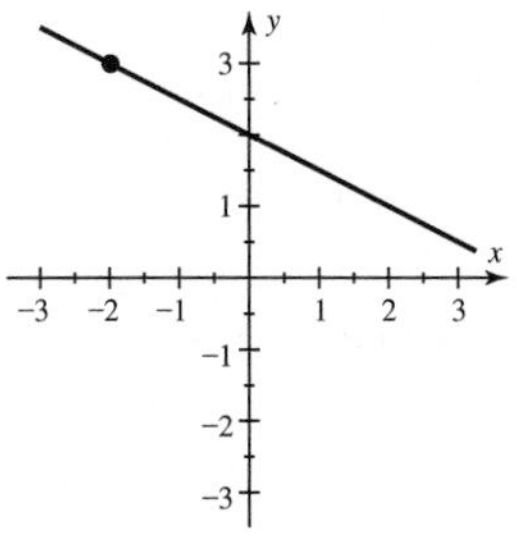

Figure 49

49. See Figure 49.

51. See Figure 51.

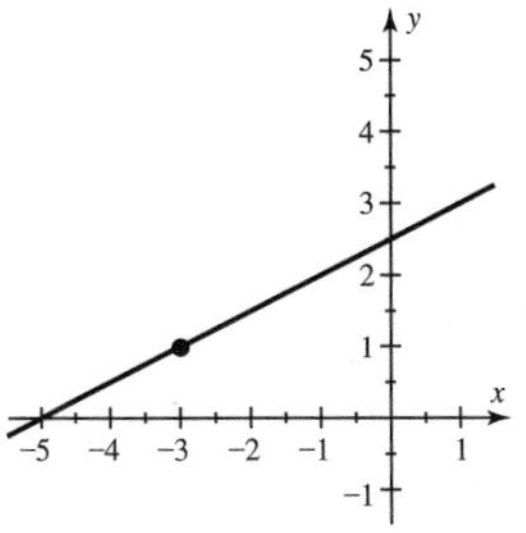

Figure 51

53. Because the y-value increases by 2 when the x-value increases by 1, the slope is 2. Because $y = 0$ when $x = 1$, the x-intercept is at $x = 1$. Because $x = 0$ when $y = -2$, the y-intercept is at $y = -2$.

55. Because the y-value decreases by 9 when the x-value increases by 1, the slope is -9. Because $y = 0$ when $x = -1$, the x-intercept is at $x = -1$. Because $x = 0$ when $y = -9$, the y-intercept is at $y = -9$.

57. Because the slope is 2, the y-value increases by 2 when the x-value increases by 1. Thus, when $x = 1$, $y = -4 + 2 = -2$; when $x = 2$, $y = -2 + 2 = 0$; when $x = 3$, $y = 0 + 2 = 2$. See Figure 57.

59. Because the slope is -3, the y-value decreases by 3 when the x-value increases by 1. Thus, when $x = 2$, $y = 4 - 3 = 1$; when $x = 3$, $y = 1 - 3 = -2$; when $x = 4$, $y = -2 - 3 = -5$; See Figure 59.

x	0	1	2	3
y	−4	−2	0	2

Figure 57

x	1	2	3	4
y	4	1	−2	−5

Figure 59

x	−4	−2	0	2
y	0	3	6	9

Figure 61

61. Because the slope is $\frac{3}{2}$, the y-value increases by $\frac{3}{2}$ when the x-value increases by 1 and the y-value increases by $2\left(\frac{3}{2}\right) = 3$ when the x-value increases by 2. Thus, when $x = -2$, $y = 0 + 3 = 3$; when $x = 0$, $y = 3 + 3 = 6$; when $x = 2$, $y = 6 + 3 = 9$. See Figure 61.

63. (a) See Figure 63.

(b) A point on the graph is $(0, -1)$ and another point is $\left(\frac{1}{2}, 0\right)$. Thus: $m = \frac{y_2 - y_1}{x_2 - x_1} = \frac{0 - (-1)}{\frac{1}{2} - 0} = \frac{1}{\frac{1}{2}} = 2$.

Therefore, the slope of the line is 2.

65. (a) See Figure 65.

(b) A point on the graph is $(1, -1)$ and another point is $(0, 2)$. Thus: $m = \frac{y_2 - y_1}{x_2 - x_1} = \frac{2 - (-1)}{0 - 1} = \frac{3}{-1} = -3$.

Therefore, the slope of the line is -3.

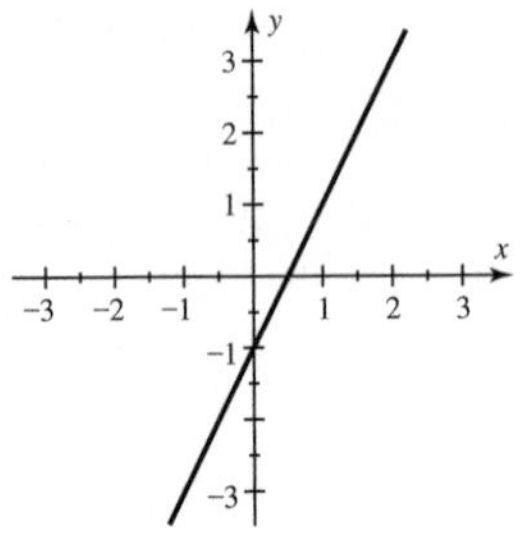

Figure 63

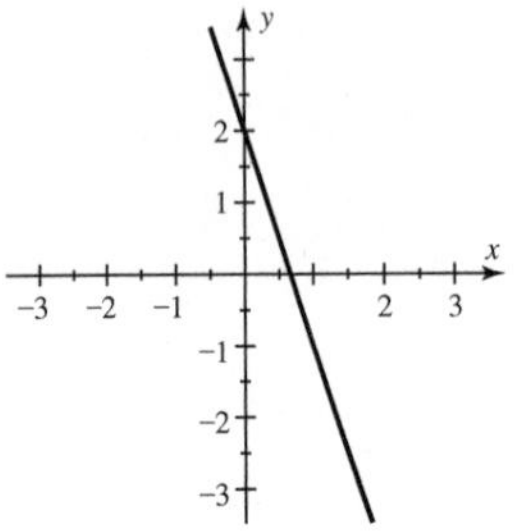

Figure 65

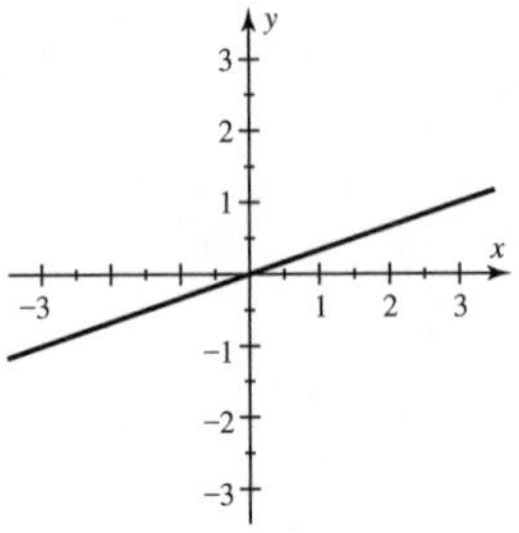

Figure 67

67. (a) See Figure 67.

(b) A point on the graph is $(0, 0)$ and another point is $(3, 1)$. Thus: $m = \frac{y_2 - y_1}{x_2 - x_1} = \frac{1 - 0}{3 - 0} = \frac{1}{3}$.

Therefore, the slope of the line is $\frac{1}{3}$.

69. (a) See Figure 69.

(b) Because the line is horizontal, the rise is always 0 and therefore the slope is 0.

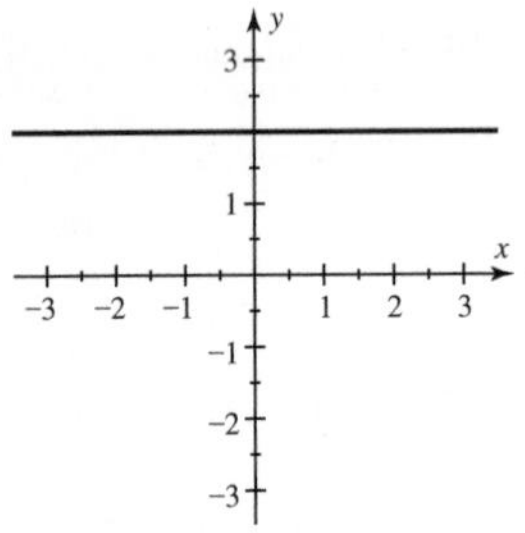

Figure 69

Slope as a Rate of Change

71. Because when $x = 0$, $y = 0$, c.

73. Because when $x = 1980$, $y > 0$ and the world population increased from 1980 to 2000, b.

75. (a) When $0 \leq x \leq 3$, the y-value increases by 1000 when x increases by 1. Therefore, $m_1 = 1000$.

When $3 \leq x \leq 5$, the y-value decreases by 1000 when x increases by 1. Therefore, $m_2 = -1000$.

(b) $m_1 = 1000$: Water is being added to the pool at a rate of 1000 gallons per hour.

$m_2 = -1000$: Water is being removed from the pool at a rate of 1000 gallons per hour.

(c) Initially the pool contained 2000 gallons of water. Over the first 3 hours, water was pumped into the pool at a rate of 1000 gallons per hour. For the next 2 hours, water was pumped out of the pool at a rate of 1000 gallons per hour.

77. (a) When $0 \le x \le 2$, the y-value increases by 50 when x increases by 1. Therefore, $m_1 = 50$.

When $2 \le x \le 3$, the y-value remains constant when x increases. Therefore, $m_2 = 0$.

When $3 \le x \le 4$, the y-value decreases by 50 when x increases by 1. Therefore, $m_3 = -50$.

(b) $m_1 = 50$: The car is moving away from home at a rate of 50 mph.

$m_2 = 0$: The car is not moving.

$m_3 = -50$: The car is moving toward home at a rate of 50 mph.

(c) Initially the car is at home. Over the first 2 hours, the car travels away from home at a rate of 50 mph. Then the car is parked for 1 hour. Finally, the car travels toward home at a rate of 50 mph.

79. See Figure 79. The graph indicates a constant decrease in distance from home (y-value) as the rider travels for x hours.

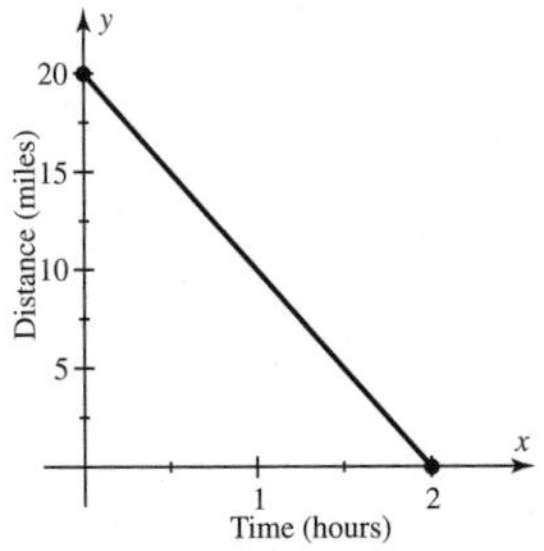

Figure 79

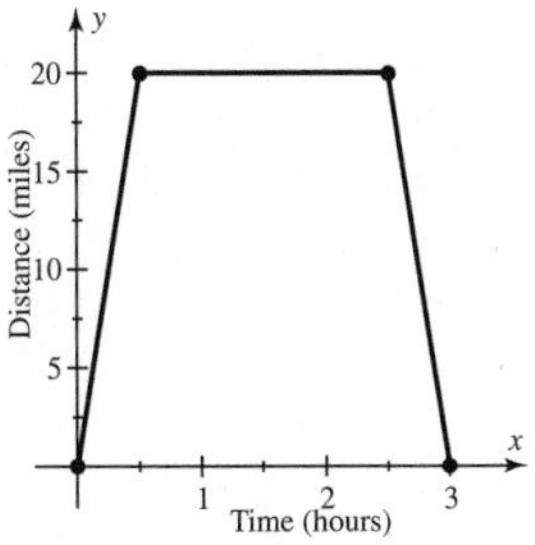

Figure 81

81. See Figure 81. The graph indicates a constant increase in distance from home as the person drives to the mall; the y-value remains constant as the person is at the mall, indicating that their distance from home neither increases or decreases, and then a decrease in distance from home when the person leaves the mall and drives home.

Applications

83. (a) $m = \dfrac{y_2 - y_1}{x_2 - x_1} = \dfrac{70 - 50}{2000 - 1990} = \dfrac{20}{10} = 2$. Thus, the slope of the line is 2.

(b) The birth rate increased on average by 2000 children per year.

85. (a) A point on the line is (40, 100) and another point is (0, 0). Thus: $m = \dfrac{y_2 - y_1}{x_2 - x_1} = \dfrac{100 - 0}{40 - 0} = \dfrac{100}{40} = 2.5$.

Thus, the slope of the line is 2.5.

(b) The revenue is \$2.50 per screwdriver.

87. (a) Substitute 50 for G and solve for O: $O = \dfrac{1}{50}G = \dfrac{1}{50}(50) = 1$. Thus, 1 gallon of oil should be added to 50 gallons of gasoline. Then substitute 100 for G and solve for O: $O = \dfrac{1}{50}G = \dfrac{1}{50}(100) = 2$. Thus, 2 gallons of oil should be added to 100 gallons of gasoline.

(b) When G increases by 1, O increases by $\dfrac{1}{50}$. Thus, the slope of the graph is $\dfrac{1}{50}$.

(c) Oil should be added at a rate of 1 gallon of oil per 50 gallons of gasoline.

89. (a) See Figure 89.

(b) $m_1 = \frac{y_2 - y_1}{x_2 - x_1} = \frac{100 - 0}{5 - 0} = \frac{100}{5} = 20$; $m_2 = \frac{y_2 - y_1}{x_2 - x_1} = \frac{250 - 100}{10 - 5} = \frac{150}{5} = 30$;

$m_3 = \frac{y_2 - y_1}{x_2 - x_1} = \frac{450 - 250}{15 - 10} = \frac{200}{5} = 40.$

(c) $m_1 = 20$: Each mile between 0 and 5 miles is worth \$20/mile.

$m_2 = 30$: Each mile between 5 and 10 miles is worth \$30/mile.

$m_3 = 40$: Each mile between 10 and 15 miles is worth \$40/mile.

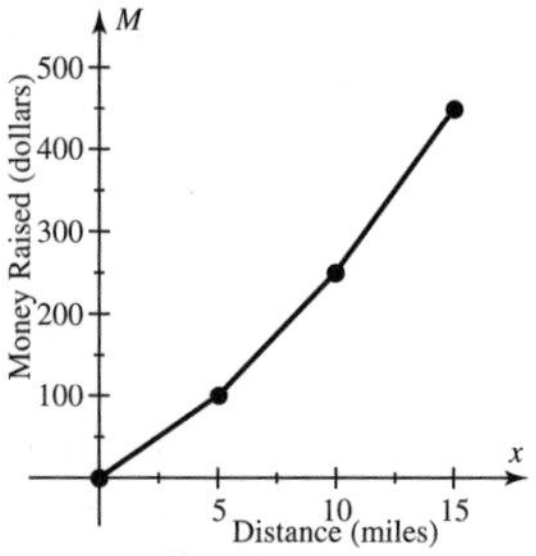

Figure 89

91. (a) $m = \frac{y_2 - y_1}{x_2 - x_1} = \frac{42{,}000 - 18{,}000}{2000 - 1980} = \frac{24{,}000}{20} = 1200$. Thus, the slope of the line is 1200.

(b) Median family income increased on average by \$1200/year over this period of time.

(c) $42{,}000 + 5(1200) = \$48{,}000$

Checking Basic Concepts for Sections 3.3 & 3.4

1. The line crosses the x-axis at $x = -2$; therefore, the x-intercept is -2.

   The line crosses the y-axis at $y = 3$; therefore, the y-intercept is 3.

2. $2x - y = 2 \Rightarrow 2x - y + y = 2 + y \Rightarrow 2x - 2 = 2 - 2 + y \Rightarrow y = 2x - 2$. Therefore:

   When $x = -1$: $y = 2(-1) - 2 \Rightarrow y = -2 - 2 \Rightarrow y = -4$; When $x = 0$: $y = 2x - 2 = 2(0) - 2 = -2$;

   When $x = 1$: $y = 2x - 2 = 2(1) - 2 = 0$; When $x = 2$: $y = 2x - 2 = 2(2) - 2 = 2$.

   Therefore, the missing values in the table are -4, -2, 0, and 1. See Figure 2.

   When $y = 0$, $x = 1$. Therefore the x-intercept is $x = 1$.

   When $x = 0$, $y = -2$. Therefore, the y-intercept is $y = -2$.

x	-2	-1	0	1	2
y	-6	-4	-2	0	2

Figure 2

3. (a) To find the x-intercept, set $y = 0$ and solve for x: $x - 2y = 6 \Rightarrow x - 2(0) = 6 \Rightarrow x = 6$. Therefore, the x-intercept is $x = 6$.

To find the y-intercept, set $x = 0$ and solve for y: $x - 2y = 6 \Rightarrow 0 - 2(y) = 6 \Rightarrow -2y = 6 \Rightarrow \frac{-2y}{-2} = \frac{6}{-2} \Rightarrow y = -3$. Therefore, the y-intercept is $y = -3$. See Figure 3a.

(b) $y = 2$ is the graph of a horizontal line. Therefore, the line does not cross the x-axis and does not have an x-intercept. The line crosses the y-axis at $y = 2$, and therefore it's y-intercept is at $y = 2$. See Figure 3b.

(c) $x = -1$ is the graph of a vertical line. Therefore, the line crosses the x-axis at $x = -1$ and therefore it's x-intercept is at $x = -1$. The line does not cross the y-axis, and therefore does not have a y-intercept. See Figure 3c.

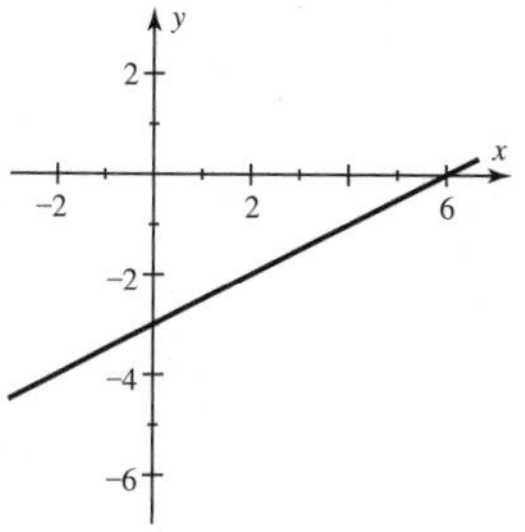

Figure 3a

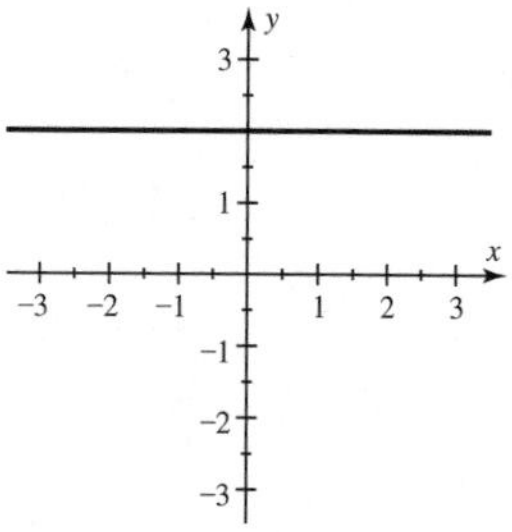

Figure 3b

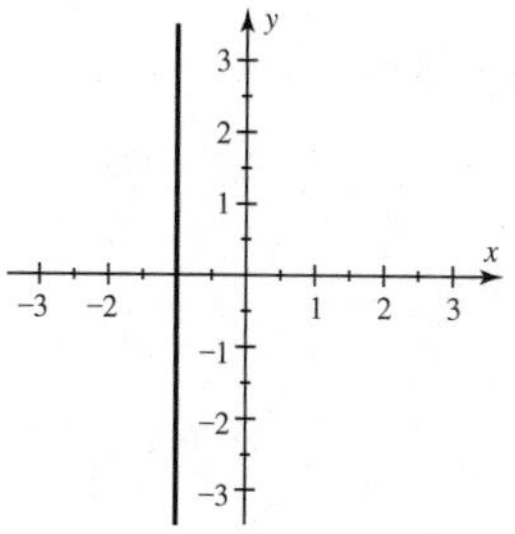

Figure 3c

4. A horizontal line passing through $(-2, 4)$ has the equation $y = 4$.

A vertical line passing through $(-2, 4)$ has the equation $x = -2$.

5. (a) $\frac{6 - 3}{2 - (-2)} = \frac{3}{4}$ Therefore, the slope of the line is $\frac{3}{4}$.

(b) $\frac{3 - 3}{0 - (-5)} = \frac{0}{5} = 0$ Therefore, the slope of the line is 0.

(c) $\frac{8 - 5}{1 - 1} = \frac{3}{0}$ Therefore, the slope of the line is undefined.

6. A point on the line is $(2, 1)$ and another point is $(0, 2)$. Thus, $\frac{2 - 1}{0 - 2} = \frac{1}{-2} = -\frac{1}{2}$.

Therefore, the slope of the line is $-\frac{1}{2}$.

7. See Figure 7.

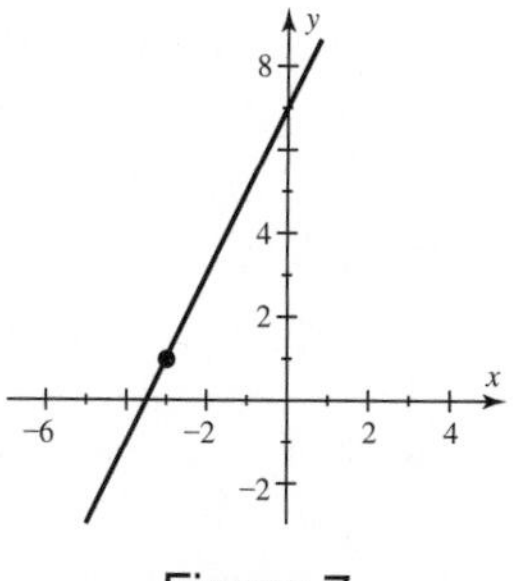

Figure 7

8. (a) $\frac{5-5}{1-0}=\frac{0}{1}=0$. Thus $m_1=0$. $\frac{7-5}{2-1}=\frac{2}{1}=2$. Thus $m_2=2$. $\frac{5-7}{5-2}=\frac{-2}{3}=-\frac{2}{3}$. Thus $m_3=-\frac{2}{3}$.

(b) $m_1=0$: before the rain, the depth of water in the pond does not change.

$m_2=2$: while it rains, the depth of water in the pond increases by 2 feet for every hour of rain.

$m_3=-\frac{2}{3}$: after it stops raining, the depth of water in the pond decreases by $-\frac{2}{3}$ feet per hour until it reaches its original depth.

(c) Initially the pond had a depth of 5 feet. For the first hour, there was no change in the depth of the pond. For the next hour, the depth of the pond increased at a rate of 2 feet per hour to a depth of 7 feet. Finally, the depth of the pond decreased for 3 hours at a rate of $\frac{2}{3}$ foot per hour until it was 5 feet deep.

9. (a) $\frac{22{,}300-18{,}100}{600-450}=\frac{4200}{150}=28$. Therefore, the slope of the line is 28.

(b) For counties between 450 and 600 mi^2, the population increases at a rate of 28 people/mi^2.

(c) No. We do not know whether this trend continues.

3.5: Slope-Intercept Form

Concepts

1. $y=mx+b$
3. y-intercept
5. origin
7. f
9. a
11. e

Slope-Intercept Form

13. The graph of the line shows the y-intercept at -1. For every x-increase of 1, the y-value increases by 1, so the slope is 1. Therefore: $y=mx+b \Rightarrow y=x-1$.

15. The graph of the line shows the y-intercept at 1. For every x-increase of 1, the y-value decreases by 2, so the slope is -2. Therefore: $y=mx+b \Rightarrow y=-2x+1$.

17. The graph of the line shows the y-intercept at -2. For every x-increase of 2, the y-value increases by 1, so the slope is $\frac{1}{2}$. Therefore: $y=mx+b \Rightarrow y=\frac{1}{2}x-2$.

19. The graph of the line shows the y-intercept at 0. For every x-increase of 1, the y-value decreases by 2, so the slope is -2. Therefore: $y=mx+b=-2x+0 \Rightarrow y=-2x$.

21. The graph of the line shows the y-intercept at 2. For every x-increase of 4, the y-value increases by 3, so the slope is $\frac{3}{4}$. Therefore: $y=mx+b \Rightarrow y=\frac{3}{4}x+2$.

23. See Figure 23. The slope-intercept form is $y = mx + b$, so with $m = 1$ and $b = 2$, $y = x + 2$.

25. See Figure 25. The slope-intercept form is $y = mx + b$, so with $m = 2$ and $b = -1$, $y = 2x - 1$.

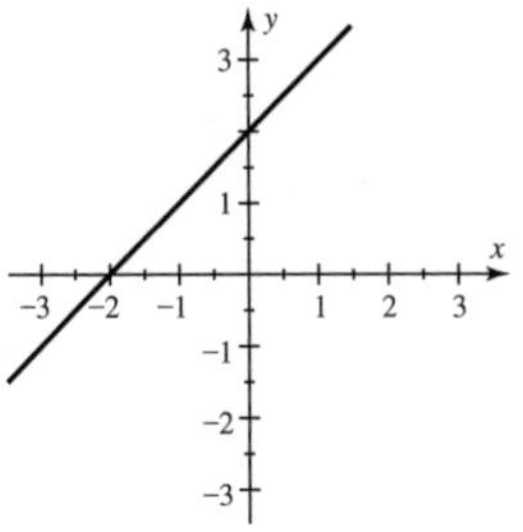

Figure 23

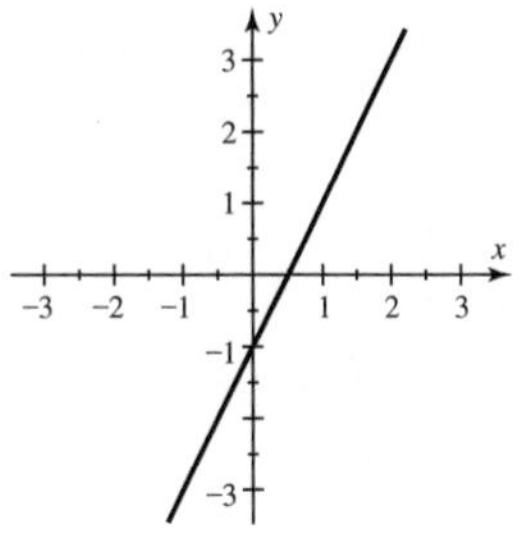

Figure 25

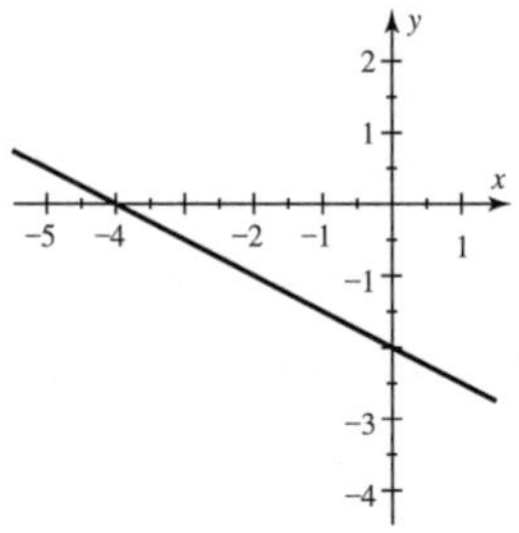

Figure 27

27. See Figure 27. The slope-intercept form is $y = mx + b$, so with $m = -\frac{1}{2}$ and $b = -2$, $y = -\frac{1}{2}x - 2$.

29. See Figure 29. $y = mx + b = \frac{1}{3}x + 0 \Rightarrow y = \frac{1}{3}x$.

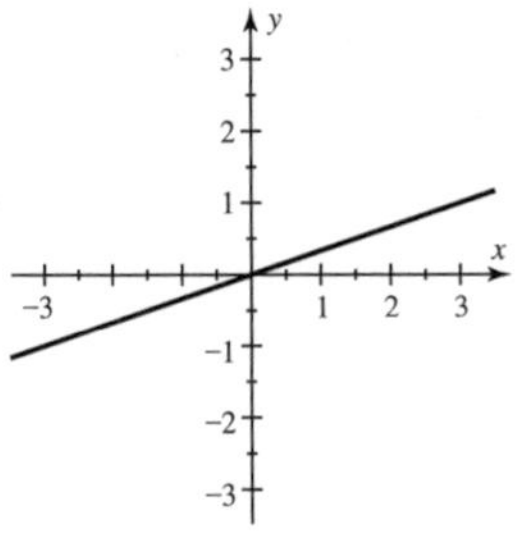

Figure 29

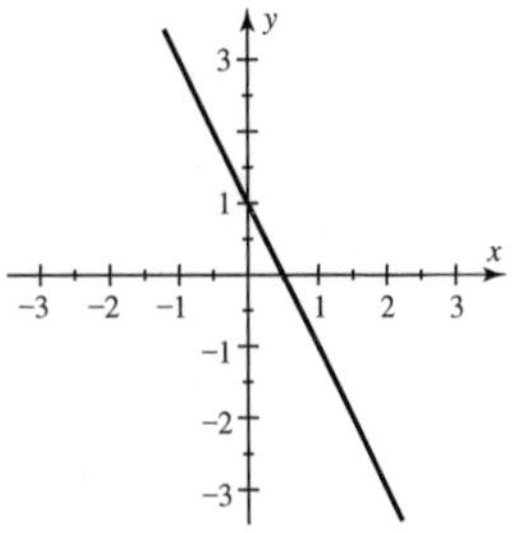

Figure 31

31. See Figure 31. $y = mx + b \Rightarrow y = -2x + 1$.

33. (a) To write the equation in slope-intercept form, solve for y:

$$x + y = 4 \Rightarrow x - x + y = 4 - x \Rightarrow y = 4 - x \Rightarrow y = -x + 4$$

(b) Because the slope-intercept form is $y = mx + b$, the slope is -1 and the y-intercept is 4.

35. (a) To write the equation in slope-intercept form, solve for y:

$$2x + y = 4 \Rightarrow 2x - 2x + y = 4 - 2x \Rightarrow y = 4 - 2x \Rightarrow y = -2x + 4$$

(b) Because the slope-intercept form is $y = mx + b$, the slope is -2 and the y-intercept is 4.

37. (a) To write the equation in slope-intercept form, solve for y: $x - 2y = -4 \Rightarrow x - x - 2y = -4 - x \Rightarrow$

$$-2y = -4 - x \Rightarrow -2y = -x - 4 \Rightarrow \frac{-2y}{-2} = \frac{-x - 4}{-2} \Rightarrow y = \frac{-x}{-2} - \frac{4}{-2} \Rightarrow y = \frac{1}{2}x + 2$$

(b) Because the slope-intercept form is $y = mx + b$, the slope is $\frac{1}{2}$ and the y-intercept is 2.

39. (a) To write the equation in slope-intercept form, solve for y: $2x - 3y = 6 \Rightarrow 2x - 2x - 3y = 6 - 2x \Rightarrow$

$$-3y = 6 - 2x \Rightarrow -3y = -2x + 6 \Rightarrow \frac{-3y}{-3} = \frac{-2x + 6}{-3} \Rightarrow y = \frac{-2x}{-3} + \frac{6}{-3} \Rightarrow y = \frac{2}{3}x - 2$$

(b) Because the slope-intercept form is $y = mx + b$, the slope is $\frac{2}{3}$ and the y-intercept is -2.

41. (a) To write the equation in slope-intercept form, solve for y: $x = 4y - 6 \Rightarrow x - 4y = 4y - 4y - 6 \Rightarrow$

$$x - 4y = -6 \Rightarrow x - x - 4 = -6 - x \Rightarrow -4y = -x - 6 \Rightarrow \frac{-4y}{-4} = \frac{-x}{-4} - \frac{6}{-4} \Rightarrow y = \frac{1}{4}x + \frac{3}{2}$$

(b) Because the slope-intercept form is $y = mx + b$, the slope is $\frac{1}{4}$ and the y-intercept is $\frac{3}{2}$.

43. (a) To write the equation in slope-intercept form, solve for y: $\frac{1}{2}x + \frac{3}{2}y = 1 \Rightarrow \frac{1}{2}x - \frac{1}{2}x + \frac{3}{2}y = 1 - \frac{1}{2}x \Rightarrow$

$$\frac{3}{2}y = -\frac{1}{2}x + 1 \Rightarrow \frac{2}{3}\left(\frac{3}{2}y\right) = \frac{2}{3}\left(-\frac{1}{2}x + 1\right) \Rightarrow y = -\frac{1}{3}x + \frac{2}{3}$$

(b) Because the slope-intercept form is $y = mx + b$, the slope is $-\frac{1}{3}$ and the y-intercept is $\frac{2}{3}$.

45. See Figure 45.

47. See Figure 47.

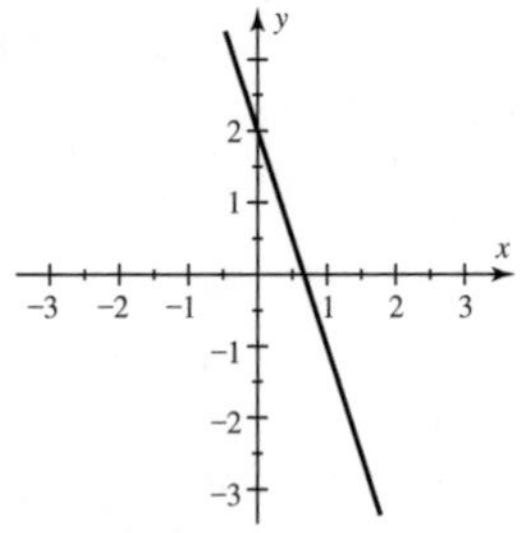

Figure 45

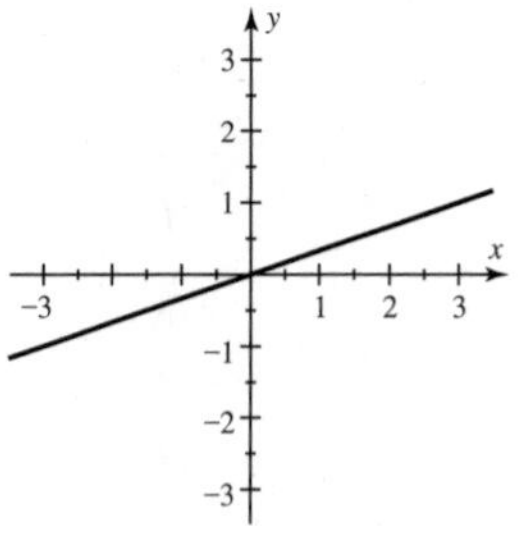

Figure 47

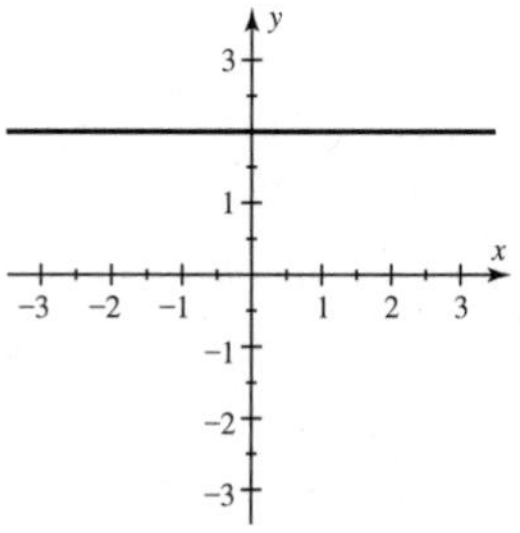

Figure 49

49. See Figure 49.

51. See Figure 51.

53. See Figure 53.

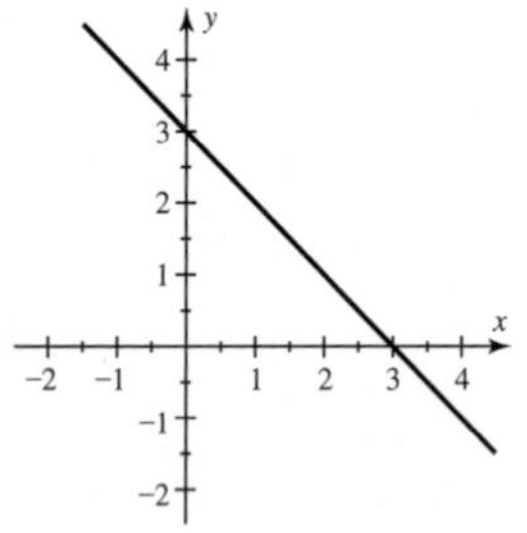

Figure 51

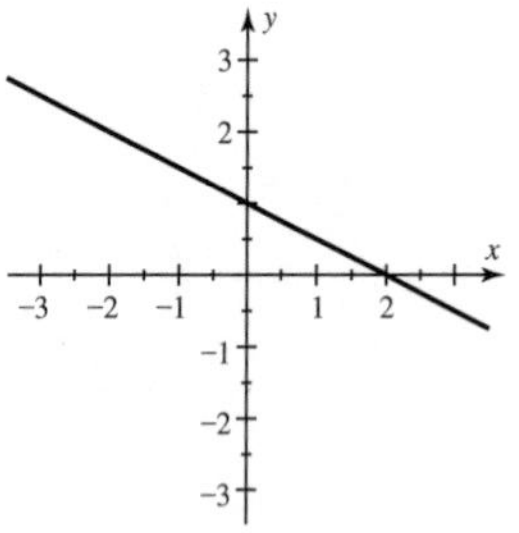

Figure 53

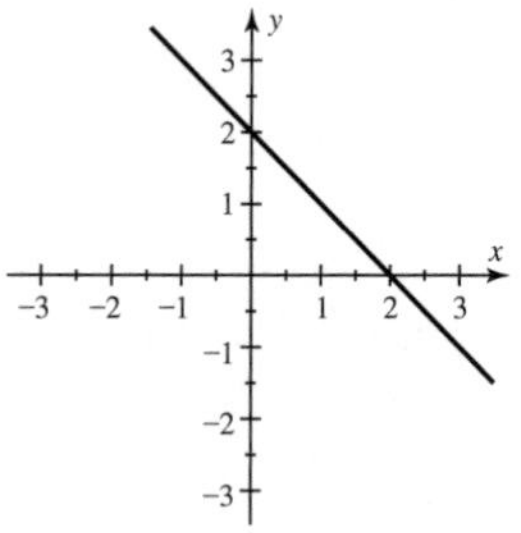

Figure 55

55. See Figure 55.

\7. For every increase in x of 1, the y-value increases by 2. Therefore, the slope $m = 2$. When $x = 0$, $y = 2$. Therefore the y-intercept $b = 2$. Therefore: $y = mx + b \Rightarrow y = 2x + 2$.

59. For every increase in x of 2, the y-value increases by 2. Therefore, the slope $m = 1$. When $x = 0$, $y = -2$. Therefore the y-intercept $b = -2$. Therefore: $y = mx + b \Rightarrow y = x - 2$.

Parallel and Perpendicular Lines

61. $y = \frac{4}{7}x + 3$

63. Because the line parallel to $y = 3x + 1$ has slope 3, $m = 3$.

Because when $x = 0$, $y = 0$, the y-intercept $b = 0$. Therefore: $y = 3x$.

65. Solve $2x + 4y = 5$ for y: $2x + 4y = 5 \Rightarrow 2x - 2x + 4y = 5 - 2x \Rightarrow 4y = -2x + 5 \Rightarrow$

$\frac{4y}{4} = \frac{-2x}{4} + \frac{5}{4} \Rightarrow y = -\frac{1}{2}x + \frac{5}{4}$.

Because the line parallel to $2x + 4y = 5$ has slope $-\frac{1}{2}$, $m = -\frac{1}{2}$. Then, to find the y-intercept b, replace x with 1 and y with 2: $y = -\frac{1}{2}x + b \Rightarrow 2 = -\frac{1}{2}(1) + b \Rightarrow 2 = -\frac{1}{2} + b \Rightarrow 2 + \frac{1}{2} = -\frac{1}{2} + \frac{1}{2} + b \Rightarrow \frac{5}{2} = b$.

Therefore, $y = -\frac{1}{2}x + \frac{5}{2}$.

67. Because the line $y = -\frac{1}{2}x - 3$ has slope $-\frac{1}{2}$, the line perpendicular to it has slope 2, the negative reciprocal of $-\frac{1}{2}$. Because when $x = 0$, $y = -4$, the y-intercept $b = -4$. Therefore, $y = mx + b \Rightarrow y = 2x - 4$.

69. Solve $x = -\frac{1}{3}y$ for y: $x = -\frac{1}{3}y \Rightarrow -3(x) = -3\left(-\frac{1}{3}y\right) \Rightarrow -3x = y \Rightarrow y = -3x$.

Because the line $y = -3x$ has slope -3, the line perpendicular to it has slope $\frac{1}{3}$, the negative reciprocal of -3.

Then, to find the y-intercept b, replace y with 0 and x with -1: $0 = \frac{1}{3}(-1) + b \Rightarrow 0 = -\frac{1}{3} + b \Rightarrow$

$0 + \frac{1}{3} = -\frac{1}{3} + \frac{1}{3} + b \Rightarrow \frac{1}{3} = b$. Therefore, $y = \frac{1}{3}x + \frac{1}{3}$.

Applications

71. (a) When $y = 0$, $x = 25$. Therefore, \$25.

(b) It costs $0.25x$ for each additional mile x. Therefore, 25 cents.

(c) When $x = 0$, $y = 25$. Therefore the y-intercept is 25. This represents the fixed cost of renting a car.

(d) The slope is 0.25. This represents the cost per mile of renting the car.

73. (a) Because $b = 3.95$ and $m = 0.07$, $y = 0.07x + 3.95$. Set $x = 50$ and solve for y:

$y = 0.07(50) + 3.95 = 3.5 + 3.95 = 7.45$. Therefore, the charge is \$7.45.

(b) $C = 0.07x + 3.95$

(c) Set $C = 8.65$ and solve for x: $8.65 = 0.07x + 3.95 \Rightarrow 8.65 - 3.95 = 0.07x \Rightarrow 4.7 = 0.07x \Rightarrow$

$\frac{4.7}{0.07} = \frac{0.07x}{0.07} \Rightarrow x \approx 67$ min.

75. (a) Because the y-value increases by \$0.30 for every increase of 1 in the x-value, the slope $m = 0.30$. Because the fixed cost of \$189.2 represents the y-value when $x = 0$, $b = 189.2$.

(b) The fixed cost of owning the car.

3.6: Point-Slope Form

Concepts

1. One

3. $y = mx + b$

5. Yes; every nonvertical line has one slope and one y-intercept.

Point-Slope Form

7. Substitute -3 for x and 3 for y: $y - 1 = -\frac{2}{3}x \Rightarrow 3 - 1 = -\frac{2}{3}(-3) \Rightarrow 2 = \frac{6}{3} \Rightarrow 2 = 2$. Because this is a true statement, the point $(-3, 3)$ lies on the line.

9. Substitute 1 for x and 4 for y: $y - 3 = -(x - 1) \Rightarrow 4 - 3 = -(1 - 1) \Rightarrow 1 = 0$. Because this is not a true statement, the point $(1, 4)$ does not lie on the line.

11. Substitute 0 for x and 4 for y: $y = \frac{1}{2}(x + 4) + 2 \Rightarrow 4 = \frac{1}{2}(0 + 4) + 2 \Rightarrow 4 = \frac{1}{2}(4) + 2 \Rightarrow$ $4 = 2 + 2 \Rightarrow 4 = 4$. Because this is a true statement, the point $(0, 4)$ lies on the line.

13. The points $(1, 2)$ and $(-3, -1)$ are on the line. First, determine the slope: $m = \frac{y_2 - y_1}{x_2 - x_1} = \frac{-1 - 2}{-3 - 1} = \frac{-3}{-4} = \frac{3}{4}$. Then substitute the x and y values of the point $(1, 2)$ into the point-slope form: $y - y_1 = m(x - x_1) \Rightarrow$ $y - 2 = m(x - 1)$. Then, substitute the value of the slope for m: $y - 2 = \frac{3}{4}(x - 1)$.

15. The points $(3, -1)$ and $(-1, 1)$ are on the line. First, determine the slope:

$$m = \frac{y_2 - y_1}{x_2 - x_1} = \frac{1 - (-1)}{-1 - 3} = \frac{1 + 1}{-4} = \frac{2}{-4} = -\frac{1}{2}.$$

Then substitute the x and y values of the point $(3, -1)$ and the value of the slope into the point-slope form:

$$y - y_1 = m(x - x_1) \Rightarrow y - (-1) = -\frac{1}{2}(x - 3) \Rightarrow y + 1 = -\frac{1}{2}(x - 3).$$

17. $y - y_1 = m(x - x_1) \Rightarrow y - (-2) = -3(x - 1) \Rightarrow y + 2 = -3(x - 1)$

19. $y - y_1 = m(x - x_1) \Rightarrow y - 30 = 1.5(x - 2000)$

21. First, determine the slope: $m = \frac{y_2 - y_1}{x_2 - x_1} = \frac{-3 - 4}{-1 - 2} = \frac{-7}{-3} = \frac{7}{3}$. Then, insert the values of the first point and the value of the slope into the point-slope form: $y - y_1 = m(x - x_1) \Rightarrow y - 4 = \frac{7}{3}(x - 2)$.

23. First determine the slope: $m = \frac{y_2 - y_1}{x_2 - x_1} = \frac{-3 - 0}{0 - 5} = \frac{-3}{-5} = \frac{3}{5}$. Then, insert the values of the first point and the value of the slope into the point-slope form: $y - y_1 = m(x - x_1) \Rightarrow y - 0 = \frac{3}{5}(x - 5) \Rightarrow y = \frac{3}{5}(x - 5)$.

25. First determine the slope: $m = \frac{y_2 - y_1}{x_2 - x_1} = \frac{65 - 15}{2000 - 1990} = \frac{50}{10} = 5$. Then, insert the values of the first point and the value of the slope into the point-slope form: $y - y_1 = m(x - x_1) \Rightarrow y - 15 = 5(x - 1990)$.

27. To convert to slope-intercept form, use the distributive property of multiplication and solve for y: $y - 4 = 3(x - 2) \Rightarrow y - 4 = 3x - 6 \Rightarrow y - 4 + 4 = 3x - 6 + 4 \Rightarrow y = 3x - 2$.

29. To convert to slope-intercept form, use the distributive property of multiplication and solve for y:

$y + 2 = \frac{1}{3}(x + 6) \Rightarrow y + 2 = \frac{1}{3}x + 2 \Rightarrow y + 2 - 2 = \frac{1}{3}x + 2 - 2 \Rightarrow y = \frac{1}{3}x.$

31. Use the distributive property of multiplication and solve for y: $y = -2(x - 2) + 5 \Rightarrow y = -2x + 4 + 5 \Rightarrow$

$y = -2x + 9.$

33. $y = -16(x + 1.5) + 5 \Rightarrow y = -16x - 24 + 5 \Rightarrow y = -16x - 19$

$y = -15(x - 1) + 100 \Rightarrow y = -15x + 15 + 100 \Rightarrow y = -15x + 115$

35. First, find the point-slope form for the line:.

Then, to find the slope-intercept form, use the distributive property of multiplication, then solve for y:

$y + 3 = -2x + 8 \Rightarrow y + 3 - 3 = -2x + 8 - 3 \Rightarrow y = -2x + 5.$

37. First, find the slope of the line: $m = \frac{y_2 - y_1}{x_2 - x_1} = \frac{-1 - (-2)}{2 - 3} = \frac{-1 + 2}{-1} = \frac{1}{-1} = -1$. Then, find the point-slope form for the line by inserting the values of the point $(3, -2)$ and the value of the slope into the point-slope form: $y - y_1 = m(x - x_1) \Rightarrow y - (-2) = -1(x - 3) \Rightarrow y + 2 = -1(x - 3)$. Then, use the distributive property of multiplication and solve for y: $y + 2 = -x + 3 \Rightarrow y + 2 - 2 = -x + 3 - 2 \Rightarrow y = -x + 1.$

39. The points $(3, 0)$ and $\left(0, \frac{1}{3}\right)$ are on the line. First find the slope of the line:

$m = \frac{y_2 - y_1}{x_2 - x_1} = \frac{\frac{1}{3} - 0}{0 - 3} = \frac{\frac{1}{3}}{-3} = \frac{1}{3}\left(-\frac{1}{3}\right) = -\frac{1}{9}$. Then, insert the values of the point $(3, 0)$ and the value of the slope into the point-slope form: $y - y_1 = m(x - x_1) \Rightarrow y - 0 = -\frac{1}{9}(x - 3).$

Then, use the distributive property of multiplication and solve for y: $y = -\frac{1}{9}x + \frac{1}{3}.$

41. The line parallel to $y = 2x - 1$ has slope 2. Insert the values of the point $(2, -3)$ and the value of the slope into the point-slope form: $y - y_1 = m(x - x_1) \Rightarrow y - (-3) = 2(x - 2) \Rightarrow y + 3 = 2(x - 2)$. Then, convert to slope-intercept form: $y + 3 = 2x - 4 \Rightarrow y + 3 - 3 = 2x - 4 - 3 \Rightarrow y = 2x - 7.$

43. The line perpendicular to $y = -\frac{1}{2}x + 3$ has slope 2. Insert the values of the point $(6, -3)$ and the value of the slope into the point-slope form: $y - y_1 = m(x - x_1) \Rightarrow y - (-3) = 2(x - 6) \Rightarrow y + 3 = 2(x - 6)$. Then, convert to slope-intercept form: $y + 3 = 2x - 12 \Rightarrow y + 3 - 3 = 2x - 12 - 3 \Rightarrow y = 2x - 15.$

45. As x increases by 1, y decreases by 2. Thus, the slope is -2. Insert the values of the point $(1, -3)$ and the value of the slope into the point slope form: $y - y_1 = m(x - x_1) \Rightarrow y - (-3) = -2(x - 1) \Rightarrow y + 3 = -2(x - 1)$. Then, convert to slope-intercept form: $y + 3 = -2x + 2 \Rightarrow y + 3 - 3 = -2x + 2 - 3 \Rightarrow y = -2x - 1.$

47. As x increases by 2, y increases by 1. Thus, the slope is $\frac{1}{2}$. Insert the values of the point $(-1, -3)$ and the value of the slope into the point slope form: $y - y_1 = m(x - x_1) \Rightarrow y - (-3) = \frac{1}{2}(x - (-1)) \Rightarrow y + 3 = \frac{1}{2}(x + 1).$

Then, convert to slope-intercept form: $y + 3 = \frac{1}{2}x + \frac{1}{2} \Rightarrow y + 3 - 3 = \frac{1}{2}x + \frac{1}{2} - 3 \Rightarrow y = \frac{1}{2}x - \frac{5}{2}.$

Graphical Interpretation

49. (a) As x increases, the y-value decreases. Because y represents the distance from home, the person is traveling toward home.

(b) After 1 hour, the person is 250 miles from home; after 4 hours, the person is 100 miles from home.

(c) Because in 3 hours the person travels 150 miles, the driver is traveling at 50 mph.

(d) First, find the slope: $m = \frac{y_2 - y_1}{x_2 - x_1} = \frac{100 - 250}{4 - 1} = \frac{-150}{3} = -50$. Then, $y = -50x + b$. Because when $x = 0$, $y = 300$, the y-intercept b is 300. Then, $y = -50x + 300$. The car is traveling toward home at 50 mph.

51. (a) Because y increases as x increases, water is entering the tank. After 4 minutes, 300 gallons.

(b) When $x = 0$, $y = 100$. therefore, the y-intercept is 100. This means that the tank held 100 gallons of water initially.

(c) First, find the slope: $m = \frac{y_2 - y_1}{x_2 - x_1} = \frac{200 - 100}{2 - 0} = \frac{100}{2} = 50$.

Then: $y = mx + b \Rightarrow y = 50x + 100$; the amount of water is increasing at a rate of 50 gal/min.

(d) The tank will be full after 8 minutes.

53. (a) Find the slope: $m = \frac{y_2 - y_1}{x_2 - x_1} = \frac{15 - 40}{6 - 1} = \frac{-25}{5} = -5°\text{F}/\text{hr}$.

(b) One point of the graph of the line is $(1, 40)$ and another point is $(2, 35)$. First, find the point-slope form of the line: $y - y_1 = m(x - x_1) \Rightarrow y - 40 = -5(x - 1)$. Then convert to slope-intercept form: $T = -5x + 5 + 40 \Rightarrow T = -5x + 45$. The temperature is decreasing at a rate of 5°F per hour.

(c) To find the x-intercept, use the slope-intercept form of the line and set $T = 0$: $T = -5x + 45 \Rightarrow 0 = -5x + 45 \Rightarrow 5x = 45 \Rightarrow x = 9$. Therefore, at 9 A.M. the temperature was 0°F.

(d) See Figure 53.

(e) At 4 A.M., the temperature was 25°F.

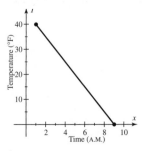

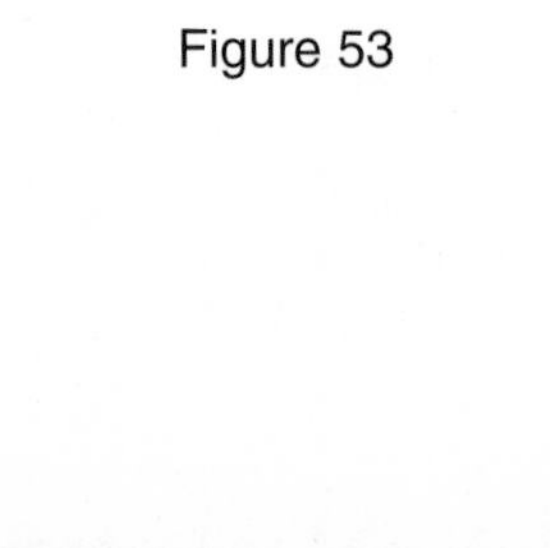

Figure 53

Applications

55. (a) First, substitute 1988 for x: $y = 64(x - 1998) + 628 = 64(1998 - 1998) + 628 = 64(0) + 628 = 628.$

Thus, in 1998 the were 628,000 inmates.

Then, substitute 2000 for x: $y = 64(x - 1998) + 628 = 64(2000 - 1998) + 628 = 64(12) + 628 =$ $768 - 628 = 1396$. Thus, in 2000 the were 1,396,000 inmates.

(b) One point on the graph of the line is (1998, 628) and another point is (2000, 1396), Thus:

$m = \frac{y_2 - y_1}{x_2 - x_1} = \frac{1396 - 628}{2000 - 1988} = \frac{768}{12} = 64$. Therefore, the number of inmates increased on average by 64,000/yr.

57. (a) In 1984, tuition and fees were \$1225; in 1987, tuition and fees were \$1621.

(b) First, find the slope: $m = \frac{y_2 - y_1}{x_2 - x_1} = \frac{1621 - 1225}{1987 - 1984} = \frac{396}{3} = 132$. Then, substitute the value of the first point and the value of the slope into the point-slope form: $y - y_1 = m(x - x_1) \Rightarrow$ $y - 1225 = 132(x - 1984)$; tuition and fees increased on average by \$132/yr.

(c) Substitute 1990 for x: $y - 1225 = 132(1990 - 1984) \Rightarrow y - 1225 = 132(6) \Rightarrow y - 1225 = 792 \Rightarrow$ $y - 1225 + 1225 = 792 + 1225 \Rightarrow y = 2017$. Thus, in 1990, tuition and fees would be about \$2017.

59. (a) The slope-intercept form is $y = mx + b$. Solve for b by setting y equal to 22, m equal to 3.1, and x equal to 1996: $22 = 3.1(1996) + b \Rightarrow 22 = 6187.6 + b \Rightarrow 22 - 6187.6 = 6187.6 - 6187.6 + b \Rightarrow -6165.6 = b.$

Therefore, $y = 3.1x - 6165.6$.

(b) Substitute 2003 for x: $y = 3.1(2003) - 6165.6 = 6209.3 - 6165.6 \Rightarrow y = 43.7$ million.

Checking Basic Concepts for Sections 3.5 & 3.6

1. For every x-value increase of 1, the y-value decreases by 3. Therefore, the slope is -3. When $x = 0, y = 1$. Thus, the y-intercept is 1. Therefore: $y = mx + b \Rightarrow y = -3x + 1$.

2. To convert to slope-intercept form, solve for y: $4x - 5y = 20 \Rightarrow 4x - 4x - 5y = 20 - 4x \Rightarrow$ $-5y = -4x + 20 \Rightarrow \frac{-5y}{-5} = \frac{-4x}{-5} + \frac{20}{-5} \Rightarrow y = \frac{4}{5}x - 4$. Therefore, the slope is $\frac{4}{5}$ and the y-intercept is -4.

3. See Figure 3.

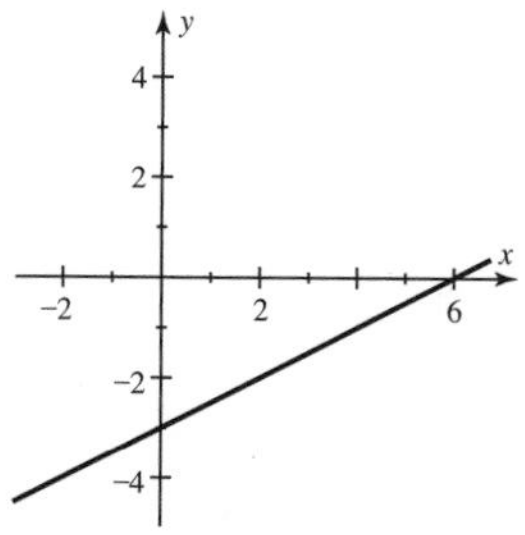

Figure 3

4. (a) The slope m is 3 and the y-intercept b is -2. Therefore: $y = mx + b \Rightarrow y = 3x - 2$.

(b) The slope of the line $y = \frac{2}{3}x$ is $\frac{2}{3}$. Therefore, the slope of the line perpendicular to $y = \frac{2}{3}x$ has slope $-\frac{3}{2}$.

Because for every 2 units of increase in run the rise decreases by 3, the y-intercept b exists when $x = 0$.

Thus, $b = 0$. Then: $y = mx + b \Rightarrow y = -\frac{3}{2}x + 0 \Rightarrow y = -\frac{3}{2}x$.

(c) First, find the slope: $m = \frac{y_2 - y_1}{x_2 - x_1} = \frac{3 - (-4)}{-2 - 1} = \frac{3 + 4}{-2 - 1} = \frac{7}{-3} = -\frac{7}{3}$. Then insert the values of the point $(1, -4)$ and the value of the slope into the point-slope form: $y - y_1 = m(x - x_1) \Rightarrow$

$y - (-4) = -\frac{7}{3}(x - 1) \Rightarrow y + 4 = -\frac{7}{3}(x - 1)$. Then, convert to slope-intercept form:

$y + 4 = -\frac{7}{3}x + \frac{7}{3} \Rightarrow y + 4 - 4 = -\frac{7}{3}x + \frac{7}{3} - 4 \Rightarrow y = -\frac{7}{3}x + \frac{7}{3} - \frac{12}{3} \Rightarrow y = -\frac{7}{3}x - \frac{5}{3}$.

5. First, use the points $(0, 3)$ and $(1, 5)$ to find the slope: $m = \frac{y_2 - y_1}{x_2 - x_1} = \frac{5 - 3}{1 - 0} = \frac{2}{1} = 2$.

When $x = 0$, $y = 3$. Thus, the y-intercept b is 3. Therefore: $y = mx + b \Rightarrow y = 2x + 3$.

6. (a) First, find the slope: $m = \frac{y_2 - y_1}{x_2 - x_1} = \frac{12 - 36}{3 - 1} = \frac{-24}{2} = -12$. Then, insert the values for the point $(1, 36)$ and the value of the slope into the point-slope form: $y - y_1 = m(x - x_1) \Rightarrow y - 36 = -12(x - 1)$. Then convert to slope-intercept form: $y - 36 = -12x + 12 \Rightarrow y - 36 + 36 = -12x + 12 + 36 \Rightarrow$

$y = -12x + 48$.

(b) Because the slope is -12, the bicyclist gets 12 miles closer to home every hour ridden. Therefore the bicyclist is traveling at 12 mph.

(c) The y-value will equal 0 when the rider reaches home Therefore, substitute 0 for y in the slope-intercept form and solve for x: $y = -12x + 48 \Rightarrow 0 = -12x + 48 \Rightarrow 0 - 48 = -12x + 48 - 48 \Rightarrow$

$-48 = -12x \Rightarrow \frac{-48}{-12} = \frac{-12x}{-12} \Rightarrow 4 = x \Rightarrow x = 4$. Therefore, the rider will arrive home at 4 pm.

(d) At noon, $x = 0$. Substitute 0 for x in the slope-intercept form and solve for y: $y = -12x + 48 \Rightarrow$

$y = -12(0) + 48 \Rightarrow y = 48$. Therefore, at noon the rider was 48 miles from home.

7. (a) At noon, $t = 0$. Substitute 0 for t in the equation and solve for s: $s = 2t + 5 = 2(0) + 5 \Rightarrow s = 5$.

Therefore, 5 inches of snow fell by noon.

(b) Because the slope equals 2, the snow fell at a rate of 2 inches per hour in the afternoon.

(c) The y-intercept is 5. This represents the total inches of snow that fell before noon.

(d) The slope is 2. This represents that the rate of snowfall was 2 inches per hour.

3.7: Introduction to Modeling

Concepts

1. abstraction

3. linear

5. approximate

7. f

9. a

11. e

Modeling Linear Data

13. For the linear equation $y = 2x + 2$, the y-intercept is 2 and the slope is 2. The ordered pairs in the table are modeled exactly by the linear equation.

15. For the linear equation $y = -4x$, the y-intercept is 0 and the slope is -4. The ordered pairs in the table are not modeled exactly by the linear equation.

17. For the linear equation $y = 1.4x - 4$, the y-intercept is -4 and the slope is 1.4. The ordered pairs in the table are not modeled exactly by the linear equation.

19. Because the line goes through the points on the graph, the linear model is exact. To find the equation of the line, first find the slope: $m = \dfrac{y_2 - y_1}{x_2 - x_1} = \dfrac{6 - 4}{4 - 3} = \dfrac{2}{1} = 2$. Then to find the y-intercept b, insert the values of the point (4, 6) and the value of the slope into the slope-intercept form and solve for b: $y = mx + b \Rightarrow 6 = 2(4) + b \Rightarrow 6 = 8 + b \Rightarrow 6 - 8 = 8 - 8 + b \Rightarrow -2 = b \Rightarrow b = -2$. Thus, the equation of the line is $y = 2x - 2$.

21. Because the line does not go through all the points on the graph, the linear model is approximate. To find the equation of the line, first find the slope: $m = \dfrac{y_2 - y_1}{x_2 - x_1} = \dfrac{6 - 4}{2 - 1} = \dfrac{2}{1} = 2$. Then to find the y-intercept b, insert the values of the point (2, 6) and the value of the slope into the slope-intercept form and solve for b: $y = mx + b \Rightarrow 6 = 2(2) + b \Rightarrow 6 = 4 + b \Rightarrow 6 - 4 = 4 - 4 + b \Rightarrow 2 = b \Rightarrow b = 2$. Thus, the equation of the line is $y = 2x + 2$.

23. Because the line does not go through all the points on the graph, the linear model is approximate. The equation of the line is $y = 2$ because the slope is 0 and because the y-intercept is at $y = 2$.

25. The initial value is 40, so the y-intercept b is 40. The rate of increase is 5 per minute, so the slope is 5. Thus: $y = mx + b \Rightarrow y = 5x + 40$.

27. The initial value is -5, so the y-intercept b is -5. The rate of decrease is 20 per day, so the slope is -20. Thus: $y = mx + b \Rightarrow y = -20x - 5$.

29. The initial value is 8, so the y-intercept b is 8. Because y remains constant, the slope is 0. Thus: $y = mx + b \Rightarrow y = 0(x) + 8 \Rightarrow y = 8$.

31. (a) See Figure 31a. A line could pass through all five points.

(b) See Figure 31b.

(c) Because y decreases by 2 for every increase in x, the slope m is -2. Because when $x = 0$, $y = 4$, the y-intercept b is 4. Thus: $y = mx + b \Rightarrow y = -2x + 4$.

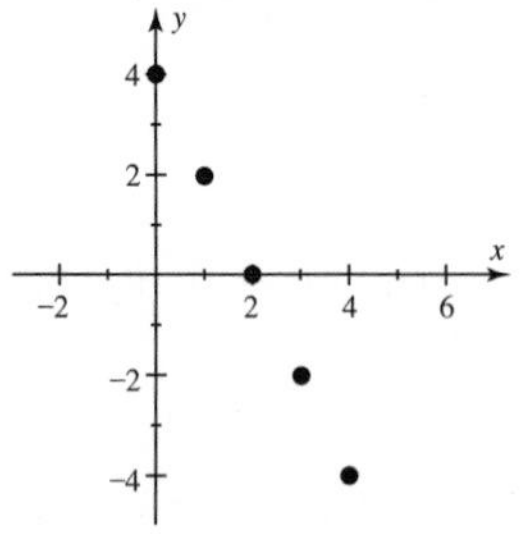

Figure 31a

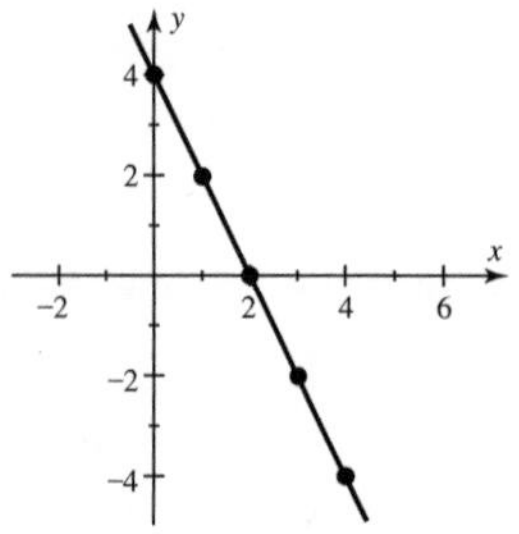

Figure 31b

33. (a) See Figure 33a. A line could not pass through all five points.

(b) See Figure 33b.

(c) To find the equation of the line, first find the slope: $m = \dfrac{y_2 - y_1}{x_2 - x_1} = \dfrac{0 - 4}{0 - (-2)} = \dfrac{-4}{2} = -2$.

Then, the line passes through the origin, so the y-intercept b is 0. Thus: $y = mx + b \Rightarrow y = -2x + 0 \Rightarrow$ $y = -2x$.

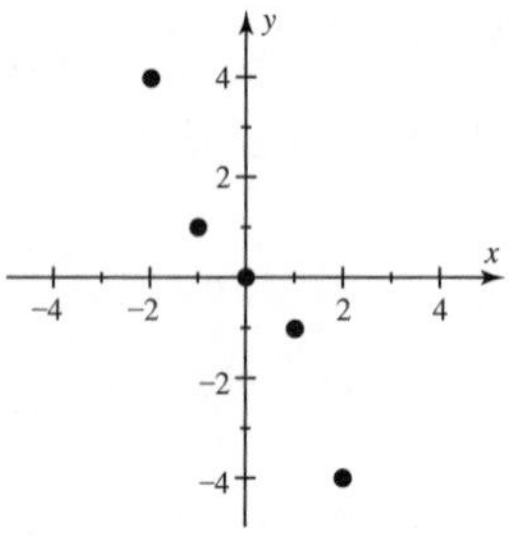

Figure 33a

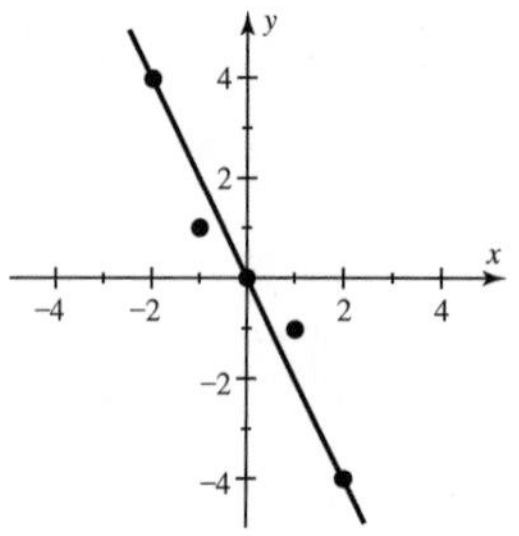

Figure 33b

35. (a) See Figure 35a. A line could pass through all five points.

(b) See Figure 35b.

(c) To find the equation of the line, first find the slope: $m = \dfrac{y_2 - y_1}{x_2 - x_1} = \dfrac{-2 - 0}{0 - (-4)} = \dfrac{-2}{4} = -\dfrac{1}{2}$.

Then, when $x = 0$, $y = -2$, the y-intercept b is -2. Thus: $y = mx + b \Rightarrow y = -\dfrac{1}{2}x - 2$.

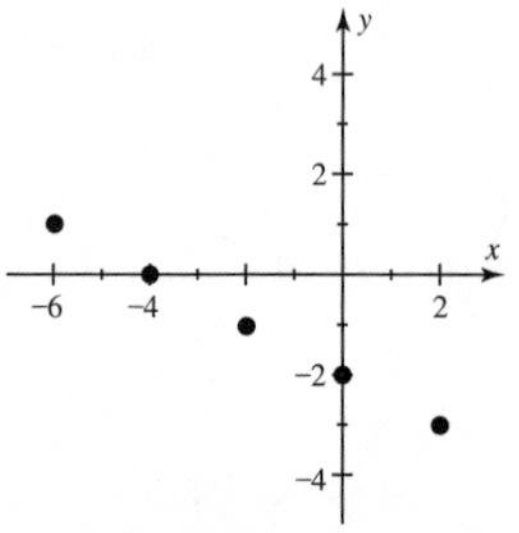

Figure 35a

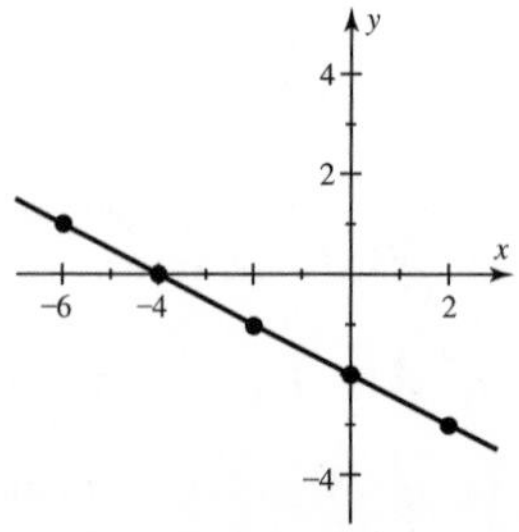

Figure 35b

37. (a) See Figure 37a. A line could not pass through all five points.

(b) See Figure 37b.

(c) To find the equation of the line, first find the slope: $m = \frac{y_2 - y_1}{x_2 - x_1} = \frac{0 - (-1)}{3 - 0} = \frac{1}{3}$.

Then, when $x = 0$, $y = -1$, the y-intercept b is -1. Thus: $y = mx + b \Rightarrow y = \frac{1}{3}x - 1$.

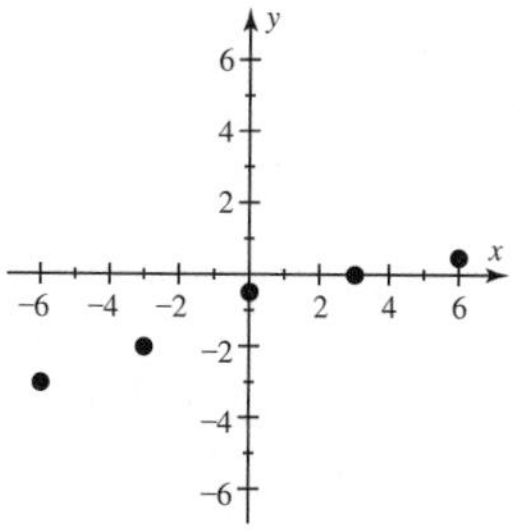

Figure 37a

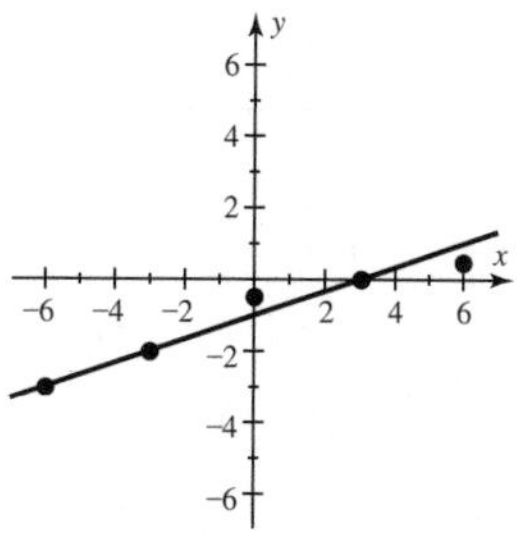

Figure 37b

Applications

39. The initial value is 200, so the g-intercept b is 200. The barrel is being filled at a rate of 5 gallons per minute, so the slope m is 5. Thus: $g = mt + b \Rightarrow g = 5t + 200$, where g represents gallons of water and t represents time in minutes.

41. The initial value is 5, so the d-intercept b is 5. The athlete is jogging at 6 miles per hour, so the slope m is 6. Thus: $d = mt + b \Rightarrow d = 6t + 5$, where d represents distance in miles and t represents time in hours.

43. The initial value is 200, so the p-intercept b is 200. The worker is being paid \$8 per hour, so the slope m is 8. Thus: $p = mt + b \Rightarrow p = 8t + 200$, where p represents total pay in dollars and t represents time in hours.

45. The initial value is 5, so the r-intercept b is 5. The carpenter is shingling roofs at a rate of 1 per day, so the slope m is 1. Thus: $r = mt + b \Rightarrow r = t + 5$, where r represents total number of roofs shingled and t represents time in days.

47. (a) A point on the graph of the volume of the glacier is (1912, 5) and another point is (2002, 1). Because there is assumed to be a constant melt rate, to find the yearly rate find the slope of the line connecting the two points: $m = \frac{y_2 - y_1}{x_2 - x_1} = \frac{1 - 5}{2002 - 1912} = \frac{-4}{90} = -\frac{2}{45}$ acres per year.

(b) The slope m is $-\frac{2}{45}$. The initial value b is 5. Thus: $A = mt + b \Rightarrow A = -\frac{2}{45}t + 5$, where A represents acres of glacier and t represents time in years.

49. (a) First, use the first and last date points to determine slope: $m = \dfrac{y_2 - y_1}{x_2 - x_1} = \dfrac{145 - 113}{2000 - 1997} = \dfrac{32}{3}$. Then, insert the values of the first point into the point-slope form: $y - y_1 = m(x - x_1) \Rightarrow$ $y - 113 = \dfrac{32}{3}(x - 1997)$. Then, convert to slope-intercept form: $y - 113 = \dfrac{32}{3}x - \dfrac{63{,}904}{3} \Rightarrow$ $y - 113 + 113 = \dfrac{32}{3}x - \dfrac{63{,}904}{3} + 113 \Rightarrow y = \dfrac{32}{3}x - \dfrac{63{,}904}{3} + \dfrac{339}{3} \Rightarrow y = \dfrac{32}{3}x - \dfrac{63{,}565}{3} \Rightarrow$ $y = \dfrac{32}{3}x - 21{,}188$ (approx.).

(b) Set $x = 2003$ and solve for y: $y = \dfrac{32}{3}(2003) - 21{,}188 = \dfrac{64{,}096}{3} - \dfrac{63{,}565}{3} = \dfrac{531}{3} \approx 177$. Thus, the prison population in 2003 is about 177,000.

51. (a) See Figure 51a.

(b) See Figure 51b.

(c) $m = \dfrac{y_2 - y_1}{x_2 - x_1} = \dfrac{120 - 60}{6 - 3} = \dfrac{60}{3} = 20$. For every gallon of gasoline, the car travels 20 miles.

(d) Because when $x = 0$, $y = 0$, the y-intercept b is 0. Thus, $y = 20x$.

(e) $y = 20x = 20(7) = 140$ miles.

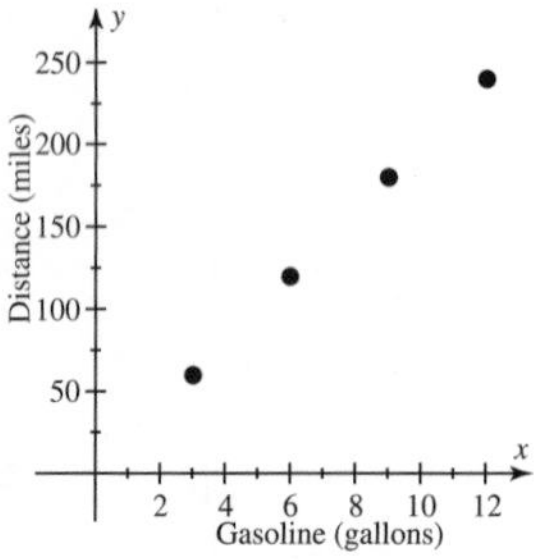

Figure 51a

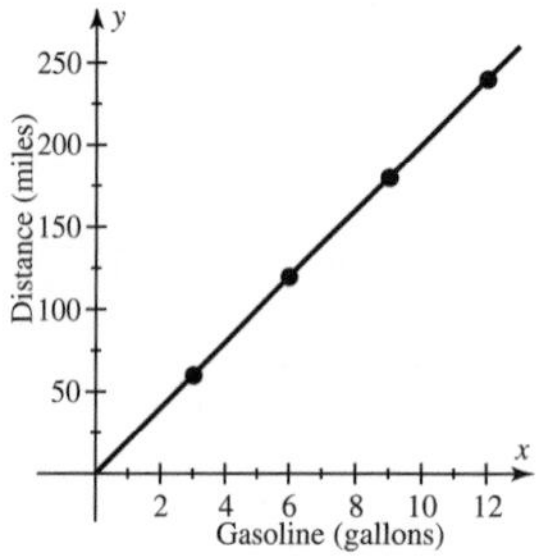

Figure 51b

Checking Basic Concepts for Section 3.7

1. The ordered pairs in the table indicate that the y-intercept is 10 and the slope is -5. Thus, the line $y = -5x + 10$ models exactly the ordered pairs.

2. Because the line does not pass through each point on the graph, the linear model is approximate. For each increase in run of 1, the value of the rise increases by 1, so the slope m is 1. When $x = 0$, $y = -1$, so the y-intercept b is -1. Thus: $y = mx + b \Rightarrow y = x - 1$.

3. (a) The initial value b is 50 and the slope m is 10. Thus: $y = 10x + 50$.

(b) The initial value b is 200 and the slope m is -2. Thus: $y = -2x + 200$.

4. (a) See Figure 4a. A line could pass through all four points.

   (b) See Figure 4b.

   (c) The y-intercept b is 1 and the slope m is $\frac{1-2}{0-(-2)} = \frac{-1}{2} = -\frac{1}{2}$. Thus: $y = -\frac{1}{2}x + 1$.

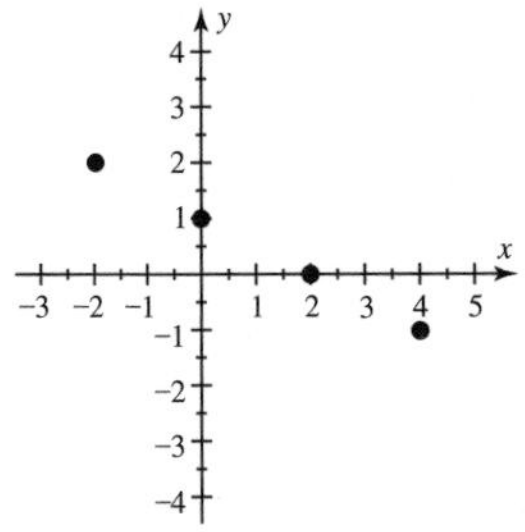

Figure 4a

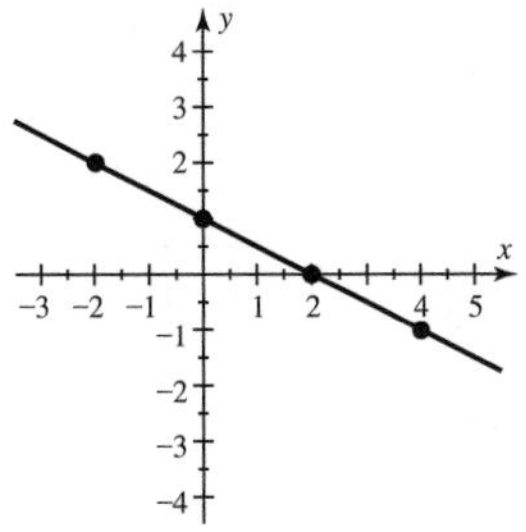

Figure 4b

5. (a) The slope m is 0.05 and the y-intercept is 0. Thus, $T = 0.05x$.

   (b) First substitute 1975 for x and solve for T: $T = 0.05(1975) = 98.75$. Thus, a point on the graph is (1975, 98.75). Then, substitute 1959 for x and solve for T: $T = 0.05(1959) = 97.95$. Thus, a second point on the graph is (1959, 97.95). Then, subtract 97.95 from 98.75 to obtain the temperature increase: $98.75 - 97.95 = 0.8°$F.

Chapter 3 Review Exercises

Section 3.1

1. $(-2, 0)$: none; $(-1, 2)$: Quadrant II; $(0, 0)$: none; $(1, -2)$: Quadrant IV; $(1, 3)$: Quadrant I

2. See Figure 2.

3. See Figure 3.

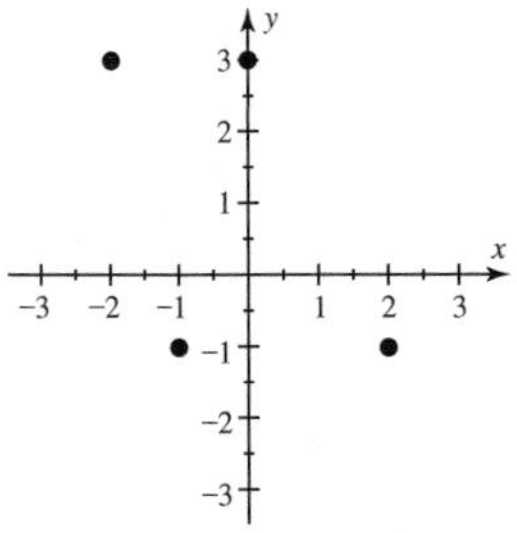

Figure 2

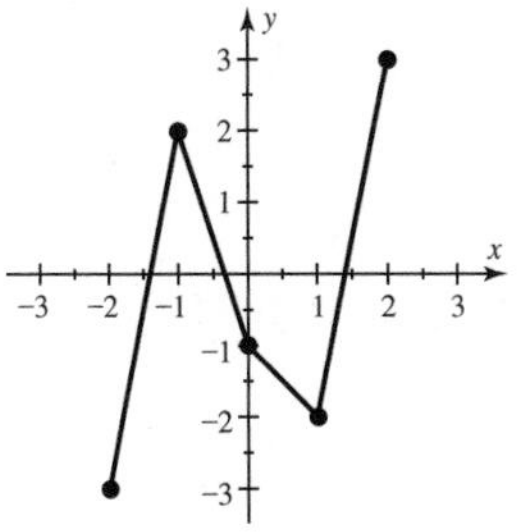

Figure 3

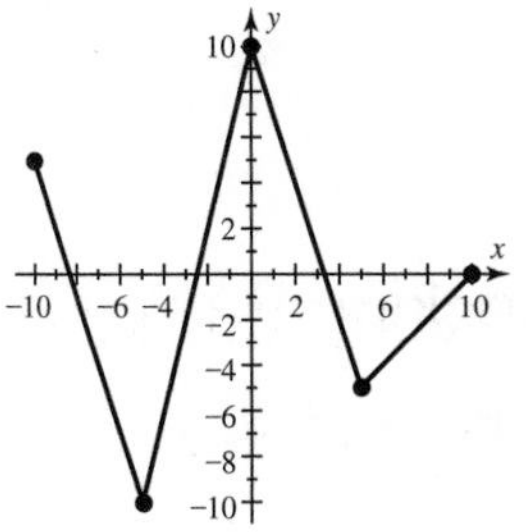

Figure 4

4. See Figure 4.

Section 3.2

5. Substitute 6 for x and 3 for y: $y = x - 3 \Rightarrow 3 = 6 - 3 \Rightarrow 3 = 3$. Because this is a true statement, the ordered pair (6, 3) is a solution.

6. Substitute -2 for x and 1 for y: $y = 5 - 2x \Rightarrow 1 = 5 - 2(-2) \Rightarrow 1 = 5 + 4 \Rightarrow 1 = 9$. Because this is not a true statement, the ordered pair $(-2, 1)$ is not a solution.

7. Substitute -1 for x and 6 for y: $3x - y = 3 \Rightarrow 3(-1) - 6 = 3 \Rightarrow -3 - 6 = 3 \Rightarrow -9 = 3$. Because this is not a true statement, the ordered pair $(-1, 6)$ is not a solution.

8. Substitute -4 for x and -3 for y: $\frac{1}{2}x + 2y = -8 \Rightarrow \frac{1}{2}(-4) + 2(-3) = -8 \Rightarrow -2 - 6 = -8 \Rightarrow -8 = -8$. Because this is a true statement, the ordered pair $(-4, -3)$ is a solution.

9. For $x = -2$: $y = -3x = -3(-2) \Rightarrow y = 6$; for $x = -1$: $y = -3x = -3(-1) \Rightarrow y = 3$; for $x = 0$: $y = -3x = -3(0) \Rightarrow y = 0$; for $x = 1$: $y = -3x = -3(1) \Rightarrow y = -3$; for $x = 2$: $y = -3x = -3(2) \Rightarrow y = -6$. Therefore, the missing values in the table are 6, 3, 0, -3, and -6. See Figure 9.

10. For $y = -3$: $2x + y = 5 \Rightarrow 2x + (-3) = 5 \Rightarrow 2x - 3 = 5 \Rightarrow 2x + 3 - 3 = 5 + 3 \Rightarrow 2x = 8 \Rightarrow \frac{2x}{2} = \frac{8}{2} \Rightarrow x = 4$; for $y = -1$: $2x + y = 5 \Rightarrow 2x + (-1) = 5 \Rightarrow 2x - 1 = 5 \Rightarrow 2x - 1 + 1 = 5 + 1 \Rightarrow 2x = 6 \Rightarrow \frac{2x}{2} = \frac{6}{2} \Rightarrow x = 3$; for $y = 0$: $2x + y = 5 \Rightarrow 2x + 0 = 5 \Rightarrow 2x = 5 \Rightarrow \frac{2x}{2} = \frac{5}{2} \Rightarrow x = 2.5$; for $y = 1$: $2x + y = 5 \Rightarrow 2x + 1 = 5 \Rightarrow 2x + 1 - 1 = 5 - 1 \Rightarrow 2x = 4 \Rightarrow \frac{2x}{2} = \frac{4}{2} \Rightarrow x = 2$; for $y = 3$: $2x + y = 5 \Rightarrow 2x + 3 = 5 \Rightarrow 2x + 3 - 3 = 5 - 3 \Rightarrow 2x = 2 \Rightarrow \frac{2x}{2} = \frac{2}{2} \Rightarrow x = 1$. Therefore, the missing values in the tables are 4, 3, 2.5, 2, and 1. See Figure 10.

x	−2	−1	0	1	2
y	6	3	0	−3	−6

Figure 9

x	4	3	2.5	2	1
y	−3	−1	0	1	3

Figure 10

x	−2	0	2	4
y	−4	2	8	14

Figure 11

11. See Figure 11.

12. See Figure 12.

13. See Figure 13.

x	1	2	3	4
y	6	5	4	3

Figure 12

x	−0.5	0	0.5	1
y	−1	0	1	2

Figure 13

x	−1	−3	−5	−7
y	1	2	3	4

Figure 14

14. See Figure 14.

15. See Figure 15.

16. See Figure 16.

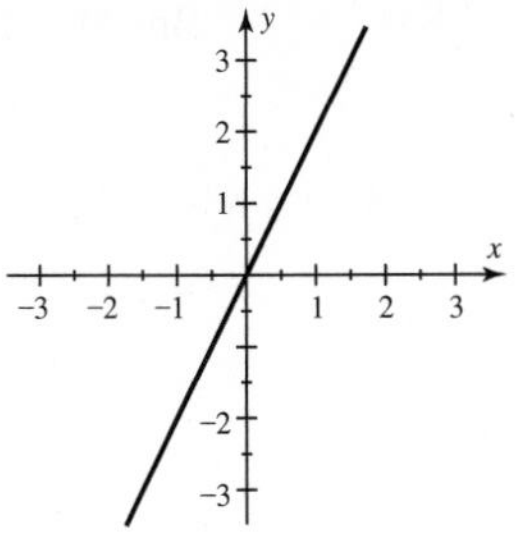

Figure 15

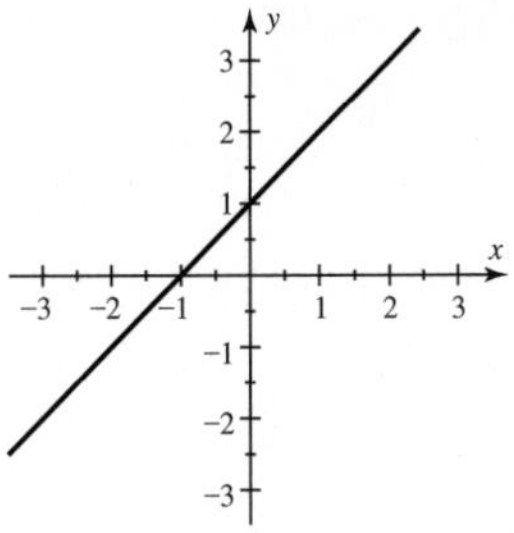

Figure 16

17. See Figure 17.

18. See Figure 18.

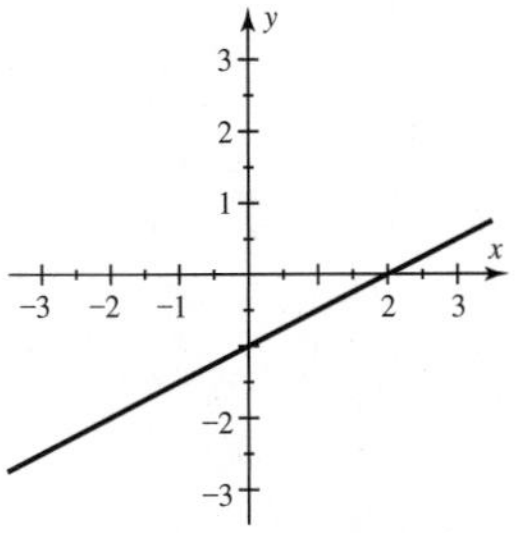

Figure 17

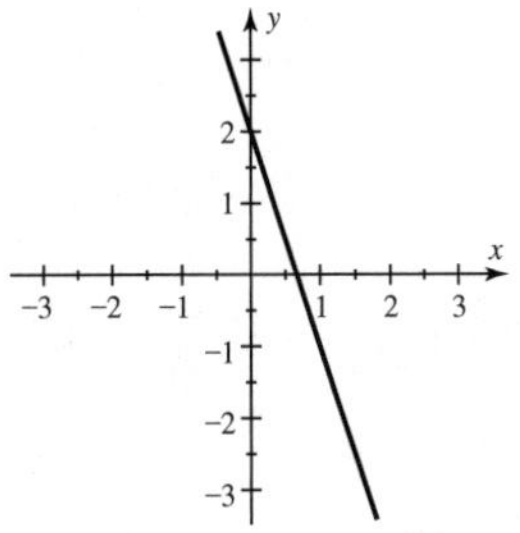

Figure 18

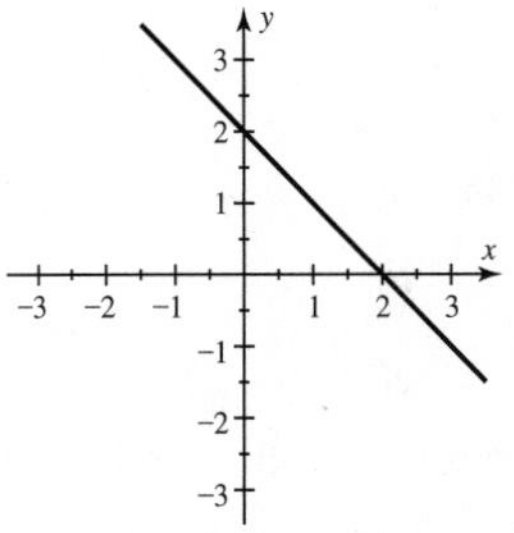

Figure 19

19. See Figure 19.

20. See Figure 20.

21. See Figure 21.

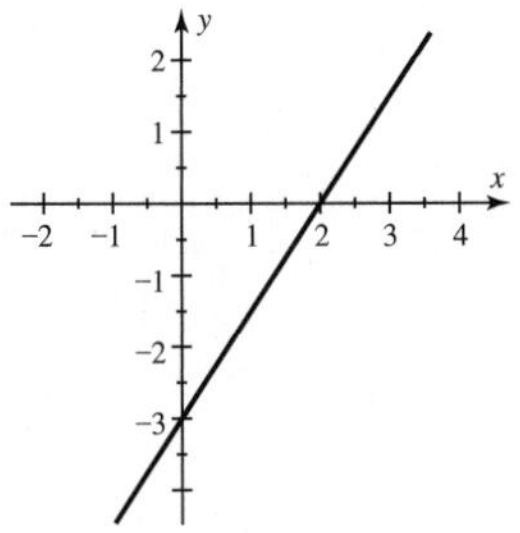

Figure 20

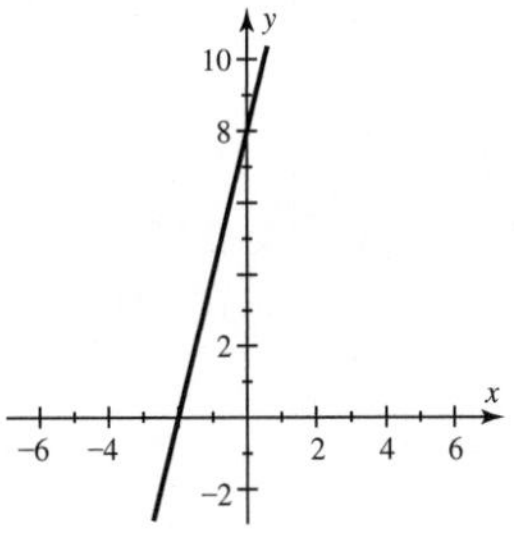

Figure 21

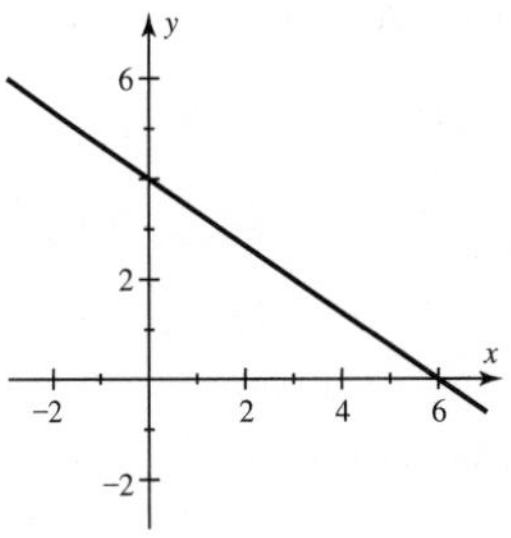

Figure 22

22. See Figure 22.

Section 3.3

23. The line crosses the x-axis at $x = 3$, therefore the x-intercept is 3. The line crosses the y-axis at $y = -2$, therefore the y-intercept is -2.

24. The graph crosses the x-axis at $x = -2$ and $x = 2$. Therefore, the x-intercepts are $2, -2$. The graph crosses the y-axis at $y = -4$, therefore, the y-intercept is -4.

25. For $x = -2$: $y = 2 - x = 2 - (-2) \Rightarrow y = 4$; for $x = -1$: $y = 2 - x = 2 - (-1) = 2 + 1 \Rightarrow y = 3$; for $x = 0$: $y = 2 - x = 2 - 0 \Rightarrow y = 2$; for $x = 1$: $y = 2 - x = 2 - 1 \Rightarrow y = 1$; for $x = 2$: $y = 2 - x = 2 - 2 \Rightarrow y = 0$. Therefore, the missing values in the table are 4, 3, 2, 2 ,1 ,0. See Figure 25. When $y = 0, x = 2$. Therefore the x-intercept is 2. When $x = 0, y = 2$. Therefore, the y-intercept is 2.

x	−2	−1	0	1	2
y	4	3	2	1	0

Figure 25

x	−4	−2	0	2	4
y	−4	−3	−2	−1	0

Figure 26

26 For $x = -4$: $x - 2y = 4 \Rightarrow -4 - 2y = 4 \Rightarrow -4 + 4 - 2y = 4 + 4 \Rightarrow -2y = 8 \Rightarrow \frac{-2y}{-2} = \frac{8}{-2} \Rightarrow$ $y = -4$; for $x = -2$: $x - 2y = 4 \Rightarrow -2 - 2y = 4 \Rightarrow -2 + 2 - 2y = 4 + 2 \Rightarrow -2y = 6 \Rightarrow$ $\frac{-2y}{-2} = \frac{6}{-2} \Rightarrow y = -3$; for $x = 0$: $x - 2y = 4 \Rightarrow 0 - 2y = 4 \Rightarrow -2y = 4 \Rightarrow \frac{-2y}{-2} = \frac{4}{-2} \Rightarrow y = -2$; for $x = 2$: $x - 2y = 4 \Rightarrow 2 - 2y = 4 \Rightarrow 2 - 2 - 2y = 4 - 2 \Rightarrow -2y = 2 \Rightarrow \frac{-2y}{-2} = \frac{2}{-2} \Rightarrow y = -1$; for $x = 4$: $x - 2y = 4 \Rightarrow 4 - 2y = 4 \Rightarrow 4 - 4 - 2y = 4 - 4 \Rightarrow -2y = 0 \Rightarrow \frac{-2y}{-2} = \frac{0}{-2} \Rightarrow y = 0$. Therefore, the missing values in the table are −4, −3, −2, −1, 0. See Figure 26. When $y = 0, x = 4$. Therefore, the x-intercept is 4. When $x = 0, y = -2$. Therefore, the y-intercept is −2.

27 To find the x-intercept, set $y = 0$: $2x - 3y = 6 \Rightarrow 2x - 3(0) = 6 \Rightarrow 2x = 6 \Rightarrow \frac{2x}{2} = \frac{6}{2} \Rightarrow x = 3$. Therefore, the x-intercept is 3.

To find the y-intercept, set $x = 0$: $2x - 3y = 6 \Rightarrow 2(0) - 3y = 6 \Rightarrow -3y = 6 \Rightarrow \frac{-3y}{-3} = \frac{6}{-3} \Rightarrow y = -2$. Therefore, the y-intercept is −2. See Figure 27.

28. Set $y = 0$ and solve for x: $5x - y = 5 \Rightarrow 5x - 0 = 5 \Rightarrow 5x = 5 \Rightarrow \frac{5x}{5} = \frac{5}{5} \Rightarrow x = 1$. Therefore, the x-intercept is 1. Then set $x = 0$ and solve for y: $5x - y = 5 \Rightarrow 5(0) - y = 5 \Rightarrow -y = 5 \Rightarrow$ $-1(-y) = -1(5) \Rightarrow y = -5$. Therefore, the y-intercept is −5. See Figure 28.

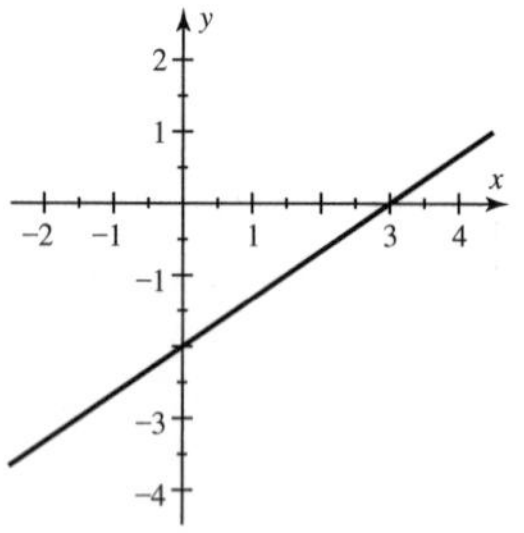

Figure 27

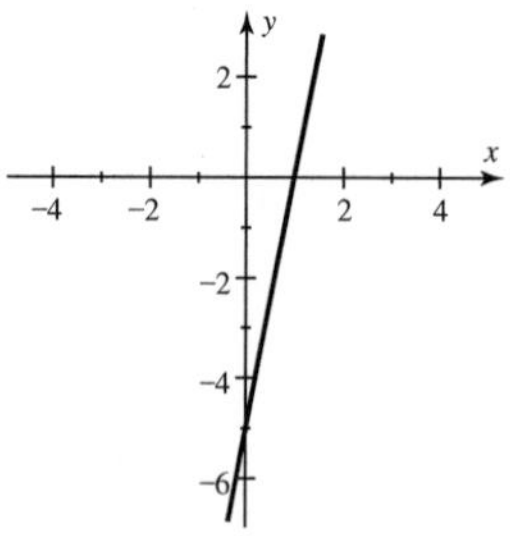

Figure 28

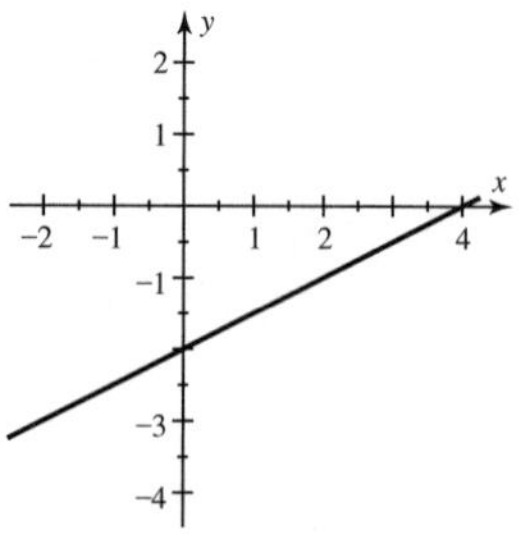

Figure 29

29. Set $y = 0$ and solve for x: $0.1x - 0.2y = 0.4 \Rightarrow 0.1x - 0.2(0) = 0.4 \Rightarrow 0.1x = 0.4 \Rightarrow \frac{0.1x}{0.1} = \frac{0.4}{0.1} \Rightarrow$ $x = 4$. Therefore the x-intercept is 4. Then set $x = 0$ and solve for y: $0.1x - 0.2y = 0.4 \Rightarrow$ $0.1(0) - 0.2y = 0.4 \Rightarrow -0.2y = 0.4 \Rightarrow \frac{-0.2y}{-0.2} = \frac{0.4}{-0.2} \Rightarrow y = -2$. Therefore, the y-intercept is −2. See Figure 29.

30. Set $y = 0$ and solve for x: $\frac{x}{2} + \frac{y}{3} = 1 \Rightarrow \frac{x}{2} + \frac{0}{3} = 1 \Rightarrow \frac{x}{2} = 1 \Rightarrow 2\left(\frac{x}{2}\right) = 2(1) \Rightarrow x = 2.$

Therefore the x-intercept is 2. Then set $x = 0$ and solve for y: $\frac{x}{2} + \frac{y}{3} = 1 \Rightarrow \frac{0}{2} + \frac{y}{3} = 1 \Rightarrow \frac{y}{3} = 1 \Rightarrow$

$3\left(\frac{y}{3}\right) = 3(1) \Rightarrow y = 3$. Therefore, the y-intercept is 3. See Figure 30.

31. (a) See Figure 31a.

(b) See Figure 31b.

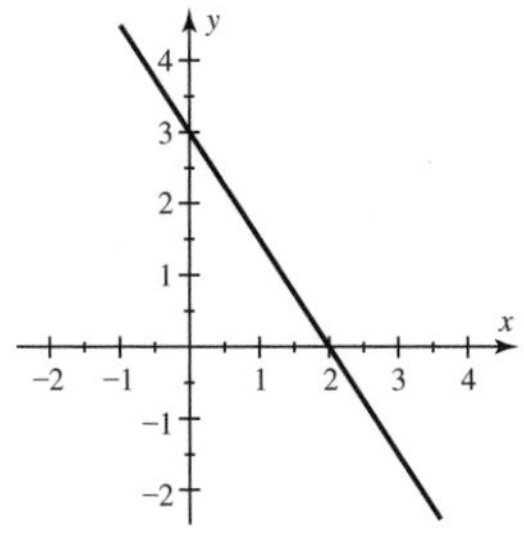

Figure 30

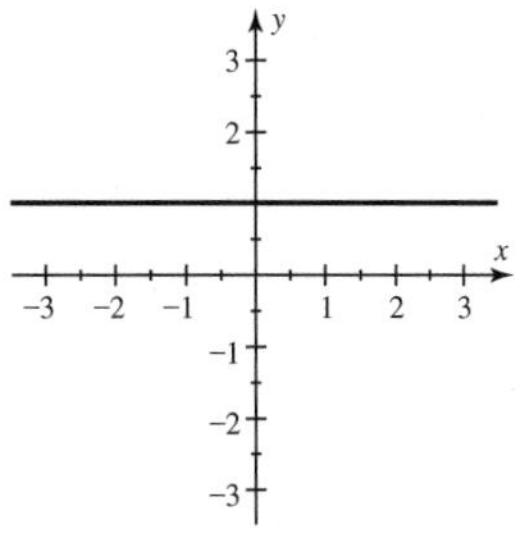

Figure 31a

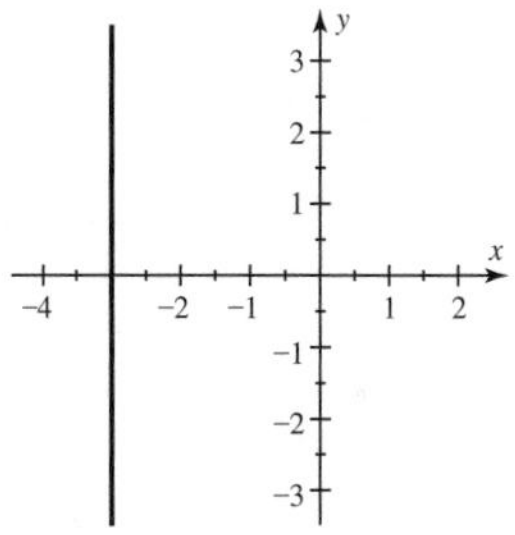

Figure 31b

32. $x = -1; y = 1$

33. Because the y-value is constant, the slope $m = 0$. Because when $x = 0, y = 1$, the y-intercept $b = 1$.

Thus: $y = mx + b \Rightarrow y = 0x + 1 \Rightarrow y = 1$.

34. Because the x-value is a constant 3, the graph is a vertical line with slope m undefined. Thus, $x = 3$.

35. horizontal line: $y = 3$; vertical line: $x = -2$

36. (a) When $x = 0, y = 90$. Therefore, the y-intercept is 90. When $y = 0, x = 3$. Therefore, the x-intercept is 3.

(b) The driver is initially 90 miles from home; the driver arrives home after 3 hours.

Section 3.4

37. $m = \frac{y_2 - y_1}{x_2 - x_1} = \frac{7 - 3}{4 - 2} = \frac{4}{2} = 2.$

38. $m = \frac{y_2 - y_1}{x_2 - x_1} = \frac{-1 - 1}{2 - (-3)} = \frac{-2}{2 + 3} = \frac{-2}{5} = -\frac{2}{5}.$

39. $m = \frac{y_2 - y_1}{x_2 - x_1} = \frac{1 - 1}{5 - 2} = \frac{0}{3} = 0.$

40. $m = \frac{y_2 - y_1}{x_2 - x_1} = \frac{10 - 6}{-5 - (-5)} = \frac{4}{-5 + 5} = \frac{4}{0}.$ Thus, undefined.

41. The points (1, 3) and (0, 0) are on the graph. Insert these two points into the slope formula:

$m = \frac{y_2 - y_1}{x_2 - x_1} = \frac{0 - 3}{0 - 1} = \frac{-3}{-1} = 3.$

42. The points $(-2, 3)$ and $(0, 2)$ are on the graph. Insert these two points into the slope formula:

$$m = \frac{y_2 - y_1}{x_2 - x_1} = \frac{2 - 3}{0 - (-2)} = \frac{-1}{0 + 2} = \frac{-1}{2} = -\frac{1}{2}.$$

43. (a) See Figure 43.

(b) The slope is -2 and the y-intercept is 0.

44. (a) See Figure 44.

(b) The slope is 1 and the y-intercept is -1.

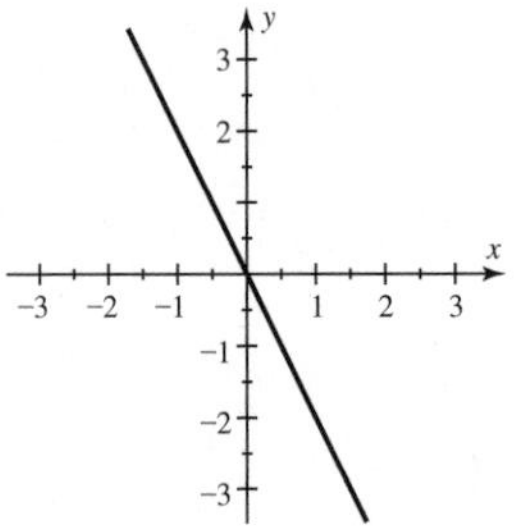

Figure 43

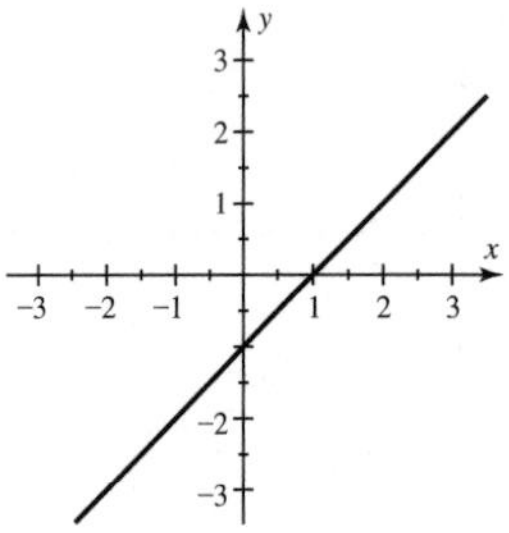

Figure 44

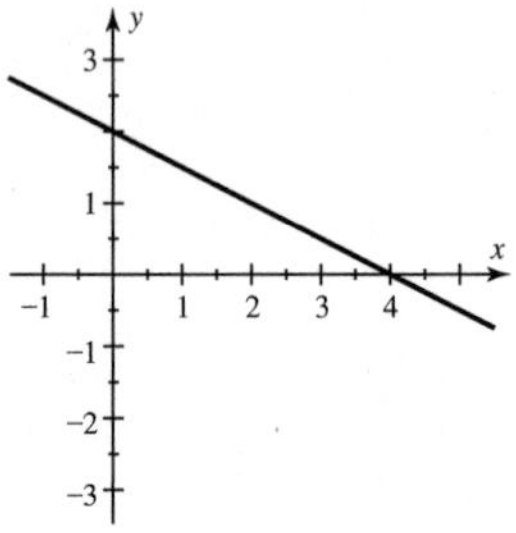

Figure 45

45. (a) See Figure 45.

(b) Solve for y:

$$x + 2y = 4 \Rightarrow x - x + 2y = 4 - x \Rightarrow 2y = -x + 4 \Rightarrow \frac{1}{2}(2y) = \frac{1}{2}(-x + 4) \Rightarrow y = -\frac{1}{2}x + 2.$$

Therefore, the slope is $-\frac{1}{2}$ and the y-intercept is 2.

46. (a) See Figure 46.

(b) Solve for y:

$$2x - 3y = -6 \Rightarrow 2x - 2x - 3y = -6 - 2x \Rightarrow -3y = -2x - 6 \Rightarrow -\frac{1}{3}(-3y) = -\frac{1}{3}(-2x - 6) \Rightarrow$$

$y = \frac{2}{3}x + 2$. Therefore, the slope is $\frac{2}{3}$ and the y-intercept is 2.

47. See Figure 47.

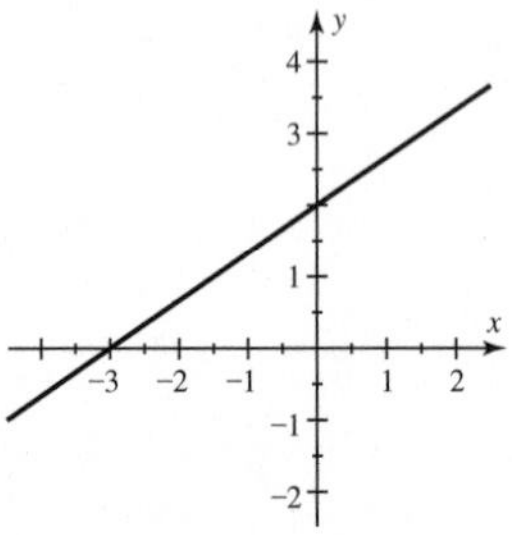

Figure 46

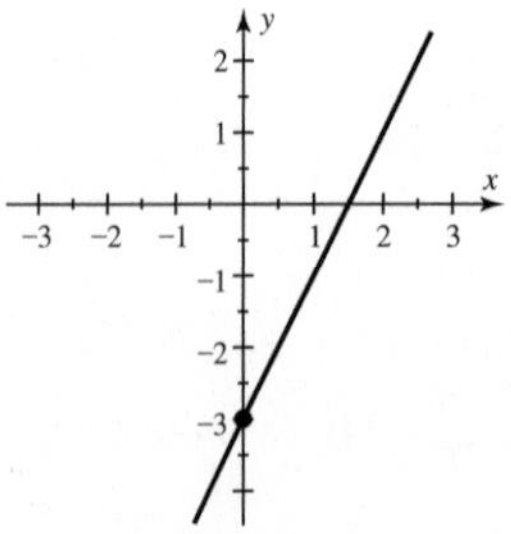

Figure 47

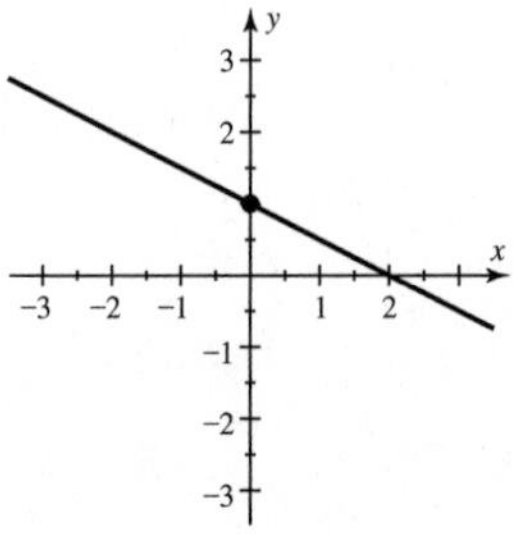

Figure 48

48. See Figure 48.

49. See Figure 49.

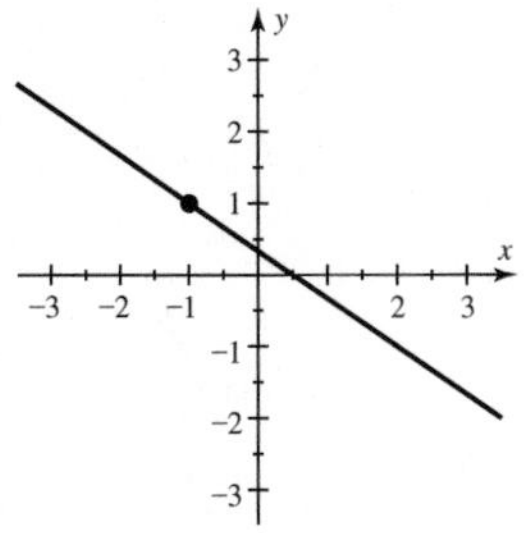

Figure 49

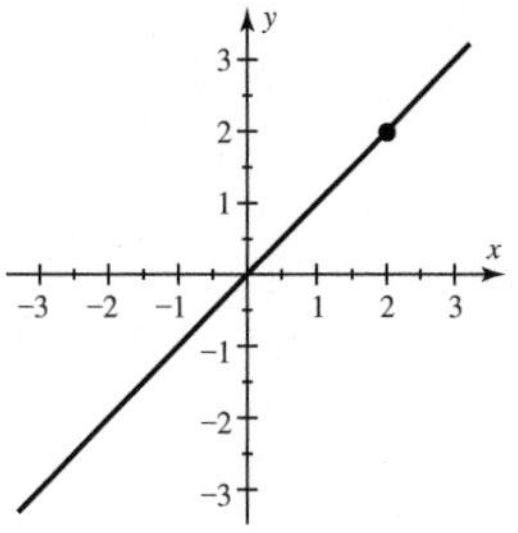

Figure 50

x	0	1	2	3
y	1	$\frac{3}{2}$	2	$\frac{5}{2}$

Figure 52

50. See Figure 50.

51. For every increase of 1 in the run, the rise increases by 2. Thus, the slope is 2. When $y = 0, x = 1$. Thus, the x-intercept is 1. When $x = 0, y = -2$. Thus, the y-intercept is -2.

52. Because the slope is $\frac{1}{2}$, for every increase of 1 in the run, the rise increases by $\frac{1}{2}$. Thus, when $x = 1, y = 1 + \frac{1}{2} = \frac{3}{2}$. When $x = 2, y = \frac{3}{2} + \frac{1}{2} = \frac{4}{2} = 2$. When $x = 3, y = 2 + \frac{1}{2} = \frac{4}{2} + \frac{1}{2} = \frac{5}{2}$. See Figure 52.

Section 3.5

53. For every increase of 1 in the run, the rise increases by 1. Therefore, the slope m is 1. When $x = 0, y = 1$. Therefore, the y-intercept is 1. Thus, $y = mx + b \Rightarrow y = 1x + 1 \Rightarrow y = x + 1$.

54. For every increase of 1 in the run, the rise decreases by 2. Therefore, the slope m is -2. When $x = 0, y = 2$. Therefore, the y-intercept is 2. Thus, $y = mx + b \Rightarrow y = -2x + 2$.

55. See Figure 55. $y = mx + b \Rightarrow y = 2x - 2$

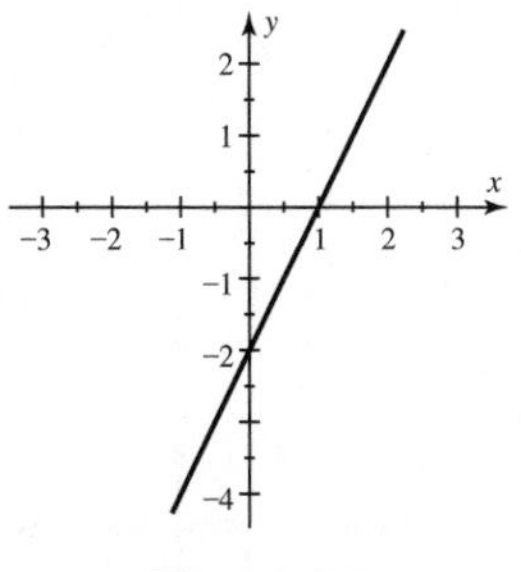

Figure 55

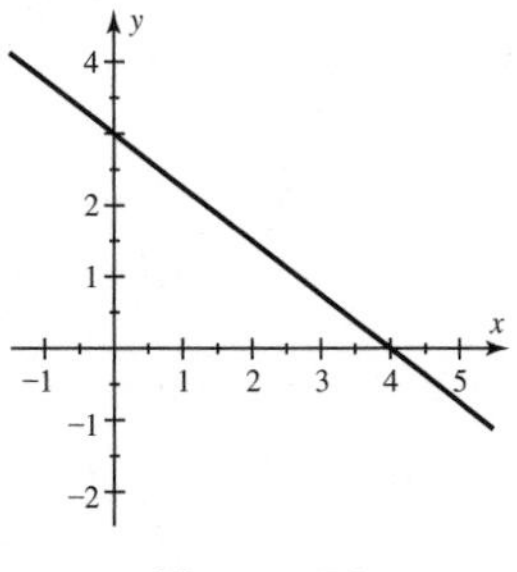

Figure 56

56. See Figure 56. $y = mx + b \Rightarrow y = -\frac{3}{4}x + 3$

57. (a) Solve for y: $x + y = 3 \Rightarrow x - x + y = 3 - x \Rightarrow y = -x + 3$.

(b) The slope is -1 and the y-intercept is 3.

58. (a) Solve for y: $-3x + 2y = -6 \Rightarrow -3x + 3x + 2y = -6 + 3x \Rightarrow 2y = 3x - 6 \Rightarrow$

$\frac{1}{2}(2y) = \frac{1}{2}(3x - 6) \Rightarrow y = \frac{3}{2}x - 3.$

(b) The slope is $\frac{3}{2}$ and the y-intercept is -3.

59. (a) Solve for y: $20x - 10y = 200 \Rightarrow 20x - 20x - 10y = 200 - 20x \Rightarrow -10y = -20x + 200 \Rightarrow$

$-\frac{1}{10}(-10y) = -\frac{1}{10}(-20x + 200) \Rightarrow y = 2x - 20.$

(b) The slope is 2 and the y-intercept is -20.

60. (a) Solve for y: $5x - 6y = 30 \Rightarrow 5x - 5x - 6y = 30 - 5x \Rightarrow -6y = -5x + 30 \Rightarrow$

$-\frac{1}{6}(-6y) = -\frac{1}{6}(-5x + 30) \Rightarrow y = \frac{5}{6}x - 5.$

(b) The slope is $\frac{5}{6}$ and the y-intercept is -5.

61. See Figure 61.

62. See Figure 62.

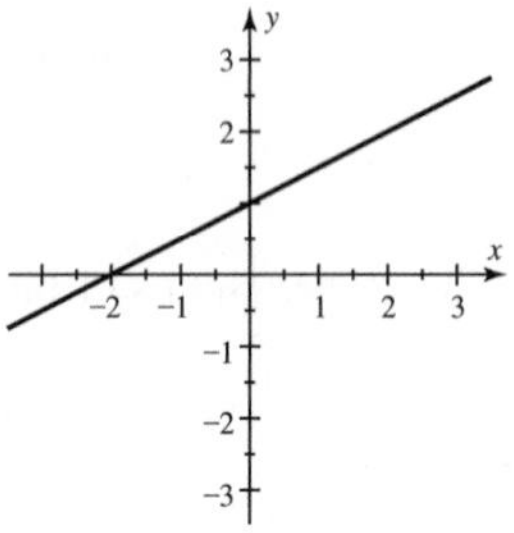

Figure 61

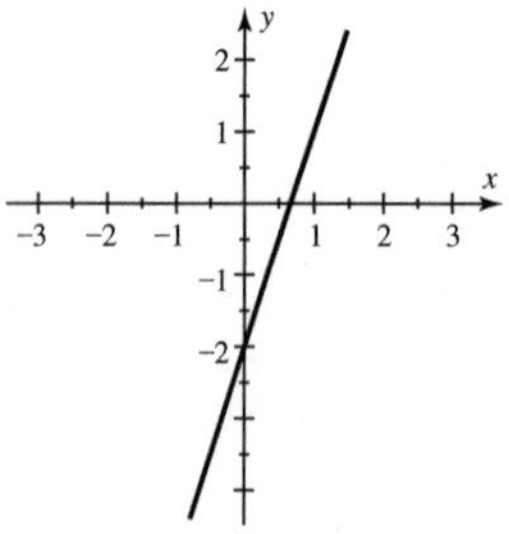

Figure 62

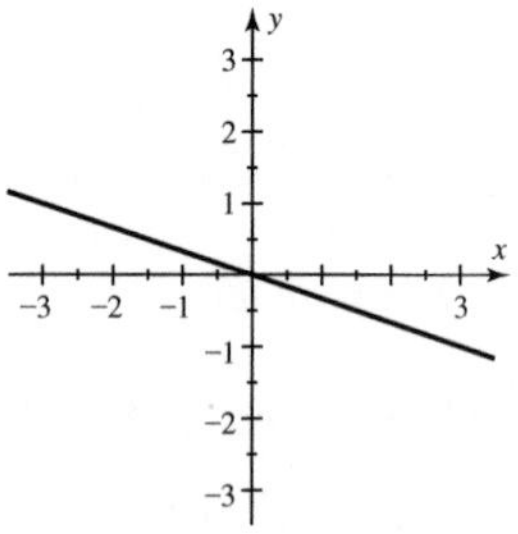

Figure 63

63. See Figure 63.

64. See Figure 64.

65. See Figure 65.

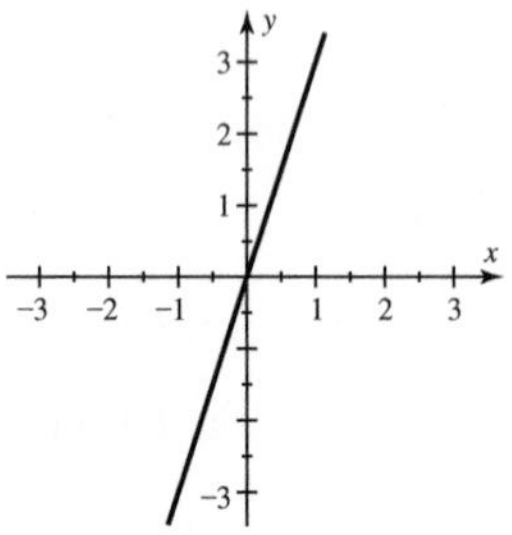

Figure 64

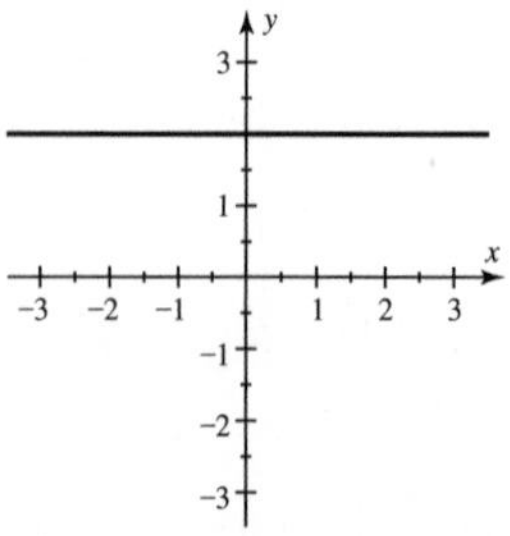

Figure 65

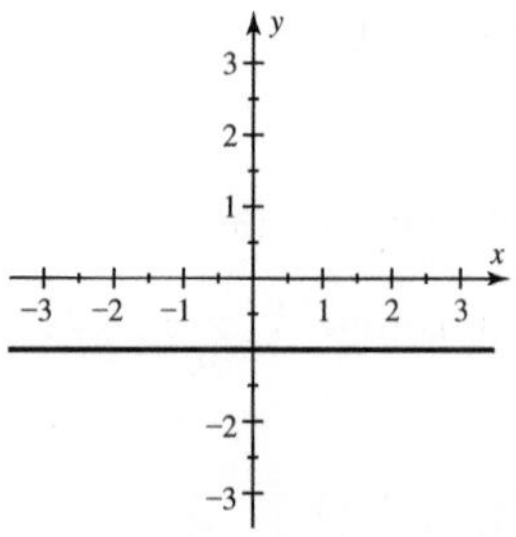

Figure 66

66. See Figure 66.

67. See Figure 67.

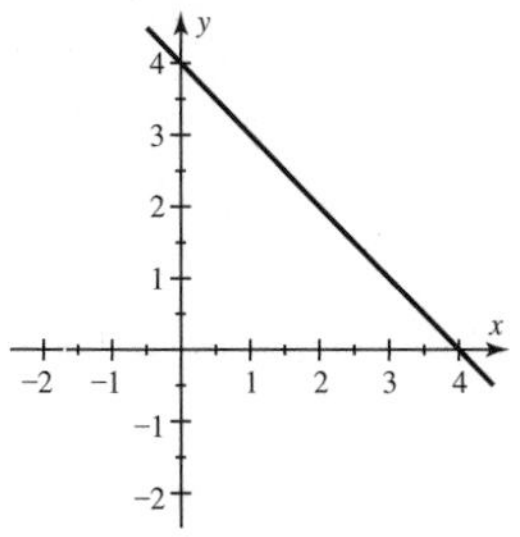

Figure 67

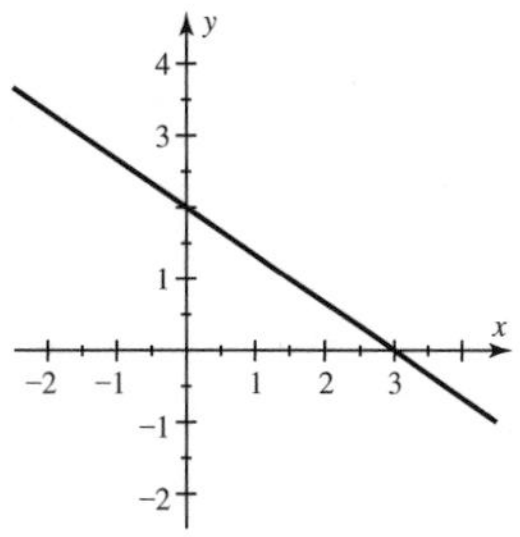

Figure 68

68. See Figure 68.

69. When the run increases by 1, the rise increases by 5. Thus, the slope m is 5. When $x = 0, y = -5$. Therefore, the y-intercept b is -5. Thus, $y = mx + b \Rightarrow y = 5x - 5$.

70. When the run increases by 1, the rise decreases by 2. Thus, the slope m is -2. When $x = 0, y = -5$. Therefore, the y-intercept b is 0. Thus, $y = mx + b \Rightarrow y = -2x + 0 \Rightarrow y = -2x$.

71. $y = mx + b \Rightarrow y = -\frac{5}{6}x + 2$.

72. The line parallel to $y = -2x + 1$ has slope -2. Insert the values of the point $(1, -1)$ and the value of the slope into the slope-intercept form and solve for b: $y = mx + b \Rightarrow -1 = -2(1) + b \Rightarrow -1 = -2 + b \Rightarrow -1 + 2 = -2 + 2 + b \Rightarrow 1 = b \Rightarrow b = 1$. Thus, the equation of the line is $y = -2x + 1$.

73. The line perpendicular to $y = -\frac{3}{2}x$ has slope $\frac{2}{3}$, the negative reciprocal *of* $-\frac{3}{2}$. Insert the values of the point $(3, 0)$ and the value of the slope into the slope-intercept form and solve for b: $y = mx + b \Rightarrow 0 = \frac{2}{3}(3) + b \Rightarrow 0 = 2 + b \Rightarrow 0 - 2 = 2 - 2 + b \Rightarrow -2 = b \Rightarrow b = -2$. Thus, $y = \frac{2}{3}x - 2$.

74. The line perpendicular to $y = 5x - 3$ has slope $-\frac{1}{5}$, the negative reciprocal *of* 5. Insert the values of the point $(0, -2)$ and the value of the slope into the slope-intercept form and solve for b: $y = mx + b \Rightarrow -2 = -\frac{1}{5}(0) + b \Rightarrow -2 = 0 + b \Rightarrow -2 = b \Rightarrow b = -2$. Thus, $y = -\frac{1}{5}x - 2$.

Section 3.6

75. Substitute -3 for x and 1 for y: $y - 1 = 2(x + 3) \Rightarrow \ - 1 - \ = 2(-3 + 3) \Rightarrow 0 = 2(0) \Rightarrow 0 = 0$. Because this is a true statement, the point $(-3, 1)$ lies on the line.

76. Substitute 3 for x and -8 for y: $y = -3(x - 1) + 2 \Rightarrow -8 = -3(3 - 1) + 2 \Rightarrow -8 = -3(2) + 2 \Rightarrow -8 = -6 + 2 \Rightarrow -8 = -4$. Because this is not a true statement, the point $(3, -8)$ is not on the line.

77. Substitute the values of the point $(1, 2)$ and the value of the slope into the slope-intercept form and solve for b: $y = mx + b \Rightarrow 2 = 5(1) + b \Rightarrow 2 = 5 + b \Rightarrow 2 - 5 = 5 - 5 + b \Rightarrow -3 = b \Rightarrow b = -3$. Thus, $y = mx + b \Rightarrow y = 5x - 3$.

78. $y = mx + b \Rightarrow -5 = 20(3) + b \Rightarrow -5 = 60 + b \Rightarrow -5 - 60 = 60 - 60 + b \Rightarrow -65 = b \Rightarrow b = -65$.

Thus, $y = mx + b \Rightarrow y = 20x - 65$.

79. Find the slope: $m = \dfrac{y_2 - y_1}{x_2 - x_1} = \dfrac{-1 - 1}{1 - (-2)} = \dfrac{-2}{1 + 2} = \dfrac{-2}{3} = -\dfrac{2}{3}$. Then, insert the values of the point $(-2, 1)$ and the value of the slope into the point-slope form: $y - y_1 = m(x - x_1) \Rightarrow y - 1 = -\dfrac{2}{3}(x - (-2)) \Rightarrow$ $y - 1 = -\dfrac{2}{3}(x + 2)$. Then, convert to slope-intercept form: $y - 1 = -\dfrac{2}{3}x - \dfrac{4}{3} \Rightarrow$ $y - 1 + 1 = -\dfrac{2}{3}x - \dfrac{4}{3} + 1 \Rightarrow y = -\dfrac{2}{3}x - \dfrac{4}{3} + \dfrac{3}{3} \Rightarrow y = -\dfrac{2}{3}x - \dfrac{1}{3}$.

80. Find the slope: $m = \dfrac{y_2 - y_1}{x_2 - x_1} = \dfrac{30 - (-30)}{40 - 20} = \dfrac{60}{20} = 3$. Then, insert the values of the point $(20, -30)$ and the value of the slope into the point-slope form: $y - y_1 = m(x - x_1) \Rightarrow y - (-30) = 3(x - 20) \Rightarrow$ $y + 30 = 3(x - 20)$. Then, convert to slope-intercept form: $y + 30 = 3(x - 20) \Rightarrow$ $y + 30 - 30 = 3(x - 20) - 30 \Rightarrow y = 3x - 60 - 30 \Rightarrow y = 3x - 90$.

81. One point on the line is $(3, 0)$ and another point is $(0, -4)$. Find the slope: $m = \dfrac{y_2 - y_1}{x_2 - x_1} = \dfrac{-4 - 0}{0 - 3} = \dfrac{-4}{-3} = \dfrac{4}{3}$. Then, insert the values of the point $(3, 0)$ and the value of the slope into the point-slope form: $y - y_1 = m(x - x_1) \Rightarrow y - 0 = \dfrac{4}{3}(x - 3)$. Then, convert to slope-intercept form: $y = \dfrac{4}{3}x - 4$.

82. One point on the line is $\left(\dfrac{1}{2}, 0\right)$ and another point is $(0, -1)$. Find the slope: $m = \dfrac{-1 - 0}{0 - \frac{1}{2}} = \dfrac{-1}{-\frac{1}{2}} = -2(-1) = 2$. The y-intercept b is -1. Thus, $y = mx + b \Rightarrow y = 2x - 1$.

83. The line parallel to $y = 2x$ has slope 2. Insert the values of the point $(5, 7)$ and the value of the slope into the point-slope form: $y - y_1 = m(x - x_1) \Rightarrow y - 7 = 2(x - 5)$. Then, convert to slope-intercept form: $y - 7 = 2x - 10 \Rightarrow y - 7 + 7 = 2x - 10 + 7 \Rightarrow y = 2x - 10 + 7 \Rightarrow y = 2x - 3$.

84. First, find the slope by converting to slope-intercept form: $y - 4 = \dfrac{3}{2}(x + 1) \Rightarrow y - 4 = \dfrac{3}{2}x + \dfrac{3}{2} \Rightarrow$ $y - 4 + 4 = \dfrac{3}{2}x + \dfrac{3}{2} + 4 \Rightarrow y = \dfrac{3}{2}x + \dfrac{3}{2} + \dfrac{8}{2} \Rightarrow y = \dfrac{3}{2}x + \dfrac{11}{2}$. The line perpendicular to $y = \dfrac{3}{2}x + \dfrac{11}{2}$ slope $-\dfrac{2}{3}$, the negative reciprocal of $\dfrac{3}{2}$. Insert the values of the point $(-1, 0)$ and the value of the slope into the point-slope form: $y - y_1 = m(x - x_1) \Rightarrow y - 0 = -\dfrac{2}{3}(x - (-1)) \Rightarrow y - 0 = -\dfrac{2}{3}(x + 1)$. Then, convert to slope-intercept form: $y = -\dfrac{2}{3}x - \dfrac{2}{3}$.

Section 3.7

85. Because a straight line would not pass through all the points, no.

86. Because the line does not pass through all the points, the linear model is approximate. When the runs increase by 1, the rise decreases by 1. Therefore, the slope is -1. When $x = 0$, $y = 5$. Thus the y-intercept is 5. Therefore: $y = mx + b \Rightarrow y = -1x + 5 \Rightarrow y = -x + 5$.

87. Because the initial value is 40, $b = 40$. Because y decreases at a rate of 2 pounds per minute, the slope is -2.

    Therefore: $y = mx + b \Rightarrow y = -2x + 40$.

88. Because the initial value is 200, $b = 200$. Because the rate of increase is 20 gallons per hour, the slope is 20.

    Therefore: $y = mx + b \Rightarrow y = 20x + 200$.

89. Because the initial value is 50, $b = 50$. Because y remains constant, the slope is 0. Therefore: $y = 50$.

90. Because the initial value is -20, $b = -20$. Because the rise is 5 feet per second, the slope is 5. Therefore:

    $y = 5x - 20$.

91. (a) See Figure 91a. The line could pass through all five points.

    (b) See Figure 91b

    (c) The initial value is 10, and the slope is -4. Thus, $y = -4 + 10$.

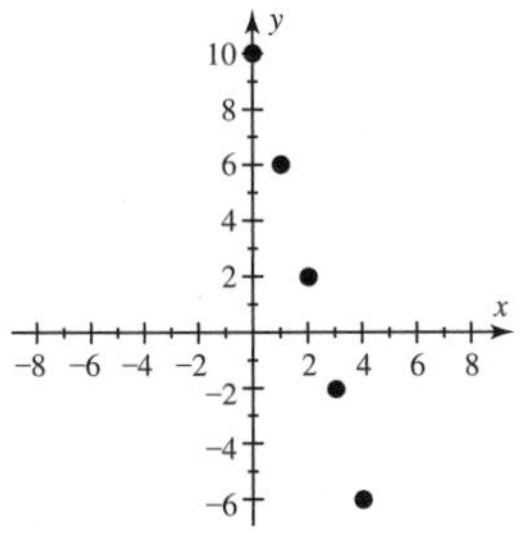

Figure 91a

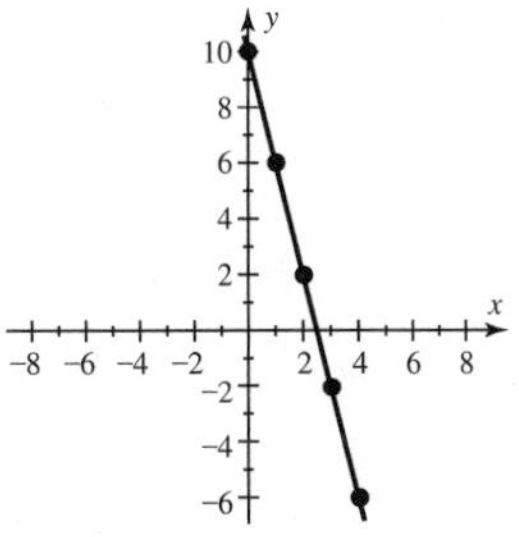

Figure 91b

92. (a) See Figure 92a. The line could not pass through all five points.

    (b) See Figure 92b.

    (c) $\dfrac{3-1}{0-(-4)} = \dfrac{2}{4} = \dfrac{1}{2}$, so the slope is $\dfrac{1}{2}$. The y-intercept is 3, so $y = \dfrac{1}{2}x + 3$.

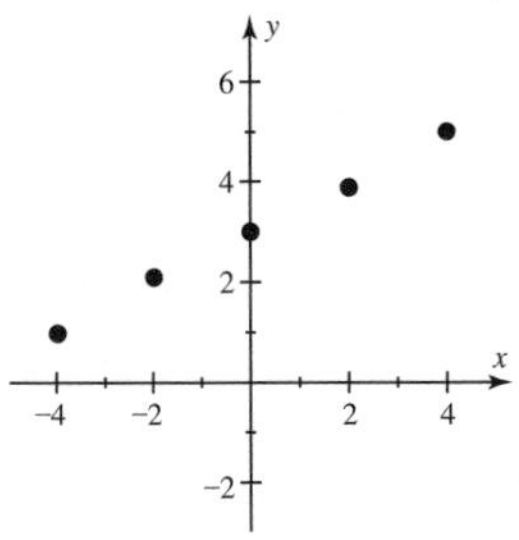

Figure 92a

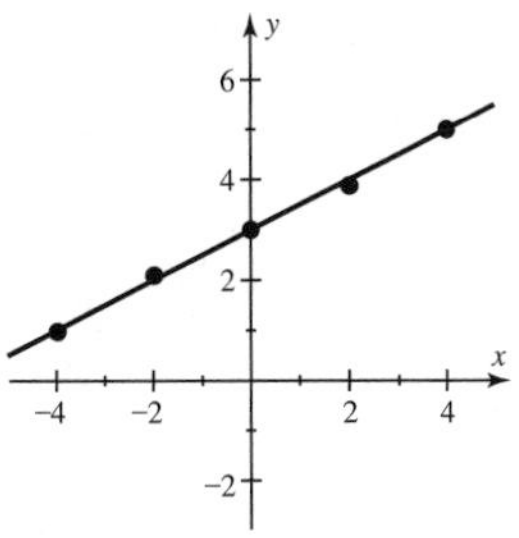

Figure 92b

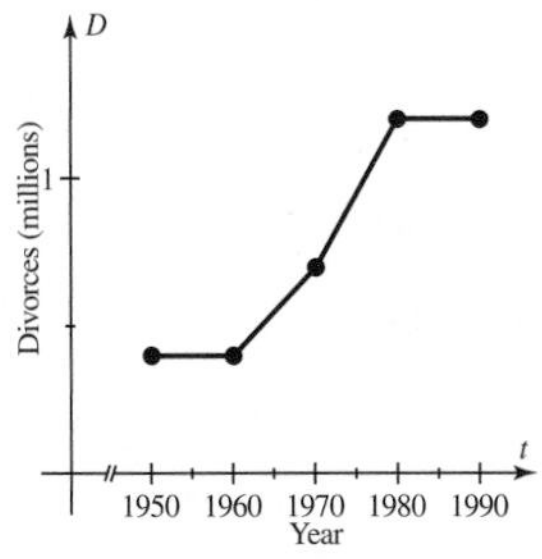

Figure 93

Applications

93. (a) See Figure 93.

    (b) The number of divorces remained unchanged from 1950 to 1960, increased significantly between 1960 and 1980, and then remined unchanged from 1980 to 1990.

94. (a) $G = 100t$

(b) See Figure 94.

(c) When $y = 5, x = 50$. Therefore, 50 days.

95. (a) See Figure 95.

(b) v-intercept, 160; t-intercept, 5; the initial velocity was 160 ft/sec. and the velocity after 5 seconds was 0.

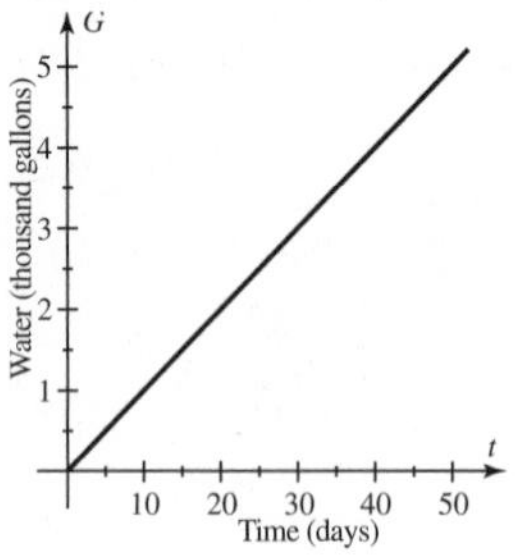

Figure 94

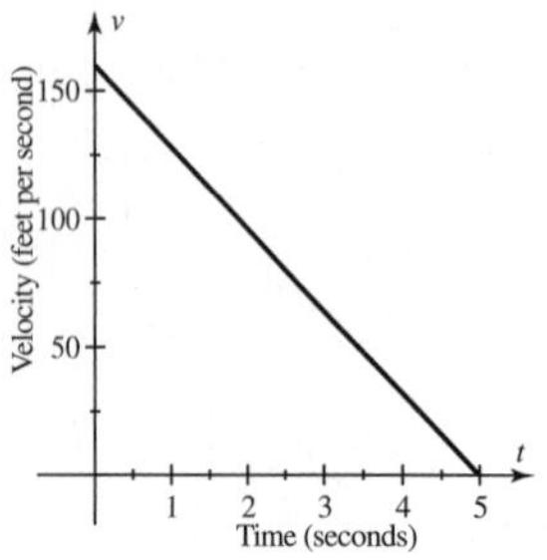

Figure 95

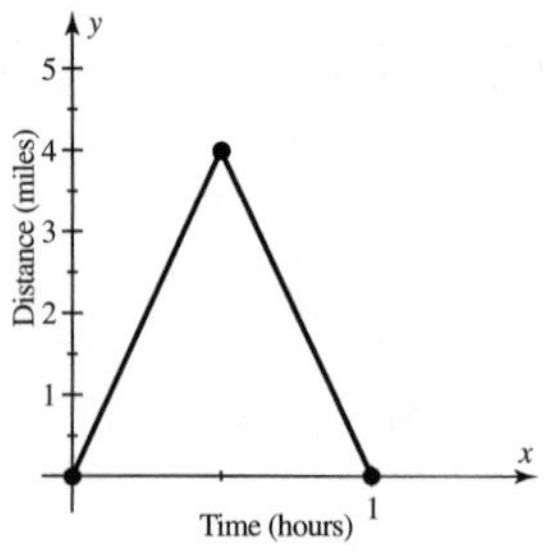

Figure 97

96. (a) $m_1 = 0$; $m_2 = -1500$; $m_3 = 500$

(b) $m_1 = 0$: The population remained unchanged. $m_2 = -1500$: The population decreased at a rate of 1500 insects per week. $m_3 = 500$: The population increased at a rate of 500 insects per week.

(c) For the first week the population did not change from the initial value of 4000. Over the next two weeks the population decreased at a rate of 1500 insects per week until it reached 1000. Finally, the population increased at a rate of 500 per week fro two weeks, reaching 2000.

97. See Figure 97.

98. (a) $\dfrac{17{,}000 - 19{,}100}{1997 - 1985} = \dfrac{-2100}{12} = -175$

(b) The number of nursing homes decreased on average at a rate of 175/yr.

99. (a) $\dfrac{70 - 60}{2010 - 1990} = \dfrac{10}{20} = \dfrac{1}{2} = 0.5$

(b) School enrollment is increasing on average at a rate of 0.5 million students/yr.

(c) $70 + 0.5(20) = 70 + 10 = 80$ million students.

100. (a) Because the initial value is 35, \$35.

(b) Because the slope is 0.2, each additional mile costs 20¢.

(c) 35; the fixed cost of renting the car.

(d) The slope is 0.2; the cost of each mile driven.

101. (a) The person is driving toward home; the slope is negative.

(b) After 1 hour the car is 200 miles from home, after 3 hours the car is 100 miles from home.

(c) The initial value is 250, so the y-intercept b is 250. For each increase of 1 in run, the rise decreases by 50, so the slope is -50. Thus, $y = -50x + 250$. The car is moving toward home at 50 mph.

(d) When time $= 2$, the distance from home is 150. Because the initial value was 250, the person has traveled 100 miles.

Then: $y = -50x + 250 = -50(2) + 250 = -100 + 250 = 150$, so $250 - 150 = 100$.

102. (a) Substitute 1990 for x: $D = 1.59(1990 - 1990) + 77.4 = 1.59(0) + 77.4 = 0 + 77.4 = 77.4 \Rightarrow$ $D = 77{,}400$. Then, substitute 1998 for x: $D = 1.59(1998 - 1990) + 77.4 = 1.59(8) + 77.4 =$ $12.72 + 77.4 = 90.12 \Rightarrow D = 90{,}120$.

(b) $\dfrac{90.12 - 77.4}{1998 - 1990} = \dfrac{12.72}{8} = 1.59$; deaths from pneumonia increased at a rate of 1590 per year.

103. (a) See Figure 103.

(b) Find the slope: $\dfrac{600 - 400}{1980 - 1970} = \dfrac{200}{10} = 20$. Then, insert the values of the point (1970, 400) and the value of the slope into the point-slope form: $y - y_1 = m(x - x_1) \Rightarrow y - 400 = 20(x - 1970)$. Then, convert to slope-intercept form: $y - 400 = 20x - 39{,}400 \Rightarrow y - 400 + 400 = 20x - 39{,}400 + 400 \Rightarrow$ $y = 20x - 39{,}000$; the number of icebergs increased at a rate of 20 per year.

(c) Because you could draw a straight line through all the points on the graph, yes.

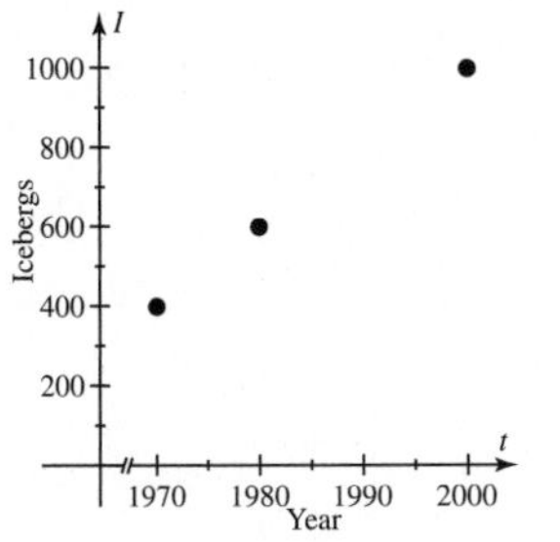

Figure 103

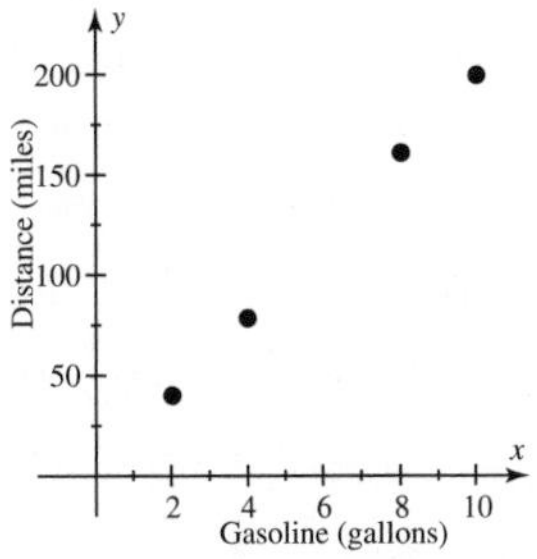

Figure 104a

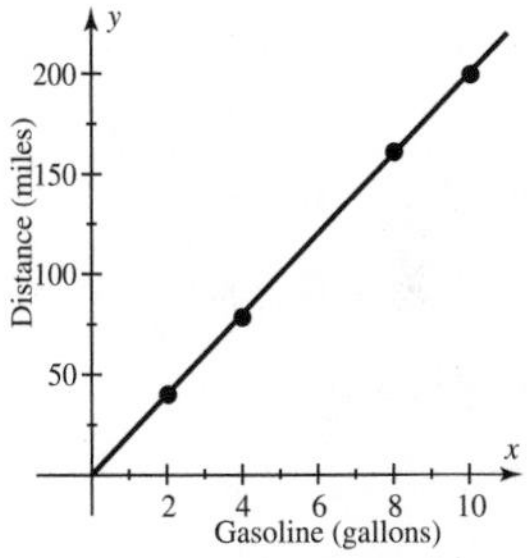

Figure 104b

104. (a) See Figure 104a.

(b) See Figure 104b.

(c) $\dfrac{200 - 40}{10 - 2} = \dfrac{160}{8} = 20$; The mileage is 20 miles per gallon.

(d) $y = 20x$; it is not an exact model.

(e) $y = 20(9) = 180$; about 180 miles.

Chapter 3 Test

1. $(-2, -2)$: Quadrant III; $(-2, 1)$: Quadrant II; $(0, -2)$: none; $(1, 0)$: none; $(2, 3)$: Quadrant I; $(3, -1)$: Quadrant IV; $(3, 1)$: Quadrant I.

2. See Figure 2.

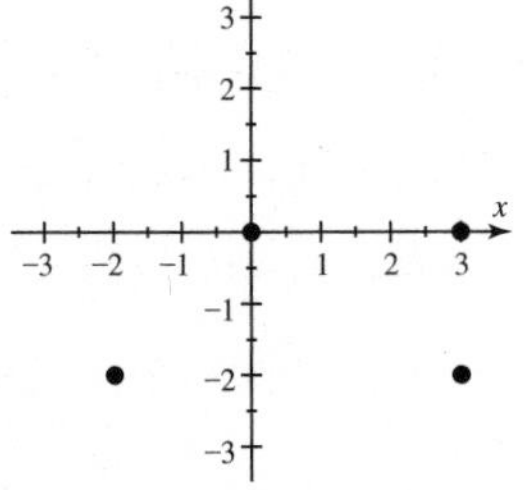

Figure 2

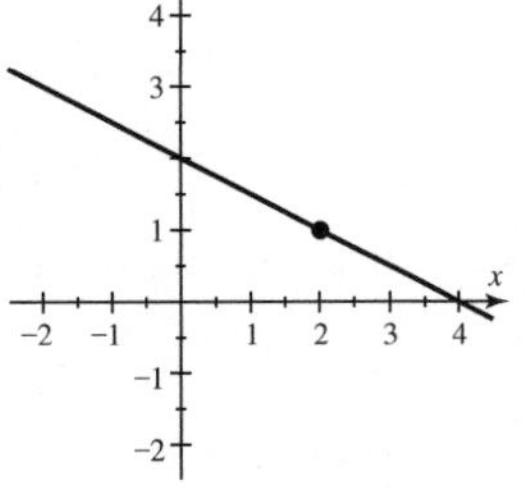

Figure 4

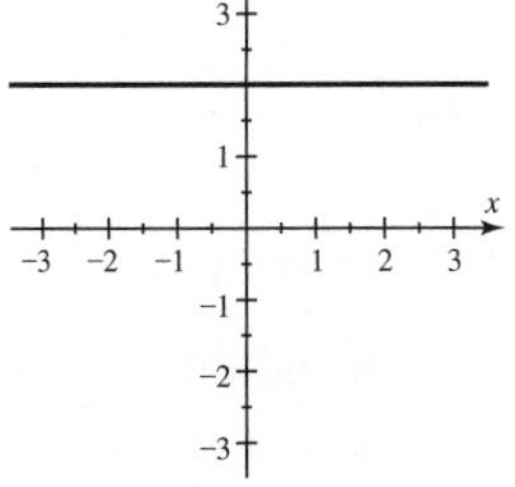

Figure 5

3. For $x = -2$: $y = 2x - 4 = 2(-2) - 4 = -4 - 4 \Rightarrow y = -8$.

   For $x = -1$: $y = 2x - 4 = 2(-1) - 4 = -2 - 4 \Rightarrow y = -6$.

   For $x = 0$: $y = 2x - 4 = 2(0) - 4 \Rightarrow y = -4$.

   For $x = 1$: $y = 2x - 4 = 2(1) - 4 = 2 - 4 \Rightarrow y = -2$.

   For $x = 2$: $y = 2x - 4 = 2(2) - 4 = 4 - 4 \Rightarrow y = 0$. See Figure 3.

   The x-intercept is 2 and the y-intercept is -4.

x	−2	−1	0	1	2
y	−8	−6	−4	−2	0

Figure 3

4. See Figure 4.

5. See Figure 5.

6. See Figure 6.

7. See Figure 7.

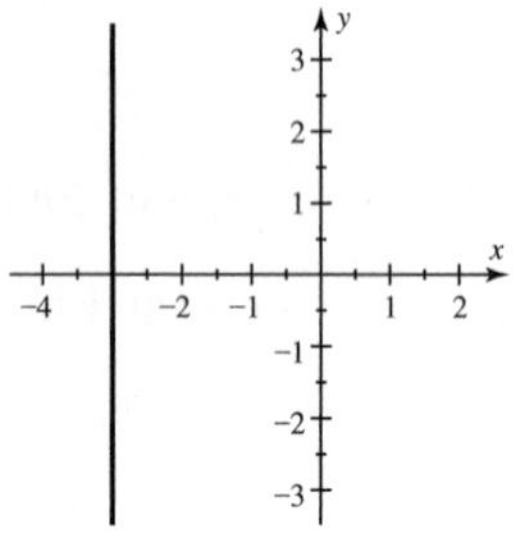

Figure 6

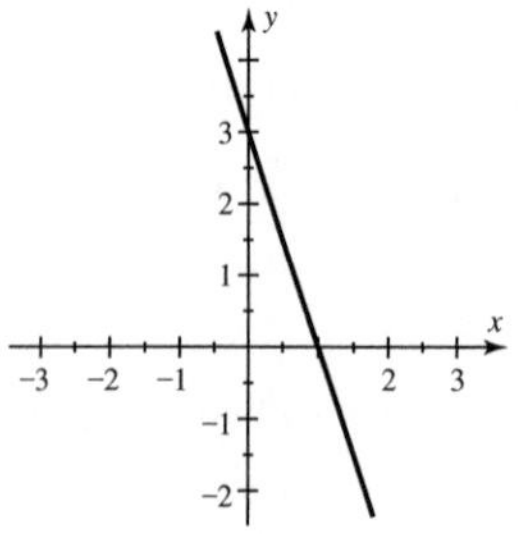

Figure 7

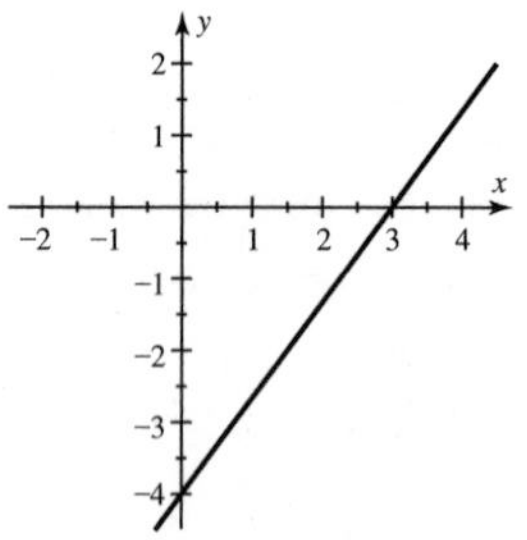

Figure 8

8. See Figure 8.

9. For every increase of 1 in the run, the rise decreases by 1, so the slope is -1. When $x = 0$, $y = 2$, so the y-intercept is 2. Therefore, the equation of the line is $y = -x + 2$.

10. Solve for y: $-4x + 2y = 1 \Rightarrow -4x + 4x + 2y = 1 + 4x \Rightarrow 2y = 4x + 1 \Rightarrow \frac{2y}{2} = \frac{4x}{2} + \frac{1}{2} \Rightarrow$

    $y = 2x + \frac{1}{2}$. The slope is 2 and the y-intercept is $\frac{1}{2}$.

11. $y = -\frac{4}{3}x - 5$

12. The line parallel to $y = 3x - 1$ has slope 3. Insert the values of the point $(2, -5)$ and the value of the slope into the point-slope form: $y - y_1 = m(x - x_1) \Rightarrow y - (-5) = 3(x - 2) \Rightarrow y + 5 = 3(x - 2)$. Then, convert to slope-intercept form: $y + 5 = 3x - 6 \Rightarrow y + 5 - 5 = 3x - 6 - 5 \Rightarrow y = 3x - 11$.

13. The line perpendicular to $y = \frac{1}{3}x$ has slope -3, the negative reciprocal to $\frac{1}{3}$. Insert the values of the point $(1, 2)$ and the value of the slope into the point-slope form: $y - y_1 = m(x - x_1) \Rightarrow y - 2 = -3(x - 1)$. Then, convert to slope-intercept form: $y - 2 = -3x + 3 \Rightarrow y - 2 + 2 = -3x + 3 + 2 \Rightarrow y = -3x + 5$.

14. Find the slope: $\frac{-1 - 2}{2 - (-4)} = \frac{-3}{6} = -\frac{1}{2}$. Then, insert the values of the point $(-4, 2)$ and the value of the slope into the point-slope form: $y - 2 = -\frac{1}{2}(x - (-4)) \Rightarrow y - 2 = -\frac{1}{2}(x + 4)$. Then, convert to slope-intercept form: $y - 2 = -\frac{1}{2}x - 2 \Rightarrow y - 2 + 2 = -\frac{1}{2}x - 2 + 2 \Rightarrow y = -\frac{1}{2}x$.

15. The linear model is approximate, because it does not go through all the points exactly. For every increase of 1 in the run, the rise is 1, so the slope is 1. Insert the values of the point $(3, 2)$ and the value of the slope into the point-slope form: $y - 2 = 1(x - 3)$. Then, convert to slope-intercept form: $y - 2 = x - 3 \Rightarrow$ $y - 2 + 2 = x - 3 + 2 \Rightarrow y = x - 1$.

16. (a) $m_1 = 2$; $m_2 = -9$; $m_3 = 2$; $m_4 = 5$

(b) $m_1 = 2$: The population increased at a rate of 2000 fish per year. $m_2 = -9$: The population decreased at a rate of 9000 fish per year. $m_3 = 2$: The population increased at a rate of 2000 fish per year. $m_4 = 5$: The population increased at a rate of 5000 fish per year.

(c) For the first year the population increased from an initial value of 8000 to 10,000 at a rate of 2000 fish per year. During the second year the population dropped dramatically to 1000 at a rate of 9000 fish per year. Over the third year the population grew to 3000 at a rate of 2000 fish per year. Finally, over the fourth year, the population grew at a rate of 5000 fish per year to reach 8000.

17. See Figure 17.

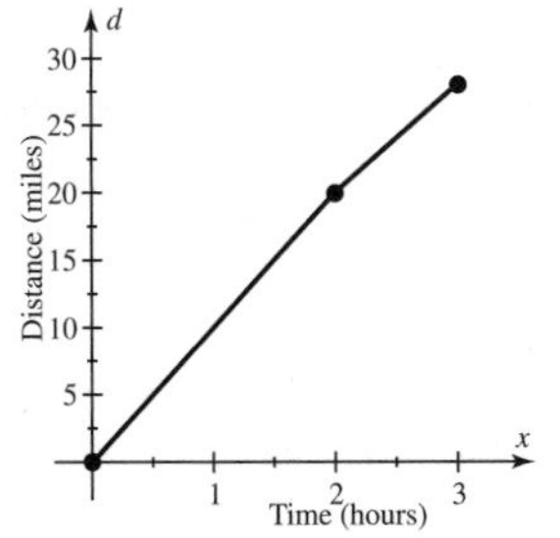

Figure 17

18. (a) $\frac{60 - 47}{1998 - 1988} = \frac{13}{10} = 1.3$

(b) Delinquency cases increased at a rate of 1.3 cases per 1000 youths per year, on average.

(c) $2004 - 1998 = 6$. Because the slope is 1.3, $6 \cdot 1.3 = 7.8$. Thus, $60 + 7.8 = 67.8$ cases per 1000 youths.

19. $n = 100x + 2000$

Chapter 3 Extended and Discovery Exercises

1. (a) See Figure 1.

   (b) Find the slope: $\dfrac{281 - 179}{2000 - 1960} = \dfrac{102}{40} = 2.55$. Then, insert the values of the point (1960, 179) and the value of the slope into the point-slope form: $P - 179 = 2.55(x - 1960) \Rightarrow$ $P - 179 + 179 = 2.55(x - 1960) + 179 \Rightarrow P = 2.55(x - 1960) + 179$. *Answers may vary.*

   (c) Substitute 2005 for x in the equation and solve for P: $P = 2.55(2005 - 1960) + 179 \Rightarrow$ $P = 2.55(45) + 179 \Rightarrow P \approx 294$ million.

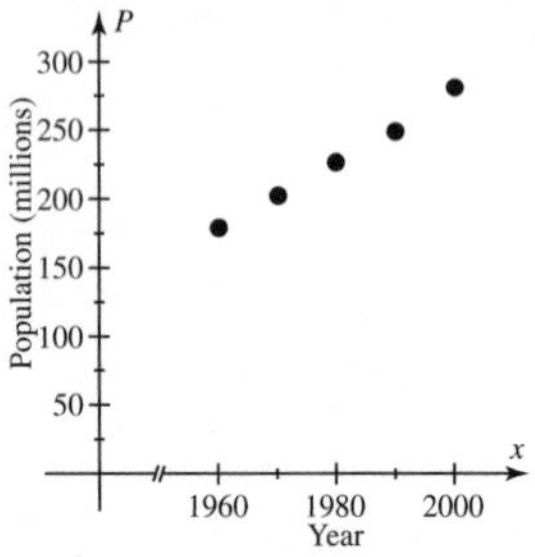

Figure 1

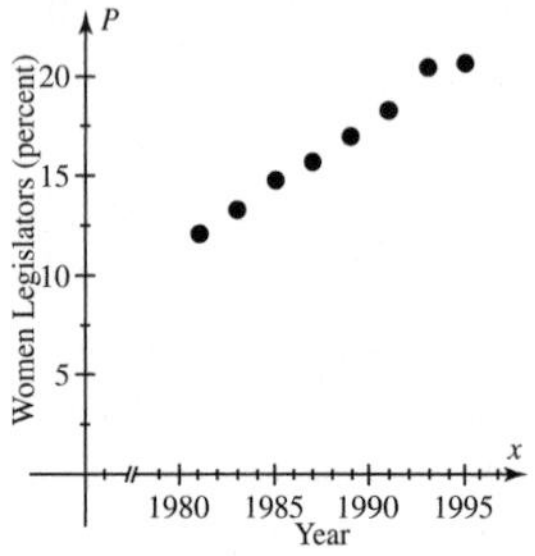

Figure 2

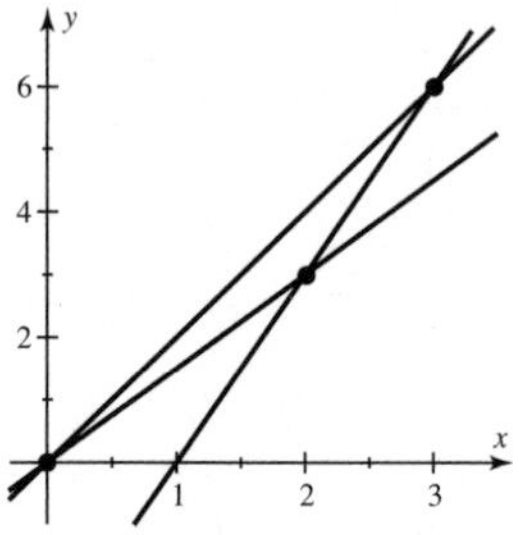

Figure 3

2. (a) See Figure 2.

   (b) Insert the values of the points (1995, 20.7) and (1981, 12.1) into the slope formula: $\dfrac{20.7 - 12.1}{1995 - 1981} = \dfrac{8.6}{14} = 0.62$. Then insert the values of the point (1981, 12.1) and the value of the slope into the point-slope form: $P - 12.1 = 0.62(x - 1981) \Rightarrow P - 12.1 + 12.1 = 0.62(x - 1981) + 12.1 \Rightarrow$ $P = 0.62(x - 1981) + 12.1$.

   (c) Substitute 2000 for x and solve for P: $P = 0.62(2000 - 1981) + 12.1 \Rightarrow P = 0.62(19) + 12.1 \Rightarrow$ $P \approx 23.9$ percent.

Creating Geometric Shapes

3. (a) The slope of the line connecting the points (0, 0) and (2, 3) is $\dfrac{3}{2}$, and the y-intercept is 0. Therefore the equation of the line is $y = \dfrac{3}{2}x$. The slope of the line connection the points (2, 3) and (3, 6) is 3. Therefore the point-slope form is: $y - 3 = 3(x - 2)$. The slope-intercept form is thus: $y - 3 + 3 = 3x - 6 + 3 \Rightarrow$ $y = 3x - 3$. The slope of the line connecting the points (3, 6) and (0, 0) is 2. The y-intercept is 0. Therefore the equation of the line is: $y = 2x$.

   (b) See Figure 3. A triangle is formed by the line segments connecting the three points.

4. (a) $y = -x + 1$

(b) See Figure 4. A parallelogram is formed.

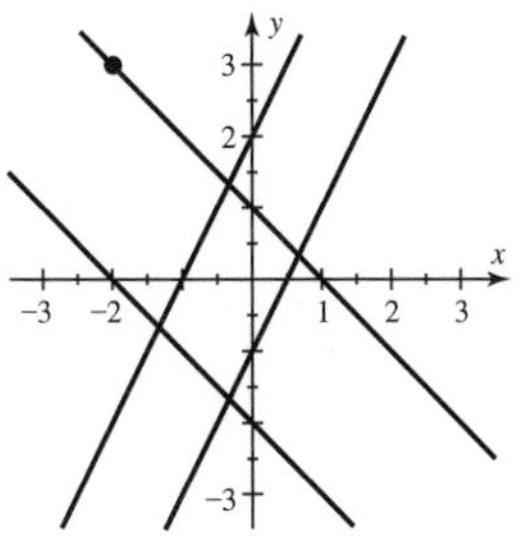

Figure 4

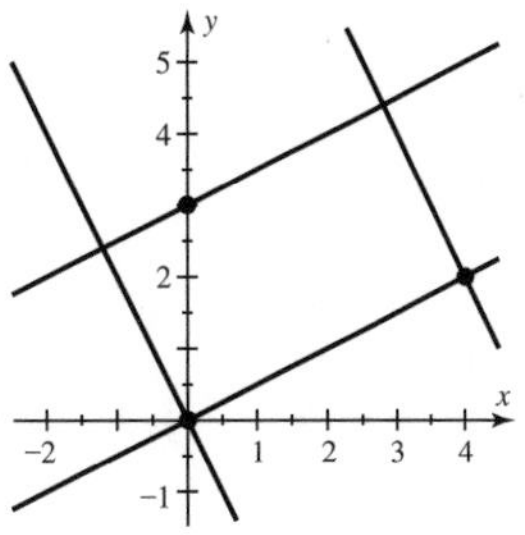

Figure 5

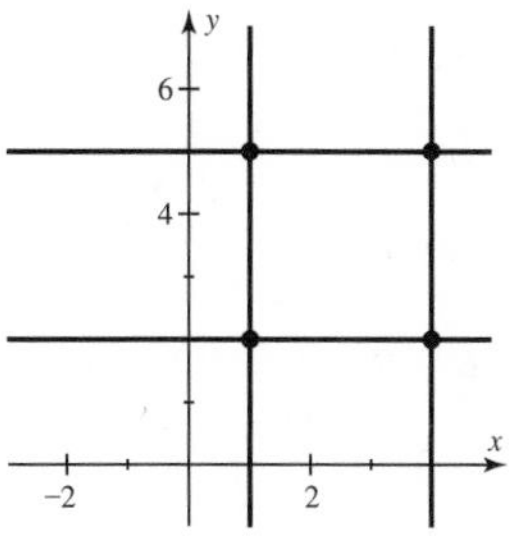

Figure 6

5. (a) $y = \frac{1}{2}x$; $y = \frac{1}{2}x + 3$; $y = -2x$; $y = -2x + 10$

(b) See Figure 5. A rectangle is formed.

6. (a) (1, 5)

(b) $x = 1$; $x = 4$; $y = 2$; $y = 5$

(c) See Figure 6. A square is formed.

Chapters 1-3 Cumulative Review Exercises

1. Composite; $40 = 2 \times 2 \times 2 \times 5$

2. Prime

3. $5x - 4y \Rightarrow 5(3) - 4(2) = 15 - 8 = 7$

4. $y = \dfrac{10}{4 + 1} = \dfrac{10}{5} = 2$

5. $n + 10$

6. $n^2 - 2$

7. Factors of 32 are: $32 \times 1, 16 \times 2, 8 \times 4$. Factors of 24 are $24 \times 1, 12 \times 2, 8 \times 3, 6 \times 4$.

Thus, the greatest common factor is 8.

8. $\dfrac{32}{40} = \dfrac{8 \cdot 4}{8 \cdot 5} = \dfrac{4}{5}$

9. $\dfrac{1}{4} \cdot \dfrac{2}{5} = \dfrac{2}{20} = \dfrac{1}{10}$

10. $\dfrac{3}{7}$

11. $\dfrac{4}{3} \cdot \dfrac{21}{24} = \dfrac{84}{72} = \dfrac{12 \cdot 7}{12 \cdot 6} = \dfrac{7}{6}$

12. $\dfrac{3}{4} \div \dfrac{9}{8} = \dfrac{3}{4} \cdot \dfrac{8}{9} = \dfrac{24}{36} = \dfrac{12 \cdot 2}{12 \cdot 3} = \dfrac{2}{3}$

13. $\frac{3}{4} \div \frac{9}{8} = \frac{3}{4} \cdot \frac{8}{9} = \frac{24}{36} = \frac{12 \cdot 2}{12 \cdot 3} = \frac{2}{3}$

14. $\frac{7}{10} - \frac{2}{15} = \frac{7 \cdot 3}{10 \cdot 3} - \frac{2 \cdot 2}{15 \cdot 2} = \frac{21}{30} - \frac{4}{30} = \frac{21 - 4}{30} = \frac{17}{30}$

15. 4^3

16. $2^4 = 2 \times 2 \times 2 \times 2 = 16$

17. $20 - 2 \cdot 3 = 20 - (2 \cdot 3) = 20 - 6 = 14$

18. $14 - 5 - 2 = (14 - 5) - 2 = 9 - 2 = 7$

19. $\frac{1 + 4}{1 + 2} = \frac{5}{3}$

20. $-3^2 = -(3^2) = -(9) = -9$

21. $10 \div 2 \cdot 5 = (10 \div 2) \cdot 5 = (5) \cdot 5 = 25$

22. $10 - 2^3 = 10 - (2 \times 2 \times 2) = 10 - 8 = 2$

23. Rational

24. Irrational, because $\sqrt{3}$ cannot be expressed as a fraction.

25. 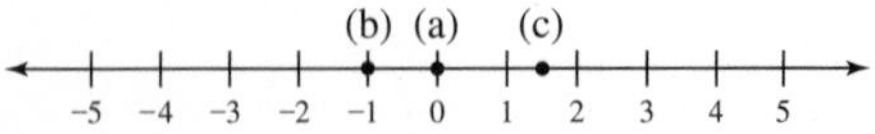

26. $|3 - 5| = |-2| = 2$

27. $-3.1, -\frac{1}{2}, \sqrt{2}, 3, \pi$

28. $2^2 - (-4)$; $2^2 - (-4) = 2^2 + 4 = 4 + 4 = 8$

29. $-10 - (-4) = -10 + 4 = -6$

30. $-5 \cdot (-3) = 15$

31. $-12 \div \left(-\frac{2}{3}\right) = -\frac{12}{1} \cdot \left(-\frac{3}{2}\right) = \frac{36}{2} = 18$

32. $-\frac{2x}{5y} \div \left(\frac{x}{10y}\right) = -\frac{2x}{5y} \cdot \frac{10y}{x} = -\frac{20xy}{5xy} = -\frac{20}{5} \cdot \frac{xy}{xy} = -4 \cdot 1 = -4$

33. Commutative and associative properties.

34. $11 + 22 + 8 + 9 = (11 + 22) + (8 + 9) = 33 + 17 = 50$

35. $3 + 4x - 2 + 3x = 3 - 2 + 4x + 3x = 1 + 7x = 7x + 1$

36. $2(x - 1) - (x + 2) = 2x - 2 - x - 2 = 2x - x - 2 - 2 = x - 4$

37. $x + 5 = 2 \Rightarrow x + 5 - 5 = 2 - 5 \Rightarrow x = -3$. To check the solution, replace x with -3 in the original equation: $x + 5 = 2 \Rightarrow -3 + 5 = 2 \Rightarrow 2 = 2$. The solution checks.

38. $\frac{1}{3}z = 7 \Rightarrow 3\left(\frac{1}{3}z\right) = 3(7) \Rightarrow z = 21$. Replace z with 21 in the original equation:

$\frac{1}{3}z = 7 \Rightarrow \frac{1}{3}(21) = 7 \Rightarrow \frac{21}{3} = 7 \Rightarrow 7 = 7$. The solution checks.

39. $3t - 5 = 1 \Rightarrow 3t - 5 + 5 = 1 + 5 \Rightarrow 3t = 6 \Rightarrow \frac{3t}{3} = \frac{6}{3} \Rightarrow t = 2$. Replace t with 2 in the original

equation: $3t - 5 = 1 \Rightarrow 3(2) - 5 = 1 \Rightarrow 6 - 5 = 1 \Rightarrow 1 = 1$. The solution checks.

40. $\frac{1}{2}(x - 2) = 3 - (x + 4) \Rightarrow \frac{1}{2}x - 1 = 3 - x - 4 \Rightarrow \frac{1}{2}x + x - 1 = 3 - x + x - 4 \Rightarrow$

$\frac{3}{2}x - 1 = 3 - 4 \Rightarrow \frac{3}{2}x - 1 + 1 = 3 - 4 + 1 \Rightarrow \frac{3}{2}x = 0 \Rightarrow \frac{2}{3}\left(\frac{3}{2}x\right) = 0\left(\frac{2}{3}\right) \Rightarrow x = 0$. Replace x with

0 in the original equation: $\frac{1}{2}(x - 2) = 3 - (x + 4) \Rightarrow \frac{1}{2}(0 - 2) = 3 - (0 + 4) \Rightarrow \frac{1}{2}(-2) = 3 - 4 \Rightarrow$

$-1 = -1$. The solution checks.

41. When $x = -2$: $6 - 2x = 6 - 2(-2) = 6 - (-4) = 6 + 4 = 10$;

when $x = -1$: $6 - 2x = 6 - 2(-1) = 6 - (-2) = 6 + 2 = 8$;

when $x = 0$: $6 - 2x = 6 - 2(0) = 6 - 0 = 6$; when $x = 1$: $6 - 2x = 6 - 2(1) = 6 - 2 = 4$;

when $x = 2$: $6 - 2x = 6 - 2(2) = 6 - 4 = 2$; thus, the missing values in the table are 10, 8, 6, 4, and 2.

See Figure 41. From the table, $6 - 2x = 4$, when $x = 1$.

x	−2	−1	0	1	2
y	10	8	6	4	2

Figure 41

42. $2n + 2 = n - 5 \Rightarrow 2n - n + 2 = n - n - 5 \Rightarrow n + 2 = -5 \Rightarrow n + 2 - 2 = -5 - 2 \Rightarrow n = -7$

43. Let n represent the lowest integer. Then: $n + (n + 1) + (n + 2) + (n + 3) = -98 \Rightarrow$

$n + n + 1 + n + 2 + n + 3 = -98 \Rightarrow 4n + 6 = -98 \Rightarrow 4n + 6 - 6 = -98 - 6 \Rightarrow$

$4n = -104 \Rightarrow \frac{4n}{4} = -\frac{104}{4} \Rightarrow n = -26$. Thus, the four integers are $-26, -25, -24$ and -23.

44. $9.8\% = \frac{9.8}{100} = \frac{9.8 \cdot 5}{100 \cdot 5} = \frac{49}{500}$; $9.8\% = \frac{9.8}{100} = 0.098$

45. $0.234 = 23.4\%$

46. $d = rt \Rightarrow 80 = 10t \Rightarrow \frac{80}{10} = \frac{10t}{10} \Rightarrow 8 = t \Rightarrow t = 8$ hours.

47. Area of a rectangle is width multiplied by length, $A = lw$. Replace w with 18 and l with 40 and solve for A:

$A = lw \Rightarrow 18 \cdot 40 = 720\ \text{ft}^2$.

48. Area of a triangle is $\frac{1}{2}$ times base times height, $A = \frac{1}{2}bh$. Replace b with 8 and h with 5 and solve for A:

$A = \frac{1}{2}bh \Rightarrow A = \frac{1}{2}(8)(5) = \frac{1}{2}(40) = 20 \text{ ft}^2$.

49. Area of a circle is π times radius squared. Because the diameter is 4, the radius is $\frac{4}{2} = 2$. Thus:

$A = \pi(2)^2 = \pi(4) = 4\pi \approx 12.6 \text{ ft}^2$.

50. Because the angles of a triangle add up to 180, $23 + 95 + x = 180$. Thus:

$23 + 95 + x = 180 \Rightarrow 118 + x = 180 \Rightarrow 118 - 118 + x = 180 - 118 \quad x = 62°$.

51. $A = \frac{1}{2}bh \Rightarrow 2A = 2\left(\frac{1}{2}bh\right) \Rightarrow 2A = bh \Rightarrow \frac{2A}{h} = \frac{bh}{h} \Rightarrow \frac{2A}{h} = b \Rightarrow b = \frac{2A}{h}$

52. $P = 2w + 2l \Rightarrow P - 2w = 2w - 2w + 2l \Rightarrow P - 2w = 2l \Rightarrow \frac{P - 2w}{2} = \frac{2l}{2} \Rightarrow \frac{P - 2w}{2} = l \Rightarrow$

$l = \frac{P - 2w}{2}$

53. $x < 2$

54. 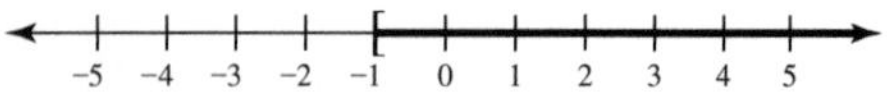

55. Replace x with 2: $3x - 2(1 + x) \geq 0 \Rightarrow 3(2) - 2(1 + 2) \geq 0 \Rightarrow 6 - 2(3) \geq 0 \Rightarrow 6 - 6 \geq 0 \Rightarrow 0 \geq 0$.

Because this is a true statement, 2 is a solution.

56. When $x = 0$: $2x - 3 = 2(0) - 3 = 0 - 3 = -3$; when $x = 1$: $2x - 3 = 2(1) - 3 = 2 - 3 = -1$;

when $x = 2$: $2x - 3 = 2(2) - 3 = 4 - 3 = 1$; when $x = 3$: $2x - 3 = 2(3) - 3 = 6 - 3 = 3$;

when $x = 4$: $2x - 3 = 2(4) - 3 = 8 - 3 = 5$; thus, the missing values in the table are −3, −1, 1, 3 and 5.

See Figure 56. From the table, $2x - 3 \leq 1$, when $x \leq 2$.

x	0	1	2	3	4
$2x - 3$	−3	−1	1	3	5

Figure 56

57. $3 - 6x < 3 \Rightarrow 3 - 3 - 6x < 3 - 3 \Rightarrow -6x < 0 \Rightarrow \frac{-6x}{-6} > \frac{0}{-6} \Rightarrow x > 0$; $\{x \mid x > 0\}$

58. $2x \leq 1 - (2x - 1) \Rightarrow 2x \leq 1 - 2x + 1 \Rightarrow 2x + 2x \leq 1 - 2x + 2x + 1 \Rightarrow 4x \leq 2 \Rightarrow \frac{4x}{4} \leq \frac{2}{4} \Rightarrow$

$x \leq \frac{1}{2}$; $\left\{x \,\middle|\, x \leq \frac{1}{2}\right\}$

59. (−2, −3): Quadrant III; (0, 3): none; (2, −2): Quadrant IV; (2, 1): Quadrant I

60. See Figures 60a and 60b.

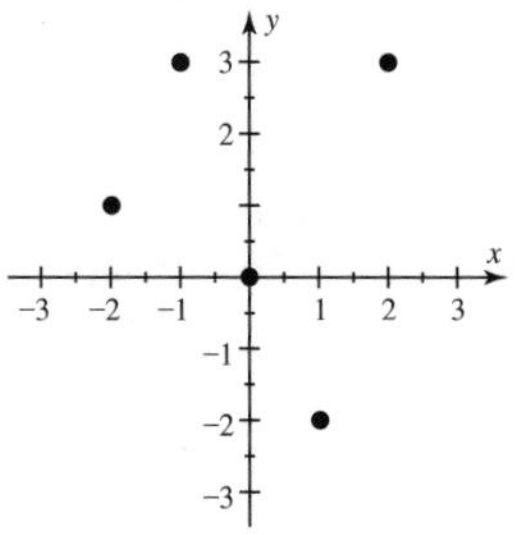

Figure 60a

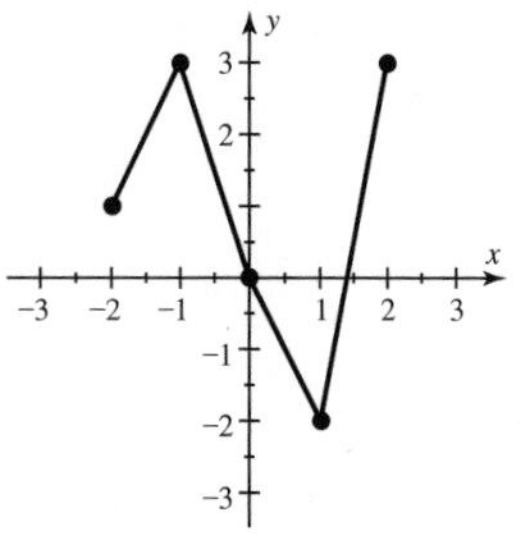

Figure 60b

x	-2	-1	0	1	2
y	3	2.5	2	1.5	1

Figure 62

61. Replace x with 5 and y with -1: $x - 3y = 8 \Rightarrow 5 - 3(-1) = 8 \Rightarrow 5 + 3 = 8 \Rightarrow 8 = 8$. Because this is a true statement, $(5, -1)$ is a solution.

62. Solve the equation for y: $x + 2y = 4 \Rightarrow x - x + 2y = 4 - x \Rightarrow 2y = 4 - x \Rightarrow \frac{2y}{2} = \frac{4}{2} - \frac{x}{2} \Rightarrow$

$y = 2 - \frac{x}{2}$. Then, when $x = -2$: $y = 2 - \frac{x}{2} \Rightarrow y = 2 - \frac{-2}{2} = 2 - (-1) = 2 + 1 = 3$;

when $x = -1$: $y = 2 - \frac{x}{2} \Rightarrow y = 2 - \left(\frac{-1}{2}\right) = 2 + \frac{1}{2} = \frac{5}{2} = 2.5$;

when $x = 0$: $y = 2 - \frac{x}{2} \Rightarrow y = 2 - \frac{0}{2} = 2 - 0 = 2$; when $x = 1$: $y = 2 - \frac{x}{2} \Rightarrow y = 2 - \frac{1}{2} = \frac{3}{2} = 1.5$;

when $x = 2$: $y = 2 - \frac{x}{2} \Rightarrow y = 2 - \frac{2}{2} = 2 - 1 = 1$. Thus, the missing values in the table are 3, 2.5, 2, 1.5, and 1. See Figure 62.

63. See Figure 63.

64. See Figure 64.

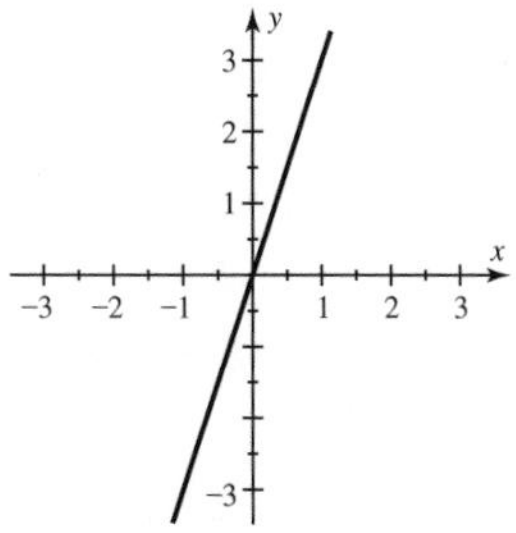

Figure 63

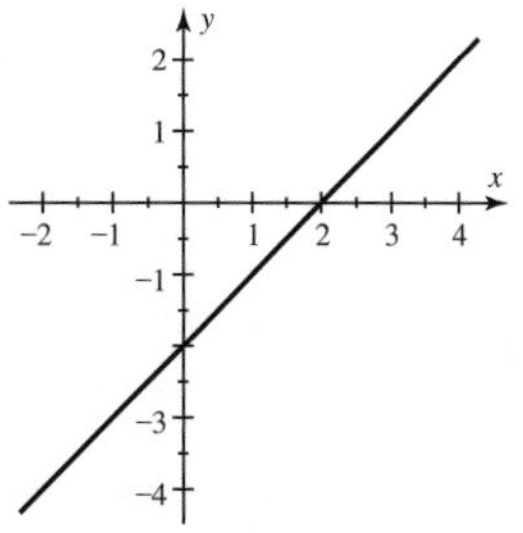

Figure 64

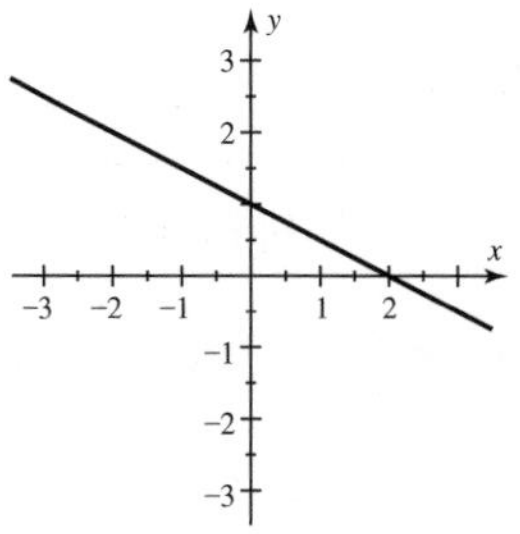

Figure 65

65. See Figure 65.

66. See Figure 66.

67. See Figure 67.

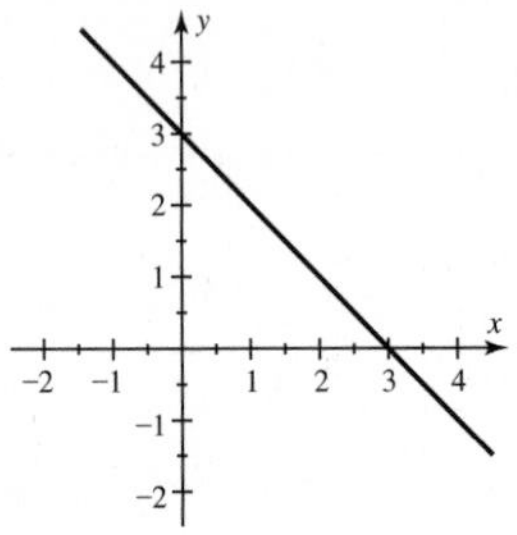

Figure 66

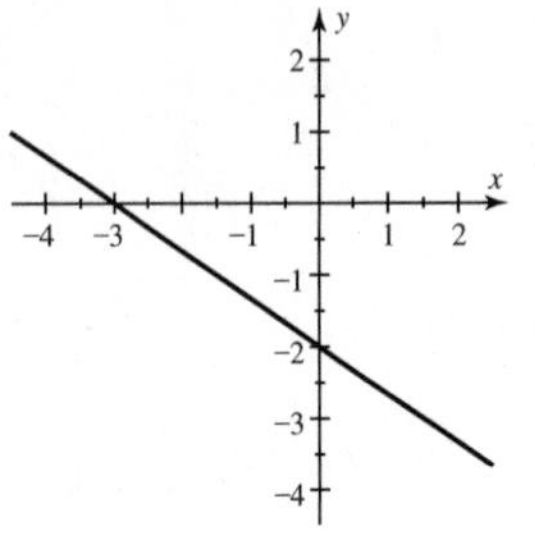

Figure 67

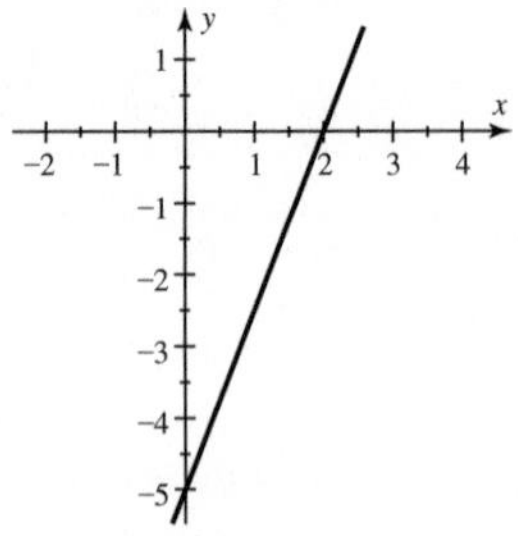

Figure 68

68. See Figure 68.

69. See Figure 69.

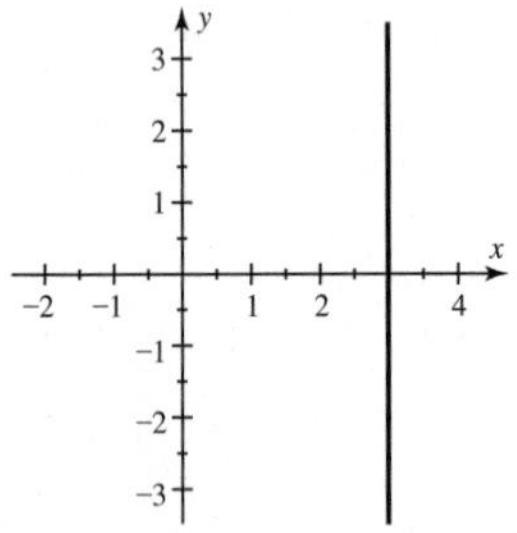

Figure 69

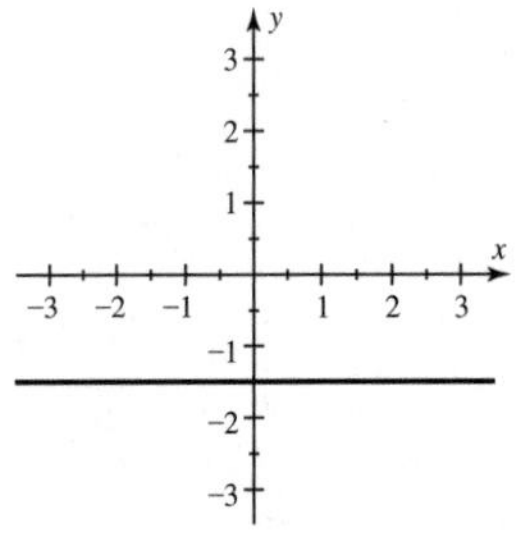

Figure 70

70. See Figure 70.

71. The x-intercept is $\frac{3}{2}$ and the y-intercept is -3. When the run increases by 1, the rise increases by 2, so the slope is 2. Thus, the equation of the line is $y = 2x - 3$.

72. The x-intercept is 2 and the y-intercept is 1. When the run increases by 2, the rise decreases by 1, so the slope is $-\frac{1}{2}$. Thus, the equation of the line is $y = -\frac{1}{2}x + 1$.

73. To find the x-intercept, set $y = 0$ and solve for x: $-4x + 5y = 40 \Rightarrow -4x + 5(0) = 40 \Rightarrow -4x + 0 = 40 \Rightarrow$ $-4x = 40 \Rightarrow \frac{-4x}{-4} = \frac{40}{-4} \Rightarrow x = -10$. Thus, the x-intercept is -10.

To find the y-intercept, set $x = 0$ and solve for y: $-4x + 5y = 40 \Rightarrow -4(0) + 5y = 40 \Rightarrow 0 + 5y = 40 \Rightarrow$ $5y = 40 \Rightarrow \frac{5y}{5} = \frac{40}{5} \Rightarrow y = 8$. Thus, the y-intercept is 8.

74. $x = \frac{3}{2}$; $y = -2$

75. See Figure 75.

76. See Figure 76.

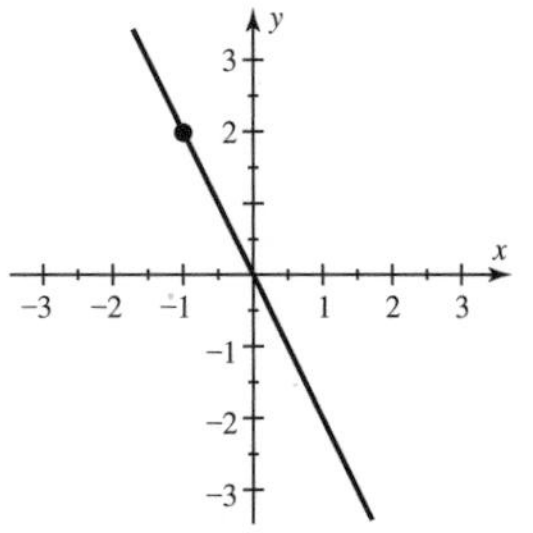

Figure 75

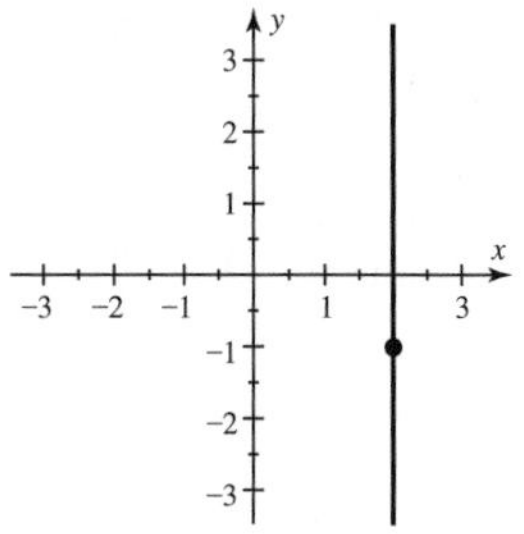

Figure 76

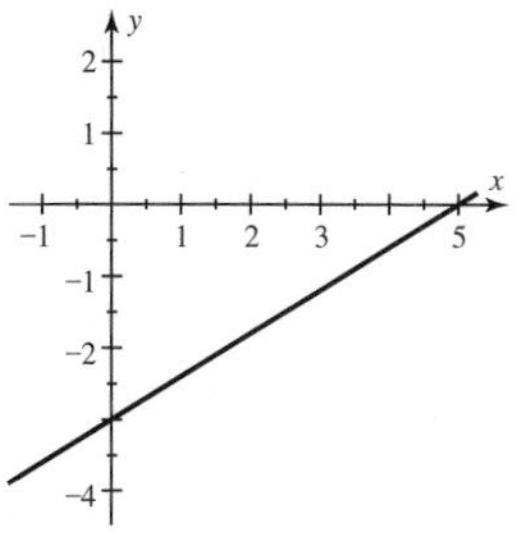

Figure 78

77. When x increases by 1, y increases by 3; therefore the slope is 3. When $x = 0$, $y = -3$; therefore the y-intercept is -3. Thus, the slope-intercept form of the line is $y = 3x - 3$.

78. Solve for y: $3x - 5y = 15 \Rightarrow 3x - 3x - 5y = 15 - 3x \Rightarrow -5y = -3x + 15 \Rightarrow$
$\frac{-5y}{-5} = \frac{-3x}{-5} + \frac{15}{-5} \Rightarrow y = \frac{3}{5}x - 3$. See Figure 78.

79. The line parallel to $y = -\frac{1}{3}x - 5$ has slope $-\frac{1}{3}$. Insert the values of the point $(-3, 8)$ and the value of the slope into the point-slope form: $y - 8 = -\frac{1}{3}(x - (-3)) \Rightarrow y - 8 = -\frac{1}{3}(x + 3)$. Then, convert to slope-intercept form: $y - 8 + 8 = -\frac{1}{3}x - 1 + 8 \Rightarrow y = -\frac{1}{3}x + 7$.

80. First, solve for y: $3x - 2y = 6 \Rightarrow 3x - 3x - 2y = 6 - 3x \Rightarrow -2y = -3x + 6 \Rightarrow \frac{-2y}{-2} = \frac{-3x}{-2} + \frac{6}{-2} \Rightarrow$
$y = \frac{3}{2}x - 3$. The line perpendicular to $y = \frac{3}{2}x - 3$ has slope $-\frac{2}{3}$, the negative reciprocal of $\frac{3}{2}$. Insert the values of the point $(0, -3)$ and the value of the point-slope form:
$y - (-3) = -\frac{2}{3}(x - 0) \Rightarrow y + 3 + (-3) = -\frac{2}{3}x - 3 \Rightarrow y = -\frac{2}{3}x - 3$.

81. First, find the slope: $\frac{-3 - 3}{2 - (-1)} = \frac{-6}{2 + 1} = \frac{-6}{3} = -2$. Then, insert the values of the point $(-1, 3)$ and the value of the slope into the point-slope form: $y - 3 = -2(x - (-1)) \Rightarrow y - 3 = -2(x + 1) \Rightarrow$
$y - 3 = -2x - 2 \Rightarrow y - 3 + 3 = -2x - 2 + 3 \Rightarrow y = -2x + 1$.

82. One point on the line is $(-2, 0)$ and another point is $\left(0, \frac{1}{2}\right)$. Find the slope: $\frac{\frac{1}{2} - 0}{0 - (-2)} = \frac{\frac{1}{2}}{2} = \frac{1}{2} \cdot \frac{1}{2} = \frac{1}{4}$.
The y-intercept is $\frac{1}{2}$. Thus, $y = \frac{1}{4}x + \frac{1}{2}$.

83. The linear model is approximate because it does not pass exactly through all the points. When the run increases by 2, the rise increases by 1. Thus, the slope is $\frac{1}{2}$. The y-intercept is 1. Thus, $y = \frac{1}{2}x + 1$.

84. $y = 5x + 100$

85. $I = 5000x + 20{,}000$

86. (a) See Figure 86a. A line could pass though all four points.

(b) See Figure 86b.

(c) The y-intercept is 5 and the slope is -2. Thus, $y = -2x + 5$.

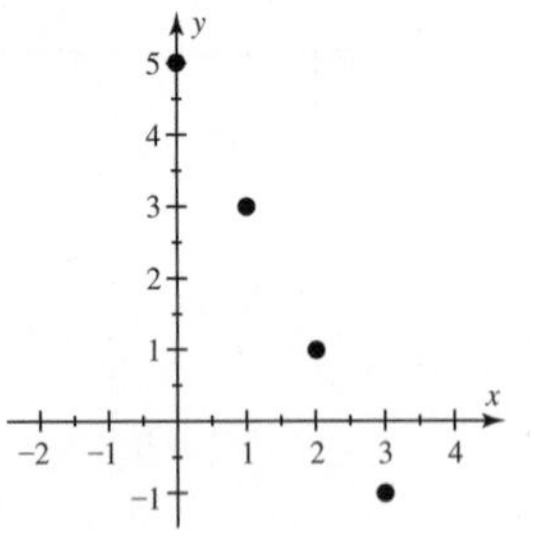

Figure 86a

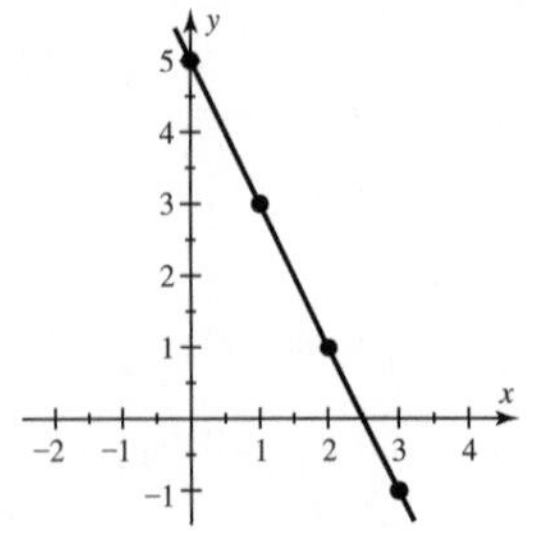

Figure 86b

87. (a) Let x represent the number of minutes. Then, $50x + 30x = 80x$.

(b) $80x = 20{,}000 \Rightarrow \dfrac{80x}{80} = \dfrac{20{,}000}{80} \Rightarrow x = 250$ minutes.

88. $C = 8x$

89. 9 out of 10, or $\dfrac{9}{10}$, of the portion of mail consisting of first-class mail and periodicals were first class mail.

Thus, $\dfrac{9}{10} \cdot \dfrac{11}{20} = \dfrac{99}{200}$ represents the fraction of all mail that was first-class mail.

90. Add the distances: $\dfrac{5}{2} + \dfrac{19}{4} + \dfrac{13}{4} = \dfrac{10}{4} + \dfrac{19}{4} + \dfrac{13}{4} = \dfrac{42}{4} = 10\dfrac{1}{2}$ miles.

91. Let x represent the cost of the car. Then, $0.06x = 330 \Rightarrow \dfrac{0.06x}{0.06} = \dfrac{330}{0.06} \Rightarrow x = \$5500$.

92. (a) The slope of the line of the equation $I = 807.4x - 1{,}587{,}300$ is 807.4. Thus, the yearly average increase is \$807.40.

(b) Set I equal to 19,400 and solve for x: $19{,}400 = 807.4x - 1{,}587{,}300 \Rightarrow$

$19{,}400 + 1{,}587{,}300 = 807.4x - 1{,}587{,}300 + 1{,}587{,}300 \Rightarrow 1{,}603{,}700 = 807.4x \Rightarrow$

$\dfrac{1{,}603{,}700}{807.4} = \dfrac{807.4x}{807.4} \Rightarrow 1990 = x \Rightarrow x = 1990$.

93. $127 - 112 = 15$. Divide 15 by 112 to find the percentage increase: $\dfrac{15}{112} \approx 0.134 \approx 13.4\%$.

94. Let x represent the amount of money invested at 3%. Then, $2x$ represent the amount of money invested at 4%.

Thus, $0.03x + 0.04(2x) = 110 \Rightarrow 0.03x + 0.08x = 110 \Rightarrow 0.11x = 110 \Rightarrow \dfrac{0.11x}{0.11} = \dfrac{110}{0.11} \Rightarrow x = 1000$.

Thus, \$1000 is invested at 3% and \$2000 is invested at 4%.

95. Let x represent the length. Then, $x - 5$ represent the width. Thus: $2x + 2(x - 5) > 4550 \Rightarrow$

$2x + 2x - 10 > 4550 \Rightarrow 4x - 10 + 10 > 4550 + 10 \Rightarrow 4x > 4560 \Rightarrow \frac{4x}{4} > \frac{4560}{4} \Rightarrow x > 1140.$

Because x represents the length, and the width is 5 inches less that the length, the values possible for the width are $w > 1135$ inches.

96. (a) $C = 0.25x + 200$

(b) $R = 10x$

(c) $P = R - C \Rightarrow P = 10x - (0.25x + 200) \Rightarrow P = 10x - 0.25x - 200 \Rightarrow P = 9.75x - 200$

(d) $9.75x - 200 > 0 \Rightarrow 9.75x - 200 + 200 > 0 + 200 \Rightarrow 9.75x > 200 \Rightarrow \frac{9.75x}{9.75} > \frac{200}{9.75} \Rightarrow$

$x > 20.5$. Thus, 21 CDs must be sold to yield a profit.

97. (a) $m_1 = 1.5;\ m_2 = 1;\ m_3 = 0$

(b) $m_1 = 1.5$: The fish grew 1.5 inches for each additional pound of food. $m_2 = 1$: The fish grew 1 inch for each additional pound of food. $m_3 = 0$: The fish stopped growing.

98. (a) $\frac{27.2 - 22.4}{2000 - 1970} = \frac{4.8}{30} = 0.16$

(b) Participation increased at a rate of 0.16 million students/year.

(c) 2005 is 5 additional years beyond 2000. Since the slope is 0.16, $5 \cdot 0.16 = 0.80$ additional students. Because the number in 2000 was 27.2, $27.2 + 0.80 = 28$ million.

99. (a) Replace x with 200: $C = 0.3(200) + 25 = 60 + 25 = \$85$.

(b) Because the initial value is 25, it costs \$25 to rent the car but not drive it.

(c) Because the slope is 0.3, it costs 30¢ to drive the car 1 additional mile.

100. (a) Selling 20 hats generates \$240 in revenue; selling 50 hats generates \$600 in revenue.

(b) The slope is $\frac{600 - 240}{50 - 20} = 12$. The initial value when $x = 0$ is 0. Thus, the equation of the line is $y = 12x$; the hats cost \$12 each.

Critical Thinking Solutions for Chapter 3

Section 3.1

- *Answers may vary.*

Section 3.3

- $y = 0$; the x-axis has y-intercept 0.
- $x = 0$; the y-axis has x-intercept 0.

Section 3.4

- See Figure 4. The slope of the two segments are 10 and −5, which are the two speeds of the runner. The second slope is negative because the distance between the runner and home is decreasing.

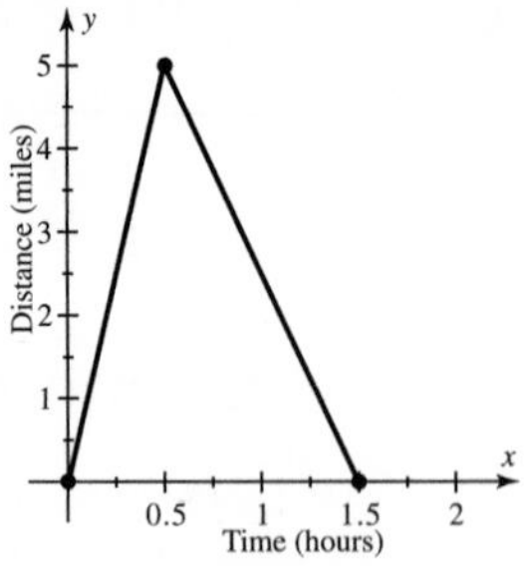

Figure 4

Section 3.6

- A positive slope indicates that water is entering the pool. A negative slope indicates water is leaving the pool.

Chapter 4: Systems of Linear Equations in Two Variables

4.1: Solving Systems of Linear Equations Graphically and Numerically

Concepts

1. ordered

3. The intersection is the solution $\Rightarrow (11, 9)$.

5. table

Solving Systems of Equations

7. Graph the system $y = 2, y = 2x$. See Figure 7. The intersection $x = 1$ is the solution.

9. Graph the system $y = 2, y = 4 - x \Rightarrow y = -x + 4$. See Figure 9. The intersection $x = 2$ is the solution.

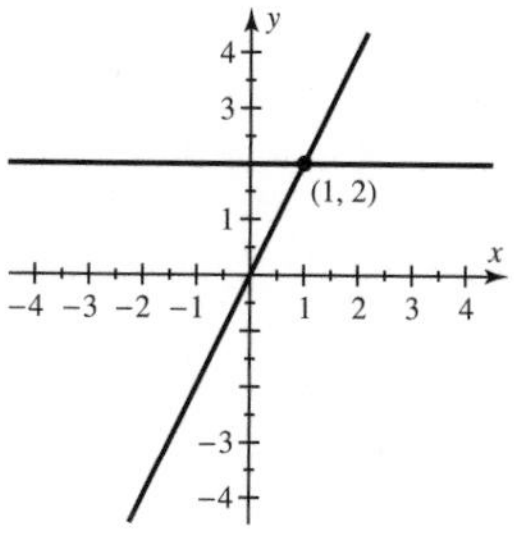

Figure 7

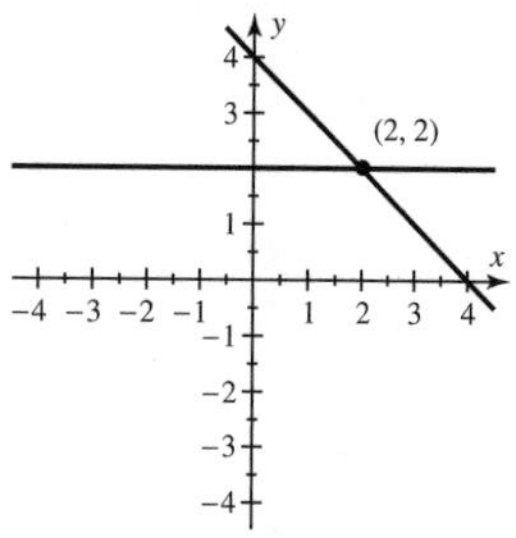

Figure 9

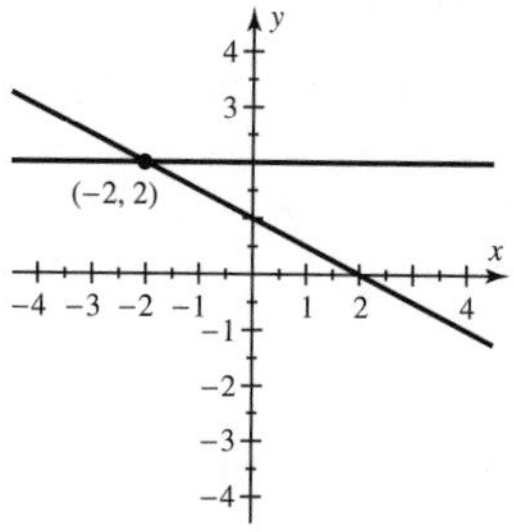

Figure 11

11. Graph the system $y = 2, y = -\frac{1}{2}x + 1$. See Figure 11. The intersection $x = -2$ is the solution.

13. Graph the system $y = 2, y = 2x + y = 6 \Rightarrow y = -2x + 6$. See Figure 13. The intersection $x = 2$ is the solution.

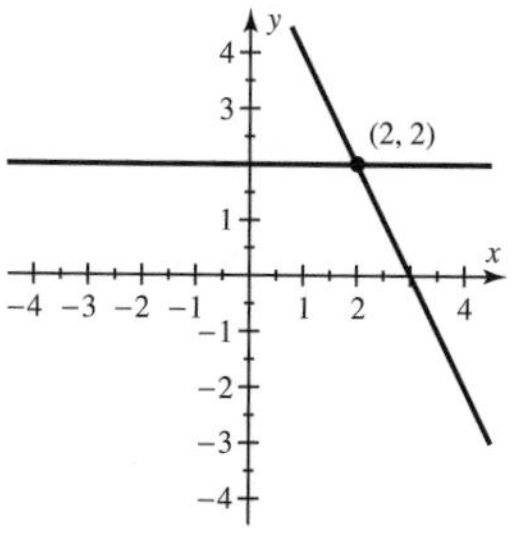

Figure 13

15. For the system $x + y = 2$ and $x - y = 0$, $(1, 1)$ is the solution because $(1) + (1) = 2$ and $(1) - (1) = 0$.

17. For the system $2x + 3y = -5$ and $4x - 5y = 23$, $(2, -3)$ is the solution because $2(2) + 3(-3) = 4 + -9 = -5$ and $4(2) - 5(-3) = 8 - (-15) = 8 + 15 = 23$.

19. For the system $-5x + 5y = -10$ and $4x + 9y = 8$, $(2, 0)$ is the solution because $-5(2) + 5(0) = -10 + 0 = -10$ and $4(2) + 9(0) = 8 + 0 = 8$.

21. The intersection and solution is $(2, 1)$, $y = 1$ and $2 + 1 = 3$.

23. The intersection and solution is $(3, 2)$, $3 + 2 = 5$ and $3 - 2 = 1$.

25. The intersection and solution is $(-1, 1)$, $-(-1) + 2(1) = 1 + 2 = 3$ and $2(-1) + 3(1) = -2 + 3 = 1$.

27. Since $y = 4$ for both equations when $x = 2$, the solution is $(2, 4)$.

29. Since $y = 1$ for both equations when $x = 3$, the solution is $(3, 1)$.

31. See Figure 31. Since $Y_1 = Y_2 = 3$ when $x = 1$, the solution is $(1, 3)$.

x	0	1	2	3
$y = x + 2$	2	3	4	5
$y = 4 - x$	4	3	2	1

Figure 31

33. (a) Graph the system. See Figure 33a. The intersection and solution is $(-1, 1)$.

(b) See Figure 33b. Since $y = 1$ for both equations, when $x = -1$ the solution is $(-1, 1)$.

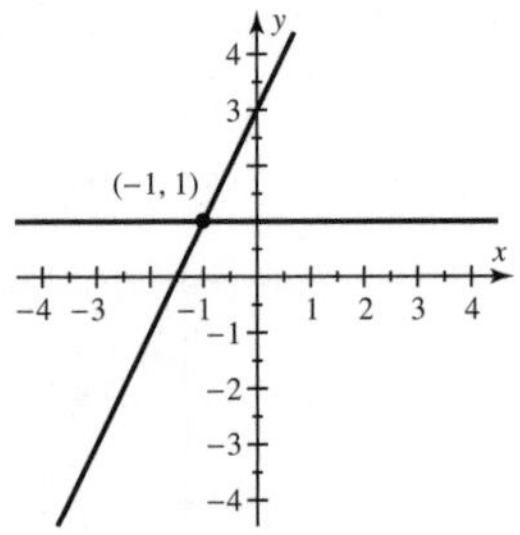

Figure 33a

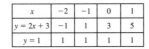

x	−2	−1	0	1
$y = 2x + 3$	−1	1	3	5
$y = 1$	1	1	1	1

Figure 33b

35. (a) Graph the system. See Figure 35a. The intersection and solution is $(3, 1)$.

(b) See Figure 35b. Since $y = 1$ for both equations, when $x = 3$ the solution is $(3, 1)$.

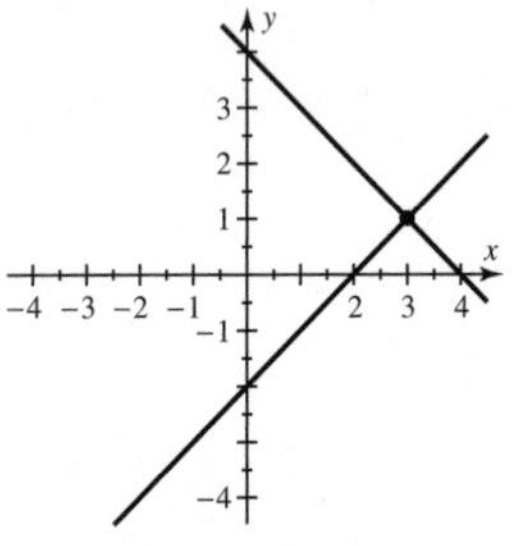

Figure 35a

x	2	3	4	5
$y = 4 - x$	2	1	0	−1
$y = x - 2$	0	1	2	3

Figure 35b

37. (a) Graph the system. See Figure 37a. The intersection and solution is $(1, 3)$.

(b) See Figure 37b. Since $y = 3$ for both equations, when $x = 1$ the solution is $(1, 3)$.

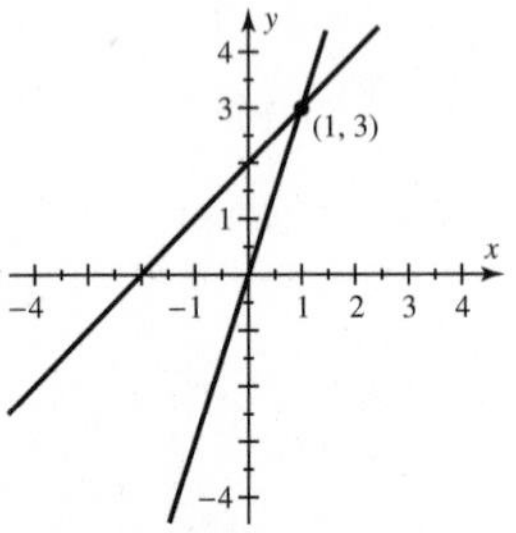

Figure 37a

x	−1	0	1	2
$y = 3x$	−3	0	3	6
$y = x + 2$	1	2	3	4

Figure 37b

39. Graph the system. See Figure 39. The intersection and solution is $(-1, -2)$.

41. Graph the system. See Figure 41. The intersection and solution is $(1, -1)$.

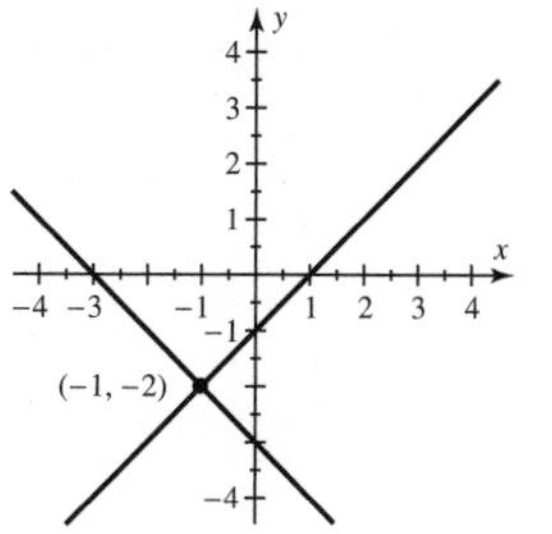

Figure 39

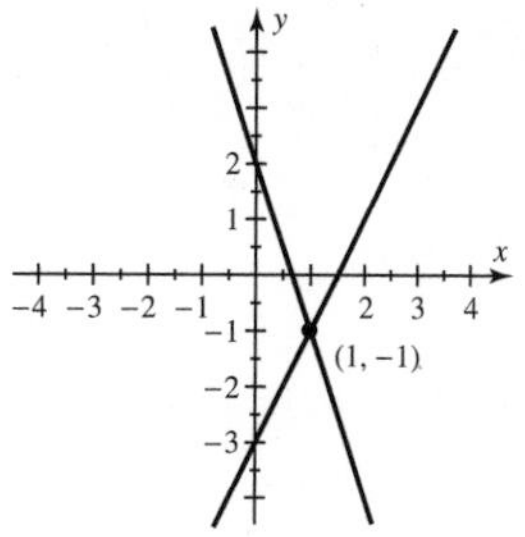

Figure 41

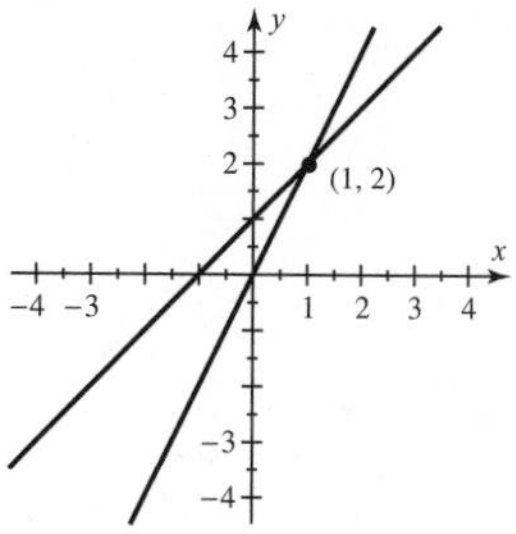

Figure 43

43. Graph the system. See Figure 43. The intersection and solution is $(1, 2)$.

45. Graph the system. See Figure 45. The intersection and solution is $(3, 2)$.

47. Graph the system. See Figure 47. The intersection and solution is $(3, 1)$.

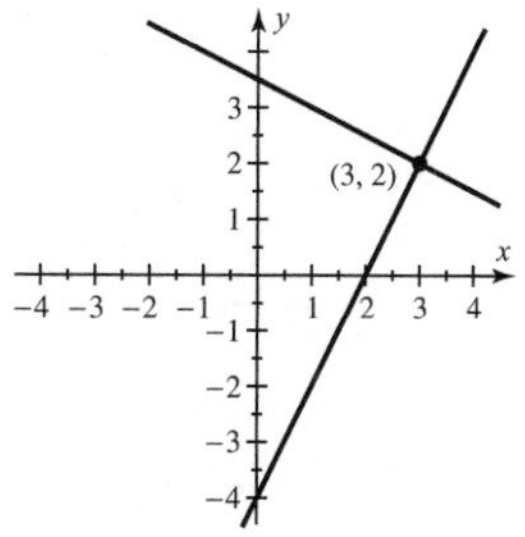

Figure 45

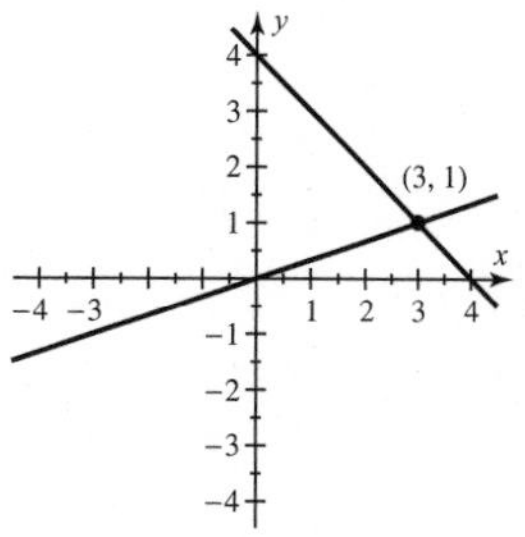

Figure 47

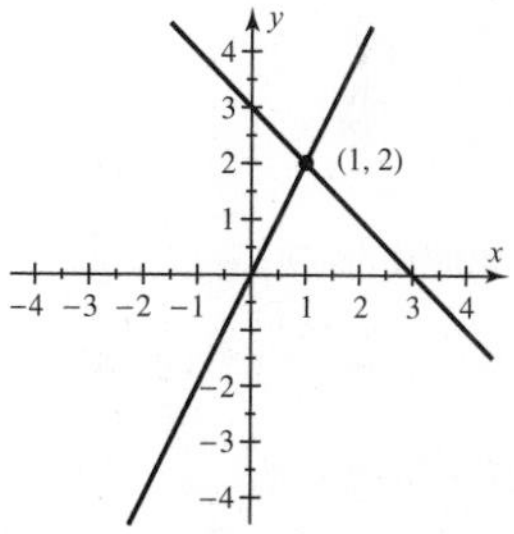

Figure 49

49. Graph the system. See Figure 49. The intersection and solution is $(1, 2)$.

Applications

51. (a) x = miles, c = cost, then $c = 0.5x + 50$.

(b) Graph $c = 0.5x + 50$ and $c = 80$. See Figure 51b. The intersection and solution $(60, 80) \Rightarrow$ 60 miles.

(c) See Figure 51c. Since $c = 80$ for both equations when $x = 60$, the solution is $(60, 80) \Rightarrow$ 60 miles.

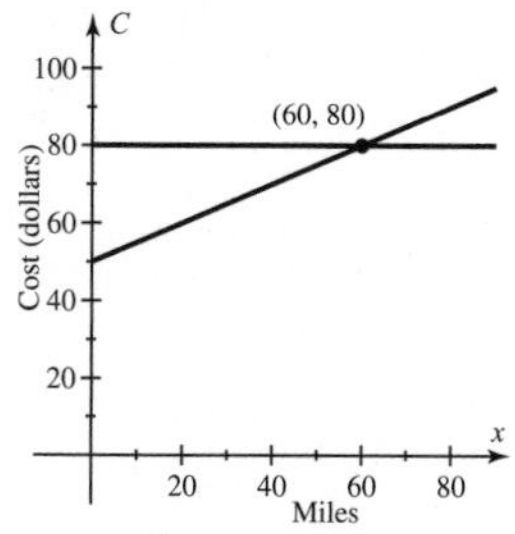

Figure 51b

x	40	50	60	70
$C = 0.5x + 50$	70	75	80	85

Figure 51c

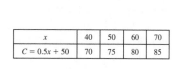

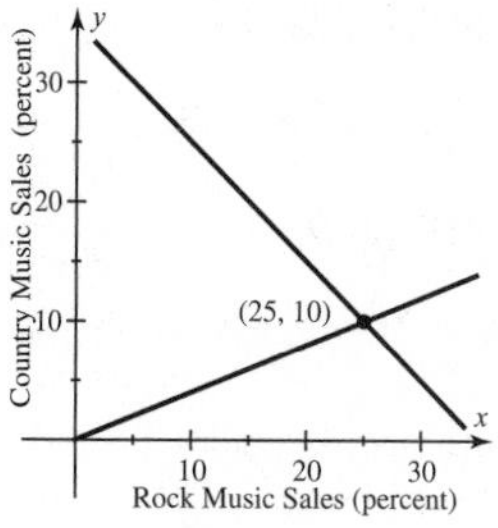

Figure 53

53. (a) x = % rock music, y = % country music, then $x + y = 35$ and $x = 2.5y$.

(b) Graph $x + y = 35$ and $x = 2.5y$. See Figure 53. The intersection and solution is $(25, 10)$.

55. (a) Let x = length, y = width, then $2x + 2y = 28$ and $x = y + 4$ or $x - y = 4$.

(b) Graph $2x + 2y = 28$ and $x - y = 4$. See Figure 55. The intersection and solution is $(9, 5) \Rightarrow 9$ in $\times$ 5 in.

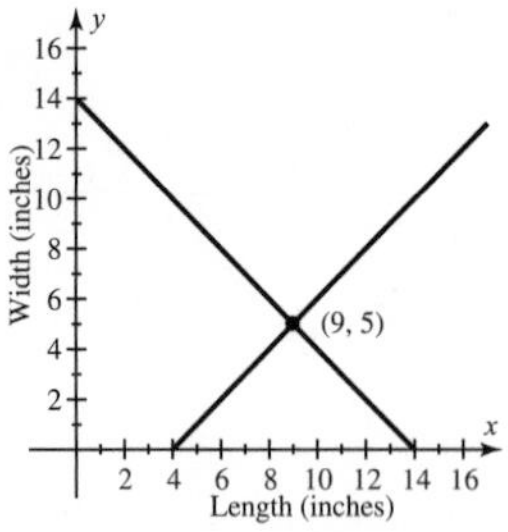

Figure 55

4.2: Solving Systems of Linear Equations by Substitution

Concepts

1. substitution

3. Because $1 = 1$ is true, it has infinitely many solutions.

5. consistent

7. independent

Solving System of Equations

9. Substituting $y = 2x$ into the first equation yields the following: $x + (2x) = 9 \Rightarrow 3x = 9 \Rightarrow x = 3$ and so $y = 2(3) \Rightarrow y = 6$. The solution is $(3, 6)$.

11. Substituting $x = 2y$ into the first equation yields the following: $(2y) + 2y = 4 \Rightarrow 4y = 4 \Rightarrow y = 1$ and so $x = 2(1) \Rightarrow x = 2$. The solution is $(2, 1)$.

13. Substituting $y = x + 1$ into the first equation yields the following: $2x + (x + 1) = -2 \Rightarrow 3x + 1 = -2 \Rightarrow$ $3x = -3 \Rightarrow x = -1$ and so $y = -1 + 1 \Rightarrow y = 0$. The solution is $(-1, 0)$.

15. Substituting $x = y + 3$ into the first equation yields the following: $(y + 3) + 3y = 3 \Rightarrow 4y + 3 = 3 \Rightarrow$ $4y = 0 \Rightarrow y = 0$ and so $x = 0 + 3 \Rightarrow x = 3$. The solution is $(3, 0)$.

17. Substituting $y = 2x - 1$ into the first equation yields the following: $-3x + 2(2x - 1) = \frac{3}{2} \Rightarrow$

$-3x + 4x - 2 = \frac{3}{2} \Rightarrow 7x - 2 = \frac{3}{2} \Rightarrow 7x = \frac{7}{2} \Rightarrow x = \frac{1}{2}$ and so $y = 2\left(\frac{1}{2}\right) - 1 \Rightarrow y = 0$.

The solution is $\left(\frac{1}{2}, 0\right)$.

19. Substituting $x = 2 - \frac{1}{2}y$ into the first equation yields the following: $2\left(2 - \frac{1}{2}y\right) - 3y = -12 \Rightarrow$ $4 - y - 3y = -12 \Rightarrow 4 - 4y = -12 \Rightarrow 4y = -16 \Rightarrow y = 4$ and so $x = 2 - \frac{1}{2}(4) \Rightarrow x = 2 - 2 \Rightarrow$ $x = 0$. The solution is $(0, 4)$.

21. Note that $3x - y = 1 \Rightarrow -y = -3x + 1 \Rightarrow y = 3x - 1$, substituting $y = 3x - 1$ into the first equation yields the following: $2x - 3(3x - 1) = -4 \Rightarrow 2x - 9x + 3 = -4 \Rightarrow -7x + 3 = -4 \Rightarrow -7x = -7 \Rightarrow x = 1$ and so $y = 3(1) - 1 \Rightarrow y = 2$. The solution is $(1, 2)$.

23. Note that $x - 5y = 26 \Rightarrow x = 5y + 26$, substituting $x = 5y + 26$ into the second equation yields the following: $2(5y + 26) + 6y = -12 \Rightarrow 10y + 52 + 6y = -12 \Rightarrow 16y + 52 = -12 \Rightarrow 16y = -64 \Rightarrow$ $y = -4$ and so $x = 5(-4) + 26 \Rightarrow x = 6$. The solution is $(6, -4)$.

25. Note that $y - 3z = 13 \Rightarrow y = 3z + 13$, substituting $y = 3z + 13$ into the first equation yields the following: $\frac{1}{2}(3z + 13) - z = 5 \Rightarrow \frac{3}{2}z + \frac{13}{2} - z = 5 \Rightarrow \frac{1}{2}z + \frac{13}{2} = 5 \Rightarrow \frac{1}{2}z = -\frac{3}{2} \Rightarrow z = -3$ and so $y = 3(-3) + 13 \Rightarrow y = -9 + 13 \Rightarrow y = 4$. The solution is $(4, -3)$.

27. Note that $r + 60t = -29 \Rightarrow r = -60t - 29$, substituting $r = -60t - 29$ into the first equation yields the following: $10(-60t - 29) - 20t = 20 \Rightarrow -600t - 290 - 20t = 20 \Rightarrow -620t - 290 = 20 \Rightarrow$ $-620t = 310 \Rightarrow t = -\frac{1}{2}$ and so $r = -60\left(-\frac{1}{2}\right) - 29 \Rightarrow r = 30 - 29 \Rightarrow r = 1$. The solution is $\left(1, -\frac{1}{2}\right)$.

29. Note that $3x + 2y = 9 \Rightarrow 3x = -2y + 9 \Rightarrow x = -\frac{2}{3}y + 3$, substituting $x = -\frac{2}{3}y + 3$ into the second equation yields the following: $2\left(-\frac{2}{3}y + 3\right) - 3y = -7 \Rightarrow \frac{4}{3}y + 6 - 3y = -7 \Rightarrow -\frac{13}{3}y + 6 = -7 \Rightarrow$ $-\frac{13}{3}y = -13 \Rightarrow y = 3$ and so $x = -\frac{2}{3}(3) + 3 \Rightarrow x = -2 + 3 \Rightarrow x = 1$. The solution is $(1, 3)$.

31. Note that $2a - 3b = 6 \Rightarrow 2a = 3b + 6 \Rightarrow a = \frac{3}{2}b + 3$, substituting $a = \frac{3}{2}b + 3$ into the first equation yields the following: $-5\left(\frac{3}{2}b + 3\right) - 3b = 6 \Rightarrow -\frac{15}{2}b - 15 - 3b = 6 \Rightarrow -\frac{21}{2}b - 15 = 6 \Rightarrow$ $-\frac{21}{2}b = 21 \Rightarrow b = -2$ and so $a = \frac{3}{2}(-2) + 3 \Rightarrow a = -3 + 3 \Rightarrow a = 0$. The solution is $(0, -2)$.

33. Note that $2x - \frac{1}{2}y = 3 \Rightarrow -\frac{1}{2}y = -2x + 3 \Rightarrow y = 4x - 6$, substituting $y = 4x - 6$ into the first equation yields the following: $-\frac{1}{2}x + 3(4x - 6) = 5 \Rightarrow -\frac{1}{2}x + 12x - 18 = 5 \Rightarrow \frac{23}{2}x - 18 = 5 \Rightarrow$ $\frac{23}{2}x = 23 \Rightarrow x = 2$ and so $y = 4(2) - 6 \Rightarrow y = 8 - 6 \Rightarrow y = 2$. The solution is $(2, 2)$.

35. Note that $-8a + 2b = 34 \Rightarrow 2b = 8a + 34 \Rightarrow b = 4a + 17$, substituting $y = 4a + 17$ into the first equation yields the following: $3a + 5(4a + 17) = 16 \Rightarrow 3a + 20a + 85 = 16 \Rightarrow 23a = -69 \Rightarrow a = -3$ and so $b = 4(-3) + 17 \Rightarrow b = -12 + 17 \Rightarrow b = 5$. The solution is $(-3, 5)$.

37. The lines intersect at one point, so there is one solution $\Rightarrow$ the system is consistent and the equations independent.

39. The lines coincide, so the are infinitely many solutions $\Rightarrow$ the system is consistent and the equations are dependent.

41. The lines are parallel, so there are zero solutions $\Rightarrow$ the system is inconsistent.

43. Note that $x + y = 4 \Rightarrow y = -x + 4$, substituting $y = -x + 4$ into the second equation yields the following: $x + (-x + 4) = 2 \Rightarrow 4 = 2$, which is false $\Rightarrow$ there are no solutions.

Graph the system. See Figure 43. The lines are parallel $\Rightarrow$ there are no solutions. The system is inconsistent.

45. Note that $x - 2y = 0 \Rightarrow x = 2y$, substituting $x = 2y$ into the first equation yields the following: $2(2y) - y = 3 \Rightarrow 3y = 3 \Rightarrow y = 1$ and so $x = 2(1) \Rightarrow x = 2$. The solution is $(2, 1)$.

Graph the system. See Figure 45. The lines intersect at the solution $(2, 1)$. The system has one solution $\Rightarrow$ the system is consistent and the equations are independent.

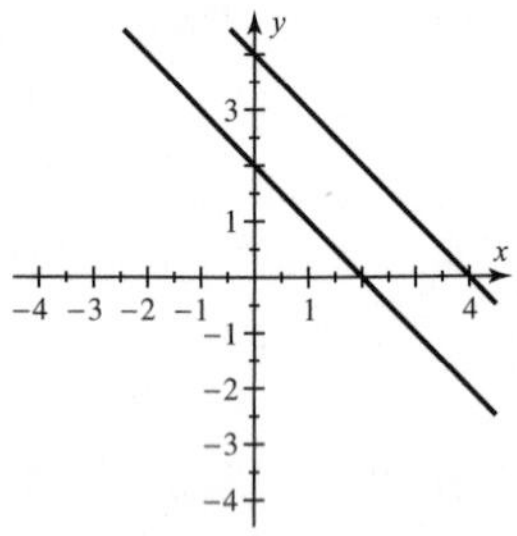

Figure 43

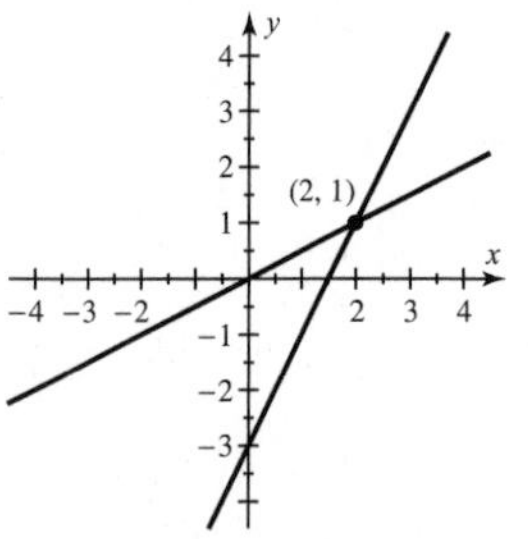

Figure 45

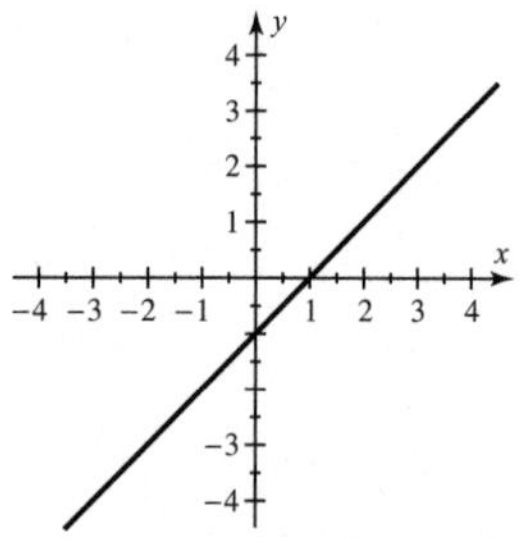

Figure 47

47. Note that $x - y = 1 \Rightarrow x = y + 1$, substituting $x = y + 1$ into the second equation yields the following: $2(y + 1) - 2y = 2 \Rightarrow 2y + 2 - 2y = 2 \Rightarrow 2 = 2$, which is true $\Rightarrow$ infinitely many solutions.

Graph the system. See Figure 47. The lines coincide $\Rightarrow$ infinitely many solutions.The system has infinitely many solutions $\Rightarrow$ the system is consistent and the equations dependent.

49. Substituting $x + 2y$ into the first equation yields the following: $(2y) - 2y = 4 \Rightarrow 0 = 4$ which is false $\Rightarrow$ no solution. Graph the system. See Figure 49. The lines are parallel $\Rightarrow$ no solutions. The system has no solutions $\Rightarrow$ the system is inconsistent.

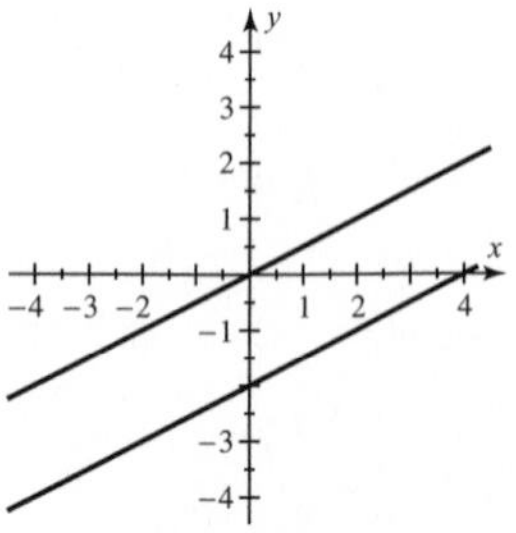

Figure 49

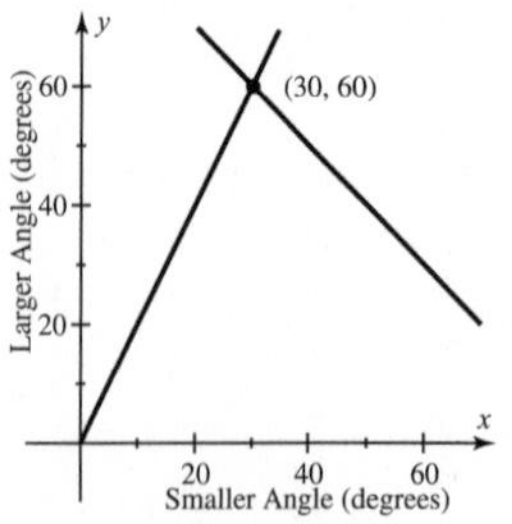

Figure 71

51. Note that $x + y = 7 \Rightarrow y = -x + 7$, substituting $y = -x + 7$ into the first equation yields the following: $x + (-x + 7) = 9 \Rightarrow 7 = 9$, which is false $\Rightarrow$ no solutions.

53. Note that $x - y = 4 \Rightarrow x = y + 4$, substituting $x = y + 4$ into the second equation yields the following: $2(y + 4) - 2y = 8 \Rightarrow 2y + 8 - 2y = 8 \Rightarrow 8 = 8$, which is true $\Rightarrow$ infinitely many solutions.

55. Note that $x + y = 4 \Rightarrow y = -x + 4$, substituting $y = -x + 4$ into the second equation yields the following: $x - (-x + 4) = 2 \Rightarrow 2x = 6 \Rightarrow x = 3$ and so $y = -(3) + 4 \Rightarrow y = 1$. The solution is (3, 1).

57. Note that $-x + y = -7 \Rightarrow y = x - 7$, substituting $y = x - 7$ into the first equation yields the following: $x - (x - 7) = 7 \Rightarrow 7 = 7$, which is true $\Rightarrow$ infinitely many solutions.

59. Note that $u - 2v = 5 \Rightarrow u = 2v + 5$, substituting $u = 2v + 5$ into the second equation yields the following: $2(2v + 5) - 4v = -2 \Rightarrow 4v + 10 - 4v = -2 \Rightarrow 10 = -2$, which is false $\Rightarrow$ no solutions.

61. Note that $r - 3t = -5 \Rightarrow r = 3t - 5$, substituting $r = 3t - 5$ into the first equation yields the following: $2(3t - 5) + 3t = 1 \Rightarrow 6t - 10 + 3t = 1 \Rightarrow 9t - 10 = 1 \Rightarrow 9t = 11 \Rightarrow t = \frac{11}{9}$ and so $r = 3\left(\frac{11}{9}\right) - 5 \Rightarrow r = \frac{11}{3} - 5 \Rightarrow r = -\frac{4}{3}$. The solution is $\left(-\frac{4}{3}, \frac{11}{9}\right)$.

63. Substituting $y = 5x$ into the second equation yields the following: $5x = -3x \Rightarrow 8x = 0 \Rightarrow x = 0$, and so $y = 5(0) \Rightarrow y = 0$. The solution is (0, 0).

65. Note that $5a = 4 - b \Rightarrow a = \frac{4}{5} - \frac{1}{5}b$, substituting $a = \frac{4}{5} - \frac{1}{5}b$ into the second equation yields the following: $5\left(\frac{4}{5} - \frac{1}{5}b\right) = 3 - b \Rightarrow 4 - b = 3 - b \Rightarrow 4 = 3$, which is false $\Rightarrow$ no solutions.

67. Note that $2x + 4y = 0 \Rightarrow 2x = -4y \Rightarrow x = -2y$, substituting $x = -2y$ into the second equation yields the following: $3(-2y) + 6y = 5 \Rightarrow -6y + 6y = 5 \Rightarrow 0 = 5$, which is false $\Rightarrow$ no solutions.

Applications

69. (a) $2L + 2W = 72$ and $L = W + 10$

(b) Substituting $L = W + 10$ into the first equation yields the following: $2(W + 10) + 2W = 72 \Rightarrow 2W = 20 + 2W = 72 \Rightarrow 4W = 52 \Rightarrow W = 13$ and so $L = 13 + 10 \Rightarrow L = 23$. The solution is (23, 13). Checking: $2(23) + 2(13) = 46 + 26 = 72$, yes. $23 = 13 + 10$, yes.

71. (a) $x + y = 90$ and $x = \frac{1}{2}y$

(b) Substituting $x = \frac{1}{2}y$ into the first equation yields the following: $\frac{1}{2}y + y = 90 \Rightarrow \frac{3}{2}y = 90 \Rightarrow y = 60$ and so $x = \frac{1}{2}(60) \Rightarrow x = 30$. The solution is (30, 60).

(c) Graph the system. See Figure 71. The lines intersect at the solution (30, 60).

73. (a) $x - y = 1.68$ and $y = 0.98x$

(b) Substituting $y = 0.98x$ into the first equation yields the following: $x - 0.98x = 1.68 \Rightarrow 0.02x = 1.68 \Rightarrow x = 84$ and so $84 - y = 1.68 \Rightarrow y = 82.32$. The solution is (84, 82.32).

75. Let L = length and W = width, then let $L = W + 44$ and $2L + 2W = 288$, substituting $L = W + 44$ into the second equation yields the following: $2(W + 44) + 2W = 288 \Rightarrow 2W + 88 + 2W = 288 \Rightarrow 4W = 200 \Rightarrow W = 50$ and so $L = 50 + 44 \Rightarrow L = 94$. The solution is (94, 50) or 94 ft $\times$ 50 ft.

77. Let x = larger number and y = smaller number, then $x + y = 70$ and $x = 3y + 2$, substituting $x = 3y + 2$ into the first equation yields the following: $(3y + 2) + y = 70 \Rightarrow 4y + 2 = 70 \Rightarrow 4y = 68 \Rightarrow y = 17$ and so $x = 3(17) + 2 \Rightarrow x = 51 + 2 \Rightarrow x = 53$. The numbers are 17 and 53.

79. Let x = liters of 20% solution and y = liters of 50% solution, then $x + y = 10$ and $0.2x + 0.5y = 0.4(10) \Rightarrow$ $0.2x + 0.5y = 4$. Note that $x + y = 10 \Rightarrow y = -x + 10$, substituting $y = -x + 10$ into the second equation yields the following: $0.2x + 0.5(-x + 10) = 4 \Rightarrow 0.2x - 0.5x + 5 = 4 \Rightarrow -0.3x = -1 \Rightarrow x = 3.33$ and so $3.33 + y = 10 \Rightarrow y = 6.67$. The amounts are: 3.33% liters of 20 % solution and 6.67 liters of 50% solution.

81. Let x = speed of tugboat and y = speed of current, then $15x - 15y = 120$ and $10x + 10y = 120$. Note that $10x + 10y = 120 \Rightarrow 10y = -10x + 120 \Rightarrow y = -x + 12$, substituting $y = -x + 12$ into the first equation yields the following: $15x - 15(-x + 12) = 120 \Rightarrow 15x + 15x - 180 = 120 \Rightarrow 30x = 300 \Rightarrow x = 10$ and so $y = -10 + 2 \Rightarrow y = 2$. The tugboat speed is 10 mph and the current's speed is 2 mph.

83. Let x = mi^2 of Lake Superior and y = mi^2 of Lake Michigan, then $x + y = 54{,}000$ and $x = y + 10{,}000$, substituting $x = y + 10{,}000$ into the first equation yields the following: $(y + 10{,}000) + y = 54{,}000 \Rightarrow$ $2y + 10{,}000 = 54{,}000 \Rightarrow 2y = 44{,}000 \Rightarrow y = 22{,}000$ and so $x = 22{,}000 + 10{,}000 \Rightarrow x = 32{,}000$. So Lake Superior has 32,000 mi^2 and Lake Michigan has 22,000 mi^2.

Checking Basic Concepts for Sections 4.1 & 4.2

1. (a) Graph the system $y = 2$ and $y = 1 - \frac{1}{2}x$. See Figure 1a. The intersection and solution is $(-2, 2) \Rightarrow x = -2$.

   (b) Graph the system $y = 2$ and $2x - 3y = 6$. See Figure 1b. The intersection and solution is $(6, 2) \Rightarrow x = 6$.

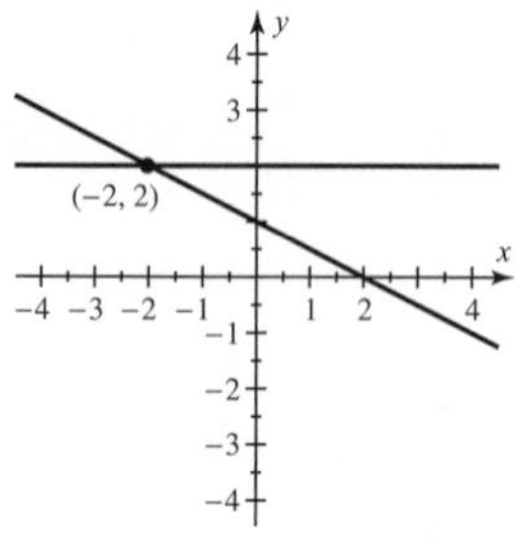

Figure 1a

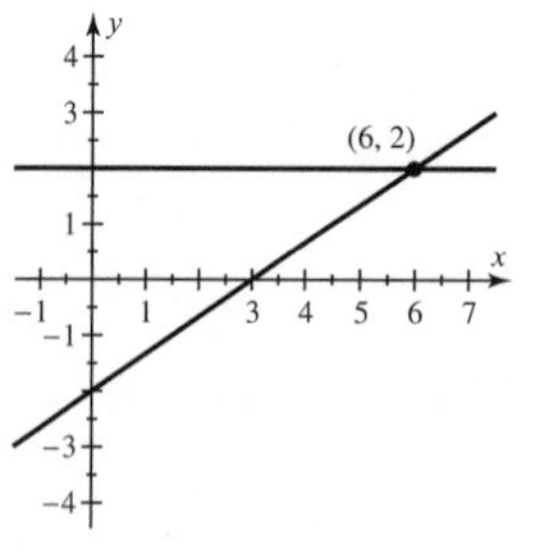

Figure 1b

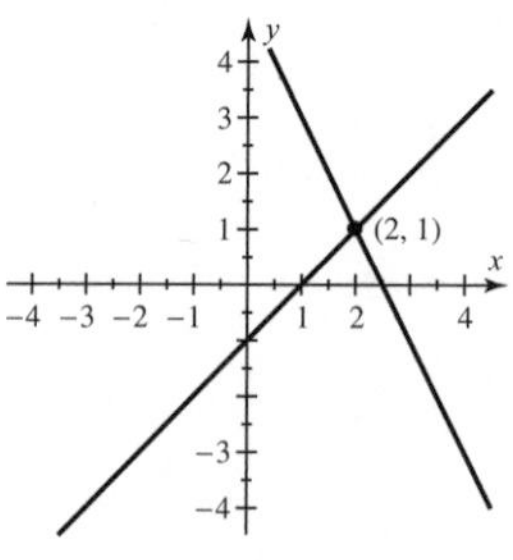

Figure 3

2. (4, 2) is the solution because $2(4) - 5(2) = 8 - 10 = -2$ and $3(4) + 2(2) = 12 + 4 = 16$.

3. Graph the system. See Figure 3. The intersection and solution is (2, 1).

   Checking: $2 - 1 = 1$ (yes) and $2(2) + 1 = 5$ (yes).

4. (a) Substituting $y = 2 - x$ into the first equation yields the following: $x + (2 - x) = -1 \Rightarrow 2 = -1$ which is false $\Rightarrow$ no solution.

   (b) Note that $-x + y = -2 \Rightarrow y = x - 2$, substituting $y = x - 2$ into the first equation yields the following: $4x - (x - 2) = 5 \Rightarrow 3x + 2 = 5 \Rightarrow 3x = 3 \Rightarrow x = 1$ and so $y = 1 - 2 \Rightarrow y = -1$. The solution is $(1, -1)$, one solution.

   (c) Note that $x + 2y = 3 \Rightarrow x = -2y + 3$, substituting $x = -2y + 3$ into the second equation yields the following: $-(-2y + 3) - 2y = -3 \Rightarrow 2y - 3 - 2y = -3 \Rightarrow -3 = -3$, which is true $\Rightarrow$ infinitely many solutions.

5. (a) $x + y = 300$, $50x + 60y = 17{,}000$

   (b) Note that $x + y = 300 \Rightarrow y = -x + 300$, substituting $y = -x + 300$ into the second equation yields the following: $50x + 60(-x + 300) = 17{,}000 \Rightarrow 50x - 60x + 18{,}000 = 17{,}000 \Rightarrow -10x = -1000 \Rightarrow$ $x = 100$ and so $y = -100 + 300 \Rightarrow y = 200$. The solution is (100, 200). Checking the answer $100 + 200 = 300$ (yes) and $50(100) + 60(200) = 5000 + 12{,}000 = 17{,}000$ (true).

4.3: Solving Systems of Linear Equations by Elimination

Concepts

1. Substitution; elimination

3. $=$

5. Add the equation to eliminate the y variable.

Using Elimination

7. Adding the two equations will eliminate the variable y.

$$\begin{array}{r} x + y = 2 \\ x - y = 0 \\ \hline 2x = 2 \end{array}$$

Thus, $x = 1$. And so $1 + y = 2 \Rightarrow y = 1$. The solution is (1, 1).

The result is supported by the graph's intersection point of (1, 1).

9. Adding the two equations will eliminate the variable y.

$$\begin{array}{r} 2x + 3y = -1 \\ 2x - 3y = -7 \\ \hline 4x = -8 \end{array}$$

Thus, $x = -2$. And so $2(-2) + 3y = -1 \Rightarrow -4 + 3y = -1 \Rightarrow 3y = 3 \Rightarrow y = 1$.

The solution is $(-2, 1)$. The result is supported by the graph's intersection point of $(-2, 1)$.

11. Multiplying the first equation by -1 and adding the two equations will eliminate both variables.

$$\begin{array}{r} -x - y = -3 \\ x + y = -1 \\ \hline 0 = -4 \end{array}$$

This is false $\Rightarrow$ no solution. This result is supported by the graph's parallel lines which has no solution.

13. Multiplying the second equation by -2 and adding the two equations will eliminate both variables.

$$\begin{aligned} 2x + 2y &= 6 \\ -2x - 2y &= -6 \\ \hline 0 &= 0 \end{aligned}$$

Which is true $\Rightarrow$ there are infinitely many solutions. This result is supported by the graph having two lines that coincide.

15. Adding the two equations will eliminate the variable y.

$$\begin{aligned} 2x + y &= 7 \\ x - y &= 5 \\ \hline 2x &= 12 \end{aligned}$$

Thus, $x = 6$. And so $6 + y = 7 \Rightarrow y = 1$. The solution is $(6, 1)$.

17. Adding the two equations will eliminate the variable x.

$$\begin{aligned} -x + y &= 5 \\ x + y &= 3 \\ \hline 2y &= 8 \end{aligned}$$

Thus, $y = 4$. And so $x + 4 = 3 \Rightarrow x = -1$. The solution is $(-1, 4)$.

19. Adding the two equations will eliminate the variable y.

$$\begin{aligned} 2x + y &= 8 \\ 3x - y &= 2 \\ \hline 5x &= 10 \end{aligned}$$

Thus, $x = 2$. And so $2(2) + y = 8 \Rightarrow 4 + y = 8 \Rightarrow y = 4$. The solution is $(2, 4)$.

21. Adding the two equations will eliminate the variable x.

$$\begin{aligned} -2x + y &= -3 \\ 2x - 4y &= 0 \\ \hline -3y &= -3 \end{aligned}$$

Thus, $y = 1$. And so $-2x + 1 = -3 \Rightarrow -2x = -4 \Rightarrow x = 2$. The solution is $(2, 1)$.

23. Multiplying the second equation by -1 and adding the two equations will eliminate the variable a.

$$\begin{aligned} a + 6b &= 2 \\ -a - 3b &= 1 \\ \hline 3b &= 3 \end{aligned}$$

Thus, $b = 1$. And so $a + 6(1) = 2 \Rightarrow a = -4$. The solution is $(-4, 1)$.

25. Multiplying the second equation by -1 and adding the two equations will eliminate the variable t.

$$\begin{aligned} 3r - t &= 7 \\ -2r + t &= -2 \\ \hline r &= 5 \end{aligned}$$

And so, $-2(5) + t = -2 \Rightarrow t = 8$. The solution is $(5, 8)$.

27. Multiplying the second equation by -2 and adding the two equations will eliminate the variable v.

$$\begin{aligned} 3u + 2v &= -16 \\ -4u - 2v &= 18 \\ \hline -u &= 2 \end{aligned}$$

Thus $u = -2$. And so $3(-2) + 2v = -16 \Rightarrow -6 + 2v = -16 \Rightarrow 2v = -10 \Rightarrow v = -5$. The solution is $(-2, -5)$.

29. Multiplying the first equation by -2 and adding the two equations will eliminate the variable x.

$$\begin{aligned} -4x - 14y &= -12 \\ 4x - 3y &= -22 \\ \hline -17y &= -34 \end{aligned}$$

Thus $y = 2$. And so $4x - 3(2) = -22 \Rightarrow 4x - 6 = -22 \Rightarrow 4x = -16 \Rightarrow x = -4$. The solution is $(-4, 2)$.

31. Multiplying the second equation by -5 and adding the two equations will eliminate the variable x.

$$\begin{array}{r} 5x - 3y = 4 \\ -5x - 20y = -50 \\ \hline -23y = -46 \end{array}$$

Thus $y = 2$. And so $5x - 3(2) = 4 \Rightarrow 5x - 6 = 4 \Rightarrow 5x = 10 \Rightarrow x = 2$.

The solution is $(2, 2)$.

33. Adding the two equations will eliminate the variable y.

$$\begin{array}{r} \frac{1}{2}x - y = 3 \\ \frac{3}{2}x + y = 5 \\ \hline 2x = 8 \end{array}$$

Thus, $x = 4$. And so $\frac{1}{2}(4) - y = 3 \Rightarrow 2 - y = 3 \Rightarrow -y = 1 \Rightarrow y = -1$.

The solution is $(4, -1)$.

35. Multiplying the first equation by 2 and adding the two equations will eliminate the variable x.

$$\begin{array}{r} -10x - 20y = -44 \\ 10x + 15y = 35 \\ \hline -5y = -9 \end{array}$$

Thus $y = \frac{9}{5}$. And so $10x + 15\left(\frac{9}{5}\right) = 35 \Rightarrow 10x + 27 = 35 \Rightarrow 10x = 8 \Rightarrow x = \frac{4}{5}$.

The solution is $\left(\frac{4}{5}, \frac{9}{5}\right)$.

37. Since $y = 2$, when $x = 3$ for both equations $\Rightarrow$ the solution is $(3, 2)$.

39. Since $y = 1$, when $x = 0$ for both equations $\Rightarrow$ the solution is $(0, 1)$.

Using More Than One Method

41. (a) Adding the two equations will eliminate the variable y.

$$\begin{array}{r} 2x + y = 5 \\ x - y = 1 \\ \hline 3x = 6 \end{array}$$

Thus, $x = 2$. And so $2 - y = 1 \Rightarrow y = 1$. The solution is $(2, 1)$.

(b) Graph the system. See Figure 41b. The intersection and solution is $(2, 1)$.

(c) See Figure 41c. Since $y = 1$ when $x = 2$ for both equations the solution is $(2, 1)$.

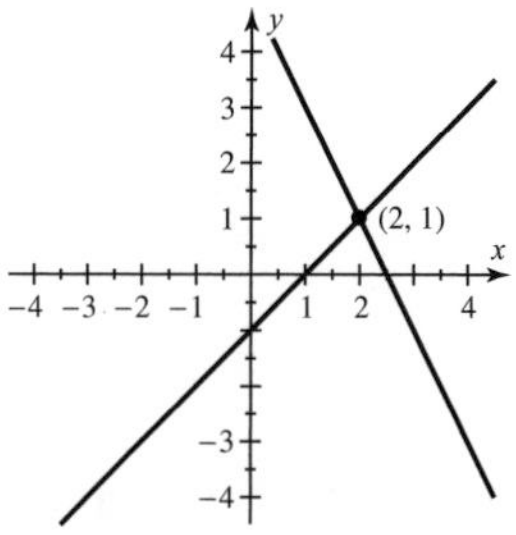

Figure 41b

x	0	1	2	3
$y = 5 - 2x$	5	3	1	−1
$y = x - 1$	−1	0	1	2

Figure 41c

43. (a) Multiplying the second equation by -1 and adding the two equations will eliminate the variable y.

$$\begin{array}{l} 2x + y = 5 \\ -x - y = -1 \\ \hline x = 4 \end{array}$$

And so $-4 - y = -1 \Rightarrow -y = 3 \Rightarrow y = -3$. The solution is $(4, -3)$.

(b) Graph the system. See Figure 43b. The intersection and solution is $(4, -3)$.

(c) See Figure 43c. Since $y = -3$ when $x = 4$ for both equations the solution is $(4, -3)$.

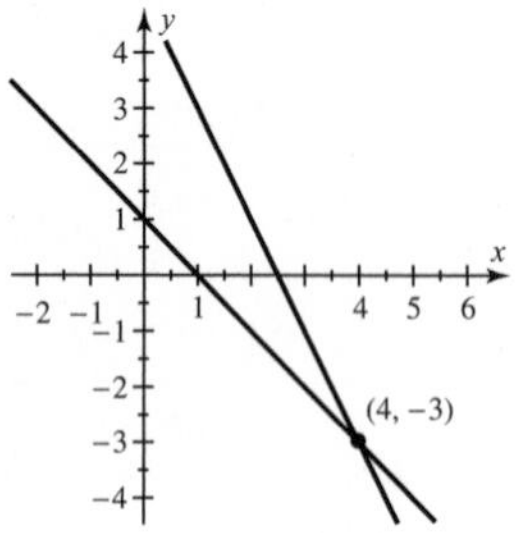

Figure 43b

x	2	3	4	5
$y = 5 - 2x$	1	−1	−3	−5
$y = 1 - x$	−1	−2	−3	−4

Figure 43c

45. (a) Multiplying the second equation by 3 and adding the two equations will eliminate the variable x.

$$\begin{array}{l} 6x + 3y = 6 \\ -6x + 6y = -6 \\ \hline 9y = 0 \end{array}$$

Thus, $y = 0$. And so $6x + 3(0) = 6 \Rightarrow 6x = 6 \Rightarrow x = 1$. The solution is $(1, 0)$.

(b) Graph the system. See Figure 45b. The intersection and solution is $(1, 0)$.

(c) See Figure 45c. Since $y = 0$ when $x = 1$ for both equations the solution is $(1, 0)$.

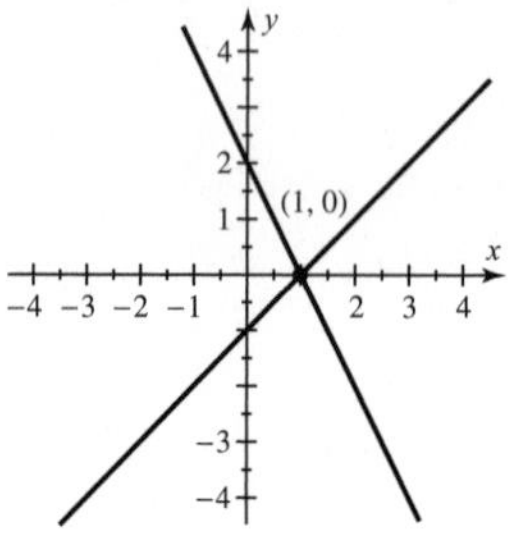

Figure 45b

x	−1	0	1	2
$y = 2 - 2x$	4	2	0	−1
$y = x - 1$	−2	−1	0	1

Figure 45c

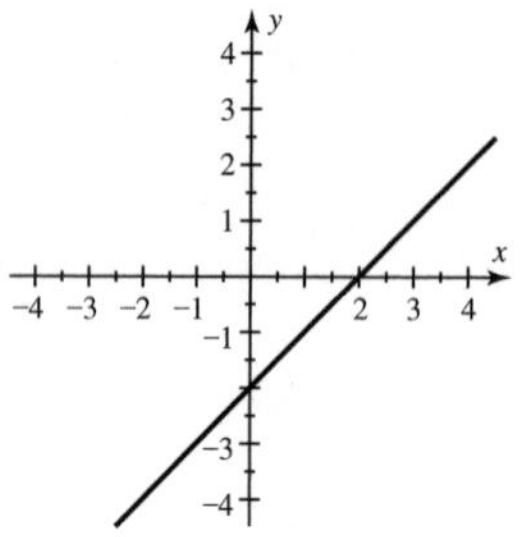

Figure 47

Elimination and Other Types of Systems

47. Multiplying the second equation by 2 and adding the two equations will eliminate both variables.

$$\begin{array}{l} 2x - 2y = 4 \\ -2x + 2y = -4 \\ \hline 0 = 0 \end{array}$$

This is always true $\Rightarrow$ infinitely many solutions. See Figure 47.

49. Adding the two equations will eliminate the variable y.

$$\begin{array}{l} x - y = 0 \\ x + y = 0 \\ \hline 2x = 0 \end{array}$$

Thus, $x = 0$. And so $0 - y = 0 \Rightarrow -y = 0 \Rightarrow y = 0$. The solution is $(0, 0) \Rightarrow$ one solution.

See Figure 49.

51. Multiplying the first equation by −1 and adding the two equations will eliminate both variables.

$$\begin{array}{r} -x + y = -4 \\ \underline{x - y = 1} \\ 0 = -3 \end{array}$$ This is never true ⇒ zero solutions. See Figure 51.

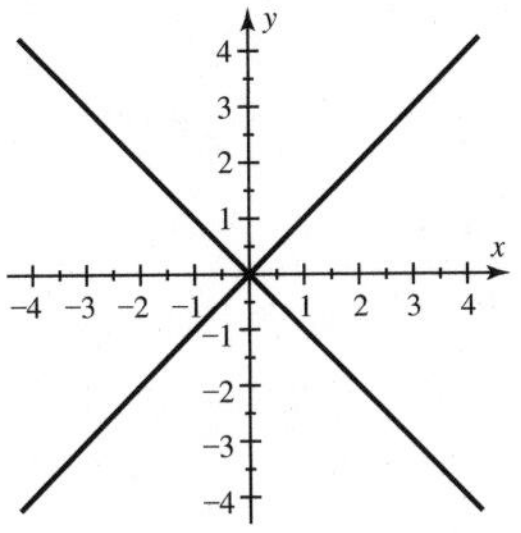

Figure 49

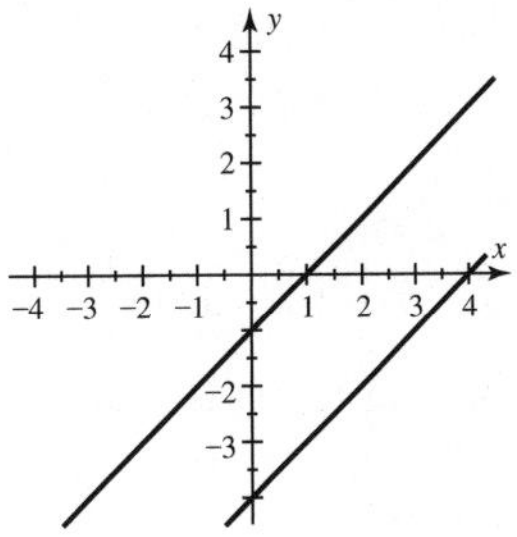

Figure 51

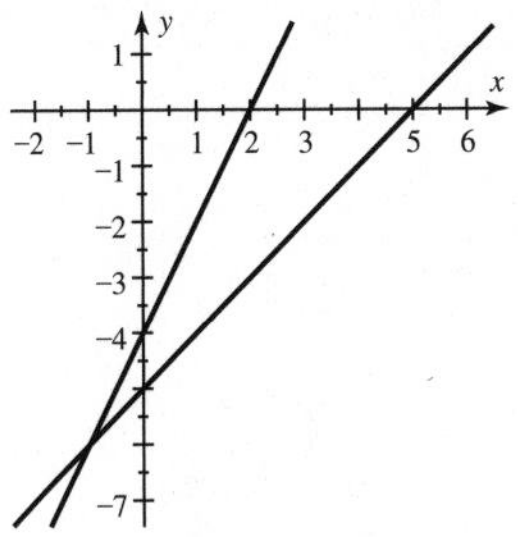

Figure 53

53. Multiplying the first equation by −1 and adding the two equations will eliminate the variable y.

$$\begin{array}{r} -x + y = -5 \\ \underline{2x - y = 4} \\ x = -1 \end{array}$$ And so $-(-1) + y = -5 \Rightarrow 1 + y = -5 \Rightarrow y = -6$. The solution is $(-1, -6) \Rightarrow$ one solution. See Figure 53.

55. Multiplying the first equation by 3, the second by −2 and adding the two equations will eliminate both variables.

$$\begin{array}{r} 12x - 24y = 72 \\ \underline{-12x - 24y = 72} \\ 0 = 0 \end{array}$$ This is always true ⇒ infinitely many solutions. See Figure 55.

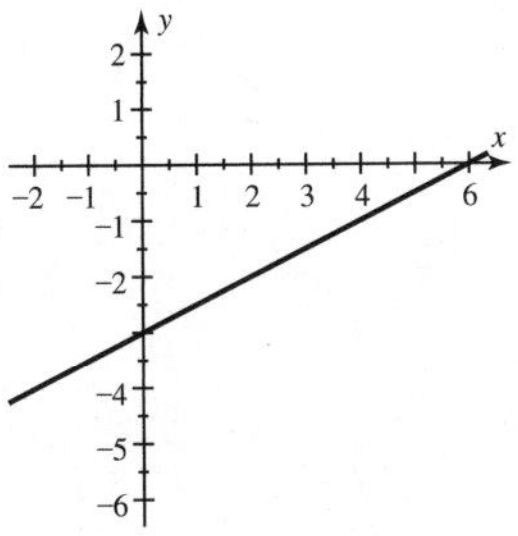

Figure 55

Applications

57. Let x = skin cancer in men and let y = skin cancer in women. Then $x + y = 56{,}400$ and $x = y + 7000$. Note that $x = y + 7000 \Rightarrow x - y = 7000$. Adding the two equations will eliminate the variable y.

$$\begin{array}{r} x + y = 56{,}400 \\ \underline{x - y = 7000} \\ 2x = 63{,}400 \end{array}$$ Thus $x = 31{,}700$. And so $31{,}700 - y = 7000 \Rightarrow -y = -24{,}700 \Rightarrow y = 24{,}700$. Therefore men: 31,700; Women: 24,700.

59. Let x = minutes on a stationary bike and let y = minutes on a stair climber. Then $x + y = 30$ and $9x + 11.5y = 300$. Multiplying the first equation by -9 and adding the two equations will eliminate the variable x.

$$\begin{array}{r} -9x - 9y = -270 \\ 9x + 11.5y = 300 \\ \hline 2.5y = 30 \end{array}$$

Thus $y = 12$. And so $x + 12 = 30 \Rightarrow x = 18$. Therefore bicycle: 18 minutes; stairclimber: 12 minutes.

61. Let x = speed of riverboat and let y = speed of the current. Then $8x + 8y = 64$ and $16x - 16y = 64$. Multiplying the first equation by 2 and adding the two equations will eliminate the variable y.

$$\begin{array}{r} 16x + 16y = 128 \\ 16x - 16y = 64 \\ \hline 32x = 192 \end{array}$$

Thus $x = 6$. And so $8(6) + 8y = 64 \Rightarrow 48 + 8y = 64 \Rightarrow 8y = 16 \Rightarrow y = 2$. Therefore current: 2 mph; boat: 6 mph.

63. Let x = amount of money invested at 3% and let y = amount of money invested at 5%. Then $x + y = 5000$ and $0.03x - 0.05y = 210$. Multiplying the second equation by -20 and adding the two equations will eliminate the variable y.

$$\begin{array}{r} x + y = 5000 \\ -0.6x - y = 4200 \\ \hline 0.4x = 800 \end{array}$$

Thus $x = 2000$. And so $2000 + y = 5000 \Rightarrow y = 3000$. Therefore \$2000 invested at 3%; \$3000 invested at 5%.

65. Let x = one of two integers and let y = the other of two integers. Then $x + y = -17$ and $x - y = 69$. Adding the two equations will eliminate the variable y.

$$\begin{array}{r} x + y = -17 \\ x - y = 69 \\ \hline 2x = 52 \end{array}$$

Thus $x = 26$. And so $26 + y = -17 \Rightarrow y = -43$. Therefore the numbers are -43 and 26.

67. (a) The graphs intersection is 20×40 in.

(b) Note that $l = 2w \Rightarrow -2w + l = 0$, using this and $2w + 2l = 120$ and adding the two equations will eliminate the variable w.

$$\begin{array}{r} -2w + l = 0 \\ 2w + 2l = 120 \\ \hline 3l = 120 \end{array}$$

Thus $l = 40$. And so $2w + 2(40) = 120 \Rightarrow 2w + 80 = 120 \Rightarrow 2w = 40 \Rightarrow w = 20$. Therefore $l = 40$ and $w = 20$ so 20×40 in.

4.4: Systems of Linear Inequalities

Concepts

1. All points below and including the line $y = k$.

3. All points above and including the line $y = x$.

5. dashed

7. $Ax + By = C$

Solutions to Linear Inequalities

9. Yes, $3 > 2$ is true.

11. No, $0 \geq 2$ is false.

13. No, $4 \geq 5$ is false.

15. Yes, $0 < 3 - 1 \Rightarrow 0 < 2$ is true.

17. Yes, $-2 + 6 \leq 4 \Rightarrow 4 \leq 4$ is true.

19. No, $2(-1) + (-1) \geq -1 \Rightarrow -2 + (-1) \geq -1 \Rightarrow -3 \geq -1$ is false.

21. *Answers may vary.* (3, 1), because $3 > 2$ is true. Shade side of the line with point (3, 1). See Figure 21.

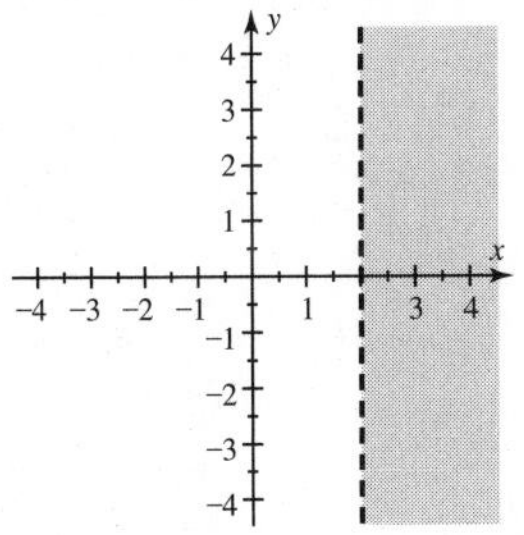

Figure 21

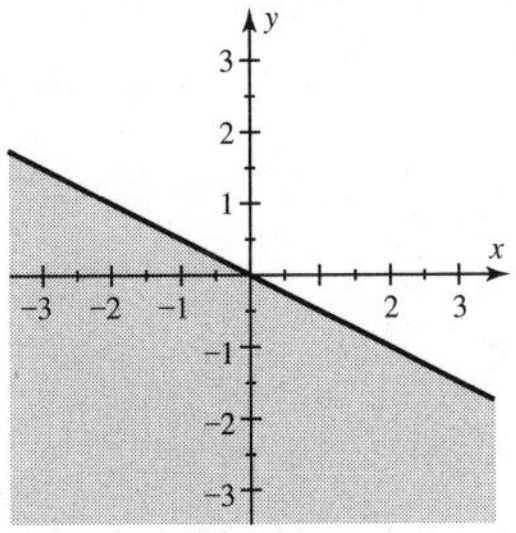

Figure 23

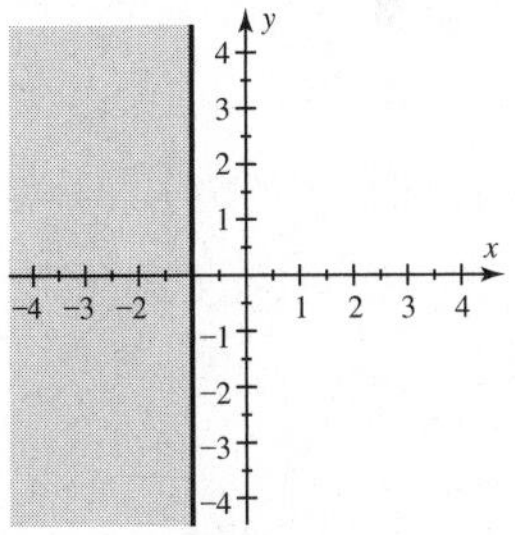

Figure 43

23. *Answers may vary.* (−2, −1), because $\frac{1}{2}(-2) + (-1) \leq 0 \Rightarrow -2 \leq 0$ is true. Shade side of the line with point (−2, −1). See Figure 23.

25. Yes, because $3 - 1 < 3 \Rightarrow 2 < 3$ is true and $3 + 1 > 3 \Rightarrow 4 > 3$ is true.

27. No, because $3(-2) - 2(3) \geq 1 \Rightarrow -6 - 6 \geq 1 \Rightarrow -12 \geq 1$ is false.

29. Yes, because $4 - 2(-2) \geq 8 \Rightarrow 4 + 4 \geq 8 \Rightarrow 8 \geq 8$ is true and $-2(4) - 5(-2) > 0 \Rightarrow -8 + 10 > 0 \Rightarrow 2 > 0$ is true.

31. The region containing (1, 2), because $1 \leq 2$ is true and $1 + 2 \geq 2 \Rightarrow 3 \geq 2$ is true.

33. The region containing (1, 0), because $1 + 0 \leq 3 \Rightarrow 1 \leq 3$ is true and $0 \leq 2(1) \Rightarrow 0 \leq 2$ is true.

35. $x > 1$

37. $y \geq 2$

39. $y < x$

41. $-x + y \leq 1$

43. See Figure 43.

45. See Figure 45.

47. See Figure 47.

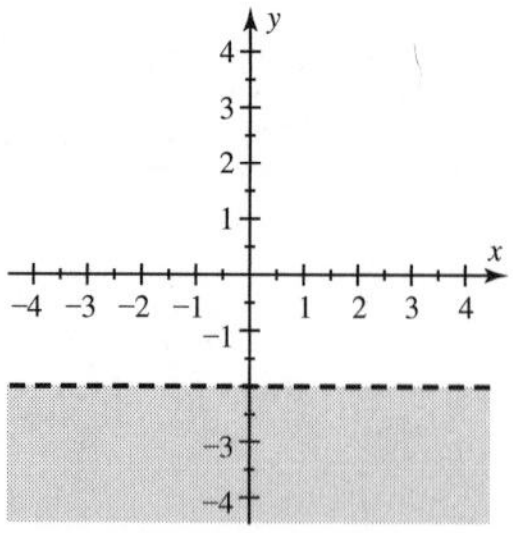

Figure 45

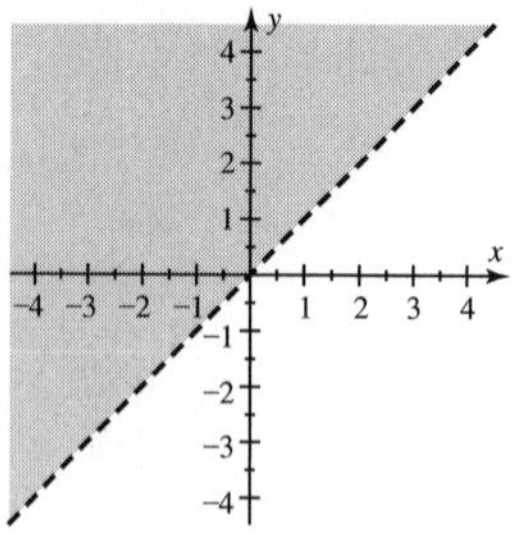

Figure 47

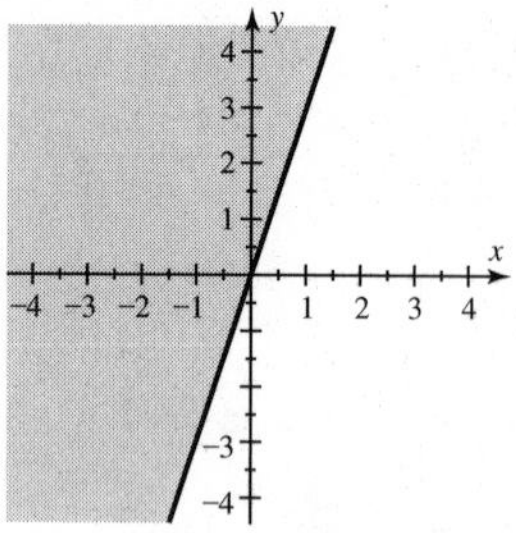

Figure 49

49. See Figure 49.

51. See Figure 51.

53. See Figure 53.

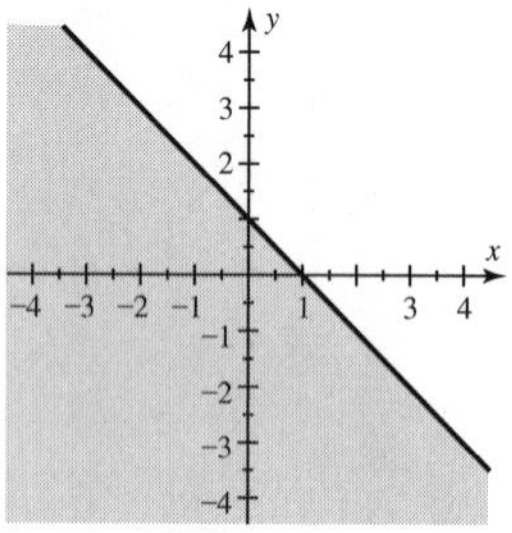

Figure 51

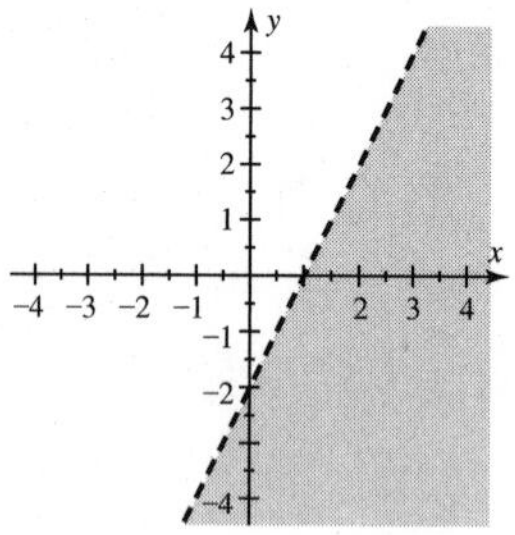

Figure 53

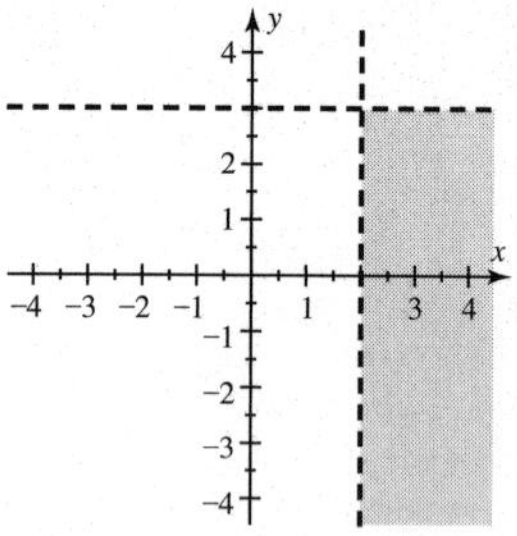

Figure 55

55. See Figure 55.

57. See Figure 57.

59. See Figure 59.

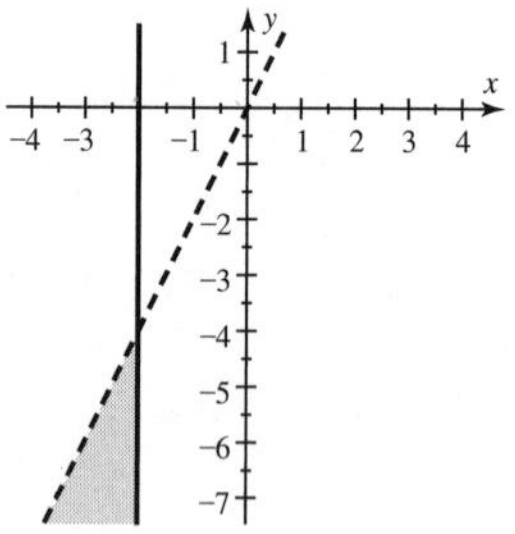

Figure 57

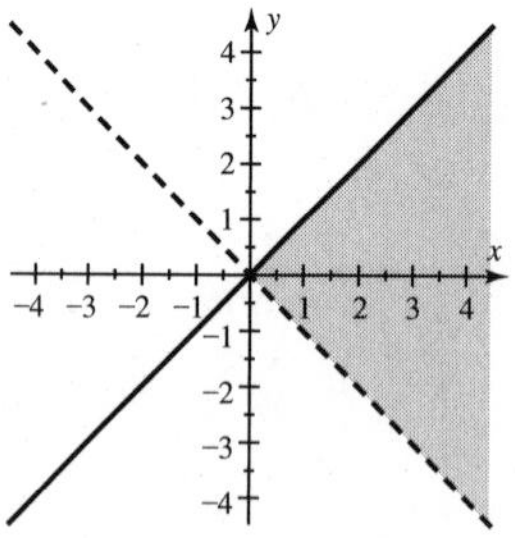

Figure 59

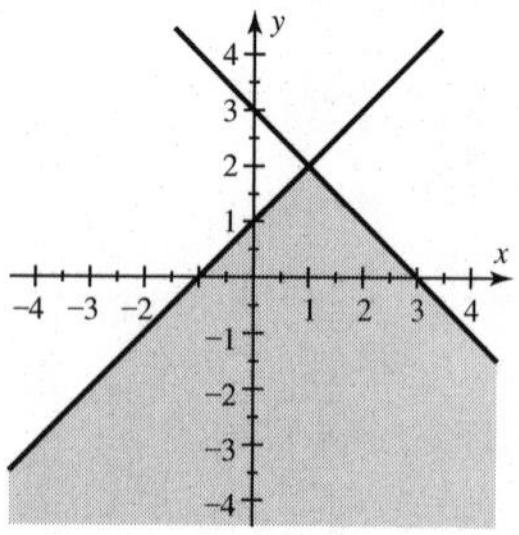

Figure 61

61. See Figure 61.

63. See Figure 63.

65. See Figure 65.

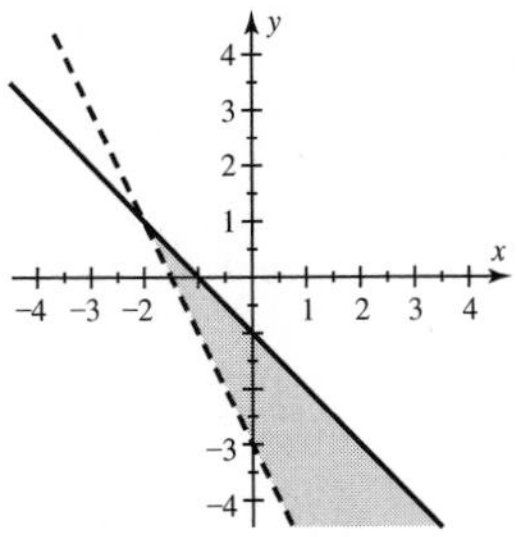

Figure 63

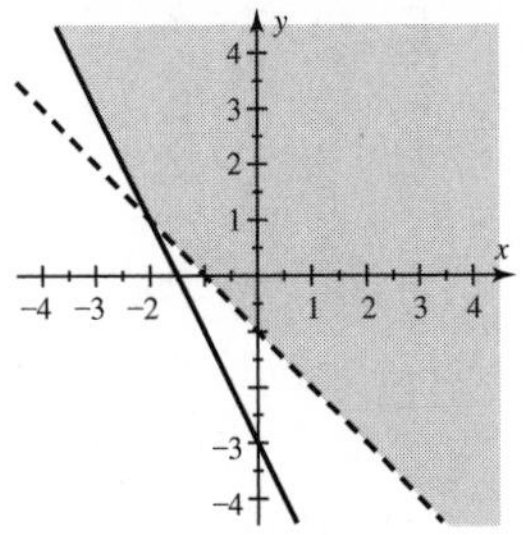

Figure 65

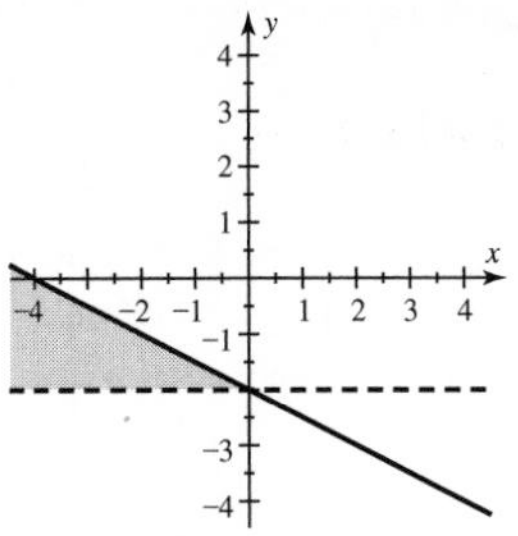

Figure 67

67. See Figure 67.

69. See Figure 69.

71. See Figure 71.

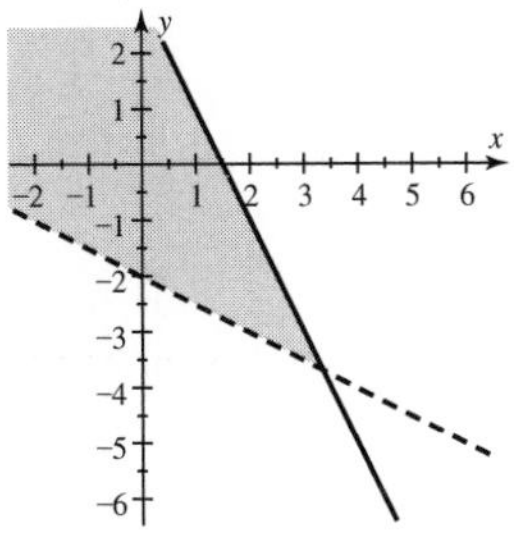

Figure 69

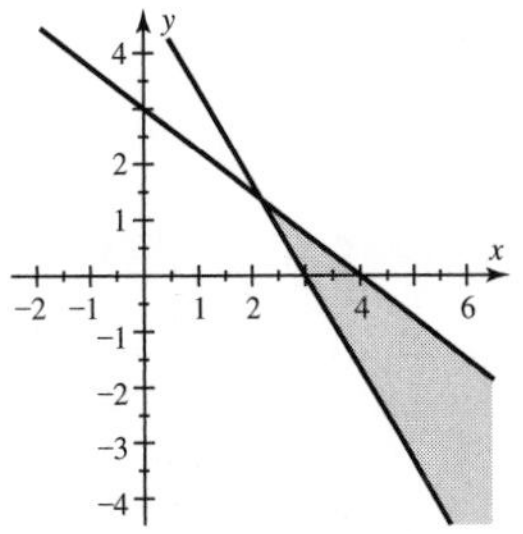

Figure 71

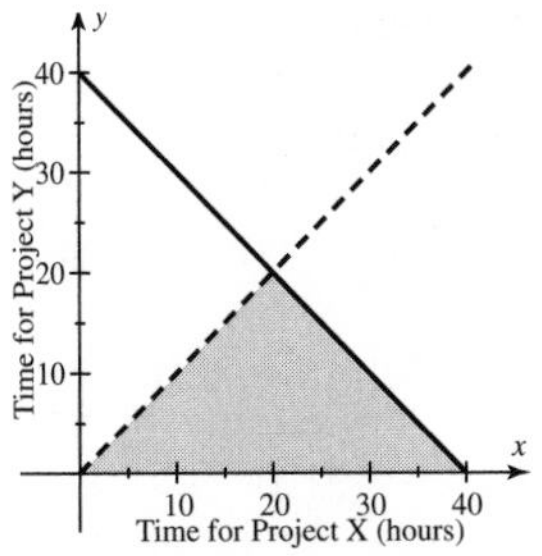

Figure 73

Applications

73. Graph the system, $x > y$ and $x + y \leq 40$. See Figure 73.

75. (a) $R = 220 - 20 \Rightarrow R = 200$ bpm for a 20 year old person and $R = 220 - 70 \Rightarrow R = 150$ bpm for a 70 year old person.

  (b) See Figure 75.

  (c) The shaded region represents possible heart rates for ages 20 to 70.

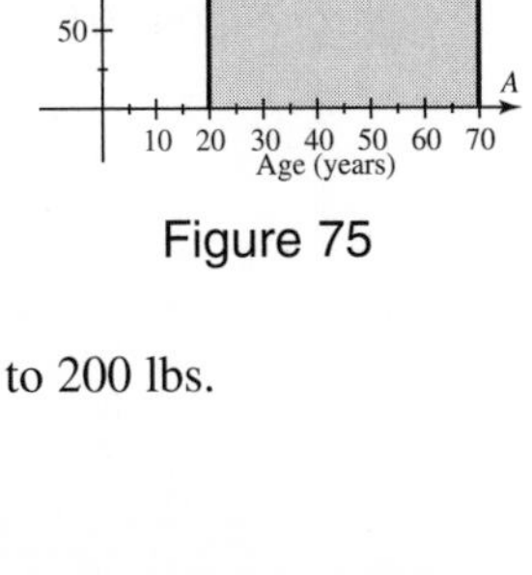

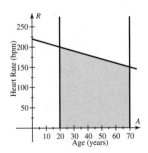

Figure 75

77. 150 to 200 lbs.

Checking Basic Concepts for Sections 4.3 & 4.4

1. Multiplying the second equation by −2 and adding the two equations will eliminate the variable x.

$$\begin{array}{r} 2x + 3y = 5 \\ -2x + 14y = 12 \\ \hline 17y = 17 \end{array}$$

Thus $y = 1$. And so $x - 7(1) = -6 \Rightarrow x = 1$. The solution is $(1, 1)$.

2. (a) Multiplying the first equation by −1 and adding the two equations will eliminate the variable x.

$$\begin{array}{r} -x - y = 1 \\ x - 2y = 2 \\ \hline -3y = 3 \end{array}$$

Thus $y = -1$. And so $x - 2(-1) = 2 \Rightarrow x + 2 = 2 \Rightarrow x = 0$. The solution is $(0, -1)$.

There is one solution.

(b) Adding the two equations will eliminate both variables.

$$\begin{array}{r} 5x - 6y = 4 \\ -5x + 6y = 1 \\ \hline 0 = 5 \end{array}$$

This is false, therefore there are no solutions.

(c) Multiplying the first equation by −2 and adding the two equations will eliminate both variables.

$$\begin{array}{r} -2x + 6y = 0 \\ 2x - 6y = 0 \\ \hline 0 = 0 \end{array}$$

This is true, therefore there are infinitely many solutions.

3. Substituting $y = 2x$ into the first equation yields the following: $-2x + (2x) = 0 \Rightarrow 0 = 0$. This is true $\Rightarrow$ infinitely many solutions. Graph the system. See Figure 3a. Line coincides $\Rightarrow$ infinitely many solutions. Numerically: See Figure 3b. Since for all values of x both equations produce the same solutions $\Rightarrow$ infinitely many solutions.

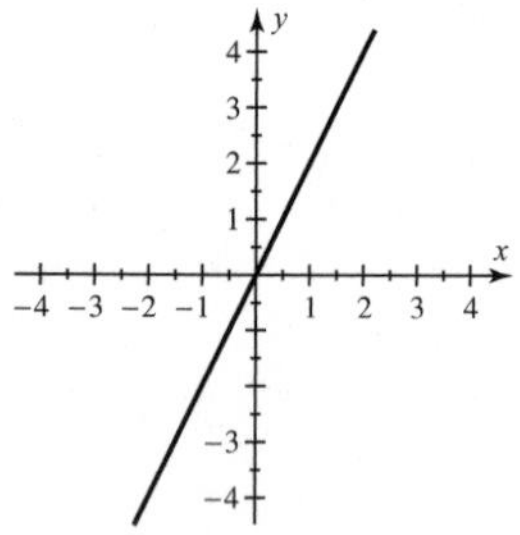

Figure 3a

x	0	1	2	3
$y = 2x$	0	2	4	6
$y = 2x$	0	2	4	6

Figure 3b

4. (a) See Figure 4a.

(b) See Figure 4b.

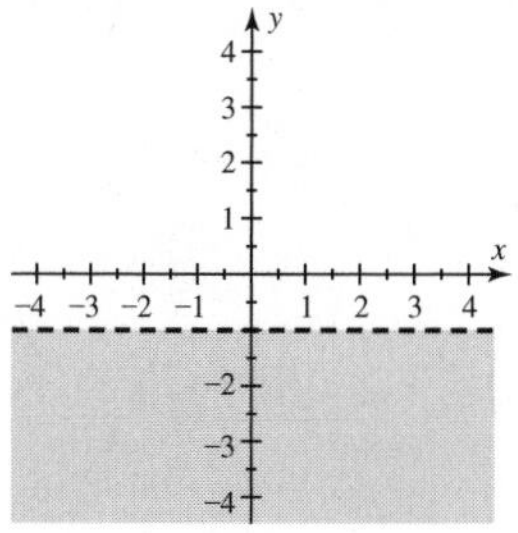

Figure 4a

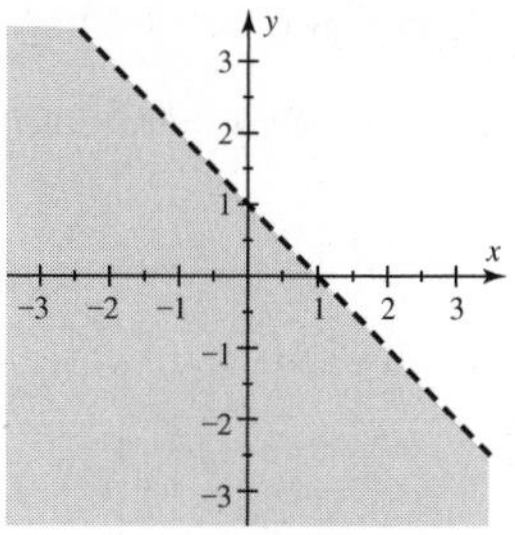

Figure 4b

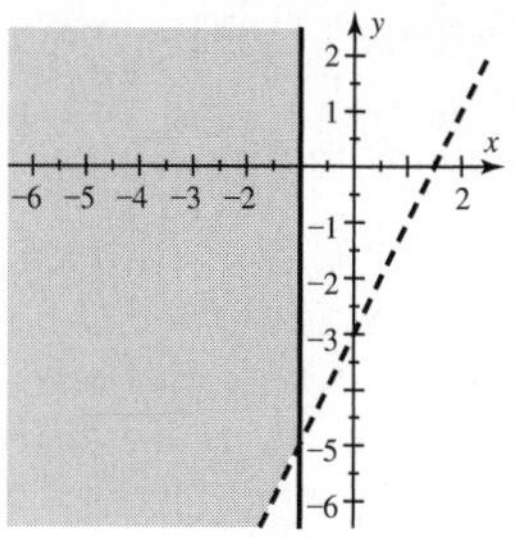

Figure 5

5. See Figure 5.
6. (a) $x + y = 11$

   $x = y + 5$ or $x - y = 5$.

   (b) Substituting $x = y + 5$ into the first equation yields the following: $(y + 5) + y = 11 \Rightarrow$ $2y + 5 = 11 \Rightarrow 2y = 6 \Rightarrow y = 3$. And so $x + 3 = 11 \Rightarrow x = 8$. The solution is (8, 3) or New York has a population of 8 million people and Chicago has a population of 3 million people.

Chapter 4 Review Exercises

Section 4.1

1. Graph the system $y = 3$ and $y = 2x - 3$. See Figure 1. The intersection and solution is $(3, 3) \Rightarrow x = 3$.

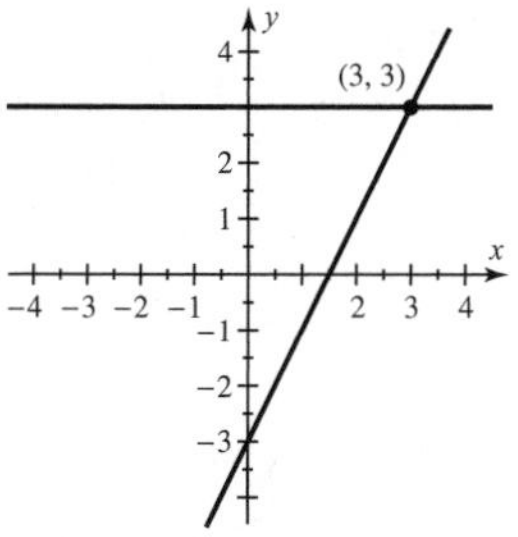

Figure 1

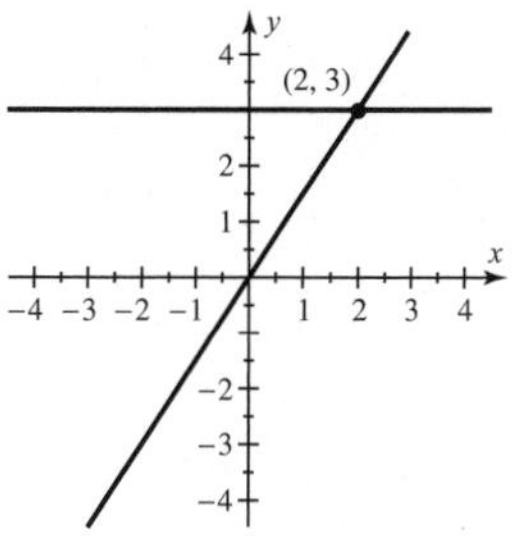

Figure 2

2. Graph the system $y = 3$ and $y = \frac{3}{2}x$. See Figure 2. The intersection and solution is $(2, 3) \Rightarrow x = 2$.
3. (1, 2), because $1 + 2(2) = 5 \Rightarrow 1 + 4 = 5$ is true and $1 - (2) = -1$ is true.
4. (5, 2), because $2(5) - 2 = 8 \Rightarrow 10 - 2 = 8$ is true and $5 + 3(2) = 11 \Rightarrow 5 + 6 = 11$ is true.
5. (4, 3), because $\frac{1}{2}(4) = 3 - 1 \Rightarrow 2 = 2$ is true and $2(4) = 3(3) - 1 \Rightarrow 8 = 9 - 1$ is true.
6. (2, −4), because $5(2) - 2(-4) = 18 \Rightarrow 10 + 8 = 18$ is true and $-4 = -2(2)$ is true.
7. The intersection and solution is (2, 2). Checking: $2 = 2$ is true and $-2(2) + 2 = -2 \Rightarrow -4 + 2 = -2$ is true.
8. The intersection and solution is (1, 2). Checking: $1 + 2 = 3$ is true and $2 = 2(1)$ is true.
9. Since when $x = 2$, $y = 6$ for both equations $\Rightarrow$ the solution is (2, 6).
10. Since when $x = 1$, $y = 1$ for both equations $\Rightarrow$ the solution is (1, 1).

11. Graph the system. See Figure 11. The intersection and solution is $(4, -3)$.

12. Graph the system. See Figure 12. The intersection and solution is $(1, 2)$.

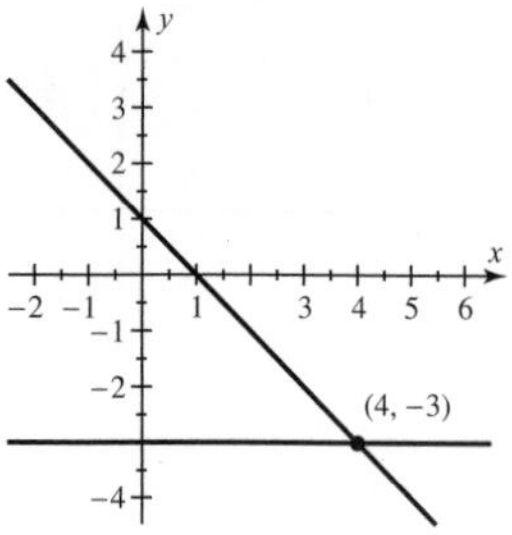

Figure 11

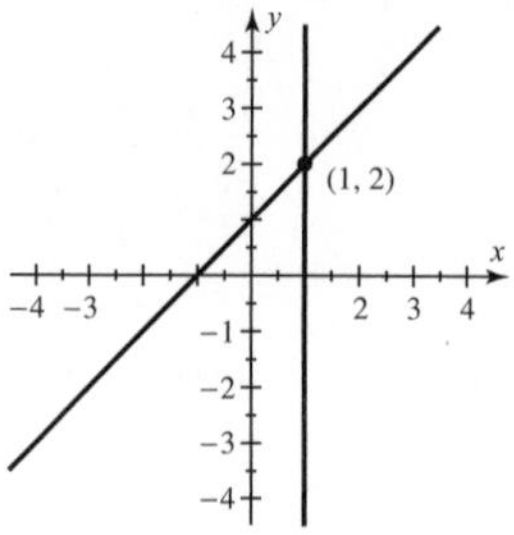

Figure 12

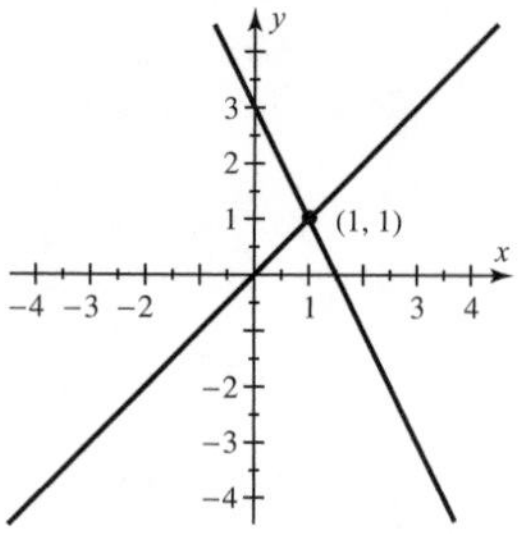

Figure 13

13. Graph the system. See Figure 13. The intersection and solution is $(1, 1)$.

14. Graph the system. See Figure 14. The intersection and solution is $(1, 2)$.

15. Graph the system. See Figure 15. The intersection and solution is $(1, 1)$.

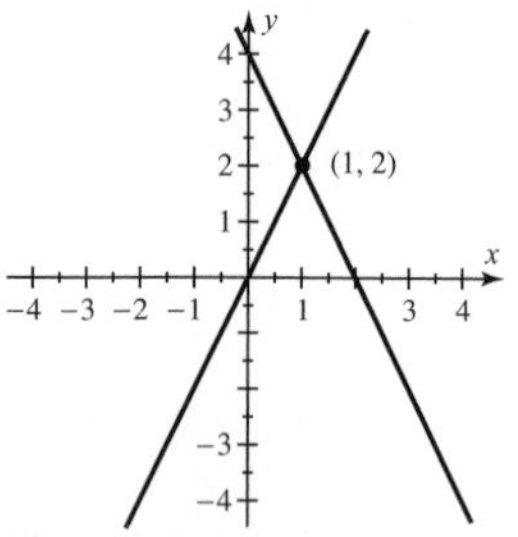

Figure 14

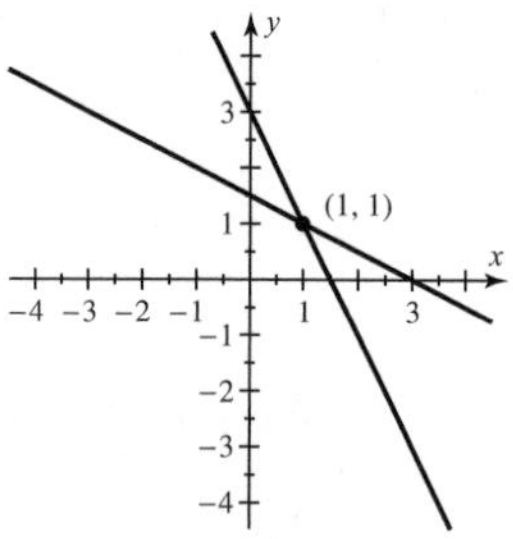

Figure 15

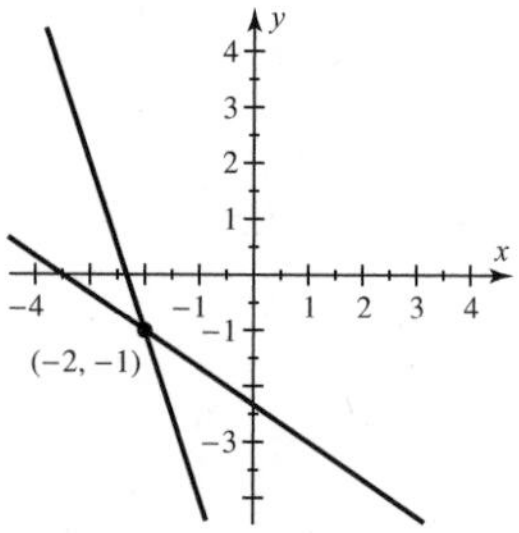

Figure 16

16. Graph the system. See Figure 16. The intersection and solution is $(-2, -1)$.

Section 4.2

17. Substituting $y = 3x$ into the first equation yields the following: $x + (3x) = 8 \Rightarrow 4x = 8 \Rightarrow x = 2$, and so $y = 3(2) \Rightarrow y = 6$. The solution is $(2, 6)$.

18. Substituting $y = -5x$ into the first equation yields the following: $x - 2(-5x) = 22 \Rightarrow x + 10x = 22 \Rightarrow 11x = 22 \Rightarrow x = 2$, and so $y = -5(2) \Rightarrow y = -10$. The solution is $(2, -10)$.

19. Note that $2x + y = 5 \Rightarrow y = -2x + 5$. Substituting $y = -2x + 5$ into the second equation yields the following: $-3x + (-2x + 5) = 0 \Rightarrow -5x + 5 = 0 \Rightarrow -5x = -5 \Rightarrow x = 1$, and so $y = -2(1) + 5 \Rightarrow y = 3$. The solution is $(1, 3)$.

20. Note that $x - y = -5 \Rightarrow x = y - 5$. Substituting $x = y - 5$ into the first equation yields the following: $3(y - 5) - y = 5 \Rightarrow 3y - 15 - y = 5 \Rightarrow 2y = 20 \Rightarrow y = 10$, and so $x = 10 - 5 \Rightarrow x = 5$. The solution is $(5, 10)$.

21. Note that $x + 3y = 1 \Rightarrow x = -3y + 1$. Substituting $x = -3y + 1$ into the second equation yields the following: $-2(-3y + 1) + 2y = 6 \Rightarrow 6y - 2 + 2y = 6 \Rightarrow 8y - 2 = 6 \Rightarrow 8y = 8 \Rightarrow y = 1$, and so $x = -3(1) + 1 \Rightarrow x = -2$. The solution is $(-2, 1)$.

22. Note that $2x - y = -4 \Rightarrow -y = -2x - 4 \Rightarrow y = 2x + 4$. Substituting $y = 2x + 4$ into the first equation yields the following: $3x - 2(2x + 4) = -4 \Rightarrow 3x - 4x - 8 = -4 \Rightarrow -x - 8 = -4 \Rightarrow -x = 4 \Rightarrow x = -4$, and so $y = 2(-4) + 4 \Rightarrow y = -8 + 4 \Rightarrow y = -4$. The solution is $(-4, -4)$.

23. (a) Parallel lines so zero solutions.

    (b) No solutions so inconsistent.

24. (a) An intersection so one solution.

    (b) One solution is consistent and dependent.

25. (a) Coinciding lines so infinitely many solutions.

    (b) Infinitely many solutions is consistent and dependent.

26. (a) parallel lines so no solutions.

    (b) No solutions is inconsistent.

27. Substituting $y = -x$ into the first equation yields the following: $x + (-x) = 2 \Rightarrow 0 = 2$. This is not true $\Rightarrow$ no solutions. See Figure 27. The lines are parallel so no solutions.

28. Substituting $x + y = -2 \Rightarrow y = -x - 2$ into the second equation yields the following: $x + (-x - 2) = 3 \Rightarrow -2 = 3$. This is not true $\Rightarrow$ no solutions. See Figure 28. The lines are parallel so no solutions.

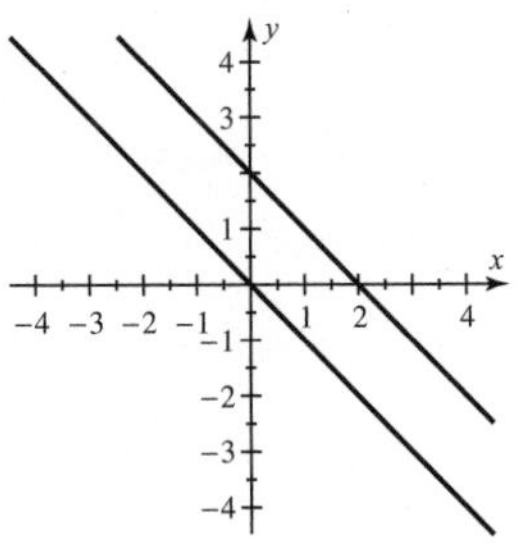

Figure 27

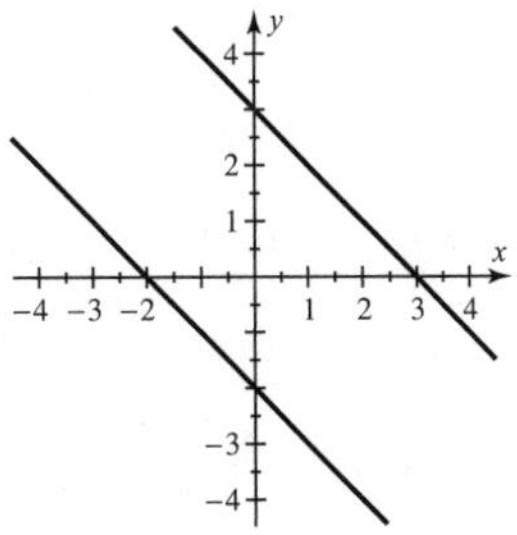

Figure 28

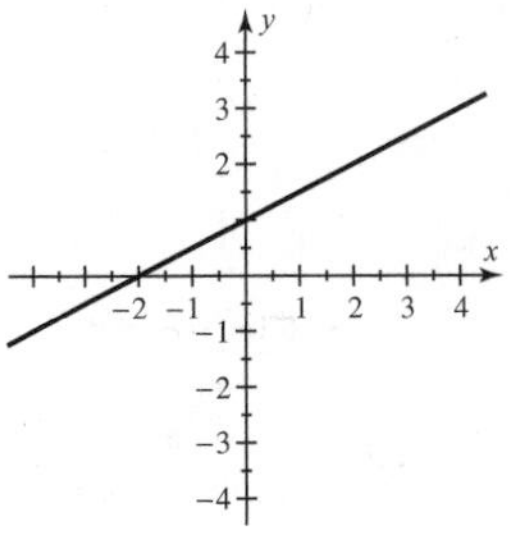

Figure 29

29. Note that $x - 2y = -2 \Rightarrow x = 2y - 2$. Substituting $x = 2y - 2$ into the first equation yields the following: $-(2y - 2) + 2y = 2 \Rightarrow -2y + 2 + 2y = 2 \Rightarrow 2 = 2$. This is true $\Rightarrow$ infinitely many solutions. See Figure 29. The lines coincide, so there are infinitely many solutions.

30. Note that $-x - y = -2 \Rightarrow -y = x - 2 \Rightarrow y = -x + 2$. Substituting $y = -x + 2$ into the second equation yields the following: $2x - (-x + 2) = 1 \Rightarrow 2x + x - 2 = 1 \Rightarrow 3x = 3 \Rightarrow x = 1$, and so $y = -1 + 2 \Rightarrow y = 1$. The solution is $(1, 1)$. See Figure 30. The lines intersect at the solution $(1, 1)$.

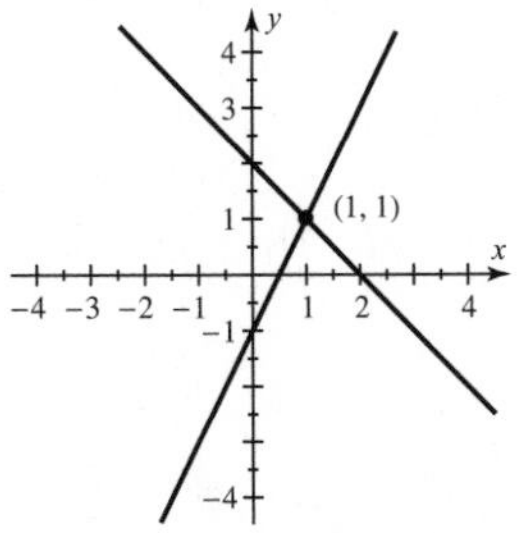

Figure 30

Section 4.3

31. The lines intersect at the solution (2, 1). Adding the two equations will eliminate the variable y.

$$\begin{array}{r} x + y = 3 \\ x - y = 1 \\ \hline 2x = 4 \end{array}$$

Thus $x = 2$. And so $2 + y = 3 \Rightarrow y = 1$. The solution is (2, 1).

32. The lines intersect at the solution $(-1, 2)$. Multiplying the second equation by -2 and adding the two equations will eliminate the variable x.

$$\begin{array}{r} 2x + 3y = 4 \\ -2x + 4y = 10 \\ \hline 7y = 14 \end{array}$$

Thus $y = 2$. And so $2x + 3(2) = 4 \Rightarrow 2x + 6 = 4 \Rightarrow 2x = -2 \Rightarrow x = -1$. The solution is $(-1, 2)$.

33. Adding the two equations will eliminate the variable y.

$$\begin{array}{r} x + y = 10 \\ x - y = 12 \\ \hline 2x = 22 \end{array}$$

Thus $x = 11$. And so $11 + y = 10 \Rightarrow y = -1$. The solution is $(11, -1)$.

34. Adding the two equations will eliminate the variable y.

$$\begin{array}{r} 2x - y = 2 \\ 3x + y = 3 \\ \hline 5x = 5 \end{array}$$

Thus $x = 1$. And so $2(1) - y = 2 \Rightarrow 2 - y = 2 \Rightarrow -y = 0 \Rightarrow y = 0$. The solution is (1, 0).

35. Multiplying the second equation by 2 and adding the two equations will eliminate the variable x.

$$\begin{array}{r} -2x + 2y = -1 \\ 2x - 6y = -6 \\ \hline -4y = -7 \end{array}$$

Thus $y = \frac{7}{4}$. And so $-2x + 2\left(\frac{7}{4}\right) = -1 \Rightarrow -2x + \frac{14}{4} = -1 \Rightarrow -2x = -\frac{18}{4} \Rightarrow x = \frac{9}{4}$.

The solution is $\left(\frac{9}{4}, \frac{7}{4}\right)$.

36. Multiplying the first equation by -1 and adding the two equations will eliminate the variable x.

$$\begin{array}{r} -2x + 5y = 0 \\ 2x + 4y = 9 \\ \hline 9y = 9 \end{array}$$

Thus $y = 1$. And so $2x + 4(1) = 9 \Rightarrow 2x + 4 = 9 \Rightarrow 2x = 5 \Rightarrow x = \frac{5}{2}$.

The solution is $\left(\frac{5}{2}, 1\right)$.

37. Multiplying the first equation by 2 and adding the two equations will eliminate the variable b.

$$\begin{array}{r} 4a + 2b = 6 \\ -3a - 2b = -1 \\ \hline a = 5 \end{array}$$

And so $4(5) + 2b = 6 \Rightarrow 20 + 2b = 6 \Rightarrow 2b = -14 \Rightarrow b = -7$. The solution is $(5, -7)$.

38. Multiplying the first equation by -3 and adding the two equations will eliminate the variable a.

$$\begin{array}{r} -3a + 9b = -6 \\ 3a + b = 26 \\ \hline 10b = 20 \end{array}$$

Thus $b = 2$. And so $3a + 2 = 26 \Rightarrow 3a = 24 \Rightarrow a = 8$. The solution is (8, 2).

39. Multiplying the first equation by 2, the second equation by 5 and adding the two equations will eliminate the variable r.

$$\begin{array}{r} 10r + 6t = -2 \\ -10r - 25t = -55 \\ \hline -19t = -57 \end{array}$$

Thus $t = 3$. And so $10r + 6(3) = -2 \Rightarrow 10r + 18 = -2 \Rightarrow 10r = -20 \Rightarrow r = -2$. The solution is $(-2, 3)$.

40. Multiplying the first equation by 7, the second equation by 2 and adding the two equations will eliminate the variable t.

$$\begin{array}{r} 35r + 14t = 35 \\ 6r - 14t = 6 \\ \hline 41r = 41 \end{array}$$

Thus $r = 1$. And so $6(1) - 14t = 6 \Rightarrow 6 - 14t = 6 \Rightarrow -14t = 0 \Rightarrow t = 0$. The solution is $(1, 0)$.

41. (a) Adding the two equations will eliminate the variable y.

$$\begin{array}{r} 3x + y = 6 \\ x - y = -2 \\ \hline 4x = 4 \end{array}$$

Thus $x = 1$. And so $1 - y = -2 \Rightarrow -y = -3 \Rightarrow y = 3$. The solution is $(1, 3)$.

(b) See Figure 41b. The intersection and solution is $(1, 3)$.

(c) See Figure 41c. Since when $x = 1$, $y = 3$ for both equations the solution is $(1, 3)$.

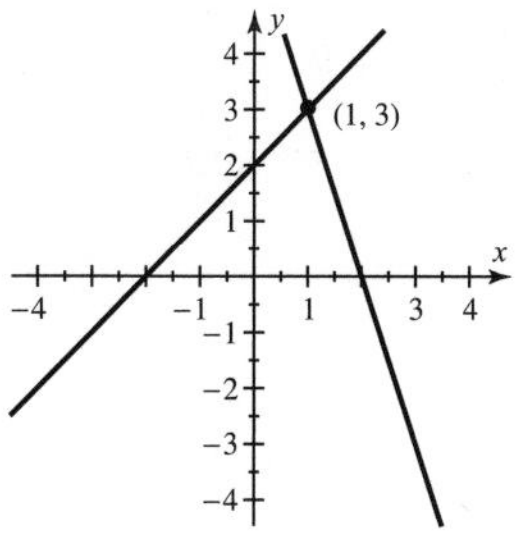

Figure 41b

x	−1	0	1	2
$y = 6 - 3x$	9	6	3	0
$y = x + 2$	1	2	3	4

Figure 41c

42. (a) Multiplying the second equation by 2 and adding the two equations will eliminate the variable x.

$$\begin{array}{r} 2x + y = 3 \\ -2x + 4y = -8 \\ \hline 5y = -5 \end{array}$$

Thus $y = -1$. And so $2x - 1 = 3 \Rightarrow 2x = 4 \Rightarrow x = 2$. The solution is $(2, -1)$.

(b) See Figure 42b. The intersection and solution is $(2, -1)$.

(c) See Figure 42c. Since when $x = 2$, $y = -1$ for both equations the solution is $(2, -1)$.

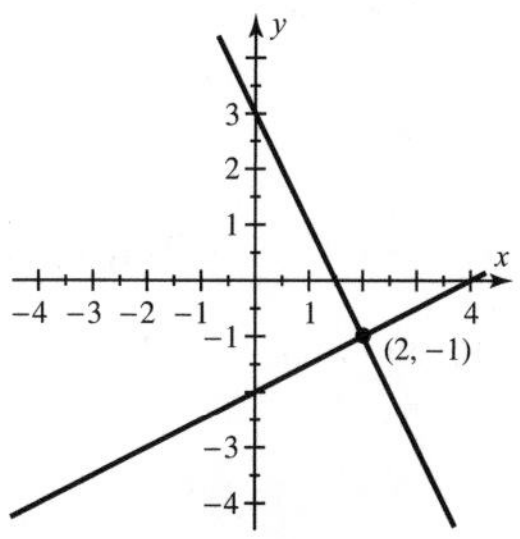

Figure 42b

x	−2	0	2	4
$y = 3 - 2x$	7	3	−1	−5
$y = (x - 4)/2$	−3	−2	−1	0

Figure 42c

43. Adding the two equations will eliminate both variables.

$$\begin{array}{r} x - y = 5 \\ -x + y = -5 \\ \hline 0 = 0 \end{array}$$ Since this is true, there are infinitely many solutions.

44. Multiplying the second equation by 3 and adding the two equations will eliminate both variables.

$$\begin{array}{r} 3x - 3y = 0 \\ -3x + 3y = 0 \\ \hline 0 = 0 \end{array}$$ Since this is true, there are infinitely many solutions.

45. Adding the two equations will eliminate both variables.

$$\begin{array}{r} -2x + y = 3 \\ 2x - y = 3 \\ \hline 0 = 6 \end{array}$$ Since this is false, there are zero solutions.

46. Adding the two equations will eliminate the variable y.

$$\begin{array}{r} -2x + y = 2 \\ 3x - y = 3 \\ \hline x = 5 \end{array}$$ And so $3(5) - y = 3 \Rightarrow 15 - y = 3 \Rightarrow -y = -12 \Rightarrow y = 12$. The solution is $(5, 12)$, therefore there is one solution.

Section 4.4

47. Yes, because $-3 \leq 2$ is true.

48. No, because $-1 > -1$ is false.

49. No, because $1 + 2 < -2$ is false.

50. Yes, because $2(1) - 3(-4) \geq 2 \Rightarrow 2 + 12 \geq 2$ is true.

51. Point $(1, -2)$ is a solution because $-2 \leq -1$ is true. See Figure 51.

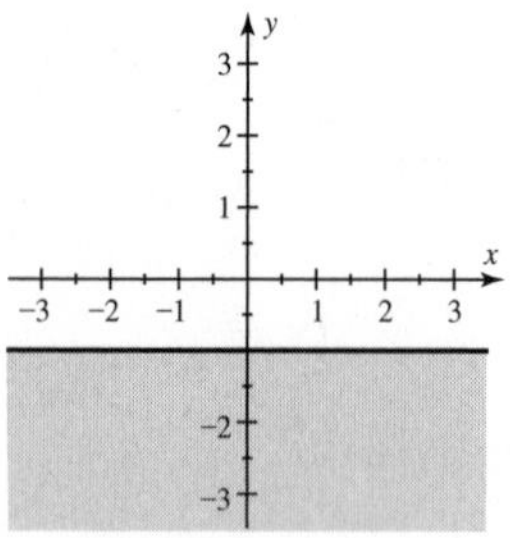

Figure 51

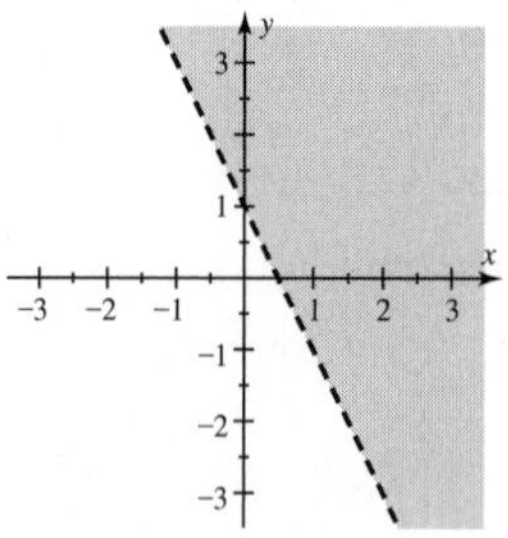

Figure 52

52. Point $(1, 1)$ is a solution because $2(1) + 1 > 1$ is true. See Figure 52.

53. Yes, because $1 - 2(-2) > 3 \Rightarrow 1 + 4 > 3$ is true and $2(1) + (-2) < 3 \Rightarrow 0 < 3$ is true.

54. No, because $4 - (-3) \geq 1 \Rightarrow 4 + 3 \geq 1$ is true but $4(4) + 3(-3) \leq 4 \Rightarrow 16 - 9 \leq 4$is false.

55. The region containing $(2, -2)$, because $-2 < 1$ is true and $2(2) + (-2) \geq -1 \Rightarrow 4 - 2 \geq -1$ is true.

56. The region containing (1, 3), because $3 \geq 1$ is true and $1 + 3 \geq 2$ is true.

57. $y > 1$

58. $y \leq 2x + 1$

59. See Figure 59.

60. See Figure 60.

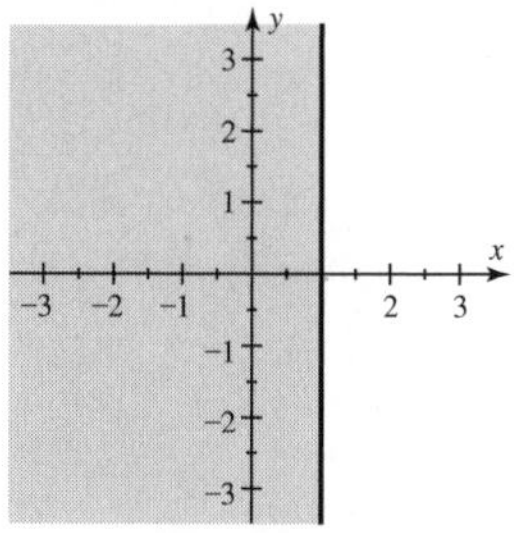

Figure 59

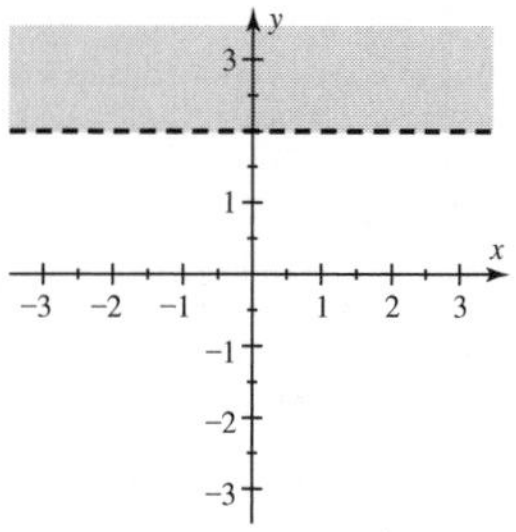

Figure 60

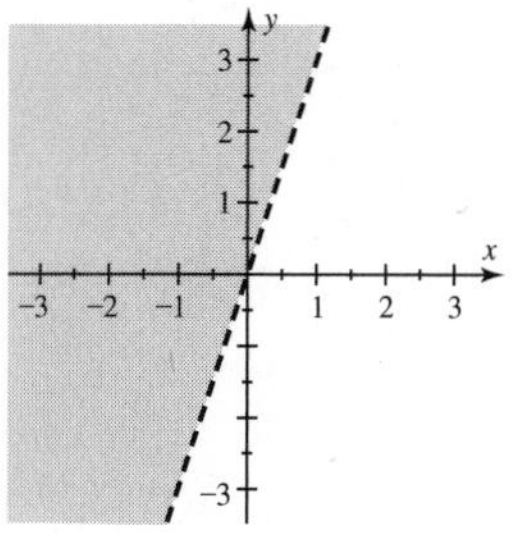

Figure 61

61. See Figure 61.

62. See Figure 62.

63. See Figure 63.

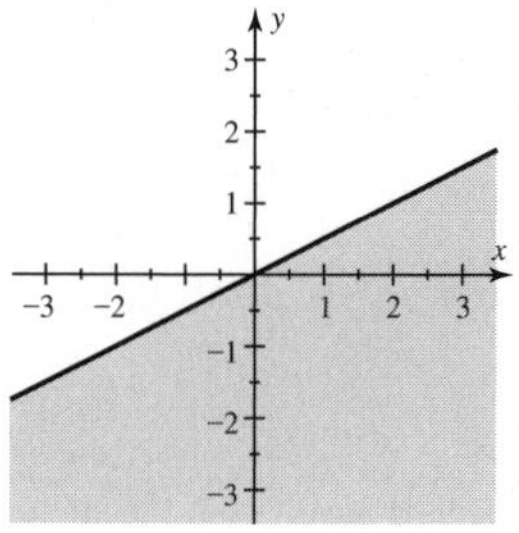

Figure 62

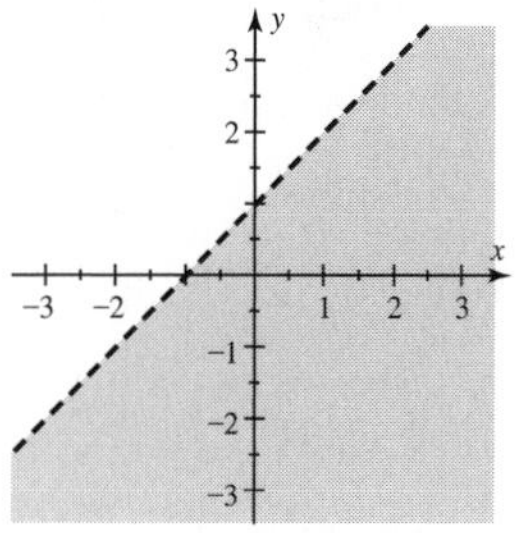

Figure 63

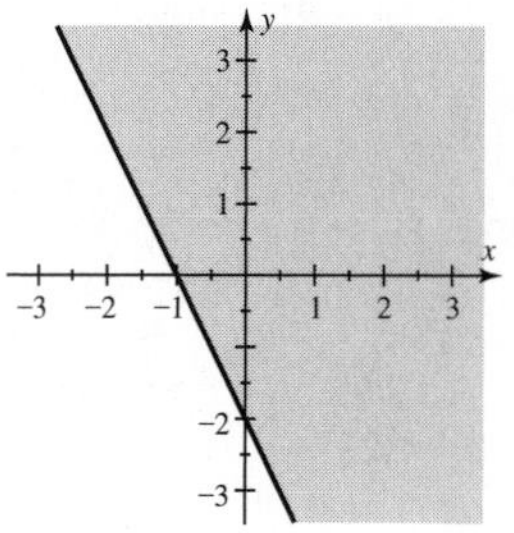

Figure 64

64. See Figure 64.

65. See Figure 65.

66. See Figure 66.

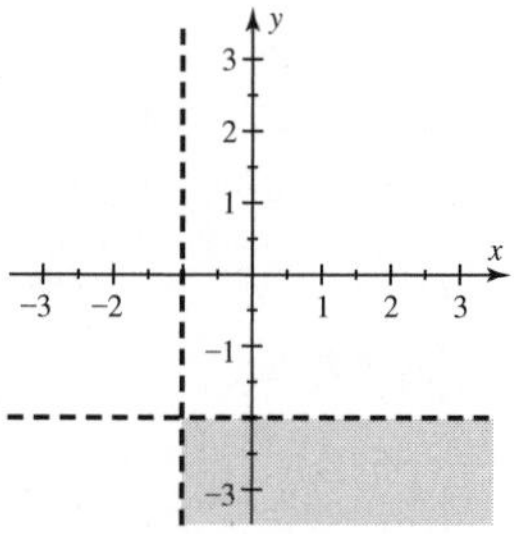

Figure 65

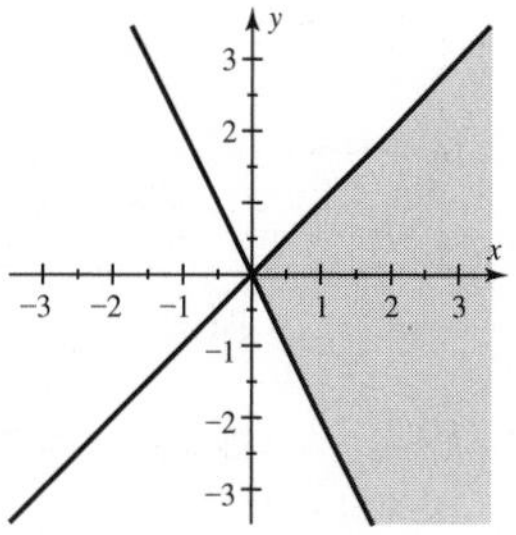

Figure 66

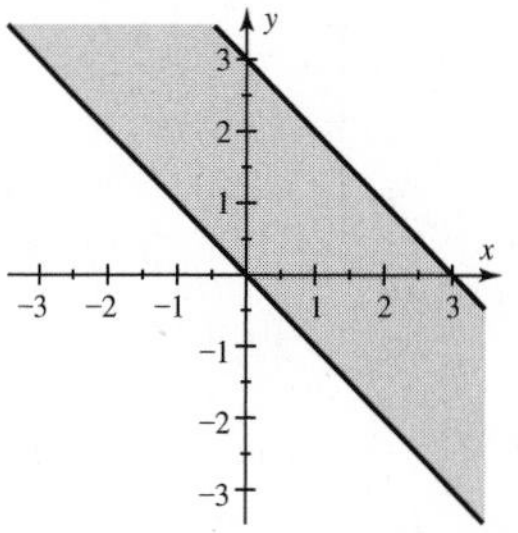

Figure 67

67. See Figure 67.

68. See Figure 68.

69. See Figure 69.

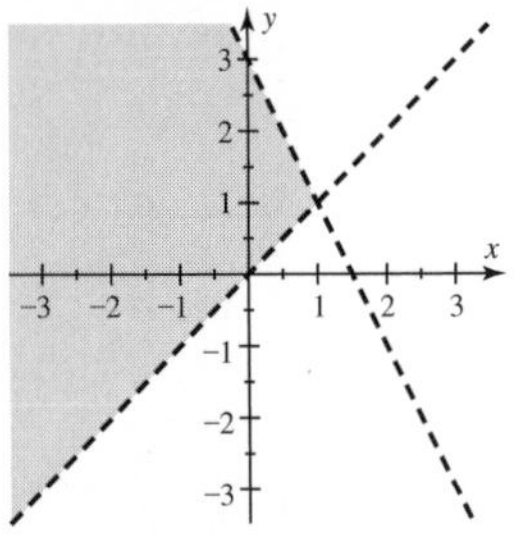
Figure 68

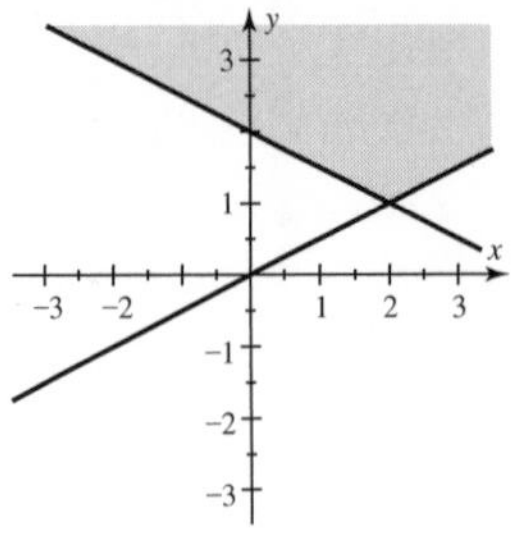
Figure 69

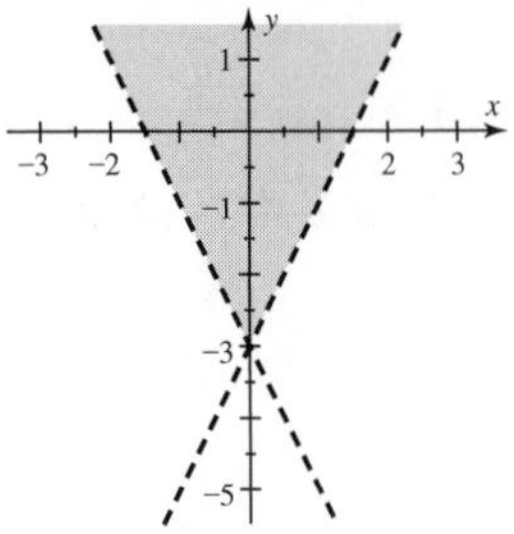
Figure 70

70. See Figure 70.

Applications

71. Let x = number of motor vehicle deaths in 1912 and let y = number of motor vehicle deaths in 1999. Then $13.3x = y$ and $y = x + 38{,}130$. Substituting $13.3x = y$ into the second equation yields the following: $13.3x = x + 38{,}130 \Rightarrow 12.3x = 38{,}130 \Rightarrow x = 3100$, and so $y = 3100 + 38{,}130 \Rightarrow y = 41{,}230$. Therefore 3100 deaths in 1912 and 41,230 deaths in 1999.

72. Let x = lung cancer cases in men and let y = lung cancer cases in women. Then $x + y = 185{,}000$ and $x = y + 20{,}000$. Substituting $x = y + 20{,}000$ into the first equation yields the following: $(y + 20{,}000) + y = 185{,}000 \Rightarrow 2y = 165{,}000 \Rightarrow y = 82{,}500$, and so $x = 82{,}500 + 20{,}000 \Rightarrow x = 102{,}500$. Therefore men will have 102,500 cases of lung cancer reported and women will have 82,500 cases of lung cancer reported.

73. (a) $c = 0.2x + 40$

(b) See Figure 73b. The intersection and solution is (250, 90) or 250 miles.

(c) See Figure 73c. Since when $x = 250$, $c = 90$ for both equations, the solution is $(250, 90) \Rightarrow$ 250 miles.

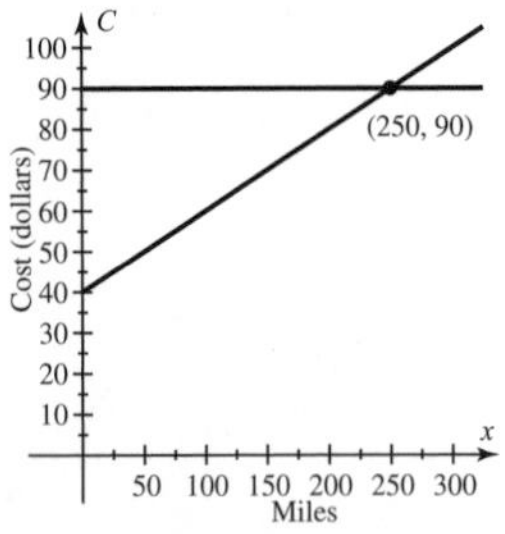

Figure 73b

x	150	200	250	300
$C = 0.2x + 40$	70	80	90	100

Figure 73c

74. Let x = gardens width and let y = gardens length. Then $2x + 2y = 88$ and $y = x + 4$. Substituting $y = x + 4$ into the first equation yields the following: $2x + 2(x + 4) = 88 \Rightarrow 2x + 2x + 8 = 88 \Rightarrow 4x + 8 = 88 \Rightarrow 4x = 80 \Rightarrow x = 20$, and so $y = 20 + 4 \Rightarrow y = 24$. The solution is (20, 24). The dimensions of the garden are 20×24 feet.

75. (a) $2x + y = 180$ and $2x = y + 40$

(b) Note that $2x + y = 180 \Rightarrow y = -2x + 180$. Substituting $y = -2x + 180$ into the second equation yields the following: $2x = (-2x + 180) + 40 \Rightarrow 2x = -2x + 220 \Rightarrow 4x = 220 \Rightarrow x = 55$, and so $y = -2(55) + 180 \Rightarrow y = -110 + 180 \Rightarrow y = 70$. The solution is (55, 70) or two angles at 55° and one at 70°.

(c) Note that $2x = y + 40 \Rightarrow 2x - y = 40$. Adding the two equations will eliminate the variable y.

$$\begin{array}{r} 2x + y = 180 \\ \underline{2x - y = 40} \\ 4x = 220 \end{array}$$

Thus $x = 55$. And so $2(55) = y + 40 \Rightarrow 110 = y + 40 \Rightarrow y = 70$. The solution is (55, 70) or two angles at 55° and one angle at 70°.

76. Let x = smaller angle and let y = larger angle. Then $x + y = 180$ and $x = y - 30$. Substituting $x = y - 30$ into the first equation yields the following: $(y - 30) + y = 180 \Rightarrow 2y = 210 \Rightarrow y = 105$, and so $x = 105 - 30 \Rightarrow x = 75$. The angles are 75° and 105°.

77. (a) Let x = number of \$80 rooms and let y = number of \$120 rooms. Then $x + y = 10$ and $80x + 120y = 920$.

(b) Multiplying the first equation by -80 and adding the two equations will eliminate the variable x.

$$\begin{array}{r} -80x - 80y = -800 \\ \underline{80x + 120y = 920} \\ 40y = 120 \end{array}$$

Thus $y = 3$. And so $x + 3 = 10 \Rightarrow x = 7$. The solution is (7, 3) or 7 \$80 rooms and 3 \$120 rooms.

78. Let x = pounds of \$2 candy and let y = pounds of \$3 candy. Then $x + y = 18$ and $2x + 3y = 47$. Multiplying the first equation by -2 and adding the two equations will eliminate the variable x.

$$\begin{array}{r} -2x - 2y = -36 \\ \underline{2x + 3y = 47} \\ y = 11 \end{array}$$

And so $x + 11 = 18 \Rightarrow x = 7$. The solution is (7, 11) or 7 pounds of \$2 candy and 11 pounds of \$3 candy.

79. Let x = minutes on the stationary bike and let y = minutes on the stair climber. Then $x + y = 60$ and $9x + 11y = 590$. Multiplying the first equation by -9 and adding the two equations will eliminate the variable x.

$$\begin{array}{r} -9x - 9y = -540 \\ \underline{9x + 11y = 590} \\ 2y = 50 \end{array}$$

Thus $y = 25$. And so $x + 25 = 60 \Rightarrow x = 35$. The solution is (35, 25) or 35 minutes on the bike and 25 minutes on the stair climber.

80. Let x = speed of the boat and let y = speed of the current. Then $10x + 10y = 140$ and $14x - 14y = 140$. Multiplying the first equation by 7, the second by 5 and adding the two equations will eliminate the variable y.

$$\begin{array}{r} 70x + 70y = 980 \\ \underline{70x - 70y = 700} \\ 140x = 1680 \end{array}$$

Thus $x = 12$. And so $10(12) + 10y = 140 \Rightarrow 120 + 10y = 140 \Rightarrow 10y = 20 \Rightarrow y = 2$. The solution is (12, 2). The current is 2 mph.

81. (a) The intersection and solution is approximately 16×24 feet.

(b) Using the system $2L + 2W = 80$ and $L = \frac{3}{2}W$ and substituting $L = \frac{3}{2}W$ into the first equation yields the following: $2\left(\frac{3}{2}W\right) + 2W = 80 \Rightarrow 3W + 2W = 80 \Rightarrow 5W = 80 \Rightarrow W = 16$, and so $L = \frac{3}{2}(16) \Rightarrow L = 24$. The dimensions are 16×24 feet.

82. Let x = number of wheels made and let y = number of trailers made. Then $x + y \leq 30$ and $x \geq 2y$. Graph this system and shade. See Figure 82.

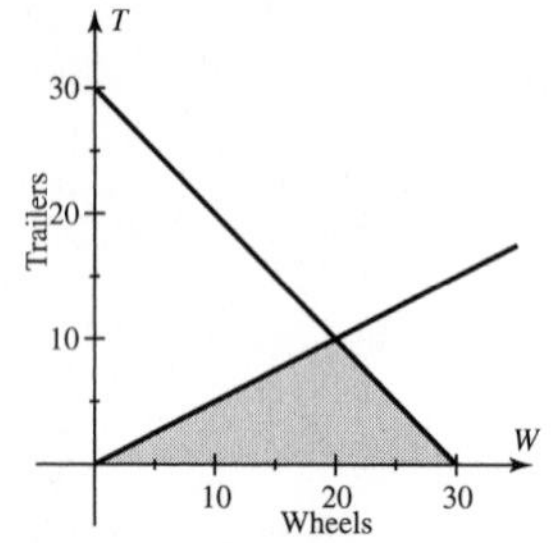

Figure 82

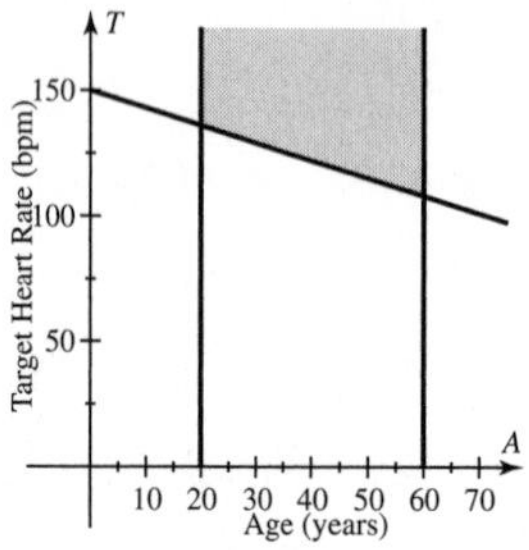

Figure 83

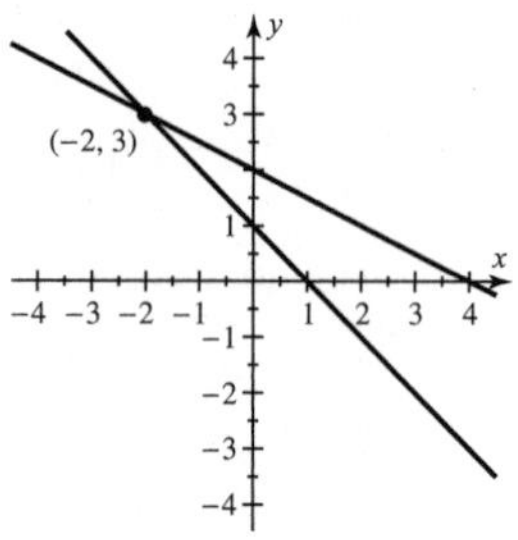

Figure 4

83. (a) $T = 150 - 0.7(20) \Rightarrow T = 150 - 14 \Rightarrow T = 136$ bpm for a 20 year old person and $T = 150 - 0.7(60) \Rightarrow T = 150 - 42 \Rightarrow T = 108$ bpm for a 60 year old person.

(b) See Figure 83.

(c) The shaded region represents target heart rates above 70% of the maximum heart rate for ages 20 to 60.

Chapter 4 Test

1. $(1, 2)$, because $3(1) + 2(2) = 7 \Rightarrow 3 + 4 = 7 \Rightarrow$ is true and $2(1) - 2 = 0$ is true.
2. The intersection and solution is $(-2, -1)$. Checking: $-2 + 4(-1) = -6 \Rightarrow -2 + (-4) = -6$ is true and $2(-2) + (-1) = -5 \Rightarrow -4 + (-1) = -5$.
3. Since when $x = -1$, $y = -2$ for both equations, the solution is $(-1, -2)$.
4. See Figure 4. The intersection and solution is $(-2, 3)$.
5. Substituting $y = 3x$ into the first equation yields the following: $3x + 2(3x) = 9 \Rightarrow 3x + 6x = 9 \Rightarrow 9x = 9 \Rightarrow x = 1$, and so $y = 3(1) \Rightarrow y = 3$. The solution is $(1, 3)$.
6. (a) Multiplying the first equation by -3 and adding the two equations will eliminate the variable x.

$$\begin{array}{r} -3x - 9y = -15 \\ 3x - 2y = 4 \\ \hline -11y = -11 \end{array}$$

Thus $y = 1$. And so $3x - 2(1) = 4 \Rightarrow 3x - 2 = 4 \Rightarrow 3x = 6 \Rightarrow x = 2$. The solution is $(2, 1) \Rightarrow$ one solution $\Rightarrow$ consistent.

(b) Multiplying the first equation by 2 and adding the two equations will eliminate both variables.

$$\begin{array}{r} -2x + y = 24 \\ 2x - y = -4 \\ \hline 0 = 20 \end{array}$$

This is false $\Rightarrow$ no solutions $\Rightarrow$ inconsistent.

7. Adding the two equations will eliminate the variable y.

$$\begin{array}{r} x + 2y = 5 \\ 3x - 2y = -17 \\ \hline 4x = -12 \end{array}$$

Thus $x = -3$. And so $-3 + 2y = 5 \Rightarrow 2y = 8 \Rightarrow y = 4$. The solution is $(-3, 4)$.

8. Multiplying the second equation by 2 and adding the two equations will eliminate both variables.

$$\begin{array}{r} 2x - 2y = 3 \\ -2x + 2y = 10 \\ \hline 0 = 13 \end{array}$$

This is false $\Rightarrow$ no solutions.

9. $y \leq -\frac{1}{2}x$

10. See Figure 10.

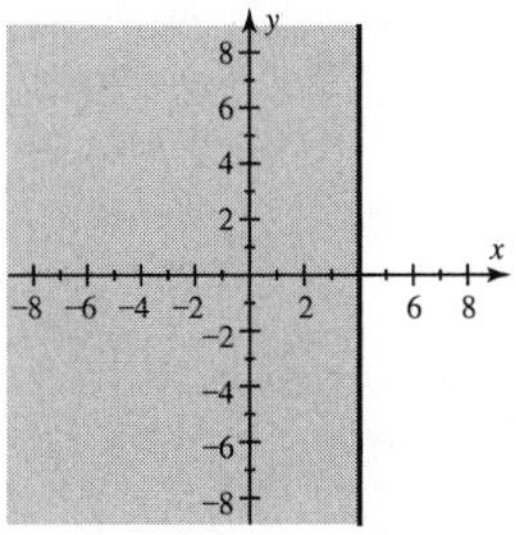

Figure 10

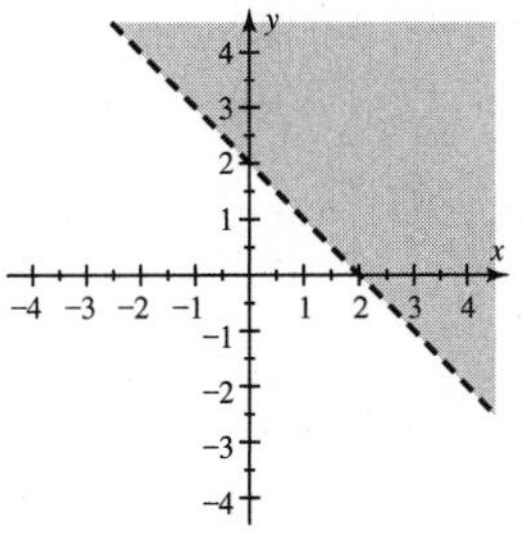

Figure 11

11. See Figure 11.

12. See Figure 12.

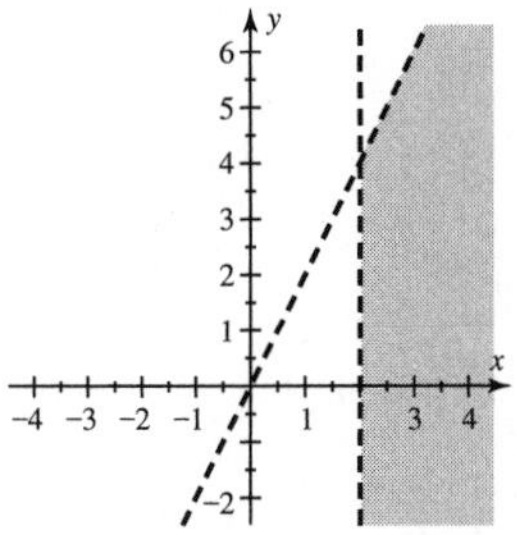

Figure 12

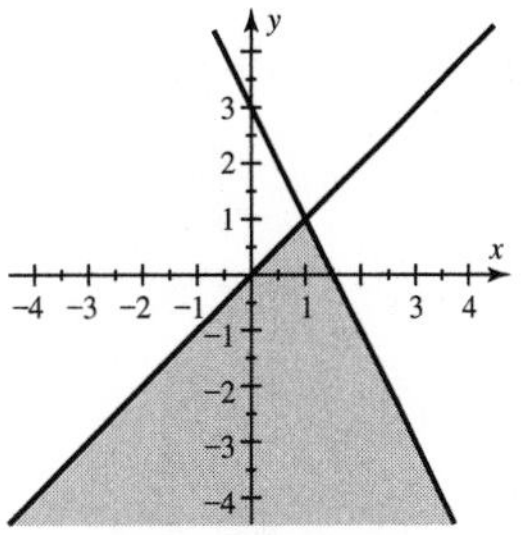

Figure 13

13. See Figure 13.

14. Let $x =$ taxes collected in 1998 and let $y =$ taxes collected in 1999. Then $x + y = 3.7$ and $y = x + 0.1$. Substituting $y = x + 0.1$ into the first equation yields the following: $x + (x + 0.1) = 3.7 \Rightarrow 2x + 0.1 = 3.7 \Rightarrow 2x = 3.6 \Rightarrow x = 1.8$, and so $y = 1.8 + 0.1 \Rightarrow y = 1.9$. The solution is $(1.8, 1.9)$ or \$1.8 trillion collected in 1998 and \$1.9 trillion collected in 1999.

15. Let $x =$ hrs jogged at 6 mph and let $y =$ hrs jogged at 9 mph. Then $x + y = 1$ and $6x + 9y = 7$. Multiplying the first equation by -6 and adding the two equations will eliminate the variable x.

$$\begin{array}{r} -6x - 6y = -6 \\ 6x + 9y = 7 \\ \hline 3y = 1 \end{array}$$

Thus $y = \frac{1}{3}$. And so $x + \frac{1}{3} = 1 \Rightarrow x = \frac{2}{3}$. The solution is $\left(\frac{2}{3}, \frac{1}{3}\right)$ or $\frac{2}{3}$ hour at 6 miles per hour and $\frac{1}{3}$ hour at 9 miles per hour.

Chapter 4 Extended and Discovery Exercises

1. The forest has higher precipitation for higher temperatures than grasslands $\Rightarrow 7P - 5T \geq -70$.
2. The deserts have less precipitation for high temperatures than grasslands $\Rightarrow 35P - 3T \leq 140$.
3. The grassland is lower precipitation for higher temperatures than forests and higher than desert $\Rightarrow 7P - 5T \leq -70$ and $35P - 3T \geq 140$.
4. From the graph, grasslands would be the type of plant growth, and $7(14) - 5(50) \leq -70 \Rightarrow 98 - 250 \leq -70$ is true and $35(14) - 3(50) \geq 140 \Rightarrow 490 - 150 \geq 140$ is true $\Rightarrow$ yes.
5. -0.5; average the x-values -1 and 0 because the solution y-value 0 is half way between their corresponding y-values -1 and 1.
6. 0.5; average the x-values 0 and 1 because the solution y-value 5 is half way between their corresponding y-values 3 and 7.
7. 1.5; average the x-values 1 and 2 because the solution y-value 3.75 is half way between their corresponding y-values 3.5 and 4.
8. $\frac{1}{3}$; because 0 is one-third of the way between the y-values -1 and 2, you must choose a value one-third of the way between the corresponding x-values 0 and 1.

Critical Thinking Solutions for Chapter 4

Section 4.1

- Parallel lines have no intersection, therefore there are no solutions.

Section 4.2

- Since it helps downstream and hurts upstream the current would be half the difference $\Rightarrow \frac{16 - 10}{2} = 3$ mph.

Section 4.4

- No, $(2, -2)$ is not a true solution for both equations, it does not satisfy $x + 2y < -2$ because $2 + 2(-2) < -2 \Rightarrow -2 < -2$ which is false.
- This region represents heavier weights and shorter heights. These ordered pairs correspond to people who weigh more than recommended.

Chapter 5: Polynomials and Exponents

5.1: Rules for Exponents

Concepts

1. b = base; n = exponent

3. $\frac{1}{2} \cdot \frac{1}{2} \cdot \frac{1}{2} = \left(\frac{1}{2}\right)^3$

5. a^{m+n}

7. $a^n b^n$

Properties of Exponents

9. $8^2 = 8 \cdot 8 = 64$

11. $(-2)^3 = (-2) \cdot (-2) \cdot (-2) = -8$

13. $-2^3 = -(2 \cdot 2 \cdot 2) = -8$

15. $6^0 = 1$

17. $2 \cdot 4^2 = 2 \cdot (4 \cdot 4) = 2 \cdot 16 = 32$

19. $1 + 5^2 = 1 + (5 \cdot 5) = 1 + 25 = 26$

21. $\frac{4^2}{2} = \frac{(4 \cdot 4)}{2} = \frac{16}{2} = 8$

23. $4 \cdot \frac{1}{2^3} = 4 \cdot \frac{1}{(2 \cdot 2 \cdot 2)} = 4 \cdot \frac{1}{8} = \frac{4}{8} = \frac{1}{2}$

25. $4^2 \cdot 4^6 = 4^{2+6} = 4^8 = 65{,}536$

27. $2^3 \cdot 2^2 = 2^{3+2} = 2^5 = 32$

29. $x^3 \cdot x^6 = x^{3+6} = x^9$

31. $z^0 z^4 = z^{0+4} = z^4$

33. $x^2 x^2 x^2 = x^{2+2+2} = x^6$

35. $4x^2 \cdot 5x^5 = 20x^{2+5} = 20x^7$

37. $3(-xy^3)(x^2y) = 3(-x^{1+2}y^{3+1}) = 3(-x^3y^4) = -3x^3y^4$

39. $(2^3)^2 = 2^{2 \cdot 3} = 2^6 = 64$

41. $(n^3)^4 = n^{3 \cdot 4} = n^{12}$

43. $x(x^3)^2 = x(x^{3 \cdot 2}) = x(x^6) = x^{1+6} = x^7$

45. $(-7b)^2 = (-7) \cdot (-7) \cdot (b \cdot b) = 49b^2$

47. $(ab)^3 = (a \cdot a \cdot a)(b \cdot b \cdot b) = a^3b^3$

49. $(2x^2)^2 = (2 \cdot 2)(x^{2 \cdot 2}) = 4x^4$

51. $(-4b^2)^3 = (-4) \cdot (-4) \cdot (-4)(b^{2 \cdot 3}) = -64b^6$

53. $(x^2y^3)^7 = (x^{2 \cdot 7}y^{3 \cdot 7}) = x^{14}y^{21}$

55. $(y^3)^2(x^4y)^3 = (y^{3\cdot 2})(x^{4\cdot 3}y^{1\cdot 3}) = (y^6)(x^{12}y^3) = x^{12}y^{6+3} = x^{12}y^9$

57. $\left(\dfrac{2}{3}\right)^3 = \dfrac{(2\cdot 2\cdot 2)}{(3\cdot 3\cdot 3)} = \dfrac{8}{27}$

59. $\left(\dfrac{a}{b}\right)^5 = \dfrac{(a\cdot a\cdot a\cdot a\cdot a)}{(b\cdot b\cdot b\cdot b\cdot b)} = \dfrac{a^5}{b^5}$

61. $\left(\dfrac{2x}{5}\right)^3 = \dfrac{(2\cdot 2\cdot 2)(x^{1\cdot 3})}{(5\cdot 5\cdot 5)} = \dfrac{8x^3}{125}$

63. $\left(\dfrac{3x^2}{5y^4}\right)^3 = \dfrac{(3\cdot 3\cdot 3)(x^{2\cdot 3})}{(5\cdot 5\cdot 5)(y^{4\cdot 3})} = \dfrac{27x^6}{125y^{12}}$

65. $(a+b)^2(a+b)^3 = (a+b)^{2+3} = (a+b)^5$

67. $6(x^4y^6)^0 = 6(x^{4\cdot 0}y^{6\cdot 0}) = 6(x^0y^0) = 6\cdot 1\cdot 1 = 6$

69. $a(a^2+2b^2) = a^{1+2} + 2ab^2 = a^3 + 2ab^2$

71. $(r+t)(rt) = (r^{1+1}t) + (rt^{1+1}) = r^2t + rt^2$

Applications

73. $2x^2\cdot 5x^2 = 10x^{2+2} = 10x^4$ square units

75. $x\cdot 2x\cdot 4x = 8x^{1+1+1} = 8x^3$

77. $\pi(3x^2)^2 = \pi(3\cdot 3)(x^{2\cdot 2}) = \pi(9x^4) = 9\pi x^4$

79. $1000(1+0.05)^3 = 1000(1.05)^3 = 1000(1.05\cdot 1.05\cdot 1.05) = 1000(1.157625) \approx \$1157.63$

81. See Figure 81.

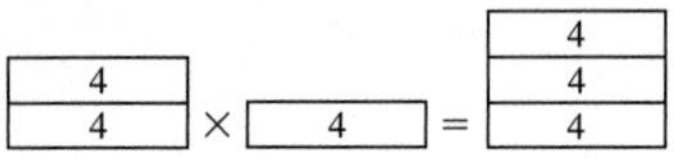

Figure 81

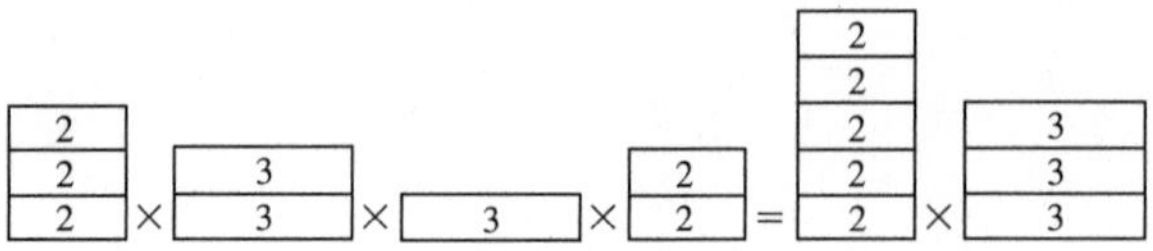

Figure 83

83. See Figure 83.

5.2: Addition and Subtraction of Polynomials

Concepts

1. monomial

3. polynomial

5. binomial

7. 2 terms; degree = 3

9. like

11. opposite

Properties of Polynomials

13. Because $x^2 \Rightarrow$ the degree is 2; the coefficient is 3.

15. Because $ab = a^1b^1$ and $1 + 1 = 2 \Rightarrow$ the degree is 2; $-ab = -1ab \Rightarrow$ the coefficient is −1.

17. Because $rt = r^1t^1$ and $1 + 1 = 2 \Rightarrow$ the degree is 2; the coefficient is −5.

19. Because there are no variables the degree is 0; the coefficient is −6.

21. Yes it is polynomial; 1 term $-x$; one variable x; $x^1 \Rightarrow$ degree is 1.

23. Yes it is polynomial; 3 terms $4x^2$, $-5x$, and 9; one variable x; $x^2 \Rightarrow$ degree is 2.

25. Not a polynomial because it has a variable in the denominator.

27. Yes it is polynomial; 2 terms $3x^2y$ and $-xy^3$; two variables x and y; $xy^3 = x^1y^3$ and $1 + 3 = 4 \Rightarrow$ degree is 4.

29. Yes, $5x + (-4x) = (5 - 4)x = 1x = x$.

31. Yes, $x^3 + (-6x^3) = [1 + (-6)]x^3 = -5x^3$.

33. No, x and y are not like terms.

35. Yes $\Rightarrow ab + ba = (1 + 1)ab = 2ab$.

37. Yes $\Rightarrow 7xy^2 + (-3xy^2) = (7 - 3)xy^2 = 4xy^2$.

Addition of Polynomials

39. $(3x + 5) + (-4x + 4) = 3x + (-4x) + 5 + 4 = (3 - 4)x + (5 + 4) = -x + 9$

41. $(3x^2 + 4x + 1) + (x^2 + 4x - 6) = 3x^2 + x^2 + 4x + 4x + 1 + (-6) = (3 + 1)x^2 + (4 + 4)x + (1 - 6) =$
$4x^2 + 8x - 5$

43. $(a^3 - 6) + (4a^3 + 7) = 4a^3 + a^3 + 7 + (-6) = (4 + 1)a^3 + (7 - 6) = 5a^3 + 1$

45. $(y^3 + 3y^2 - 5) + (3y^3 + 4y - 4) = 3y^3 + y^3 + 3y^2 + 4y + (-5) + (-4) =$
$(3 + 1)y^3 + 3y^2 + 4y + (-5 - 4) = 4y^3 + 3y^2 + 4y - 9$

47. $(-xy + 5) + (5xy - 4) = 5xy + (-xy) + 5 + (-4) = (5 - 1)xy + (5 - 4) = 4xy + 1$

49. $(a^3b^2 + a^2b^3) + (a^2b^3 - a^3b^2) = a^3b^2 + (-a^3b^2) + a^2b^3 + a^2b^3 = (1 - 1)a^3b^2 + (1 + 1)a^2b^3 =$
$0a^3b^2 + 2a^2b^3 = 2a^2b^3$

51.
$$\begin{array}{r} 4x^2 - 2x + 1 \\ +\ 5x + 3x - 7 \\ \hline 9x^2 + x - 6 \end{array}$$

53.
$$\begin{array}{r} -x^2 + x + 0 \\ +\ 2x^2 - 8x - 1 \\ \hline x^2 - 7x - 1 \end{array}$$

Subtraction of Polynomials

55. $-5x^2$

57. $-3a^2 + a - 4$

59. $2t^2 + 3t - 4$

61. $3x^3 + x - 5$

63. $-9xy + x^2$

65. $(3x + 1) - (-x + 3) = (3x + 1) + (x - 3) = (3 + 1)x + (1 - 3) = 4x - 2$

67. $(-x^2 + 6x + 8) - (2x^2 + x - 2) = (-x^2 + 6x + 8) + (2x^2 - x + 2) =$

$(-1 - 2)x^2 + (6 - 1)x + (8 + 2) = -3x^2 + 5x + 10$

69. $(a^2 - 2a) - (4a^2 + 3a) = (a^2 - 2a) + (-4a^2 - 3a) = (1 - 4)a^2 + (-2 - 3)a = -3a^2 - 5a$

71. $(z^3 - 2z^2 - z) - (4z^2 + 5z + 1) = (z^3 - 2z^2 - z) + (-4z^2 - 5z - 1) =$

$z^3 + (-2 - 4)z^2 + (-1 - 5)z - 1 = z^3 - 6z^2 - 6z - 1$

73. $(4xy + x^2y^2) - (xy - x^2y^2) = (4xy + x^2y^2) + (-xy + x^2y^2) = (4 - 1)xy + (1 + 1)x^2y^2 = 3xy + 2x^2y^2$

75. $(ab^2) - (ab^2 + a^3b) = (ab^2) + (-ab^2 - a^3b) = (1 - 1)ab^2 - a^3b = 0ab^2 - a^3b = -a^3b$

77. $(x^2 + 2x - 3) - (2x^2 + 7x + 1) = $

$$\begin{array}{r} x^2 + 2x - 3 \\ + (-2x^2) - 7x - 1 \\ \hline -x^2 - 5x - 4 \end{array}$$

79. $(3x^3 - 2x) - (5x^3 + 4x + 2) = $

$$\begin{array}{r} 3x^3 - 2x + 0 \\ + (-5x^3) - 4x - 2 \\ \hline -2x^3 - 6x - 2 \end{array}$$

Applications

81. $x = 3$ in., $x^3 = 3^3 = 27$ in^3

83. (a) Let $t = 0$, then $1.6t^2 - 28t + 200 = 1.6(0^2) - 28(0) + 200 = 0 - 0 + 200 = 200$ bpm.

(b) Let $t = 5$, then $1.6t^2 - 28t + 200 = 1.6(5^2) - 28(5) + 200 = 1.6(25) - 28(5) + 200 =$

$40 - 140 + 200 = 100$ bpm.

(c) It decreases quickly at first and then more slowly.

85. $z^2 + z^2 = (1 + 1)z^2$; Let $z = 10$ in., then $2(10^2) = 2(100) = 200$ in^2

87. $2x \cdot x + x \cdot x = 2x^2 + x^2$ or $3x^2$; Let $x = 6$ feet, then $3x^2 = 3(6^2) = 3(36) = 108$ ft^2

89. $\pi x^2 + \pi y^2$; Let $x = 2$ feet and $y = 3$ feet, then $\pi x^2 + \pi y^2 = \pi(2^2) + \pi(3^2) = \pi(4) + \pi(9) = 13\pi$ ft^2

91. (a) Slope $m = \dfrac{P_2 - P_1}{t_2 - t_1}$, so $m_1 = \dfrac{5 - 4}{1987 - 1974} = \dfrac{1}{13} \Rightarrow m_1 = 0.077$; $m_2 = \dfrac{6 - 5}{1999 - 1987} = \dfrac{1}{12} \Rightarrow$

$m_2 = 0.083$; $m_3 = \dfrac{7 - 6}{2012 - 1999} = \dfrac{1}{13} \Rightarrow m_3 = 0.077$. A line is a reasonable estimate, it is not exact.

(b) Substituting different years for t shows that the polynomial gives a reasonable estimate. Example:

$0.077(1987) - 148 = 4.999$ million, close to the five million estimate of 1987.

Checking Basic Concepts for Sections 5.1 & 5.2

1. (a) $-5^2 = -(5 \cdot 5) = -25$

(b) $3^2 - 2^3 = (3 \cdot 3) - (2 \cdot 2 \cdot 2) = 9 - 8 = 1$

2. (a) $10^3 \cdot 10^5 = 10^{3+5} = 10^8$

(b) $(3x^2)(-4x^5) = -12x^{2+5} = -12x^7$

(c) $(a^3b)^2 = a^{3\cdot 2}b^{1\cdot 2} = a^6b^2$

(d) $\left(\frac{x}{z^3}\right)^4 = \frac{x^{1\cdot 4}}{z^{3\cdot 4}} = \frac{x^4}{z^{12}}$

3. 3 terms $5x^3y$, $-2x^2y$, and 5; 2 variables x and y; $x^3y = x^3y^1$, $3 + 1 = 4 \Rightarrow$ the degree is 4.

4. (a) Let length $= 2W$, width $= W$, and height $= H$, then $2W \cdot W \cdot H = 2W^2H$.

(b) Let $W = 12$ and $H = 10$, then $2W^2H = 2(12^2)(10) = 2(144)(10) = 2880 \text{ in}^3$.

5. (a) $(2a^2 + 3a - 1) + (a^2 - 3a + 7) = 2a^2 + a^2 + 3a + (-3a) + (-1) + 7 =$

$(2 + 1)a^2 + (3 - 3)a + (-1 + 7) = 3a^2 + 0a + 6 = 3a^2 + 6$

(b) $(4z^3 + 5z) - (2z^3 - 2z + 8) = (4z^3 + 5z) + (-2z^3 + 2z - 8) = (4 - 2)z^3 + (5 + 2)z - 8 =$

$2z^3 + 7z - 8$

(c) $(x^2 + 2xy + y^2) - (x^2 - 2xy + y^2) = (x^2 + 2xy + y^2) + (-x^2 + 2xy - y^2) =$

$(1 - 1)x^2 + (2 + 2)xy + (1 - 1)y^2 = 0x^2 + 4xy + 0y^2 = 4xy$

6. Let $x = -2$, then $5x^2 - 7x = 5(-2)^2 - 7(-2) = 5(4) - 7(-2) = 20 - (-14) = 20 + 14 = 34$.

5.3: Multiplication of Polynomials

Concepts

1. The product rule

3. $x^2 - 7$; *Answers may vary.*

5. term; term

Multiplication of Monomials

7. $x^2 \cdot x^5 = x^{2+5} = x^7$

9. $-3a \cdot 4a = (-3)(4)aa = -12a^{1+1} = -12a^2$

11. $4x^3 \cdot 5x^2 = (4)(5)x^3x^2 = 20x^{3+2} = 20x^5$

13. $xy^2 \cdot 4xy = (1)(4)xxy^2y = 4x^{1+1}y^{2+1} = 4x^2y^3$

15. $(-3xy^2)(4x^2y) = (-3)(4)xx^2y^2y = -12x^{1+2}y^{2+1} = -12x^3y^3$

Multiplication of Monomials and Polynomials

17. $3(x + 4) = 3 \cdot x + 3 \cdot 4 = 3x + 12$

19. $-5(9x + 1) = -5 \cdot 9x + (-5 \cdot 1) = -45x - 5$

21. $(4 - z)z = 4 \cdot z + (-z \cdot z) = 4z - z^2$

23. $-y(5 + 3y) = -y \cdot 5 + (-y \cdot 3y) = -5y - 3y^2$

25. $3x(5x^2 - 4) = 3x \cdot 5x^2 + 3x \cdot (-4) = (3)(5)xx^2 - 12x = 15x^{1+2} - 12x = 15x^3 - 12x$

27. $(6x - 6)x^2 = 6x \cdot x^2 + (-6) \cdot x^2 = 6x^{1+2} - 6x^2 = 6x^3 - 6x^2$

29. $-8(4t^2 + t + 1) = -8 \cdot 4t^2 + (-8)(t) + (-8)(1) = -32t^2 - 8t - 8$

31. $4m(-2m^2 + 7m - 6) = 4m \cdot (-2m^2) + (4m)(7m) + (4m)(-6) = (4)(-2)mm^2 + (4)(7)mm - 24m =$
$-8m^{1+2} + 28m^{1+1} - 24m = -8m^3 + 28m^2 - 24m$

33. $n^2(-5n^2 + n - 2) = (n^2)(-5n^2) + (n^2)(n) + (n^2)(-2) = -5n^{2+2} + n^{2+1} - 2n^2 = -5n^4 + n^3 - 2n^2$

35. $xy(x + y) = xy \cdot x + xy \cdot y = x^{1+1}y + xy^{1+1} = x^2y + xy^2$

37. $x^2(x^2y - xy^2) = x^2 \cdot x^2y + (x^2)(-xy^2) = x^{2+2}y - x^{2+1}y^2 = x^4y - x^3y^2$

39. $-ab(a^3 - 2b^3) = -ab \cdot a^3 + (-ab)(-2b^3) = -a^{1+3}b + 2ab^{3+1} = -a^4b + 2ab^4$

Multiplication of Polynomials

41. (a) Area $= x^2 + 3x$. See Figure 41.
(b) $x(x + 3) = x \cdot x + x \cdot 3 = x^{1+1} + 3x = x^2 + 3x$

43. (a) Area $= x^2 + 2x + 2x + 4 = x^2 + 4x + 4$. See Figure 43.
(b) $(x + 2)(x + 2) = x \cdot x + x \cdot 2 + 2 \cdot x + 2 \cdot 2 = x^{1+1} + 2x + 2x + 4 = x^2 + 4x + 4$

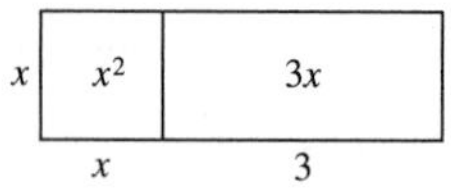

Figure 41

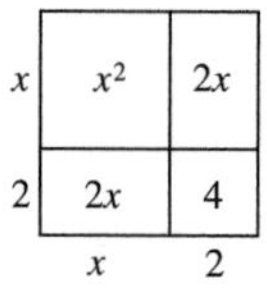

Figure 43

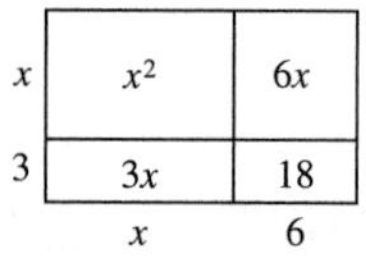

Figure 45

45. (a) Area $= x^2 + 3x + 6x + 18 = x^2 + 9x + 18$. See Figure 45.
(b) $(x + 3)(x + 6) = x \cdot x + x \cdot 6 + 3 \cdot x + 3 \cdot 6 = x^{1+1} + 6x + 3x + 18 = x^2 + 9x + 18$

47. $(x + 3)(x + 5) = x \cdot x + x \cdot 5 + 3 \cdot x + 3 \cdot 5 = x^{1+1} + 5x + 3x + 15 = x^2 + 8x + 15$

49. $(x - 8)(x - 9) = x \cdot x + (x)(-9) + (-8)(x) + (-8)(-9) = x^{1+1} + (-9x) + (-8x) + 72 = x^2 - 17x + 72$

51. $(3z - 2)(2z - 5) = 3z \cdot 2z + (3z)(-5) + (-2)(2z) + (-2)(-5) = 6z^{1+1} + (-15z) + (-4z) + 10 =$
$6z^2 - 19z + 10$

53. $(8b - 1)(8b + 1) = 8b \cdot 8b + 8b \cdot 1 + (-1)(8b) + (-1)(1) = 64b^{1+1} + 8b - 8b - 1 = 64b^2 - 1$

55. $(10y + 7)(y - 1) = 10y \cdot y + (10y)(-1) + 7 \cdot y + (7)(-1) = 10y^{1+1} - 10y + 7y - 7 = 10y^2 - 3y - 7$

57. $(5 - 3a)(1 - 2a) = 5 \cdot 1 + (5)(-2a) + (-3a)(1) + (-3a)(-2a) = 5 + (-10a) + (-3a) + 6a^{1+1} =$
$5 - 13a + 6a^2$

59. $(1 - 3x)(1 + 3x) = 1 \cdot 1 + 1 \cdot 3x + (-3x)(1) + (-3x)(3x) = 1 + 3x - 3x - 9x^{1+1} = 1 - 9x^2$

61. $(x - 1)(x^2 + 1) = x \cdot x^2 + x \cdot 1 + (-1)(x^2) + (-1)(1) = x^{1+2} + x - x^2 - 1 = x^3 - x^2 + x - 1$

63. $(x^2 + 4)(4x - 3) = x^2 \cdot 4x + (x^2)(-3) + 4 \cdot 4x + (4)(-3) = 4x^{2+1} - 3x^2 + 16x - 12 =$
$4x^3 - 3x^2 + 16x - 12$

65. $(2n + 1)(n^2 + 3) = 2n \cdot n^2 + 2n \cdot 3 + 1 \cdot n^2 + 1 \cdot 3 = 2n^{1+2} + 6n + n^2 + 3 = 2n^3 + n^2 + 6n + 3$

67. $(m + 1)(m^2 + 3m + 1) = m \cdot m^2 + m \cdot 3m + m \cdot 1 + 1 \cdot m^2 + 1 \cdot 3m + 1 \cdot 1 =$
$m^{1+2} + 3m^{1+1} + m + m^2 + 3m + 1 = m^3 + 3m^2 + m + m^2 + 3m + 1 = m^3 + 4m^2 + 4m + 1$

69. $(3x - 2)(2x^2 - x + 4) = 3x \cdot 2x^2 + (3x)(-x) + 3x \cdot 4 + (-2)(2x^2) + (-2)(-x) + (-2)(4) =$
$6x^{1+2} - 3x^{1+1} + 12x - 4x^2 + 2x - 8 = 6x^3 - 3x^2 + 12x - 4x^2 + 2x - 8 = 6x^3 - 7x^2 + 14x - 8$

71. $(x + 1)(x^2 - x + 1) = x \cdot x^2 + (x)(-x) + x \cdot 1 + 1 \cdot x^2 + (1)(-x) + 1 \cdot 1 =$
$x^{1+2} - x^{1+1} + x + x^2 - x + 1 = x^3 - x^2 + x + x^2 - x + 1 = x^3 + 1$

73. $(4b^2 + 3b + 7)(b^2 + 3) = 4b^2 \cdot b^2 + 4b^2 \cdot 3 + 3b \cdot b^2 + 3b \cdot 3 + 7 \cdot b^2 + 7 \cdot 3 =$
$4b^{2+2} + 12b^2 + 3b^{1+2} + 9b + 7b^2 + 21 = 4b^4 + 12b^2 + 3b^3 + 9b + 7b^2 + 21 =$
$4b^4 + 3b^3 + 19b^2 + 9b + 21$

Applications

75. (a) Let h = height, ht^2 = length, and $h - 4$ = width, then $(h - 4)(h + 2) =$
$h \cdot h + h \cdot 2 + (-4)(h) + (-4)(2) = h^{1+1} + 2h - 4h - 8 = h^2 - 2h - 8 \Rightarrow (h)(h^2 - 2h - 8) =$
$h \cdot h^2 + (h)(-2h) + (h)(-8) = h^{1+2} - 2h^{1+1} - 8h = h^3 - 2h^2 - 8h.$
(b) $h^3 - 2h^2 - 8h = 25^3 - 2(25)^2 - 8(25) = 15{,}625 - 2(625) - 200 = 15{,}625 - 1250 - 200 =$
$14{,}175 \text{ in}^3$

77. $(x + 1)(x + 1) = x \cdot x + x \cdot 1 + 1 \cdot x + 1 \cdot 1 = x^{1+1} + x + x + 1 = x^2 + 2x + 1 \Rightarrow$ 1 side $=$
$x^2 + 2x + 1$. A cube has all sides the same $\Rightarrow$ 6 sides $= (6)(x^2 + 2x + 1) = 6 \cdot x^2 + 6 \cdot 2x^2 + 6 \cdot 1 =$
$6x^2 + 12x + 6$.

79. (a) $t(64 - 16t) = t \cdot 64 + (t)(-16t) = 64t - 16t^{1+1} = 64t - 16t^2$
(b) $64 - 16t^2 = 64(2) - 16(2)^2 = 128 - 16(4) = 128 - 64 = 64;$
$t(64 - 16t) = 2(64 - 16(2)) = 2(64 - 32) = 2(32) = 64$
(c) Yes; yes.

81. (a) $x(50 - x) = x \cdot 50 + (x)(-x) = 50x - x^{1+1} = 50x - x^2$
(b) $50x - x^2 = 50(25) - (25^2) = 1250 - 625 = 625$

5.4: Special Products

Concepts

1. $(a + b)(a - b) = (a)^2 - (b)^2 = a^2 - b^2$
3. $(a + b)^2 = (a)^2 + 2(a)(b) + (b)^2 = a^2 + 2ab + b^2$
5. No, let $x = 1, y = 1$, then $(1 + 1)^2 = 2^2 = 4$ and $1^2 + 1^2 = 1 + 1 = 2$, *Answers may vary.*
7. No, let $z = 1$, then $(1 + 5)^3 = 6^3 = 216$ and $1^3 + 5^3 = 1 + 125 = 126$, *Answers may vary.*

Product of a Sum and Difference

9. $(x + 1)(x - 1) = (x)^2 - (1)^2 = x^2 - 1$

11. $(4x - 1)(4x + 1) = (4x)^2 - (1)^2 = 16x^2 - 1$

13. $(1 + 2a)(1 - 2a) = (1)^2 - (2a)^2 = 1 - 4a^2$

15. $(2x + 3y)(2x - 3y) = (2x)^2 - (3y)^2 = 4x^2 - 9y^2$

17. $(ab - 5)(ab + 5) = (ab)^2 - (5)^2 = a^2b^2 - 25$

19. $(ab + 4)(ab - 4) = (ab)^2 - (4)^2 = a^2b^2 - 16$

21. $(a^2 - b^2)(a^2 + b^2) = (a^2)^2 - (b^2)^2 = a^4 - b^4$

23. $(x^3 - y^3)(x^3 + y^3) = (x^3)^2 - (y^3)^2 = x^6 - y^6$

25. $101 \cdot 99 = (100 + 1)(100 - 1) = (100)^2 - (1)^2 = 10{,}000 - 1 = 9999$

27. $23 \cdot 17 = (20 + 3)(20 - 3) = (20)^2 - (3)^2 = 400 - 9 = 391$

29. $90 \cdot 110 = (100 - 10)(100 + 10) = (100)^2 - (10)^2 = 10{,}000 - 100 = 9900$

Squaring Binomials

31. $(x + 1)^2 = (x)^2 + 2(x)(1) + (1)^2 = x^2 + 2x + 1$

33. $(a - 2)^2 = (a)^2 - 2(a)(2) + (2)^2 = a^2 - 4a + 4$

35. $(2x + 3)^2 = (2x)^2 + 2(2x)(3) + (3)^2 = 4x^2 + 12x + 9$

37. $(3b + 5)^2 = (3b)^2 + 2(3b)(5) + (5)^2 = 9b^2 + 30b + 25$

39. $\left(\frac{3}{4}a - 4\right)^2 = \left(\frac{3}{4}a\right)^2 - 2\left(\frac{3}{4}a\right)(4) + (4)^2 = \frac{9}{16}a^2 - 6a + 16$

41. $(1 - b)^2 = (1)^2 - 2(1)(b) + (b)^2 = 1 - 2b + b^2$

43. $(5 + y^3)^2 = (5)^2 + 2(5)(y^3) + (y^3)^2 = 25 + 10y^3 + y^6$

45. $(a^2 + b)^2 = (a^2)^2 + 2(a^2)(b) + (b)^2 = a^4 + 2a^2b + b^2$

Cubing Binomials

47. $(a + 1)^3 = (a + 1)(a + 1)^2 = (a + 1)(a^2 + 2a + 1) =$

$a \cdot a^2 + a \cdot 2a + a \cdot 1 + 1 \cdot a^2 + 1 \cdot 2a + 1 \cdot 1 = a^3 + 2a^2 + a + a^2 + 2a + 1 = a^3 + 3a^2 + 3a + 1$

49. $(x - 2)^3 = (x - 2)(x - 2)^2 = (x - 2)(x^2 - 4x + 4) =$

$x \cdot x^2 + x \cdot (-4x) + x \cdot 4 + (-2) \cdot x^2 + (-2)(-4x) + (-2)4 =$

$x^3 + (-4x^2) + 4x + (-2x^2) + 8x + (-8) = x^3 - 6x^2 + 12x - 8$

51. $(2x + 1)^3 = (2x + 1)(2x + 1)^2 = (2x + 1)(4x^2 + 4x + 1) =$

$2x \cdot 4x^2 + 2x \cdot 4x + 2x \cdot 1 + 1 \cdot 4x^2 + 1 \cdot 4x + 1 \cdot 1 =$

$8x^3 + 8x^2 + 2x + 4x^2 + 4x + 1 = 8x^3 + 12x^2 + 6x + 1$

53. $(6u - 1)^3 = (6u - 1)(6u - 1)^2 = (6u - 1)(36u^2 - 12u + 1) =$

$6u \cdot 36u^2 + 6u \cdot (-12u) + 6u \cdot 1 + (-1) \cdot 36u^2 + (-1) \cdot (-12u) + (-1) \cdot 1 =$

$216u^3 + (-72u^2) + 6u + (-36u^2) + 12u + (-1) = 216u^3 - 108u^2 + 18u - 1$

55. $t(t + 2)^3 = t(t + 2)(t + 2)^2 = t(t + 2)(t^2 + 4t + 4) = (t^2 + 2t)(t^2 + 4t + 4) =$

$t^2 \cdot t^2 + t^2 \cdot 4t + t^2 \cdot 4 + 2t \cdot t^2 + 2t \cdot 4t + 2t \cdot 4 =$

$t^4 + 4t^3 + 4t^2 + 2t^3 + 8t^2 + 8t = t^4 + 6t^3 + 12t^2 + 8t$

Multiplication of Polynomials

57. $4(5x + 9) = 4 \cdot 5x + 4 \cdot 9 = 20x + 36$

59. $(x - 5)(x + 7) = x \cdot x + x \cdot 7 + (-5)(x) + (-5)(7) = x^2 + 2x - 35$

61. $(3x - 5)^2 = (3x)^2 - 2(3x)(5) + (5x)^2 = 9x^2 - 30x + 25$

63. $(5x + 3)(5x + 4) = 5x \cdot 5x + 5x \cdot 4 + 3 \cdot 5x + 3 \cdot 4 = 25x^2 + 35x + 12$

65. $(4b - 5)(4b + 5) = (4b)^2 - (5)^2 = 16b^2 - 25$

67. $-5x(4x^2 - 7x + 2) = (-5x)(4x^2) + (-5x)(-7x) + (-5x)(2) = -20x^3 + 35x^2 - 10x$

69. $(4 - a)^3 = (4 - a)(4 - a)^2 = (4 - a)(16 - 8a + a^2) =$

$4 \cdot 16 + (4)(-8a) + 4 \cdot a^2 + (-a)(16) + (-a)(-8a) + (-a)(a^2) = 64 - 48a + 12a^2 - a^3$

Applications

71. (a) $(x + 2)(x + 2) = (x)^2 + 2(x)(2) + (2)^2 = x^2 + 4x + 4$

(b) $x \cdot x + 2 \cdot x + x \cdot 2 + 2 \cdot 2 = x^2 + 2x + 2x + 4 = x^2 + 4x + 4$

73. (a) $(2x + 3)(2x + 3) = (2x)^2 + 2(2x)(3) + (3)^2 = 4x^2 + 12x + 9$

(b) $2x \cdot 2x + 3 \cdot 2x + 2x \cdot 3 + 3 \cdot 3 = 4x^2 + 6x + 6x + 9 = 4x^2 + 12x + 9$

75 (a) $6(x + 5)^2 = 6(x^2 + 10x + 25) = 6x^2 + 60x + 150$

(b) $(x + 5)^3 = (x + 5)(x + 5)^2 = (x + 5)(x^2 + 10x + 25) =$

$x \cdot x^2 + x \cdot 10x + x \cdot 25 + 5 \cdot x^2 + 5 \cdot 10x + 5 \cdot 25 = x^3 + 15x^2 + 75x + 125$

77. (a) $(1 + x)^2 = (1)^2 + 2(1)(x) + (x)^2 = 1 + 2x + x^2$

(b) $1 + 2x + x^2 = 1 + 2(0.10) + (0.10)^2 = 1 + 0.20 + 0.01 = 1.21$; the money increases by 1.21 times in 2 years if the interest rate is 10%.

79. (a) $(1 - x)^2 = (1)^2 - 2(1)(x) + (x)^2 = 1 - 2x + x^2$

(b) $1 - 2x + x^2 = 1 - 2(0.50) + (0.50)^2 = 1 - 1 + 0.25 = 0.25$; if the chance of rain on each day is 50%, then there is a 25% chance of no rain on either day.

81. (a) $(z + 16)^2 - (z)^2 = (z^2 + 32z + 256) - (z^2) = 32z + 256$

(b) $32z + 256 = 32(60) + 256 = 1920 + 256 = 2176$; the area of an 8 foot wide sidewalk around a 60×60 pool is 2176 ft^2.

Checking Basic Concepts for Sections 5.3 & 5.4

1. (a) $(-3xy^4)(5x^2y) = (-3)(5)xx^2y^4y = -15x^3y^5$

(b) $-x(6 - 4x) = (-x)(6) + (-x)(-4x) = -6x + 4x^2$

(c) $3ab(a^2 - 2ab + b^2)3ab \cdot a^2 + (3ab)(-2ab) + 3ab \cdot b^2 = 3a^3b - 6a^2b^2 + 3ab^3$

2. (a) $(x + 3)(4x - 3) = x \cdot 4x + (x)(-3) + 3 \cdot 4x + (3)(-3) = 4x^2 + 9x - 9$

(b) $(x^2 - 1)(2x^2 + 2) = x^2 \cdot 2x^2 + x^2 \cdot 2 + (-1)(2x^2) + (-1)(2) = 2x^4 - 2$

(c) $(x + y)(x^2 - xy + y^2) = x \cdot x^2 + (x)(-xy) + x \cdot y^2 + y \cdot x^2 + (y)(-xy) + y \cdot y^2 = x^3 + y^3$

3. (a) $(5x + 2)(5x - 2) = (5x)^2 - (2)^2 = 25x^2 - 4$

(b) $(x + 3)^2 = (x)^2 + 2(x)(3) - (3)^2 = x^2 + 6x + 9$

(c) $(2 - 7x)^2 = (2)^2 - 2(2)(7x) + (7x)^2 = 4 - 28x + 49x^2$

(d) $(t + 2)^3 = (t + 2)(t + 2)^2 = (t + 2)(t^2 + 4t + 4) = t \cdot t^2 + t \cdot 4t + t \cdot 4 + 2 \cdot t^2 + 2 \cdot 4t + 2 \cdot 4 =$
$t^3 + 6t^2 + 12t + 8$

4. (a) $4\pi(a + 7)^2 = 4\pi(a^2 + 14a + 49) = 4\pi(a^2) + 4\pi(14a) + 4\pi(49) = 4\pi a^2 + 56\pi a + 196\pi$

(b) $4\pi a^2 + 56\pi a + 196\pi = 4\pi(8)^2 + 56\pi(8) + 196\pi = 256\pi + 448\pi + 196\pi = 900\pi$

5. (a) $(m + 5)^2 = (m)^2 + 2(5)(m) + (5)^2 = m^2 + 10m + 25$

(b) $m \cdot m + m \cdot 5 + 5 \cdot m + 5 \cdot 5 = m^2 + 5m + 5m + 25 = m^2 + 10m + 25$

5.5: Integer Exponents and the Quotient Rule

Concepts

1. $a^{-n} = \dfrac{1}{a^n}$

3. $\dfrac{1}{a^{-n}} = \dfrac{a^n}{1} = a^n$

5. $\dfrac{a^m}{a^n} = a^{m-n}$

7. $\left(\dfrac{a}{b}\right)^{-n} = \left(\dfrac{b}{a}\right)^n$

9. $1 \le |b| < 10$

Negative Exponents

11. $4^{-1} = \dfrac{1}{4^1} = \dfrac{1}{4}$

13. $\left(\dfrac{1}{3}\right)^{-2} = \left(\dfrac{3}{1}\right)^2 = \dfrac{3^2}{1^2} = \dfrac{3 \cdot 3}{1 \cdot 1} = \dfrac{9}{1} = 9$

15. $2^3 \cdot 2^{-2} = 2^{3+(-2)} = 2^1 = 2$

17. $10^4 \cdot 10^{-2} = 10^{4+(-2)} = 10^2 = 10 \cdot 10 = 100$

19. $3^{-2} \cdot 3^{-1} \cdot 3^{-1} = 3^{-2+(-1)+(-1)} = 3^{-4} = \dfrac{1}{3^4} = \dfrac{1}{3 \cdot 3 \cdot 3 \cdot 3} = \dfrac{1}{81}$

21. $(2^3)^{-1} = 2^{(3)(-1)} = 2^{-3} = \frac{1}{2^3} = \frac{1}{2 \cdot 2 \cdot 2} = \frac{1}{8}$

23. $(3^2 4^3)^{-1} = 3^{(2)(-1)} 4^{(3)(-1)} = 3^{-2} 4^{-3} = \frac{1}{3^2 4^3} = \frac{1}{(3 \cdot 3)(4 \cdot 4 \cdot 4)} = \frac{1}{9 \cdot 64} = \frac{1}{576}$

25. $\frac{4^5}{4^2} = 4^{5-2} = 4^3 = 4 \cdot 4 \cdot 4 = 64$

27. $\frac{1^9}{1^7} = 1^{9-7} = 1^2 = 1 \cdot 1 = 1$

29. $\frac{1}{4^{-3}} = 4^3 = 4 \cdot 4 \cdot 4 = 64$

31. $\frac{5^{-2}}{5^{-4}} = 5^{-2-(-4)} = 5^2 = 5 \cdot 5 = 25$

33. $\left(\frac{2}{7}\right)^{-2} = \left(\frac{7}{2}\right)^2 = \frac{7^2}{2^2} = \frac{7 \cdot 7}{2 \cdot 2} = \frac{49}{4}$

35. $x^{-1} = \frac{1}{x}$

37. $a^{-4} = \frac{1}{a^4}$

39. $x^{-2} \cdot x^{-1} \cdot x = x^{-2+(-1)+1} = x^{-2} = \frac{1}{x^2}$

41. $a^{-5} \cdot a^{-2} \cdot a^{-1} = a^{-5+(-2)+(-1)} = a^{-8} = \frac{1}{a^8}$

43. $x^2 y^{-3} x^{-5} y^6 = x^{2+(-5)} y^{-3+6} = x^{-3} y^3 = \frac{y^3}{x^3}$

45. $(xy)^{-3} = x^{-3} y^{-3} = \frac{1}{x^3 y^3}$

47. $(2t)^{-4} = 2^{-4} t^{-4} = \frac{1}{2^4 t^4} = \frac{1}{16t^4}$

49. $(x+1)^{-7} = \frac{1}{(x+1)^7}$

51. $(a^{-2})^{-4} = a^{(-2)(-4)} = a^8$

53. $(rt^3)^{-2} = r^{-2} t^{(3)(-2)} = r^{-2} t^{-6} = \frac{1}{r^2 t^6}$

55. $(ab)^2 (a^2)^{-3} = (a^2 b^2)(a^{(2)(-3)}) = (a^2 b^2)(a^{-6}) = a^{2+(-6)} b^2 = a^{-4} b^2 = \frac{b^2}{a^4}$

57. $\frac{x^4}{x^2} = x^{4-2} = x^2$

59. $\frac{a^{10}}{a^{-3}} = a^{10-(-3)} = a^{13}$

61. $\frac{4z}{2z^4} = \frac{4}{2} \cdot \frac{z}{z^4} = 2z^{1-4} = 2z^{-3} = \frac{2}{z^3}$

63. $\frac{-4xy^5}{6x^3 y^2} = \frac{-4}{6} \cdot \frac{xy^5}{x^3 y^2} = \frac{-2}{3} x^{1-3} y^{5-2} = \frac{-2}{3} x^{-2} y^3 = -\frac{2y^3}{3x^2}$

65. $\frac{x^{-4}}{x^{-1}} = x^{-4-(-1)} = x^{-3} = \frac{1}{x^3}$

67. $\dfrac{10b^{-4}}{5b^{-5}} = \dfrac{10}{5} \cdot \dfrac{b^{-4}}{b^{-5}} = 2b^{-4-(-5)} = 2b$

69. $\left(\dfrac{a}{b}\right)^3 = \dfrac{a^3}{b^3}$

71. $\dfrac{1}{y^{-5}} = y^5$

73. $\dfrac{4}{2t^{-3}} = \dfrac{4}{2} \cdot \dfrac{1}{t^{-3}} = 2 \cdot t^3 = 2t^3$

75. $\dfrac{1}{(xy)^{-2}} = \dfrac{1}{x^{-2}y^{-2}} = x^2y^2$

77. $\dfrac{1}{(a^2b)^{-3}} = \dfrac{1}{a^{(2)(-3)}b^{-3}} = \dfrac{1}{a^{-6}b^{-3}} = a^6b^3$

79. $\left(\dfrac{a}{b}\right)^{-2} = \left(\dfrac{b}{a}\right)^2 = \dfrac{b^2}{a^2}$

81. $\left(\dfrac{u}{4v}\right)^{-1} = \left(\dfrac{4v}{u}\right)^1 = \dfrac{4v}{u}$

Scientific Notation

83. Thousand

85. Billion

87. Hundredth

89. Move the decimal point three places to the right, $2 \times 10^3 = 2000$.

91. Move the decimal point four places to the right, $4.5 \times 10^4 = 45{,}000$.

93. Move the decimal point three places to the left, $8 \times 10^{-3} = 0.008$.

95. Move the decimal point four places to the left, $4.56 \times 10^{-4} = 0.000456$.

97. Move the decimal point seven places to the right, $3.9 \times 10^7 = 39{,}000{,}000$.

99. Move the decimal point five places to the right, $-5 \times 10^5 = -500{,}000$.

101. Move the decimal point three places to the left, $2000 = 2 \times 10^3$.

103. Move the decimal point two places to the left, $567 = 5.67 \times 10^2$.

105. Move the decimal point seven places to the left, $12{,}000{,}000 = 1.2 \times 10^7$.

107. Move the decimal point three places to the right, $0.004 = 4 \times 10^{-3}$.

109. Move the decimal point four places to the right, $0.000895 = 8.95 \times 10^{-4}$.

111. Move the decimal point two places to the right, $-0.05 = -5 \times 10^{-2}$.

113. $(5 \times 10^3)(3 \times 10^2) = (5 \cdot 3) \times (10^3 \cdot 10^2) = 15 \times 10^{3+2} = 15 \times 10^5 = 1.5 \times 10^6$;

Move the decimal point six places to the right, $1.5 \times 10^6 = 1{,}500{,}000$.

115. $(-3 \times 10^{-3})(5 \times 10^2) = (-3 \cdot 5) \times (10^{-3} \cdot 10^2) = -15 \times 10^{-3+2} = -15 \times 10^{-1} = -1.5 \times 10^0 = -1.5$

117. $\dfrac{4 \times 10^5}{2 \times 10^2} = \dfrac{4}{2} \cdot \dfrac{10^5}{10^2} = 2 \times 10^{5-2} = 2 \times 10^3$;

Move the decimal point three places to the right, $2 \times 10^3 = 2000$.

119. $\dfrac{8 \times 10^{-6}}{4 \times 10^{-3}} = \dfrac{8}{4} \cdot \dfrac{10^{-6}}{10^{-3}} = 2 \times 10^{-6-(-3)} = 2 \times 10^{-3}$;

Move the decimal point two places to the left, $2 \times 10^{-3} = 0.002$.

Applications

121. (a) $(1.86 \times 10^5)(3.15 \times 10^7) = (1.86 \cdot 3.15) \times (10^5 \cdot 10^7) \approx 5.859 \times 10^{5+7} \approx 5.859 \times 10^{12}$ miles.

(b) $(5.859 \times 10^{12})(4.27) = (5.859 \cdot 4.27) \times (10^{12}) \approx 25 \times 10^{12} \approx 2.5 \times 10^{13}$ miles.

123. $\dfrac{10^5 \cdot \pi \text{ (light years)}}{1} \div \dfrac{2 \times 10^8 \text{ (years)}}{1} \cdot \dfrac{5.859 \times 10^{12}}{1} \approx 9.2 \times 10^9$ miles.

125. (a) Move the decimal point 12 places to the left, $9{,}963{,}000{,}000{,}000 = 9.963 \times 10^{12}$.

(b) $\dfrac{9.963 \times 10^{12}}{2.81 \times 10^8} = \dfrac{9.963}{2.81} \cdot \dfrac{10^{12}}{10^8} \approx 3.5456 \times 10^{12-8} \approx 3.5456 \times 10^4 \approx \$35{,}456$

5.6: Division of Polynomials

Concepts

1. $\dfrac{a + b}{d} = \dfrac{a}{d} + \dfrac{b}{d}$

3. $\dfrac{5x^2 + 2x}{2x} = \dfrac{5x^2}{2x} + \dfrac{2x}{2x} = \dfrac{5x}{2} + 1 \neq 5x^2 + 1$; No

5. $9 \cdot 4 + 1 = 37$

Division by a Monomial

7. $\dfrac{6x^2}{3x} = \dfrac{6}{3} \cdot \dfrac{x^2}{x} = 2x^{2-1} = 2x$; Checking: $3x \cdot 2x = (3 \cdot 2)(x \cdot x) = 6x^2$

9. $\dfrac{z^4 + z^3}{z} = \dfrac{z^4}{z} + \dfrac{z^3}{z} = z^{4-1} + x^{3-1} = z^3 + z^2$; Checking: $(z)(z^3 + z^2) = (z^3)(z) + (z^2)(z) = z^4 + z^3$

11. $\dfrac{a^5 - 6a^3}{2a^3} = \dfrac{a^5}{2a^3} - \dfrac{6a^3}{2a^3} = \dfrac{1}{2}a^{5-3} - 3a^{3-3} = \dfrac{a^2}{2} - 3a^0 = \dfrac{a^2}{2} - 3$

Checking: $(2a^3)\left(\dfrac{a^2}{2} - 3\right) = (2a^3)\left(\dfrac{a^2}{2}\right) - (2a^3)(3) = \dfrac{2a^{3+2}}{2} - 6a^3 = a^5 - 6a^3$

13. $\dfrac{4x - 7x^4}{x^2} = \dfrac{4x}{x^2} - \dfrac{7x^4}{x^2} = 4x^{1-2} - 7x^{4-2} = 4x^{-1} - 7x^2 = \dfrac{4}{x} - 7x^2$

15. $\dfrac{9x^4 - 3x + 6}{3x} = \dfrac{9x^4}{3x} - \dfrac{3x}{3x} + \dfrac{6}{3x} = 3x^{4-1} - 1 + \dfrac{2}{x} = 3x^3 - 1 + \dfrac{2}{x}$

17. $\dfrac{12y^4 - 3y^2 + 6y}{3y^2} = \dfrac{12y^4}{3y^2} - \dfrac{3y^2}{3y^2} + \dfrac{6y}{3y^2} = 4y^{4-2} - 1 + 2y^{1-2} = 4y^2 - 1 + 2y^{-1} = 4y^2 - 1 + \dfrac{2}{y}$

19. $\dfrac{15m^4 - 10m^3 + 20m^2}{5m^2} = \dfrac{15m^4}{5m^2} - \dfrac{10m^3}{5m^2} + \dfrac{20m^2}{5m^2} = 3m^{4-2} - 2m^{3-2} + 4m^{2-2} = 3m^2 - 2m + 4$

21.

$$\begin{array}{r} 2x + 1 \\ x - 2\overline{)2x^2 - 3x + 1} \\ \underline{2x^2 - 4x} \\ x + 1 \\ \underline{x - 2} \\ 3 \end{array}$$

The solution is: $2x + 1 + \dfrac{3}{x - 2}$

Checking:

$(x - 2)(2x + 1) + 3 = x \cdot 2x + x \cdot 1 + (-2)(2x) + (-2)(1) + 3 = 2x^2 + x - 4x - 2 + 3 = 2x^2 - 3x + 1$

23.

$$\begin{array}{r} x + 1 \\ x + 1\overline{)x^2 + 2x + 1} \\ \underline{x^2 + x} \\ x + 1 \\ \underline{x + 1} \\ 0 \end{array}$$

The solution is: $x + 1$

Checking: $(x + 1)(x + 1) = (x)^2 + (2)(x)(1) + (1)^2 = x^2 + 2x + 1$

25.

$$\begin{array}{r} x^2 + 1 \\ x - 1\overline{)x^3 - x^2 + x - 2} \\ \underline{x^3 - x^2} \\ x - 2 \\ \underline{x - 1} \\ -1 \end{array}$$

The solution is: $x^2 + 1 + \dfrac{-1}{x - 1}$

Checking: $(x - 1)(x^2 + 1) + (-1) = x \cdot x^2 + x \cdot 1 + (-1)(x^2) + (-1)(1) + (-1) =$

$x^3 + x - x^2 - 1 - 1 = x^3 - x^2 + x - 2$

27.

$$\begin{array}{r} x^2 - x + 2 \\ 4x + 1\overline{)4x^3 - 3x^2 + 7x + 3} \\ \underline{4x^3 + x^2} \\ -4x^2 + 7x \\ \underline{-4x^2 - x} \\ 8x + 3 \\ \underline{8x + 2} \\ 1 \end{array}$$

The solution is: $x^2 - x + 2 + \dfrac{1}{4x + 1}$

29.

$x - 2\overline{)x^3 - x + 2} \Rightarrow$

$$\begin{array}{r} x^2 + 2x + 3 \\ x - 2\overline{)x^3 - 0x^2 - x + 2} \\ \underline{x^3 - 2x^2} \\ 2x^2 - x \\ \underline{2x^2 - 4x} \\ 3x + 2 \\ \underline{3x - 6} \\ 8 \end{array}$$

The solution is: $x^2 + 2x + 3 + \dfrac{8}{x - 2}$

31. $x - 1\overline{)3x^3 + 2} \Rightarrow$

$$\begin{array}{r} 3x^2 + 3x + 3 \qquad\qquad\quad \\ x - 1\overline{)3x^3 - 0x^2 + 0x + 2} \\ \underline{3x^3 - 3x^2} \qquad\qquad\quad \\ 3x^2 + 0x \qquad\quad \\ \underline{3x^2 - 3x} \qquad\quad \\ 3x + 2 \\ \underline{3x - 3} \\ 5 \end{array}$$

The solution is: $3x^2 + 3x + 3 + \dfrac{5}{x - 1}$

33. $x^2 + 1\overline{)x^3 + 3x^2 + 1} \Rightarrow$

$$\begin{array}{r} x + 3 \qquad\qquad\quad \\ x^2 + 1\overline{)x^3 + 3x^2 + 0x + 1} \\ \underline{x^3 + 0x^2 + x} \qquad\quad \\ 3x^2 - x + 1 \\ \underline{3x^2 + 0x + 3} \\ -x - 2 \end{array}$$

The solution is: $x + 3 + \dfrac{-x - 2}{x^2 + 1}$

35. $x^2 - x + 1\overline{)x^3 + 1} \Rightarrow$

$$\begin{array}{r} x + 1 \qquad\qquad\quad \\ x^2 - x + 1\overline{)x^3 + 0x^2 + 0x + 1} \\ \underline{x^3 - x^2 + x} \qquad\quad \\ x^2 - x + 1 \\ \underline{x^2 - x + 1} \\ 0 \end{array}$$

The solution is: $x + 1$

37. $x + 2\overline{)x^3 + 8} \Rightarrow$

$$\begin{array}{r} x^2 - 2x + 4 \qquad\qquad\quad \\ x + 2\overline{)x^3 + 0x^2 + 0x + 8} \\ \underline{x^3 + 2x^2} \qquad\qquad\quad \\ -2x^2 + 0x \qquad\quad \\ \underline{-2x^2 - 4x} \qquad\quad \\ 4x + 8 \\ \underline{4x + 8} \\ 0 \end{array}$$

The solution is: $x^2 - 2x + 4$

Applications

39. $2x \cdot L = 8x^2 \Rightarrow L = \dfrac{8x^2}{2x} \Rightarrow L = 4x^{2-1} \Rightarrow L = 4x$

41. $2x^2 \cdot H = 2x^2 + 4x^2 \Rightarrow H = \dfrac{2x^3 + 4x^2}{2x^2} \Rightarrow H = \dfrac{2x^3}{2x^2} + \dfrac{4x^2}{2x^2} = x^{3-2} + 2x^{2-2} = x + 2$. See Figure 41.

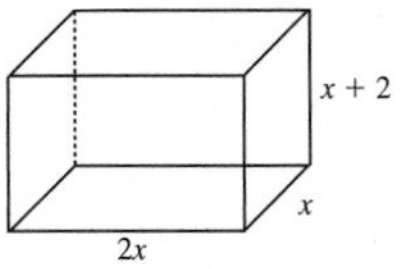

Figure 41

Checking Basic Concepts for Sections 5.5 & 5.6

1. (a) $9^{-2} = \dfrac{1}{9^2} = \dfrac{1}{9 \cdot 9} = \dfrac{1}{81}$

   (b) $\dfrac{3x^{-3}}{6x^4} = \dfrac{1}{2}x^{-3-4} = \dfrac{1}{2}x^{-7} = \dfrac{1}{2x^7}$

   (c) $(4ab^{-4})^{-2} = 4^{-2}a^{-2}b^8 = \dfrac{b^8}{16a^2}$

2. (a) $\dfrac{1}{z^{-5}} = z^5$

   (b) $\dfrac{x^{-3}}{y^{-6}} = \dfrac{y^6}{x^3}$

   (c) $\left(\dfrac{3}{x^2}\right)^{-3} = \left(\dfrac{x^2}{3}\right)^3 = \dfrac{x^{2\cdot 3}}{3^3} = \dfrac{x^6}{27}$

3. (a) Move the decimal point four places to the left: $45{,}000 = 4.5 \times 10^4$.

   (b) Move the decimal point four places to the right: $0.000234 = 2.34 \times 10^{-4}$.

   (c) Move the decimal point two places to the right: $0.01 = 1 \times 10^{-2}$.

4. (a) Move the decimal point four places to the right: $4.71 \times 10^4 = 47{,}100$.

   (b) Move the decimal point three places to the left: $6 \times 10^{-3} = 0.006$.

5. $\dfrac{25a^4 - 15a^3}{5a^3} = \dfrac{25a^4}{5a^3} - \dfrac{15a^3}{5a^3} = 5a^{4-3} - 3a^{3-3} = 5a - 3$

6. $$\begin{array}{r l} & 3x + 2 \\ x - 1 \overline{)} & 3x^2 - x - 4 \\ & \underline{3x^2 - 3x} \\ & \quad 2x - 4 \\ & \quad \underline{2x - 2} \\ & \quad\quad -2 \end{array}$$
   The quotient is: $3x + 2$; The remainder is: -2

7. (a) Move the decimal point seven places to the left: $93{,}000{,}000 = 9.3 \times 10^7$.

   (b) $\dfrac{9.3 \times 10^7}{1.86 \times 10^5} = \dfrac{9.3}{1.86} \cdot \dfrac{10^7}{10^5} \approx 5 \times 10^{7-5} \approx 5 \times 10^2 \approx 500$ seconds. (About 8 minutes 20 seconds)

Chapter 5 Review Exercises

Section 5.1

1. $5^3 = 5 \cdot 5 \cdot 5 = 125$
2. $-3^4 = -(3 \cdot 3 \cdot 3 \cdot 3) = -81$
3. $4(-2)^0 = 4(1) = 4$
4. $3 + 3^2 - 3^0 = 3 + (3 \cdot 3) - 1 = 3 + 9 - 1 = 11$
5. $\dfrac{-5^2}{5} = \dfrac{-(5 \cdot 5)}{5} = \dfrac{-25}{5} = -5$
6. $\left(\dfrac{-5}{5}\right)^2 = \dfrac{(-5)(-5)}{(5)(5)} = \dfrac{25}{25} = 1$

7. $6^2 \cdot 6^3 = 6^{2+3} = 6^5$

8. $10^5 \cdot 10^7 = 10^{5+7} = 10^{12}$

9. $z^4 \cdot z^5 = z^{4+5} = z^9$

10. $y^2 \cdot y \cdot y^3 = y^{2+1+3} = y^6$

11. $5x^2 \cdot 6x^7 = 5 \cdot 6 \cdot x^{2+7} = 30x^9$

12. $(ab^3)(a^3b) = a^{1+3}b^{3+1} = a^4b^4$

13. $(2^5)^2 = 2^{5\cdot 2} = 2^{10}$

14. $(m^4)^5 = m^{4\cdot 5} = m^{20}$

15. $(ab)^3 = a^3b^3$

16. $(x^2y^3)^4 = x^{2\cdot 4}y^{3\cdot 4} = x^8y^{12}$

17. $(xy)^3(x^2y^4)^2 = (x^3y^3)(x^{2\cdot 2}y^{4\cdot 2}) = (x^3y^3)(x^4y^8) = x^{3+4}y^{3+8} = x^7y^{11}$

18. $(a^2b^9)^0 = 1$

19. $(r - t)^4(r - t)^5 = (r - t)^{4+5} = (r - t)^9$

20. $(a + b)^2(a + b)^4 = (a + b)^{2+4} = (a + b)^6$

Section 5.2

21. degree is 7; coefficient is 6

22. degree is 5; coefficient is −1

23. Yes, it is a polynomial; 1 term: $8y$; 1 variable: y; y^1 so it is a 1st degree polynomial.

24. Yes, it is a polynomial; 4 terms: $8x^3$, $-3x^2$, x and -5; 1 variable: x; x^3 so it is a 3rd degree polynomial.

25. Yes, it is a polynomial; 3 terms: a^2, $2ab$ and b^2; 2 variable: a and b; a^2 so it is a 2nd degree polynomial.

26. No, it is not a polynomial, because there are variables in the denominator.

27.
$$\begin{array}{r} 3x^2 + 4x + 8 \\ +\ 2x^2 - 5x - 5 \\ \hline 5x^2 - x + 3 \end{array}$$

28. $-6x^2 + 3x + 7$

29. $(4x - 3) + (-x + 7) = 4x + (-x) + (-3) + 7 = 3x + 4$

30. $(3x^2 - 1) - (5x^2 + 12) = (3x^2 - 1) + (-5x^2 - 12) = 3x^2 + (-5x^2) + (-1) + (-12) = -2x^2 - 13$

31. $(x^2 + 5x + 6) - (3x^2 - 4x + 1) = (x^2 + 5x + 6) + (-3x^2 + 4x - 1) =$
$x^2 + (-3x^2) + 5x + 4x + 6 + (-1) = -2x^2 + 9x + 5$

32. $(a^3 + 4a^2) + (a^3 - 5a^2 + 7a) = a^3 + a^3 + 4a^2 + (-5a^2) + 7a = 2a^3 - a^2 + 7a$

33. $(xy + y^2) + (4y^2 - 4xy) = y^2 + 4y^2 + xy + (-4xy) = 5y^2 - 3xy$

34. $(7x^2 + 2xy + y^2) - (7x^2 - 2xy + y^2) = (7x^2 + 2xy + y^2) + (7x^2 + 2xy - y^2) =$
$7x^2 + (-7x^2) + 2xy + 2xy + y^2 + (-y^2) = 4xy$

Section 5.3

35. $-x^2 \cdot x^3 = -x^{2+3} = -x^5$

36. $-(r^2t^3)(rt) = -(r^{2+1}t^{3+1}) = -r^3t^4$

37. $-3(2t - 5) = (-3)(2t) + (-3)(-5) = -6t + 15$

38. $2y(1 - 6y) = 2y \cdot 1 + 2y(-6y) = 2y - 12y^2$

39. $6x^3(3x^2 + 5x) = 6x^3 \cdot 3x^2 + 6x^3 \cdot 5x = 18x^{3+2} + 30x^{3+1} = 18x^5 + 30x^4$

40. $-x(x^2 - 2x + 9) = (-x)(x^2) + (-x)(-2x) + (-x)(9) = -x^{1+2} + 2x^{1+1} - 9x = -x^3 + 2x^2 - 9x$

41. $-ab(a^2 - 2ab + b^2) = -ab \cdot a^2 + (-ab)(-2ab) + (-ab)(b^2) = -a^3b + 2a^2b^2 - ab^3$

42. $(a - 2)(a + 5) = a \cdot a + a \cdot 5 + (-2)(a) + (-2)(5) = a^2 + 5a - 2a - 10 = a^2 + 3a - 10$

43. $(8x - 3)(x + 2) = 8x \cdot x + 8x \cdot 2 + (-3)(x) + (-3)(2) = 8x^2 + 16x - 3x - 6 = 8x^2 + 13x - 6$

44. $(2x - 1)(1 - x) = 2x \cdot 1 + (2x)(-x) + (-1)(1) + (-1)(-x) = 2x - 2x^2 - 1 + x = -2x^2 + 3x - 1$

45. $(y^2 + 1)(2y + 1) = y^2 \cdot 2y + y^2 \cdot 1 + 1 \cdot 2y + 1 \cdot 1 = 2y^3 + y^2 + 2y + 1$

46. $(y^2 - 1)(2y^2 + 1) = y^2 \cdot 2y^2 + y^2 \cdot 1 + (-1)(2y^2) + (-1)(1) = 2y^4 + y^2 - 2y^2 - 1 = 2y^4 - y^2 - 1$

47. $(z + 1)(z^2 - z + 1) = z \cdot z^2 + (z)(-z) + z \cdot 1 + 1 \cdot z^2 + (1)(-z) + 1 \cdot 1 = z^3 - z^2 + z + z^2 - z + 1 =$
$z^3 + 1$

48. $(4z - 3)(z^2 - 3z + 1) = 4z \cdot z^2 + (4z)(-3z) + 4z \cdot 1 + (-3)(z^2) + (-3)(-3z) + (-3)(1) =$
$4z^3 - 12z^2 + 4z - 3z^2 + 9z - 3 = 4z^3 - 15z^2 + 13z - 3$

49. (a) $z^2 + z$; See Figure 49.

    (b) $z(z + 1) = z \cdot z + z \cdot 1 = z^2 + 1$

50. (a) $2x^2 + 4x$; See Figure 50.

    (b) $2x(x + 2) = 2x \cdot x + 2x \cdot 2 = 2x^2 + 4x$

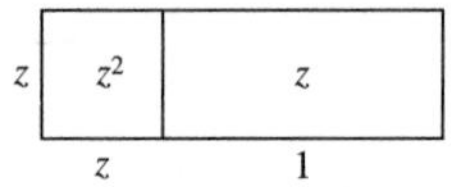

Figure 49

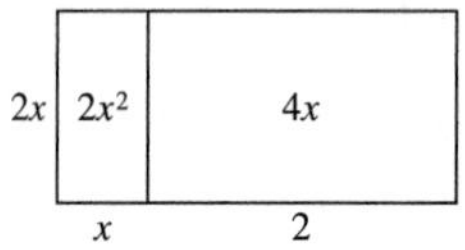

Figure 50

Section 5.4

51. $(z + 2)(z - 2) = (z)^2 - (2)^2 = z^2 - 4$

52. $(5z - 9)(5z + 9) = (5z)^2 - (9)^2 = 25z^2 - 81$

53. $(1 - 3y)(1 + 3y) = (1)^2 - (3y)^2 = 1 - 9y^2$

54. $(5x + 4y)(5x - 4y) = (5x)^2 - (4y)^2 = 25x^2 - 16y^2$

55. $(rt + 1)(rt - 1) = (rt)^2 - (1)^2 = r^2t^2 - 1$

56. $(2m^2 - n^2)(2m^2 + n^2) = (2m^2)^2 - (n^2)^2 = 4m^4 - n^4$

57. $(x + 1)^2 = (x)^2 + (2)(x)(1) + (1)^2 = x^2 + 2x + 1$

58. $(4x + 3)^2 = (4x)^2 + (2)(4x)(3) + (3)^2 = 16x^2 + 24x + 9$

59. $(y-3)^2 = (y)^2 - (2)(y)(3) + (3)^2 = y^2 - 6y + 9$

60. $(2y-5)^2 = (2y)^2 - (2)(2y)(5) + (5)^2 = 4y^2 - 20y + 25$

61. $(4+a)^2 = (4)^2 + (2)(4)(a) + (a)^2 = 16 + 8a + a^2$

62. $(4-a)^2 = (4)^2 - (2)(4)(a) + (a)^2 = 16 - 8a + a^2$

63. $(x^2+y^2)^2 = (x^2)^2 + (2)(x^2)(y^2) + (y^2)^2 = x^4 + 2x^2y^2 + y^4$

64. $(xy-2)^2 = (xy)^2 - (2)(xy)(2) + (2)^2 = x^2y^2 - 4xy + 4$

65. $(z+5)^3 = (z+5)(z+5)^2 = (z+5)(z^2+10z+25) =$

$z \cdot z^2 + z \cdot 10z + z \cdot 25 + 5 \cdot z^2 + 5 \cdot 10z + 5 \cdot 25 = z^3 + 10z^2 + 25z + 5z^2 + 50z + 125 =$

$z^3 + 15z^2 + 75z + 125$

66. $(2z-1)^3 = (2z-1)(2z-1)^2 = (2z-1)(4z^2-4z+1) =$

$2z \cdot 4z^2 + (2z)(-4z) + 2z \cdot 1 + (-1)(4z^2) + (-1)(-4z) + (-1)(1) = 8z^3 - 8z^2 + 2z - 4z^2 + 4z - 1 =$

$8z^3 - 12z^2 + 6z - 1$

Section 5.5

67. $9^{-1} = \frac{1}{9}$

68. $3^{-2} = \frac{1}{3^2} = \frac{1}{3 \cdot 3} = \frac{1}{9}$

69. $4^3 \cdot 4^{-2} = 4^{3+(-2)} = 4^1 = 4$

70. $10^{-6} \cdot 10^3 = 10^{-6+3} = 10^{-3} = \frac{1}{10^3} = \frac{1}{10 \cdot 10 \cdot 10} = \frac{1}{1000}$

71. $\frac{1}{6^{-2}} = 6^2 = 36$

72. $\frac{5^7}{5^9} = 5^{7-9} = 5^{-2} = \frac{1}{5^2} = \frac{1}{5 \cdot 5} = \frac{1}{25}$

73. $z^{-2} = \frac{1}{z^2}$

74. $y^{-4} = \frac{1}{y^4}$

75. $a^{-4} \cdot a^2 = a^{-4+2} = a^{-2} = \frac{1}{a^2}$

76. $x^2 \cdot x^{-5} \cdot x = x^{2+(-5)+1} = x^{-2} = \frac{1}{x^2}$

77. $(2t)^{-2} = 2^{-2}t^{-2} = \frac{1}{2^2t^2} = \frac{1}{4t^2}$

78. $(ab^2)^{-3} = a^{-3}b^{(2)(-3)} = a^{-3}b^{-6} = \frac{1}{a^3b^6}$

79. $(xy)^{-2}(x^{-2}y)^{-1} = (x^{-2}y^{-2})(x^{(-2)(-1)}y^{-1}) = x^{-2+2}y^{-2+(-1)} = y^{-3} = \frac{1}{y^3}$

80. $\frac{x^6}{x^2} = x^{6-2} = x^4$

81. $\frac{4x}{2x^4} = 2x^{1-4} = 2x^{-3} = \frac{2}{x^3}$

82. $\dfrac{20x^5y^3}{30xy^6} = \dfrac{2}{3}x^{5-1}y^{3-6} = \dfrac{2}{3}x^4y^{-3} = \dfrac{2x^4}{3y^3}$

83. $\left(\dfrac{a}{b}\right)^5 = \dfrac{a^5}{b^5}$

84. $\dfrac{4}{t^{-4}} = 4t^4$

85. $\left(\dfrac{x}{3}\right)^{-3} = \left(\dfrac{3}{x}\right)^3 = \dfrac{3^3}{x^3} = \dfrac{27}{x^3}$

86. $\dfrac{2}{(ab)^{-1}} = 2ab$

87. $\left(\dfrac{x}{y}\right)^{-2} = \left(\dfrac{y}{x}\right)^2 = \dfrac{y^2}{x^2}$

88. $\left(\dfrac{3u}{2v}\right)^{-1} = \left(\dfrac{2v}{3u}\right)^1 = \dfrac{2v}{3u}$

89. Move the decimal point two places to the right, $6 \times 10^2 = 600$.

90. Move the decimal point four places to the right, $5.24 \times 10^4 = 52{,}400$.

91. Move the decimal point three places to the left, $3.7 \times 10^{-3} = 0.0037$.

92. Move the decimal point two places to the left, $6.234 \times 10^{-2} = 0.06234$.

93. Move the decimal point four places to the left, $10{,}000 = 1 \times 10^4$.

94. Move the decimal point seven places to the left, $56{,}100{,}000 = 5.61 \times 10^7$.

95. Move the decimal point five places to the right, $0.000054 = 5.4 \times 10^{-5}$.

96. Move the decimal point three places to the right, $0.001 = 1 \times 10^{-3}$.

97. $(4 \times 10^2)(6 \times 10^4) = (4 \cdot 6) \times (10^2 \cdot 10^4) = 24 \times 10^6 = 2.4 \times 10^7$;

Move the decimal point seven places to the right, $2.4 \times 10^7 = 24{,}000{,}000$.

98. $\left(\dfrac{8 \times 10^3}{4 \times 10^4}\right) = \dfrac{8}{4} \times \dfrac{10^3}{10^4} = 2 \times 10^{3-4} = 2 \times 10^{-1}$;

Move the decimal point one place to the left, $2 \times 10^{-1} = 0.2$.

Section 5.6

99. $\dfrac{5x^2 + 3x}{3x} = \dfrac{5x^2}{3x} + \dfrac{3x}{3x} = \dfrac{5}{3}x^{2-1} + 1 = \dfrac{5}{3}x + 1$; Checking: $3x\left(\dfrac{5}{3}x + 1\right) = 3x \cdot \dfrac{5}{3}x + 3x \cdot 1 = 5x^2 + 3x$

100. $\dfrac{6b^4 - 4b^2 + 2}{2b^2} = \dfrac{6b^4}{2b^2} - \dfrac{4b^2}{2b^2} + \dfrac{2}{2b^2} = 3b^{4-2} - 2b^{2-2} + \dfrac{1}{b^2} = 3b^2 - 2 + \dfrac{1}{b^2}$;

Checking: $(2b^2)\left(3b^2 - 2 + \dfrac{1}{b^2}\right) = 2b^2 \cdot 3b^2 + (2b^2)(-2) + 2b^2 \cdot \dfrac{1}{b^2} = 6b^4 - 4b^2 + 2$

101.

$$\begin{array}{r}
3x + 2 \\
x - 1 \overline{)\, 3x^2 - x + 2} \\
\underline{3x^2 - 3x} \\
2x + 2 \\
\underline{2x - 2} \\
4
\end{array}$$

The solution is: $3x + 2 + \dfrac{4}{x - 1}$

Checking: $(x - 1)(3x + 2) + 4 = x \cdot 3x + x \cdot 2 + (-1)(3x) + (-1)(2) + 4 =$

$3x^2 + 2x - 3x - 2 + 4 = 3x^2 - x + 2$

102.

$$\begin{array}{r}
3x - 4 \\
3x + 2 \overline{)\, 9x^2 - 6x - 2} \\
\underline{9x^2 + 6x} \\
-12x - 2 \\
\underline{-12x - 8} \\
6
\end{array}$$

The solution is: $3x - 4 + \dfrac{6}{3x + 2}$

Checking: $(3x + 2)(3x - 4) + 6 = 3x \cdot 3x + (3x)(-4) + 2 \cdot 3x + (2)(-4) + 6 =$

$9x^2 - 12x + 6x - 8 + 6 = 9x^2 - 6x - 2$

103.

$$\begin{array}{r}
x^2 - 3x - 1 \\
4x + 1 \overline{)\, 4x^3 - 11x^2 - 7x - 1} \\
\underline{4x^3 + x^2} \\
-12x^2 - 7x \\
\underline{-12x^2 - 3x} \\
-4x - 1 \\
\underline{-4x - 1} \\
0
\end{array}$$

The solution is: $x^2 - 3x - 1$

Checking: $(4x + 1)(x^2 - 3x - 1) = 4x \cdot x^2 + (4x)(-3x) + (4x)(-1) + 1 \cdot x^2 + (1)(-3x) + (1)(-1) =$

$4x^3 - 12x^2 - 4x + x^2 - 3x - 1 = 4x^3 - 11x^2 - 7x - 1$

104.

$$\begin{array}{r}
x^2 \\
2x - 1 \overline{)\, 2x^3 - x^2 - 1} \\
\underline{2x^3 - x^2} \\
\underline{0 - 1} \\
-1
\end{array}$$

The solution is: $x^2 + \dfrac{-1}{2x - 1}$

Checking: $(x^2)(2x - 1) + (-1) = x^2 \cdot 2x + (x^2)(-1) + (-1) = 2x^3 - x^2 - 1$

105.

$$\begin{array}{r}
x - 1 \\
x^2 + 1 \overline{)\, x^3 - x^2 - x + 1} \\
\underline{x^3 + 0x^2 + x} \\
-x^2 - 2x \\
\underline{-x^2 + 0x - 1} \\
-2x + 2
\end{array}$$

The solution is: $x - 1 + \dfrac{-2x + 2}{x^2 + 1}$

Checking: $(x - 1)(x^2 + 1) + (-2x + 2) = x \cdot x^2 + x \cdot 1 + (-1)(x^2) + (-1)(1) + (-2x + 2) =$

$x^3 + x - x^2 - 1 - 2x + 2 = x^3 - x^2 - x + 1$

106. $$\begin{array}{r} x^2 + 2x + 5 \\ x^2 + x + 1 \overline{) x^4 + 3x^3 + 8x^2 + 7x + 5} \\ \underline{x^4 + x^3 + x^2} \qquad\qquad \\ 2x^3 + 7x^2 + 7x \qquad \\ \underline{2x^3 + 2x^2 + 2x} \qquad \\ 5x^2 + 5x + 5 \\ \underline{5x^2 + 5x + 5} \\ 0 \end{array}$$

The solution is: $x^2 + 2x + 5$

Checking: $(x^2 + x + 1)(x^2 + 2x + 5) =$

$x^2 \cdot x^2 + x^2 \cdot 2x + x^2 \cdot 5 + x \cdot x^2 + x \cdot 2x + x \cdot 5 + 1 \cdot x^2 + 1 \cdot 2x + 1 \cdot 5 =$

$x^4 + 2x^3 + 5x^2 + x^3 + 2x^2 + 5x + x^2 + 2x + 5 = x^4 + 3x^3 + 8x^2 + 7x + 5$

Applications

107. (a) $t^2 + 60 \Rightarrow 0^2 + 60 = 60$ bpm

(b) $t^2 + 60 \Rightarrow 10^2 + 60 = 100 + 60 = 160$ bpm

(c) It increases.

108. $L \times W = 2xy = 1$ rectangle $\Rightarrow$ 3 rectangles $= 3 \cdot 2xy = 6xy$; for $x = 3$ ft, $y = 4$ ft, $6xy = 6(3)(4) =$ 72 ft^2

109. $5 \cdot 3z = 15z$, $5 \cdot 2z = 10z$, $2z \cdot (3z + 2z) = 6z^2 + 4z^2 \Rightarrow 15z + 10z + 6z^2 + 4z^2 = 10z^2 + 25z$; for $z = 6$ in $\Rightarrow 10z^2 + 25z = 10(6)^2 + 25(6) = 10(36) + 150 = 360 + 150 = 510$ in^2

110. $(x^2y)(x^2y) = x^{2+2}y^{1+1} = x^4y^2$

111. $P(1 + 0.06)^3 = P(1.06)^3 = P(1.191016)$; let $P = \$700 \Rightarrow \$700(1.191016) = \$833.71$.

112. (a) $(2x)(x + 5) = 2x \cdot x + 2x \cdot 5 = 2x^2 + 10x$

(b) $(x + 2)(x + 5) = x \cdot x + x \cdot 5 + 2 \cdot x + 2 \cdot 5 = x^2 + 5x + 2x + 10 = x^2 + 7x + 10$

(c) $(2x)(x + 2) = 2x \cdot x + 2x \cdot 2 = 2x^2 + 4x$

(d) 3 sides $= (2x^2 + 10x) + (x^2 + 7x + 10) + (2x^2 + 4x) = 5x^2 + 21x + 10$

6 sides $= 2(5x^2 + 21x + 10) = 10x^2 + 42x + 20$

113. $\frac{4}{3}\pi(x + 2)^3 = \frac{4}{3}\pi(x + 2)(x + 2)^2 = \frac{4}{3}\pi(x + 2)(x^2 + 4x + 4) =$

$\frac{4}{3}\pi(x \cdot x^2 + x \cdot 4x + x \cdot 4 + 2 \cdot x^2 + 2 \cdot 4x + 2 \cdot 4) = \frac{4}{3}\pi(x^3 + 4x^2 + 4x + 2x^2 + 8x + 8) =$

$\frac{4}{3}\pi(x^3 + 6x^2 + 12x + 8) = \frac{4}{3}\pi \cdot x^3 + \frac{4}{3}\pi \cdot 6x^2 + \frac{4}{3}\pi \cdot 12x + \frac{4}{3}\pi \cdot 8 = \frac{4}{3}\pi x^3 + 8\pi x^2 + 16\pi x + \frac{32}{3}\pi$

114. (a) $t(96 - 16t) = 96t - 16t^2$

(b) $t = 2 \Rightarrow 96t - 16t^2 = 96(2) = 16(2)^2 = 192 - 16(4) = 192 - 64 = 128$, after 2 seconds the ball is 128 feet high.

115. (a) If $P = 2L + 2W$ then $1200 = 2L + 2W \Rightarrow 1200 - 2L = 2W \Rightarrow 600 - L = W$. Now $A = L \cdot W$ so $A = L \cdot (600 - L) \Rightarrow A = 600L - L^2$.

(b) $L = 50 \Rightarrow 600L - L^2 = 600(50) - (50)^2 = 30{,}000 - 2500 = 27{,}500$. A rectangular building with a perimeter of 1200 ft and a side of length 50 ft has an area of 27,500 ft^2.

116. (a) $(x + 5)(x + 5) = (x)^2 + 2(x)(5) + (5)^2 = x^2 + 10x + 25$

(b) $x \cdot x + 5 \cdot x + x \cdot 5 + 5 \cdot 5 = x^2 + 5x + 5x + 25 = x^2 + 10x + 25$

117. (a) $(x + 4)(x + 4) - (x - 4)(x - 4) = x^2 + 8x + 16 - (x^2 - 8x + 16) = 16x$

(b) $x = 100 \Rightarrow 16x = 16(100) = 1600$

118. $P = 6(1.014)^x \Rightarrow P = 6(1.014)^5 \Rightarrow P = 6(1.07199) \Rightarrow P \approx 6.43$ billion.

119. 2.19 trillion $= 2.19 \times 10^{12}$, 249 million $= 2.49 \times 10^8$

$$\frac{2.19 \times 10^{12}}{2.49 \times 10^8} = \frac{2.19}{2.49} \times \frac{10^{12}}{10^8} = 0.8795 \times 10^{12-8} = 0.8795 \times 10^4 = 8.795 \times 10^3 \approx \$8{,}795/\text{person}.$$

120. 211 million $= 2.11 \times 10^8$;

$(2.21)(2.11 \times 10^8) = (2.21)(2.11) \times 10^8 = 4.6631 \times 10^8 \approx 466{,}310{,}000$ gal. or 4.6631×10^8 gal.

Chapter 5 Test

1. Yes, it is a polynomial; 3 terms $5x^2, -3xy, -7y^3$; 2 variables x and y; $y^3 \Rightarrow$ 3rd degree.

2. $x^3 - 4x + 8$

3. $(-3x + 4) + (7x + 2) = (-3x) + (7x) + 4 + 2 = 4x + 6$

4. $(5x^2 - x + 3) - (4x^2 - 2x + 10) = (5x^2 - x + 3) + (-4x^2 + 2x - 10) =$
$5x^2 + (-4x^2) + (-x) + 2x + 3 + (-10) = x^2 + x - 7$

5. $(a^3 + 5ab) + (3a^3 - 3ab) = a^3 + 3a^3 + 5ab + (-3ab) = 4a^3 + 2ab$

6. (a) $-4^2 + 10 = -(4 \cdot 4) + 10 = -16 + 10 = -6$

(b) $8^{-2} = \dfrac{1}{8^2} = \dfrac{1}{8 \cdot 8} = \dfrac{1}{64}$

(c) $\dfrac{1}{2^{-3}} = 2^3 = 2 \cdot 2 \cdot 2 = 8$

7. $x^7 \cdot x^{-3} = x^{7+(-3)} = x^4$

8. $(a^{-1}b^2)^{-3} = a^{(-1)(-3)}b^{(2)(-3)} = a^3b^{-6} = \dfrac{a^3}{b^6}$

9. $ab(a^2 - b^2) = ab \cdot a^2 + ab(-b^2) = a^3b - ab^3$

10. $\left(\dfrac{3a^2}{2b^{-3}}\right)^{-2} = \dfrac{3^{-2}a^{(2)(-2)}}{2^{-2}b^{(-3)(-2)}} = \dfrac{2^2}{3^2a^4b^6} = \dfrac{4}{9a^4b^6}$

11. $\dfrac{12xy^4}{6x^2y} = 2x^{1-2}y^{4-1} = 2x^{-1}y^3 = \dfrac{2y^3}{x}$

12. $3x^2(4x^3 - 6x + 1) = 3x^2 \cdot 4x^3 + (3x^2)(-6x) + 3x^2 \cdot 1 = 12x^5 - 18x^3 + 3x^2$

13. $(z - 3)(2z + 4) = z \cdot 2z + z \cdot 4 + (-3)(2z) + (-3)(4) = 2z^2 + 4z - 6z - 12 = 2z^2 - 2z - 12$

14. $(7y^2 - 3)(7y^2 + 3) = (7y^2)^2 - (3)^2 = 49y^4 - 9$

15. $(3x - 2)^2 = (3x)^2 - (2)(3x)(2) + (2)^2 = 9x^2 - 12x + 4$

16. $(m + 3)^3 = (m + 3)(m + 3)^2 = (m + 3)(m^2 + 6m + 9) =$

$m \cdot m^2 + m \cdot 6m + m \cdot 9 + 3 \cdot m^2 + 3 \cdot 6m + 3 \cdot 9 = m^3 + 6m^2 + 9m + 3m^2 + 18m + 27 =$

$m^3 + 9m^2 + 27m + 27$

17. Move the decimal point three places to the left, $6.1 \times 10^{-3} = 0.0061$.

18. Move the decimal point three places to the left, $5410 = 5.41 \times 10^3$.

19. $\dfrac{9x^3 - 6x^2 + 3x}{3x^2} = \dfrac{9x^3}{3x^2} - \dfrac{6x^2}{3x^2} + \dfrac{3x}{3x^2} = 3x^{3-2} - 2x^{2-2} + \dfrac{1}{x} = 3x - 2 + \dfrac{1}{x}$

20.
$$\begin{array}{r|l} & x^2 - x + 1 \\ \hline x + 2 & x^3 + x^2 - x + 1 \\ & \underline{x^3 + 2x^2} \\ & -x^2 - x \\ & \underline{-x^2 - 2x} \\ & x + 1 \\ & \underline{x + 2} \\ & -1 \end{array}$$

The solution is: $x^2 - x + 1 + \dfrac{-1}{x + 2}$

21. (a) $20t$

(b) $2t + 2000$

(c) $(20t) - (2t + 2000) = 20t - 2t - 2000 = 18t - 2000$; profit from selling t tickets.

22. $(3x)(2x) + (3x)(2x) = 6x^2 + 6x^2 = 12x^2$; For $x = 10$ feet $\Rightarrow 12x^2 = 12(10)^2 = 12(100) = 1200$ ft^2

23. $(3x)(x + 3)(x + 6) = (3x)(x \cdot x + x \cdot 6 + 3 \cdot x + 3 \cdot 6) = (3x)(x^2 + 9x + 18) =$

$3x \cdot x^2 + 3x \cdot 9x + 3x \cdot 18 = 3x^3 + 27x^2 + 54x$

24. (a) $t(88 - 16t) = t \cdot 88 - t \cdot 16t = 88t - 16t^2$

(b) $t = 3 \Rightarrow 88t - 16t^2 = 88(3) - 16(3)^2 = 264 - 16(9) = 264 - 144 = 120$

After 3 seconds the ball is 120 feet high.

Chapter 5 Extended and Discovery Exercises

1. Conjecture: Make the power of the 10's the same and you can add or subtract the lead numbers and multiply by that power of 10. $(4 \times 10^3) + (3 \times 10^3) = (4 + 3) \times 10^3 = 7 \times 10^3$; Answer checks.

2. Conjecture: Make the power of the 10's the same and you can add or subtract the lead numbers and multiply by that power of 10. $(5 \times 10^{-2}) - (2 \times 10^{-2}) = (5 - 2) \times 10^{-2} = 3 \times 10^{-2}$; Answer checks.

3. Conjecture: Make the power of the 10's the same and you can add or subtract the lead numbers and multiply by that power of 10. $(1.2 \times 10^4) - (3 \times 10^3) = (12 \times 10^3) - (3 \times 10^3) = (12 - 3) \times 10^3 = 9 \times 10^3$; Answer checks.

4. Conjecture: Make the power of the 10's the same and you can add or subtract the lead numbers and multiply by that power of 10. $(2 \times 10^2) + (6 \times 10^1) = (2 \times 10^2) + (0.6 \times 10^2) = (2 + 0.6) \times 10^2 = 2.6 \times 10^2$; Answer checks.

5. Conjecture: Make the power of the 10's the same and you can add or subtract the lead numbers and multiply by that power of 10. $(2 \times 10^{-1}) + (4 \times 10^{-2}) = (2 \times 10^{-1}) + (0.4 \times 10^{-1}) = (2 + 0.4) \times 10^{-1} = 2.4 \times 10^{-1}$; Answer checks.

6. Conjecture: Make the power of the 10's the same and you can add or subtract the lead numbers and multiply by that power of 10. $(2 \times 10^{-3}) - (5 \times 10^{-2}) = (0.2 \times 10^{-2}) - (5 \times 10^{-2}) = (0.2 - 5) \times 10^{-2} = -4.8 \times 10^{-2}$; Answer checks.

7. (a) The length of the box is $30 - 2x$, the width is $20 - 2x$, and the height is x. If $V = L \times W \times H$ then, $V = (30 - 2x)(20 - 2x)(x) = (600 - 60x - 40x + 4x^2)(x) = (4x^2 - 100x + 600)(x) = 4x^3 - 100x^2 + 600x$

   (b) Let $x = 4$, then $4(4)^3 - 100(4)^2 + 600(4) = 4(64) - 100(16) - 600(4) = 256 - 1600 + 2400 = 1056 \text{ in}^3$

8. (a) The length and width would be $25 - 2x$ and the height would be x. Therefore the base is equal to $(25 - 2x)^2 = 625 - 100x + 4x^2$ and the four sides are each $(25 - 2x)(x) = 25x - 2x^2 \cdot 4$ sides $= 100x - 8x^2$. Adding $625 - 100x + 4x^2 + 100x - 8x^2 = 625 - 4x^2$.

   (b) Let $x = 3$, then $625 - 4(3)^2 = 625 - 4(9) = 625 - 36 = 589 \text{ in}^2$.

9. See Figure 9a & 9b. No, not equal for all values of x; $3x(4 - 5x) = 12x - 15x^2$

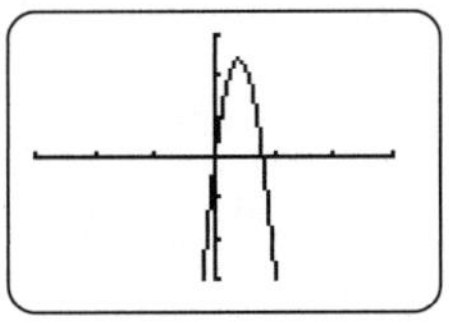

Figure 9a

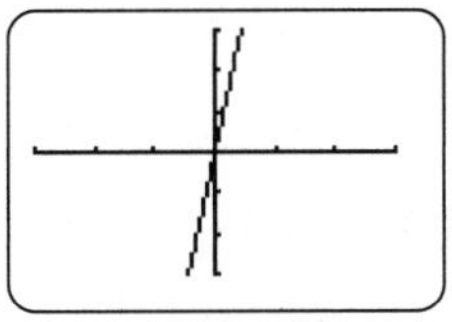

Figure 9b

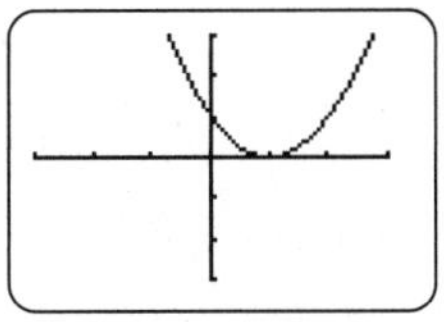

Figure 10a

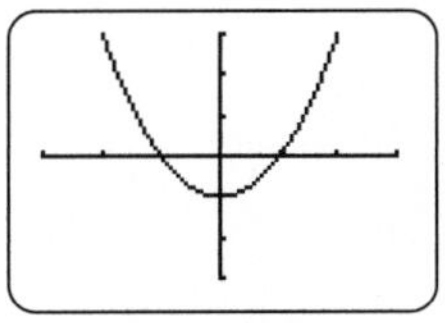

Figure 10b

10. See Figure 10a & 10b. No, not equal for all values of x; $(x - 1)^2 = x^2 - 2x + 1$

11. See Figure 11a & 11b. Yes, equal for all values of x.

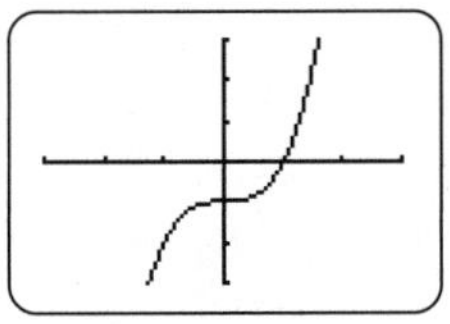

Figure 11a

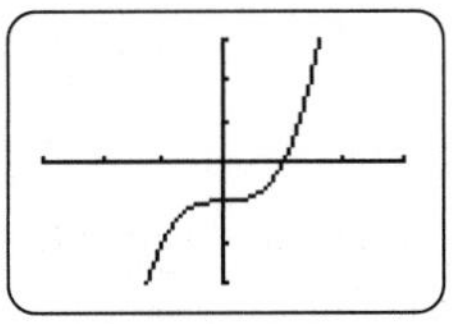

Figure 11b

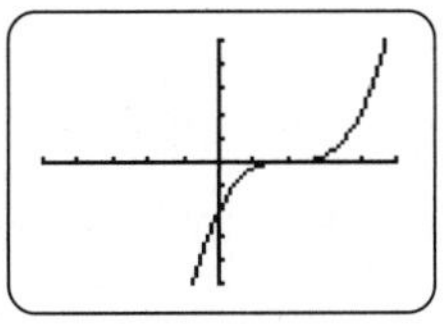

Figure 12a

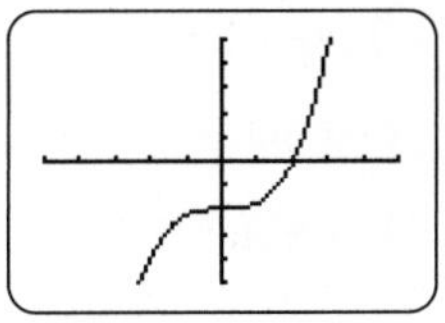

Figure 12b

12. See Figure 12a & 12b. No, not equal for all values of x; $(x - 2)^3 = (x - 2)^2(x - 2) = (x^2 - 4x + 4)(x - 2) = x^3 - 4x^2 + 4x - 2x^2 + 8x - 8 = x^3 - 6x^2 + 12x - 8$

Critical Thinking Solutions for Chapter 5

Section 5.2

- Volume of a cube is side cubed $\Rightarrow L^3$, then multiply by 6 of them $\Rightarrow 6L^3$.
- The result is zero.

Section 5.4

- Let $x = 2$ and $y = 3$, then $(x + y)^3 = (2 + 3)^3 = 5^3 = 125$ and $x^3 + y^3 = 2^3 + 3^3 = 8 + 27 = 35$, $125 \neq 35$ therefore $(x + y)^3 \neq x^3 + y^3$

Section 5.6

- $P = m + n$ or degree of dividend = degree of divisor + degree of quotient

Chapter 6: Factoring Polynomials and Solving Equations

6.1: Introduction to Factoring

Concepts

1. factoring

3. greatest common factor (GCF)

5. Factors of $2x^2$ are 1, 2, $2x$, x^2 and $2x^2$; factors of $4x$ are 1, 2, 4, $2x$ and $4x$. Therefore, common factors are 1, 2, x and $2x$.

Common Factors

7. $2x = 2 \cdot x$ and $4 = 2 \cdot 2 \Rightarrow 2(x + 2)$. See Figure 7.

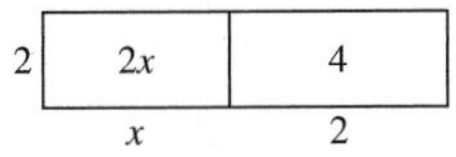

Figure 7

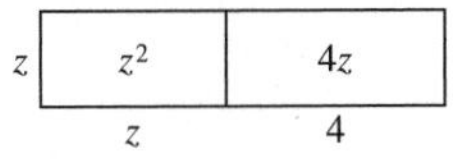

Figure 9

9. $z^2 = z \cdot z$ and $4z = 4 \cdot z \Rightarrow z(z + 4)$. See Figure 9.

11. $6x - 18x^2$; because $6x = 2 \cdot 3 \cdot x$ and $18x^2 = 3 \cdot 3 \cdot 2 \cdot x \cdot x$, common factors are $2 \cdot 3 \cdot x \Rightarrow$ GCF $= 6x$ and $\Rightarrow 6x(1 - 3x)$.

13. $8y^3 - 12y^2$; because $8y^3 = 2 \cdot 2 \cdot 2 \cdot y \cdot y \cdot y$ and $12y^2 = 2 \cdot 2 \cdot 3 \cdot y \cdot y$, common factors are $2 \cdot 2 \cdot y \cdot y \Rightarrow$ GCF $= 4y^2$ and $\Rightarrow 4y^2(2y - 3)$.

15. $6z^3 + 3z^2 + 9z$; because $6z^3 = 2 \cdot 3 \cdot z \cdot z \cdot z$ and $3z^2 = 3 \cdot z \cdot z$ and $9z = 3 \cdot 3 \cdot z$, common factors are $3 \cdot z \Rightarrow$ GCF $= 3z$ and $\Rightarrow 3z(2z^2 + z + 3)$.

17. $x^4 - 5x^3 - 4x^2$; because $x^4 = x \cdot x \cdot x \cdot x$ and $5x^3 = 5 \cdot x \cdot x \cdot x$ and $4x^2 = 2 \cdot 2 \cdot x \cdot x$, common factors are $x \cdot x \Rightarrow$ GCF $= x^2$ and $\Rightarrow x^2(x^2 - 5x - 4)$.

19. $5y^5 + 10y^4 - 15y^3 + 10y^2$; because $5y^5 = 5 \cdot y \cdot y \cdot y \cdot y \cdot y$ and $10y^4 = 2 \cdot 5 \cdot y \cdot y \cdot y \cdot y$ and $15y^3 = 3 \cdot 5 \cdot y \cdot y \cdot y$ and $10y^2 = 2 \cdot 5 \cdot y \cdot y$, common factors are $5 \cdot y \cdot y \Rightarrow$ GCF $= 5y^2$ and $\Rightarrow 5y^2(y^3 + 2y^2 - 3y + 2)$.

21. $xy + xz$; because $xy = x \cdot y$ and $xz = x \cdot z$, common factors are $x \Rightarrow$ GCF $= x$ and $\Rightarrow x(y + z)$.

23. $ab^2 - a^2b$; because $ab^2 = a \cdot b \cdot b$ and $a^2b = a \cdot a \cdot b$, common factors are $a \cdot b \Rightarrow$ GCF $= ab$ and $\Rightarrow ab(b - a)$.

25. $5x^2y^4 + 10x^3y^3$; because $5x^2y^4 = 5 \cdot x \cdot x \cdot y \cdot y \cdot y \cdot y$ and $10x^3y^3 = 2 \cdot 5 \cdot x \cdot x \cdot x \cdot y \cdot y \cdot y$, common factors are $5 \cdot x \cdot x \cdot y \cdot y \cdot y \Rightarrow$ GCF $= 5x^2y^3$ and $\Rightarrow 5x^2y^3(y + 2x)$.

27. $a^2b + ab^2 + ab$; because $a^2b = a \cdot a \cdot b$ and $ab^2 = a \cdot b \cdot b$ and $ab = a \cdot b$, common factors $= a \cdot b \Rightarrow$ *GCF* $= ab$ *and* $\Rightarrow ab(a + b + 1)$.

Factoring by Grouping

29. $x(x + 1) - 2(x + 1)$ has common binomial $(x + 1) \Rightarrow (x - 2)(x + 1)$

31. $(z + 5)z + (z + 5)4$ has common binomial $(z + 5) \Rightarrow (z + 4)(z + 5)$

33. $y^2(y + 7) - 4y(y + 7) \Rightarrow (y^2 - 4y)(y + 7) \Rightarrow y(y - 4)(y + 7)$

35. $4x^3(x - 5) + (x - 5)$ has common binomial $(x - 5) \Rightarrow (4x^3 + 1)(x - 5)$

37. $x^3 + 2x^2 + 3x + 6$ by associative property $= (x^3 + 2x^2) + (3x + 6) \Rightarrow$

    common factors $= x^2(x + 2) + 3(x + 2) \Rightarrow (x^2 + 3)(x + 2)$

39. $2y^3 + y^2 + 2y + 1$ by associative property $= (2y^3 + y^2) + (2y + 1) \Rightarrow$

    common factors $= y^2(2y + 1) + (2y + 1) \Rightarrow (y^2 + 1)(2y + 1)$

41. $2z^3 - 6z^2 + 5z - 15$ by associative property $= (2z^3 - 6z^2) + (5z - 15) \Rightarrow$

    common factors $= 2z^2(z - 3) + 5(z - 3) \Rightarrow (2z^2 + 5)(z - 3)$

43. $4t^3 - 20t^2 + 3t - 15$ by associative property $= (4t^3 - 20t^2) + (3t - 15) \Rightarrow$

    common factors $= 4t^2(t - 5) + 3(t - 5) \Rightarrow (4t^2 + 3)(t - 5)$

45. $9r^3 + 6r^2 - 6r - 4$ by associative property $= (9r^3 + 6r^2) - (6r - 4) \Rightarrow$

    common factors $= 3r^2(3r + 2) - 2(3r + 2) \Rightarrow (3r^2 - 2)(3r + 2)$

47. $7x^3 + 21x^2 - 2x - 6$ by associative property $= (7x^3 + 21x^2) - (2x - 6) \Rightarrow$

    common factors $= 7x^2(x + 3) - 2(x + 3) \Rightarrow (7x^2 - 2)(x + 3)$

49. $2y^3 - 7y^2 - 4y + 14$ by associative property $= (2y^3 - 7y^2) - (4y + 14) \Rightarrow$

    common factors $= y^2(2y - 7) - 2(2y - 7) \Rightarrow (y^2 - 2)(2y - 7)$

51. $z^3 - 4z^2 - 7z + 28$ by associative property $= (z^3 - 4z^2) - (7z + 28) \Rightarrow$

    common factors $= z^2(z - 4) - 7(z - 4) \Rightarrow (z^2 - 7)(z - 4)$

53. $2x^4 - 3x^3 + 4x - 6$ by associative property $= (2x^4 - 3x^3) + (4x - 6) \Rightarrow$

    common factors $= x^3(2x - 3) + 2(2x - 3) \Rightarrow (x^3 + 2)(2x - 3)$

55. $ax + bx + ay + by$ by associative property $= (ax + bx) + (ay + by) \Rightarrow$

    common factors $= x(a + b) + y(a + b) \Rightarrow (x + y)(a + b)$

Applications

57. (a) $80t = 2 \cdot 2 \cdot 2 \cdot 2 \cdot 5 \cdot t$ and $16t^2 = 2 \cdot 2 \cdot 2 \cdot 2 \cdot t \cdot t$, common factors are $2 \cdot 2 \cdot 2 \cdot 2 \cdot t \Rightarrow$

    GCF $= 2 \cdot 2 \cdot 2 \cdot 2 \cdot t = 16t$.

    (b) $80t - 16t^2 = 16t(5 - t)$

59. (a) $x = 3$, $4x^3 - 60x^2 + 200x \Rightarrow 4(3)^3 - 60(3)^2 + 200(3) = 108 - 540 + 600 = 168 \Rightarrow V = 168$ in^3.

    (b) $4x^3 = 2 \cdot 2 \cdot x \cdot x \cdot x$ and $60x^2 = 2 \cdot 2 \cdot 3 \cdot 5 \cdot x \cdot x$ and $200x = 2 \cdot 2 \cdot 2 \cdot 5 \cdot 5 \cdot x$, common factors are

    $2 \cdot 2 \cdot x \Rightarrow$ GCF $= 4x \Rightarrow 4x(x^2 - 15x + 50)$.

6.2: Factoring Trinomials I (x^2 + bx + c)

Concepts

1. F: multiply the first term; O: multiply the outside term; I: multiply the inside term; L: multiply the last term

3. $x^2 + bx + c$, so c is the third term $\Rightarrow mn = c$ and b is the second term $\Rightarrow m + n = b$.

5. Product of 12 by factors: 1, 12; 2, 6; and 3, 4.

7. Factors of 28 are 1, 28; 2, 14; 4, 7 and only $4 + 7 = 11 \Rightarrow 4, 7$.

9. Factors of 30 are 1, 30; 2, 15; 3, 10; 5, 6 and only $3 + 10 = 13 \Rightarrow 3, 10$.

11. Factors of -50 are $-1, 50;\ 1, -50;\ -2, 25;\ 2, -25;\ -5, 10;\ 5, -10$ and only $-5 + 10 = 5 \Rightarrow -5, 10$.

13. Factors of 28 are $1, 28;\ -1, -28;\ 2, 14;\ -2, -14;\ 4, 7;\ -4, -7$ and only $(-4) + (-7) = -11 \Rightarrow -4, -7$.

Factoring Trinomials

15. Factors of 2 with sum of 3 are 1 and 2 $\Rightarrow x^2 + 3x + 2 = (x + 1)(x + 2)$.

17. Factors of 4 with sum of 4 are 2 and 2 $\Rightarrow y^2 + 4y + 4 = (y + 2)(y + 2)$.

19. Factors of 9 with sum of 6 are 3 and 3 $\Rightarrow z^2 + 6z + 9 = (z + 3)(z + 3)$.

21. Factors of 15 with sum of 8 are 3 and 5 $\Rightarrow x^2 + 8x + 15 = (x + 3)(x + 5)$.

23. Factors of 36 with sum of 13 are 4 and 9 $\Rightarrow m^2 + 13m + 36 = (m + 4)(m + 9)$.

25. Factors of 100 with sum of 20 are 10 and 10 $\Rightarrow n^2 + 20n + 100 = (n + 10)(n + 10)$.

27. Factors of 5 with sum of -6 are -1 and $-5 \Rightarrow x^2 - 6x + 5 = (x - 1)(x - 5)$.

29. Factors of 12 with sum of -7 are -3 and $-4 \Rightarrow y^2 - 7y + 12 = (y - 3)(y - 4)$.

31. Factors of 40 with sum of -13 are -5 and $-8 \Rightarrow z^2 - 13z + 40 = (z - 5)(z - 8)$.

33. Factors of 63 with sum of -16 are -7 and $-9 \Rightarrow a^2 - 16a + 63 = (a - 7)(a - 9)$.

35. Factors of 125 with sum of -30 are -5 and $-25 \Rightarrow b^2 - 30b + 125 = (b - 5)(b - 25)$.

37. Factors of -90 with sum of 13 are -5 and $18 \Rightarrow x^2 + 13x - 90 = (x - 5)(x + 18)$.

39. Factors of -45 with sum of 4 are -5 and $9 \Rightarrow m^2 + 4m - 45 = (m - 5)(m + 9)$.

41. Factors of -200 with sum of 10 are -10 and $20 \Rightarrow n^2 + 10n - 200 = (n - 10)(n + 20)$.

43. Factors of -23 with sum of 22 are -1 and $23 \Rightarrow x^2 + 22x - 23 = (x - 1)(x + 23)$.

45. Factors of -32 with sum of 4 are -4 and $8 \Rightarrow a^2 + 4a - 32 = (a - 4)(a + 8)$.

47. Factors of -20 with sum of -1 are 4 and $-5 \Rightarrow b^2 - b - 20 \Rightarrow (b + 4)(b - 5)$.

49. Factors of -72 with sum of -1 are 8 and $-9 \Rightarrow x^2 - x - 72 \Rightarrow (x + 8)(x - 9)$.

51. Factors of -34 with sum of -15 are 2 and $-17 \Rightarrow y^2 - 15y - 34 \Rightarrow (y + 2)(y - 17)$.

53. Factors of -66 with sum of -5 are 6 and $-11 \Rightarrow z^2 - 5z - 66 \Rightarrow (z + 6)(z - 11)$.

55. $5 + 6x + x^2$ in standard form $x^2 + 6x + 5$ and factors of 5 with a sum of $6 = 1, 5 \Rightarrow (x + 5)(x + 1)$.

57. $3 - 4x + x^2$ in standard form is $x^2 - 4x + 3$ and factors of 3 with a sum of $-4 = -1, -3 \Rightarrow (x - 1)(x - 3)$.

59. Using the hint, the answer will be in the form of $(m - x)(n + x)$ we need to find m and n. Factors of 12 with a difference of 4 are 6 and 2 $\Rightarrow 12 + 4x - x^2 = (6 - x)(2 + x)$.

61. Factors of 32 with a difference of 4 are 8 and 4 $\Rightarrow 32 - 4x - x^2 = (8 + x)(4 - x)$.

Geometry

63. $x^2 + 2x + 1 \Rightarrow (x + 1)(x + 1) \Rightarrow L \cdot W = x^2 + 2x + 1 \Rightarrow L = x + 1$. See Figure 63.

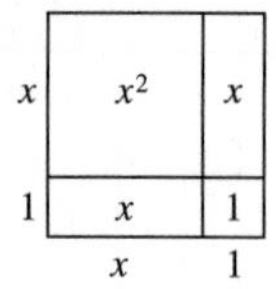

Figure 63

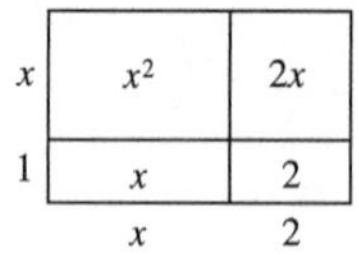

Figure 65

65. $x^2 + 3x + 2 = (x + 2)(x + 1) = L \cdot W \Rightarrow L = x + 2$ or $x + 1$. See Figure 65.

67. $6x^2 + 12x + 6$ divided by 6 (for 6 surfaces) $= x^2 + 2x + 1 = (x + 1)(x + 1) \Rightarrow$ each side is $x + 1$.

69. Add the four regions: $x^2 + 2x + 6x + 12 = x^2 + 8x + 12 = (x + 2)(x + 6)$.

Checking Basic Concepts for Sections 6.1 & 6.2

1. $8x^3 = 2 \cdot 2 \cdot 2 \cdot x \cdot x \cdot x$ and $12x^2 = 2 \cdot 2 \cdot 3 \cdot x \cdot x$ and $24x = 2 \cdot 2 \cdot 2 \cdot 3 \cdot x \Rightarrow \text{GCF} = 2 \cdot 2 \cdot x = 4x$.

2. GCF of $12z^3$ and $18z^2$ is $6z^2 \Rightarrow 6z^2(2z - 3)$.

3. (a) $6y(y - 2) + 5(y - 2) = (6y + 5)(y - 2)$

   (b) $(2x^3 + x^2) + (10x + 5) = x^2(2x + 1) + 5(2x + 1) = (x^2 + 5)(2x + 1)$

4. (a) Factors of 8 with a sum of 6 are 2 and 4 $\Rightarrow (x + 2)(x + 4)$.

   (b) Factors of -42 with a sum of -1 are -7 and 6 $\Rightarrow (x - 7)(x + 6)$.

5. $x^2 + 5x + 5x + 25 \Rightarrow x^2 + 10x + 25 \Rightarrow (x + 5)(x + 5)$

6.3: Factoring Trinomials II ($ax^2 + bx + c$)

Concepts

1. ac; b

3. By $ax^2 + bx + c$, if $a > 0$, $b > 0$ and $c > 0$ then: $+$; $+$

5. By $ax^2 + bx + c$, if $a > 0$, $b < 0$ and $c > 0$ then: $-$; $-$

7. If $(4x + a)(b + 2) = 4x^2 + 11x + 6$, then by FOIL: $4x \cdot b = 4x^2 \Rightarrow b = x$ and $a \cdot 2 = 6 \Rightarrow a = 3 \Rightarrow 3; x$.

9. If $(2x - a)(b + 3) = 4x^2 + 4x - 3$, then by FOIL: $2x \cdot b = 4x^2 \Rightarrow b = 2x$ and $-a \cdot 3 = -3 \Rightarrow$

   $a = 1 \Rightarrow 1; 2x$.

Factoring Trinomials

11. Using factoring by grouping: For $2x^2 + 7x + 3$, $m \cdot n = a \cdot c = 2 \cdot 3 = 6$ and $m + n = b = 7 \Rightarrow$

    $m = 6, n = 1 \Rightarrow 2x^2 + 6x + x + 3 \Rightarrow 2x(x + 3) + (x + 3) \Rightarrow (2x + 1)(x + 3)$.

13. Using factoring by grouping: For $3x^2 + 4x + 1$, $m \cdot n = a \cdot c = 3 \cdot 1 = 3$ and $m + n = b = 4 \Rightarrow$
$m = 3, n = 1 \Rightarrow 3x^2 + 3x + x + 1 \Rightarrow 3x(x + 1) + (x + 1) \Rightarrow (3x + 1)(x + 1)$.

15. Using factoring by grouping: For $6x^2 + 11x + 3$, $m \cdot n = a \cdot c = 6 \cdot 3 = 18$ and $m + n = b = 11 \Rightarrow$
$m = 9, n = 2 \Rightarrow 6x^2 + 9x + 2x + 3 \Rightarrow 3x(2x + 3) + (2x + 3) \Rightarrow (3x + 1)(2x + 3)$.

17. Using factoring by grouping: For $5x^2 - 11x + 2$, $m \cdot n = a \cdot c = 5 \cdot 2 = 10$ and $m + n = b = -11 \Rightarrow$
$m = -10, n = -1 \Rightarrow 5x^2 - 10x - x + 2 \Rightarrow 5x(x - 2) - (x - 2) \Rightarrow (5x - 1)(x - 2)$.

19. Using factoring by grouping: For $2y^2 - 7y + 5$, $m \cdot n = a \cdot c = 2 \cdot 5 = 10$ and $m + n = b = -7 \Rightarrow$
$m = -5, n = -2 \Rightarrow 2y^2 - 5y - 2y + 5 \Rightarrow y(2y - 5) - (2y - 5) \Rightarrow (y - 1)(2y - 5)$.

21. Using factoring by grouping: For $7z^2 - 37z + 10$, $m \cdot n = a \cdot c = 7 \cdot 10 = 70$ and $m + n = b = -37 \Rightarrow$
$m = -35, n = -2 \Rightarrow 7z^2 - 35z - 2z + 10 \Rightarrow 7z(z - 5) - 2(z - 5) \Rightarrow (7z - 2)(z - 5)$.

23. Using factoring by grouping: For $3t^2 - 7t - 6$, $m \cdot n = a \cdot c = 3 \cdot (-6) = -18$ and $m + n = b = -7 \Rightarrow$
$m = -9, n = 2 \Rightarrow 3t^2 - 9t + 2t - 6 \Rightarrow 3t(t - 3) + 2(t - 3) \Rightarrow (3t + 2)(t - 3)$.

25. Using factoring by grouping: For $15r^2 + r - 6$, $m \cdot n = a \cdot c = 15 \cdot (-6) = -90$ and $m + n = b = 1 \Rightarrow$
$m = 10, n = -9 \Rightarrow 15r^2 + 10r - 9r - 6 \Rightarrow 5r(3r + 2) - 3(3r + 2) \Rightarrow (5r - 3)(3r + 2)$.

27. Using factoring by grouping:
For $24m^2 - 23m - 12$, $m \cdot n = a \cdot c = 24 \cdot (-12) = -288$ and $m + n = b = -23 \Rightarrow$
$m = -32, n = 9 \Rightarrow 24m^2 - 32m + 9m - 12 \Rightarrow 8m(3m - 4) + 3(3m - 4) \Rightarrow (8m + 3)(3m - 4)$.

29. Using factoring by grouping: For $25x^2 + 5x - 2$, $m \cdot n = a \cdot c = 25 \cdot (-2) = -50$ and $m + n = b = 5 \Rightarrow$
$m = 10, n = -5 \Rightarrow 25x^2 + 10x - 5x - 2 \Rightarrow 5x(5x + 2) - (5x + 2) \Rightarrow (5x - 1)(5x + 2)$.

31. Using factoring by grouping: For $6x^2 + 11x - 2$, $m \cdot n = a \cdot c = 6 \cdot (-2) = -12$ and $m + n = b = 11 \Rightarrow$
$m = 12, n = -1 \Rightarrow 6x^2 + 12x - x - 2 \Rightarrow 6x(x + 2) - (x + 2) \Rightarrow (6x - 1)(x + 2)$.

33. Using factoring by grouping: For $21n^2 + 4n - 1$, $m \cdot n = a \cdot c = 21 \cdot (-1) = -21$ and $m + n = b = 4 \Rightarrow$
$m = 7, n = -3 \Rightarrow 21n^2 + 7n - 3n - 1 \Rightarrow 7n(3n + 1) - (3n + 1) \Rightarrow (7n - 1)(3n + 1)$.

35. Using factoring by grouping: For $14y^2 + 23y + 3$, $m \cdot n = a \cdot c = 14 \cdot 3 = 42$ and $m + n = b = 23 \Rightarrow$
$m = 21, n = 2 \Rightarrow 14y^2 + 21y + 2y + 3 \Rightarrow 7y(2y + 3) + (2y + 3) \Rightarrow (7y + 1)(2y + 3)$.

37. Using factoring by grouping: For $28z^2 - 25z + 3$, $m \cdot n = a \cdot c = 28 \cdot 3 = 84$ and $m + n = b = -25 \Rightarrow$
$m = -21, n = -4 \Rightarrow 28z^2 - 21z - 4z + 3 \Rightarrow 7z(4z - 3) - (4z - 3) \Rightarrow (7z - 1)(4z - 3)$.

39. Using factoring by grouping: For $30x^2 - 29x + 6$, $m \cdot n = a \cdot c = 30 \cdot 6 = 180$ and $m + n = b = -29 \Rightarrow$
$m = -20, n = -9 \Rightarrow 30x^2 - 20x - 9x + 6 \Rightarrow 10x(3x - 2) - 3(3x - 2) \Rightarrow (10x - 3)(3x - 2)$.

41. Using factoring by grouping: For $18t^2 + 23t - 6$, $m \cdot n = a \cdot c = 18 \cdot (-6) = -108$ and $m + n = b = 23 \Rightarrow$
$m = 27, n = -4 \Rightarrow 18t^2 + 27t - 4t - 6 \Rightarrow 9t(2t + 3) - 2(2t + 3) \Rightarrow (9t - 2)(2t + 3)$.

43. Put $2 + 15x + 7x^2$ in standard form $7x^2 + 15x + 2$, $m \cdot n = a \cdot c = 7 \cdot 2 = 14$ and $m + n = b = 15 \Rightarrow$
$m = 14, n = 1 \Rightarrow 7x^2 + 14x + x + 2 \Rightarrow 7x(x + 2) + (x + 2) \Rightarrow (7x + 1)(x + 2)$.

45. Put $2 - 5x + 2x^2$ in standard form $2x^2 - 5x + 2$, $m \cdot n = a \cdot c = 2 \cdot 2 = 4$ and $m + n = b = -5 \Rightarrow$
$m = -4, n = -1 \Rightarrow 2x^2 - 4x - x + 2 \Rightarrow 2x(x - 2) - (x - 2) \Rightarrow (2x - 1)(x - 2)$.

47. Put $3 - 2x - 8x^2$ in standard form $-8x^2 - 2x + 3 = -(8x^2 + 2x - 3)$, $m \cdot n = a \cdot c = 8 \cdot (-3) = -24$ and $m + n = b = 2 \Rightarrow m = 6, n = -4 \Rightarrow -(8x^2 + 6x - 4x - 3) \Rightarrow -[2x(4x + 3) - (4x + 3)] \Rightarrow -(2x - 1)(4x + 3)$.

49. $-2x^2 - 7x + 15 = -(2x^2 + 7x - 15)$, $m \cdot n = a \cdot c = 2 \cdot (-15) = -30$ and $m + n = b = 7 \Rightarrow m = 10, n = -3 \Rightarrow -(2x^2 + 10x - 3x - 15) \Rightarrow -[2x(x + 5) - 3(x + 5)] \Rightarrow -(2x - 3)(x + 5)$.

51. $-5x^2 + 14x + 3 = -(5x^2 - 14x - 3)$, $m \cdot n = a \cdot c = 5 \cdot (-3) = -15$ and $m + n = b = -14 \Rightarrow m = -15, n = 1 \Rightarrow -(5x^2 - 15x + x - 3) \Rightarrow -[5x(x - 3) + (x - 3)] \Rightarrow -(5x + 1)(x - 3)$.

53. $6x^2 + 7x + 2$, $m \cdot n = a \cdot c = 6 \cdot 2 = 12$ and $m + n = b = 7 \Rightarrow m = 4, n = 3 \Rightarrow (6x^2 + 4x + 3x + 2) \Rightarrow 2x(3x + 2) + (3x + 2) \Rightarrow (2x + 1)(3x + 2)$. See Figure 53.

$2x$	$6x^2$	$4x$
1	$3x$	2
	$3x$	2

Figure 53

55. $(2x^2 + 6x + x + 3) \Rightarrow 2x(x + 3) + (x + 3) \Rightarrow (2x + 1)(x + 3)$.

6.4: Special Types of Factoring

Concepts

1. $a^2 - b^2 = (a - b)(a + b)$
3. $36x^2 - 49y^2 = (6x)^2 - (7y)^2 \Rightarrow a = 6x$ and $b = 7y$.
5. $a^2 - 2ab + b^2 = (a - b)^2$
7. $a^2 - 2ab + b^2 = (a - b)^2 \Rightarrow 4r^2 = (2r)^2$ and $25t^2 = (5t)^2$ and so by $2ab = 2(2r)(5t) = 20rt$.
9. $a^3 - b^3 = (a - b)(a^2 + ab + b^2)$
11. $y^3 - 8 = (y - 2)(y + 2y + 4) \Rightarrow -; +$

Factoring the Difference of Two Squares

13. $x^2 - 1 = (x)^2 - (1)^2 \Rightarrow (x - 1)(x + 1)$
15. $z^2 - 100 = (z)^2 - (10)^2 \Rightarrow (z - 10)(z + 10)$
17. $4y^2 - 1 = (2y)^2 - (1)^2 \Rightarrow (2y - 1)(2y + 1)$
19. $36z^2 - 25 = (6z)^2 - (5)^2 \Rightarrow (6z - 5)(6z + 5)$
21. $9 - x^2 = (3) - (x)^2 \Rightarrow (3 - x)(3 + x)$
23. $1 - 9y^2 = (1) - (3y)^2 \Rightarrow (1 - 3y)(1 + 3y)$
25. $4a^2 - 9b^2 = (2a)^2 - (3b)^2 \Rightarrow (2a - 3b)(2a + 3b)$
27. $36m^2 - 25n^2 = (6m)^2 - (5n)^2 \Rightarrow (6m - 5n)(6m + 5n)$
29. $81r^2 - 49t^2 = (9r)^2 - (7t)^2 \Rightarrow (9r - 7t)(9r + 7t)$

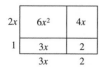

Factoring Perfect Square Trinomials

31. $x^2 + 8x + 16$ is a perfect square trinomial, $a^2 = x^2$ so $a = x$, $b^2 = 4^2$ so $b = 4$, $2ab = 8x$, the middle term $\Rightarrow$

$(a + b)^2 \Rightarrow (x + 4)^2$.

33. $z^2 + 12z + 25$ is not a perfect square trinomial because $a^2 = z^2$ so $a = z$, $b^2 = 5^2$ so $b = 5$, $2ab = 10z \neq 12z$, the middle term and also, FOIL does not work, therefore: Not possible.

35. $x^2 - 6x + 9$ is a perfect square trinomial, $a^2 = x^2$ so $a = x$, $b^2 = (\pm 3)^2$ so $b = \pm 3$, using $b = -3$,

$2ab = -6x$, the middle term $\Rightarrow (a + b)^2 \Rightarrow (x - 3)^2$.

37. $9y^2 + 6y + 1$ is a perfect square trinomial,

$a^2 = (3y)^2$ so $a = 3y$, $b^2 = 1^2$ so $b = 1$, $2ab = 6y$, the middle term $\Rightarrow (a + b)^2 \Rightarrow (3y + 1)^2$.

39. $4z^2 - 4z + 1$ is a perfect square trinomial, $a^2 = (2z)^2$ so $a = 2z$, $b^2 = (\pm 1)^2$ so $b = \pm 1$,

using $b = -1$, $2ab = -4z$, the middle term $\Rightarrow (a + b)^2 \Rightarrow (2z - 1)^2$.

41. $9t^2 + 16t + 4$ is not a perfect square trinomial because $a^2 = (3t)^2$ so $a = 3t$, $b^2 = (\pm 1)^2$ so $b = \pm 1$,

$2ab = \pm 6t \neq 16t$, the middle term and also, FOIL does not work, therefore: Not possible.

43. $9x^2 + 30x + 25$ is a perfect square trinomial, $a^2 = (3x)^2$ so $a = 3x$, $b^2 = (5)^2$ so $b = 5$,

$2ab = 30x$, the middle term $\Rightarrow (a + b)^2 \Rightarrow (3x + 5)^2$.

45. $4a^2 - 36a + 81$ is a perfect square trinomial, $a^2 = (2a)^2$ so $a = 2a$, $b^2 = (\pm 9)^2$ so $b = \pm 9$, using $b = -9$,

$2ab = -36a$, the middle term $\Rightarrow (a + b)^2 \Rightarrow (2a - 9)^2$.

47. $x^2 + 2xy + y^2$ is a perfect square trinomial, $a^2 = x^2$ so $a = x$, $b^2 = \sqrt{y^2}$ so $b = y$,

$2ab = 2xy$, the middle term $\Rightarrow (a + b)^2 \Rightarrow (x + y)^2$.

49. $r^2 - 10rt + 25t^2$ is a perfect square trinomial, $a^2 = r^2$ so $a = r$, $b^2 = (\pm 5t)^2$ so $b = \pm 5t$, using $b = -5t$,

$2ab = -10rt$, the middle term $\Rightarrow (a + b)^2 \Rightarrow (r - 5t)^2$.

51. $4y^2 - 10yz + 9z^2$ is not a perfect square trinomial because $a^2 = (2y)^2$ so $a = 2y$, $b^2 = (\pm 3z)^2$ so $b = \pm 3z$,

$2ab = \pm 6z \neq -10yz$, the middle term and also, FOIL does not work, therefore: Not possible.

Factoring Sums and Differences of Two Cubes

53. Using the sum of cubes for $z^3 + 1$, $a^3 = z^3$ so $a = z$, $b^3 = 1^3$ so $b = 1 \Rightarrow$

$(a + b)(a^2 - ab + b^2) \Rightarrow (z + 1)(z^2 - z + 1)$.

55. Using the sum of cubes for $x^3 + 64$, $a^3 = x^3$ so $a = x$, $b^3 = 4^3$ so $b = 4 \Rightarrow$

$(a + b)(a^2 - ab + b^2) \Rightarrow (x + 4)(x^2 - 4x + 16)$.

57. Using the difference of cubes for $y^3 - 8$, $a^3 = y^3$ so $a = y$, $b^3 = 2^3$ so $b = 2 \Rightarrow$

$(a - b)(a^2 + ab + b^2) \Rightarrow (y - 2)(y^2 + 2y + 4)$.

59. Using the difference of cubes for $n^3 - 1$, $a^3 = n^3$ so $a = n$, $b^3 = 1^3$ so $b = 1 \Rightarrow$

$(a - b)(a^2 + ab + b^2) \Rightarrow (n - 1)(n^2 + n + 1)$.

61. Using the sum of cubes for $8x^3 + 1$, $a^3 = (2x)^3$ so $a = 2x$, $b^3 = 1^3$ so $b = 1 \Rightarrow$

$(a + b)(a^2 - ab + b^2) \Rightarrow (2x + 1)(4x^2 - 2x + 1)$.

63. Using the differences of cubes for $m^3 - 64n^3$, $a^3 = m^3$ so $a = m$, $b^3 = (4n)^3$ so $b = 4n \Rightarrow$

$(a - b)(a^2 + ab + b^2) \Rightarrow (m - 4n)(m^2 + 4mn + 16n^2)$.

65. Using the sum of cubes for $16a^3 + 2b^3 = 2(8a^3 + b^3)$, $a^3 = (2a)^3$ so $a = 2a$, $b^3 = b^3$ so $b = b \Rightarrow$

$(a + b)(a^2 - ab + b^2) \Rightarrow 2(2a + b)(4a^2 - 2ab + b^2)$.

67. Using the sum of cubes for $8x^3 + 125y^3$, $a^3 = (2x)^3$ so $a = 2x$, $b^3 = (5y)^3$ so $b = 5y \Rightarrow$

$(a + b)(a^2 - ab + b^2) \Rightarrow (2x + 5y)(4x^2 - 10xy + 25y^2)$.

69. Using the differences of cubes for $500r^3 - 32t^3 = 4(125r^3 - 8t^3)$,

$a^3 = (5r)^3$ so $a = 5r$, $b^3 = (2t)^3$ so $b = 2t \Rightarrow (a - b)(a^2 + ab + b^2) \Rightarrow 4(5r - 2t)(25r^2 + 10rt + 4t^2)$.

71. $9x^4 - 3x^3 = 3x^3(3x - 1)$

73. $4y^2 - 9$ (difference of squares) $\Rightarrow (2y + 3)(2y - 3)$

75. $25z^2 - 80z + 64$ (perfect trinomial square), $a^2 = (5z)^2$ so $a = 5z$, $b^2 = (\pm 8)^2$ so $b = \pm 8$, using $b = -8$,

$2ab = -80z$ the middle term $\Rightarrow (a + b)^2 \Rightarrow (5z - 8)^2$.

77. $2x^2 - 15x + 7$ (factor by grouping), $m \cdot n = 14$, $m + n = -15 \Rightarrow m = -14$, $n = -1 \Rightarrow$

$2x^2 - 14x - x + 7 \Rightarrow 2x(x - 7) - (x - 7) \Rightarrow (2x - 1)(x - 7)$.

79. $2n^2 + 21n + 27$ (factor by grouping), $m \cdot n = 54$, $m + n = 21 \Rightarrow m = 18$, $n = 3 \Rightarrow$

$2n^2 + 18n + 3n + 27 \Rightarrow 2n(n + 9) + 3(n + 9) \Rightarrow (2n + 3)(n + 9)$.

81. $8x^3 - 27$ (difference of cubes), $a^3 = (2x)^3$ so $a = 2x$, $b^3 = 3^3$ so $b = 3 \Rightarrow (2x - 3)(4x^2 + 6x + 9)$.

83. $x^3 + 2x^2 - 5x - 10$ (factor by grouping) $\Rightarrow x^2(x + 2) - 5(x + 2) \Rightarrow (x^2 - 5)(x + 2)$.

85. $a^2 + 18ab + 81b^2$ (perfect trinomial square), $a^2 = a^2$ so $a = a$, $b^2 = (9b)^2$ so $b = 9b$,

$2ab = 18ab$ the middle term $\Rightarrow (a + 9b)^2$.

87. Sides must be the same $\Rightarrow$ perfect trinomial, $4x^2 + 12x + 9$, $a^2 = (2x)^2$ so $a = 2x$, $b^2 = 3^2$ so $b = 3$,

$2ab = 12x$ the middle term $\Rightarrow (2x + 3)^2$. See Figure 87.

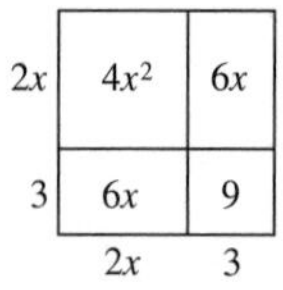

Figure 87

Checking Basic Concepts for Sections 6.3 & 6.4

1. (a) $2x^2 - 5x - 12$ (factor by grouping), $m \cdot n = -24$, $m + n = -5 \Rightarrow m = -8$, $n = 3 \Rightarrow$

$2x^2 - 8x + 3x - 12 \Rightarrow 2x(x - 4) + 3(x - 4) \Rightarrow (2x + 3)(x - 4)$.

(b) $6x^2 + 17x - 14$ (factor by grouping), $m \cdot n = -84$, $m + n = 17 \Rightarrow m = 21$, $n = -4 \Rightarrow$

$6x^2 + 21x - 4x - 14 \Rightarrow 3x(2x + 7) - 2(2x + 7) \Rightarrow (3x - 2)(2x + 7)$.

2. $3x^2 + 2x + 9x + 6 \Rightarrow x(3x + 2) + 3(3x + 2) \Rightarrow (x + 3)(3x + 2)$

3. (a) $z^2 - 64$ (difference of squares), $a^2 = z^2$ so $a = z$, $b^2 = 8^2$ so $b = 8 \Rightarrow (z + 8)(z - 8)$.

(b) $9r^2 - 4t^2$ (difference of squares), $a^2 = (3r)^2$ so $a = 3r$, $b^2 = (2t)^2$ so $b = 2t \Rightarrow (3r + 2t)(3r - 2t)$.

(c) $x^2 + 12x + 36$ (FOIL in reverse) $\Rightarrow (x + 6)(x + 6) \Rightarrow (x + 6)^2$.

(d) $9a^2 - 12ab + 4b^2$ (perfect trinomial square), $a^2 = (3a)^2$ so $a = 3a$, $b^2 = (\pm 2b)^2$ so $b = \pm 2b$, using $b = -2b$, $2ab = -12ab$ the second term $\Rightarrow (3a - 2b)^2$.

4. (a) $m^3 - 27$ (difference of cubes), $a^3 = m^3$ so $a = m$, $b^3 = 3^3$ so $b = 3 \Rightarrow (m - 3)(m^2 + 3m + 9)$.

(b) $125n^3 + 27$ (sum of cubes), $a^3 = (5n)^3$ so $a = 5n$, $b^3 = 3^3$ so $b = 3 \Rightarrow (5n + 3)(25n^2 - 15n + 9)$.

6.5: Solving Equations by Factoring I (Quadratics)

Concepts

1. 0, 0
3. $2x = 0, x + 6 = 0$
5. Apply the zero-product property by setting $x + 5 = 0$ and $x - 4 = 0$.
7. $ax^2 + bx + c = 0$ with $a \neq 0$.

Zero-Product Property

9. $x = 0$ or $y = 0$.
11. $2x = 0$ or $x + 8 = 0$, so $x = -8, 0$.
13. $y - 1 = 0$ or $y - 2 = 0$, so $y = 1, 2$.
15. $2z - 1 = 0$ or $4z - 3 = 0$, then $2z - 1 = 0 \Rightarrow 2z = 1 \Rightarrow z = \frac{1}{2}$ or $4z - 3 = 0 \Rightarrow 4z = 3 \Rightarrow z = \frac{3}{4}$, so $z = \frac{1}{2}, \frac{3}{4}$.
17. $1 - 3n = 0$ or $3 - 7n = 0$, then $1 - 3n = 0 \Rightarrow -3n = -1 \Rightarrow n = \frac{-1}{-3} = \frac{1}{3}$ or $3 - 7n = 0 \Rightarrow -7n = -3 \Rightarrow n = \frac{-3}{-7} = \frac{3}{7}$, so $n = \frac{1}{3}, \frac{3}{7}$.
19. $x = 0$ or $x - 5 = 0$ or $x - 8 = 0$, then $x - 5 = 0 \Rightarrow x = 5$ or $x - 8 = 0 \Rightarrow x = 8$, so $x = 0, 5, 8$.

Solving Quadratic Equations

21. $x^2 - x = 0 \Rightarrow x(x - 1) = 0$, then $x = 0$ or $x - 1 = 0 \Rightarrow x = 1$, so $x = 0, 1$.
23. $z^2 - 5z = 0 \Rightarrow z(z - 5) = 0$, then $z = 0$ or $z - 5 = 0 \Rightarrow z = 5$, so $z = 0, 5$.
25. $10y^2 + 15y = 0 \Rightarrow 5y(2y + 3) = 0$, then $5y = 0 \Rightarrow y = 0$ or $2y + 3 = 0 \Rightarrow 2y = -3 \Rightarrow y = \frac{-3}{2}$, so $y = 0, \frac{-3}{2}$.
27. $x^2 - 1 = 0 \Rightarrow (x + 1)(x - 1)$ then $x + 1 = 0 \Rightarrow x = -1$ or $x - 1 = 0 \Rightarrow x = 1$ so $x = -1, 1$.
29. $4n^2 - 1 = 0 \Rightarrow (2n + 1)(2n - 1) = 0$, then $2n + 1 = 0 \Rightarrow 2n = -1 \Rightarrow n = \frac{-1}{2}$ or $2n - 1 = 0 \Rightarrow 2n = 1 \Rightarrow n = \frac{1}{2}$, so $n = -\frac{1}{2}, \frac{1}{2}$.

31. $z^2 + 3z + 2 = 0 \Rightarrow (z + 2)(z + 1) = 0$, then $z + 2 = 0 \Rightarrow z = -2$ or $z + 1 = 0 \Rightarrow z = -1$, so $z = -2, -1$.

33. $x^2 - 12x + 35 = 0 \Rightarrow (x - 7)(x - 5) = 0$, then $x - 7 = 0 \Rightarrow x = 7$ or $x - 5 = 0 \Rightarrow x = 5$, so $x = 5, 7$.

35. $2b^2 + 3b - 2 = 0 \Rightarrow (2b - 1)(b + 2) = 0$, then $2b - 1 = 0 \Rightarrow 2b = 1 \Rightarrow$

$b = \frac{1}{2}$ or $b + 2 = 0 \Rightarrow b = -2$, so $b = -2, \frac{1}{2}$.

37. $6y^2 + 19y + 10 = 0$, (factor by grouping), $m \cdot n = 60$, $m + n = 19 \Rightarrow m = 15, n = 4 \Rightarrow$

$6y^2 + 15y + 4y + 10 = 0 \Rightarrow 3y(2y + 5) + 2(2y + 5) = 0 \Rightarrow (3y + 2)(2y + 5) = 0$, then $3y + 2 = 0 \Rightarrow$

$3y = -2 \Rightarrow y = \frac{-2}{3}$ or $2y + 5 = 0 \Rightarrow 2y = -5 \Rightarrow y = \frac{-5}{2}$, so $y = -\frac{5}{2}, -\frac{2}{3}$.

39. $x^2 = 25 \Rightarrow x^2 - 25 = 0 \Rightarrow (x + 5)(x - 5) = 0$, then $x + 5 = 0 \Rightarrow x = -5$ or $x - 5 = 0 \Rightarrow$

$x = 5$, so $x = -5, 5$.

41. $t^2 = 5t \Rightarrow t^2 - 5t = 0 \Rightarrow t(t - 5) = 0$, then $t = 0$ or $t - 5 = 0 \Rightarrow t = 5$, so $x = 0, 5$.

43. $3m^2 = -9m \Rightarrow 3m^2 + 9m = 0 \Rightarrow 3m(m + 3) = 0$, then $3m = 0 \Rightarrow m = 0$ or $m + 3 = 0 \Rightarrow$

$m = -3$, so $m = -3, 0$.

45. $x^2 = 5x + 6 \Rightarrow x^2 - 5x - 6 = 0 \Rightarrow (x + 1)(x - 6) = 0$, then $x + 1 = 0 \Rightarrow x = -1$ or $x - 6 = 0 \Rightarrow$

$x = 6$, so $x = -1, 6$.

47. $12z^2 + 11z = 15 \Rightarrow 12z^2 + 11z - 15 = 0$, (factor by grouping), $m \cdot n = -180$, $m + n = 11 \Rightarrow$

$m = 20, n = -9 \Rightarrow 12z^2 + 20z - 9z - 15 = 0 \Rightarrow 4z(3z + 5) - 3(3z + 5) = 0 \Rightarrow (4z - 3)(3z + 5) = 0$,

then $4z - 3 = 0 \Rightarrow 4z = 3 \Rightarrow z = \frac{3}{4}$ or $3z + 5 = 0 \Rightarrow 3z = -5 \Rightarrow z = \frac{-5}{3}$, so $z = -\frac{5}{3}, \frac{3}{4}$.

49. $t(t + 1) = 2 \Rightarrow t^2 + t = 2 \Rightarrow t^2 + t - 2 = 0 \Rightarrow (t + 2)(t - 1) = 0$, then $t + 2 = 0 \Rightarrow$

$t = -2$ or $t - 1 = 0 \Rightarrow t = 1$, so $t = -2, 1$.

51. $x(2x + 5) = 3 \Rightarrow 2x^2 + 5x = 3 \Rightarrow 2x^2 + 5x - 3 = 0 \Rightarrow (2x - 1)(x + 3) = 0$, then $2x - 1 = 0 \Rightarrow$

$2x = 1 \Rightarrow x = \frac{1}{2}$ or $x + 3 = 0 \Rightarrow x = -3$, so $x = -3, \frac{1}{2}$.

Geometry

53. Both sides are the same so $x^2 = 144 \Rightarrow x^2 - 144 = 0 \Rightarrow (x + 12)(x - 12) = 0$, then $x + 12 = 0 \Rightarrow$

$x = -12$ or $x - 12 = 0 \Rightarrow x = 12$, so $x = -12, 12$, but length is not negative so $x = 12$ feet.

55. Area of circle πr^2 – circumference of circle $2\pi r = 8\pi \Rightarrow r^2\pi - 2r\pi = 8\pi \Rightarrow r^2 - 2r = 8 \Rightarrow$

$r^2 - 2r - 8 = 0 \Rightarrow (r - 4)(r + 2) = 0$, then $r - 4 = 0 \Rightarrow r = 4$ or $r + 2 = 0 \Rightarrow r = -2$, so $r = -2, 4$,

but radius cannot be -2 inches long so $r = 4$ inches.

57. Using pythagorean theorem $a^2 + b^2 = c^2$, $(x - 1)^2 + x^2 = (x + 1)^2 \Rightarrow x^2 - 2x + 1 + x^2 = x^2 + 2x + 1 \Rightarrow$

$2x^2 - 2x + 1 = x^2 + 2x + 1 \Rightarrow x^2 - 4x = 0 \Rightarrow x(x - 4) = 0$, then $x = 0$ or $x - 4 = 0 \Rightarrow$

$x = 4$, so $x = 0, 4$, but length cannot be 0 so $x = 4$.

Applications

59. (a) Height is zero at ground, $0 = 96t - 16t^2 \Rightarrow 0 = 16t(6 - t) = 0$, then $16t = 0 \Rightarrow t = 0$ or $6 - t = 0 \Rightarrow -t = -6 \Rightarrow t = 6$, so $t = 0, 6$, but $t = 0$ is when it was first hit, so after it was hit, it took 6 seconds to hit the ground.

(b) 3 seconds. See figure 59.

Time (t)	0	1	2	3	4	5	6
Height (h)	0	80	128	144	128	80	0

Figure 59

61. (a) For $x = 30$, $D = \frac{1}{11}(30)^2 \Rightarrow D = \frac{1}{11}(900) \Rightarrow d = 81.8$ feet.

For $x = 60$, $D = \frac{1}{11}(60)^2 \Rightarrow D = \frac{1}{11}(3600) \Rightarrow d = 327.3$ feet.

When the speed doubles, the braking distance quadruples.

(b) $33 = \frac{1}{11}x^2 \Rightarrow 363 = x^2 \Rightarrow x \approx 19$ mph.

(c) See Figure 61. About 19 miles per hour: yes.

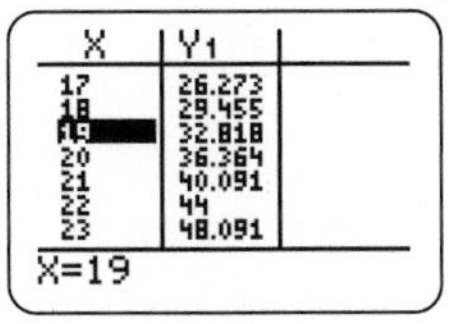

Figure 61

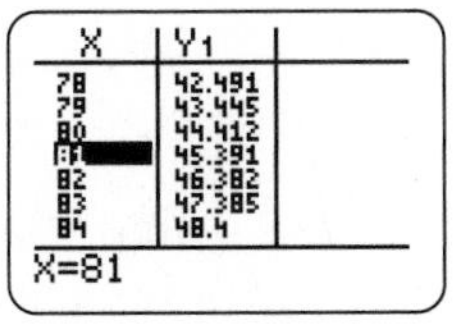

Figure 63

63. (a) 1930, $x = 30 \Rightarrow W = \frac{19}{3125}(30)^2 + \frac{11}{2} \Rightarrow W = \frac{19}{3125}(900) + \frac{11}{2} \Rightarrow$

$W = 10.972$ million ≈ 11 million.

2000, $x = 100 \Rightarrow W = \frac{19}{3125}(100)^2 + \frac{11}{2} \Rightarrow W = \frac{19}{3125}(10{,}000) + \frac{11}{2} \Rightarrow$

$W = 66.3$ million ≈ 66 million.

(b) See Figure 63. About 1981.

65. Width $= x$, Length $= x + 10$, $x(x + 10) = 2000 \Rightarrow x^2 + 10x = 2000 \Rightarrow x^2 + 10x - 2000 = 0 \Rightarrow (x + 50)(x - 40) = 0$, then $x + 50 = 0 \Rightarrow x = -50$ or $x - 40 = 0 \Rightarrow x = 40$, so $x = -50, 40$, but we can not have -50 pixels, so $x = 40 \Rightarrow$ width 40 and length $40 + 10 = 50 \Rightarrow 40 \times 50$ pixels.

6.6: Solving Equations by Factoring II (Higher Degrees)

Concepts

1. GCF

3. $(z^2 + 1)(z^2 + 2)$

5. Subtract x from both sides.

Factoring Polynomials

7. $5x^2 - 5x - 30 \Rightarrow 5(x^2 - x - 6) \Rightarrow 5(x + 2)(x - 3)$

9. $-4y^2 - 32y - 48 \Rightarrow -4(y^2 + 8y + 12) \Rightarrow -4(y + 6)(y + 2)$

11. $-20z^2 - 110z - 50 \Rightarrow -10(2z^2 + 11z + 5) \Rightarrow -10(2z + 1)(z + 5)$

13. $60 - 64t - 28t^2 \Rightarrow -4(7t^2 + 16t - 15) \Rightarrow -4(7t - 5)(t + 3)$

15. $r^3 - r \Rightarrow r(r^2 - 1) \Rightarrow r(r + 1)(r - 1)$

17. $3x^3 + 3x^2 - 18x \Rightarrow 3x(x^2 + x - 6) \Rightarrow 3x(x + 3)(x - 2)$

19. $72z^3 + 12z^2 - 24z \Rightarrow 12z(6z^2 + z - 2) \Rightarrow 12z(3z + 2)(2z - 1)$

21. $x^4 - 4x^2 \Rightarrow x^2(x^2 - 4) \Rightarrow x^2(x + 2)(x - 2)$

23. $t^4 + t^3 - 2t^2 \Rightarrow t^2(t^2 + t - 2) \Rightarrow t^2(t + 2)(t - 1)$

25. $x^4 - 5x^2 + 6 \Rightarrow (x^2 - 2)(x^2 - 3)$

27. $2x^4 + 7x^2 + 3 \Rightarrow (2x^2 + 1)(x^2 + 3)$

29. $y^4 + 6y^2 + 9 \Rightarrow (y^2 + 3)(y^2 + 3) \Rightarrow (y^2 + 3)^2$

31. $x^4 - 9 \Rightarrow (x^2 + 3)(x^2 - 3)$

33. $x^4 - 81 \Rightarrow (x^2 + 9)(x^2 - 9) \Rightarrow (x^2 + 9)(x + 3)(x - 3)$

35. $z^5 + 2z^4 + z^3 \Rightarrow z^3(z^2 + 2z + 1) \Rightarrow z^3(z + 1)(z + 1) \Rightarrow z^3(z + 1)^2$

37. $2x^2 + xy - y^2 \Rightarrow (2x - y)(x + y)$

39. $a^4 - 2a^2b^2 + b^4 \Rightarrow (a^2 - b^2)(a^2 - b^2) \Rightarrow (a + b)(a - b)(a + b)(a - b) \Rightarrow (a + b)^2(a - b)^2$

41. $x^3 - xy^2 \Rightarrow x(x^2 - y^2) \Rightarrow x(x + y)(x - y)$

43. $4x^3 + 4x^2y + xy^2 \Rightarrow x(4x^2 + 4xy + y^2) \Rightarrow x(2x + y)(2x + y) \Rightarrow x(2x + y)^2$

Solving Equations

45. (a) $x^3 - 4x \Rightarrow x(x^2 - 4) \Rightarrow x(x + 2)(x - 2)$

    (b) $x(x + 2)(x - 2) = 0$, then $x = 0$ or $x + 2 = 0$ or $x - 2 = 0 \Rightarrow x = -2, 0, 2$.

47. (a) $2y^3 - 6y^2 - 36y \Rightarrow 2y(y^2 - 3y - 18) \Rightarrow 2y(y - 6)(y + 3)$

    (b) $2y(y - 6)(y + 3) = 0$, then $2y = 0$ or $y - 6 = 0$ or $y + 3 = 0 \Rightarrow y = -3, 0, 6$.

49. $3x^2 + 33x + 72 = 0 \Rightarrow 3(x^2 + 11x + 24) = 0 \Rightarrow 3(x + 8)(x + 3) = 0$, then $x + 8 = 0$ or $x + 3 = 0 \Rightarrow$ $x = -8, -3$.

51. $25x^2 = 50x + 75 \Rightarrow 25x^2 - 50x - 75 = 0 \Rightarrow 25(x^2 - 2x - 3) = 0 \Rightarrow 25(x - 3)(x + 1) = 0$, then $x - 3 = 0$ or $x + 1 = 0 \Rightarrow x = -1, 3$.

53. $y^3 - 3y^2 - 4y = 0 \Rightarrow y(y^2 - 3y - 4) = 0 \Rightarrow y(y - 4)(y + 1) = 0$, then $y = 0$ or $y - 4 = 0$ or $y + 1 = 0 \Rightarrow y = -1, 0, 4$.

55. $3z^3 + 6z^2 = 72z \Rightarrow 3z^3 + 6z^2 - 72z = 0 \Rightarrow 3z(z^2 + 2z - 24) = 0 \Rightarrow 3z(z + 6)(z - 4) = 0$, then $3z = 0$ or $z + 6 = 0$ or $z - 4 = 0 \Rightarrow z = -6, 0, 4$.

57. $x^4 - 36x^2 = 0 \Rightarrow x^2(x^2 - 36) = 0 \Rightarrow x^2(x + 6)(x - 6) = 0$, then $x^2 = 0$ or $x + 6 = 0$ or $x - 6 = 0 \Rightarrow$ $x = -6, 0, 6$.

59. $r^4 + 6r^3 = 7r^2 \Rightarrow r^4 + 6r^3 - 7r^2 = 0 \Rightarrow r^2(r^2 + 6r - 7) = 0 \Rightarrow r^2(r + 7)(r - 1) = 0$, then $r^2 = 0$ or $r + 7 = 0$ or $r - 1 = 0 \Rightarrow r = -7, 0, 1$.

61. $x^4 - 13x^2 + 36 = 0 \Rightarrow (x^2 - 9)(x^2 - 4) = 0 \Rightarrow (x + 3)(x - 3)(x + 2)(x - 2) = 0$, then $x + 3 = 0$ or $x - 3 = 0$ or $x + 2 = 0$ or $x - 2 = 0 \Rightarrow x = -3, -2, 2, 3$.

63. $x^4 + 1 = 2x^2 \Rightarrow x^4 - 2x^2 + 1 = 0 \Rightarrow (x^2 - 1)(x^2 - 1) = 0 \Rightarrow (x + 1)(x - 1)(x + 1)(x - 1) = 0$, then $x + 1 = 0$ or $x - 1 = 0 \Rightarrow x = -1, 1$.

65. $a^4 = 81 \Rightarrow a^4 - 81 = 0 \Rightarrow (a^2 + 9)(a^2 - 9) = 0 \Rightarrow (a^2 + 9)(a + 3)(a - 3) = 0$, then $a^2 + 9 = 0$ or $a + 3 = 0$ or $a - 3 = 0$, but $a^2 + 9 = 0$ does not produce real solutions so $x = -3, 3$.

67. $x^3 - 2x^2 - x + 2 = 0 \Rightarrow x^2(x - 2) - (x - 2) = 0 \Rightarrow (x^2 - 1)(x - 2) = 0 \Rightarrow$ $(x + 1)(x - 1)(x - 2) = 0$, then $x + 1 = 0$ or $x - 1 = 0$ or $x - 2 = 0 \Rightarrow x = -1, 1, 2$.

69. $x^3 - 5x^2 + x - 5 = 0 \Rightarrow x^2(x - 5) + (x - 5) = 0 \Rightarrow (x^2 + 1)(x - 5) = 0 \Rightarrow$ then $x^2 + 1 = 0$ or $x - 5 = 0$ but $x^2 + 1 = 0$ does not produce real solutions so $x = 5$.

Applications

71. (a) $x < 7.5$ because the width is 15 inches.
    (b) Area of rectangle with 4 cut out pieces $15 \times 20 = 300$. Area of cut out piece $x^2 \cdot 4$ pieces $= 4x^2 \Rightarrow$ surface area $300 - 4x^2$.
    (c) $300 - 4x^2 = 275 \Rightarrow 0 = 4x^2 - 25 \Rightarrow (2x + 5)(2x - 5) = 0$, then $2x + 5 = 0$ or $2x - 5 = 0$, but $2x + 5 = 0$ produces a negative length which we can not have so $2x - 5 = 0 \Rightarrow 2x = 5 \Rightarrow$ $x = \frac{5}{2} \Rightarrow x = 2.5$ inches.

73. $1990 = 30 \Rightarrow 0.0013(30)^3 - 0.085(30)^2 + 1.6(30) + 12 = 35.1 - 76.5 + 48 + 12 = 18.6$ trillion ft^3

75. Factoring is very difficult.

Checking Basic Concepts for Sections 6.5 & 6.6

1. (a) $4y^2 - 6y = 0 \Rightarrow 2y(2y - 3) = 0$, then $2y = 0$ or $2y - 3 = 0 \Rightarrow y = 0, \frac{3}{2}$
   (b) $5z^2 + 2z = 3 \Rightarrow 5z^2 + 2z - 3 = 0 \Rightarrow (5z - 3)(z + 1) = 0$, then $5z - 3 = 0 \Rightarrow 5z = 3 \Rightarrow z = \frac{3}{5}$ or $z + 1 = 0$, so $z = -1, \frac{3}{5}$

2. $x^2 + 2x - 3 = 0 \Rightarrow (x + 3)(x - 1) = 0$, then $x + 3 = 0$ or $x - 1 = 0$, so $x = -3, 1$

3. $88t - 16t^2 = 0 \Rightarrow -8t(2t - 11) = 0$, then $-8t = 0$ or $2t - 11 = 0 \Rightarrow 2t = 11 \Rightarrow t = \frac{11}{2}$, so $t = 0, \frac{11}{2}$; $t = 0$ is when the ball was hit so the golf ball will hit the ground 5.5 seconds after it is hit.

4. (a) $x^4 - 8x^2 + 16 \Rightarrow (x^2 - 4)(x^2 - 4) \Rightarrow (x + 2)(x - 2)(x + 2)(x - 2) \Rightarrow (x + 2)^2(x - 2)^2$
   (b) $2y^3 + 17y^2 - 30y \Rightarrow y(2y^2 + 17y - 30) \Rightarrow y(2y - 3)(y + 10)$
   (c) $x^4 - 16y^4 \Rightarrow (x^2 + 4y^2)(x^2 - 4y^2) \Rightarrow (x^2 + 4y^2)(x + 2y)(x - 2y)$

5. $t^4 + t^3 = 12t^2 \Rightarrow t^4 + t^3 - 12t^2 = 0 \Rightarrow t^2(t^2 + t - 12) = 0 \Rightarrow t^2(t + 4)(t - 3) = 0$, then $t^2 = 0$ or $t + 4 = 0$ or $t - 3 = 0 \Rightarrow t = -4, 0, 3$.

Chapter 6 Review Exercises

Section 6.1

1. Factors of $8z^3 = 2 \cdot 2 \cdot 2 \cdot z \cdot z \cdot z \Rightarrow$ factors of $4z^2 = 2 \cdot 2 \cdot z \cdot z \Rightarrow \text{GCF} = 2 \cdot 2 \cdot z \cdot z = 4z^2$; $4z^2(2z - 1)$
2. Factors of $6x^4 = 2 \cdot 3 \cdot x \cdot x \cdot x \cdot x \Rightarrow$ factors of $3x^3 = 3 \cdot x \cdot x \cdot x \Rightarrow$ factors of $12x^2 = 2 \cdot 2 \cdot 3 \cdot x \cdot x \Rightarrow$ $GCF = 3 \cdot x \cdot x = 3x^2$; $3x^2(2x^2 + x - 4)$.
3. Factors of $9xy = 3 \cdot 3 \cdot x \cdot y \Rightarrow$ factors of $15yz^2 = 3 \cdot 5 \cdot y \cdot z \cdot z \Rightarrow \text{GCF} = 3 \cdot y = 3y$; $3y(3x + 5z^2)$.
4. Factors of $a^2b^3 = a \cdot a \cdot b \cdot b \cdot b \Rightarrow$ factors of $a^3b^2 = a \cdot a \cdot a \cdot b \cdot b \Rightarrow \text{GCF} = a \cdot a \cdot b \cdot b = a^2b^2$; $a^2b^2(b + a)$.
5. $x(x + 2) - 3(x + 2) \Rightarrow (x - 3)(x + 2)$
6. $y^2(x - 5) + 3y(x - 5) \Rightarrow (y^2 + 3y)(x - 5) \Rightarrow y(y + 3)(x - 5)$
7. $z^3 - 2z^2 + 5z - 10 \Rightarrow z^2(z - 2) + 5(z - 2) \Rightarrow (z^2 + 5)(z - 2)$
8. $t^3 + t^2 + 8t + 8 \Rightarrow t^2(t + 1) + 8(t + 1) \Rightarrow (t^2 + 8)(t + 1)$
9. $x^3 - 3x^2 + 6x - 18 \Rightarrow x^2(x - 3) + 6(x - 3) \Rightarrow (x^2 + 6)(x - 3)$
10. $ax + bx - ay - by \Rightarrow x(a + b) - y(a + b) \Rightarrow (x - y)(a + b)$

Section 6.2

11. 4, 5
12. −3, 7
13. −9, −4
14. −25, 4
15. Product −12, sum −1 is −4, 3 $\Rightarrow (x - 4)(x + 3)$.
16. Product 24, sum 10 is 4, 6 $\Rightarrow (x + 4)(x + 6)$.
17. Product −16, sum 6 is −2, 8 $\Rightarrow (x - 2)(x + 8)$.
18. Product −42, sum −1 is −7, 6 $\Rightarrow (x - 7)(x + 6)$.
19. Product −3, sum 2 is −1, 3 $\Rightarrow (x - 1)(x + 3)$.
20. Product 120, sum 22 is 10, 12 $\Rightarrow (x + 10)(x + 12)$.
21. Product 10, sum −7 is −5, −2 $\Rightarrow (2 - x)(5 - x)$.
22. Product 24, sum 2 is 6, −4 $\Rightarrow (6 - x)(4 + x)$.

Section 6.3

23. Using FOIL: $9x^2 + 3x - 2 = (3x + 2)(3x - 1)$.

24. Using FOIL: $2x^2 + 3x - 5 = (2x + 5)(x - 1)$.

25. Using FOIL: $3x^2 + 14x + 15 = (3x + 5)(x + 3)$.

26. Using FOIL: $35x^2 - 2x - 1 = (5x - 1)(7x + 1)$.

27. Using FOIL: $24x^2 - 7x - 5 = (8x - 5)(3x + 1)$.

28. Using FOIL: $4x^2 + 33x - 27 = (x + 9)(4x - 3)$.

29. Using FOIL: $12 - 5x - 2x^2 = (3 - 2x)(4 + x)$.

30. Using FOIL: $1 + 3x - 10x^2 = (1 + 5x)(1 - 2x)$.

Section 6.4

31. Difference of squares, $x^2 - 4 = (x + 2)(x - 2)$.

32. Difference of squares, $9z^2 - 64 = (3z + 8)(3z - 8)$.

33. Difference of squares, $36 - y^2 = (6 + y)(6 - y)$.

34. Difference of squares, $100a^2 - 81b^2 = (10a + 9b)(10a - 9b)$.

35. Perfect trinomial, $a^2 = x^2$ so $a = x$, $b^2 = 7^2$ so $b = 7$, then $2ab = 2 \cdot 7 \cdot x = 14x$ the middle term $\Rightarrow$ $(x + 7)^2$.

36. Perfect trinomial, $a^2 = x^2$ so $a = x$, $b^2 = (\pm 5)^2$ so $b = \pm 5$, using $b = -5$, then $2ab = 2 \cdot (-5)x = -10x$ the middle term $\Rightarrow (x - 5)^2$.

37. Perfect trinomial, $a^2 = (2x)^2$ so $a = 2x$, $b^2 = (\pm 3)^2$ so $b = \pm 3$, using $b = -3$, then $2ab = 2 \cdot (-3)2x = -12x$ the middle term $\Rightarrow (2x - 3)^2$.

38. Perfect trinomial, $a^2 = 3x^2$ so $a = 3x$, $b^2 = 8^2$ so $b = 8$, then $2ab = 2 \cdot 8 \cdot 3x = 48x$ the middle term $\Rightarrow$ $(3x + 8)^2$.

39. Difference of cubes, $8t^3 - 1$, $a^3 = (2t)^3$ so $a = 2t$, $b^3 = 1^3$ so $b = 1 \Rightarrow (2t - 1)(4t^2 + 2t + 1)$.

40. Sum of cubes, $27r^3 + 8t^3$, $a^3 = (3r)^3$ so $a = 3r$, $b^3 = (2t)^3$ so $b = 2t \Rightarrow (3r + 2t)(9r^2 - 6rt + 4t^2)$.

Section 6.5

41. $m = 0$ or $n = 0$

42. $y = 0$

43. $(4x - 3)(x + 9) = 0$, then $4x - 3 = 0 \Rightarrow 4x = 3 \Rightarrow x = \frac{3}{4}$ or $x + 9 = 0 \Rightarrow x = -9$, so $x = -9, \frac{3}{4}$.

44. $(1 - 4x)(6 + 5x) = 0$, then $1 - 4x = 0 \Rightarrow -4x = -1 \Rightarrow x = \frac{-1}{-4} \Rightarrow x = \frac{1}{4}$ or $6 + 5x = 0 \Rightarrow 5x = -6 \Rightarrow$ $x = \frac{-6}{5}$, so $x = -\frac{6}{5}, \frac{1}{4}$.

45. $z(z - 1)(z - 2) = 0$, then $z = 0$ or $z - 1 = 0 \Rightarrow z = 1$ or $z - 2 = 0 \Rightarrow z = 2$, so $z = 0, 1, 2$.

46. $z^2 - 7z = 0 \Rightarrow z(z - 7) = 0$, then $z = 0$ or $z - 7 = 0 \Rightarrow z = 7$, so $z = 0, 7$.

47. $y^2 - 64 = 0$, difference of squares $(y + 8)(y - 8) = 0$, then $y + 8 = 0 \Rightarrow y = -8$ or $y - 8 = 0 \Rightarrow$ $y = 8$, so $y = -8, 8$.

48. $y^2 + 9y + 14 = 0 \Rightarrow (y + 2)(y + 7) = 0$, then $y + 2 = 0 \Rightarrow y = -2$ or $y + 7 = 0 \Rightarrow$ $y = -7$, so $y = -2, -7$.

49. $x^2 = x + 6 \Rightarrow x^2 - x - 6 = 0 \Rightarrow (x - 3)(x + 2) = 0$, then $x - 3 = 0 \Rightarrow x = 3$ or $x + 2 = 0 \Rightarrow$ $x = -2$, so $x = -2, 3$.

50. $10x^2 + 11x = 6 \Rightarrow 10x^2 + 11x - 6 = 0 \Rightarrow (2x + 3)(5x - 2) = 0$, then $2x + 3 = 0 \Rightarrow 2x = -3 \Rightarrow$ $x = \frac{-3}{2}$ or $5x - 2 = 0 \Rightarrow 5x = 2 \Rightarrow x = \frac{2}{5}$, so $x = -\frac{3}{2}, \frac{2}{5}$.

51. $t(t - 14) = 72 \Rightarrow t^2 - 14t = 72 \Rightarrow t^2 - 14t - 72 = 0 \Rightarrow (t - 18)(t + 4) = 0$, then $t - 18 = 0 \Rightarrow$ $t = 18$ or $t + 4 = 0 \Rightarrow t = -4$, so $t = -4, 18$.

52. $t(2t - 1) = 10 \Rightarrow 2t^2 - t = 10 \Rightarrow 2t^2 - t - 10 = 0 \Rightarrow (2t - 5)(t + 2) = 0$, then $2t - 5 = 0 \Rightarrow$ $2t = 5 \Rightarrow t = \frac{5}{2}$ or $t + 2 = 0 \Rightarrow t = -2$, so $t = -2, \frac{5}{2}$.

Section 6.6

53. $5x^2 - 15x - 50 \Rightarrow 5(x^2 - 3x - 10) \Rightarrow 5(x - 5)(x + 2)$

54. $-3x^2 - 6x + 45 \Rightarrow -3(x^2 + 2x - 15) \Rightarrow -3(x + 5)(x - 3)$

55. $y^3 - 4y \Rightarrow y(y^2 - 4) \Rightarrow y(y + 2)(y - 2)$

56. $3y^3 + 6y^2 - 9y \Rightarrow 3y(y^2 + 2y - 3) \Rightarrow 3y(y + 3)(y - 1)$

57. $2z^4 + 14z^3 + 20z^2 \Rightarrow 2z^2(z^2 + 7z + 10) \Rightarrow 2z^2(z + 2)(z + 5)$

58. $8z^4 - 32z^2 \Rightarrow 8z^2(z^2 - 4) \Rightarrow 8z^2(z + 2)(z - 2)$

59. $x^4 - 6x^2 + 9 \Rightarrow (x^2 - 3)(x^2 - 3) \Rightarrow (x^2 - 3)^2$

60. $2x^4 - 15x^2 - 27 \Rightarrow (2x^2 + 3)(x^2 - 9) \Rightarrow (2x^2 + 3)(x + 3)(x - 3)$

61. $a^2 + 10ab + 25b^2 \Rightarrow (a + 5b)(a + 5b) \Rightarrow (a + 5b)^2$

62. $x^3 - xy^2 \Rightarrow x(x^2 - y^2) \Rightarrow x(x + y)(x - y)$

63. $16x^2 - 72x - 40 = 0 \Rightarrow 8(2x^2 - 9x - 5) = 0 \Rightarrow 8(2x + 1)(x - 5) = 0$, then $2x + 1 = 0 \Rightarrow 2x = -1 \Rightarrow$ $x = -\frac{1}{2}$ or $x - 5 = 0 \Rightarrow x = 5$, so $x = -\frac{1}{2}, 5$.

64. $2x^3 - 11x^2 - 15x = 0 \Rightarrow x(2x^2 - 11x + 15) = 0 \Rightarrow x(2x - 5)(x - 3) = 0$, then $x = 0$ or $2x - 5 = 0 \Rightarrow$ $2x = 5 \Rightarrow x = \frac{5}{2}$ or $x - 3 = 0 \Rightarrow x = 3$, so $x = 0, \frac{5}{2}, 3$.

65. $t^3 - 25t = 0 \Rightarrow t(t^2 - 25) = 0 \Rightarrow t(t + 5)(t - 5) = 0$, then $t = 0$ or $t + 5 = 0 \Rightarrow$ $t = -5$ or $t - 5 = 0 \Rightarrow t = 5$, so $t = -5, 0, 5$.

66. $t^4 - 7t^3 + 12t^2 = 0 \Rightarrow t^2(t^2 - 7t + 12) = 0 \Rightarrow t^2(t - 3)(t - 4) = 0$, then $t^2 = 0$ or $t - 3 = 0 \Rightarrow$ $t = 3$ or $t - 4 = 0 \Rightarrow t = 4$, so $t = 0, 3, 4$.

67. $z^4 + 16 = 8z^2 \Rightarrow z^4 - 8z^2 + 16 = 0 \Rightarrow (z^2 - 4)(z^2 - 4) = 0 \Rightarrow (z + 2)(z - 2)(z + 2)(z - 2) = 0$, then $z + 2 = 0 \Rightarrow z = -2$ or $z - 2 = 0 \Rightarrow z = 2$, so $z = -2, 2$.

68. $z^4 - 256 = 0 \Rightarrow (z^2 + 16)(z^2 - 16) = 0 \Rightarrow (z^2 + 16)(z + 4)(z - 4) = 0$, then $z^2 + 16 = 0$ which produces no real solutions, or $z + 4 = 0 \Rightarrow z = -4$ or $z - 4 = 0 \Rightarrow z = 4$, so $z = -4, 4$.

69. $y^3 = -64 \Rightarrow y^3 + 64 = 0 \Rightarrow (y + 4)(y^2 - 4y + 16) = 0$, then $y + 4 = 0 \Rightarrow$
$y = -4$ or $y^2 - 4y + 16 = 0$ which produces no real solutions, so $y = -4$.

70. $y^3 - y^2 - y + 1 = 0 \Rightarrow y^2(y - 1) - 1(y - 1) = 0 \Rightarrow (y^2 - 1)(y - 1) = 0 \Rightarrow$
$(y + 1)(y - 1)(y - 1) = 0$, then $y + 1 = 0 \Rightarrow y = -1$ or $y - 1 = 0 \Rightarrow y = 1$, so $y = -1, 1$.

Applications

71. The sides of a square are equal so the trinomial must be a perfect trinomial, $a^2 = (3x)^2$ so $a = 3x$, $b^2 = 7^2$ so $b = 7$, then $2ab = 2 \cdot 3x \cdot 7 = 42x$ the middle term, so $(3x + 7)^2$, so each side is $3x + 7$. See Figure 71.

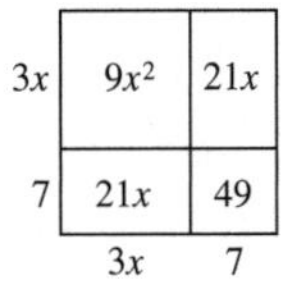

Figure 71

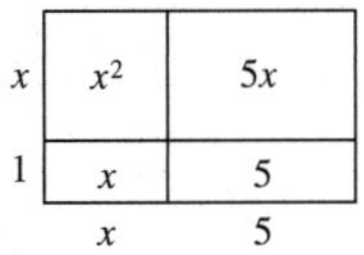

Figure 72

72. $x^2 + 6x + 5 = 0 \Rightarrow (x + 5)(x + 1) = 0$ so the sides are $(x + 5)$ by $(x + 1)$. See Figure 72.

73. A cube has six sides, so $(6x^2 + 12x + 6) \div 6 = x^2 + 2x + 1$, the area of each side $\Rightarrow (x + 1)(x + 1) \Rightarrow$ each side is $(x + 1)$.

74. $x^2 + 3x + x + 3 = x^2 + 4x + 3 \Rightarrow (x + 3)(x + 1)$

75. $2x^2 + 3x + 12x + 18 = 2x^2 + 15x + 18 \Rightarrow (2x + 3)(x + 6)$

76. (area) $\pi r^2 = 2r\pi$ (circumference) $\Rightarrow r^2 = 2r \Rightarrow r = 2$

77. $x(x + 7) = 120 \Rightarrow x^2 + 7x - 120 = 0 \Rightarrow (x + 15)(x - 8) = 0$, $x = -15$ (not possible), 8, so rectangle 8×15.

78. $100 = -16t^2 + 80t + 4 \Rightarrow 16t^2 - 80t + 96 = 0 \Rightarrow 16(t^2 - 5t + 6) = 0 \Rightarrow 16(t - 2)(t - 3) = 0$, so $x = 2, 3$ so at 2 seconds and 3 seconds.

79. (a) $D = \frac{1}{9}(45)^2 + \frac{11}{3}(45) \Rightarrow D = \frac{1}{9}(2025) + \frac{11}{3}(45) \Rightarrow D = 225 + 165 \Rightarrow D = 390$ feet.

(b) $80 = \frac{1}{9}x^2 + \frac{11}{3}x \Rightarrow \frac{1}{9}x^2 + \frac{11}{3}x - 80 = 0 \Rightarrow$ multiply by 9 $\Rightarrow x^2 + 33x - 720 = 0 \Rightarrow$
$(x + 48)(x - 15) = 0$, so $D = -48$ (not possible) or 15mph.

(c) See Figure 79. 15mph, yes.

80. (a) $R = 100(200 - 100) \Rightarrow R = 100(100) \Rightarrow R = \$10{,}000$

(b) $7500 = p(200 - p) \Rightarrow 7500 = 200p - p^2 \Rightarrow p^2 - 200p + 7500 = 0 \Rightarrow (p - 50)(p - 150) = 0 \Rightarrow$
$p = 50, 150 \Rightarrow$ \$50 or \$150.

(c) See Figure 80. \$50 or \$150, yes.

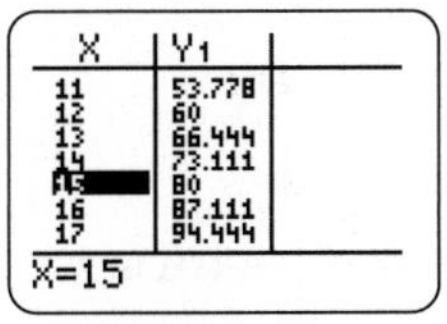

Figure 79

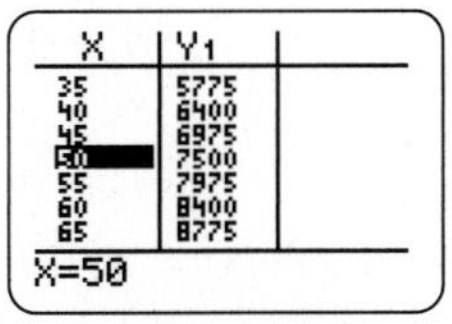

Figure 80

81. (a) $x = 20$ for 1970, $N = 0.68(20)^2 + 3.8(20) + 24 \Rightarrow N = 272 + 76 + 24 \Rightarrow N = 372$ million.

(b) See Figure 81. 1975.

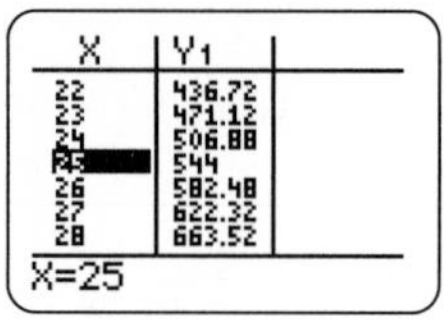

Figure 81

82. $x(x + 30) = 4000 \Rightarrow x^2 + 30x - 4000 = 0 \Rightarrow (x + 80)(x - 50) = 0$, so $x = -80$ (not possible) or 50, so 50×80 pixels.

83. (a) Bottom $(50 - 2x)(40 - 2x) = 2000 - 80x - 100x + 4x^2 = 2000 - 180 + 4x^2$;

2 sides $x(50 - 2x) = 50x - 2x^2(2) = 100x - 4x^2$; 2 sides $x(40 - 2x) = 40x - 2x^2(2) = 80x - 4x^2$.

Add all sides $2000 - 180x + 4x^2 + 100x - 4x^2 + 80x - 4x^2 = 2000 - 4x^2$.

(b) $1900 = 2000 - 4x^2 \Rightarrow -100 = -4x^2 \Rightarrow 25 = x^2 \Rightarrow x = 5$ inches.

Chapter 6 Test

1. $4x^2y = 2 \cdot 2 \cdot x \cdot x \cdot y$; $20xy^2 = 2 \cdot 2 \cdot 5 \cdot x \cdot y \cdot y$; $12xy = 2 \cdot 2 \cdot 3 \cdot x \cdot y \Rightarrow$ $\text{GCF} = 2 \cdot 2 \cdot x \cdot y = 4xy \Rightarrow 4x^2y - 20xy^2 + 12xy = 4xy(x - 5y + 3)$

2. $9a^3b^2 = 3 \cdot 3 \cdot a \cdot a \cdot a \cdot b \cdot b$; $3a^2b^2 = 3 \cdot a \cdot a \cdot b \cdot b \Rightarrow \text{GCF} = 3 \cdot a \cdot a \cdot b \cdot b = 3a^2b^2 \Rightarrow$ $9a^3b^2 + 3a^2b^2 = 3a^2b^2(3a + 1)$

3. $ay + by + az + bx \Rightarrow y(a + b) + z(a + b) \Rightarrow (y + z)(a + b)$

4. $3x^3 + x^2 - 15x - 5 \Rightarrow x^2(3x + 1) - 5(3x + 1) \Rightarrow (x^2 - 5)(3x + 1)$

5. $y^2 + 4y - 12 = (y + 6)(y - 2)$

6. $4x^2 + 20x + 25 = (2x + 5)(2x + 5) = (2x + 5)^2$

7. $4z^2 - 19z + 12 = (4z - 3)(z - 4)$

8. $21 - 17t + 2t^2 = 2t^2 - 17t + 21 = (2t - 3)(t - 7)$

9. $x^2 - 16 = 0 \Rightarrow (x + 4)(x - 4) = 0$, then $x + 4 = 0$ or $x - 4 = 0$, so $x = -4, 4$.

10. $y^2 = y + 20 \Rightarrow y^2 - y - 20 = 0 \Rightarrow (y - 5)(y + 4) = 0$, then $y - 5 = 0$ or $y + 4 = 0$, so $y = -4, 5$.

11. $9z^2 + 16 = 24z \Rightarrow 9z^2 - 24z + 16 = 0$ is a perfect trinomial $a^2 = (3z)^2$ so $a = 3z$, $b^2 = \pm 4^2$ so $b = \pm 4$, using $b = -4$, $2ab = 2 \cdot 3z \cdot -4 = -24z$ the middle term $\Rightarrow (3z - 4)^2$, then $3z - 4 = 0 \Rightarrow$ $3z = 4 \Rightarrow z = \dfrac{4}{3}$.

12. $x(x - 5) = 66 \Rightarrow x^2 - 5x - 66 = 0 \Rightarrow (x - 11)(x + 6) = 0$, then $x - 11 = 0$ or $x + 6 = 0$, so $x = -6, 11$

13. $6x^3 + 3x^2 - 3x \Rightarrow 3x(2x^2 + x - 1) \Rightarrow 3x(2x - 1)(x + 1)$

14. $2z^4 - 12z^2 - 54 \Rightarrow 2(z^4 - 6z - 27) \Rightarrow 2(z^2 - 9)(z^2 + 3) \Rightarrow 2(z + 3)(z - 3)(z^2 + 3)$

15. $y^3 = 9y \Rightarrow y^3 - 9y = 0 \Rightarrow y(y^2 - 9) = 0 \Rightarrow y(y + 3)(y - 3) = 0$, then $y = 0$ or $y + 3 = 0$ or $y - 3 = 0$, so $y = -3, 0, 3$.

16. $x^4 - 5x^2 + 4 = 0 \Rightarrow (x^2 - 4)(x^2 - 1) = 0 \Rightarrow (x + 2)(x - 2)(x + 1)(x - 1) = 0$, then $x + 2 = 0$ or $x - 2 = 0$ or $x + 1 = 0$ or $x - 1 = 0$, so $x = -2, -1, 1, 2$.

17. In a square the sides must be equal so $9x^2 + 30x + 25$ must be a perfect trinomial $\Rightarrow a^2 = (3x)^2$ so $a = 3x$, $b^2 = 5^2$ so $b = 5$, $2ab = 2(3x)5 = 30x$ the middle term $\Rightarrow (3x + 5)^2 \Rightarrow$ each side is $3x + 5$.

18. $x^2 + 3x + 2x + 6 = x^2 + 5x + 6 = (x + 2)(x + 3)$

19. (a) $D = \frac{1}{11}(55)^2 = \frac{1}{11}(3025) = 275$ ft.

    (b) $99 = \frac{1}{11}x^2 \Rightarrow \frac{1}{11}x^2 - 99 = 0 \Rightarrow x^2 - 1089 = 0 \Rightarrow (x + 33)(x - 33) = 0$, then $x + 33 = 0$ or $x - 33 = 0$, so $x = -33$ (not possible) or 33, so 33 mph.

20. $36 = -16t^2 + 48t + 4 \Rightarrow 16t^2 - 48t + 32 = 0 \Rightarrow 16(t^2 - 3t + 2) = 0 \Rightarrow 16(t - 2)(t - 1) = 0$, then $t - 2 = 0$ or $t - 1 = 0$, so $t = 1, 2$ so 1 sec. or 2 sec.

Chapter 6 Extended and Discovery Exercises

1. $x^2 - 5 = (x + \sqrt{5})(x - \sqrt{5})$

2. $y^2 - 7 = (x + \sqrt{7})(x - \sqrt{7})$

3. $3z^2 - 25 = (\sqrt{3}z + 5)(\sqrt{3}z - 5)$

4. $7t^2 - 11 = (\sqrt{7}t + \sqrt{11})(\sqrt{7}t - \sqrt{11})$

5. $x - 4 = (\sqrt{x} + 2)(\sqrt{x} - 2)$

6. $x - 7 = (\sqrt{x} + \sqrt{7})(\sqrt{x} - \sqrt{7})$

7. $x^2 - 3 = 0 \Rightarrow (x + \sqrt{3})(x - \sqrt{3}) = 0$, then $x + \sqrt{3} = 0 \Rightarrow x = -\sqrt{3}$ or $x - \sqrt{3} = 0 \Rightarrow x = \sqrt{3}$, so $x = -\sqrt{3}, \sqrt{3}$.

8. $y^2 - 7 = 0 \Rightarrow (y + \sqrt{7})(y - \sqrt{7}) = 0$, then $y + \sqrt{7} = 0 \Rightarrow y = -\sqrt{7}$ or $y - \sqrt{7} = 0 \Rightarrow y = \sqrt{7}$, so $x = -\sqrt{7}, \sqrt{7}$.

9. $3x^2 - 25 = 0 \Rightarrow (\sqrt{3}x + 5)(\sqrt{3}x - 5) = 0$, then $\sqrt{3}x + 5 = 0 \Rightarrow \sqrt{3}x = -5 \Rightarrow x = \frac{-5}{\sqrt{3}}$ or $\sqrt{3}x - 5 = 0 \Rightarrow \sqrt{3}x = 5 \Rightarrow x = \frac{5}{\sqrt{3}}$, so $x = \frac{-5}{\sqrt{3}}, \frac{5}{\sqrt{3}}$.

10. $3x^2 - 11 = 0 \Rightarrow (\sqrt{7}x + \sqrt{11})(\sqrt{7}x - \sqrt{11}) = 0$, then $\sqrt{7}x + \sqrt{11} = 0 \Rightarrow \sqrt{7}x = -\sqrt{11} \Rightarrow$ $x = \frac{-\sqrt{11}}{\sqrt{7}}$ or $\sqrt{7}x - \sqrt{11} = 0 \Rightarrow \sqrt{7}x = \sqrt{11} \Rightarrow x = \frac{\sqrt{11}}{\sqrt{7}}$, so $x = \frac{-\sqrt{11}}{\sqrt{7}}, \frac{\sqrt{11}}{\sqrt{7}}$.

11. $x^4 - 9 = 0 \Rightarrow (x^2 + 3)(x^2 - 3) = 0 \Rightarrow (x^2 + 3)(x + \sqrt{3})(x - \sqrt{3}) = 0$, then $x^2 + 3 = 0 \Rightarrow x^2 = -3$, which has no real solutions, or $x + \sqrt{3} = 0 \Rightarrow x = -\sqrt{3}$ or $x - \sqrt{3} = 0 \Rightarrow x = \sqrt{3}$, so $x = -\sqrt{3}, \sqrt{3}$.

12. $x^4 - 25 = 0 \Rightarrow (x^2 + 5)(x^2 - 5) = 0 \Rightarrow (x^2 + 5)(x + \sqrt{5})(x - \sqrt{5}) = 0$, then $x^2 + 5 = 0 \Rightarrow x^2 = -5$, which has no real solutions, or $x + \sqrt{5} = 0 \Rightarrow x = -\sqrt{5}$ or $x - \sqrt{5} = 0 \Rightarrow x = \sqrt{5}$, so $x = -\sqrt{5}, \sqrt{5}$.

Chapters 1-6 Cumulative Review Exercises

1. $144 = 2 \times 2 \times 2 \times 2 \times 3 \times 3$

2. $-2(-2) + 3(4) = 4 + 12 = 16$

3. $2n + 5$

4. $-\frac{5}{8}$

5. $\frac{3}{5} \cdot \frac{15}{21} = \frac{45}{105} = \frac{3}{7}$

6. $\frac{1}{2} \div \frac{5}{4} = \frac{1}{2} \cdot \frac{4}{5} = \frac{4}{10} = \frac{2}{5}$

7. $\frac{5}{8} + \frac{1}{8} = \frac{6}{8} = \frac{3}{4}$

8. $\frac{4}{5} - \frac{1}{10} = \frac{8}{10} - \frac{1}{10} = \frac{7}{10}$

9. $26 - 3 \cdot 6 \div 2 = 26 - 18 \div 2 = 26 - 9 = 17$

10. $-2^2 + \frac{3+2}{8+2} = -(2^2) + \frac{5}{10} = -4 + \frac{1}{2} = -\frac{8}{2} + \frac{1}{2} = -\frac{7}{2}$

11. 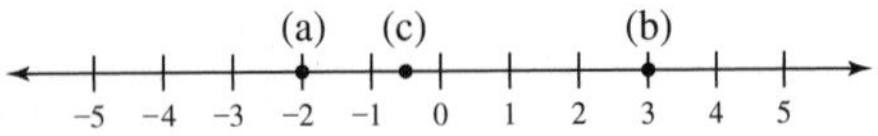

12. $\frac{4x}{9y} \div \frac{6x}{3y} = \frac{4x}{9y} \cdot \frac{3y}{6x} = \frac{12xy}{54xy} = \frac{2}{9}$

13. $-2 + 7x + 4 - 5x = 2x + 2$

14. $-4(4 - y) + (5 - 3y) = -16 + 4y + 5 - 3y = y - 11$

15. $4t - 7 = 25 \Rightarrow 4t = 32 \Rightarrow t = \frac{32}{4}$, so $t = 8$.

16. See Figure 16. $2x + 3 = 5$ when $x = 1$.

x	−2	−1	0	1	2
$2x + 3$	−1	1	3	5	7

Figure 16

17. $3n - 5 = n - 7$; $3n - 5 = n - 7 \Rightarrow 3n - n = -7 + 5 \Rightarrow 2n = -2 \Rightarrow n = -1$

18. $\frac{5.7}{100} = \frac{57}{1000}$; 0.057

19. $0.123 = 12.3\%$

20. For $r = 60$, $d = 150$, $d = rt \Rightarrow 150 = 60t \Rightarrow \frac{150}{60} = t \Rightarrow t = \frac{5}{2} \Rightarrow t = 2.5$ hrs.

21. $d = 5 \Rightarrow r = \frac{5}{2}$, $A = \pi r^2 \Rightarrow A = \pi\left(\frac{5}{2}\right)^2 \Rightarrow A = \pi\frac{25}{4}$, so $A = \frac{25}{4}\pi$ ft^2

22. $P = 2W + 2L \Rightarrow P - 2L = 2W \Rightarrow \frac{P - 2L}{2} = W \Rightarrow W = \frac{P - 2L}{2}$

23. 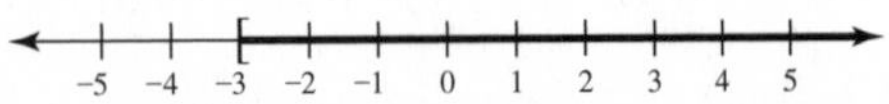

24. $5 - 3z < -1 \Rightarrow -3z < -6 \Rightarrow z > 2 \Rightarrow \{z \mid z > 2\}$

25. See Figure 25.

26. See Figure 26.

x-intercept: $0 = 3x - 2 \Rightarrow 2 = 3x \Rightarrow x = \frac{2}{3}$; y-intercept: $y = 3(0) - 2 \Rightarrow y = 0 - 2 \Rightarrow y = -2$

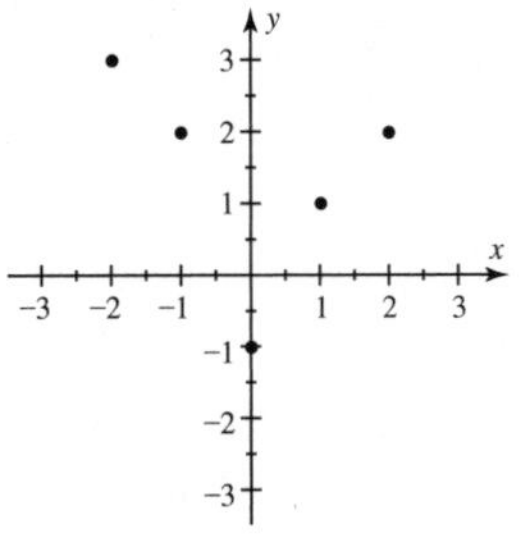

Figure 25

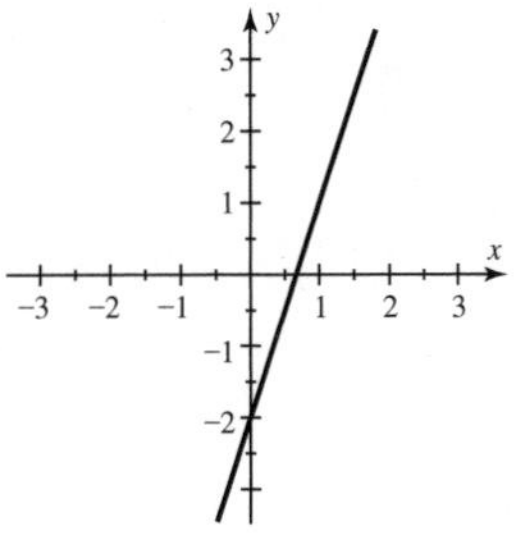

Figure 26

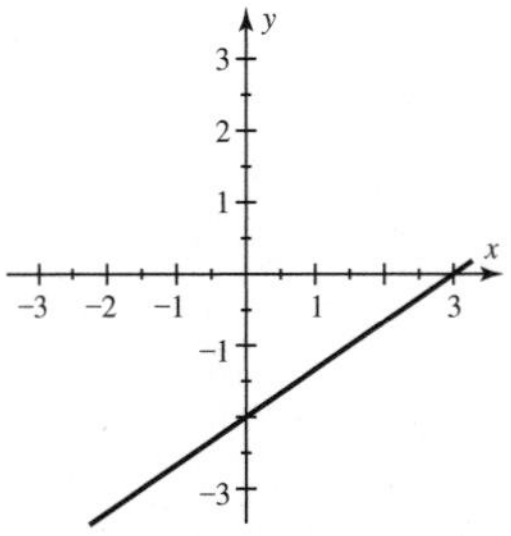

Figure 27

27. See Figure 27.

x-intercept: $2x - 3(0) = 6 \Rightarrow 2x = 6 \Rightarrow x = 3$; y-intercept: $2(0) - 3y = 6 \Rightarrow -3y = 6 \Rightarrow y = -2$.

28. See Figure 28. x-intercept: $x = 1$; y-intercept: None.

29. See Figure 29. x-intercept: None; y-intercept: $y = -2$.

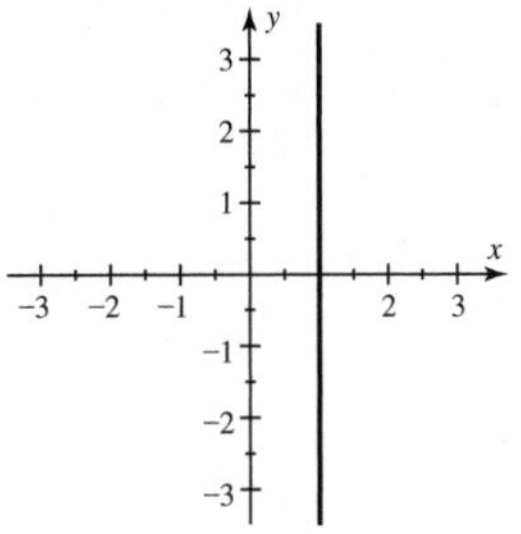

Figure 28

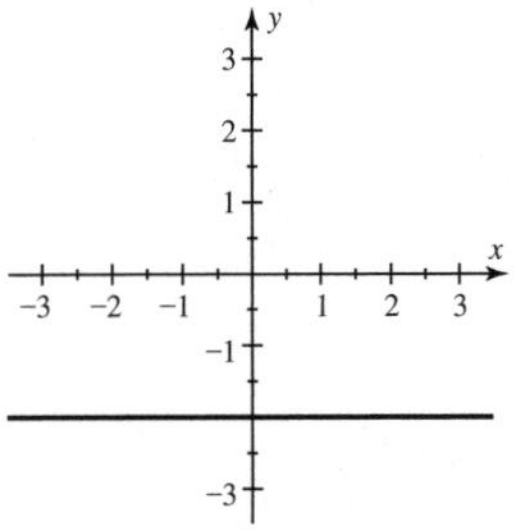

Figure 29

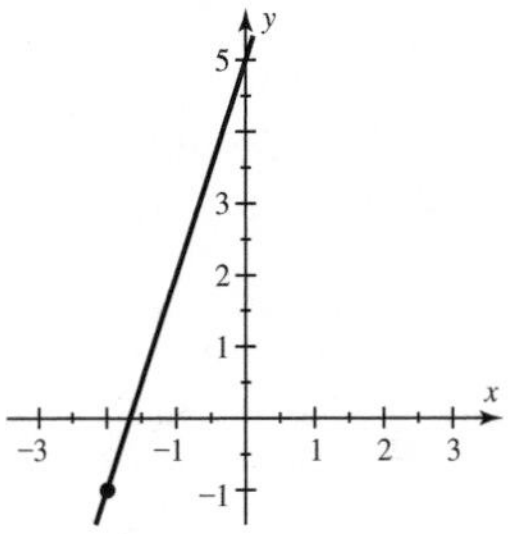

Figure 31

30. x-intercept: $x = -1 \Rightarrow (-1, 0)$; y-intercept: $y = -2 \Rightarrow (0, -2)$; $m = \frac{-2 - 0}{0 - (-1)} = \frac{-2}{1} = -2$;

$y = mx + b \Rightarrow y = -2x - 2$.

31. See Figure 31. Using $y = mx + b \Rightarrow y = 3x + 5$.

32. Using $(-2, -5)$ and $(-1, -3)$, $m = \frac{-5 - (-3)}{-2 - (-1)} = \frac{-2}{-1} = 2$, the y-intercept is $(0, -1)$ or $b = -1$, so $y = 2x - 1$.

33. Parallel lines have equal slopes $\Rightarrow m = -\frac{2}{3}$, now using $(2, -1)$ and $y - y_1 = m(x - x_1) \Rightarrow$

$y - (-1) = -\frac{2}{3}(x - 2) \Rightarrow y + 1 = -\frac{2}{3}x + \frac{4}{3} \Rightarrow y = -\frac{2}{3}x + \frac{1}{3}$.

34. $2x - 3y = -6 \Rightarrow -2y = -2x - 6 \Rightarrow y = \frac{2}{3}x + 2$, since perpendicular lines have a negative reciprocal slope, $m = -\frac{3}{2}$, now using $(1, 2)$ and $y - y_1 = m(x - x_1) \Rightarrow y - 2 = -\frac{3}{2}(x - 1) \Rightarrow$

$y - 2 = -\frac{3}{2}x + \frac{3}{2} \Rightarrow y = -\frac{3}{2}x + \frac{7}{2}$.

35. $m = \dfrac{5 - 1}{1 - (-2)} = \dfrac{4}{3}$, using $(-2, 1)$ and $y - y_1 = m(x - x_1) \Rightarrow y - 1 = \dfrac{4}{3}[x - (-2)] \Rightarrow$

$y - 1 = \dfrac{4}{3}x + \dfrac{8}{3} \Rightarrow y = \dfrac{4}{3}x + \dfrac{11}{3}$.

36. $N = 200x + 2000$

37. Using $(2, -4)$ for $4x + y = 2 \Rightarrow 4(2) + (-4) = 2 \Rightarrow 8 - 4 = 2$, No;

Using $(2, -4)$ for $x - 4y = 9 \Rightarrow 2 - 4(-4) = 9 \Rightarrow 2 + 16 = 9$, No;

Using $(1, -2)$ for $4x + y = 2 \Rightarrow 4(1) + (-2) = 2 \Rightarrow 4 - 2 = 2$, Yes;

Using $(1, -2)$ for $x - 4y = 9 \Rightarrow 1 - 4(-2) = 9 \Rightarrow 1 + 8 = 9$, Yes; $(1, -2)$ is true for both equations, therefore a solution to the system of equations.

38. $(1, 2)$; $x + y = 3 \Rightarrow 1 + 2 = 3$, Yes; $-2x + y = 0 \Rightarrow -2(1) + 2 = 0 \Rightarrow -2 + 2 = 0$, Yes

39. When $x = 1$ both solutions are 2, therefore $(1, 2)$ is a solution to both equations.

40. Using substitution $y = -1$ into $2x + y = 1 \Rightarrow 2x + (-1) = 1 \Rightarrow 2x = 2 \Rightarrow x = 1 \Rightarrow (1, -1)$.

41. Using substitution $5x + y = -5 \Rightarrow y = -5x - 5$, substituting into $-x + 2y = 12 \Rightarrow$

$-x + 2(-5x - 5) = 12 \Rightarrow -x - 10x - 10 = 12 \Rightarrow -11x = 22 \Rightarrow x = -2$ and $y = -5(-2) - 5 \Rightarrow$

$y = 10 - 5 \Rightarrow y = 5 \Rightarrow (-2, 5)$.

42. Using substitution $2r + t = -4 \Rightarrow t = -2r - 4$, substituting into $-3r - t = 2 \Rightarrow$

$-3r - (-2r - 4) = 2 \Rightarrow -r + 4 = 2 \Rightarrow -r = -2 \Rightarrow r = 2$ and $t = -2(2) - 4 \Rightarrow$

$t = -4 - 4 \Rightarrow t = -8 \Rightarrow (2, -8)$.

43. (a) One solution, the intersection of the lines.

(b) Consistent, independent.

44. (a) Zero solutions, no intersection of the lines.

(b) Inconsistent

45.
$$\begin{array}{r} 2x - y = 5 \\ -2x + y = -5 \\ \hline \end{array}$$
$0 = 0$, if $0 = 0$ then infinitely many solutions.

46.
$$\begin{array}{rr} (4x - 6y = 12)3 = & 12x - 18y = 36 \\ (-6x + 9y = 18)2 = & -12x + 18y = 36 \\ \hline \end{array}$$
$0 = 72$, if $0 = 72$ then no solutions.

47.
$$\begin{array}{r} -2x + y = 0 \\ -x - y = -3 \\ \hline \end{array}$$
$-3x = -3 \Rightarrow x = 1$, then $1 + y = 3 \Rightarrow y = 2 \Rightarrow (1, 2)$.

48. See Figure 48. $(0, 0)$; answers may vary.

49. See Figure 49. $x \leq 2$

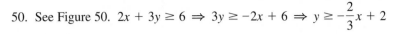

50. See Figure 50. $2x + 3y \geq 6 \Rightarrow 3y \geq -2x + 6 \Rightarrow y \geq -\frac{2}{3}x + 2$

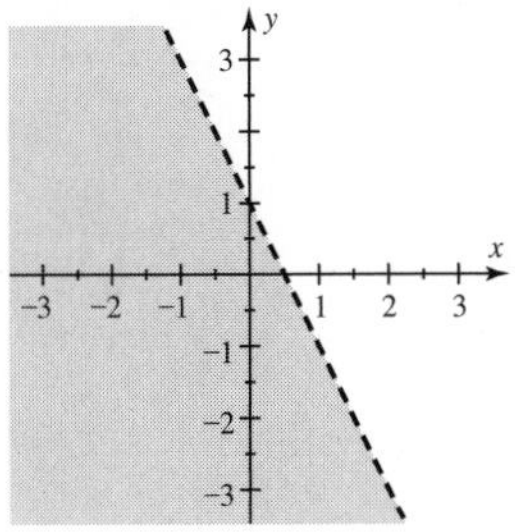

Figure 48

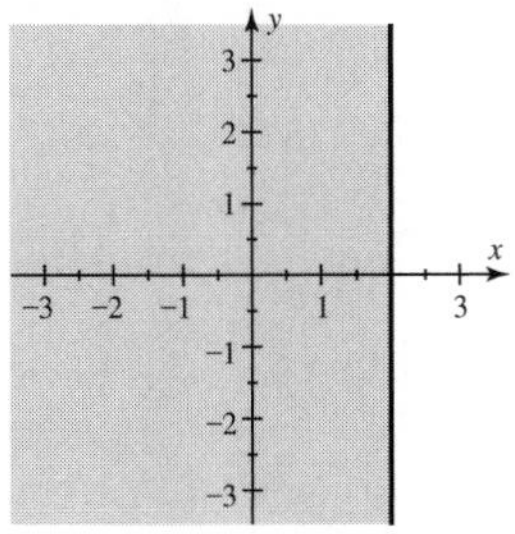

Figure 49

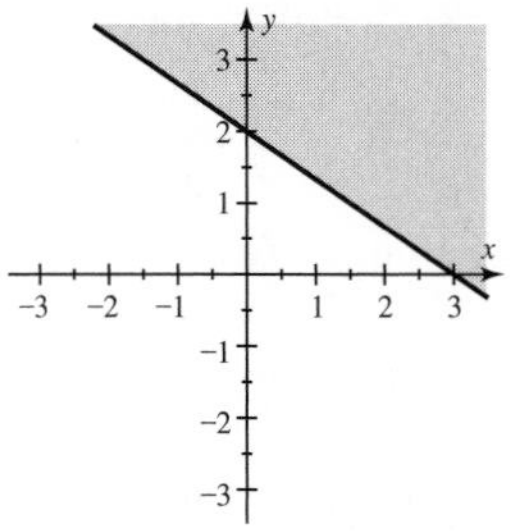

Figure 50

51. See Figure 51.

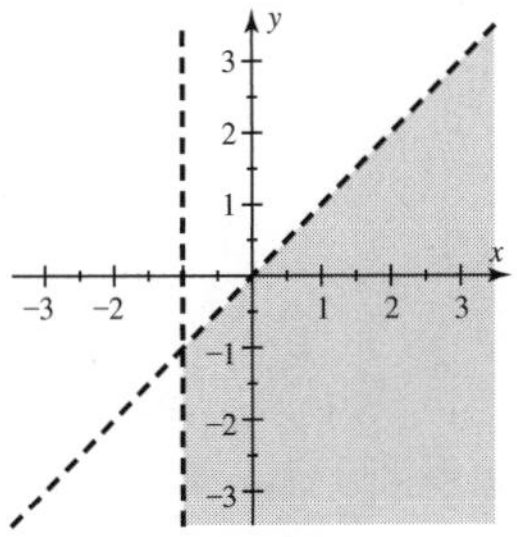

Figure 51

52. See figure 52. $2x - y \leq 4 \Rightarrow -y \leq -2x + 4 \Rightarrow y \geq 2x - 4$ and $x + 2y \geq 2 \Rightarrow 2y \geq -x + 2 \Rightarrow$

$y \geq -\frac{1}{2}x + 1.$

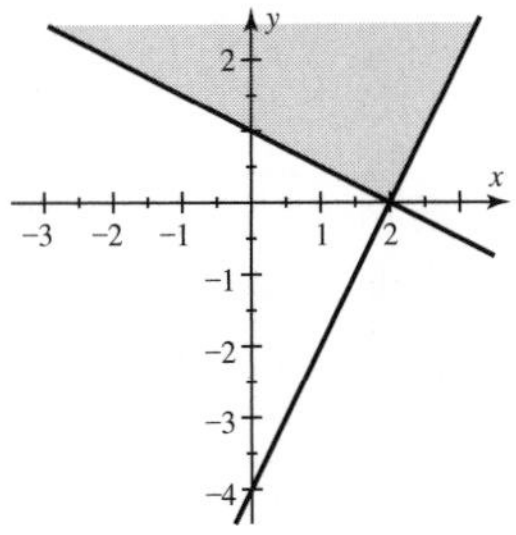

Figure 52

53. $(5x^2 - 3) + (-x^2 + 4) \Rightarrow 5x^2 - 3 - x^2 + 4 \Rightarrow 4x^2 + 1$

54. $(2xy + x^2) - (2x^2 - 5xy) \Rightarrow 2xy + x^2 - 2x^2 + 5xy \Rightarrow -x^2 + 7xy$

55. $-2^4 = -(2^4) = -16$

56. $(xy)^0 = 1$

57. $3z^2 \cdot 5z^6 = 3 \cdot 5 \cdot z^2 \cdot z^6 = 15z^8$

58. $(a^2b^4)(ab^2) = a^2 \cdot a \cdot b^4 \cdot b^2 = a^3b^6$

59. $(ab)^3 = a^3b^3$

60. $(xy)^4(x^3y^{-4}) = x^4 \cdot y^4 \cdot x^6 \cdot y^{-8} = x^{10}y^{-4} = \dfrac{x^{10}}{y^4}$

61. $7x^3(-2x^2 + 3x) = -14x^5 + 21x^4$

62. $(a - b)(a^2 + ab + b^2) = a^3 + a^2b + ab^2 - a^2b - ab^2 - b^3 = a^3 - b^3$

63. By FOIL, $(7x - 2)(3x + 5) = 21x^2 + 35x - 6x - 10 = 21x^2 + 29x - 10$.

64. By FOIL, $(2y^2 - 3)(5y^2 + 2) = 10y^4 + 4y^2 - 15y^2 - 6 = 10y^4 - 11y^2 - 6$.

65. By FOIL, $(2rt + 3)(2rt - 3) = 4r^2t^2 - 6rt + 6rt - 9 = 4r^2t^2 - 9$.

66. By FOIL, $(2t + 5)^2 = (2t + 5)(2t + 5) = 4t^2 + 10t + 10t + 25 = 4t^2 + 20t + 25$.

67. By FOIL, $(x - 7)^2 = (x - 7)(x - 7) = x^2 - 7x - 7x + 49 = x^2 - 14x + 49$.

68. By FOIL, $(x^2 - y^2)^2 = (x^2 - y^2)(x^2 - y^2) = x^4 - x^2y^2 - x^2y^2 + y^4 = x^4 - 2x^2y^2 + y^4$.

69. $2^{-4} \cdot 2^5 = 2^1 = 2$

70. $\dfrac{1}{3^{-2}} = \dfrac{3^2}{1} = 9$

71. $a^{-4} \cdot a^2 = a^{-2} = \dfrac{1}{a^2}$

72. $(2t^3)^{-2} = 2^{-2} \cdot t^{-6} = \dfrac{1}{2^2} \cdot \dfrac{1}{t^6} = \dfrac{1}{4t^6}$

73. $(xy)^{-3}(x^{-1}y^2)^{-1} = x^{-3}y^{-3} \cdot x^1 \cdot y^{-2} = x^{-2} \cdot y^{-5} = \dfrac{1}{x^2y^5}$

74. $\dfrac{4x^2}{2x^4} = \dfrac{4}{2} \cdot \dfrac{x^2}{x^4} = \dfrac{2}{1} \cdot \dfrac{1}{x^2} = \dfrac{2}{x^2}$

75. $\left(\dfrac{2x}{y^{-2}}\right)^5 = \dfrac{2^5x^5}{y^{-10}} = \dfrac{32x^5}{y^{-10}} = 32x^5y^{10}$

76. $8.3 \times 10^4 = 83{,}000$

77. $6.23 \times 10^{-3} = 0.00623$

78. $543{,}000 = 5.43 \times 10^5$

79. $0.00123 = 1.23 \times 10^{-3}$

80. $\dfrac{6x^3 + 12x^2}{3x} = \dfrac{6x^3}{3x} + \dfrac{12x^2}{3x} = 2x^2 + 4x$

81.

$$
\begin{array}{r|l}
 & 2x + 1 + \frac{4}{x-1} \\
x - 1 & 2x^2 - x + 3 \\
 & \underline{2x^2 - 2x} \\
 & x + 3 \\
 & \underline{x - 1} \\
 & 4
\end{array}
$$

82.
$$\begin{array}{r} 3x + \frac{-4x+1}{x^2+1} \\ x^2 + 1 \overline{)\,3x^3 - x + 1} \\ \underline{3x^3 + 3x} \\ -4x + 1 \end{array}$$

83. $20z^3 = 2 \cdot 2 \cdot 5 \cdot z \cdot z \cdot z$ and $15z^2 = 3 \cdot 5 \cdot z \cdot z \Rightarrow \text{GCF} = 5 \cdot z \cdot z = 5z^2$; $20z^3 - 15z^2 = 5z^2(4z - 3)$

84. $12x^2y = 2 \cdot 2 \cdot 3 \cdot x \cdot x \cdot y$ and $15xy^2 = 3 \cdot 5 \cdot x \cdot y \cdot y \Rightarrow \text{GCF} = 3 \cdot x \cdot y = 3xy$;

$12x^2y + 15xy^2 = 3xy(4x + 5y)$

85. $2y^2(x + 2) - 5(x + 2) = (2y^2 - 5)(x + 2)$

86. $t^3 + 6t^2 + t + 6 = (t^3 + 6t^2) + (t + 6) = t^2(t + 6) + (t + 6) = (t^2 + 1)(t + 6)$

87. FOIL, $x^2 + 3x - 28 = (x - 4)(x + 7)$

88. FOIL, $6y^2 + y - 12 = (2y + 3)(3y - 4)$

89. FOIL, $6 + 13x - 5x^2 = (3 - x)(2 + 5x)$

90. Difference of squares, $9z^2 - 4 = (3z + 2)(3z - 2)$

91. Difference of squares, $25x^2 - 4y^2 = (5x + 2y)(5x - 2y)$

92. FOIL, $t^2 + 16t + 64 = (t + 8)(t + 8) = (t + 8)^2$

93. FOIL, $64x^2 - 16x + 1 = (8x - 1)(8x - 1) = (8x - 1)^2$

94. Difference of cubes, $27t^3 - 8 = (3t - 2)(9t^2 + 6t + 4)$

95. $-4x^2 + 4x + 24 = -4(x^2 - x - 6) \Rightarrow$ FOIL, $-4(x - 3)(x + 2)$

96. $x^3 - 16x = x(x^2 - 16) \Rightarrow$ Difference of squares, $x(x - 4)(x + 4)$

97. $x^3 + 2x^2 - 99x = x(x^2 + 2x - 99) \Rightarrow$ FOIL, $x(x + 11)(x - 9)$

98. FOIL, $x^4 - 12x^2 + 27 = (x^2 - 3)(x^2 - 9) = (x^2 - 3)(x + 3)(x - 3)$

99. FOIL, $a^2 + 6ab + 9b^2 = (a + 3b)(a + 3b) = (a + 3b)^2$

100. $x^3y - x^2y^2 = x^2y(x - y)$

101. $(2x - 7)(x + 5) = 0 \Rightarrow 2x - 7 = 0 \Rightarrow 2x = 7 \Rightarrow x = \frac{7}{2}$ or $x + 5 = 0 \Rightarrow x = -5$, so $x = -5, \frac{7}{2}$

102. $2x^2 - 4x = 0 \Rightarrow 2x(x - 2) = 0$, then $2x = 0 \Rightarrow x = 0$ or $x - 2 = 0 \Rightarrow x = 2$, so $x = 0, 2$

103. $y^2 + 5y - 14 = 0 \Rightarrow (y + 7)(y - 2) = 0$, then $y + 7 = 0 \Rightarrow y = -7$ or $y - 2 = 0 \Rightarrow y = 2$,

so $y = -7, 2$.

104. $y^4 = 25y^2 \Rightarrow y^4 - 25y^2 = 0 \Rightarrow y^2(y^2 - 25) = 0 \Rightarrow y^2(y + 5)(y - 5) = 0$, then $y^2 = 0 \Rightarrow y = 0$ or

$y + 5 = 0 \Rightarrow y = -5$ or $y - 5 = 0 \Rightarrow y = 5$, so $y = -5, 0, 5$.

105. $8z^2 + 8z - 16 = 0 \Rightarrow 8(z^2 + z - 2) = 0 \Rightarrow 8(z + 2)(z - 1) = 0$, then $z + 2 = 0 \Rightarrow z = -2$ or

$z - 1 = 0 \Rightarrow z = 1$, so $z = -2, 1$.

106. $4z^3 = 49z \Rightarrow 4z^3 - 49z = 0 \Rightarrow z(4z^2 - 49) = 0 \Rightarrow z(2z + 7)(2z - 7) = 0$, then $z = 0$ or

$2z + 7 = 0 \Rightarrow 2z = -7 \Rightarrow z = \frac{-7}{2}$ or $2z - 7 = 0 \Rightarrow 2z = 7 \Rightarrow z = \frac{7}{2}$, so $z = \frac{-7}{2}, 0, \frac{7}{2}$.

107. $x^4 - 18x^2 + 81 = 0 \Rightarrow (x^2 - 9)(x^2 - 9) = 0 \Rightarrow (x + 3)(x - 3)(x + 3)(x - 3) = 0$, then

$x + 3 = 0 \Rightarrow x = -3$ or $x - 3 = 0 \Rightarrow x = 3$, so $x = -3, 3$.

Applications

108. (a) $10x + 8x = 18x$

(b) $18x = 900 \Rightarrow x = 50$ min.

109. $1\frac{3}{4} + 2\frac{1}{2} + 2\frac{2}{3} = 1\frac{9}{12} + 2\frac{6}{12} + 2\frac{8}{12} = 5\frac{23}{12} = 6\frac{11}{12}$ miles.

110. $0.07(C) = 1470 \Rightarrow C = \$21{,}000$

111. Let x represent the minutes cross country skiing and $60 - x$ represent minutes running.

$12(x) + 9(60 - x) = 615 \Rightarrow 12x + 540 - 9x = 615 \Rightarrow 3x = 75 \Rightarrow x = 25$, so 25 minutes skiing and 35 minutes running.

112. (a) $m = \frac{y_2 - y_1}{x_2 - x_1}$, so $m = \frac{858 - 376}{2000 - 1980} = \frac{482}{20} = 24.1$

(b) Participating in Head Start increased by 24.1 thousand children per year on average.

(c) $24.1(10) + 858 = 241 + 858 = 1099$ thousand or 1.099 million.

113. (a) $C = 0.25x + 20$

(b) $100 = 0.25x + 20 \Rightarrow 80 = 0.25x \Rightarrow x = 320$ or 320 miles.

114. (a) $x =$ one angle $\Rightarrow x + x + y = 180 \Rightarrow 2x + y = 180$ and $2x = y + 20 \Rightarrow 2x - y = 20$

(b) Using elimination,

$$\begin{array}{r} 2x + y = 180 \\ \underline{2x - y = 20} \\ 4x = 200 \end{array} \Rightarrow x = 50 \Rightarrow 50, 50, 80 \text{ degrees.}$$

115. See Figure 115.

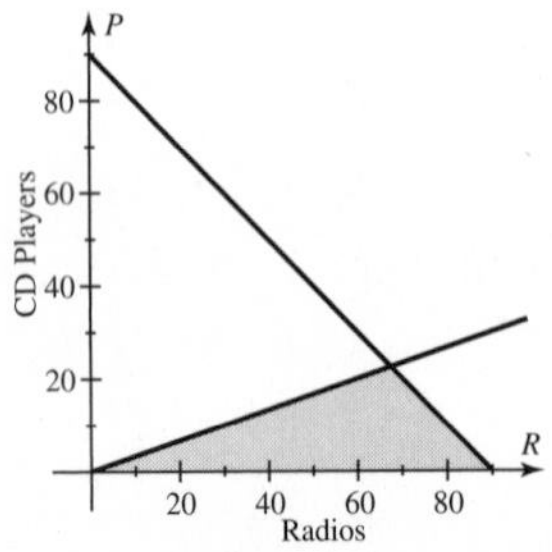

Figure 115

116. (a) $G = -0.036(5)^2 + 0.76(5) + 18.7 = -0.036(25) + 3.80 + 18.7 = -0.900 + 3.80 + 18.7 = 21.6 \Rightarrow$

$G = 21.6$ trillion ft^3 was the natural gas consumption in 1995.

(b) $22.7 = -0.036x^2 + 0.76x + 18.7 \Rightarrow 0 = -0.036x^2 + 0.76x + 4 \Rightarrow 0 = -36x^2 + 760x + 4000 \Rightarrow$

$0 = -4(9x^2 - 190x + 1000)$ (factor by grouping)

$\Rightarrow m \cdot n = 9000, m + n = -190 \Rightarrow m = -90$ and $n = -100 \Rightarrow 9x^2 - 90x - 100x + 1000 = 0 \Rightarrow$

$9x(x - 10) - 100(x - 10) = 0 \Rightarrow (9x - 100)(x - 10) = 0$, then

$9x - 100 = 0 \Rightarrow 9x = 100 \Rightarrow x = \frac{100}{9} \Rightarrow x = 11\frac{1}{9}$ or $x - 10 = 0 \Rightarrow x = 10$, so $x = 10, 11\frac{1}{9}$

Thus, $x = 10 \Rightarrow 2000$ and $x = 11\frac{1}{9} \Rightarrow > 2001$, therefore 2000.

117. $3(3x)(2y) = 18xy$; $18(2)(3) = 108 \text{ yds}^2$.

118. $V = s^3 \Rightarrow V = (2xy^2)^3 \Rightarrow V = 2^3 \cdot x^3 \cdot (y^2)^3 \Rightarrow V = 8x^3y^6$

119. (a) $(x + 2)(x + 2) = x^2 + 4x + 4$

(b) $2(x) + x \cdot x + 2 \cdot 2 + 2 \cdot x = 2x + x^2 + 4 + 2x = x^2 + 4x + 4$

120. $x^2 + 12x + 36 = (x + 6)(x + 6) = (x + 6)^2 \Rightarrow$ each side is $x + 6$

121. (a) $0 = 64t - 16t^2 \Rightarrow -16t(t - 4) = 0$, then $-16t = 0 \Rightarrow t = 0$ (when hit) or $t - 4 = 0 \Rightarrow t = 4$ sec.

(b) $48 = 64t - 16t^2 \Rightarrow 16t^2 - 64t + 48 = 0 \Rightarrow 16(t^2 - 4t + 3) = 0 \Rightarrow 16(t - 3)(t - 1) = 0$, then

$t - 3 = 0 \Rightarrow t = 3$ *or* $t - 1 = 0 \Rightarrow t = 1$, so at 1 and 3 sec.

Critical Thinking Solutions for Chapter 6

Section 6.2

- A cube has 6 sides so $(6x^2 + 24x + 24) \div 6 = x^2 + 4x + 4$, the area of each side. Factoring gives $(x + 2)(x + 2)$, so each side is $(x + 2)$.

Section 6.3

- $x^2 + x + 5$, No factors of 5 add up to equal 1, can not factor.

  $x^2 - 2x + 6$, No factors of 6 add up to equal -2, can not factor.

  $2x^2 + 3x + 2$, Using grouping, $m \cdot n = 4$ and $m + n = 3$, No factors of 4 add up to equal 3, can not factor.

  Conjecture: Not all polynomials are factorable.

Section 6.4

- Yes, $x^2 - 5 = (x - \sqrt{5})(x + \sqrt{5})$, because $a^2 = x^2$, so $a = x$ and $b^2 = 5$, so $b = \sqrt{5}$.

Section 6.5

- No, the zero-product property does not work for 1. We solve instead for zero, $x(2x + 1) = 1 \Rightarrow$ $2x^2 + x - 1 = 0 \Rightarrow (2x - 1)(x + 1) = 0$; $2x - 1 = 0 \Rightarrow x = \frac{1}{2}$ and $x + 1 = 0 \Rightarrow x = -1$. The solutions are $\frac{1}{2}$ and -1.

Section 6.6

- The area of the metal square is 100 in^2 and the area of the four cutout squares is $4x^2$, so the surface area is $100 - 4x^2$. The sum of the areas of the four sides and the bottom is $4x(10 - 2x) + (10 - 2x)^2 = 100 - 4x^2$.

Chapter 7: Rational Expressions

7.1: Introduction to Rational Expressions

Concepts

1. $\frac{P}{Q}$; polynomials

3. the denominator is zero

5. $\frac{a}{b}$

7. $-1, \frac{x-a}{a-x} = \frac{1(x-a)}{a-x} = \frac{-1(-x+a)}{a-x} = \frac{-1(a-x)}{a-x} = -1$

Evaluating Rational Expressions

9. $x = -7, \frac{3}{x} = \frac{3}{-7} = -\frac{3}{7}$

11. $x = -4, -\frac{x}{x-5} = -\frac{-4}{-4-5} = \frac{-(-4)}{-9} = \frac{4}{-9} = -\frac{4}{9}$

13. $y = -2, \frac{y+1}{y^2} = \frac{-2+1}{(-2)^2} = \frac{-1}{4} = -\frac{1}{4}$

15. $z = -2, \frac{7z}{z^2-4} = \frac{7(-2)-1}{(-2)^2-4} = \frac{-14}{4-4} = \frac{-14}{0} =$ undefined

17. $t = -2, \frac{5}{3t+6} = \frac{5}{3(-2)+6} = \frac{5}{-6+6} = \frac{5}{0} =$ undefined

19. $x = 0, -\frac{6-x}{x-6} = -\frac{6-0}{0-6} = -\frac{6}{-6} = \frac{-(6)}{-6} = \frac{-6}{-6} = 1$

21. $x = -2, \frac{x}{x+1} = \frac{-2}{-2+1} = \frac{-2}{-1} = 2$; $x = -1, \frac{x}{x+1} = \frac{-1}{-1+1} = \frac{-1}{0} =$ undefined;

$x = 0, \frac{x}{x+1} = \frac{0}{0+1} = \frac{0}{1} = 0$; $x = 1, \frac{x}{x+1} = \frac{1}{1+1} = \frac{1}{2}$; $x = 2, \frac{x}{x+1} = \frac{2}{2+1} = \frac{2}{3}$. See Figure 21.

x	-2	-1	0	1	2
$\frac{x}{x+1}$	2	—	0	$\frac{1}{2}$	$\frac{2}{3}$

Figure 21

x	-2	-1	0	1	2
$\frac{3x}{2x^2+1}$	$-\frac{2}{3}$	-1	0	1	$\frac{2}{3}$

Figure 23

23. $x = -2, \frac{3x}{2x^2+1} = \frac{3(-2)}{2(-2)^2+1} = \frac{-6}{2(4)+1} = \frac{-6}{8+1} = \frac{-6}{9} = \frac{-2}{3} = -\frac{2}{3}$;

$x = -1, \frac{3x}{2x^2+1} = \frac{3(-1)}{2(-1)^2+1} = \frac{-3}{2(1)+1} = \frac{-3}{2+1} = \frac{-3}{3} = -1$;

$x = 0, \frac{3x}{2x^2+1} = \frac{3(0)}{2(0)^2+1} = \frac{0}{2(0)+1} = \frac{0}{0+1} = \frac{0}{1} = 0$;

$x = 1, \frac{3x}{2x^2+1} = \frac{3(1)}{2(1)^2+1} = \frac{3}{2(1)+1} = \frac{3}{2+1} = \frac{3}{3} = 1$;

$x = 2, \frac{3x}{2x^2+1} = \frac{3(2)}{2(2)^2+1} = \frac{6}{2(4)+1} = \frac{6}{8+1} = \frac{6}{9} = \frac{2}{3}$. See Figure 23.

25. A rational expression is undefined when the denominator = 0. $x = 0$

27. A rational expression is undefined when the denominator = 0. $z - 3 = 0 \Rightarrow z = 3$

29. A rational expression is undefined when the denominator = 0. $5y + 4 = 0 \Rightarrow 5y = -4 \Rightarrow y = \frac{-4}{5}$

31. A rational expression is undefined when the denominator = 0. $t^2 + 1 = 0 \Rightarrow t^2 = -1$ which is impossible, so none.

33. A rational expression is undefined when the denominator = 0. $x^2 - 25 = 0 \Rightarrow x^2 = 25 \Rightarrow x = -5, 5$

35. A rational expression is undefined when the denominator = 0. $x^2 + 5x + 6 = 0 \Rightarrow (x + 3)(x + 2) = 0 \Rightarrow$ $x + 3 = 0 \Rightarrow x = -3$ or $x + 2 = 0 \Rightarrow x = -2$, so $x = -3, -2$

37. A rational expression is undefined when the denominator = 0. $2z^2 - 7z + 5 = 0 \Rightarrow (2z - 5)(z - 1) = 0 \Rightarrow$ $2z - 5 = 0 \Rightarrow 2z = 5 \Rightarrow z = \frac{5}{2}$ or $z - 1 = 0 \Rightarrow z = 1$, so $z = 1, \frac{5}{2}$

Simplifying Rational Expressions

39. $\frac{12}{18} = \frac{2}{3} \cdot \frac{6}{6} = \frac{2}{3} \cdot 1 = \frac{2}{3}$

41. $\frac{24}{48} = \frac{1}{2} \cdot \frac{24}{24} = \frac{1}{2} \cdot 1 = \frac{1}{2}$

43. $-\frac{6}{15} = -\frac{2}{5} \cdot \frac{3}{3} = -\frac{2}{5} \cdot 1 = -\frac{2}{5}$

45. $-\frac{25}{75} = -\frac{1}{3} \cdot \frac{25}{25} = -\frac{1}{3} \cdot 1 = -\frac{1}{3}$

47. $\frac{5x^4}{10x^6} = \frac{1}{2}x^{4-6} = \frac{1}{2}x^{-2} = \frac{1}{2x^2}$

49. $\frac{8xy^3}{6x^2y^2} = \frac{4}{3}x^{1-2}y^{3-2} = \frac{4}{3}x^{-1}y = \frac{4y}{3x}$

51. $\frac{x + 4}{2x + 8} = \frac{x + 4}{2(x + 4)} = \frac{1}{2} \cdot \frac{x + 4}{x + 4} = \frac{1}{2} \cdot 1 = \frac{1}{2}$

53. $\frac{3z - 9}{5z - 15} = \frac{3(z - 3)}{5(z - 3)} = \frac{3}{5} \cdot \frac{z - 3}{z - 3} = \frac{3}{5} \cdot 1 = \frac{3}{5}$

55. $\frac{(x + 1)(x - 1)}{(x + 6)(x - 1)} = \frac{x + 1}{x + 6} \cdot \frac{x - 1}{x - 1} = \frac{x + 1}{x + 6} \cdot 1 = \frac{x + 1}{x + 6}$

57. $\frac{(5y + 3)(2y - 1)}{(2y - 1)(y + 2)} = \frac{(5y + 3)(2y - 1)}{(y + 2)(2y - 1)} = \frac{5y + 3}{y + 2} \cdot \frac{2y - 1}{2y - 1} = \frac{5y + 3}{y + 2} \cdot 1 = \frac{5y + 3}{y + 2}$

59. $\frac{x - 7}{7 - x} = \frac{x - 7}{-1(-7 + x)} = \frac{x - 7}{-1(x - 7)} = -1$

61. $\frac{a - b}{b - a} = \frac{a - b}{-1(-b + a)} = \frac{a - b}{-1(a - b)} = -1$

63. $\frac{(3x + 5)(x - 1)}{(3x - 5)(1 - x)} = \frac{3x + 5}{3x - 5} \cdot \frac{(x - 1)}{-1(-1 + x)} = \frac{3x + 5}{3x - 5} \cdot \frac{x - 1}{-1(x - 1)} = \frac{3x + 5}{3x - 5} \cdot -1 = -\frac{3x + 5}{3x - 5}$

65. $\dfrac{n^2-n}{n^2-5n}=\dfrac{n(n-1)}{n(n-5)}=\dfrac{n}{n}\cdot\dfrac{n-1}{n-5}=1\cdot\dfrac{n-1}{n-5}=\dfrac{n-1}{n-5}$

67. $\dfrac{x^2-3x}{6x-18}=\dfrac{x(x-3)}{6(x-3)}=\dfrac{x}{6}\cdot\dfrac{x-3}{x-3}=\dfrac{x}{6}\cdot 1=\dfrac{x}{6}$

69. $\dfrac{z^2-3z+2}{z^2-4z+3}=\dfrac{(z-2)(z-1)}{(z-3)(z-1)}=\dfrac{z-2}{z-3}\cdot\dfrac{z-1}{z-1}=\dfrac{z-2}{z-3}\cdot 1=\dfrac{z-2}{z-3}$

71. $\dfrac{2x^2+7x-4}{6x^2+x-2}=\dfrac{(x+4)(2x-1)}{(3x+2)(2x-1)}=\dfrac{x+4}{3x+2}\cdot\dfrac{2x-1}{2x-1}=\dfrac{x+4}{3x+2}\cdot 1=\dfrac{x+4}{3x+2}$

73. $\dfrac{x-3}{3x^2-11x+6}=\dfrac{x-3}{(x-3)(3x-2)}=\dfrac{x-3}{x-3}\cdot\dfrac{1}{3x-2}=1\cdot\dfrac{1}{3x-2}=\dfrac{1}{3x-2}$

75. $-\dfrac{a-9}{9-a}=\dfrac{-(a-9)}{9-a}=\dfrac{-a+9}{9-a}=\dfrac{9-a}{9-a}=1$

77. $\dfrac{-2x-1}{4x+2}=\dfrac{-2x-1}{2(2x+1)}=\dfrac{-1(2x+1)}{2(2x+1)}=-\dfrac{1}{2}\cdot\dfrac{2x+1}{2x+1}=-\dfrac{1}{2}\cdot 1=-\dfrac{1}{2}$

Applications

79. (a) For $x=3$, $T=\dfrac{1}{5-x}\Rightarrow T=\dfrac{1}{5-3}=\dfrac{1}{2}$; When traffic arrives at an average rate of 3 vehicles/min., the average wait is one-half minute.

(b) For $x=2$, $T=\dfrac{1}{5-x}\Rightarrow T=\dfrac{1}{5-2}=\dfrac{1}{3}$;

For $x=4$, $T=\dfrac{1}{5-x}\Rightarrow T=\dfrac{1}{5-4}=\dfrac{1}{1}=1$;

For $x=4.5$, $T=\dfrac{1}{5-x}\Rightarrow T=\dfrac{1}{5-4.5}=\dfrac{1}{0.5}=2$;

For $x=4.9$, $T=\dfrac{1}{5-x}\Rightarrow T=\dfrac{1}{5-4.9}=\dfrac{1}{0.1}=10$;

For $x=4.99$, $T=\dfrac{1}{5-x}\Rightarrow T=\dfrac{1}{5-4.99}=\dfrac{1}{0.01}=100$; See Figure 79.

As x nears 5 vehicles/min., a small increase in x increases the wait dramatically.

x	2	4	4.5	4.9	4.99
T	$\frac{1}{3}$	1	2	10	100

Figure 79

81. $\dfrac{1}{2}$

83. (a) $\dfrac{3}{n}$

(b) $\dfrac{n-3}{n}$; $n=100$, $\dfrac{n-3}{n}=\dfrac{100-3}{100}=\dfrac{97}{100}$; There is a 97% chance that a winning ball will not be drawn.

85. (a) $\dfrac{360}{60}=6$ hours

(b) $\dfrac{m}{60}$

87. (a) $T = \dfrac{1}{5 - x}$, $5 - x = 0 \Rightarrow -x = -5 \Rightarrow x = 5$

(b) As the average arrival rate nears 5 cars/min., a small increase in x increases the waiting time dramatically.

7.2: Multiplication and Division of Rational Expressions

Concepts

1. $\dfrac{AC}{BD}$

3. $\dfrac{(x+7)(x+2)}{(x+1)(x+2)} = \dfrac{x+7}{x+1} \cdot \dfrac{x+2}{x+2} = \dfrac{x+7}{x+1} \cdot 1 = \dfrac{x+7}{x+1}$

5. No, it equals $1 + \dfrac{2}{x}$.

Review of Fractions

7. $\dfrac{1}{2} \cdot \dfrac{4}{5} = \dfrac{4}{10} = \dfrac{2}{5}$

9. $\dfrac{3}{7} \cdot 4 = \dfrac{3}{7} \cdot \dfrac{4}{1} = \dfrac{12}{7}$

11. $\dfrac{1}{3} \cdot \dfrac{2}{3} \cdot \dfrac{9}{11} = \dfrac{2}{9} \cdot \dfrac{9}{11} = \dfrac{18}{99} = \dfrac{2}{11}$

13. $\dfrac{2}{3} \div \dfrac{1}{6} = \dfrac{2}{3} \cdot \dfrac{6}{1} = \dfrac{12}{3} = 4$

15. $\dfrac{8}{9} \div \dfrac{5}{3} = \dfrac{8}{9} \cdot \dfrac{3}{5} = \dfrac{24}{45} = \dfrac{8}{15}$

17. $8 \div \dfrac{4}{5} = \dfrac{8}{1} \cdot \dfrac{5}{4} = \dfrac{40}{4} = 10$

Multiplying Rational Expressions

19. $\dfrac{x+5}{x+5} = 1$

21. $\dfrac{(z+1)(z+2)}{(z+4)(z+2)} = \dfrac{z+1}{z+4} \cdot \dfrac{z+2}{z+2} = \dfrac{z+1}{z+4} \cdot 1 = \dfrac{z+1}{z+4}$

23. $\dfrac{8y(y+7)}{12y(y+7)} = \dfrac{8}{12} \cdot \dfrac{y}{y} \cdot \dfrac{y+7}{y+7} = \dfrac{8}{12} \cdot 1 \cdot 1 = \dfrac{8}{12} = \dfrac{2}{3}$

25. $\dfrac{x(x+2)(x+3)}{x(x-2)(x+3)} = \dfrac{x}{x} \cdot \dfrac{x+2}{x-2} \cdot \dfrac{y+3}{y+3} = 1 \cdot \dfrac{x+2}{x-2} \cdot 1 = \dfrac{x+2}{x-2}$

27. $\dfrac{8}{x} \cdot \dfrac{x+1}{x} = \dfrac{8(x+1)}{x^2}$

29. $\dfrac{8+x}{x} \cdot \dfrac{x-3}{x+8} = \dfrac{8+x}{8+x} \cdot \dfrac{x-3}{x} = 1 \cdot \dfrac{x-3}{x} = \dfrac{x-3}{x}$

31. $\frac{z+3}{z+4}\cdot\frac{z+4}{z-7}=\frac{z+4}{z+4}\cdot\frac{z+3}{z-7}=1\cdot\frac{z+3}{z-7}=\frac{z+3}{z-7}$

33. $\frac{5x+1}{3x+2}\cdot\frac{3x+2}{5x+1}=\frac{5x+1}{5x+1}\cdot\frac{3x+2}{3x+2}=1\cdot 1=1$

35. $\frac{(t+1)^2}{t+2}\cdot\frac{(t+2)^2}{t+1}=\frac{(t-1)(t+1)}{t+2}\cdot\frac{(t+2)(t+2)}{t+1}=\frac{t+1}{t+1}\cdot\frac{t+1}{1}\cdot\frac{t+2}{t+2}\cdot\frac{t+2}{1}=$
$1\cdot(t+1)\cdot 1\cdot(t+2)=(t+1)(t+2)$

37. $\frac{x^2}{x^2+4}\cdot\frac{x+4}{x}=\frac{x^2}{x}\cdot\frac{x+4}{x^2+4}=\frac{x}{x}\cdot\frac{x(x+4)}{x^2+4}=1\cdot\frac{x(x+4)}{x^2+4}=\frac{x(x+4)}{x^2+4}$

39. $\frac{(z^2-1)}{(z^2-4)}\cdot\frac{z-2}{z+1}=\frac{(z-1)(z+1)}{(z-2)(z+2)}\cdot\frac{z-2}{z+1}=\frac{z-1}{z+2}\cdot\frac{z+1}{z+1}\cdot\frac{z-2}{z-2}=\frac{z-1}{z+2}\cdot 1\cdot 1=\frac{z-1}{z+2}$

41. $\frac{y^2-2y}{y^2-1}\cdot\frac{y+1}{y-2}=\frac{y(y-2)}{(y-1)(y+1)}\cdot\frac{y+1}{y-2}=\frac{y}{y-1}\cdot\frac{y+1}{y+1}\cdot\frac{y-2}{y-2}=\frac{y}{y-1}\cdot 1\cdot 1=\frac{y}{y-1}$

43. $\frac{2x^2-x-3}{3x^2-8x-3}\cdot\frac{3x+1}{2x-3}=\frac{(2x-3)(x+1)}{(3x+1)(x-3)}\cdot\frac{3x+1}{2x-3}=\frac{2x-3}{2x-3}\cdot\frac{3x+1}{3x+1}\cdot\frac{x+1}{x-1}=1\cdot 1\cdot\frac{x+1}{x-3}=\frac{x+1}{x-3}$

45. $\frac{(x-3)^3}{x^2-2x+1}\cdot\frac{x-1}{(x-3)^2}=\frac{(x-3)(x-3)^2}{(x-1)(x-1)}\cdot\frac{x-1}{(x-3)^2}=\frac{x-3}{x-1}\cdot\frac{(x-3)^2}{(x-3)^2}\cdot\frac{x-1}{x-1}=\frac{x-3}{x-1}\cdot 1\cdot 1=\frac{x-3}{x-1}$

47. $\frac{2}{x}\div\frac{2x+3}{x}=\frac{2}{x}\cdot\frac{x}{2x+3}=\frac{x}{x}\cdot\frac{2}{2x+3}=1\cdot\frac{2}{2x+3}=\frac{2}{2x+3}$

49. $\frac{x-2}{3x}\div\frac{2-x}{6x}=\frac{x-2}{3x}\cdot\frac{6x}{2-x}=\frac{x-2}{-1(-2+x)}\cdot\frac{6x}{3x}=\frac{x-2}{-1(-2+x)}\cdot 2=-1\cdot 2=-2$

51. $\frac{z+2}{z+1}\div\frac{z+2}{z-1}=\frac{z+2}{z+1}\cdot\frac{z-1}{z+2}=\frac{z+2}{z+2}\cdot\frac{z-1}{z+1}=1\cdot\frac{z-1}{z+1}=\frac{z-1}{z+1}$

53. $\frac{3y+4}{2y+1}\div\frac{3y+4}{y+2}=\frac{3y+4}{2y+1}\cdot\frac{y+2}{3y+4}=\frac{3y+4}{3y+4}\cdot\frac{y+2}{2y+1}=1\cdot\frac{y+2}{2y+1}=\frac{y+2}{2y+1}$

55. $\frac{t^2-1}{t^2+1}\div\frac{t+1}{4}=\frac{t^2-1}{t^2+1}\cdot\frac{4}{t+1}=\frac{(t+1)(t-1)}{t^2+1}\cdot\frac{4}{t+1}=\frac{t+1}{t+1}\cdot\frac{4(t-1)}{t^2+1}=1\cdot\frac{4(t-1)}{t^2+1}=\frac{4(t-1)}{t^2+1}$

57. $\frac{y^2-9}{y^2-25}\div\frac{y+3}{y+5}=\frac{y^2-9}{y^2-25}\cdot\frac{y+5}{y+3}=\frac{(y-3)(y+3)}{(y-5)(y+5)}\cdot\frac{y+5}{y+3}=\frac{y-3}{y-5}\cdot\frac{y+3}{y+3}\cdot\frac{y+5}{y+5}=$
$\frac{y-3}{y-5}\cdot 1\cdot 1=\frac{y-3}{y-5}$

59. $\frac{2x^2-4x}{2x-1}\div\frac{x-2}{2x-1}=\frac{2x^2-4x}{2x-1}\cdot\frac{2x-1}{x-2}=\frac{2x(x-2)}{x-2}\cdot\frac{2x-1}{2x-1}=2x\cdot 1\cdot 1=2x$

61. $\frac{2z^2-5z-3}{z^2+z-20}\div\frac{z-3}{z-4}=\frac{(2z+1)(z-3)}{(z+5)(z-4)}\cdot\frac{z-4}{z-3}=\frac{2z+1}{z+5}\cdot\frac{z-3}{z-4}\cdot\frac{z-4}{z-4}=\frac{2z+1}{z+5}\cdot 1\cdot 1=\frac{2z+1}{z+5}$

63. $\frac{t^2-1}{t^2+5t-6}\div(t+1)=\frac{(t+1)(t-1)}{(t-1)(t+6)}\cdot\frac{1}{(t+1)}=\frac{t+1}{t+1}\cdot\frac{t-1}{t-1}\cdot\frac{1}{t+6}=1\cdot 1\cdot\frac{1}{t+6}=\frac{1}{t+6}$

65. $\frac{a-b}{a+b}\div\frac{a-b}{2a+3b}=\frac{a-b}{a+b}\cdot\frac{2a+3b}{a-b}=\frac{a-b}{a-b}\cdot\frac{2a+3b}{a+b}=1\cdot\frac{2a+3b}{a+b}=\frac{2a+3b}{a+b}$

67. $\frac{x-y}{x^2+2xy+y^2}\div\frac{1}{(x+y)^2}=\frac{x-y}{(x+y)^2}\cdot\frac{(x+y)^2}{1}=\frac{x-y}{1}\cdot\frac{(x+y)^2}{(x+y)^2}=x-y\cdot 1=x-y$

Applications

69. (a) $\frac{1}{n} \cdot \frac{n}{n+1} = \frac{n}{n} \cdot \frac{1}{n+1} = 1 \cdot \frac{1}{n+1} = \frac{1}{n+1}$

(b) $\frac{1}{n+1} \Rightarrow \frac{1}{99+1} = \frac{1}{100}$

Checking Basic Concepts for Sections 7.1 & 7.2

1. For $x=-1$, $\frac{3}{x^2-1} = \frac{3}{(-1)^2-1} = \frac{3}{1-1} = \frac{3}{0} =$ undefined. For $x=3$, $\frac{3}{x^2-1} = \frac{3}{(3)^2-1} = \frac{3}{9-1} = \frac{3}{8}$

2. (a) $\frac{6x^3y^2}{15x^2y^3} = \frac{2}{5}xy^{-1} = \frac{2x}{5y}$

(b) $\frac{5x-15}{x-3} = \frac{5(x-3)}{x-3} = \frac{5}{1} \cdot \frac{x-3}{x-3} = 5 \cdot 1 = 5$

(c) $\frac{x^2-x-6}{x^2+x-12} = \frac{(x+2)(x-3)}{(x+4)(x-3)} = \frac{x+2}{x+4} \cdot \frac{x-3}{x-3} = \frac{x+2}{x+4} \cdot 1 = \frac{x+2}{x+4}$

3. (a) $\frac{4}{3x} \cdot \frac{2x}{6} = \frac{8x}{18x} = \frac{8}{18} \cdot \frac{x}{x} = \frac{8}{18} \cdot 1 = \frac{8}{18} = \frac{4}{9}$

(b) $\frac{2x+4}{x^2-1} \cdot \frac{x+1}{x+2} = \frac{2(x+2)}{(x-1)(x+1)} \cdot \frac{x+1}{x+2} = \frac{2}{x-1} \cdot \frac{x+2}{x+2} \cdot \frac{x+1}{x+1} = \frac{2}{x-1} \cdot 1 \cdot 1 = \frac{2}{x-1}$

4. (a) $\frac{7}{3z^2} \div \frac{14}{5z^3} = \frac{7}{3z^2} \cdot \frac{5z^3}{14} = \frac{35z^3}{42z^2} = \frac{35z}{42} \cdot \frac{z^2}{z^2} = \frac{35z}{42} \cdot 1 = \frac{35z}{42} = \frac{5z}{6}$

(b) $\frac{x^2+x}{x-3} \div \frac{x}{x-3} = \frac{x(x-1)}{x-3} \cdot \frac{x-3}{x} = \frac{x}{x} \cdot \frac{x-3}{x-3} \cdot \frac{x+1}{1} = 1 \cdot 1 \cdot x + 1 = x + 1$

5. (a) For $x = 0.5$, $T = \frac{1}{2-x} \Rightarrow T = \frac{1}{2-0.5} = \frac{1}{1.5} = \frac{2}{3}$;

For $x = 1$, $T = \frac{1}{2-x} \Rightarrow T = \frac{1}{2-1} = \frac{1}{1} = 1$;

For $x = 1.5$, $T = \frac{1}{2-x} \Rightarrow T = \frac{1}{2-1.5} = \frac{1}{0.5} = 2$;

For $x = 1.9$, $T = \frac{1}{2-x} \Rightarrow T = \frac{1}{2-1.9} = \frac{1}{0.1} = 10$; See Figure 5.

(b) As x nears 2 customers/min., a small increase in x increases the wait dramatically.

x	0.5	1.0	1.5	1.9
T	$\frac{2}{3}$	1	2	10

Figure 5

7.3: Addition and Subtraction with Like Denominators

Concepts

1. add, numerators; denominators

3. $\dfrac{A + B}{C}$

5. $5 - (x + 1) = 5 - x - 1 = 4 - x$

7. $3x - (2x - 5) = 3x - 2x + 5 = x + 5$

Addition and Subtraction of Fractions

9. $\dfrac{1}{2} + \dfrac{1}{2} = \dfrac{1 + 1}{2} = \dfrac{2}{2} = 1$

11. $\dfrac{4}{5} + \dfrac{2}{5} = \dfrac{4 + 2}{5} = \dfrac{6}{5}$

13. $\dfrac{1}{6} + \dfrac{5}{6} = \dfrac{1 + 1}{6} = \dfrac{6}{6} = 1$

15. $\dfrac{4}{7} - \dfrac{1}{7} = \dfrac{4 - 1}{7} = \dfrac{3}{7}$

17. $\dfrac{7}{8} - \dfrac{3}{8} = \dfrac{7 - 3}{8} = \dfrac{4}{8} = \dfrac{1}{2}$

19. $\dfrac{11}{12} - \dfrac{5}{12} = \dfrac{11 - 5}{12} = \dfrac{6}{12} = \dfrac{1}{2}$

21. $\dfrac{7}{15} + \dfrac{4}{15} - \dfrac{1}{15} = \dfrac{7 + 4 - 1}{15} = \dfrac{11 - 1}{15} = \dfrac{10}{15} = \dfrac{2}{3}$

Addition and Subtraction of Rational Expressions

23. $\dfrac{2}{x} + \dfrac{1}{x} = \dfrac{2 + 1}{x} = \dfrac{3}{x}$

25. $\dfrac{7 + 2x}{4x} - \dfrac{7}{4x} = \dfrac{(7 + 2x) - 7}{4x} = \dfrac{2x}{4x} = \dfrac{1}{2} \cdot \dfrac{x}{x} = \dfrac{1}{2} \cdot 1 = \dfrac{1}{2}$

27. $\dfrac{x + 3}{y - 3} + \dfrac{27 - 12}{y - 3} = \dfrac{(y + 3) + (2y - 12)}{y - 3} = \dfrac{3y - 9}{y - 3} = \dfrac{3(y - 3)}{y - 3} = 3 \cdot \dfrac{y - 3}{y - 3} = 3 \cdot 1 = 3$

29. $\dfrac{5z}{4z + 3} - \dfrac{z}{4z + 3} = \dfrac{5z - z}{4z + 3} = \dfrac{4z}{4z + 3}$

31. $\dfrac{t + 5}{t + 6} + \dfrac{t + 7}{t + 6} = \dfrac{(t + 5) + (t + 7)}{t + 6} = \dfrac{2t + 12}{t + 6} = \dfrac{2(t + 6)}{t + 6} = 2 \cdot \dfrac{t + 6}{t + 6} = 2 \cdot 1 = 2$

33. $\dfrac{5x}{2x + 3} - \dfrac{3x - 3}{2x + 3} = \dfrac{5x - (3x - 3)}{2x + 3} = \dfrac{2x + 3}{2x + 3} = 1$

35. $\dfrac{x^2 + 4x - 1}{4x + 2} - \dfrac{x^2 - 4x - 5}{4x + 2} = \dfrac{(x^2 + 4x - 1) - (x^2 - 4x - 5)}{4x + 2} = \dfrac{8x + 4}{4x + 2} = \dfrac{2(4x + 2)}{4x + 2} = 2 \cdot \dfrac{4x + 2}{4x + 2} =$
$2 \cdot 1 = 2$

37. $\dfrac{3y}{5} + \dfrac{2y - 5}{5} = \dfrac{3y + (2y - 5)}{5} = \dfrac{5y - 5}{5} = \dfrac{5(y - 1)}{5} = \dfrac{5}{5} \cdot (y - 1) = 1 \cdot (y - 1) = y - 1$

39. $\dfrac{x + y}{4} + \dfrac{x - y}{4} = \dfrac{(x + y) + (x - y)}{4} = \dfrac{2x}{4} = \dfrac{1x}{2} = \dfrac{x}{2}$

41. $\dfrac{z^2 + 4}{z - 2} - \dfrac{4z}{z - 2} = \dfrac{(z^2 + 4) - 4z}{z - 2} = \dfrac{z^2 - 4z + 4}{z - 2} = \dfrac{(z - 2)(z - 2)}{z - 2} = \dfrac{z - 2}{z - 2} \cdot \dfrac{z - 2}{1} = 1 \cdot z - 2 = z - 2$

43. $\frac{2x^2 - 5x}{2x + 1} - \frac{3}{2x + 1} = \frac{(2x^2 - 5x) - 3}{2x + 1} = \frac{2x^2 - 5x - 3}{2x + 1} = \frac{(2x + 1)(x - 3)}{2x + 1} = \frac{2x + 1}{2x + 1} \cdot \frac{x - 3}{1} =$
$1 \cdot x - 3 = x - 3$

45. $\frac{3n}{2n^2 - n + 5} + \frac{4n}{2n^2 - n + 5} = \frac{3n + 4n}{2n^2 - n + 5} = \frac{7n}{2n^2 - n + 5}$

47. $\frac{1}{x + 3} + \frac{2}{x + 3} + \frac{3}{x + 3} = \frac{1 + 2 + 3}{x + 3} = \frac{6}{x + 3}$

49. $\frac{x}{x + y} + \frac{y}{x + y} = \frac{x + y}{x + y} = 1$

51. $\frac{a^2}{a + b} - \frac{b^2}{a + b} = \frac{a^2 - b^2}{a + b} = \frac{(a + b)(a - b)}{a + b} = \frac{a + b}{a + b} \cdot \frac{a - b}{1} = 1 \cdot a - b = a - b$

53. $\frac{4x^2}{2x + 3y} - \frac{9y^2}{2x + 3y} = \frac{4x^2 - 9y^2}{2x + 3y} = \frac{(2x + 3y)(2x - 3y)}{2x + 3y} = \frac{2x + 3y}{2x + 3y} \cdot \frac{2x - 3y}{1} = 1 \cdot 2x - 3y = 2x - 3y$

Applications

55. (a) $\frac{6}{n + 1} + \frac{5}{n + 1} + \frac{3}{n + 1} = \frac{6 + 5 + 3}{n + 1} = \frac{14}{n + 1}$

(b) For $n = 99$, $\frac{14}{n + 1} \Rightarrow \frac{14}{99 + 1} = \frac{14}{100} = \frac{7}{50}$; there are 7 chances in 50 that a defective battery is chosen.

7.4: Addition and Subtraction with Unlike Denominators

Concepts

1. Examples include 36 and 54. *Answers may vary.*
3. $\frac{3}{3}$
5. Factoring 4 and 6 completely yields: 2^2 and $2 \cdot 3$, a list of factors is $2^2 \cdot 3 = 12$.
7. Factoring 4 and 6 completely yields: 2^2 and $2 \cdot 3$, a list of factors is $2^2 \cdot 3 = 12$.
9. 2 and 3 are both prime $\Rightarrow$ a list of factors is $2 \cdot 3 = 6$.
11. Factoring 10 and 15 completely yields: $2 \cdot 5$ and $3 \cdot 5$, a list of factors is $2 \cdot 3 \cdot 5 = 30$.
13. Factoring 24 and 36 completely yields: $2^3 \cdot 3$ and $2^2 \cdot 3^2$, a list of factors is $2^3 \cdot 3^2 = 72$.
15. Factoring $4x$ and $6x$ completely yields: $2^2 \cdot x$ and $2 \cdot 3 \cdot x$, a list of factors is $2^2 \cdot 3 \cdot x = 12x$.
17. Factoring $5x$ and $10x^2$ completely yields: $5 \cdot x$ and $2 \cdot 5 \cdot x^2$, a list of factors is $2 \cdot 5 \cdot x^2 = 10x^2$.
19. Both x and $x + 1$ are prime $\Rightarrow$ a list of factors is $x(x + 1)$.
21. Both $2x + 1$ and $x + 3$ are prime $\Rightarrow$ a list of factors is $(2x + 1)(x + 3)$.
23. Factoring $4x^2$ and $9x^3$ completely yields: $2^2 \cdot x^2$ and $3^2 \cdot x^3$, a list of factors is $3^2 \cdot 2^2 \cdot x^3 = 36x^3$.
25. Factoring $x^2 - x$ and $x^2 + x$ completely yields: $x(x - 1)$ and $x(x + 1)$, a list of factors is $x(x - 1)(x + 1)$.
27. Both $(x + 1)^2$ and $x + 1$ are factored completely $\Rightarrow$ a list of factors is $(x + 1)^2$.
29. Both $(2x - 1)^3$ and $(2x - 1)(x + 3)$ are factored completely $\Rightarrow$ a list of factors is $(2x - 1)^3(x + 3)$.

31. Factoring $4x^2 - 1$ and $2x + 1$ completely yields: $(2x + 1)(2x - 1)$ and $(2x + 1)$, a list of factors is $(2x + 1)(2x - 1)$.

33. Factoring $x^2 - 1$ and $x + 1$ completely yields: $(x + 1)(x - 1)$ and $(x + 1)$, a list of factors is $(x + 1)(x - 1)$.

35. Both $x^2 + 4$ and $4x$ are factored completely $\Rightarrow$ a list of factors is $4x(x^2 + 4)$.

37. Factoring $2x^2 + 7x + 6$ and $x^2 + 5x + 6$ completely yields: $(2x + 3)(x + 2)$ and $(x + 2)(x + 3)$, a list of factors is $(2x + 3)(x + 2)(x + 3)$.

Addition and Subtraction of Rational Expressions

39. $\frac{1}{3}, D = 9 \Rightarrow \frac{1}{3} \cdot \frac{3}{3} = \frac{3}{9}$

41. $\frac{5}{7}, D = 21 \Rightarrow \frac{5}{7} \cdot \frac{3}{3} = \frac{15}{21}$

43. $\frac{1}{4x}, D = 8x^3 \Rightarrow \frac{1}{4x} \cdot \frac{2x^2}{2x^2} = \frac{2x^2}{8x^3}$

45. $\frac{1}{x + 2}, D = x^2 - 4 \Rightarrow \frac{1}{x + 2} \cdot \frac{x - 2}{x - 2} = \frac{x - 2}{x^2 - 4}$

47. $\frac{1}{x + 1}, D = x^2 + x \Rightarrow \frac{1}{x + 1} \cdot \frac{x}{x} = \frac{x}{x^2 + x}$

49. $\frac{2x}{x + 1}, D = x^2 + 2x + 1 \Rightarrow \frac{2x}{x + 1} \cdot \frac{x + 1}{x + 1} = \frac{2x^2 + 2x}{x^2 + 2x + 1}$

51. $\frac{4}{5} + \frac{1}{2} = \frac{8}{10} + \frac{5}{10} = \frac{13}{10}$

53. $\frac{5}{9} - \frac{1}{3} = \frac{5}{9} - \frac{3}{9} = \frac{2}{9}$

55. $\frac{1}{3x} + \frac{3}{4x} = \frac{4}{12x} + \frac{9}{12x} = \frac{13}{12x}$

57. $\frac{5}{z^2} - \frac{7}{z^3} = \frac{5z}{z^3} - \frac{7}{z^3} = \frac{5z - 7}{z^3}$

59. $\frac{1}{x} - \frac{1}{y} = \frac{y}{xy} - \frac{x}{xy} = \frac{y - x}{xy}$

61. $\frac{a}{b} + \frac{b}{a} = \frac{a^2}{ab} + \frac{b^2}{ab} = \frac{a^2 + b^2}{ab}$

63. $\frac{1}{2x + 4} + \frac{3}{x + 2} = \frac{1}{2(x + 2)} + \frac{3}{x + 2} \cdot \frac{2}{2} = \frac{1}{2(x + 2)} + \frac{6}{2(x + 2)} = \frac{7}{2(x + 2)}$

65. $\frac{2}{t - 2} - \frac{1}{t} = \frac{2}{t - 2} \cdot \frac{t}{t} - \frac{1}{t} \cdot \frac{t - 2}{t - 2} = \frac{2t}{t(t - 2)} - \frac{t - 2}{t(t - 2)} = \frac{t + 2}{t(t - 2)}$

67. $\frac{5}{n - 1} + \frac{n}{n + 1} = \frac{5}{n - 1} \cdot \frac{n + 1}{n + 1} + \frac{n}{n + 1} \cdot \frac{n - 1}{n - 1} = \frac{5n + 5}{(n - 1)(n + 1)} + \frac{n^2 - n}{(n - 1)(n + 1)} = \frac{n^2 + 4n + 5}{(n - 1)(n + 1)}$

69. $\frac{3}{x - 3} + \frac{6}{3 - x} = \frac{3}{x - 3} + \frac{6}{-(x - 3)} = \frac{3}{x - 3} - \frac{6}{x - 3} = -\frac{3}{x - 3}$

71. $\frac{1}{5k - 1} + \frac{1}{1 - 5k} = \frac{1}{5k - 1} + \frac{1}{-(5k - 1)} = \frac{1}{5k - 1} - \frac{1}{5k - 1} = 0$

73. $\dfrac{2x}{(x-1)^2}+\dfrac{4}{x-1}=\dfrac{2x}{(x-1)^2}+\dfrac{4}{x-1}\cdot\dfrac{x-1}{x-1}=\dfrac{2x}{(x-1)^2}+\dfrac{4x-4}{(x-1)^2}=\dfrac{6x-4}{(x-1)^2}$

75. $\dfrac{2y}{y(2y-1)}+\dfrac{1}{2y-1}=\dfrac{2y}{y(2y-1)}+\dfrac{1}{2y-1}\cdot\dfrac{y}{y}=\dfrac{2y}{y(2y-1)}+\dfrac{y}{y(2y-1)}=\dfrac{3y}{y(2y-1)}=\dfrac{3}{2y-1}\cdot\dfrac{y}{y}=$

$\dfrac{3}{2y-1}\cdot 1=\dfrac{3}{2y-1}$

77. $\dfrac{1}{x+2}-\dfrac{1}{x^2+2x}=\dfrac{1}{x+2}\cdot\dfrac{x}{x}-\dfrac{1}{x(x+2)}=\dfrac{x}{x(x+2)}-\dfrac{1}{x(x+2)}=\dfrac{x-1}{x(x+2)}$

79. $\dfrac{x}{x^2+4x+4}+\dfrac{1}{x+2}=\dfrac{x}{(x+2)^2}+\dfrac{1}{x+2}\cdot\dfrac{x+2}{x+2}=\dfrac{x}{(x+2)^2}+\dfrac{x+2}{(x+2)^2}=\dfrac{2x+2}{(x+2)^2}$

81. $\dfrac{x}{(x+1)(x+2)}-\dfrac{1}{(x+2)(x+3)}=\dfrac{x}{(x+1)(x+2)}\cdot\dfrac{x+3}{x+3}-\dfrac{1}{(x+2)(x+3)}\cdot\dfrac{x+1}{x+1}=$

$\dfrac{x^2+3x}{(x+1)(x+2)(x+3)}-\dfrac{x+1}{(x+1)(x+2)(x+3)}=\dfrac{x^2+2x-1}{(x+1)(x+2)(x+3)}$

83. $\dfrac{1}{a+b}-\dfrac{1}{a-b}=\dfrac{1}{a+b}\cdot\dfrac{a-b}{a-b}-\dfrac{1}{a-b}\cdot\dfrac{a+b}{a+b}=\dfrac{a-b}{(a+b)(a-b)}-\dfrac{a+b}{(a+b)(a-b)}=-\dfrac{2b}{(a+b)(a-b)}$

85. $\dfrac{r}{r-t}+\dfrac{t}{t-r}-1=\dfrac{r}{r-t}+\dfrac{t}{-(r-t)}-1=\dfrac{r}{r-t}-\dfrac{t}{r-t}-1=\dfrac{r-t}{r-r}-1=1-1=0$

87. $\dfrac{1}{2a}+\dfrac{1}{3a}+\dfrac{1}{4a}=\dfrac{1}{2a}\cdot\dfrac{6}{6}+\dfrac{1}{3a}\cdot\dfrac{4}{4}+\dfrac{1}{4a}\cdot\dfrac{3}{3}=\dfrac{6}{12a}+\dfrac{4}{12a}+\dfrac{3}{12a}=\dfrac{13}{12a}$

89. $\dfrac{2}{x-y}+\dfrac{3}{y-x}+\dfrac{1}{x-y}=\dfrac{2}{x-y}+\dfrac{3}{-(x-y)}+\dfrac{1}{x-y}=\dfrac{2}{x-y}-\dfrac{3}{x-y}+\dfrac{1}{x-y}=\dfrac{0}{x-y}=0$

91. $\dfrac{3}{x-3}-\dfrac{3}{x^2-3x}-\dfrac{6}{x(x-3)}=\dfrac{3}{x-3}\cdot\dfrac{x}{x}-\dfrac{3}{x(x-3)}+\dfrac{6}{x(x-3)}=\dfrac{3x}{x(x-3)}-\dfrac{3}{x(x-3)}-\dfrac{6}{x(x-3)}=$

$\dfrac{3x-9}{x(x-3)}=\dfrac{3(x-3)}{x(x-3)}=\dfrac{3}{x}\cdot\dfrac{x-3}{x-3}=\dfrac{3}{x}\cdot 1=\dfrac{3}{x}$

Applications

93. $R=120, S=200;\ \dfrac{1}{R}+\dfrac{1}{S}\Rightarrow\dfrac{1}{120}+\dfrac{1}{200}=\dfrac{1}{120}\cdot\dfrac{5}{5}+\dfrac{1}{200}\cdot\dfrac{3}{3}=\dfrac{5}{600}+\dfrac{3}{600}=\dfrac{8}{600}=\dfrac{1}{75}$ and

$\dfrac{S+R}{RS}\Rightarrow\dfrac{120+200}{120(200)}=\dfrac{320}{24{,}000}=\dfrac{1}{75}.$ Yes, they are the same.

95. $\dfrac{1}{F}-\dfrac{1}{D}\Rightarrow F, D=F\cdot D=FD\Rightarrow\dfrac{1}{F}\cdot\dfrac{D}{D}-\dfrac{1}{D}\cdot\dfrac{F}{F}=\dfrac{D}{FD}-\dfrac{F}{FD}=\dfrac{D-F}{FD}$

Checking Basic Concepts for Sections 7.3 & 7.4

1. (a) $\dfrac{x}{x+2}+\dfrac{2}{x+2}=\dfrac{x+2}{x+2}=1$

(b) $\dfrac{2}{3x}-\dfrac{x}{3x}=\dfrac{2-x}{3x}$

(c) $\dfrac{z^2+z}{z+2}+\dfrac{z}{z+2}=\dfrac{z^2+2z}{z+2}=\dfrac{z(z+2)}{z+2}=\dfrac{z}{1}\cdot\dfrac{z+2}{z+2}=\dfrac{z}{1}\cdot 1=z$

2. (a) Factoring $3x$ and $5x$ completely yields: $3 \cdot x$ and $5 \cdot x$, a list of factors is $3 \cdot 5 \cdot x = 15x$.

(b) Factoring $4x$ and $x^2 + x$ completely yields:

$2^2 \cdot x$ and $x(x + 1)$, a list of factors is $2^2 \cdot x \cdot (x + 1) = 4x(x + 1)$.

(c) Both $x + 1$ and $x - 1$ are factored completely, a list of factors is $(x + 1)(x - 1)$.

3. (a) $\dfrac{1}{x+1} + \dfrac{5}{x} = \dfrac{1}{x+1} \cdot \dfrac{x}{x} + \dfrac{5}{x} \cdot \dfrac{x+1}{x+1} = \dfrac{x}{x(x+1)} + \dfrac{5x+5}{x(x+1)} = \dfrac{6x+5}{x(x+1)}$

(b) $\dfrac{5}{x-3} + \dfrac{1}{3-x} = \dfrac{5}{x-3} + \dfrac{1}{-(x-3)} = \dfrac{5}{x-3} - \dfrac{1}{x-3} = \dfrac{4}{x-3}$

(c) $\dfrac{-4}{4x+2} - \dfrac{x+2}{2x+1} = \dfrac{-4}{2(2x+1)} - \dfrac{x+2}{2x+1} = \dfrac{-4}{2(2x+1)} - \dfrac{x+2}{2x+1} \cdot \dfrac{2}{2} = \dfrac{-4}{2(2x+1)} - \dfrac{2x+4}{2(2x+1)} =$

$\dfrac{-2x-8}{2(2x+1)} = \dfrac{-2(x+4)}{2(2x+1)} = -\dfrac{x+4}{2x+1}$

4. $\dfrac{a}{a-b} - \dfrac{b}{a+b} = \dfrac{a}{a-b} \cdot \dfrac{a+b}{a+b} - \dfrac{b}{a+b} \cdot \dfrac{a-b}{a-b} = \dfrac{a^2+ab}{(a-b)(a+b)} - \dfrac{ab-b^2}{(a-b)(a+b)} = \dfrac{a^2+b^2}{(a-b)(a+b)}$

7.5: Complex Fractions

Concepts

1. $\dfrac{\frac{1}{2}}{\frac{3}{4}} = \dfrac{1}{2} \cdot \dfrac{4}{3} = \dfrac{4}{6} = \dfrac{2}{3}$

3. fraction

5. Division

7. $\dfrac{\frac{a}{b}}{\frac{c}{d}}$

Simplifying Complex Fractions

9. For $\dfrac{\frac{x}{5} - \frac{1}{6}}{\frac{2}{15} - 3x}$, the denominators 5, 6 and 15 have prime factorization of 5, $2 \cdot 3$ and $3 \cdot 5$, therefore $2 \cdot 3 \cdot 5 = 30$.

11. For $\dfrac{\frac{2}{x+1} - x}{\frac{2}{x-1} - x}$, the denominators $x + 1$ and $x - 1$ are prime, therefore $(x + 1)(x - 1)$.

13. For $\dfrac{\frac{1}{2x-1} - \frac{1}{2x+1}}{\frac{x+1}{x}}$, the denominators $2x - 1$, $2x + 1$ and x are prime, therefore $x(2x - 1)(2x + 1)$.

15. $\dfrac{\frac{2}{3}}{\frac{5}{6}} = \dfrac{2}{3} \div \dfrac{5}{6} = \dfrac{2}{3} \cdot \dfrac{6}{5} = \dfrac{12}{15} = \dfrac{4}{5}$

17. $\dfrac{\frac{r}{t}}{\frac{2r}{t}} = \dfrac{r}{t} \div \dfrac{2r}{t} = \dfrac{r}{t} \cdot \dfrac{t}{2r} = \dfrac{t}{t} \cdot \dfrac{1}{2} \cdot \dfrac{r}{r} = 1 \cdot \dfrac{1}{2} \cdot 1 = \dfrac{1}{2}$

19. $\dfrac{\frac{6}{x}}{\frac{2}{y}} = \dfrac{6}{x} \div \dfrac{2}{y} = \dfrac{6}{x} \cdot \dfrac{y}{2} = \dfrac{6y}{2x} = \dfrac{3y}{x}$

21. $\dfrac{\frac{6}{m-2}}{\frac{2}{m-2}} = \dfrac{6}{m-2} \div \dfrac{2}{m-2} = \dfrac{6}{m-2} \cdot \dfrac{m-2}{2} = \dfrac{m-2}{m-2} \cdot \dfrac{6}{2} = 1 \cdot 3 = 3$

23. $\dfrac{\frac{p+1}{p}}{\frac{p+2}{p}} = \dfrac{p+1}{p} \div \dfrac{p+2}{p} = \dfrac{p+1}{p} \cdot \dfrac{p}{p+2} = \dfrac{p}{p} \cdot \dfrac{p+1}{p+2} = 1 \cdot \dfrac{p+1}{p+2} = \dfrac{p+1}{p+2}$

25. $\dfrac{\frac{5}{z^2-1}}{\frac{z}{z^2-1}} = \dfrac{5}{z^2-1} \div \dfrac{z}{z^2-1} = \dfrac{5}{z^2-1} \cdot \dfrac{z^2-1}{z} = \dfrac{z^2-1}{z^2-1} \cdot \dfrac{5}{z} = 1 \cdot \dfrac{5}{z} = \dfrac{5}{z}$

27. $\dfrac{\frac{y}{y^2-9}}{\frac{1}{y+3}} = \dfrac{y}{y^2-9} \div \dfrac{1}{y+3} = \dfrac{y}{y^2-9} \cdot \dfrac{y+3}{1} = \dfrac{y}{(y+3)(y-3)} \cdot \dfrac{y+3}{1} = \dfrac{y}{y-3} \cdot \dfrac{y+3}{y+3} =$

$\dfrac{y}{y-3} \cdot 1 = \dfrac{y}{y-3}$

29. $\dfrac{\frac{3}{x+1}}{\frac{4}{x+1} - \frac{1}{x+1}} = \dfrac{\frac{3}{x+1}}{\frac{3}{x+1}} = \dfrac{3}{x+1} \div \dfrac{3}{x+1} = \dfrac{3}{x+1} \cdot \dfrac{x+1}{3} = \dfrac{x+1}{x+1} \cdot \dfrac{3}{3} = 1 \cdot 1 = 1$

31. $\dfrac{\frac{1}{m^2n} + \frac{1}{mn^2}}{\frac{1}{m^2n} - \frac{1}{mn^2}} = \dfrac{\frac{1}{m^2n} + \frac{1}{mn^2}}{\frac{1}{m^2n} - \frac{1}{mn^2}} \cdot \dfrac{m^2n^2}{m^2n^2} = \dfrac{\frac{m^2n^2}{m^2n} + \frac{m^2n^2}{mn^2}}{\frac{m^2n^2}{m^2n} - \frac{m^2n^2}{mn^2}} = \dfrac{(\frac{m^2}{m^2} \cdot \frac{n}{n} \cdot n) + (m \cdot \frac{m}{m} \cdot \frac{n^2}{n^2})}{(\frac{m^2}{m^2} \cdot \frac{n}{n} \cdot n) - (m \cdot \frac{m}{m} \cdot \frac{n^2}{n^2})} = \dfrac{(1 \cdot 1 \cdot n) + (m \cdot 1 \cdot 1)}{(1 \cdot 1 \cdot n) - (m \cdot 1 \cdot 1)} = \dfrac{n+m}{n-m}$

33. $\dfrac{\frac{1}{2x} + \frac{1}{y}}{\frac{1}{y} - \frac{1}{2x}} = \dfrac{\frac{1}{2x} + \frac{1}{y}}{\frac{1}{y} - \frac{1}{2x}} \cdot \dfrac{2xy}{2xy} = \dfrac{\frac{2xy}{2x} + \frac{2xy}{y}}{\frac{2xy}{y} - \frac{2xy}{2x}} = \dfrac{\frac{2x}{2x} \cdot y + 2x \cdot \frac{y}{y}}{2x \cdot \frac{y}{y} - \frac{2x}{2x} \cdot y} = \dfrac{1 \cdot y + 2x \cdot 1}{2x \cdot 1 - 1 \cdot y} = \dfrac{2x+y}{2x-y}$

35. $\dfrac{\frac{1}{ab} + \frac{1}{a}}{\frac{1}{ab} - \frac{1}{b}} = \dfrac{\frac{1}{ab} + \frac{b}{ab}}{\frac{1}{ab} - \frac{a}{ab}} = \dfrac{\frac{1+b}{ab}}{\frac{1-a}{ab}} = \dfrac{1+b}{ab} \div \dfrac{1-a}{ab} = \dfrac{1+b}{ab} \cdot \dfrac{ab}{1-a} = \dfrac{ab}{ab} \cdot \dfrac{1+b}{1-a} = 1 \cdot \dfrac{1+b}{1-a} = \dfrac{1+b}{1-a}$

37. $\dfrac{\frac{2}{q} - \frac{1}{q+1}}{\frac{1}{q+1}} = \dfrac{\frac{2}{q} - \frac{1}{q+1}}{\frac{1}{q+1}} \cdot \dfrac{q(q+1)}{q(q+1)} = \dfrac{\frac{2q(q+1)}{q} - \frac{q(q+1)}{q+1}}{\frac{q(q+1)}{q+1}} = \dfrac{\frac{q}{q} \cdot 2(q+1) - q \cdot \frac{q+1}{q+1}}{q \cdot \frac{q+1}{q+1}} = \dfrac{2q+2-q}{q} = \dfrac{q+2}{q}$

39. $\dfrac{\frac{1}{x+1} + \frac{1}{x+2}}{\frac{1}{x+1} - \frac{1}{x+2}} = \dfrac{\frac{1}{x+1} + \frac{1}{x+2}}{\frac{1}{x+1} - \frac{1}{x+2}} \cdot \dfrac{(x+1)(x+2)}{(x+1)(x+2)} = \dfrac{\frac{(x+1)(x+2)}{x+1} + \frac{(x+1)(x+2)}{x+2}}{\frac{(x+1)(x+2)}{x+1} - \frac{(x+1)(x+2)}{x+2}} =$

$\dfrac{\frac{x+1}{x+1} \cdot x + 2 + \frac{x+2}{x+2} \cdot x + 1}{\frac{x+1}{x+1} \cdot x + 2 - \frac{x+2}{x+2} \cdot (x+1)} = \dfrac{1 \cdot x + 2 + 1 \cdot x + 1}{1 \cdot x + 2 - 1 \cdot (x+1)} = \dfrac{x+2+x+1}{x+2-x-1} = \dfrac{2x+3}{1} = 2x+3$

41. $\dfrac{\frac{1}{2x-1} - \frac{1}{2x+1}}{\frac{x+1}{x}} = \dfrac{\frac{2x+1}{(2x-1)(2x+1)} - \frac{2x-1}{(2x-1)(2x+1)}}{\frac{x+1}{x}} = \dfrac{\frac{2}{(2x-1)(2x+1)}}{\frac{x+1}{x}} =$

$\dfrac{2}{(2x-1)(2x+1)} \div \dfrac{x+1}{x} = \dfrac{2}{(2x-1)(2x+1)} \cdot \dfrac{x}{x+1} = \dfrac{2x}{(x+1)(2x-1)(2x+1)}$

43. $\dfrac{\frac{1}{ab^2} - \frac{1}{a^2b}}{\frac{1}{b} - \frac{1}{a}} = \dfrac{\frac{a}{a^2b^2} - \frac{b}{a^2b^2}}{\frac{a}{ab} - \frac{b}{ab}} = \dfrac{\frac{a-b}{a^2b^2}}{\frac{a-b}{ab}} = \dfrac{a-b}{a^2b^2} \div \dfrac{a-b}{ab} = \dfrac{a-b}{a^2b^2} \cdot \dfrac{ab}{a-b} = \dfrac{a-b}{a-b} \cdot \dfrac{ab}{a^2b^2} = 1 \cdot \dfrac{1}{ab} = \dfrac{1}{ab}$

45. $\dfrac{1}{a^{-1} + b^{-1}} = \dfrac{1}{\frac{1}{a} + \frac{1}{b}} = \dfrac{1}{\frac{1}{a} \cdot \frac{b}{b} + \frac{1}{b} \cdot \frac{a}{a}} = \dfrac{1}{\frac{b}{ab} + \frac{a}{ab}} = \dfrac{1}{\frac{a+b}{ab}} = 1 \div \dfrac{a+b}{ab} = 1 \cdot \dfrac{ab}{a+b} = \dfrac{ab}{a+b}$

Applications

47. $\dfrac{P(1 + \frac{r}{26})^{52} - P}{\frac{r}{26}}$

49. $R = \dfrac{1}{\frac{1}{T} + \frac{1}{S}} = \dfrac{1}{\frac{1}{T} + \frac{1}{S}} \cdot \dfrac{ST}{ST} = \dfrac{ST}{\frac{ST}{T} + \frac{ST}{S}} = \dfrac{ST}{S \cdot \frac{T}{T} + \frac{S}{S} \cdot T} = \dfrac{ST}{S \cdot 1 + 1 \cdot T} = \dfrac{ST}{S + T}$

7.6: Rational Equations and Formulas

Concepts

1. rational

3. $ad = bc$; b; d

5. $12x$

Solving Rational Equations

7. $\dfrac{x}{2} = \dfrac{3}{4} \Rightarrow x \cdot 4 = 2 \cdot 3 \Rightarrow 4x = 6 \Rightarrow \dfrac{4x}{4} = \dfrac{6}{4} \Rightarrow x = \dfrac{6}{4} \Rightarrow x = \dfrac{3}{2}$

   Check: $\dfrac{\frac{3}{2}}{2} = \dfrac{3}{4} \Rightarrow \dfrac{3}{2} \div \dfrac{2}{1} = \dfrac{3}{2} \cdot \dfrac{1}{2} = \dfrac{3}{4}$

9. $\dfrac{3}{z} = \dfrac{6}{5} \Rightarrow 3 \cdot 5 = z \cdot 6 \Rightarrow 15 = 6z \Rightarrow \dfrac{15}{6} = \dfrac{6z}{6} \Rightarrow z = \dfrac{15}{6} \Rightarrow z = \dfrac{5}{2}$

   Check: $\dfrac{3}{\frac{5}{2}} = \dfrac{6}{5} \Rightarrow \dfrac{3}{1} \div \dfrac{5}{2} = \dfrac{3}{1} \cdot \dfrac{2}{5} = \dfrac{6}{5}$

11. $\dfrac{12}{7} = \dfrac{2}{t} \Rightarrow 12 \cdot t = 7 \cdot 2 \Rightarrow 12t = 14 \Rightarrow \dfrac{12t}{12} = \dfrac{14}{12} \Rightarrow t = \dfrac{14}{12} \Rightarrow t = \dfrac{7}{6}$

   Check: $\dfrac{12}{7} = \dfrac{2}{\frac{7}{6}} \Rightarrow \dfrac{2}{1} \div \dfrac{7}{6} = \dfrac{2}{1} \cdot \dfrac{6}{7} = \dfrac{12}{7}$

13. $\dfrac{3y}{4} = \dfrac{7y}{2} \Rightarrow 3y \cdot 2 = 4 \cdot 7y \Rightarrow 6y = 28y \Rightarrow 34y = 0 \Rightarrow \dfrac{34y}{34} = \dfrac{0}{34} \Rightarrow y = 0$

   Check: $\dfrac{3(0)}{4} = \dfrac{7(0)}{2} \Rightarrow \dfrac{0}{4} = \dfrac{0}{2} \Rightarrow 0 = 0$

15. $\dfrac{2}{3} = \dfrac{1}{2x + 1} \Rightarrow 2(2x + 1) = 3 \cdot 1 \Rightarrow 4x + 2 = 3 \Rightarrow 4x = 1 \Rightarrow \dfrac{4x}{4} = \dfrac{1}{4} \Rightarrow x = \dfrac{1}{4}$

   Check: $\dfrac{2}{3} = \dfrac{1}{2(\frac{1}{4}) + 1} \Rightarrow \dfrac{1}{\frac{2}{4} + 1} = \dfrac{1}{\frac{6}{4}} = \dfrac{1}{1} \div \dfrac{6}{4} = \dfrac{1}{1} \cdot \dfrac{4}{6} = \dfrac{4}{6} = \dfrac{2}{3}$

17. $\dfrac{5}{2x} = \dfrac{8}{x + 2} \Rightarrow 5(x + 2) = 2x \cdot 8 \Rightarrow 5x + 10 = 16x \Rightarrow -11x = -10 \Rightarrow \dfrac{-11x}{-11} = \dfrac{-10}{-11} \Rightarrow x = \dfrac{10}{11}$

   Check: $\dfrac{5}{2(\frac{10}{11})} = \dfrac{8}{\frac{10}{11} + 2} \Rightarrow \dfrac{5}{\frac{20}{11}} = \dfrac{8}{\frac{32}{11}} \Rightarrow \dfrac{5}{1} \div \dfrac{20}{11} = \dfrac{8}{1} \div \dfrac{32}{11} \Rightarrow \dfrac{5}{1} \cdot \dfrac{11}{20} = \dfrac{8}{1} \cdot \dfrac{11}{32} \Rightarrow \dfrac{55}{20} = \dfrac{88}{32} \Rightarrow \dfrac{11}{4} = \dfrac{11}{4}$

19. $\dfrac{1}{z - 1} = \dfrac{z}{z + 1} \Rightarrow 1 \cdot (z + 1) = (z - 1) \cdot 2 \Rightarrow z + 1 = 2z - 2 \Rightarrow 3 = z \Rightarrow z = 3$

   Check: $\dfrac{1}{3 - 1} = \dfrac{2}{3 + 1} \Rightarrow \dfrac{1}{2} = \dfrac{2}{4} \Rightarrow \dfrac{1}{2} = \dfrac{1}{2}$

21. $\dfrac{3}{n+5} = \dfrac{2}{n-5} \Rightarrow 3 \cdot (n-5) = (n+5) \cdot 2 \Rightarrow 3n - 15 = 2n + 10 \Rightarrow n = 25$

Check: $\dfrac{3}{25+5} = \dfrac{2}{25-5} \Rightarrow \dfrac{3}{30} = \dfrac{2}{20} \Rightarrow \dfrac{1}{10} = \dfrac{1}{10}$

23. $\dfrac{m}{m-1} = \dfrac{5}{4} \Rightarrow m \cdot 4 = (m-1) \cdot 5 \Rightarrow 4m = 5m - 5 \Rightarrow -m = -5 \Rightarrow \dfrac{-m}{-1} = \dfrac{-5}{-1} \Rightarrow m = 5$

Check: $\dfrac{5}{5-1} = \dfrac{5}{4} \Rightarrow \dfrac{5}{4} = \dfrac{5}{4}$

25. $\dfrac{5x}{5-x} = \dfrac{1}{3} \Rightarrow 5x \cdot 3 = (5-x) \cdot 1 \Rightarrow 15x = 5 - x \Rightarrow 16x = 5 \Rightarrow \dfrac{16x}{16} = \dfrac{5}{16} \Rightarrow x = \dfrac{5}{16}$

Check: $\dfrac{5(\frac{5}{16})}{2 - \frac{5}{16}} = \dfrac{1}{3} \Rightarrow \dfrac{\frac{25}{16}}{\frac{75}{16}} = \dfrac{25}{16} \div \dfrac{75}{16} = \dfrac{25}{16} \cdot \dfrac{16}{75} = \dfrac{16}{16} \cdot \dfrac{25}{75} = 1 \cdot \dfrac{1}{3} = \dfrac{1}{3}$

27. $\dfrac{6}{5-2x} = \dfrac{2}{1} \Rightarrow 6 \cdot 1 = (5-2x) \cdot 2 \Rightarrow 6 = 10 - 4x \Rightarrow -4 = -4x \Rightarrow \dfrac{-4}{-4} = \dfrac{-4x}{-4} \Rightarrow 1 = x \Rightarrow x = 1$

Check: $\dfrac{6}{5 - 2(1)} = 2 \Rightarrow \dfrac{6}{5-2} = \dfrac{6}{3} \Rightarrow 2 = 2$

29. $\dfrac{1}{1-x} = \dfrac{3}{1+x} \Rightarrow 1 \cdot (1+x) = (1-x) \cdot 3 \Rightarrow 1 + x = 3 - 3x \Rightarrow 4x = 2 \Rightarrow \dfrac{4x}{4} = \dfrac{2}{4} \Rightarrow x = \dfrac{1}{2}$

Check: $\dfrac{1}{1 - \frac{1}{2}} = \dfrac{3}{1 + \frac{1}{2}} \Rightarrow \dfrac{1}{\frac{1}{2}} = \dfrac{3}{\frac{3}{2}} \Rightarrow \dfrac{1}{1} \div \dfrac{1}{2} = \dfrac{3}{1} \div \dfrac{3}{2} \Rightarrow \dfrac{1}{1} \cdot \dfrac{3}{1} = \dfrac{3}{1} \cdot \dfrac{2}{3} \Rightarrow 2 = \dfrac{6}{3} \Rightarrow 2 = 2$

31. $\dfrac{1}{z+2} = \dfrac{-z}{1} \Rightarrow 1 \cdot 1 = -z(z+2) \Rightarrow 1 = -z^2 - 2z \Rightarrow z^2 + 2z + 1 = 0 \Rightarrow (z+1)^2 = 0 \Rightarrow z = -1$

Check: $\dfrac{1}{-1+2} = \dfrac{-(-1)}{1} \Rightarrow \dfrac{1}{1} = \dfrac{1}{1} \Rightarrow 1 = 1$

33. $\dfrac{-1}{2x+5} = \dfrac{x}{3} \Rightarrow -1 \cdot 3 = (2x+5) \cdot x \Rightarrow -3 = 2x^2 + 5x \Rightarrow 0 = 2x^2 + 5x + 3 \Rightarrow$

$0 = (2x+3)(x+1) \Rightarrow 0 = 2x + 3 \Rightarrow -\dfrac{3}{2} = \dfrac{2}{2}x \Rightarrow -\dfrac{3}{2} = x, 0 = x + 1 \Rightarrow -1 = x \Rightarrow x = -\dfrac{3}{2}, -1$

Check: $\dfrac{-1}{2(\frac{-3}{2}) + 5} = \dfrac{\frac{-3}{2}}{3} \Rightarrow \dfrac{-1}{\frac{4}{2}} = \dfrac{\frac{-3}{2}}{3} \Rightarrow \dfrac{-1}{1} \div \dfrac{4}{2} = \dfrac{-3}{2} \div \dfrac{3}{1} \Rightarrow \dfrac{-1}{1} \cdot \dfrac{2}{4} = \dfrac{-3}{2} \cdot \dfrac{1}{3} \Rightarrow \dfrac{-2}{4} = \dfrac{-3}{6} \Rightarrow$

$\dfrac{-1}{2} = \dfrac{-1}{2(-1) + 5} = \dfrac{-1}{3} \Rightarrow \dfrac{-1}{-2+5} \Rightarrow \dfrac{-1}{3}$

35. $\dfrac{x}{2} + \dfrac{x}{4} = 3 \Rightarrow \dfrac{x(4)}{2} + \dfrac{x(4)}{4} = 3(4) \Rightarrow \dfrac{4x}{2} + \dfrac{4x}{4} = 12 \Rightarrow 2x + x = 12 \Rightarrow 3x = 12 \Rightarrow \dfrac{3x}{3} = \dfrac{12}{3} \Rightarrow x = 4$

Check: $\dfrac{4}{2} + \dfrac{4}{4} = 3 \Rightarrow 2 + 1 = 3 \Rightarrow 3 = 3$

37. $\dfrac{3x}{4} - \dfrac{x}{2} = 1 \Rightarrow \dfrac{3x(4)}{4} - \dfrac{x(4)}{2} = 1(4) \Rightarrow \dfrac{12x}{4} - \dfrac{4x}{2} = 4 \Rightarrow 3x - 2x = 4 \Rightarrow x = 4$

Check: $\dfrac{3(4)}{4} - \dfrac{4}{2} = 1 \Rightarrow \dfrac{12}{4} - \dfrac{4}{2} = 1 \Rightarrow 3 - 2 = 1 = 1$

39. $\dfrac{4}{t+1}+\dfrac{1}{t+1}=-1 \Rightarrow \dfrac{5}{t+1}=-1 \Rightarrow (t+1)\cdot\dfrac{5}{t+1}=-1\cdot(t+1) \Rightarrow 5=-t-1 \Rightarrow 6=-t \Rightarrow$

$\dfrac{6}{-1}=\dfrac{-t}{-1} \Rightarrow t=-6$

Check: $\dfrac{4}{t+1}+\dfrac{1}{t+1}=-1 \Rightarrow \dfrac{5}{t+1}=-1 \Rightarrow \dfrac{5}{-6+1}=-1 \Rightarrow \dfrac{5}{-5}=-1 \Rightarrow -1=-1$

41. $\dfrac{1}{x}+\dfrac{2}{x}=\dfrac{1}{2} \Rightarrow \dfrac{3}{x}=\dfrac{1}{2} \Rightarrow x\cdot\dfrac{3}{x}=\dfrac{1}{2}\cdot x \Rightarrow 3=\dfrac{1}{2}x \Rightarrow 3\cdot 2=\dfrac{1}{2}x\cdot 2 \Rightarrow 6=x \Rightarrow x=6$

Check: $\dfrac{1}{6}+\dfrac{2}{6}=\dfrac{1}{2} \Rightarrow \dfrac{3}{6}=\dfrac{1}{2} \Rightarrow \dfrac{1}{2}=\dfrac{1}{2}$

43. $\dfrac{5}{4z}-\dfrac{2}{3z}=1 \Rightarrow \dfrac{5(12z)}{4z}-\dfrac{2(12z)}{3z}=1(12z) \Rightarrow \dfrac{60z}{4z}-\dfrac{24z}{3z}=12z \Rightarrow 15-8=12z \Rightarrow \dfrac{7}{12}=\dfrac{12z}{12} \Rightarrow$

$\dfrac{7}{12}=z \Rightarrow z=\dfrac{7}{12}$ Check: $\dfrac{5}{4(\frac{7}{12})}-\dfrac{2}{3(\frac{7}{12})}=1 \Rightarrow \dfrac{5}{\frac{7}{3}}-\dfrac{2}{\frac{7}{4}}=1 \Rightarrow \dfrac{5}{1}\div\dfrac{7}{3}-\dfrac{2}{1}\div\dfrac{7}{4}=1 \Rightarrow$

$\dfrac{5}{1}\cdot\dfrac{3}{7}-\dfrac{2}{1}\cdot\dfrac{4}{7}=1 \Rightarrow \dfrac{15}{7}-\dfrac{8}{7}=1 \Rightarrow \dfrac{7}{7}=1 \Rightarrow 1=1$

45. $\dfrac{4}{y-1}+\dfrac{1}{y}=\dfrac{6}{5} \Rightarrow \dfrac{4(5)(y)(y-1)}{y-1}+\dfrac{1(5)(y)(y-1)}{y}=\dfrac{6(5)(y)(y-1)}{5} \Rightarrow$

$\dfrac{20y(y-1)}{y-1}+\dfrac{5y(y-1)}{y}=\dfrac{6y^2-6y(5)}{5} \Rightarrow 20y+5y-5=6y^2-6y \Rightarrow 25y-5=6y^2-6y \Rightarrow$

$6y^2-31y+5=0 \Rightarrow (6y-1)(y-5)=0 \Rightarrow 6y-1=0 \Rightarrow 6y=1 \Rightarrow y=\dfrac{1}{6}, y-5=0 \Rightarrow$

$y=5 \Rightarrow y=\dfrac{1}{6}, 5$

Check: $\dfrac{4}{y-1}+\dfrac{1}{y}=\dfrac{6}{5} \Rightarrow \dfrac{4}{\frac{1}{6}-1}+\dfrac{1}{\frac{1}{6}}=\dfrac{6}{5} \Rightarrow \dfrac{4}{-\frac{5}{6}}+\dfrac{1}{\frac{1}{6}}=\dfrac{6}{5} \Rightarrow \dfrac{4}{1}\cdot-\dfrac{6}{5}+\dfrac{1}{1}\cdot\dfrac{6}{1}=\dfrac{6}{5} \Rightarrow -\dfrac{24}{5}+\dfrac{6}{1}=\dfrac{6}{5} \Rightarrow$

$-\dfrac{24}{5}+\dfrac{30}{5}=\dfrac{6}{5} \Rightarrow \dfrac{6}{5}=\dfrac{6}{5}, \dfrac{4}{5-1}+\dfrac{1}{5}=\dfrac{6}{5} \Rightarrow \dfrac{4}{4}+\dfrac{1}{5}=\dfrac{6}{5} \Rightarrow \dfrac{20}{20}+\dfrac{4}{20}=\dfrac{24}{20} \Rightarrow \dfrac{24}{20}=\dfrac{24}{20} \Rightarrow \dfrac{6}{5}=\dfrac{6}{5}$

47. $\dfrac{1}{2x}-\dfrac{1}{x+3}=0 \Rightarrow \dfrac{1(2x)(x+3)}{2x}-\dfrac{2(2x)(x+3)}{x+3}=0(2x)(x+3) \Rightarrow \dfrac{x+3(2x)}{2x}-\dfrac{2x(x+3)}{x+3}=0 \Rightarrow$

$x+3-2x=0 \Rightarrow -x+3=0 \Rightarrow -x=-3 \Rightarrow x=3$

Check: $\dfrac{1}{2(3)}-\dfrac{1}{3+3}=0 \Rightarrow \dfrac{1}{6}-\dfrac{1}{6}=0 \Rightarrow 0=0$

49. $\dfrac{1}{x-2}+\dfrac{1}{x+2}=\dfrac{6}{x^2-4} \Rightarrow \dfrac{1(x-2)(x+2)}{x-2}+\dfrac{1(x-1)(x+2)}{x+2}=\dfrac{6(x-2)(x+2)}{(x-2)(x+2)} \Rightarrow$

$\dfrac{x+2(x-2)}{x-2}+\dfrac{x-2(x+2)}{x+2}=\dfrac{6(x-2)(x+2)}{(x-2)(x+2)} \Rightarrow x+2+x-2=6 \Rightarrow 2x=6 \Rightarrow x=\dfrac{6}{2} \Rightarrow x=3$

Check: $\dfrac{1}{3-2}+\dfrac{1}{3+2}=\dfrac{6}{(3)^2-4} \Rightarrow \dfrac{1}{1}+\dfrac{1}{5}=\dfrac{6}{5} \Rightarrow \dfrac{5}{5}+\dfrac{1}{5}=\dfrac{6}{5} \Rightarrow \dfrac{6}{5}=\dfrac{6}{5}$

51. $\dfrac{1}{p+1} + \dfrac{1}{p+2} = \dfrac{1}{p^2+3p+2} \Rightarrow \dfrac{1}{p+1} \cdot \dfrac{p+2}{p+2} + \dfrac{1}{p+2} \cdot \dfrac{p+1}{p+1} = \dfrac{1}{(p+1)(p+2)} \Rightarrow$

$\dfrac{p+2}{(p+1)(p+2)} + \dfrac{p+1}{(p+1)(p+2)} = \dfrac{1}{(p+1)(p+2)} \Rightarrow 2p+3 = 1 \Rightarrow 2p = -2 \Rightarrow$

$p = -1$, but $p = -1$ makes $\dfrac{1}{p+1} = \dfrac{1}{0}$ which is undefined $\Rightarrow$ no solution

53. $\dfrac{1}{x-2} + \dfrac{3}{2x-4} = \dfrac{6}{3x-6} \Rightarrow \dfrac{1}{x-2} + \dfrac{3}{2(x-2)} = \dfrac{6}{3(x-2)} \Rightarrow$

$\dfrac{1}{x-2} \cdot \dfrac{6}{6} + \dfrac{3}{2(x-2)} \cdot \dfrac{3}{3} = \dfrac{6}{3(x-2)} \cdot \dfrac{2}{2} \Rightarrow \dfrac{6}{6(x-2)} + \dfrac{9}{6(x-2)} = \dfrac{12}{6(x-2)} \Rightarrow 6 + 9 = 12 \Rightarrow$

$15 = 12$, which is false $\Rightarrow$ no solution

55. $\dfrac{1}{r^2-r-2} + \dfrac{2}{r^2-2r} = \dfrac{1}{r^2+r} \Rightarrow \dfrac{1(r)(r-2)(r+1)}{(r-2)(r+1)} + \dfrac{2(r)(r-2)(r+1)}{r(r-2)} = \dfrac{1(r)(r-2)(r+1)}{r(r+1)} \Rightarrow$

$\dfrac{r(r-2)(r+1)}{(r-2)(r+1)} + \dfrac{2r+2(r)(r-2)}{r(r-2)} = \dfrac{r-2(r)(r+1)}{r(r+1)} \Rightarrow r + 2r + 2 = r - 2 \Rightarrow 3r + 2 = r - 2 \Rightarrow$

$3r = r - 4 \Rightarrow 2r = -4 \Rightarrow r = \dfrac{-4}{2} \Rightarrow r = -2$

Check: $\dfrac{1}{(-2)^2-(-2)-2} + \dfrac{2}{(-2)^2-2(-2)} = \dfrac{1}{(-2)^2+(-2)} \Rightarrow \dfrac{1}{4} + \dfrac{2}{8} = \dfrac{1}{2} \Rightarrow \dfrac{1}{4} + \dfrac{1}{4} = \dfrac{1}{2} \Rightarrow \dfrac{2}{4} = \dfrac{1}{2} \Rightarrow$

$\dfrac{1}{2} = \dfrac{1}{2}$

Graphical and Numerical Solutions

57. (a) $-3, 1$; $y_1 = \dfrac{3}{x}$, $y_2 = x + 2$. See Figure 57a.

(b) See Figure 57b. $-3, 1$

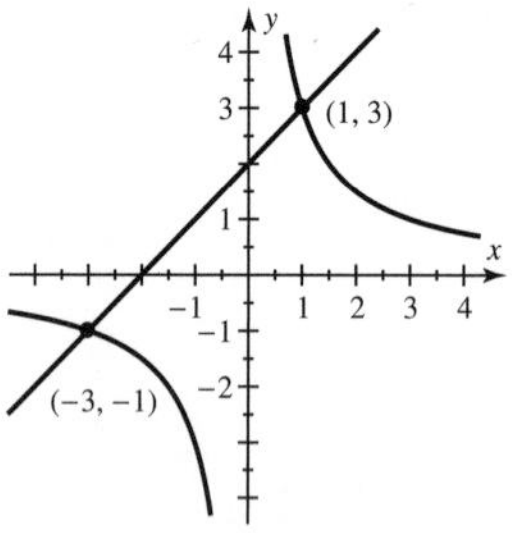

Figure 57a

x	-3	-1	1	3
$y = 3/x$	-1	-3	3	1
$y = x + 2$	-1	1	3	5

Figure 57b

59. (a) -1; $y_1 = \dfrac{3x}{2}$, $y_2 = \dfrac{1}{2}x - 1$. See Figure 59a.

(b) See Figure 59b. -1

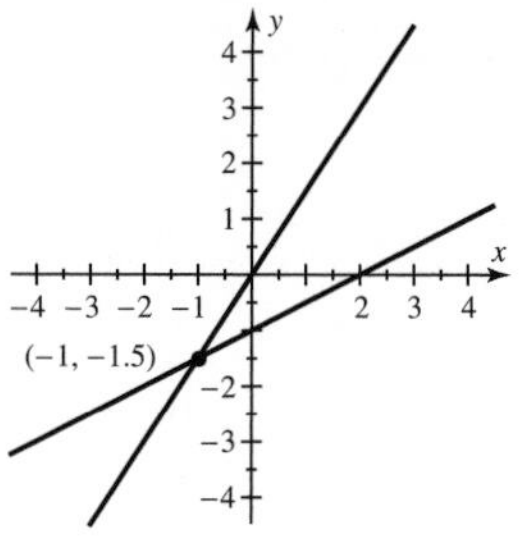

Figure 59a

x	−2	−1	1	2
$y = 3x/2$	−3	−1.5	1.5	3
$y = x/2 - 1$	−2	−1.5	−0.5	0

Figure 59b

61. (a) 2; $y_1 = \dfrac{3}{x - 1}$, $y_2 = 3$. See Figure 61a.

 (b) See Figure 61b. 2

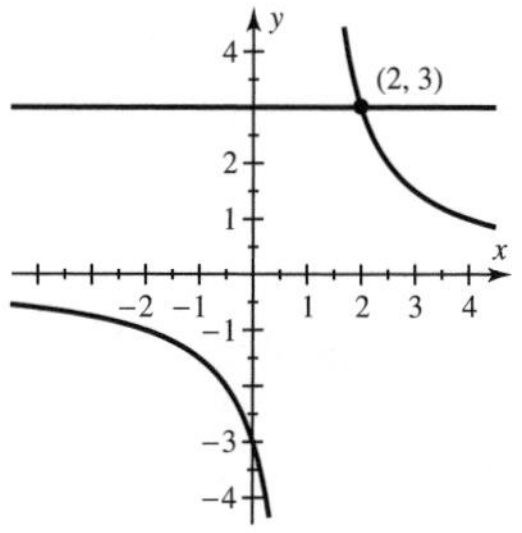

Figure 61a

x	−2	0	2	4
$y = 3/(x - 1)$	−1	−3	3	1
$y = 3$	3	3	3	3

Figure 61b

63. (a) −2, 2; $y_1 = \dfrac{4}{x^2}$, $y_2 = 1$. See Figure 63a.

 (b) See Figure 63b. −2, 2

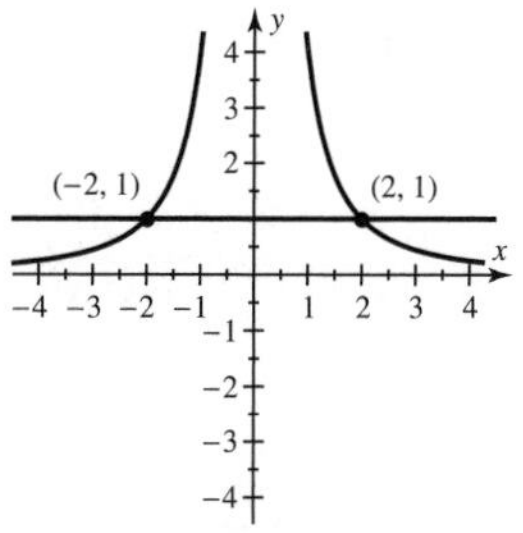

Figure 63a

x	−2	−1	1	2
$y = 4/x^2$	1	4	4	1
$y = 1$	1	1	1	1

Figure 63b

Solving an Equation for a Variable

65. $m = \dfrac{F}{a}$ for $a \Rightarrow a \cdot m = \dfrac{F}{a} \cdot a \Rightarrow am = F \Rightarrow \dfrac{am}{m} = \dfrac{F}{m} \Rightarrow a = \dfrac{F}{m}$

67. $I = \dfrac{V}{R + r}$ for $r \Rightarrow I(R + r) = \dfrac{V}{R + r} \cdot R + r \Rightarrow I(R + r) = V \Rightarrow \dfrac{I(R + r)}{I} = \dfrac{V}{I} \Rightarrow R + r = \dfrac{V}{I} \Rightarrow$

 $r = \dfrac{V}{I} - R$

69. $h = \dfrac{2A}{b}$ for $b \Rightarrow b \cdot h = \dfrac{2A}{b} \cdot b \Rightarrow bh = 2A \Rightarrow \dfrac{bh}{h} = \dfrac{2A}{h} \Rightarrow b = \dfrac{2A}{h}$

71. $\frac{3}{k} = \frac{z}{z+5}$ for $z \Rightarrow 3(z+5) = kz \Rightarrow 3z + 15 = kz \Rightarrow 15 = kz - 3z \Rightarrow 15 = z(k-3) \Rightarrow z = \frac{15}{k-3}$

73. $T = \frac{ab}{a+b}$ for $b \Rightarrow T(a+b) = ab \cdot 1 \Rightarrow aT + bT = ab \Rightarrow aT = ab - bT \Rightarrow aT = b(a-T) \Rightarrow$

$b = \frac{aT}{a-T}$

75. $\frac{3}{k} = \frac{1}{x} - \frac{2}{y}$ for $x \Rightarrow \frac{3}{k} \cdot \frac{xy}{xy} = \frac{1}{x} \cdot \frac{ky}{ky} - \frac{2}{y} \cdot \frac{xk}{xk} \Rightarrow \frac{3xy}{kxy} = \frac{ky}{kxy} - \frac{2xk}{kxy} \Rightarrow 3xy = ky - 2xk \Rightarrow$

$3xy + 2xk = ky \Rightarrow x(3y + 2k) = ky \Rightarrow x = \frac{ky}{3y+2k}$

Applications

77. $\frac{1}{10-x} = 1 \Rightarrow 10 - x \cdot \frac{1}{10-x} = 1(10-x) \Rightarrow 1 = 10 - x \Rightarrow x = 9$ cars/minute.

79. $\frac{t}{4} + \frac{t}{3} = 1 \Rightarrow \frac{t(12)}{4} + \frac{t(12)}{3} = 12 \Rightarrow \frac{12t}{4} + \frac{12t}{3} = 12 \Rightarrow 3t + 4t = 12 \Rightarrow 7t = 12 \Rightarrow t = \frac{12}{7} \Rightarrow$

$t = 1.7$ hr

81. $\frac{d}{8} + \frac{d}{4} = 1 \Rightarrow \frac{(8)d}{8} + \frac{(8)d}{4} = 8 \Rightarrow \frac{8d}{8} + \frac{8d}{4} = 8 \Rightarrow d + 2d = 8 \Rightarrow 3d = 8 \Rightarrow d = \frac{8}{3} \Rightarrow d \approx 2.7$ days

83. Let x represent the speed of the teammate. Then $x + 2$ represents the speed of the winner. The finishing time for the teammate is $\frac{6}{x}$ and the finishing time for the winner is $\frac{6}{x+2}$. Since the winner's time is 2 minutes, or $\frac{1}{30}$ hour, faster than the teammate's time, the needed equation is $\frac{6}{x} - \frac{6}{x+2} = \frac{1}{30}$. Multiply each term by the LCD, $30x(x+2)$. $\frac{6}{x} - \frac{6}{x+2} = \frac{1}{30} \Rightarrow 30x(x+2) \cdot \frac{6}{x} - 30x(x+2) \cdot \frac{6}{x+2} = 30x(x+2) \cdot \frac{1}{30} \Rightarrow$

$180x + 360 - 180x = x^2 + 2x \Rightarrow x^2 + 2x - 360 = 0 \Rightarrow (x+20)(x-18) = 0 \Rightarrow x = -20$ or 18

Since x must be positive, the teammate's speed is 18 mph and the winner's speed is $18 + 2 = 20$ mph.

85. (a) $m = -0.05, B = \frac{30}{0.3 + (-0.05)} \Rightarrow B = \frac{30}{0.25} \Rightarrow B = 120$, the breaking distance is 120 feet when the slope of the road is -0.05.

(b) $B = 150, 150 = \frac{30}{0.3 + m} \Rightarrow 0.3 + m(150) = 30 \Rightarrow 0.3 + m = \frac{30}{150} \Rightarrow 0.3 + m = .2 \Rightarrow m = -0.1$

87. $\frac{36}{x-3} = \frac{54}{x+3} \Rightarrow 36x + 108 = 54x - 162 \Rightarrow 270 = 18x \Rightarrow 15 = x \Rightarrow x = 15$ mph

89. $\frac{450}{x-50} = \frac{750}{x+50} \Rightarrow 450x + 22{,}500 = 750x - 37{,}500 \Rightarrow 60{,}000 = 300x \Rightarrow 200 = x \Rightarrow x = 200$ mph

91. Let $x =$ walking in mph and $x + 5 =$ running in mph, then $x \cdot (t+1) = 10$ and $(x+5)t = 10$, so

$t + 1 = \frac{10}{x} \Rightarrow t = \frac{10}{x} - 1$ and $t = \frac{10}{x+5}$.

Now, $\frac{10}{x} - 1 = \frac{10}{x+5} \Rightarrow \frac{10}{x} \cdot \frac{x+5}{x+5} - \frac{1}{1} \cdot \frac{x(x+5)}{x(x+5)} = \frac{10}{x+5} \cdot \frac{x}{x} \Rightarrow 10(x+5) - x(x+5) = 10x \Rightarrow$

$10x + 50 - x^2 - 5x = 10x \Rightarrow x^2 + 5x - 50 = 0 \Rightarrow (x+10)(x-5) = 0$, so $x = -10, 5$ but -10 cannot be the rate so $x = 5$. So 10 mph running and 5 mph walking.

93. $\frac{2+n}{8-n} = 1 \Rightarrow 2 + n = 8 - n \Rightarrow 2n = 6 \Rightarrow n = 3$

95. $\frac{4+6n}{4-4n} = -\frac{49}{31} \Rightarrow 124 + 186n = -196 + 196n \Rightarrow 320 = 10n \Rightarrow 32 = n \Rightarrow n = 32$

Checking Basic Concepts for Sections 7.5 & 7.6

1. (a) $\frac{\frac{x}{3}}{\frac{2x}{5}} = \frac{x}{3} \div \frac{2x}{5} = \frac{x}{3} \cdot \frac{5}{2x} = \frac{5x}{6x} = \frac{5}{6} \cdot \frac{x}{x} = \frac{5}{6} \cdot 1 = \frac{5}{6}$

(b) $\frac{\frac{2}{2x} - \frac{1}{3x}}{6x} = \frac{\frac{6}{6x} - \frac{2}{6x}}{6x} = \frac{\frac{4}{6x}}{6x} = \frac{4}{6x} \div \frac{6x}{1} = \frac{4}{6x} \cdot \frac{1}{6x} = \frac{4}{36x^2} = \frac{1}{9x^2}$

(c) $\frac{\frac{1}{a} - \frac{1}{b}}{\frac{1}{a} + \frac{1}{b}} = \frac{\frac{b}{ab} - \frac{a}{ab}}{\frac{b}{ab} + \frac{a}{ab}} = \frac{\frac{b-a}{ab}}{\frac{b+a}{ab}} = \frac{b-a}{ab} \div \frac{b+a}{ab} = \frac{b-a}{ab} \cdot \frac{ab}{b+a} = \frac{ab}{ab} \cdot \frac{b-a}{b+a} = 1 \cdot \frac{b-a}{b+a} = \frac{b-a}{b+a}$

(d) $\frac{\frac{1}{r^2} - \frac{1}{t^2}}{\frac{2}{r} - \frac{2}{t}} = \frac{\frac{t^2}{r^2t^2} - \frac{r^2}{r^2t^2}}{\frac{2t}{rt} - \frac{2r}{rt}} = \frac{\frac{t^2-r^2}{r^2t^2}}{\frac{2t-2r}{rt}} = \frac{t^2-r^2}{r^2t^2} \div \frac{2t-2r}{rt} = \frac{t^2-r^2}{r^2t^2} \cdot \frac{rt}{2t-2r} = \frac{rt}{r^2t^2} \cdot \frac{t^2-r^2}{2t-2r} =$

$\frac{1}{2rt} \cdot \frac{(t+r)(t-r)}{t-r} = \frac{t+r}{2rt} = \frac{r+t}{2rt}$

2. (a) $\frac{1}{2x} = \frac{3}{x+1} \Rightarrow 6x = x + 1 \Rightarrow 5x = 1 \Rightarrow x = \frac{1}{5}$

Check: $\frac{1}{2(\frac{1}{5})} = \frac{3}{(\frac{1}{5}) + 1} \Rightarrow \frac{1}{\frac{2}{5}} = \frac{3}{\frac{6}{5}} \Rightarrow \frac{1}{1} \cdot \frac{5}{2} = \frac{3}{1} \cdot \frac{5}{6} \Rightarrow \frac{5}{2} = \frac{15}{6} \Rightarrow \frac{5}{2} = \frac{5}{2}$

(b) $\frac{x}{2x+3} = \frac{4}{5} \Rightarrow 5x = 8x + 12 \Rightarrow -3x = 12 \Rightarrow x = \frac{12}{-3} \Rightarrow x = -4$

Check: $\frac{-4}{2(-4)+3} = \frac{4}{5} \Rightarrow \frac{-4}{-5} = \frac{4}{5} \Rightarrow \frac{4}{5} = \frac{4}{5}$

3. (a) $\frac{1}{2x} + \frac{3}{2x} = 1 \Rightarrow \frac{4}{2x} = 1 \Rightarrow 2x = 4 \Rightarrow x = \frac{4}{2} \Rightarrow x = 2$

Check: $\frac{1}{2(2)} + \frac{3}{2(2)} = 1 \Rightarrow \frac{1}{4} + \frac{3}{4} = 1 \Rightarrow \frac{4}{4} = 1 \Rightarrow 1 = 1$

(b) $\frac{3}{x+1} - \frac{2}{x} = -2 \Rightarrow \frac{3}{x+1} \cdot \frac{x}{x} - \frac{2}{x} \cdot \frac{x+1}{x+1} = \frac{-2}{1} \cdot \frac{x(x+1)}{x(x+1)} \Rightarrow 3x - 2x - 2 = -2x^2 - 2x \Rightarrow$

$x - 2 = -2x^2 - 2x \Rightarrow 2x^2 + 3x - 2 = 0 \Rightarrow (2x-1)(x+2) = 0$, so $x = \frac{1}{2}, -2$

Check: $\frac{3}{\frac{1}{2}+1} - \frac{2}{\frac{1}{2}} = -2 \Rightarrow \frac{3}{1\frac{1}{2}} - \frac{2}{\frac{1}{2}} = -2 \Rightarrow \frac{6}{3} - \frac{12}{3} = -2 \Rightarrow \frac{-6}{3} = -2 \Rightarrow -2 = -2$

Check: $\frac{3}{-2+1} - \frac{2}{-2} = -2 \Rightarrow \frac{3}{-1} - \frac{2}{-2} = -2 \Rightarrow -3 - (-1) = -2 \Rightarrow -2 = -2$

4. (a) $\frac{ax}{2} - 3y = b$ for $x \Rightarrow \frac{ax}{2} = b + 3y \Rightarrow ax = 2(b+3y) \Rightarrow x = \frac{2(b+3y)}{a}$

(b) $\frac{1}{2m-1} = \frac{k}{m}$ for $m \Rightarrow m \cdot 1 = k(2m-1) \Rightarrow m = 2km - k \Rightarrow m - 2km = -k \Rightarrow$

$m(1-2k) = -k \Rightarrow m = \frac{-k}{1-2k} \Rightarrow m = \frac{-k}{-(2k-1)} \Rightarrow m = \frac{k}{2k-1}$

5. (a) $m = 0.1, D = \dfrac{120}{0.3 + 0.1} \Rightarrow D = \dfrac{120}{0.4} \Rightarrow D = 300$; when the slope of the hill is 0.1, the braking distance is 300 ft.

(b) $D = 200,\ 200 = \dfrac{120}{0.3 + m} \Rightarrow 200(0.3 + m) = 120 \Rightarrow 0.3 + m = \dfrac{120}{200} \Rightarrow 0.3 + m = 0.6 \Rightarrow$ $m = 0.3$; the braking distance is 200 ft. when the slope of the road is 0.3.

7.7: Proportions and Variation

Concepts

1. A statement that two ratios are equal.

3. It doubles

5. constant

7. kxy

9. Directly; doubling the number being fed doubles the bill.

Proportions

11. $\dfrac{x}{14} = \dfrac{5}{7} \Rightarrow 70 = 7x \Rightarrow \dfrac{70}{7} = x \Rightarrow x = 10$

13. $\dfrac{8}{x} = \dfrac{2}{3} \Rightarrow 24 = 2x \Rightarrow \dfrac{24}{2} = x \Rightarrow x = 12$

15. $\dfrac{6}{13} = \dfrac{h}{156} \Rightarrow 936 = 13h \Rightarrow \dfrac{936}{13} = h \Rightarrow h = 72$

17. $\dfrac{3}{2} = \dfrac{2x}{9} \Rightarrow 27 = 4x \Rightarrow \dfrac{27}{4} = x \Rightarrow x = \dfrac{27}{4}$

19. (a) $\dfrac{7}{9} = \dfrac{10}{x}$

(b) $\dfrac{7}{9} = \dfrac{10}{x} \Rightarrow 90 = 7x \Rightarrow \dfrac{90}{7} = x \Rightarrow x = \dfrac{90}{7}$

21. (a) $\dfrac{3}{5} = \dfrac{6}{x}$

(b) $\dfrac{3}{5} = \dfrac{6}{x} \Rightarrow 3x = 30 \Rightarrow x = \dfrac{30}{3} \Rightarrow x = 10$

23. (a) $\dfrac{78}{6} = \dfrac{x}{8}$

(b) $\dfrac{78}{6} = \dfrac{x}{8} \Rightarrow 624 = 6x \Rightarrow \dfrac{624}{6} = x \Rightarrow x = \$104$

25. (a) $\dfrac{2}{90} = \dfrac{5}{x}$

(b) $\dfrac{2}{90} = \dfrac{5}{x} \Rightarrow 2x = 450 \Rightarrow x = \dfrac{450}{2} \Rightarrow x = 225$ min.

Variation

27. (a) $k = \frac{y}{x}, y = 6, x = 3 \Rightarrow k = \frac{6}{3} = 2$

(b) $y = kx, k = 2, x = 7 \Rightarrow y = (2)(7) = 14$

29. (a) $k = \frac{y}{x}, y = 5, x = 2 \Rightarrow k = \frac{5}{2}$

(b) $y = kx, k = \frac{5}{2}, x = 7 \Rightarrow y = \left(\frac{5}{2}\right)(7) = \frac{35}{2}$

31. (a) $k = \frac{y}{x}, y = -120, x = 16 \Rightarrow k = \frac{-120}{16} = \frac{-15}{2}$

(b) $y = kx, k = -\frac{15}{2}, x = 7 \Rightarrow y = \left(-\frac{15}{2}\right)(7) = -\frac{105}{2}$

33. (a) $k = yx, y = 5, x = 4 \Rightarrow k = 5 \cdot 4 = 20$

(b) $y = \frac{k}{x}, k = 20, x = 10 \Rightarrow y = \frac{20}{10} = 2$

35. (a) $k = yx, y = 100, x = \frac{1}{2} \Rightarrow k = 100 \cdot \frac{1}{2} = \frac{100}{2} = 50$

(b) $y = \frac{k}{x}, k = 50, x = 10 \Rightarrow y = \frac{50}{10} = 5$

37. (a) $k = yx, y = 20, x = 20 \Rightarrow k = 20 \cdot 20 = 400$

(b) $y = \frac{k}{x}, k = 400, x = 10 \Rightarrow y = \frac{400}{10} = 40$

39. (a) $k = \frac{z}{xy}, z = 6, x = 3, y = 8 \Rightarrow k = \frac{6}{3 \cdot 8} = \frac{6}{24} = \frac{1}{4}$

(b) $z = kxy, k = \frac{1}{4}, x = 5, y = 7 \Rightarrow z = \frac{1}{4} \cdot 5 \cdot 7 = \frac{35}{4}$

41. (a) $k = \frac{z}{xy}, z = 5775, x = 25, y = 21 \Rightarrow k = \frac{5775}{25 \cdot 21} = \frac{5775}{525} = 11$

(b) $z = kxy, k = 11, x = 5, y = 7 \Rightarrow z = 11 \cdot 5 \cdot 7 = 385$

43. (a) $k = \frac{z}{xy}, z = 25, x = \frac{1}{2}, y = 5 \Rightarrow k = \frac{25}{\frac{1}{2} \cdot 5} = \frac{25}{\frac{5}{2}} = \frac{25}{1} \cdot \frac{2}{5} = \frac{50}{5} = 10$

(b) $z = kxy, k = 10, x = 5, y = 7 \Rightarrow z = 10 \cdot 5 \cdot 7 = 350$

45. (a) Direct, because as x increases, y increases and $k = \frac{y}{x} \Rightarrow k = \frac{3}{2} = \frac{4.5}{3} = \frac{6}{4}$, etc.

(b) $k = \frac{y}{x} \Rightarrow k = \frac{3}{2} \Rightarrow y = kx \Rightarrow y = \frac{3}{2}x$

(c) See Figure 45.

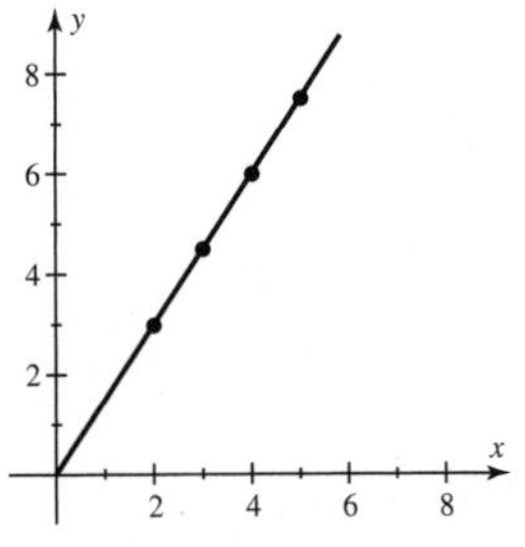

Figure 45

47. (a) Neither, because as x increases, y decreases, but $k = xy \Rightarrow 10(12) \neq 30(5)$

(b) NA

(c) NA

49. (a) Neither, because as x increases, y increases, but $k = \frac{y}{x} \Rightarrow \frac{10}{4} \neq \frac{40}{20}$

(b) NA

(c) NA

51. Direct, $k = \frac{y}{x} \Rightarrow k = \frac{3}{3} \Rightarrow k = 1$

53. Neither

55. Direct, $k = \frac{y}{x} \Rightarrow k = \frac{6}{3} \Rightarrow k = 2$

Applications

57. $\frac{68}{600} \Rightarrow 600x = 24{,}480 \Rightarrow x = \frac{24{,}480}{600} \Rightarrow x = 40.8$ minutes

59. $\frac{8}{1} \Rightarrow 8x = 11 \Rightarrow x = \frac{11}{8} \Rightarrow x = 1.375$ inches

61. (a) Direct, the ratios $\frac{R}{W}$ always equal 0.012

(b) $\frac{R}{W} = 0.012 \Rightarrow R = 0.012W$. See Figure 61.

(c) $W = 3200, R = 0.012(3200) \Rightarrow R = 38.4$ pounds.

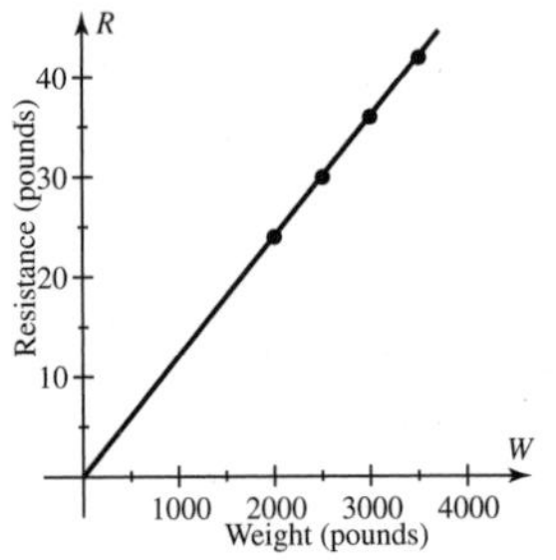

Figure 61

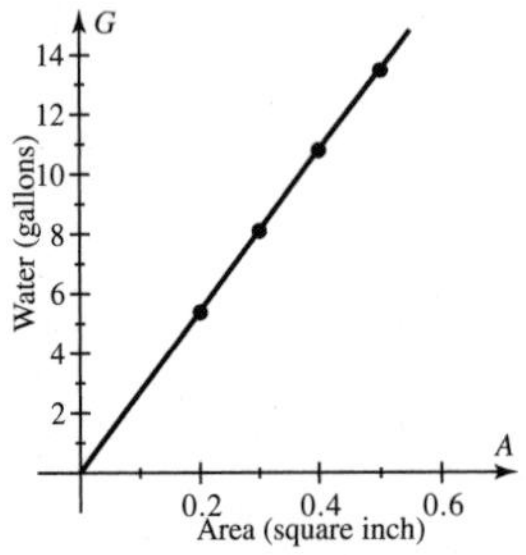

Figure 63

63. (a) Direct, the ratios $\frac{G}{A}$ always equal 27.

(b) $\frac{G}{A} = 27 \Rightarrow G = 27A$. See Figure 63.

(c) For each square inch in the cross-sectional area of the hose, the flow increases by 27 gal/min.

65. (a) $k = FL \Rightarrow k = 120 \cdot 10 \Rightarrow k = 1200 \Rightarrow F = \frac{k}{L} \Rightarrow F = \frac{1200}{L}$

(b) $L = 20 \Rightarrow F = \frac{1200}{20} \Rightarrow F = 60$ pounds

67. (a) Direct

(b) $k = \frac{y}{x} \Rightarrow k - \frac{-145}{5} \Rightarrow k = -29 \Rightarrow y = kx \Rightarrow y = -29x$

(c) Negative, for each 1-mile increase in altitude the temperature decreases by 29°F.

(d) $y = kx, k = -29, x = 3.5, y = -29 \cdot 3.5 \Rightarrow y = -101.5 \Rightarrow$ 101.5°F decrease

69. $\frac{35}{2} = \frac{25}{x} \Rightarrow 35x = 50 \Rightarrow x = \frac{50}{35} \Rightarrow x =$ about 1.43 ohms

71. $k = \frac{z}{x^2y^3}, z = 31.9, x = 2, y = 2.5 \Rightarrow k = \frac{31.9}{2^2 \cdot 2.5^3} \Rightarrow k = \frac{31.9}{4 \cdot 15.625} \Rightarrow k = \frac{31.9}{62.5} \Rightarrow k = 0.5104;$

$z = kx^2y^3, k = 0.5104 \Rightarrow z = 0.5104x^2y^3$

73. $k = \frac{s}{wt^2}, s = 300, w = 5, t = 3 \Rightarrow k = \frac{300}{5 \cdot 9} \Rightarrow k = \frac{300}{45} \Rightarrow k = 6.66;$

$s = kwt^2, k = 6.66, w = 5, t = 2 \Rightarrow s = 6.66 \cdot 5 \cdot 4 \Rightarrow$ about 133 pounds

Checking Basic Concepts for Section 7.7

1. (a) $\frac{x}{7} = \frac{2}{13} \Rightarrow 13x = 14 \Rightarrow x = \frac{14}{13}$

(b) $\frac{2}{3} \cdot \frac{5}{b} \Rightarrow 2b = 15 \Rightarrow b = \frac{15}{2}$

2. (a) $\frac{8}{12} = \frac{6}{x} \Rightarrow 8x = 72 \Rightarrow x = \frac{72}{8} \Rightarrow x = 9$

(b) $\frac{2}{148} = \frac{7}{x} \Rightarrow 2x = 1036 \Rightarrow x = \frac{1036}{2} \Rightarrow x = 518$ minutes

3. $k = xy, x = 10, y = 6 \Rightarrow k = 10 \cdot 6 \Rightarrow k = 60;\ y = \frac{k}{x}, k = 60, x = 15 \Rightarrow y = \frac{60}{15} \Rightarrow y = 4$

4. (a) Directly, the ratios $\frac{y}{x}$ always equal $\frac{3}{2}, \frac{3}{2}; \frac{x}{y} = \frac{3}{2}, \frac{6}{4} = \frac{3}{2}, \frac{9}{6} = \frac{3}{2}, \frac{12}{8} = \frac{3}{2}$

(b) Inverse, the products xy always equal 24, 24; $xy = 24, 2 \cdot 12 = 24, 4 \cdot 6 = 24, 6 \cdot 4 = 24, 8 \cdot 3 = 24$

5. $\frac{221}{17} = \frac{x}{8} \Rightarrow 1768 = 17x \Rightarrow \frac{1768}{17} = x \Rightarrow x = 104 \Rightarrow x = \$104$

Chapter 7 Review Exercises

Section 7.1

1. $x = -2, \frac{3}{x-3} = \frac{3}{-2-3} = \frac{3}{-5} = -\frac{3}{5}$

2. $x = 3, \frac{4x}{5-x^2} = \frac{4(3)}{5-(3)^2} = \frac{12}{5-9} = \frac{12}{-4} = -3$

3. $x = 7, \frac{-x}{7-x} = \frac{-(7)}{7-(7)} = \frac{-7}{0} =$ undefined

4. $x = 2, \dfrac{4x}{x^2 - 3x + 2} = \dfrac{4(2)}{(2)^2 - 3(2) + 2} = \dfrac{8}{4 - 6 + 2} = \dfrac{8}{0} =$ undefined

5. $x = -2, \dfrac{3x}{x - 1} = \dfrac{3(-2)}{-2 - 1} = \dfrac{-6}{-3} = 2;\ x = -1, \dfrac{3x}{x - 1} = \dfrac{3(-1)}{-1 - 1} = \dfrac{-3}{-2} = \dfrac{3}{2};$

$x = 0, \dfrac{3x}{x - 1} = \dfrac{3(0)}{0 - 1} = \dfrac{0}{-1} = 0;\ x = 1, \dfrac{3x}{x - 1} = \dfrac{3(1)}{1 - 1} = \dfrac{3}{0} =$ undefined;

$x = 2, \dfrac{3x}{x - 1} = \dfrac{3(2)}{2 - 1} = \dfrac{6}{1} = 6$. See Figure 5.

x	-2	-1	0	1	2
$\frac{3x}{x-1}$	2	$\frac{3}{2}$	0	—	6

Figure 5

6. $\dfrac{8}{x^2 - 4} \Rightarrow x^2 - 4 \neq 0 \Rightarrow (x - 2)(x + 2) \neq 0 \Rightarrow x - 2 = 0 \Rightarrow x \neq 2$ or $x + 2 = 0 \Rightarrow x \neq 0$

Therefore $x = 2, -2$ make the expression undefined.

7. $\dfrac{25x^3y^4}{15x^5y} = \dfrac{5}{3}x^{3-5}y^{4-1} = \dfrac{5}{3}x^{-2}y^3 = \dfrac{5y^3}{3x^2}$

8. $\dfrac{x^2 - 36}{x + 6} = \dfrac{(x + 6)(x - 6)}{x + 6} = \dfrac{x + 6}{x + 6} \cdot \dfrac{x - 6}{1} = 1 \cdot x - 6 = x - 6$

9. $\dfrac{x - 9}{9 - x} = \dfrac{x - 9}{-1(-9 + x)} = \dfrac{x - 9}{-1(x - 9)} = -1$

10. $\dfrac{x^2 - 5x}{5x} = \dfrac{x(x - 5)}{x(5)} = \dfrac{x}{x} \cdot \dfrac{x - 5}{5} = 1 \cdot \dfrac{x - 5}{5} = \dfrac{x - 5}{5}$

11. $\dfrac{2x^2 + 5x - 3}{2x + x - 1} = \dfrac{(x + 3)(2x - 1)}{(x + 1)(2x - 1)} = \dfrac{x + 3}{x + 1} \cdot \dfrac{2x - 1}{2x - 1} = \dfrac{x + 3}{x + 1} \cdot 1 = \dfrac{x + 3}{x + 1}$

12. $\dfrac{3x^2 + 10x - 8}{3x + x - 2} = \dfrac{(x + 4)(3x - 2)}{(x + 1)(3x - 2)} = \dfrac{x + 4}{x + 1} \cdot \dfrac{3x - 2}{3x - 2} = \dfrac{x + 4}{x + 1} \cdot 1 = \dfrac{x + 4}{x + 1}$

Section 7.2

13. $\dfrac{x - 3}{x + 1} \cdot \dfrac{2x + 2}{x - 3} = \dfrac{x - 3}{x + 1} \cdot \dfrac{2(x + 1)}{x - 3} = \dfrac{x - 3}{x - 3} \cdot \dfrac{x + 1}{x + 1} \cdot 2 = 1 \cdot 1 \cdot 2 = 2$

14. $\dfrac{2x + 5}{(x + 5)(x - 1)} \cdot \dfrac{x - 1}{2x + 5} = \dfrac{2x + 5}{2x + 5} \cdot \dfrac{x - 1}{x - 1} \cdot \dfrac{1}{x + 5} = 1 \cdot 1 \cdot \dfrac{1}{x + 5} = \dfrac{1}{x + 5}$

15. $\dfrac{(z + 3)^2}{(z + 3)(z - 4)} = \dfrac{z + 3}{z + 3} \cdot \dfrac{z + 3}{z - 4} = 1 \cdot \dfrac{z + 3}{z - 4} = \dfrac{z + 3}{z - 4}$

16. $\dfrac{x^2}{x^2 - 4} \cdot \dfrac{x + 2}{x} = \dfrac{x(x)}{(x - 2)(x + 2)} \cdot \dfrac{x + 2}{x} = \dfrac{x}{x} \cdot \dfrac{x + 2}{x + 2} \cdot \dfrac{x}{x - 2} = 1 \cdot 1 \cdot \dfrac{x}{x - 2} = \dfrac{x}{x - 2}$

17. $\dfrac{x + 1}{2x} \div \dfrac{3x + 3}{5x} = \dfrac{x + 1}{2x} \cdot \dfrac{5x}{3(x + 1)} = \dfrac{5}{6} \cdot \dfrac{x + 1}{x + 1} \cdot \dfrac{x}{x} = \dfrac{5}{6} \cdot 1 \cdot 1 = \dfrac{5}{6}$

18. $\dfrac{4}{x^3} \div \dfrac{x + 1}{2x^2} = \dfrac{4}{x^3} \cdot \dfrac{2x^2}{x + 1} = \dfrac{8}{x} \cdot \dfrac{x^2}{x^2} \cdot \dfrac{1}{x + 1} = \dfrac{8}{x} \cdot 1 \cdot \dfrac{1}{x + 1} = \dfrac{8}{x(x + 1)}$

19. $\dfrac{x-5}{x+2} \div \dfrac{2x-10}{x+2} = \dfrac{x-5}{x+2} \cdot \dfrac{x+2}{2(x-5)} = \dfrac{1}{2} \cdot \dfrac{x-5}{x-5} \cdot \dfrac{x+2}{x+2} = \dfrac{1}{2} \cdot 1 \cdot 1 = \dfrac{1}{2}$

20. $\dfrac{x^2-6x+5}{x^2-25} \div \dfrac{x-1}{x+5} = \dfrac{(x-1)(x-5)}{(x-5)(x+5)} \cdot \dfrac{x+5}{x-1} = \dfrac{x-1}{x-1} \cdot \dfrac{x+5}{x+5} \cdot \dfrac{x-5}{x-5} = 1 \cdot 1 \cdot 1 = 1$

21. $\dfrac{x^2-y^2}{x+y} \div \dfrac{x-y}{x+y} = \dfrac{(x-y)(x+y)}{x+y} \cdot \dfrac{x+y}{x-y} = \dfrac{x-y}{x-y} \cdot \dfrac{x+y}{x+y} \cdot x+y = 1 \cdot 1 \cdot x+y = x+y$

22. $\dfrac{a^3-b^3}{a+b} \div \dfrac{a-b}{2a+2b} = \dfrac{(a-b)(a^2+ab+b^2)}{a+b} \cdot \dfrac{2(a+b)}{a-b} = \dfrac{a-b}{a-b} \cdot \dfrac{a+b}{a+b} \cdot \dfrac{2(a^2+ab+b^2)}{1} =$
$1 \cdot 1 \cdot 2(a^2+ab+b^2) = 2(a^2+ab+b^2)$

Section 7.3

23. $\dfrac{2}{x+10} + \dfrac{8}{x+10} = \dfrac{2+8}{x+10} = \dfrac{10}{x+10}$

24. $\dfrac{9}{x-1} - \dfrac{8}{x-1} = \dfrac{9-8}{x-1} = \dfrac{1}{x-1}$

25. $\dfrac{x+2y}{2x} + \dfrac{x-2y}{2x} = \dfrac{(x+2y)+(x-2y)}{2x} = \dfrac{2x}{2x} = 1$

26. $\dfrac{x}{x+3} + \dfrac{3}{x+3} = \dfrac{x+3}{x+3} = 1$

27. $\dfrac{x}{x^2-1} - \dfrac{1}{x^2-1} = \dfrac{x-1}{x^2-1} = \dfrac{x-1}{(x-1)(x+1)} = \dfrac{x-1}{x-1} \cdot \dfrac{1}{x+1} = 1 \cdot \dfrac{1}{x+1} = \dfrac{1}{x+1}$

28. $\dfrac{2x}{x^2-25} + \dfrac{10}{x^2-25} = \dfrac{2x+10}{x^2-25} = \dfrac{2(x+5)}{(x-5)(x+5)} = \dfrac{2}{x-5} \cdot \dfrac{x+5}{x+5} = \dfrac{2}{x-5} \cdot 1 = \dfrac{2}{x-5}$

Section 7.4

29. $2x = 3 \cdot x$ and $5x = 5 \cdot x \Rightarrow 3 \cdot 5 \cdot x = 15x$

30. $5x^2 = 5 \cdot x^2$ and $10x = 2 \cdot 5 \cdot x \Rightarrow 2 \cdot 5 \cdot x^2 = 10x^2$

31. x and $x-5$ are both prime $\Rightarrow x(x-5)$

32. $10x^2 = 2 \cdot 5 \cdot x^2$ and $x^2 - x = x(x-1) \Rightarrow 2 \cdot 5 \cdot x^2 \cdot (x-1) = 10x^2(x-1)$

33. $x^2 - 1 = (x+1)(x-1)$ and $(x+1)^2$ is prime $\Rightarrow (x+1)^2(x-1)$

34. $x^2 - 4x = x(x-4)$ and $x^2 - 16 = (x+4)(x-4) \Rightarrow x(x-4)(x+4)$

35. $\dfrac{3}{8}, D = 24 \Rightarrow \dfrac{3}{8} \cdot \dfrac{3}{3} = \dfrac{9}{24}$

36. $\dfrac{4}{3x}, D = 12x \Rightarrow \dfrac{4}{3x} \cdot \dfrac{4}{4} = \dfrac{16}{12x}$

37. $\dfrac{3x}{x-2}, D = x^2 - 4 \Rightarrow \dfrac{3x}{x-2} \cdot \dfrac{x+2}{x+2} = \dfrac{3x^2+6}{x^2-4}$

38. $\dfrac{2}{x+1}, D = x^2 + x \Rightarrow \dfrac{2}{x+1} \cdot \dfrac{x}{x} = \dfrac{2x}{x^2+x}$

39. $\dfrac{3}{5x}, D = 5x^2 - 5x \Rightarrow \dfrac{3}{5x} \cdot \dfrac{x-1}{x-1} = \dfrac{3x-3}{5x^2-5x}$

40. $\dfrac{2x}{2x-3}, D = 2x^2 + x - 6 \Rightarrow \dfrac{2x}{2x-3} \cdot \dfrac{x+2}{x+2} = \dfrac{2x^2+4x}{2x^2+x-6}$

41. $\dfrac{5}{8} + \dfrac{1}{6} = \dfrac{5}{8} \cdot \dfrac{3}{3} + \dfrac{1}{6} \cdot \dfrac{4}{4} = \dfrac{15}{24} + \dfrac{4}{24} = \dfrac{19}{24}$

42. $\dfrac{3}{4x} + \dfrac{1}{x} = \dfrac{3}{4x} + \dfrac{1}{x} \cdot \dfrac{4}{4} = \dfrac{3}{4x} + \dfrac{4}{4x} = \dfrac{7}{4x}$

43. $\dfrac{5}{9x} - \dfrac{2}{3x} = \dfrac{5}{9x} - \dfrac{2}{3x} \cdot \dfrac{3}{3} = \dfrac{5}{9x} - \dfrac{6}{9x} = \dfrac{-1}{9x} = -\dfrac{1}{9x}$

44. $\dfrac{7}{x-1} - \dfrac{3}{x} = \dfrac{7}{x-1} \cdot \dfrac{x}{x} - \dfrac{3}{x} \cdot \dfrac{x-1}{x-1} = \dfrac{7x}{x(x-1)} - \dfrac{3x-3}{x(x-1)} = \dfrac{4x-3}{x(x-1)}$

45. $\dfrac{1}{x+1} + \dfrac{1}{x-1} = \dfrac{1}{x+1} \cdot \dfrac{x-1}{x-1} + \dfrac{1}{x-1} \cdot \dfrac{x+1}{x+1} = \dfrac{x-1}{(x+1)(x-1)} + \dfrac{x+1}{(x+1)(x-1)} = \dfrac{2x}{(x-1)(x+1)}$

46. $\dfrac{4}{3x^2} - \dfrac{3}{2x} = \dfrac{4}{3x^2} \cdot \dfrac{2}{2} - \dfrac{3}{2x} \cdot \dfrac{3x}{3x} = \dfrac{8}{6x^2} - \dfrac{9x}{6x^2} = \dfrac{8-9x}{6x^2}$

47. $\dfrac{1+x}{3x} - \dfrac{3}{2x} = \dfrac{1+x}{3x} \cdot \dfrac{2}{2} - \dfrac{3}{2x} \cdot \dfrac{3}{3} = \dfrac{2+2x}{6x} - \dfrac{9}{6x} = \dfrac{2x-7}{6x}$

48. $\dfrac{x}{x^2-1} - \dfrac{1}{x-1} = \dfrac{x}{(x+1)(x-1)} - \dfrac{1}{x-1} \cdot \dfrac{x+1}{x+1} = \dfrac{x}{(x+1)(x-1)} - \dfrac{x+1}{(x+1)(x-1)} = \dfrac{1}{(x-1)(x+1)}$

49. $\dfrac{2}{x-y} - \dfrac{3}{x+y} = \dfrac{2}{x-y} \cdot \dfrac{x+y}{x+y} - \dfrac{3}{x+y} \cdot \dfrac{x-y}{x-y} = \dfrac{2x+2y}{(x-y)(x+y)} - \dfrac{3x-3y}{(x-y)(x+y)} = \dfrac{5y-x}{(x-y)(x+y)}$

50. $\dfrac{2}{x} - \dfrac{1}{2x} + \dfrac{2}{3x} = \dfrac{2}{x} \cdot \dfrac{6}{6} - \dfrac{1}{2x} \cdot \dfrac{3}{3} + \dfrac{2}{3x} \cdot \dfrac{2}{2} = \dfrac{12}{6x} - \dfrac{3}{6x} + \dfrac{4}{6x} = \dfrac{12-3+4}{6x} = \dfrac{12+1}{6x} = \dfrac{13}{6x}$

Section 7.5

51. $\dfrac{\frac{3}{4}}{\frac{7}{11}} = \dfrac{3}{4} \div \dfrac{7}{11} = \dfrac{3}{4} \cdot \dfrac{11}{7} = \dfrac{33}{28}$

52. $\dfrac{\frac{x}{5}}{\frac{2x}{7}} = \dfrac{x}{5} \div \dfrac{2x}{7} = \dfrac{x}{5} \cdot \dfrac{7}{2x} = \dfrac{7x}{10x} = \dfrac{7}{10} \cdot \dfrac{x}{x} = \dfrac{7}{10} \cdot 1 = \dfrac{7}{10}$

53. $\dfrac{\frac{m}{n}}{\frac{2m}{n^2}} = \dfrac{m}{n} \div \dfrac{2m}{n^2} = \dfrac{m}{n} \cdot \dfrac{n^2}{2m} = \dfrac{m}{2m} \cdot \dfrac{n^2}{n} = \left(\dfrac{1}{2} \cdot \dfrac{m}{m}\right) \cdot \left(\dfrac{n}{n} \cdot n\right) = \left(\dfrac{1}{2} \cdot 1\right) \cdot 1 \cdot n = \dfrac{n}{2}$

54. $\dfrac{\frac{3}{p-1}}{\frac{1}{p+1}} = \dfrac{3}{p-1} \div \dfrac{1}{p+1} = \dfrac{3}{p-1} \cdot \dfrac{p+1}{1} = \dfrac{3(p+1)}{p-1}$

55. $\dfrac{\frac{3}{m-1}}{\frac{2m-2}{m+1}} = \dfrac{3}{m-1} \div \dfrac{2m-2}{m+1} = \dfrac{3}{m-1} \cdot \dfrac{m+1}{2m-2} = \dfrac{3}{m-1} \cdot \dfrac{m+1}{2(m-1)} = \dfrac{3(m+1)}{2(m-1)^2}$

56. $\dfrac{\frac{2}{2n+1}}{\frac{8}{2n-1}} = \dfrac{2}{2n+1} \div \dfrac{8}{2n-1} = \dfrac{2}{2n+1} \cdot \dfrac{2n-1}{8} = \dfrac{2}{8} \cdot \dfrac{2n-1}{2n+1} = \dfrac{2n-1}{4(2n+1)}$

57. $\dfrac{\frac{1}{2x} - \frac{1}{3x}}{\frac{2}{3x} - \frac{1}{6x}} = \dfrac{\frac{3}{6x} - \frac{2}{6x}}{\frac{4}{6x} - \frac{1}{6x}} = \dfrac{\frac{1}{6x}}{\frac{3}{6x}} = \dfrac{1}{6x} \div \dfrac{3}{6x} = \dfrac{1}{6x} \cdot \dfrac{6x}{3} = \dfrac{1}{3} \cdot \dfrac{6x}{6x} = \dfrac{1}{3} \cdot 1 = \dfrac{1}{3}$

58. $\dfrac{\frac{2}{xy} - \frac{1}{y}}{\frac{2}{xy} + \frac{1}{y}} = \dfrac{\frac{2}{xy} - \frac{1}{x}}{\frac{2}{xy} + \frac{1}{y}} \cdot \dfrac{xy}{xy} = \dfrac{\frac{2xy}{xy} - \frac{xy}{y}}{\frac{2xy}{xy} + \frac{xy}{y}} = \dfrac{2 \cdot \frac{xy}{xy} - x \cdot \frac{y}{y}}{2 \cdot \frac{xy}{xy} + x \cdot \frac{y}{y}} = \dfrac{2 \cdot 1 - x \cdot 1}{2 \cdot 1 + x \cdot 1} = \dfrac{2-x}{2+x}$

59. $\dfrac{\frac{1}{x}-\frac{1}{x+1}}{\frac{x}{x+1}}=\dfrac{\frac{x+1}{x(x+1)}-\frac{x}{x(x+1)}}{\frac{x}{x+1}}=\dfrac{\frac{1}{x(x+1)}}{\frac{x}{x+1}}=\dfrac{1}{x(x+1)}\div\dfrac{x}{x+1}=\dfrac{1}{x(x+1)}\cdot\dfrac{x+1}{x}=\dfrac{1}{x\cdot x}\cdot\dfrac{x+1}{x+1}=$

$\dfrac{1}{x^2}\cdot 1=\dfrac{1}{x^2}$

60. $\dfrac{\frac{2}{x-1}-\frac{1}{x+1}}{\frac{1}{x^2-1}}=\dfrac{\frac{2x+2}{(x-1)(x+1)}-\frac{x-1}{(x-1)(x+1)}}{\frac{1}{x^2-1}}=\dfrac{\frac{x+3}{x^2-1}}{\frac{1}{x^2-1}}=\dfrac{x+3}{x^2-1}\div\dfrac{1}{x^2-1}=\dfrac{x+3}{x^2-1}\cdot\dfrac{x^2-1}{1}=$

$\dfrac{x+3}{1}\cdot\dfrac{x^2-1}{x^2-1}=x+3\cdot 1=x+3$

Section 7.6

61. $\dfrac{x}{5}=\dfrac{4}{7}\Rightarrow 7x=20\Rightarrow x=\dfrac{20}{7}$ Check: $\dfrac{\frac{20}{7}}{5}=\dfrac{4}{7}\Rightarrow 7\left(\dfrac{20}{7}\right)=20\Rightarrow 20=20$

62. $\dfrac{4}{x}=\dfrac{3}{2}\Rightarrow 3x=8\Rightarrow x=\dfrac{8}{3}$ Check: $\dfrac{4}{\frac{8}{3}}=\dfrac{3}{2}\Rightarrow 8=3\left(\dfrac{8}{3}\right)\Rightarrow 8=8$

63. $\dfrac{3}{z+1}=\dfrac{1}{2z}\Rightarrow 6z=z+1\Rightarrow 5z=1\Rightarrow z=\dfrac{1}{5}$

Check: $\dfrac{3}{\frac{1}{5}+1}=\dfrac{1}{2(\frac{1}{5})}\Rightarrow\dfrac{3}{\frac{6}{5}}=\dfrac{1}{\frac{2}{5}}\Rightarrow\dfrac{3}{1}\cdot\dfrac{5}{6}=\dfrac{1}{1}\cdot\dfrac{5}{2}\Rightarrow\dfrac{15}{6}=\dfrac{5}{2}\Rightarrow\dfrac{5}{2}=\dfrac{5}{2}$

64. $\dfrac{x+2}{x}=\dfrac{3}{5}\Rightarrow 3x=5x+10\Rightarrow -2x=10\Rightarrow x=\dfrac{10}{-2}\Rightarrow x=-5$

Check: $\dfrac{-5+2}{-5}=\dfrac{3}{5}\Rightarrow\dfrac{-3}{-5}=\dfrac{3}{5}\Rightarrow\dfrac{3}{5}=\dfrac{3}{5}$

65. $\dfrac{1}{x+1}=\dfrac{2}{x-2}\Rightarrow x-2=2x+2\Rightarrow -x=4\Rightarrow x=-4$

Check: $\dfrac{1}{-4+1}=\dfrac{2}{-4-2}\Rightarrow\dfrac{1}{-3}=\dfrac{2}{-6}\Rightarrow -\dfrac{1}{3}=-\dfrac{1}{3}$

66. $\dfrac{x}{3}=\dfrac{-1}{x+4}\Rightarrow x^2+4x=-3\Rightarrow x^2+4x+3=0\Rightarrow (x+1)(x+3)=0\Rightarrow x+1=0\Rightarrow x=-1,$

$x+3=0\Rightarrow x=-3\Rightarrow x=-1,-3$

Check: $\dfrac{-1}{3}=\dfrac{-1}{-1+4}\Rightarrow -\dfrac{1}{3}=-\dfrac{1}{3},\ \dfrac{-3}{3}=\dfrac{-1}{-3+4}\Rightarrow -1=\dfrac{-1}{1}\Rightarrow -1=-1$

67. $\dfrac{1}{5x}+\dfrac{3}{5x}=\dfrac{1}{5}\Rightarrow\dfrac{4}{5x}=\dfrac{1}{5}\Rightarrow 5x=20\Rightarrow x=4$ Check: $\dfrac{1}{5(4)}+\dfrac{3}{5(4)}=\dfrac{1}{5}\Rightarrow\dfrac{4}{20}=\dfrac{1}{5}\Rightarrow\dfrac{1}{5}=\dfrac{1}{5}$

68. $\dfrac{1}{x-1}+\dfrac{2x}{x-1}=1\Rightarrow\dfrac{2x+1}{x-1}=1\Rightarrow\dfrac{2x+1(x-1)}{x-1}=\dfrac{x-1}{1}\Rightarrow 2x+1=x-1\Rightarrow x=-2$

Check: $\dfrac{1}{-2-1}+\dfrac{2(-2)}{-2-1}=1\Rightarrow\dfrac{-3}{-3}=1\Rightarrow 1=1$

69. $\dfrac{1}{x}+\dfrac{2}{3x}=\dfrac{1}{3}\Rightarrow\dfrac{1(3)}{3(x)}+\dfrac{2}{3x}=\dfrac{1(x)}{3(x)}\Rightarrow\dfrac{3}{3x}+\dfrac{2}{3x}=\dfrac{x}{3x}\Rightarrow\dfrac{5}{3x}=\dfrac{x}{3x}\Rightarrow 15x=3x^2\Rightarrow\dfrac{15}{3}=\dfrac{x^2}{x}\Rightarrow$

$5=x\Rightarrow x=5$ Check: $\dfrac{1}{5}+\dfrac{2}{3(5)}=\dfrac{1}{3}\Rightarrow\dfrac{1}{5}+\dfrac{2}{15}=\dfrac{1}{3}\Rightarrow\dfrac{3}{15}+\dfrac{2}{15}=\dfrac{5}{15}\Rightarrow\dfrac{5}{15}=\dfrac{5}{15}\Rightarrow\dfrac{1}{3}=\dfrac{1}{3}$

70. $\dfrac{1}{x+3}+\dfrac{2x}{x+3}=\dfrac{3}{2}\Rightarrow\dfrac{2x+1}{x+3}=\dfrac{3}{2}\Rightarrow\dfrac{2x+1(x+3)(2)}{x+3}=\dfrac{3(x+3)(2)}{2}\Rightarrow$

$\dfrac{(4x+2)(x+3)}{x+3}=\dfrac{(3x+9)(2)}{2}\Rightarrow 4x+2=3x+9\Rightarrow x=7$

Check: $\dfrac{1}{7+3}+\dfrac{2(7)}{7+3}=\dfrac{3}{3}\Rightarrow\dfrac{15}{10}=\dfrac{3}{2}\Rightarrow\dfrac{3}{2}=\dfrac{3}{2}$

71. $\dfrac{5}{x}-\dfrac{3}{x+1}=\dfrac{1}{2}\Rightarrow\dfrac{5(x)(x+1)(2)}{x}-\dfrac{3(x)(x+1)(2)}{x+1}=\dfrac{1(x)(x+1)(2)}{2}\Rightarrow$

$\dfrac{(10x+10)(x)}{x}-\dfrac{6x(x+1)}{x+1}=\dfrac{x^2+x(2)}{2}\Rightarrow 10x+10-6x=x^2+x\Rightarrow 4x+10=x^2+x\Rightarrow$

$x^2-3x-10=0\Rightarrow(x-5)(x+2)=0,\ x-5=0\Rightarrow x=5, x+2=0\Rightarrow x=-2\Rightarrow x=5,-2$

Check: $\dfrac{5}{-2}-\dfrac{3}{-2+1}=\dfrac{1}{2}\Rightarrow\dfrac{5}{-2}-\dfrac{3}{-1}=\dfrac{1}{2}\Rightarrow\dfrac{5}{-2}-\dfrac{6}{-2}=\dfrac{1}{2}\Rightarrow\dfrac{-1}{-2}=\dfrac{1}{2}\Rightarrow\dfrac{1}{2}=\dfrac{1}{2}$

Check: $\dfrac{5}{5}-\dfrac{3}{5+1}=\dfrac{1}{2}\Rightarrow\dfrac{5}{5}-\dfrac{3}{6}=\dfrac{1}{2}\Rightarrow 1-\dfrac{1}{2}=\dfrac{1}{2}\Rightarrow\dfrac{1}{2}=\dfrac{1}{2}$

72. $\dfrac{1}{x-1}-\dfrac{1}{x+1}=\dfrac{1}{4}\Rightarrow\dfrac{1(x-1)(x+1)(4)}{x-1}-\dfrac{1(x-1)(x+1)(4)}{x+1}=\dfrac{1(x-1)(x+1)(4)}{4}\Rightarrow$

$\dfrac{(4x+4)(x-1)}{x-1}-\dfrac{(4x-4)(x+1)}{x+1}=\dfrac{x^2-1(4)}{4}\Rightarrow 4x+4-(4x-4)=x^2-1\Rightarrow 8=x^2-1\Rightarrow$

$9=x^2\Rightarrow\pm3=x\Rightarrow x=-3, 3$

Check: $\dfrac{1}{-3-1}-\dfrac{1}{-3+1}=\dfrac{1}{4}\Rightarrow\dfrac{1}{-4}-\dfrac{1}{-2}=\dfrac{1}{4}\Rightarrow\dfrac{1}{-4}-\dfrac{2}{-4}=\dfrac{1}{4}\Rightarrow\dfrac{-1}{-4}=\dfrac{1}{4}\Rightarrow\dfrac{1}{4}=\dfrac{1}{4}$

Check: $\dfrac{1}{3-1}-\dfrac{1}{3+1}=\dfrac{1}{4}\Rightarrow\dfrac{1}{2}-\dfrac{1}{4}=\dfrac{1}{4}\Rightarrow\dfrac{2}{4}-\dfrac{1}{4}=\dfrac{1}{4}\Rightarrow\dfrac{1}{4}=\dfrac{1}{4}$

73. $\dfrac{4}{p}-\dfrac{5}{p+2}=0\Rightarrow\dfrac{4(p)(p+2)}{p}-\dfrac{5(p)(p+2)}{p+2}=0(p)(p+2)\Rightarrow\dfrac{(4p+8)(p)}{p}-\dfrac{5p(p+2)}{p+2}=0\Rightarrow$

$4p+8-5p=0\Rightarrow -p+8=0\Rightarrow -p=-8\Rightarrow p=8$

Check: $\dfrac{4}{8}-\dfrac{5}{8+2}=0\Rightarrow\dfrac{4}{8}-\dfrac{5}{10}=0\Rightarrow\dfrac{1}{2}-\dfrac{1}{2}=0\Rightarrow 0=0$

74. $\dfrac{1}{x-3}-\dfrac{1}{x+3}=\dfrac{1}{x^2-9}\Rightarrow\dfrac{1}{x-3}\cdot\dfrac{x+3}{x+3}-\dfrac{1}{x+3}\cdot\dfrac{x-3}{x-3}=\dfrac{1}{(x+3)(x-3)}\Rightarrow$

$\dfrac{x+3}{(x-3)(x+3)}-\dfrac{x-3}{(x-3)(x+3)}=\dfrac{1}{(x-3)(x+3)}\Rightarrow 6=1$, which is false, so no solution.

75. $\dfrac{2}{x^2-2x}+\dfrac{1}{x^2-4}=\dfrac{1}{x^2+2x}\Rightarrow\dfrac{2(x)(x-2)(x+2)}{x(x-2)}+\dfrac{1(x)(x-2)(x+2)}{(x-2)(x+2)}=\dfrac{1(x)(x-2)(x+2)}{x(x+2)}\Rightarrow$

$\dfrac{(2x+4)(x)(x-2)}{x(x-2)}+\dfrac{x(x^2-4)}{x^2-4}=\dfrac{(x-2)(x)(x+2)}{x(x+2)}\Rightarrow 2x+4+x=x-2\Rightarrow 3x+4=x-2\Rightarrow$

$2x=-6\Rightarrow x=-3$ Check: $\dfrac{2}{(-3)^2-2(-3)}+\dfrac{1}{(-3)^2-4}=\dfrac{1}{(-3)^2+2(-3)}\Rightarrow\dfrac{2}{15}+\dfrac{1}{5}=\dfrac{1}{3}\Rightarrow$

$\dfrac{2}{15}+\dfrac{3}{15}=\dfrac{5}{15}\Rightarrow\dfrac{5}{15}=\dfrac{5}{15}\Rightarrow\dfrac{1}{3}=\dfrac{1}{3}$

76. $\frac{3}{x^2-3x}-\frac{1}{x^2-9}=\frac{1}{x^2+3x}\Rightarrow\frac{3(x)(x-3)(x+3)}{x(x-3)}-\frac{1(x)(x-3)(x+3)}{(x-3)(x+3)}=\frac{1(x)(x-3)(x+3)}{x(x+3)}\Rightarrow$

$\frac{(3x+9)(x)(x-3)}{x(x-3)}-\frac{x(x^2-9)}{x^2-9}=\frac{(x-3)(x)(x+3)}{x(x+3)}\Rightarrow 3x+9-x=x-3\Rightarrow 2x+9=x-3\Rightarrow$

$x=-12$ Check: $\frac{3}{(-12)^2-3(-12)}-\frac{1}{(-12)^2-9}=\frac{1}{(-12)^2+3(-12)}\Rightarrow\frac{3}{180}-\frac{1}{135}=\frac{1}{108}\Rightarrow$

$\frac{9}{540}-\frac{4}{540}=\frac{5}{540}\Rightarrow\frac{5}{540}=\frac{5}{540}\Rightarrow\frac{1}{108}=\frac{1}{108}$

77. $\frac{1}{x^2}-\frac{5}{x^2+4x}=\frac{1}{x^2+4x}\Rightarrow\frac{1(x^2)(x^2+4x)}{x^2}-\frac{5(x^2)(x^2+4x)}{(x^2+4x)}=\frac{1(x^2)(x^2+4x)}{x^2+4x}\Rightarrow$

$\frac{(x^2+4x)(x^2)}{x^2}-\frac{5x^2(x^2+4x)}{x^2+4x}=\frac{x^2(x^2+4x)}{x^2+4x}\Rightarrow x^2+4x-5x^2=x^2\Rightarrow -4x^2+4x=x^2\Rightarrow$

$-5x^2=-4x\Rightarrow\frac{x^2}{x}=\frac{-4}{-5}\Rightarrow x=\frac{4}{5}$

Check: $\frac{1}{(\frac{4}{5})^2}-\frac{5}{(\frac{4}{5})^2+4(\frac{4}{5})}=\frac{1}{(\frac{4}{5})^2+4(\frac{4}{5})}\Rightarrow\frac{1}{\frac{16}{25}}-\frac{5}{\frac{96}{25}}=\frac{1}{\frac{96}{25}}\Rightarrow\frac{1}{1}\cdot\frac{25}{16}-\frac{5}{1}\cdot\frac{25}{96}=\frac{1}{1}\cdot\frac{25}{96}\Rightarrow$

$\frac{25}{16}-\frac{125}{96}=\frac{25}{96}\Rightarrow\frac{150}{96}-\frac{125}{96}=\frac{25}{96}\Rightarrow\frac{25}{96}=\frac{25}{96}$

78. $\frac{5}{x^2-1}-\frac{1}{x^2+2x+1}=\frac{3}{x^2-1}\Rightarrow$

$\frac{5(x+1)(x+1)(x-1)}{(x+1)(x-1)}-\frac{1(x+1)(x+1)(x-1)}{(x+1)(x+1)}=\frac{3(x+1)(x+1)(x-1)}{(x+1)(x-1)}\Rightarrow$

$\frac{(5x+5)(x^2-1)}{(x^2-1)}-\frac{(x-1)(x^2+2x+1)}{x^2+2x+1}=\frac{(3x+3)(x^2-1)}{x^2-1}\Rightarrow 5x+5-(x-1)=3x+3\Rightarrow$

$4x+6=3x+3\Rightarrow x=-3$

Check: $\frac{5}{(-3)^2-1}-\frac{1}{(-3)^2+2(-3)+1}=\frac{2}{(-3)^2-1}\Rightarrow\frac{5}{8}-\frac{1}{4}=\frac{3}{8}\Rightarrow\frac{5}{8}-\frac{2}{8}=\frac{3}{8}\Rightarrow\frac{3}{8}=\frac{3}{8}$

79. $\frac{1}{a}+\frac{2}{b}=\frac{3}{c}$ for $b\Rightarrow\frac{1}{a}\cdot\frac{bc}{bc}+\frac{2}{b}\cdot\frac{ac}{ac}=\frac{3}{c}\cdot\frac{ab}{ab}\Rightarrow bc+2ac=3ab\Rightarrow 2ac=3ab-bc\Rightarrow$

$2ac=b(3a-c)\Rightarrow b=\frac{2ac}{3a-c}$

80. $y=\frac{x}{x-1}$ for $x\Rightarrow y(x-1)=x\cdot 1\Rightarrow xy-y=x\Rightarrow xy-x=y\Rightarrow x(y-1)=y\Rightarrow x=\frac{y}{y-1}$

Section 7.7

81. $\frac{x}{6}=\frac{1}{5}\Rightarrow 5x=6\Rightarrow x=\frac{6}{5}$

82. $\frac{3}{x}=\frac{7}{3}\Rightarrow 9=7x\Rightarrow\frac{9}{7}=x\Rightarrow x=\frac{9}{7}$

83. (a) $\frac{5}{x}=\frac{11}{20}$

(b) $\frac{5}{x}=\frac{11}{20}\Rightarrow 100=11x\Rightarrow\frac{100}{11}=x\Rightarrow x=\frac{100}{11}$

84. (a) $\frac{117}{13} = \frac{x}{7}$

(b) $\frac{117}{13} = \frac{x}{7} \Rightarrow 13x = 819 \Rightarrow x = 63 \Rightarrow \$63$

85. (a) $k = \frac{y}{x},\ y = 8, x = 2 \Rightarrow k = \frac{8}{2} \Rightarrow k = 4$

(b) $y = kx,\ k = 4, x = 4 \Rightarrow y = 4 \cdot 4 \Rightarrow y = 16$

86. (a) $k = \frac{y}{x},\ y = 21, x = 7 \Rightarrow k = \frac{21}{7} \Rightarrow k = 3$

(b) $y = kx,\ k = 3, x = 4 \Rightarrow y = 3 \cdot 4 \Rightarrow y = 12$

87. (a) $k = xy,\ x = 4, y = 2.5 \Rightarrow k = 4 \cdot 2.5 \Rightarrow k = 10$

(b) $y = \frac{k}{x},\ k = 10, x = 2 \Rightarrow y = \frac{10}{2} \Rightarrow y = 5$

88. (a) $k = xy,\ x = 3, y = 7 \Rightarrow k = 3 \cdot 7 \Rightarrow k = 21$

(b) $y = \frac{k}{x},\ k = 21, x = 2 \Rightarrow y = \frac{21}{2}$

89. (a) Inverse, because as x increases y decreases and $k = xy \Rightarrow 2 \cdot 30 = 3 \cdot 20 = 4 \cdot 15$, etc.

(b) $k = xy,\ x = 2, y = 30 \Rightarrow k = 2 \cdot 30 \Rightarrow k = 60;\ y = \frac{k}{x} \Rightarrow y = \frac{60}{x}$

(c) See Figure 89.

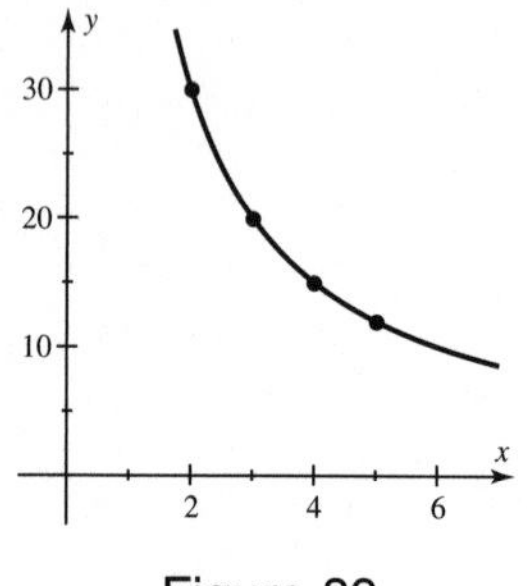

Figure 89

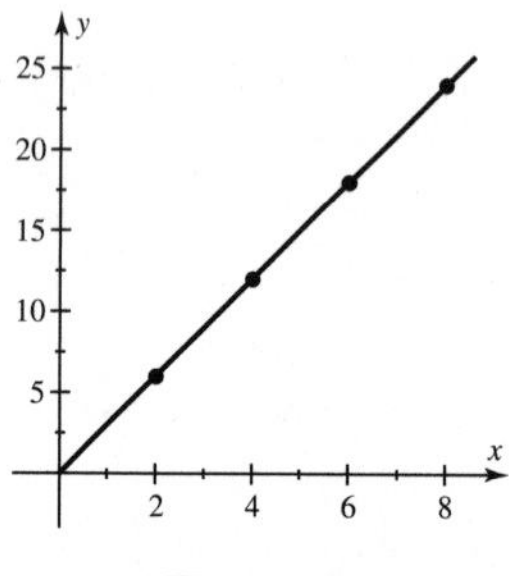

Figure 90

90. (a) Direct, because as x increases y also increases and $k = \frac{y}{x} \Rightarrow \frac{6}{2} = \frac{12}{4} = \frac{18}{6}$, etc.

(b) $k = \frac{y}{x},\ x = 2, y = 6 \Rightarrow k = \frac{6}{2} \Rightarrow k = 3;\ y = kx \Rightarrow y = 3x$

(c) See Figure 90.

91. Direct, $k = \frac{y}{x},\ y = 2, x = 4 \Rightarrow k = \frac{2}{4} \Rightarrow k = \frac{1}{2}$

92. Inverse, $k = xy,\ x = 2, y = 6 \Rightarrow k = 2 \cdot 6 \Rightarrow k = 12$

Applications

93. (a) $x = 10,\ T = \dfrac{1}{15 - x} \Rightarrow T = \dfrac{1}{15 - 10} = \dfrac{1}{5} = 0.2,$ when the rate of arrival is 10 cars/min., the wait is 0.2 minutes or 12 seconds.

(b) $x = 5,\ T = \dfrac{1}{15 - x} \Rightarrow T = \dfrac{1}{15 - 5} = \dfrac{1}{10};\ x = 10,\ T = \dfrac{1}{15 - x} \Rightarrow T = \dfrac{1}{15 - 10} = \dfrac{1}{5};$

$x = 13,\ T = \dfrac{1}{15 - x} \Rightarrow T = \dfrac{1}{15 - 13} = \dfrac{1}{2};\ x = 14,\ T = \dfrac{1}{15 - x} \Rightarrow T = \dfrac{1}{15 - 14} = \dfrac{1}{1} = 1;$

$x = 14.9,\ T = \dfrac{1}{15 - x} \Rightarrow T = \dfrac{1}{15 - 14.9} = \dfrac{1}{0.1} = 10;$ See Figure 93.

(c) It increases dramatically.

x	5	10	13	14	14.9
T	$\frac{1}{10}$	$\frac{1}{5}$	$\frac{1}{2}$	1	10

Figure 93

94. If $r \cdot t = d$, then $50 \cdot t = 150 \Rightarrow t = 3$ and $75t = 150 \Rightarrow t = 2$. The combined $d = 300$ and the combined $t = 5$. Therefore, $r \cdot 5 = 300 \Rightarrow r = 60 \Rightarrow 60$ mph.

95. $\dfrac{t}{100} + \dfrac{t}{160} = 1 \Rightarrow \dfrac{800t}{100} + \dfrac{800t}{160} = 800 \Rightarrow 8t + 5t = 800 \Rightarrow 13t = 800 \Rightarrow t = \dfrac{800}{13} \Rightarrow t = 61.5$ hrs.

96. Let x = slower jogger speed and $x + 2$ = faster jogger speed, then $\dfrac{10}{x} - \dfrac{10}{x + 2} = 1 \Rightarrow$

$10x + 20 - 10x = x^2 + 2x \Rightarrow 20 = x^2 + 2x \Rightarrow x^2 + 2x - 20 = 0 \Rightarrow (x - 10)(x + 12) = 0 \Rightarrow$

$x - 10 = 0 \Rightarrow x = 10,\ x + 12 = 0 \Rightarrow x = -12 \Rightarrow x = 10, -12.$ Therefore 10 mph and 12 mph.

97. $\dfrac{16}{x - 4} = \dfrac{48}{x + 4} \Rightarrow 16x + 64 = 48x - 192 \Rightarrow 256 = 32x \Rightarrow \dfrac{256}{32} = x \Rightarrow x = 8$ mph

98. $\dfrac{6}{5} = \dfrac{32}{x} \Rightarrow 6x = 160 \Rightarrow x = \dfrac{160}{6} \Rightarrow x \approx 26.7$ ft.

99. $\dfrac{20}{1} = \dfrac{35}{x} \Rightarrow 20x = 35 \Rightarrow x = \dfrac{35}{20} \Rightarrow x \approx 1.75$ in.

100. $k = xy,\ x = 0.25, y = 200 \Rightarrow k = 0.25 \cdot 200 \Rightarrow k = 50$

$y = \dfrac{k}{x},\ x = 0.50, k = 50 \Rightarrow y = \dfrac{50}{0.50} \Rightarrow y = 100$ vehicles

101. $k = xy,\ x = 10, y = 25 \Rightarrow k = 10 \cdot 25 \Rightarrow k = 250$

$y = \dfrac{k}{x},\ x = 12, k = 250 \Rightarrow y = \dfrac{250}{12} \Rightarrow y \approx 20.8$ lbs.

102. $k = \dfrac{y}{x},\ x = 17, k = 425 \Rightarrow k = \dfrac{425}{17} \Rightarrow y = 25$

$y = kx,\ x = 13, y = 25 \Rightarrow y = 25 \cdot 13 \Rightarrow y = \$325$

103. $k = \dfrac{z}{x^2y^3},\ x = 6, y = 20, z = 10{,}823 \Rightarrow k = \dfrac{10{,}823}{(6)^2(20)^3} \Rightarrow k = \dfrac{10{,}823}{288{,}000} \Rightarrow k = 0.0375798611$

$z = kx^2y^3,\ x = 10, y = 12, k = 0.0376 \Rightarrow z = 0.0376 \cdot 100 \cdot 1728 \Rightarrow z = 6493.8$ W

104. $k = \frac{z}{wt^2}$, $w = 8, t = 5, z = 650 \Rightarrow k = \frac{650}{8 \cdot 25} \Rightarrow k = \frac{650}{200} \Rightarrow k = 3.25$

$z = kwt^2$, $w = 6, t = 6, k = 3.25 \Rightarrow z = 3.25 \cdot 6 \cdot 36 \Rightarrow z = 702$ lbs.

105. $30 \cdot 25 = 750$ and $90 \cdot 25 = 2250$, therefore 750 to 2250 sec. or 12.5 to 37.5 min.

Chapter 7 Test

1. $x = 3, \frac{3x}{2x - 1} \Rightarrow \frac{3(3)}{2(3) - 1} = \frac{9}{6 - 1} = \frac{9}{5}$

2. $\frac{x - 1}{x + 2}$, the equation is undefined when $x + 2 = 0 \Rightarrow x = -2$.

3. $\frac{x^2 - 25}{x - 5} = \frac{(x - 5)(x + 5)}{x - 5} = \frac{x - 5}{x - 5} \cdot x + 5 = 1 \cdot x + 5 = x + 5$

4. $\frac{3x^2 - 15x}{3x} = \frac{3x(x - 5)}{3x} = \frac{3x}{3x} \cdot (x - 5) = 1 \cdot (x - 5) = x - 5$

5. $\frac{x - 2}{x + 4} \cdot \frac{3x + 12}{x - 2} = \frac{x - 2}{x - 2} \cdot \frac{3(x + 4)}{x + 4} = 1 \cdot 1 \cdot 3 = 3$

6. $\frac{z + 1}{x + 3} \cdot \frac{2z + 6}{z + 1} = \frac{z + 1}{z + 1} \cdot \frac{2(z + 3)}{z + 3} = 1 \cdot 1 \cdot 2 = 2$

7. $\frac{x + 1}{5x} \div \frac{2x + 2}{x - 1} = \frac{x + 1}{5x} \cdot \frac{x - 1}{2x + 2} = \frac{x + 1}{2(x + 1)} \cdot \frac{x - 1}{5x} = \frac{x - 1}{2(5x)} \cdot 1 = \frac{x - 1}{10x}$

8. $\frac{2}{x^2} \div \frac{x + 3}{3x} = \frac{2}{x^2} \cdot \frac{3x}{x + 3} = \frac{x}{x} \cdot \frac{2 \cdot 3}{x(x + 3)} = 1 \cdot \frac{6}{x(x + 3)} = \frac{6}{x(x + 3)}$

9. $\frac{x}{x + 4} + \frac{3x + 1}{x + 4} = \frac{4x + 1}{x + 4}$

10. $\frac{4t + 1}{2t - 3} - \frac{3t - 6}{2t - 3} = \frac{4t + 1 - (3t - 6)}{2t - 3} = \frac{t + 7}{2t - 3}$

11. $\frac{1}{y^2 + y} - \frac{y - 1}{y^2 - y} = \frac{1}{y(y + 1)} \cdot \frac{y - 1}{y - 1} - \frac{y - 1}{y(y - 1)} \cdot \frac{y + 1}{y + 1} = \frac{y - 1}{y(y + 1)(y - 1)} - \frac{y^2 - 1}{y(y + 1)(y - 1)} =$

$\frac{y - y^2}{y(y + 1)(y - 1)} = \frac{-y(y - 1)}{y(y + 1)(y - 1)} = \frac{-1}{y + 1} = -\frac{1}{y + 1}$

12. $\frac{1}{xy} + \frac{x}{y} - \frac{1}{y^2} = \frac{y}{xy^2} + \frac{x^2y}{xy^2} - \frac{x}{xy^2} = \frac{x^2y - x + y}{xy^2}$

13. $\frac{\frac{a}{3b}}{\frac{5a}{b^2}} = \frac{a}{3b} \div \frac{5a}{b^2} = \frac{a}{3b} \cdot \frac{b^2}{5a} = \frac{a}{a} \cdot \frac{b}{b} \cdot \frac{b}{15} = 1 \cdot 1 \cdot \frac{b}{15} = \frac{b}{15}$

14. $\frac{1 + \frac{1}{p - 1}}{1 - \frac{1}{p - 1}} = \frac{\frac{p - 1}{p - 1} + \frac{1}{p - 1}}{\frac{p - 1}{p - 1} - \frac{1}{p - 1}} = \frac{\frac{p}{p - 1}}{\frac{p - 2}{p - 1}} = \frac{p}{p - 1} \div \frac{p - 2}{p - 1} = \frac{p}{p - 1} \cdot \frac{p - 1}{p - 2} = \frac{p - 1}{p - 1} \cdot \frac{p}{p - 2} = 1 \cdot \frac{p}{p - 2} =$

$\frac{p}{p - 2}$

15. $\frac{2}{7} = \frac{5}{x} \Rightarrow 2x = 35 \Rightarrow x = \frac{35}{2}$

16. $\dfrac{x+3}{2x} = 1 \Rightarrow x + 3 = 2x \Rightarrow 3 = x \Rightarrow x = 3$

17. $\dfrac{1}{2x} + \dfrac{2}{5x} = \dfrac{9}{10} = \dfrac{1 \cdot 10x}{2x} + \dfrac{2 \cdot 10x}{5x} = \dfrac{9 \cdot 10x}{10} \Rightarrow 5 + 4 = 9x \Rightarrow 9 = 9x \Rightarrow x = 1$

18. $\dfrac{1}{x-1} + \dfrac{2}{x+2} = \dfrac{3}{2} \Rightarrow \dfrac{2(x-1)(x+2)}{x-1} + \dfrac{2(2)(x-1)(x+2)}{x+2} = \dfrac{3(2)(x-1)(x+2)}{2} \Rightarrow$

$2x + 4 + 4x - 4 = 3x^2 + 3x - 6 \Rightarrow 6x = 3x^2 + 3x - 6 \Rightarrow 3x^2 - 3x - 6 = 0 \Rightarrow$

$3(x+1)(x-2) = 0,\ x + 1 = 0 \Rightarrow x = -1, x - 2 = 0 \Rightarrow x = 2 \Rightarrow x = -1, 2$

19. $\dfrac{1}{x^2-1} - \dfrac{4}{x+1} = \dfrac{3}{x-1} \Rightarrow \dfrac{1}{(x+1)(x-1)} - \dfrac{4}{x+1} = \dfrac{3}{x-1} \Rightarrow$

$\dfrac{1(x+1)(x-1)}{(x+1)(x-1)} - \dfrac{4(x+1)(x-1)}{x+1} = \dfrac{3(x+1)(x-1)}{x-1} \Rightarrow 1 - (4x - 4) = 3x + 3 \Rightarrow$

$-4x + 5 = 3x + 3 \Rightarrow -7x = -2 \Rightarrow x = \dfrac{-2}{-7} \Rightarrow x = \dfrac{2}{7}$

20. $\dfrac{1}{x^2-4x} + \dfrac{2}{x^2-16} = \dfrac{2}{x^2+4x} \Rightarrow \dfrac{1}{4(x-4)} + \dfrac{2}{(x-4)(x+4)} = \dfrac{2}{x(x+4)} \Rightarrow$

$\dfrac{1(x)(x+4)(x-4)}{x(x-4)} + \dfrac{2(x)(x+4)(x-4)}{(x-4)(x+4)} = \dfrac{2(x)(x+4)(x-4)}{x(x+4)} \Rightarrow x + 4 + 2x = 2x - 8 \Rightarrow$

$3x + 4 = 2x - 8 \Rightarrow x = -12$

21. $y = \dfrac{2}{3x-5}$ for x, $y(3x-5) = 2 \Rightarrow 3x - 5 = \dfrac{2}{y} \Rightarrow 3x = \dfrac{2}{y} + 5 \Rightarrow x = \left(\dfrac{2}{y} + 5\right)\dfrac{1}{3} \Rightarrow$

$x = \dfrac{2}{3y} + \dfrac{5}{3} \Rightarrow x = \dfrac{2}{3y} + \dfrac{5y}{3} \Rightarrow x = \dfrac{2+5y}{3y}$

22. $\dfrac{a+b}{ab} = 1$ for b, $ab = a + b \Rightarrow ab - b = a \Rightarrow b(a-1) = a \Rightarrow b = \dfrac{a}{a-1}$

23. (a) $k = \dfrac{y}{x} \Rightarrow k = \dfrac{10}{4} \Rightarrow k = \dfrac{5}{2}$

(b) $y = kx \Rightarrow y = \dfrac{5}{2}(6) \Rightarrow y = \dfrac{30}{2} \Rightarrow y = 15$

24. Inversely, as x increases y decreases and for all $k = xy$, $k = 64$.

25. $\dfrac{t}{40} + \dfrac{t}{60} = 1 \Rightarrow \dfrac{120t}{40} + \dfrac{120t}{60} = 120 \Rightarrow 3t + 2t = 120 \Rightarrow 5t = 120 \Rightarrow t = 24$ hours

26. $\dfrac{5}{4} = \dfrac{x}{54} \Rightarrow 4x = 270 \Rightarrow x = 67.5$ ft.

27. $N = \dfrac{x^2}{900 - 30x}$ for $x = 24$, $N = \dfrac{24^2}{900 - 30(24)} \Rightarrow N = \dfrac{576}{900 - 720} \Rightarrow N = \dfrac{576}{180} \Rightarrow N = \dfrac{16}{5}$ or 3.2;

when the arrival rate is 24 people/hr., there are about 3 people in line.

Chapter 7 Extended and Discovery Exercises

1. (a) $x = 3, N = \dfrac{3^2}{225 - 15(3)} = \dfrac{9}{225 - 45} = \dfrac{9}{180} = \dfrac{1}{20} \Rightarrow N = 0.05;$

$x = 9, N = \dfrac{9^2}{225 - 15(9)} = \dfrac{81}{225 - 135} = \dfrac{81}{90} = \dfrac{9}{10} \Rightarrow N = 0.9;$

$x = 12, N = \dfrac{12^2}{225 - 15(12)} = \dfrac{144}{225 - 180} = \dfrac{144}{45} = \dfrac{16}{5} \Rightarrow N = 3.2;$

$x = 13, N = \dfrac{13^2}{225 - 15(13)} = \dfrac{169}{225 - 195} = \dfrac{169}{30} \Rightarrow N = 5.6\overline{3};$

$x = 14, N = \dfrac{14^2}{225 - 15(14)} = \dfrac{196}{225 - 210} = \dfrac{196}{15} \Rightarrow N = 13.0\overline{6}$ See Figure 1a.

(b) $x = 15$, because $\dfrac{15^2}{225 - 15(15)} = \dfrac{225}{0}$, which is undefined.

(c) See Figure 1c.

(d) See Figure 1d.

(e) As x approaches 15, the wait increases dramatically.

(f) The formula is only valid for arrival rates under 15 cars per hour, but it can be inferred that the line of cars will continue to grow.

x	3	9	12	13	14
N	0.05	0.9	3.2	$5.6\overline{3}$	$13.0\overline{6}$

Figure 1a

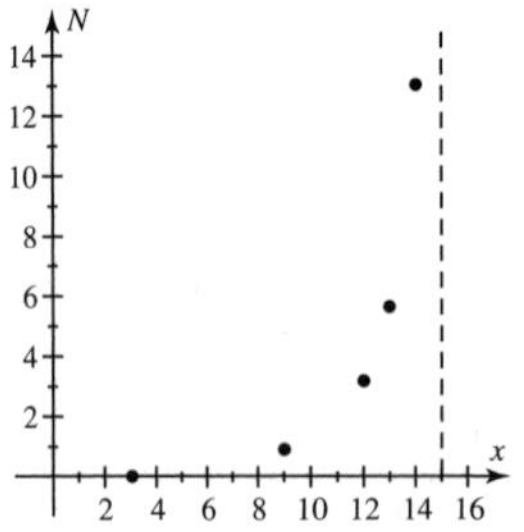

Figure 1c

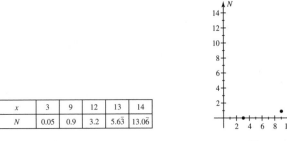

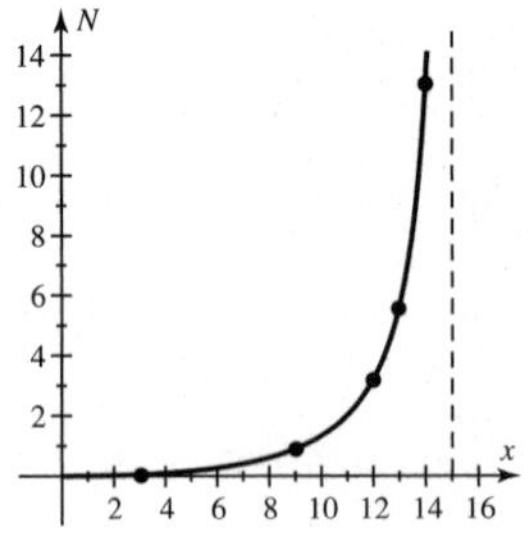

Figure 1d

2. (a) $x = -4,\ y = \dfrac{1}{-4 - 1} \Rightarrow y = -\dfrac{1}{5};\ x = -3,\ y = \dfrac{1}{-3 - 1} \Rightarrow y = -\dfrac{1}{4};$

$x = -2,\ y = \dfrac{1}{-2 - 1} \Rightarrow y = -\dfrac{1}{3};\ x = -1,\ y = \dfrac{1}{-1 - 1} \Rightarrow y = -\dfrac{1}{2};$

$x = 0,\ y = \dfrac{1}{0 - 1} \Rightarrow y = -\dfrac{1}{1} = -1;\ x = 1,\ y = \dfrac{1}{1 - 1} \Rightarrow y = \dfrac{1}{0} \Rightarrow y =$ undefined;

$x = 2,\ y = \dfrac{1}{2 - 1} \Rightarrow y = \dfrac{1}{1} \Rightarrow y = 1;\ x = 3,\ y = \dfrac{1}{3 - 1} \Rightarrow y = \dfrac{1}{2};$

$x = 4,\ y = \dfrac{1}{4 - 1} \Rightarrow y = \dfrac{1}{3};$ See Figure 2a.

(b) $x = 1$ yields $\dfrac{1}{0}$ which is undefined.

(c) See Figure 2c-e.

(d) See Figure 2c-e.

(e) See Figure 2c-e.

x	−4	−3	−2	−1	0	1	2	3	4
y	−0.2	−0.25	$-0.\overline{3}$	−0.5	−1	—	1	0.5	$0.\overline{3}$

Figure 2a

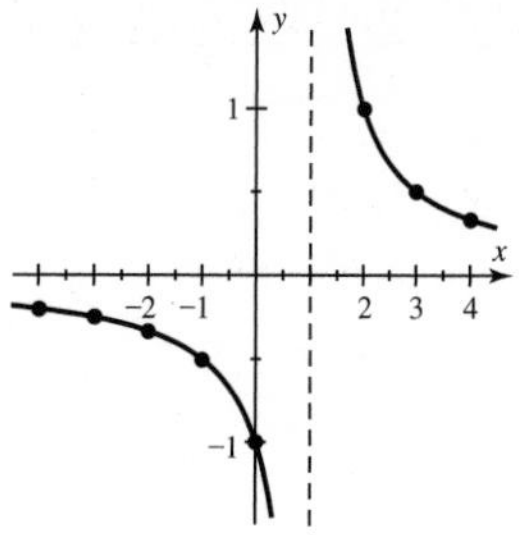

Figure 2c-e

3. (a) $x=-4,\ y=\dfrac{1}{-4+1}\Rightarrow y=-\dfrac{1}{3};\ x=-3,\ y=\dfrac{1}{-3+1}\Rightarrow y=-\dfrac{1}{2};$

$x=-2,\ y=\dfrac{1}{-2+1}\Rightarrow y=-\dfrac{1}{1}=-1;\ x=-1,\ y=\dfrac{1}{-1+1}\Rightarrow y=\dfrac{1}{0}\Rightarrow y=\text{undefined};$

$x=0,\ y=\dfrac{1}{0+1}\Rightarrow y=\dfrac{1}{1}=1;\ x=1,\ y=\dfrac{1}{1+1}\Rightarrow y=\dfrac{1}{2};$

$x=2,\ y=\dfrac{1}{2+1}\Rightarrow y=\dfrac{1}{3};\ x=3,\ y=\dfrac{1}{3+1}\Rightarrow y=\dfrac{1}{4};$

$x=4,\ y=\dfrac{1}{4+1}\Rightarrow y=\dfrac{1}{5};$ See Figure 3a.

(b) $x=-1$ yields $\dfrac{1}{0}$ which is undefined.

(c) See Figure 3c-e.

(d) See Figure 3c-e.

(e) See Figure 3c-e.

x	−4	−3	−2	−1	0	1	2	3	4
y	$-0.\overline{3}$	−0.5	−1	—	1	0.5	$0.\overline{3}$	0.25	0.2

Figure 3a

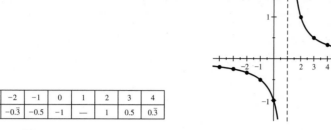

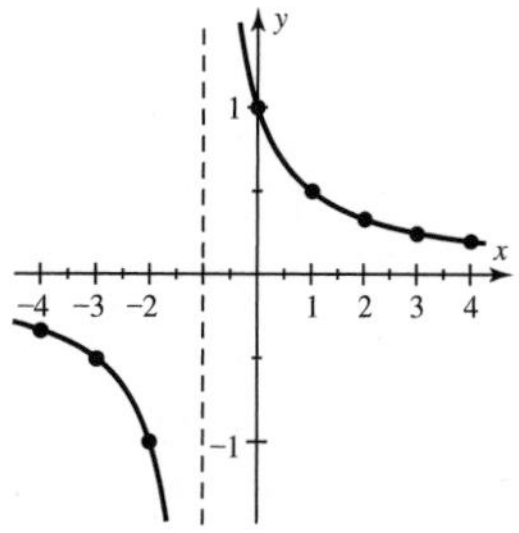

Figure 3c-e

4. (a) $x = -4,\ y = \dfrac{4}{16 + 1} \Rightarrow y = \dfrac{4}{17};\ x = -3,\ y = \dfrac{4}{9 + 1} \Rightarrow y = \dfrac{4}{10};$

$x = -2,\ y = \dfrac{4}{4 + 1} \Rightarrow y = \dfrac{4}{5};\ x = -1,\ y = \dfrac{4}{1 + 1} \Rightarrow y = \dfrac{4}{2} \Rightarrow y = 2;$

$x = 0,\ y = \dfrac{4}{0 + 1} \Rightarrow y = \dfrac{4}{1} = 4;\ x = 1,\ y = \dfrac{4}{1 + 1} \Rightarrow y = \dfrac{4}{2} = 2;$

$x = 2,\ y = \dfrac{4}{4 + 1} \Rightarrow y = \dfrac{4}{5};\ x = 3,\ y = \dfrac{4}{9 + 1} \Rightarrow y = \dfrac{4}{10};$

$x = 4,\ y = \dfrac{4}{16 + 1} \Rightarrow y = \dfrac{4}{17};$ See Figure 4a.

(b) No points are undefined.

(c) See Figure 4c-e.

(d) See Figure 4c-e.

(e) See Figure 4c-e.

x	−4	−3	−2	−1	0	1	2	3	4
y	0.235	0.4	0.8	2	4	2	0.8	0.4	0.235

Figure 4a

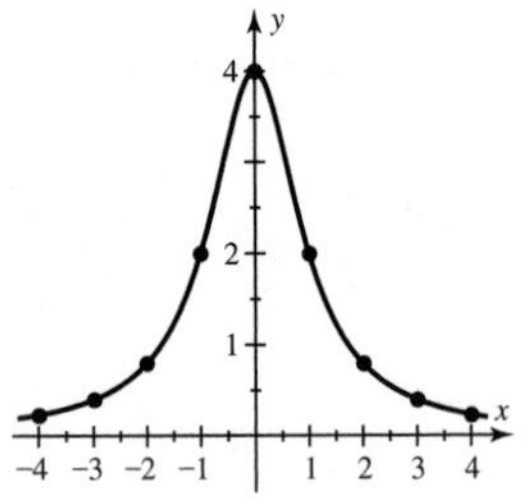

Figure 4c-e

5. (a) $x = -4,\ y = \dfrac{-4}{-4 + 1} \Rightarrow y = \dfrac{4}{3};\ x = -3,\ y = \dfrac{-3}{-3 + 1} \Rightarrow y = \dfrac{3}{2};$

$x = -2,\ y = \dfrac{-2}{-2 + 1} \Rightarrow y = \dfrac{2}{1} = 2;\ x = -1,\ y = \dfrac{-1}{-1 + 1} \Rightarrow y = \dfrac{-1}{0} \Rightarrow y = \text{undefined};$

$x = 0,\ y = \dfrac{0}{0 + 1} \Rightarrow y = \dfrac{0}{1} = 0;\ x = 1,\ y = \dfrac{1}{1 + 1} \Rightarrow y = \dfrac{1}{2};$

$x = 2,\ y = \dfrac{2}{2 + 1} \Rightarrow y = \dfrac{2}{3};\ x = 3,\ y = \dfrac{3}{3 + 1} \Rightarrow y = \dfrac{3}{4};$

$x = 4,\ y = \dfrac{4}{4 + 1} \Rightarrow y = \dfrac{4}{5};$ See Figure 5a.

(b) $x = -1$ yields $\dfrac{-1}{0}$ which is undefined.

(c) See Figure 5c-e.

(d) See Figure 5c-e.

(e) See Figure 5c-e.

x	−4	−3	−2	−1	0	1	2	3	4
y	$1.\overline{3}$	1.5	2	—	0	0.5	$0.\overline{6}$	0.75	0.8

Figure 5a

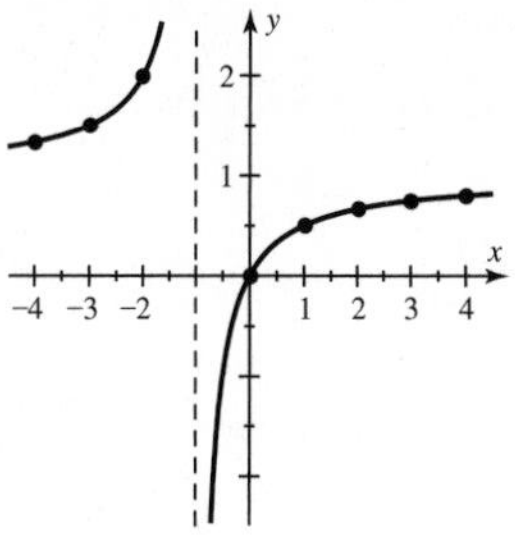

Figure 5c-e

6. (a) $x=-4,\ y=\dfrac{-4}{-4-1}\Rightarrow y=\dfrac{4}{5};\ x=-3,\ y=\dfrac{-3}{-3-1}\Rightarrow y=\dfrac{3}{4};$

$x=-2,\ y=\dfrac{-2}{-2-1}\Rightarrow y=\dfrac{2}{3};\ x=-1,\ y=\dfrac{-1}{-1-1}\Rightarrow y=\dfrac{1}{2};$

$x=0,\ y=\dfrac{0}{0-1}\Rightarrow y=\dfrac{0}{-1}=0;\ x=1,\ y=\dfrac{1}{1-1}\Rightarrow y=\dfrac{1}{0}\Rightarrow y=$ undefined;

$x=2,\ y=\dfrac{2}{2-1}\Rightarrow y=\dfrac{2}{1}=2;\ x=3,\ y=\dfrac{3}{3-1}\Rightarrow y=\dfrac{3}{2};$

$x=4,\ y=\dfrac{4}{4-1}\Rightarrow y=\dfrac{4}{3};$ See Figure 6a.

(b) $x=1$ yields $\dfrac{1}{0}$ which is undefined.

(c) See Figure 6c-e.

(d) See Figure 6c-e.

(e) See Figure 6c-e.

x	−4	−3	−2	−1	0	1	2	3	4
y	0.8	0.75	$0.\overline{6}$	0.5	0	—	2	1.5	$1.\overline{3}$

Figure 6a

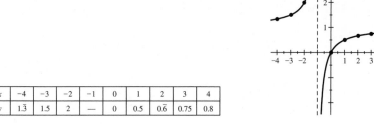

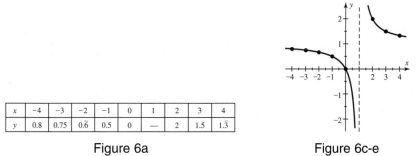

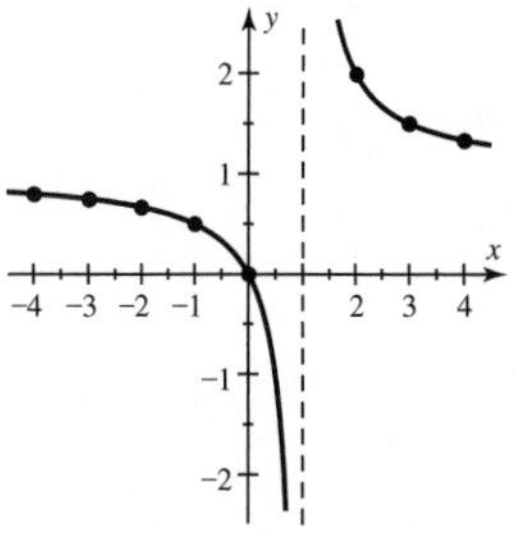

Figure 6c-e

Critical Thinking Solutions for Chapter 7

Section 7.1

- With n winning numbers, the number of nonwinners out of 100 is $100-n$. Therefore the probability of not drawing a winning number is $\dfrac{100-n}{100}$.

Section 7.2

- $\dfrac{x^2 - 1}{x + 5} \div \dfrac{x - 1}{x + 5} \div x + 1 = \dfrac{(x + 1)(x - 1)}{x + 5} \cdot \dfrac{x + 5}{x - 1} \cdot \dfrac{1}{x + 1} = \dfrac{1}{1} = 1$

Section 7.4

- $x + \dfrac{1}{x} = \dfrac{x}{1} + \dfrac{1}{x} = \dfrac{x^2}{x} + \dfrac{1}{x} = \dfrac{x^2 + 1}{x}$, then the reciprocal is $\dfrac{x}{x^2 + 1}$

Section 7.5

- No, $\dfrac{\frac{a}{b}}{\frac{a}{b} + 1} = \dfrac{\frac{a}{b}}{\frac{a}{b} + \frac{b}{b}} = \dfrac{\frac{a}{b}}{\frac{a + b}{b}} = \dfrac{a}{b} \div \dfrac{a + b}{b} = \dfrac{a}{b} \cdot \dfrac{b}{a + b} = \dfrac{a}{a + b}$, which is not equal to $\dfrac{1}{1 + 1}$.

  Yes, $\dfrac{\frac{a + b}{b}}{\frac{a}{b}} = \dfrac{a + b}{b} \div \dfrac{a}{b} = \dfrac{a + b}{b} \cdot \dfrac{b}{a} = \dfrac{b}{b} \cdot \dfrac{a + b}{a} = 1 \cdot \dfrac{a + b}{a} = \dfrac{a + b}{a} = 1 + \dfrac{b}{a}$, which does equal $1 + \dfrac{b}{a}$.

Section 7.6

- Solving $y = \dfrac{2}{x}$ and $y = x + 1$ by substitution, we get $\dfrac{2}{x} = x + 1 \Rightarrow 2 = x^2 + x \Rightarrow x^2 + x - 2 = 0 \Rightarrow$ $(x - 1)(x + 2) = 0 \Rightarrow x - 1 = 0 \Rightarrow x = 1$ and $x + 2 = 0 \Rightarrow x = -2$, so $x = 1, -2$, the same answers from the graph and table.
- $\dfrac{t}{x} + \dfrac{t}{y} = 1 \Rightarrow \dfrac{txy}{x} + \dfrac{txy}{y} = xy \Rightarrow ty + tx = xy \Rightarrow t(x + y) = xy \Rightarrow t = \dfrac{xy}{x + y}$

Section 7.7

- Using $S = kwt^2$ and width w and thickness t; when width doubles, $w = 2w$, stength $S = k2wt^2 \Rightarrow$ $S = 2kwt^2$ or strength doubles. When thickness t doubles, $t = 2t$, strength $S = kw(2t)^2 \Rightarrow S = 4kwt^2$ or strength quadruples. And when both triple, $w = 3w$ and $t = 3t$, strength $S = k3w(3t)^2 \Rightarrow S = 27kwt^2$ or strength is 27 times greater.

Chapter 8: Introduction to Functions

8.1: Functions and Their Representations

Concepts

1. function
3. symbolic
5. domain
7. one
9. The four types of representations for a function are verbal, numerical, symbolic and graphical.
11. Yes, there is only one output for each input.
13. No, one exam can have many students who pass.

Representing and Evaluating Functions

15. $f(-1) = 4(-1) - 2 = -6$; $f(0) = 4(0) - 2 = -2$
17. $f(0) = \sqrt{0} = 0$; $f\left(\frac{9}{4}\right) = \sqrt{\frac{9}{4}} = \frac{3}{2}$
19. $f(-5) = (-5)^2 = 25$; $f\left(\frac{3}{2}\right) = \left(\frac{3}{2}\right)^2 = \frac{9}{4}$
21. $f(-8) = 3$; $f\left(\frac{7}{3}\right) = 3$
23. $f(-5) = \frac{2}{-5 + 1} = \frac{2}{-4} = -\frac{1}{2}$; $f(4) = \frac{2}{4 + 1} = \frac{2}{5}$
25. (a) Because there are 36 inches in 1 yard, the formula is $I(x) = 36x$.

    (b) $I(10) = 36(10) = 360$. There are 360 inches in 10 yards.
27. (a) The area formula for a circle is $A(r) = \pi r^2$.

    (b) $A(10) = \pi(10)^2 = 100\pi \approx 314.2$. The area of a circle with radius 10 is about 314.2.
29. (a) Because there are 43,560 square feet in 1 acre, the formula is $F(x) = 43{,}560x$.

    (b) $F(10) = 43{,}560(10) = 435{,}600$. There are 435,600 square feet in 10 acres.
31. See Figure 31.
33. See Figure 33.

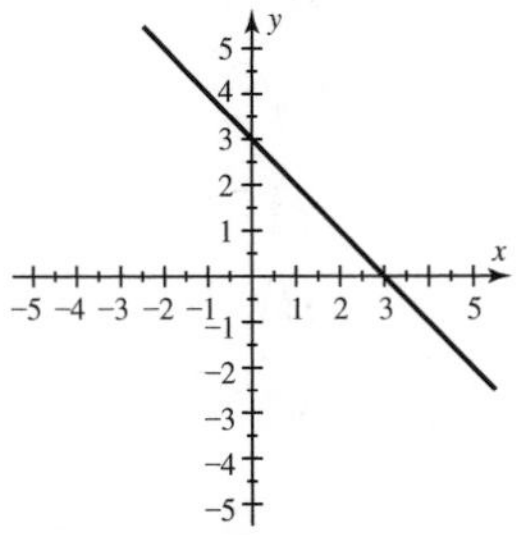

Figure 31

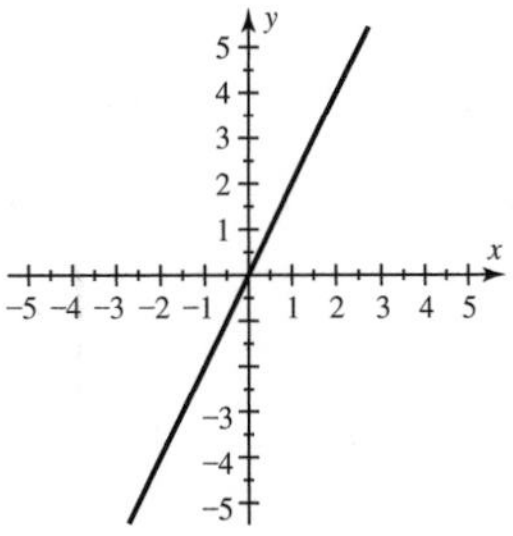

Figure 33

35. See Figure 35.

37. See Figure 37.

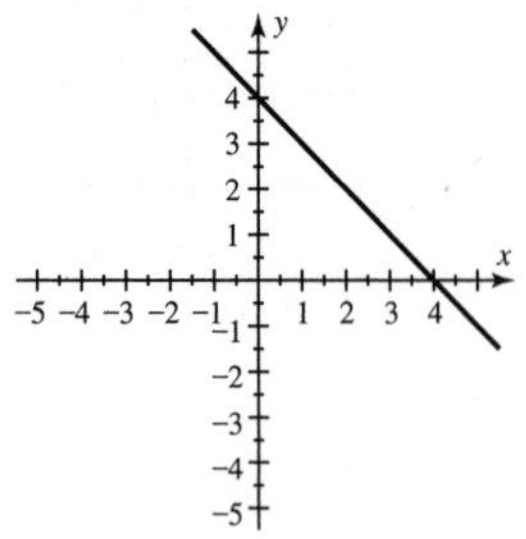

Figure 35

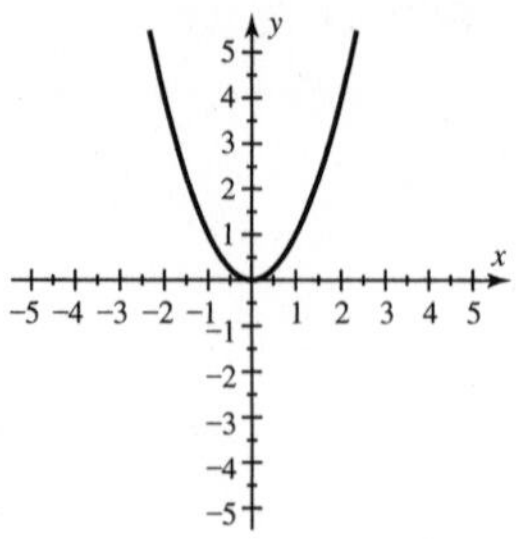

Figure 37

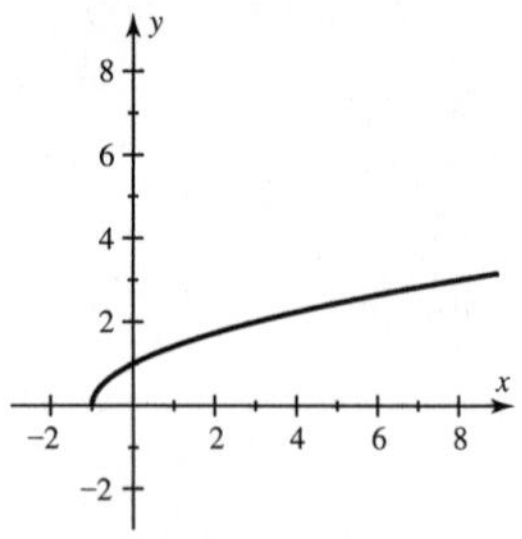

Figure 39

39. See Figure 39.

41. $f(0) = 3; f(2) = -1$

43. $f(-2) = 0; f(1) = 2$

45. $f(1) = -4; f(2) = -3$

47. $f(0) = 5.5; f(2) = 3.7$

49. $f(1990) = 26.9$ mpg

51. Symbolic: $y = x + 5$. Numerical: See the table in Figure 51a. Graphical: See the graph in Figure 51b.

x	−3	−2	−1	0	1	2	3
$y = f(x)$	2	3	4	5	6	7	8

Figure 51a

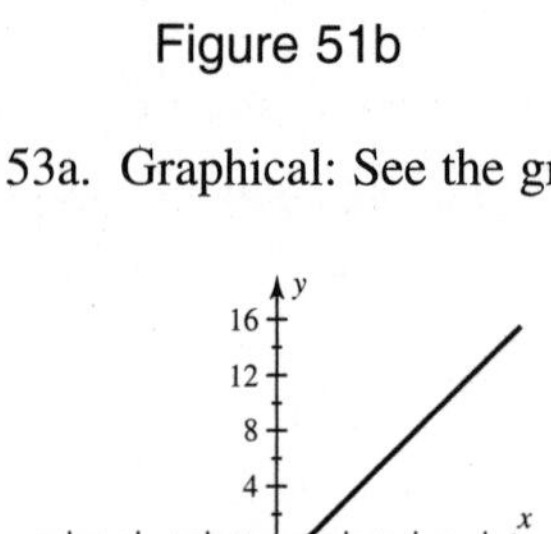

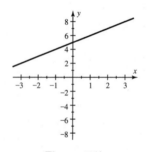

Figure 51b

53. Symbolic: $y = 5x - 2$. Numerical: See the table in Figure 53a. Graphical: See the graph in Figure 53b.

x	−3	−2	−1	0	1	2	3
$y = f(x)$	−17	−12	−7	−2	3	8	13

Figure 53a

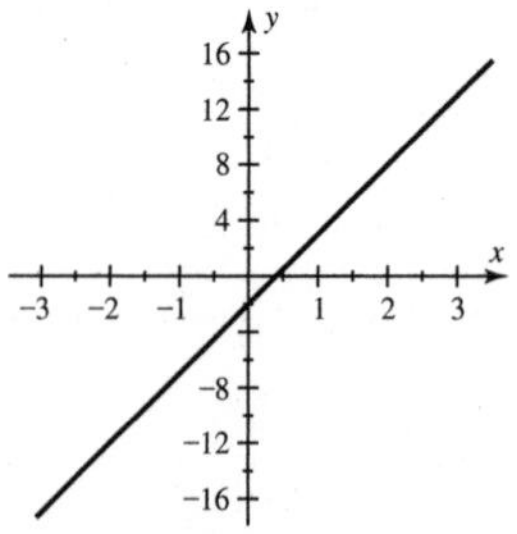

Figure 53b

55. Subtract $\frac{1}{2}$ from the input x to obtain the output y.

57. Divide the input x by 3 to obtain the output y.

59. Symbolic: $f(x) = 0.50x$. Graphical: See the graph in Figure 59a. Numerical: See the table in Figure 59b.

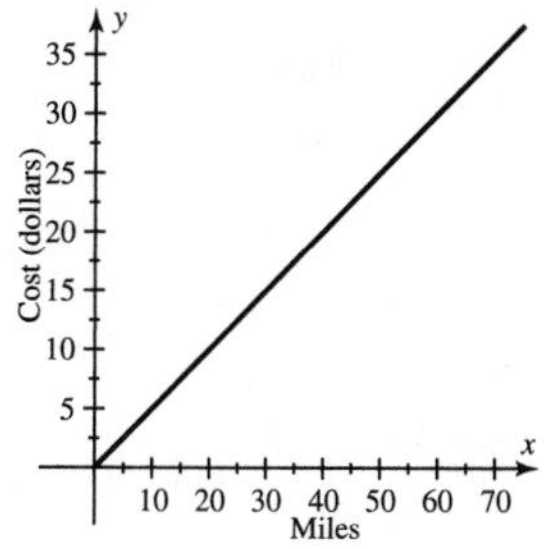

Figure 59a

Miles	10	20	30	40	50	60	70
Cost	\$5	\$10	\$15	\$20	\$25	\$30	\$35

Figure 59b

61. $P(1986) = 3.421(1986 - 1980) + 61 = 3.421(6) + 61 = 20.526 + 61 = 81.526$

In 1986 the median price for a single-family home was \$81,526.

63. (a) The point $(-1, -2)$ appears to be on the graph (not shown) of $f(x) = 3x + 1$. Therefore $f(-1) = -2$.

(b) $f(-1) = 3(-1) + 1 = -3 + 1 = -2$

65. (a) The point $(-1, 0.5)$ appears to be on the graph (not shown) of $f(x) = 0.5x^2$. Therefore $f(-1) = 0.5$.

(b) $f(-1) = 0.5(-1)^2 = 0.5(1) = 0.5$

Identifying Domains and Ranges

67. $D: -2 \leq x \leq 2; R: 0 \leq y \leq 2$

69. $D: -2 \leq x \leq 4; R: -2 \leq y \leq 2$

71. D: all real numbers; $R: y \geq -1$

73. $D: -3 \leq x \leq 3; R: -3 \leq y \leq 2$

75. $D = \{1, 2, 3, 4\}; R = \{5, 6, 7\}$

77. Any real number is a valid input for this function. D: all real numbers.

79. Any real number is a valid input for this function. D: all real numbers.

81. The denominator of this function cannot equal zero. $D: x \neq 5$.

83. The denominator of this function will never equal zero because the variable is squared. D: all real numbers.

85. The radicand must be greater than or equal to zero. $D: x \geq 1$.

87. (a) $f(1950) = 60.3$; In 1950 there were 60.3 accidental deaths per 100,000 people.

(b) $D = \{1910, 1930, 1950, 1970, 1990, 2000\}; R = \{35.5, 36.9, 56.2, 60.3, 80.5, 84.4\}$

(c) The number of accidental deaths per 100,000 people decreased over this time period.

Identifying a Function

89. (a) May is month number 5. The corresponding value for P is 0.2.

(b) Yes. Each month has exactly one average precipitation.

(c) Months 2, 3, 7 and 11.

91. No. The value 1 in the domain corresponds to more than one value in the range.

93. Yes. Each value in the domain corresponds to exactly one value in the range.

95. Yes. The graph passes the vertical line test.; *D*: all real numbers; *R*: all real numbers

97. No. The graph does not pass the vertical line test.

99. Yes. The graph passes the vertical line test.; $D: -4 \leq x \leq 4$; $R: 0 \leq y \leq 4$

101. Yes. The graph passes the vertical line test.; *D*: all real numbers; $R: y = 3$

103. No. The graph does not pass the vertical line test when $x = -2$.

105. Yes. Each value in the domain corresponds to exactly one value in the range.

107. No. The value 5 in the domain corresponds to more than one value in the range.

8.2: Linear Functions

Concepts

1. $ax + b$

3. line

5. 7

Identifying Linear Functions

7. Linear: $a = \frac{1}{2}, b = -6$

9. Nonlinear

11. Linear: $a = 0, b = -9$

13. Linear: $a = -9, b = 0$

15. Yes. The graph is a straight line.

17. No. The graph is not a straight line.

19. Yes. For each unit increase in x, the values of $f(x)$ increase by 3 units, so $a = \frac{3}{1} = 3$.

    Because $f(x) = -6$ when $x = 0$, the y-intercept is $b = -6$. The function can be written $f(x) = 3x - 6$.

21. Yes. For each 2-unit increase in x, the values of $f(x)$ increase by 3 units, so $a = \frac{3}{2}$.

    Because $f(x) = 3$ when $x = 0$, the y-intercept is $b = 3$. The function can be written $f(x) = \frac{3}{2}x + 3$.

23. No. For each unit increase in x, the values of $f(x)$ do not increase by a constant amount.

25. Yes. For each unit increase in x, the values of $f(x)$ increase by 2 units, so $a = \frac{2}{1} = 2$.

    Because $f(x) = 0$ when $x = 1$, the y-intercept is $b = -2$. The function can be written $f(x) = 2x - 2$.

Evaluating Linear Functions

27. $f(-4) = 4(-4) = -16$; $f(5) = 4(5) = 20$

29. $f\left(-\frac{2}{3}\right) = 5 - \left(-\frac{2}{3}\right) = \frac{15}{3} + \frac{2}{3} = \frac{17}{3}$; $f(3) = 5 - 3 = 2$

31. $f\left(-\frac{3}{4}\right) = -22;\ f(13) = -22$

33. $f(-1) = -2;\ f(0) = 0$

35. $f(-2) = -1;\ f(4) = -4$

37. $f(-3) = 1;\ f(1) = 1$

39. $f(x) = 6x; f(3) = 6(3) = 18$

41. $f(x) = \frac{x}{6} - \frac{1}{2}; f(3) = \frac{(3)}{6} - \frac{1}{2} = \frac{1}{2} - \frac{1}{2} = 0$

Representing Linear Functions

43. The graph should have a positive slope and pass through (0, 0). d

45. The graph should have a positive slope and pass through (0, –2). b

47. See Figure 47.

49. See Figure 49.

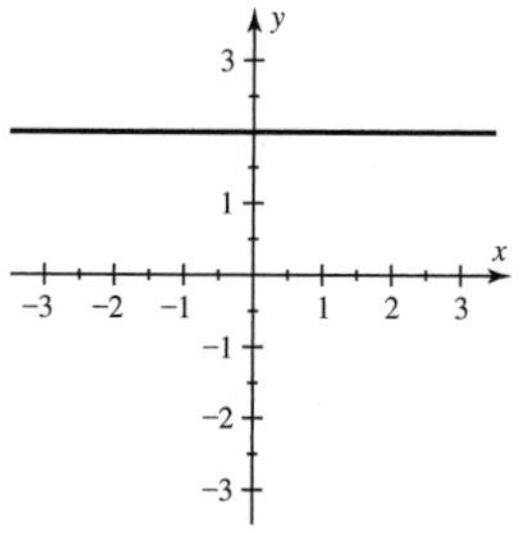

Figure 47

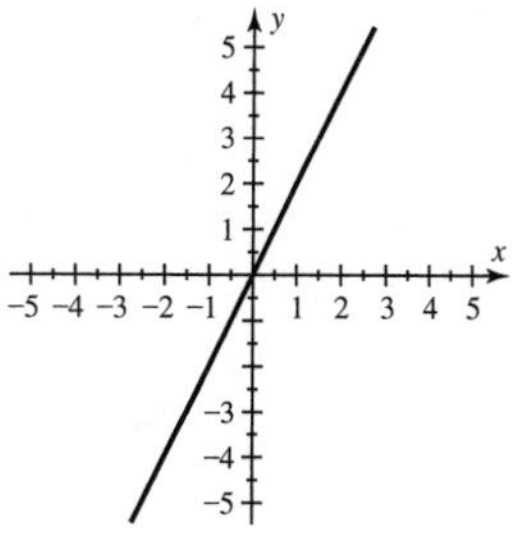

Figure 49

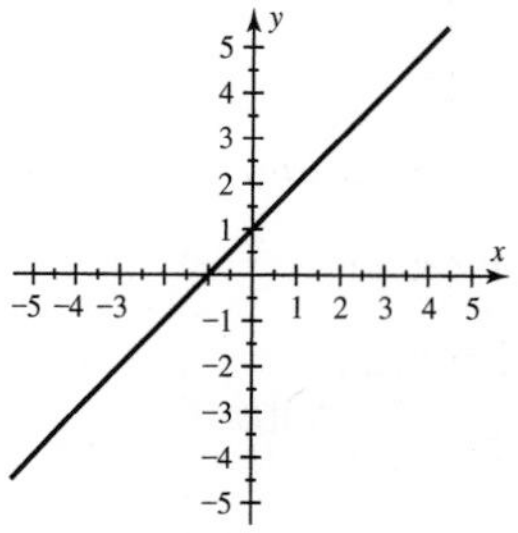

Figure 51

51. See Figure 51.

53. See Figure 53.

55. See Figure 55.

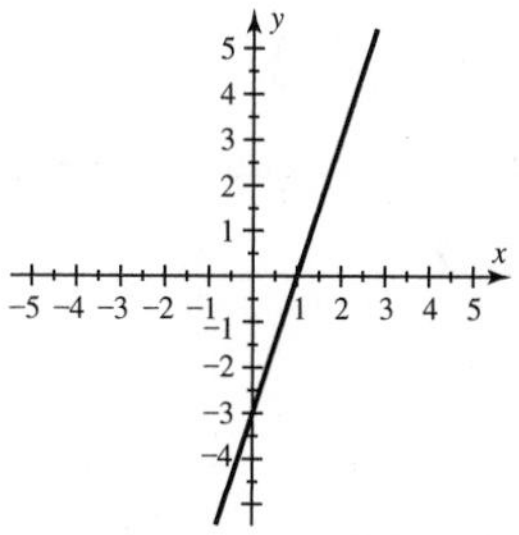

Figure 53

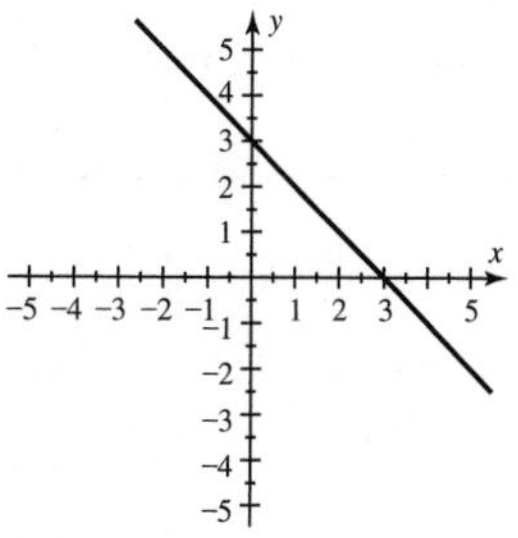

Figure 55

57. Since each pound is divided into 16 ounces: $f(x) = \frac{1}{16}x$

59. Since the car travels 65 miles each hour: $f(t) = 65t$

61. Since every day has 24 hours: $f(x) = 24$

Modeling

63. The graph should increase since the cost of tuition has been rising but it should not start at zero. b

65. The graph should be a horizontal line since this distance has not changed over the past 10 years. c

Applications

67. (a) Symbolic: $f(x) = 70$

Graphical: A graph of the function is shown in Figure 67a.

(b) A table of the function is shown in Figure 67b.

(c) The function f is a constant function.

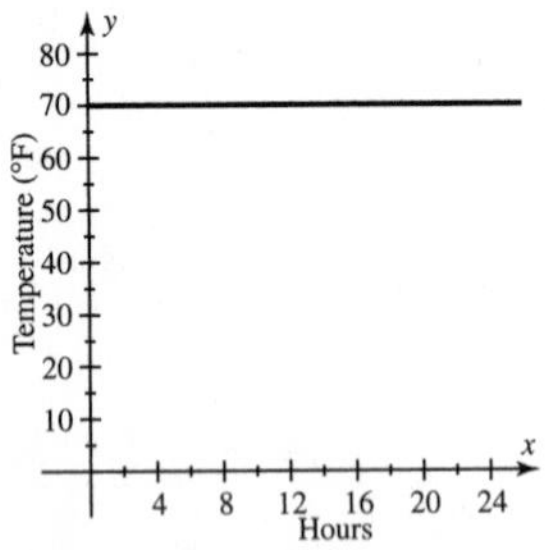

Figure 67a

Hours	0	4	8	12	16	20	24
Temp. (°F)	70	70	70	70	70	70	70

Figure 67b

69. For each 2-hour increase in t, the distance increases by 120 miles, so $a = \dfrac{120}{2} = 60$.

Because $D = 50$ when $t = 0$, the y-intercept is $b = 50$. The function can be written $D(t) = 60t + 50$.

71. (a) Because the average person disposed of 2.7 pounds of garbage each day, the function is $f(x) = 2.7x$.

$f(60) = 2.7(60) = 162$; In 1960 the average person disposed of 162 pounds of garbage in 60 days.

(b) Because the average person disposed of 4.3 pounds of garbage each day, the function is $g(x) = 4.3x$.

$g(60) = 4.3(60) = 258$; In 2003 the average person disposed of 258 pounds of garbage in 60 days.

73. (a) Graph $Y_1 = 0.09X - 147.1$ in [1820, 1995, 20] by [0, 40, 10]. See Figure 73a. Median age is increasing.

(b) Table $Y_1 = 0.09X - 147.1$ with TblStart = 1820 and ΔTbl = 20. See Figure 73b.

$f(1900) = 23.9$; In 1900 the median age of the U.S. population was 23.9 years.

(c) Each year the median age increases by 0.09 year, on average.

[1820, 1995, 20] by [0, 40, 10]

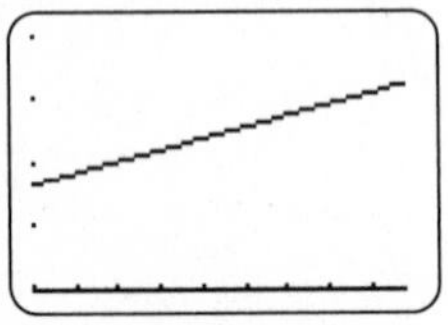

Figure 73a

Year (x)	1820	1840	1860	1880	1900	1920	1940
Median Age	16.7	18.5	20.3	22.1	23.9	25.7	27.5

Figure 73b

75. (a) Because each 1°C increase in temperature results in a 0.5 cubic centimeter increase in volume, $a = 0.5$.

Because the volume is 137 cubic centimeters when the temperature is 0°C, the y-intercept is $b = 137$.

The formula is $V(T) = 0.5T + 137$.

(b) $V(50) = 0.5(50) + 137 = 25 + 137 = 162$ cubic centimeters.

77. (a) From the table, the average length of a baseball game in 2000 was 180 minutes.

(b) Each year the average length of a game decreased by 4 minutes.

(c) Because the constant change is a decrease of 4 minutes, $a = -4$. Because the initial length is 180, $b = 180$.

The formula is $f(x) = -4x + 180$.

(d) The year 2004 corresponds to $x = 4$. $f(4) = -4(4) + 180 = -16 + 180 = 164$ minutes.79.

$f(x) = 40x$

In 30 days each additional pound of muscle will burn $40(30) = 1200$ calories. Then the amount of muscle necessary to lose 1 pound of fat is $3500 \div 1200 \approx 2.92$ lb.

Checking Basic Concepts for Sections 8.1 & 8.2

1. Symbolic: $f(x) = x^2 - 1$

Graphical: The graph is shown in Figure 1.

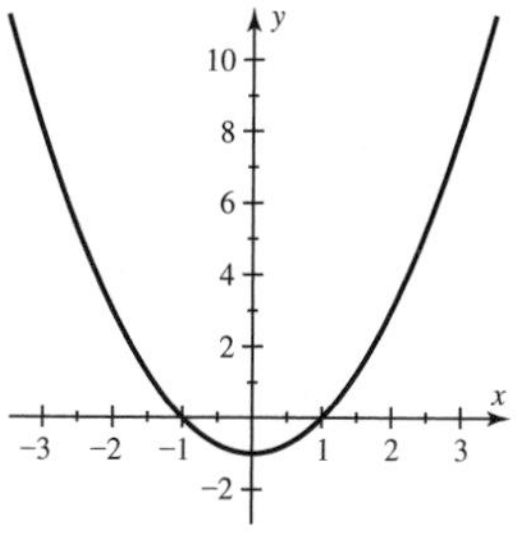

Figure 1

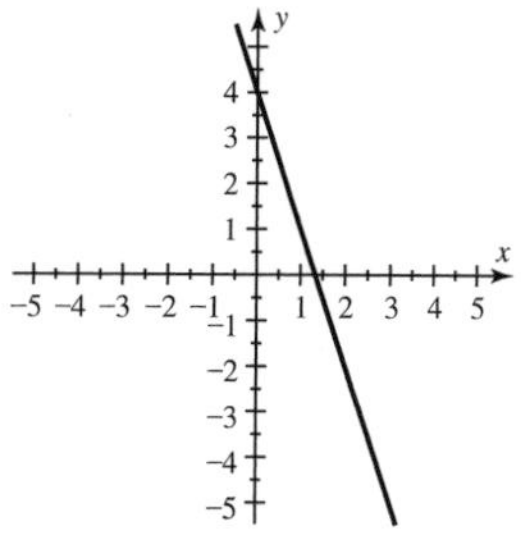

Figure 4

2. (a) $D: -3 \leq x \leq 3$; $R: -4 \leq y \leq 4$

(b) $f(0) = 0$; $f(2) = 4$

(c) No. The graph is not a straight line.

3. (a) Yes. The function is of the form $f(x) = ax + b$.

(b) No. The function can not be written in the form $f(x) = ax + b$.

(c) Yes. The function could be written $f(x) = 0x - 9$ which is of the form $f(x) = ax + b$.

(d) Yes. The function could be written $f(x) = 3x + 9$ which is of the form $f(x) = ax + b$.

4. The graph is shown in Figure 4. $f(-2) = 4 - 3(-2) = 4 + 6 = 10$.

5. For each 2-unit increase in x, the values of $f(x)$ increase by 1 unit, so $a = \frac{1}{2}$.

Because $f(x) = -1$ when $x = 0$, the y-intercept is $b = -1$. The function can be written $f(x) = \frac{1}{2}x - 1$.

6. (a) $f(20) = 0.264(20) + 27.7 = 5.28 + 27.7 = 32.98$; In 1990 the median age was about 33 years.

   (b) The number 0.264 means that the median age increased by 0.264 year each year. The number 27.7 means that the initial median age in 1970 was 27.7 years.

8.3: Compound Inequalities

Concepts

1. An example of a compound inequality containing the word *and* is $x > 1$ and $x \leq 7$; *Answers may vary.*
3. No, $1 \not> 3$.
5. Yes. The inequality can be written in either form.
7. Yes, $x = 2$ satisfies both inequalities. No, $x = 6$ does not satisfy $x - 1 < 5$.
9. No, $x = 0$ does not satisfy either inequality. Yes, $x = 3$ satisfies $2x \geq 3$.
11. No, $x = -3$ does not satisfy $2 - x \leq 4$. Yes, $x = 0$ satisfies both inequalities.

Interval Notation

13. $[2, 10]$
15. $(5, 8]$
17. $(-\infty, 4)$
19. $(-2, \infty)$
21. $(-\infty, -2] \cup [4, \infty)$
23. $(-\infty, 1) \cup [5, \infty)$
25. $(-3, 5]$
27. $(-\infty, -2)$
29. $(-\infty, 4)$
31. $(-\infty, 1) \cup (2, \infty)$

Symbolic Solutions

33. $x \leq 3$ and $x \geq -1 \Rightarrow -1 \leq x \leq 3$; $\{x \mid -1 \leq x \leq 3\}$; See Figure 33.

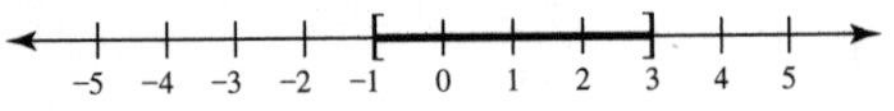

Figure 33

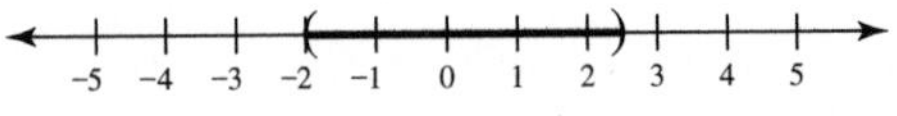

Figure 35

35. $2x < 5$ and $2x > -4 \Rightarrow x < \frac{5}{2}$ and $x > \frac{-4}{2} \Rightarrow -2 < x < 2.5$; $\{x \mid -2 < x < 2.5\}$; See Figure 35.

37. $x \leq -1$ or $x \geq 2$; $\{x \mid x \leq -1 \text{ or } x \geq 2\}$; See Figure 37.

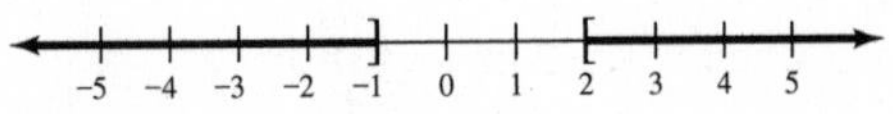

Figure 37

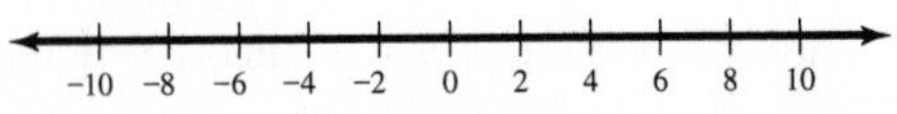

Figure 39

39. $5 - x > 1$ or $x + 3 \ge -1 \Rightarrow -x > -4$ or $x \ge -4 \Rightarrow x < 4$ or $x \ge -4$; All real numbers; See Figure 39.

41. $x - 3 \le 4 \Rightarrow x \le 7$ and $x + 5 \ge -1 \Rightarrow x \ge -6$

The solutions must satisfy both of these inequalities. The interval is $[-6, 7]$.

43. $3t - 1 > -1 \Rightarrow 3t > 0 \Rightarrow t > 0$ and $2t - \frac{1}{2} > 6 \Rightarrow 2t > \frac{13}{2} \Rightarrow t > \frac{13}{4}$

The solutions must satisfy both of these inequalities. The interval is $\left(\frac{13}{4}, \infty\right)$.

45. $x - 4 \ge -3 \Rightarrow x \ge 1$ or $x - 4 \le 3 \Rightarrow x \le 7$

The solutions may satisfy either one or both of these inequalities. The interval is $(-\infty, \infty)$.

47. $-x < 1 \Rightarrow x > 1$ or $5x + 1 < -10 \Rightarrow 5x < -11 \Rightarrow x < -\frac{11}{5}$

The solutions may satisfy either one or both of these inequalities. The interval is $\left(-\infty, -\frac{11}{5}\right) \cup (-1, \infty)$.

49. $1 - 7x < -48 \Rightarrow -7x < -49 \Rightarrow x > 7$ and $3x + 1 \le -9 \Rightarrow 3x \le -10 \Rightarrow x \le -\frac{10}{3}$

The solutions must satisfy both of these inequalities. This is not possible. No solutions.

51. $-2 \le t + 4 < 5 \Rightarrow -6 \le t < 1$; $[-6, 1)$

53. $-\frac{5}{8} \le y - \frac{3}{8} < 1 \Rightarrow -\frac{1}{4} \le y < \frac{11}{8}$; $\left[-\frac{1}{4}, \frac{11}{8}\right)$

55. $-27 \le 3x \le 9 \Rightarrow -9 \le x \le 3$; $[-9, 3]$

57. $\frac{1}{2} < -2y \le 8 \Rightarrow -\frac{1}{4} > y \ge -4 \Rightarrow -4 \le y < -\frac{1}{4}$; $\left[-4, -\frac{1}{4}\right)$

59. $-4 < 5z + 1 \le 6 \Rightarrow -5 < 5z \le 5 \Rightarrow -1 < z \le 1$; $(-1, 1]$

61. $3 \le 4 - n \le 6 \Rightarrow -1 \le -n \le 2 \Rightarrow 1 \ge n \ge -2 \Rightarrow -2 \le n \le 1$; $[-2, 1]$

63. $-1 < 2z - 1 < 3 \Rightarrow 0 < 2z < 4 \Rightarrow 0 < z < 2$; $(0, 2)$

65. $-2 \le 5 - \frac{1}{3}m < 2 \Rightarrow -7 \le -\frac{1}{3}m < -3 \Rightarrow 21 \ge m > 9 \Rightarrow 9 < m \le 21$; $(9, 21]$

67. $100 \le 10(5x - 2) \le 200 \Rightarrow 10 \le 5x - 2 \le 20 \Rightarrow 12 \le 5x \le 22 \Rightarrow \frac{12}{5} \le x \le \frac{22}{5}$; $\left[\frac{12}{5}, \frac{22}{5}\right]$

69. $-3 < \frac{3z + 1}{4} < 1 \Rightarrow -12 < 3z + 1 < 4 \Rightarrow -13 < 3z < 3 \Rightarrow -\frac{13}{3} < z < 1$; $\left(-\frac{13}{3}, 1\right)$

71. $-\frac{5}{2} \le \frac{2 - m}{4} \le \frac{1}{2} \Rightarrow -10 \le 2 - m \le 2 \Rightarrow -12 \le -m \le 0 \Rightarrow 12 \ge m \ge 0 \Rightarrow 0 \le m \le 12$; $[0, 12]$

Numerical and Graphical Solutions

73. The values of $3x$ are between -3 and 6 when $-1 \le x \le 2$. The interval is $[-1, 2]$.

75. The values of $1 - x$ are between -1 and 2 when $-1 < x < 2$. The interval is $(-1, 2)$.

77. The values of y_1 are between the lines $y = -2$ and $y = 2$ when $-3 \le x \le 1$. The interval is $[-3, 1]$.

79. The values of y_1 are below the line $y = -2$ and above the line $y = 2$ when $x < -2$ or $x > 0$.

The interval is $(-\infty, -2) \cup (0, \infty)$.

81. (a) The car is moving toward Omaha since the distance is decreasing.

(b) The car is 100 miles from Omaha when $x = 4$ hr. The car is 200 miles from Omaha when $x = 2$ hr.

(c) The car is 100 to 200 miles from Omaha when the elapsed time is between 2 and 4 hours.

(d) The car's distance from Omaha is greater than or equal to 200 miles during the first 2 hours.

83. Numerical: Table $Y_1 = 2X - 4$ with TblStart = 0 and ΔTbl = 1. See Figure 83a.

Graphical: Graph $Y_1 = -2$, $Y_2 = 2X - 4$ and $Y_3 = 4$ in [–5, 5, 1] by [–5, 5, 1]. See Figure 83b.

The solution is $[1, 4]$.

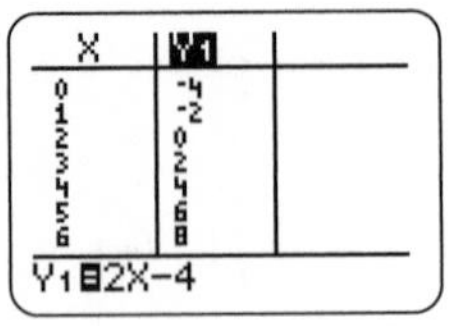

Figure 83a

[–5, 5, 1] by [–5, 5, 1]

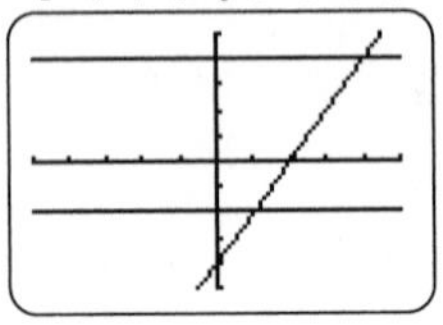

Figure 83b

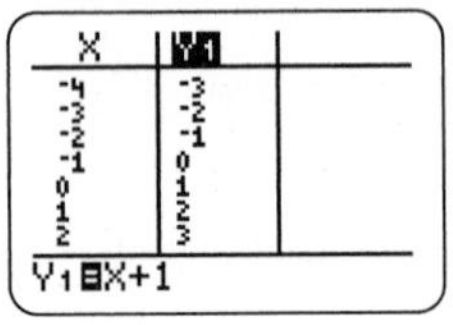

Figure 85a

[–5, 5, 1] by [–5, 5, 1]

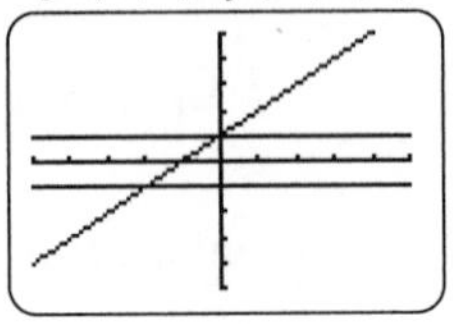

Figure 85b

85. Numerical: Table $Y_1 = X + 1$ with TblStart = –4 and ΔTbl = 1. See Figure 85a.

Graphical: Graph $Y_1 = -1$, $Y_2 = X + 1$ and $Y_3 = 1$ in [–5, 5, 1] by [–5, 5, 1]. See Figure 85b.

The solution is $(-\infty, -2) \cup (0, \infty)$.

Using More Than One Method

87. $4 \leq 5x - 1 \leq 14 \Rightarrow 5 \leq 5x \leq 15 \Rightarrow 1 \leq x \leq 3$; $[1, 3]$

Graphical: Graph $Y_1 = 4$, $Y_2 = 5X - 1$ and $Y_3 = 14$ in [0, 10, 1] by [0, 20, 1]. See Figure 87a.

Numerical: Table $Y_1 = 5X - 1$ with TblStart = 0 and ΔTbl = 1. See Figure 87b.

The solution is $[1, 3]$.

[0, 10, 1] by [0, 20, 1]

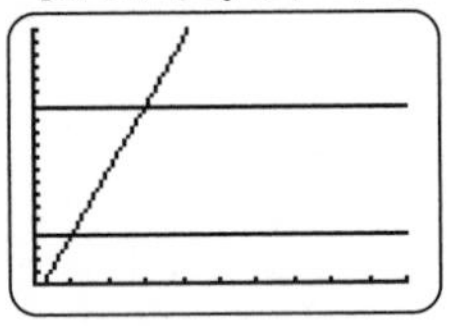

Figure 87a

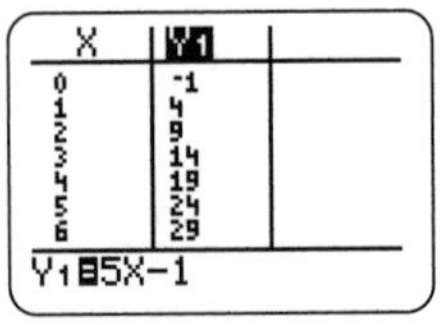

Figure 87b

[–5, 5, 1] by [–5, 5, 1]

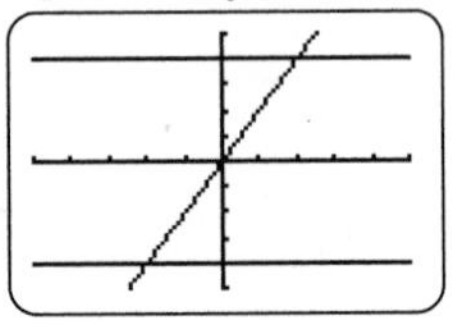

Figure 88a

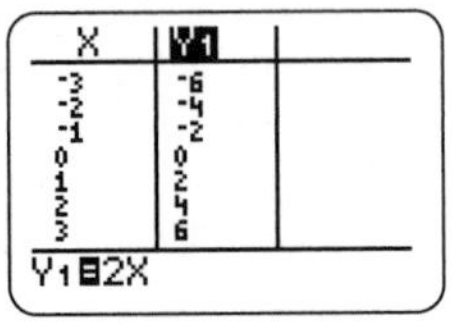

Figure 88b

89. $4 - x \geq 1$ or $4 - x < 3 \Rightarrow -x \geq -3$ or $-x < -1 \Rightarrow x \leq 3$ or $x > 1$; $(-\infty, \infty)$

Graphical: Graph $Y_1 = 1$, $Y_2 = 4 - X$ and $Y_3 = 3$ in [–10, 10, 1] by [–10, 10, 1]. See Figure 89a.

Numerical: Table $Y_1 = 4 - X$ with TblStart = –1 and ΔTbl = 1. See Figure 89b.

The solution is $(-\infty, \infty)$.

[–10, 10, 1] by [–10, 10, 1]

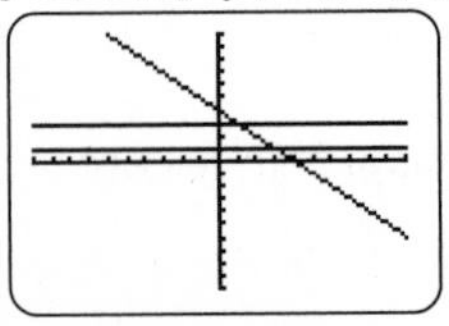

Figure 89a

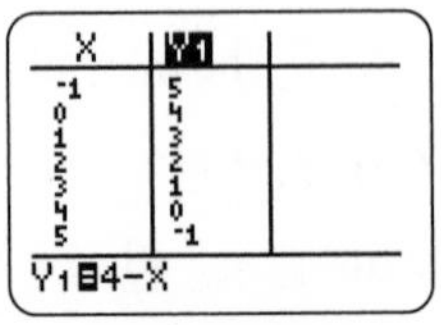

Figure 89b

Applications

91. The percentage was from 6% to 17% during the years from about 1950 to 1980.

93. $250 \le 18x - 35{,}750 \le 340 \Rightarrow 36{,}000 \le 18x \le 36{,}090 \Rightarrow 2000 \le x \le 2005$

Medicare costs will be from 250 to 340 billion dollars from 2000 to 2005.

95. The perimeter of the rectangle is given by $2(x + 3) + 2(2x)$.

$40 \le 2(x + 3) + 2(2x) \le 60 \Rightarrow 40 \le 6x + 6 \le 60 \Rightarrow 34 \le 6x \le 54 \Rightarrow 5.\overline{6} \le x \le 9$

97. (a) Table $Y_1 = 70X + 50$ with TblStart = 4 and ΔTbl = 1. See Figure 97. $[6, 9]$

The car is from 470 to 680 miles from the rest stop for times from 6 to 9 hours.

(b) $470 \le 70x + 50 \le 680 \Rightarrow 420 \le 70x \le 630 \Rightarrow 6 \le x \le 9$; $[6, 9]$

x	4	5	6	7	8	9	10
$f(x) = 70x + 50$	330	400	470	540	610	680	750

Figure 97

99. $-90 \le \frac{9}{5}C + 32 \le 98 \Rightarrow -122 \le \frac{9}{5}C \le 66 \Rightarrow -122\left(\frac{5}{9}\right) \le C \le 66\left(\frac{5}{9}\right) \Rightarrow -67.\overline{7} \le C \le 36.\overline{6}$

The temperature range in Celsius is $-67.\overline{7}$°C to $36.\overline{6}$°C.

8.4: Other Functions and Their Properties

Concepts

1. domain

3. $[1, \infty)$

5. $(-\infty, \infty)$

7. absolute value

9. 2

11. rational

Domain and Range

13. All real number inputs valid and all real number outputs possible. Therefore $D = (-\infty, \infty)$; $R = (-\infty, \infty)$.

15. All real number inputs valid and all real number outputs possible. Therefore $D = (-\infty, \infty)$; $R = (-\infty, \infty)$.

17. All real number inputs valid and $z^2 \ge 0$ for all possible real number outputs, then $z^2 + 2 \ge 2$.

Therefore $D = (-\infty, \infty)$; $R = [2, \infty)$.

19. All real number inputs valid and $z^2 \le 0$ for all possible real number outputs.

Therefore $D = (-\infty, \infty)$; $R = (-\infty, 0]$.

21. Since $\sqrt{}$ of negative numbers is undefined, then for $\sqrt{x + 1}$, $x + 1 \ge 0 \Rightarrow x \ge -1$ and all possible outputs will be positive. Therefore $D = [-1, \infty)$; $R = [0, \infty)$.

23. All real number inputs valid and absolute value outputs will be positive. Therefore $D = (-\infty, \infty)$; $R = [0, \infty)$.

25. The function will only be undefined when the denominator $x - 1 = 0 \Rightarrow x - 1 \neq 0 \Rightarrow x \neq 1$.

Therefore $D = (-\infty, 1)\cup(1, \infty)$.

27. The function will only be undefined when the denominator $6 - 3x = 0 \Rightarrow 6 - 3x \neq 0 \Rightarrow -3x \neq -6 \Rightarrow$ $x \neq 2$. Therefore $D = (-\infty, 2)\cup(2, \infty)$.

29. The function will only be undefined when the denominator $t^2 - 4 = 0 \Rightarrow t^2 - 4 \neq 0 \Rightarrow t^2 \neq 4 \Rightarrow$ $t \neq -2$ or 2. Therefore $D = (-\infty, -2)\cup(-2, 2)\cup(2, \infty)$.

31. The function will only be undefined when the denominator $t^2 - 2t = 0 \Rightarrow t^2 - 2t \neq 0 \Rightarrow t(t - 2) \neq 0 \Rightarrow$ $t \neq 0$ or 2. Therefore $D = (-\infty, 0)\cup(0, 2)\cup(2, \infty)$.

33. The function will only be undefined when the denominator $z^3 - 1 = 0 \Rightarrow z^3 - 1 \neq 0 \Rightarrow z^3 \neq 1 \Rightarrow z \neq 1$.

Therefore $D = (-\infty, 1)\cup(1, \infty)$.

35. The function will only be undefined when the denominator $x^2 - 2x - 3 = 0 \Rightarrow x^2 - 2x - 3 \neq 0 \Rightarrow$ $(x - 3)(x + 1) \neq 0 \Rightarrow x - 3 \neq 0$ or $x + 1 \neq 0 \Rightarrow x \neq 3$ or $x \neq -1$.

Therefore $D = (-\infty, -1)\cup(-1, 3)\cup(3, \infty)$.

37. All x or inputs possible, all y or outputs possible. Therefore, $D = (-\infty, \infty)$; $R = (-\infty, \infty)$.

39. Only inputs $-2 \leq x \leq 2$ graphed, only outputs $-2 \leq y \leq 2$. Therefore, $D = [-2, 2]$; $R = [-2, 2]$.

41. Only inputs $-2 \leq x \leq 3$ graphed, only outputs $-2 \leq y \leq 2$. Therefore, $D = [-2, 3]$; $R = [-2, 2]$.

Identifying Polynomial Functions

43. Yes, the function is a polynomial; variable to first power, so 1st degree; first degree polynomials are linear functions.

45. Yes, the function is a polynomial; variable to third power, so 3rd degree; third degree polynomials are cubic functions.

47. No, functions that include any variables in the denominator are rational functions and not polynomial functions.

49. Yes, the function is a polynomial; highest exponent on the variable is the second power, so 2nd degree; second degree polynomials are quadratic functions.

51. No, functions with negative exponents are not polynomial functions.

53. Yes, the function is a polynomial; highest exponent on the variable is the fourth power, so 4th degree; fourth degree polynomials are called fourth degree polynomials.

Evaluating Functions

55. $|4t|$ for $t = 3 \Rightarrow |4(3)| = |12| = 12$; $|4t|$ for $t = 0 \Rightarrow |4(0)| = |0| = 0$

57. $|t - 2|$ for $t = 1 \Rightarrow |1 - 2| = |-1| = 1$; $|t - 2|$ for $t = -\frac{3}{4} \Rightarrow \left|-\frac{3}{4} - 2\right| = \left|-\frac{11}{4}\right| = \frac{11}{4}$

59. $t^2 - t - 6$ for $t = 3 \Rightarrow (3)^2 - 3 - 6 = 9 - 3 - 6 = 0$

$t^2 - t - 6$ for $t = -3 \Rightarrow (-3)^2 - (-3) - 6 = 9 + 3 - 6 = 6$

61. $2t^3 - t$ for $t = 2 \Rightarrow 2(2)^3 - 2 = 2(8) - 2 = 16 - 2 = 14$

$2t^3 - t$ for $t = -2 \Rightarrow 2(-2)^3 - (-2) = 2(-8) - (-2) = -16 + 2 = -14$

63. $t^2 - 2t - 6$ for $t = 0 \Rightarrow (0)^2 - 2(0) - 6 = 0 - 0 - 6 = -6$

$t^2 - 2t - 6$ for $t = -3 \Rightarrow (-3)^2 - 2(-3) - 6 = 9 - (-6) - 6 = 9 + 6 - 6 = 9$

65. $\frac{1}{t}$ for $t = 11 \Rightarrow \frac{1}{11}$; $\frac{1}{t}$ for $t = -7 \Rightarrow \frac{1}{-7} = -\frac{1}{7}$

67. $-\frac{t}{t+1}$ for $t = 5 \Rightarrow -\frac{5}{5+1} = -\frac{5}{6}$; $-\frac{t}{t+1}$ for $t = -1 \Rightarrow -\frac{-1}{-1+1} = -\frac{-1}{0}$ = undefined

69. $\frac{t^2}{t^2 - t}$ for $t = -5 \Rightarrow \frac{(-5)^2}{(-5)^2 - (-5)} = \frac{25}{25 + 5} = \frac{25}{30} = \frac{5}{6}$;

$\frac{t^2}{t^2 - t}$ for $t = 1 \Rightarrow \frac{(1)^2}{(1)^2 - 1} = \frac{1}{1 - 1} = \frac{1}{0}$ = undefined

71. Evaluating from the graph should be similar to evaluating using the formula. Evaluating from the formula gives:

$1 - 2x$ for $x = 0 \Rightarrow 1 - 2(0) = 1 - 0 = 1$; $1 - 2x$ for $x = 1 \Rightarrow 1 - 2(1) = 1 - 2 = -1$.

73. Evaluating from the graph should be similar to evaluating using the formula. Evaluating from the formula gives:

$3x - x^3$ for $x = -1 \Rightarrow 3(-1) - (-1)^3 = -3 - (-1) = -2$; $3x - x^3$ for $x = 2 \Rightarrow 3(2) - (2)^3 = 6 - 8 = -2$.

75. Evaluating from the graph should be similar to evaluating using the formula. Evaluating from the formula gives:

$x - \frac{1}{2}x^2$ for $x = -2 \Rightarrow (-2) - \frac{1}{2}(-2)^2 = (-2) - \frac{1}{2}(4) = (-2) - 2 = -4$;

$x - \frac{1}{2}x^2$ for $x = 2 \Rightarrow 2 - \frac{1}{2}(2)^2 = 2 - \frac{1}{2}(4) = 2 - 2 = 0$.

77. Evaluating from the graph should be similar to evaluating using the formula. Evaluating from the formula gives:

$\frac{2}{x+1}$ for $x = -3 \Rightarrow \frac{2}{-3+1} = \frac{2}{-2} = -1$; $\frac{2}{x+1}$ for $x = -1 \Rightarrow \frac{2}{-1+1} = \frac{2}{0}$ = undefined.

79. See Figure 79.

81. See Figure 81.

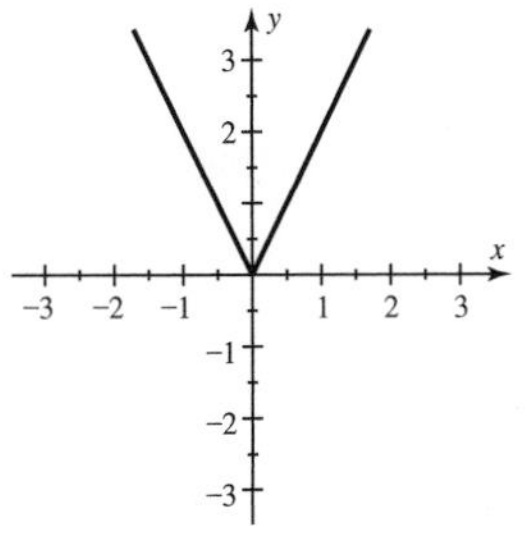

Figure 79

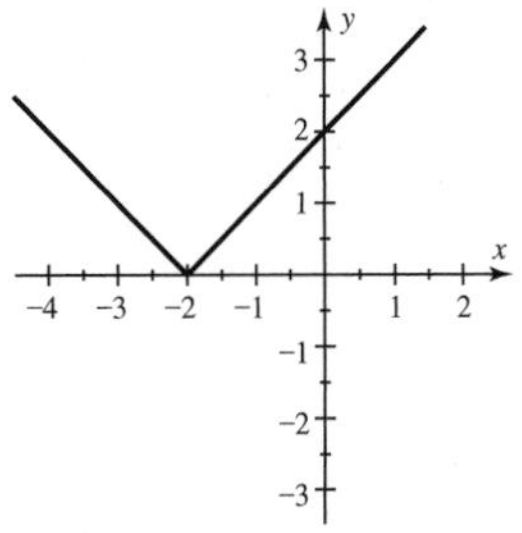

Figure 81

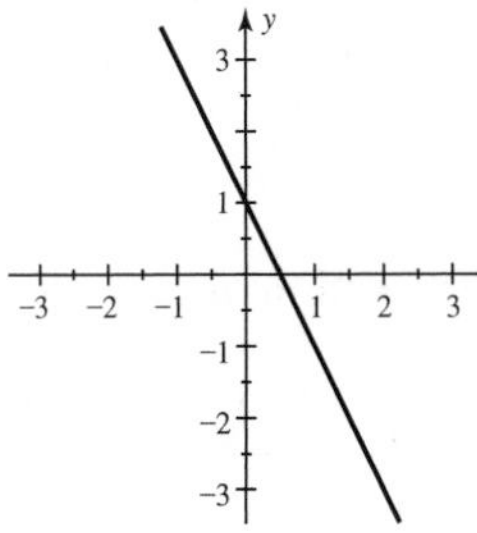

Figure 83

83. See Figure 83.

85. See Figure 85.

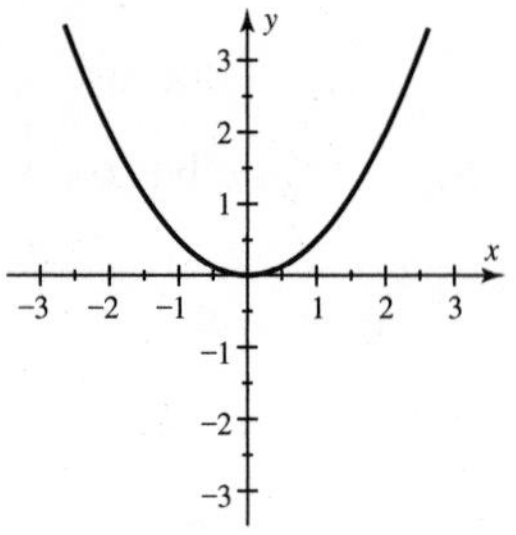

Figure 85

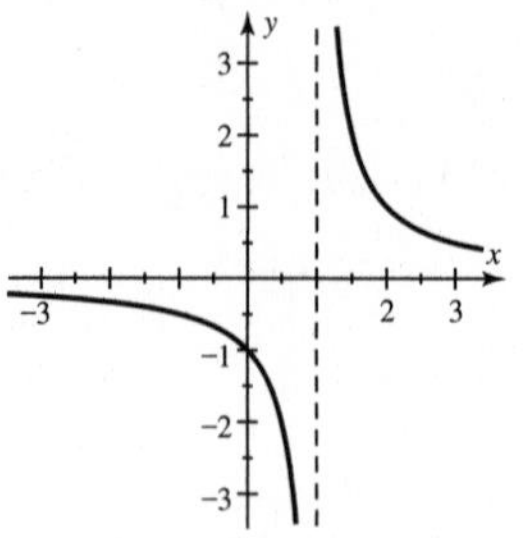

Figure 87

87. See Figure 87.

Applications

89. (a) No, only get exact outputs at 0 and 10 seconds, others are only close.

(b) Yes, all output answers are reasonably close.

(c) No, the problem tells us the race lasts 10 seconds. The domain is $0 \le t \le 10$.

91. (a) Yes, walking 0 minutes burns 0 calories.

(b) Linear, the data forms a straight line.

(c) $C(t) = x \cdot t \Rightarrow 32 = x \cdot 6 \Rightarrow \frac{32}{6} = x \Rightarrow \frac{16}{3} = x \Rightarrow C(t) = \frac{16}{3}t.$

93. c

95. d

97. (a) $\frac{2540}{r}$ for $r = 300 \Rightarrow \frac{2540}{300} = 8.4\overline{6}$; the elevation of the outer rail should be about 8.5 inches when the radius of the curve is 300 feet.

(b) Graph $Y_1 = 2540/X$ in [0, 600, 100] by [0, 50, 10]. See Figure 97.

(c) The higher the radius the more gradual the curve, therefore, as the radius increases the change in the elevation of the outer rail decreases.

[0, 600, 100] by [0, 50, 10]

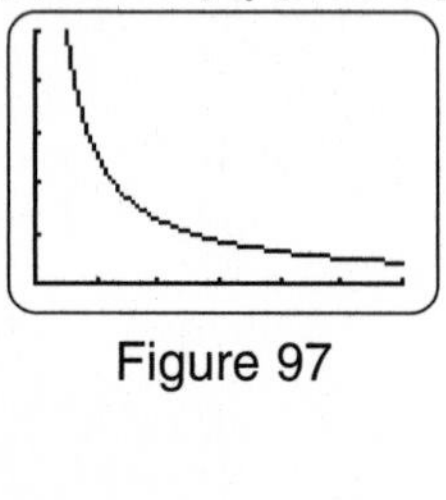

Figure 97

Checking Basic Concepts for Sections 8.3 & 8.4

1. (a) Evaluate $x = 3$ for $x + 2 < 4$ or $2x - 1 \geq 3$.

   $3 + 2 < 4 \Rightarrow 5 < 4 \Rightarrow$ False; $2(3) - 1 \geq 3 \Rightarrow 6 - 1 \geq 3 \Rightarrow 5 \geq 3 \Rightarrow$ True. Because an (or) compound inequality must satisfy at least one of the two inequalities to be true, and this has one; Yes.

   (b) Evaluate $x = 3$ for $x + 2 < 4$ or $2x - 1 \geq 3$. As shown in part (a), one is false and one is true. For an (and) compound inequality both must be true for the statement to be true; No.

2. (a) $-5 \leq 2x + 1 \leq 3 \Rightarrow -6 \leq 2x \leq 2 \Rightarrow -3 \leq x \leq 1 \Rightarrow [-3, 1]$

   (b) $1 - x \leq -2$ or $1 - x \geq 2$; $1 - x \leq -2 \Rightarrow -x \leq -3 \Rightarrow x \geq 3$ or $1 - x \geq 2 \Rightarrow -x \geq 1 \Rightarrow x \leq -1$

   Therefore, $x \leq -1$ and $x \geq 3 \Rightarrow (-\infty, -1] \cup [3, \infty)$.

   (c) $-2 < \dfrac{4 - 3x}{2} \leq 6 \Rightarrow -4 < 4 - 3x \leq 12 \Rightarrow -8 < -3x \leq 8 \Rightarrow \dfrac{8}{3} > x \geq -\dfrac{8}{3} \Rightarrow$

   $-\dfrac{8}{3} \leq x < \dfrac{8}{3} \Rightarrow \left[-\dfrac{8}{3}, \dfrac{8}{3}\right)$

3. (a) All inputs for x valid, therefore $D = (-\infty, \infty)$.

   (b) The function will only be undefined when the denominator $t - 1 = 0 \Rightarrow t - 1 \neq 0 \Rightarrow t \neq 1 \Rightarrow$ $D = (-\infty, 1) \cup (1, \infty)$.

   (c) Since $\sqrt{}$ of negative numbers is undefined, then for $\sqrt{z}$, $z \geq 0 \Rightarrow D = [0, \infty)$.

4. (a) $D = [-2, 1]$; $R = [-3, 1]$

   (b) 1; -3

5. See Figure 5.

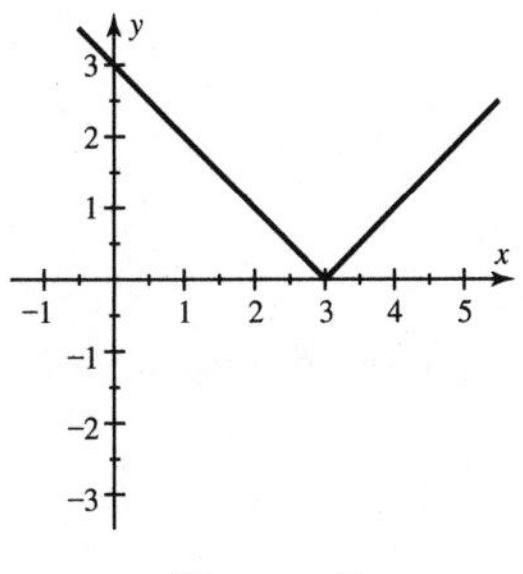

Figure 5

8.5: Absolute Value Equations and Inequalities

Concepts

1. An example of an absolute value equation is $|3x + 2| = 6$. *Answers may vary.*

3. Yes, since $|-3| = 3$.

5. Yes

7. No, $|2(-3) - 5| = |-11| = 11 \neq 1$. Yes, $|2(3) - 5| = |1| = 1$.

9. No, $|7 - 4(-2)| = |15| = 15 \nleq 5$. Yes, $|7 - 4(2)| = |-1| = 1 \leq 1$.

11. Yes, $\left|7\left(-\frac{4}{7}\right)+4\right| = |-4+4| = |0| = 0 > -1$. Yes, $|7(2)+4| = |18| = 18 > -1$.

13. $x = 0$ or $x = 4$

Symbolic Solutions

15. $x = -7$ or $x = 7$

17. $x = 0$

19. $4x = 9 \Rightarrow x = \frac{9}{4}$ or $4x = -9 \Rightarrow x = -\frac{9}{4}$

21. Since $|-2x| - 6 = 2 \Rightarrow |-2x| = 8$: $-2x = 8 \Rightarrow x = -4$ or $-2x = -8 \Rightarrow x = 4$

23. $2x + 1 = 11 \Rightarrow 2x = 10 \Rightarrow x = 5$ or $2x + 1 = -11 \Rightarrow 2x = -12 \Rightarrow x = -6$

25. Since $|-2x+3| + 3 = 4 \Rightarrow |-2x+3| = 1$:

$-2x + 3 = 1 \Rightarrow -2x = -2 \Rightarrow x = 1$ or $-2x + 3 = -1 \Rightarrow -2x = -4 \Rightarrow x = 2$

27. $\frac{1}{2}x - 1 = 5 \Rightarrow \frac{1}{2}x = 6 \Rightarrow x = 12$ or $\frac{1}{2}x - 1 = -5 \Rightarrow \frac{1}{2}x = -4 \Rightarrow x = -8$

29. An absolute value can not be negative. No solution.

31. Since $\left|\frac{2}{3}z - 1\right| - 3 = 8 \Rightarrow \left|\frac{2}{3}z - 1\right| = 11$:

$\frac{2}{3}z - 1 = 11 \Rightarrow \frac{2}{3}z = 12 \Rightarrow z = 18$ or $\frac{2}{3}z - 1 = -11 \Rightarrow \frac{2}{3}z = -10 \Rightarrow z = -15$

33. $z - 1 = 2z \Rightarrow -z = 1 \Rightarrow z = -1$ or $z - 1 = -2z \Rightarrow 3z = 1 \Rightarrow z = \frac{1}{3}$

35. $3t + 1 = 2t - 4 \Rightarrow t = -5$ or $3t + 1 = -2t + 4 \Rightarrow 5t = 3 \Rightarrow t = \frac{3}{5}$

37. $\frac{1}{4}x = 3 + \frac{1}{4}x \Rightarrow 0 = 3$ (no solution) or $\frac{1}{4}x = -3 - \frac{1}{4}x \Rightarrow \frac{1}{2}x = -3 \Rightarrow x = -6$

39. (a) $2x = 8 \Rightarrow x = 4$ or $2x = -8 \Rightarrow x = -4$

(b) $\{x \mid -4 < x < 4\}$

(c) $\{x \mid x < -4 \text{ or } x > 4\}$

41. (a) $5 - 4x = 3 \Rightarrow -4x = -2 \Rightarrow x = \frac{1}{2}$ or $5 - 4x = -3 \Rightarrow -4x = -8 \Rightarrow x = 2$

(b) $\left\{x \mid \frac{1}{2} \le x \le 2\right\}$

(c) $\left\{x \mid x \le \frac{1}{2} \text{ or } x \ge 2\right\}$

43. The solutions to $|x| \le 3$ satisfy $c \le x \le d$ where c and d are the solutions to $|x| = 3$.

$|x| = 3$ is equivalent to $x = -3$ and $x = 3$. The interval is $[-3, 3]$.

45. The solutions to $|k| > 4$ satisfy $k < c$ or $k > d$ where c and d are the solutions to $|k| = 4$.

$|k| = 4$ is equivalent to $k = -4$ and $k = 4$. The interval is $(-\infty, -4) \cup (4, \infty)$.

47. The inequality $|t| \le -3$ has no solutions because absolute value is never negative.

49. The inequality $|z| > 0$ is true for any value of z except $z = 0$. The interval is $(-\infty, 0) \cup (0, \infty)$.

51. The solutions to $|2x| > 7$ satisfy $x < c$ or $x > d$ where c and d are the solutions to $|2x| = 7$.

    $|2x| = 7$ is equivalent to $2x = -7 \Rightarrow x = -\frac{7}{2}$ and $2x = 7 \Rightarrow x = \frac{7}{2}$.

    The interval is $\left(-\infty, -\frac{7}{2}\right) \cup \left(\frac{7}{2}, \infty\right)$.

53. The solutions to $|-4x + 4| < 16$ satisfy $c < x < d$ where c and d are the solutions to $|-4x + 4| = 16$.

    $|-4x + 4| = 16$ is equivalent to $-4x + 4 = -16 \Rightarrow x = 5$ and $-4x + 4 = 16 \Rightarrow x = -3$.

    The interval is $(-3, 5)$.

55. First divide each side of $2|x + 5| \geq 8$ by 2 to obtain $|x + 5| \geq 4$.

    The solutions to $|x + 5| \geq 4$ satisfy $x \leq c$ or $x \geq d$ where c and d are the solutions to $|x + 5| = 4$.

    $|x + 5| = 4$ is equivalent to $x + 5 = -4 \Rightarrow x = -9$ and $x + 5 = 4 \Rightarrow x = -1$.

    The interval is $(-\infty, -9] \cup [-1, \infty)$.

57. First add 1 to each side of $|8 - 6x| - 1 \leq 2$ to obtain $|8 - 6x| \leq 3$.

    The solutions to $|8 - 6x| \leq 3$ satisfy $c \leq x \leq d$ where c and d are the solutions to $|8 - 6x| = 3$.

    $|8 - 6x| = 3$ is equivalent to $8 - 6x = -3 \Rightarrow x = \frac{11}{6}$ and $8 - 6x = 3 \Rightarrow x = \frac{5}{6}$. The interval is $\left[\frac{5}{6}, \frac{11}{6}\right]$.

59. First subtract 5 from each side of $5 + \left|\frac{2 - x}{3}\right| \leq 9$ to obtain $\left|\frac{2 - x}{3}\right| \leq 4$.

    The solutions to $\left|\frac{2 - x}{3}\right| \leq 4$ satisfy $c \leq x \leq d$ where c and d are the solutions to $\left|\frac{2 - x}{3}\right| = 4$.

    $\left|\frac{2 - x}{3}\right| = 4$ is equivalent to $\frac{2 - x}{3} = -4 \Rightarrow x = 14$ and $\frac{2 - x}{3} = 4 \Rightarrow x = -10$. The interval is $[-10, 14]$.

61. The inequality $|2x - 1| \leq -3$ has no solutions because absolute value is never negative.

63. First add 1 to each side of $|x + 1| - 1 > -3$ to obtain $|x + 1| > -2$.

    The inequality $|x + 1| > -2$ is true for all values of x because absolute value is never negative

    The interval is $(-\infty, \infty)$.

65. The inequality $|2z - 4| \leq -1$ has no solutions because absolute value is never negative.

67. The inequality $|3z - 1| > -3$ is true for all values of z because absolute value is never negative.

    The interval is $(-\infty, \infty)$.

69. The solutions to $\left|\frac{2 - t}{3}\right| \geq 5$ satisfy $t \leq c$ or $t \geq d$ where c and d are the solutions to $\left|\frac{2 - t}{3}\right| = 5$.

    $\left|\frac{2 - t}{3}\right| = 5$ is equivalent to $\frac{2 - t}{3} = -5 \Rightarrow t = 17$ and $\frac{2 - t}{3} = 5 \Rightarrow x = -13$.

    The interval is $(-\infty, -13] \cup [17, \infty)$.

    The interval is $(-\infty, -19] \cup [16, \infty)$.

71. The solutions to $|t - 1| \leq 0.1$ satisfy $c \leq t \leq d$ where c and d are the solutions to $|t - 1| = 0.1$.

    $|t - 1| = 0.1$ is equivalent to $t - 1 = -0.1 \Rightarrow t = 0.9$ and $t - 1 = 0.1 \Rightarrow t = 1.1$. The interval is $[0.9, 1.1]$.

73. The solutions to $|b - 10| > 0.5$ satisfy $b < c$ or $b > d$ where c and d are the solutions to $|b - 10| = 0.5$.

$|b - 10| = 0.5$ is equivalent to $b - 10 = -0.5 \Rightarrow b = 9.5$ and $b - 10 = 0.5 \Rightarrow b = 10.5$.

The interval is $(-\infty, 9.5) \cup (10.5, \infty)$.

Numerical and Graphical Solutions

75. (a) From the table, $y = 2$ when $x = -1$ or $x = 3$.

(b) $y < 2$ when $-1 < x < 3$. The interval is $(-1, 3)$.

(c) $y > 2$ when $x < -1$ or $x > 3$. The interval is $(-\infty, -1) \cup (3, \infty)$.

77. (a) From the graph $y_1 = 1$ when $x = -1$ or $x = 0$.

(b) $y_1 \le 1$ when $-1 \le x \le 0$. The interval is $[-1, 0]$.

(c) $y_1 \ge 1$ when $x \le -1$ or $x \ge 0$. The interval is $(-\infty, -1] \cup [0, \infty)$.

79. Graph Y_1 = abs(X) and Y_2 = 1 in [−3, 3, 1] by [−3, 3, 1]. See Figures 79a and 79b. $(-\infty, -1] \cup [1, \infty)$

[−3, 3, 1] by [−3, 3, 1]

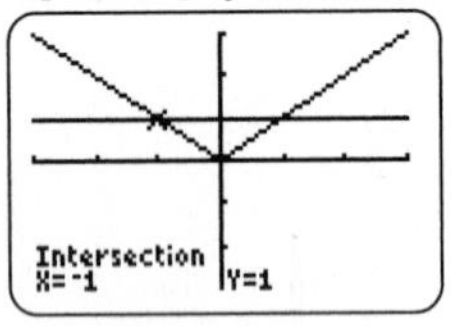

Figure 79a

[−3, 3, 1] by [−3, 3, 1]

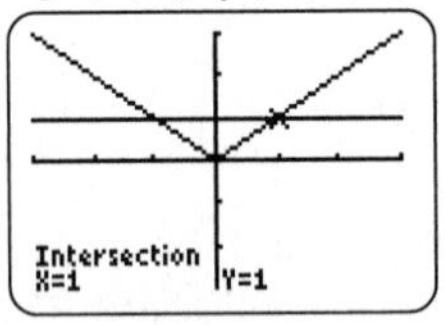

Figure 79b

[−5, 5, 1] by [−5, 5, 1]

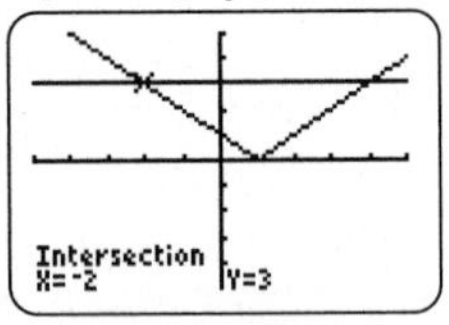

Figure 81a

[−5, 5, 1] by [−5, 5, 1]

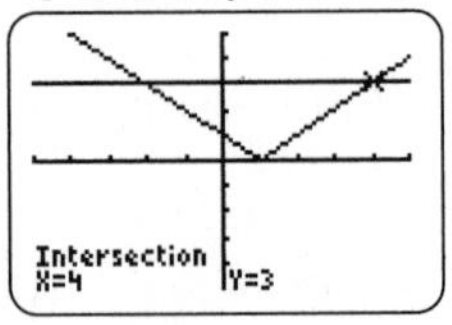

Figure 81b

81. Graph Y_1 = abs(X − 1) and Y_2 = 3 in [−5, 5, 1] by [−5, 5, 1]. See Figures 81a and 81b. $[-2, 4]$

83. Graph Y_1 = abs(4 − 2X) and Y_2 = 2 in [0, 5, 1] by [0, 5, 1]. See Figures 83a and 83b. $(-\infty, 1) \cup (3, \infty)$

[0, 5, 1] by [0, 5, 1]

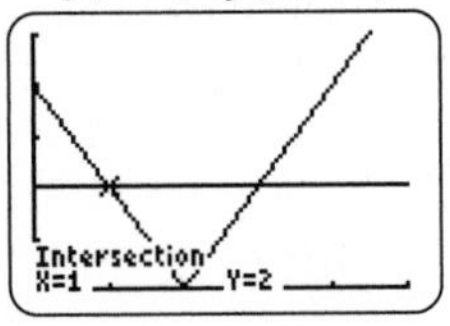

Figure 83a

[0, 5, 1] by [0, 5, 1]

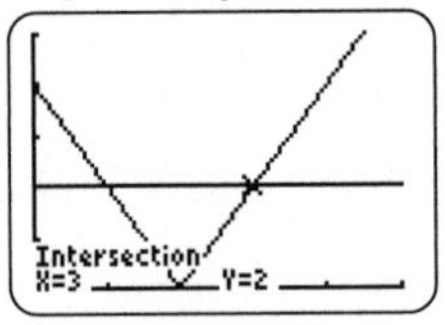

Figure 83b

[−8, 8, 1] by [0, 10, 1]

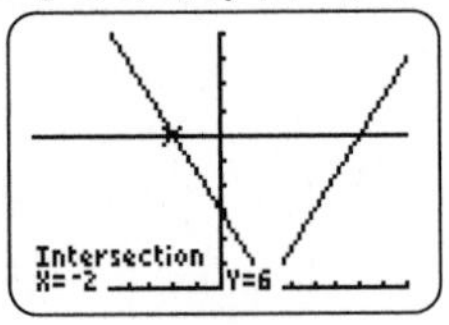

Figure 85a

[−8, 8, 1] by [0, 10, 1]

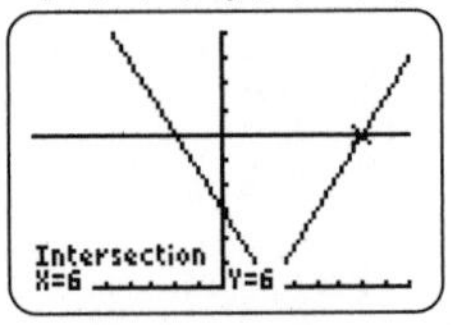

Figure 85b

85. Graph Y_1 = abs(1.5X − 3) and Y_2 = 6 in [−8, 8, 1] by [0, 10, 1]. See Figures 85a and 85b. $(2, 4.\overline{6})$

87. Graph Y_1 = abs(8.1 − X) and Y_2 = −2 in [0, 15, 1] by [−5, 5, 1]. See Figure 87. $(-\infty, \infty)$

[0, 15, 1] by [−5, 5, 1]

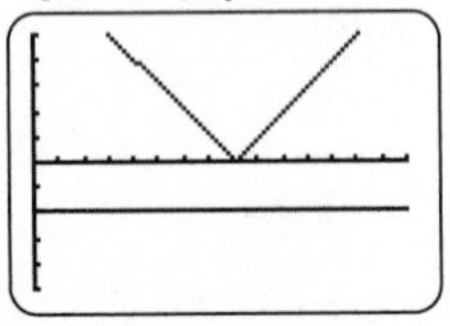

Figure 87

Using More Than One Method

89. (a) $3x = 9 \Rightarrow x = 3$ or $3x = -9 \Rightarrow x = -3$; $\{x \mid -3 \le x \le 3\}$

(b) Graph $Y_1 = \text{abs}(3X)$ and $Y_2 = 9$ in $[-5, 5, 1]$ by $[-5, 15, 1]$. See Figures 89a and 89b.

(c) Table $Y_1 = \text{abs}(3X)$ with TblStart = –7 and ΔTbl = 2. See Figure 89c.

The solution set is $\{x \mid -3 \le x \le 3\}$.

[–5, 5, 1] by [–5, 15, 1]

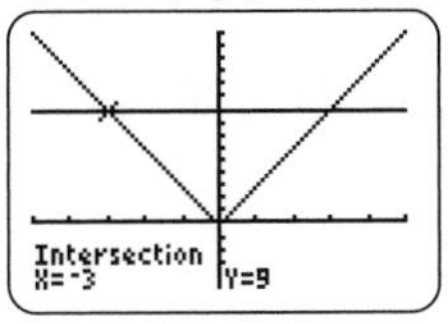

Figure 89a

[–5, 5, 1] by [–5, 15, 1]

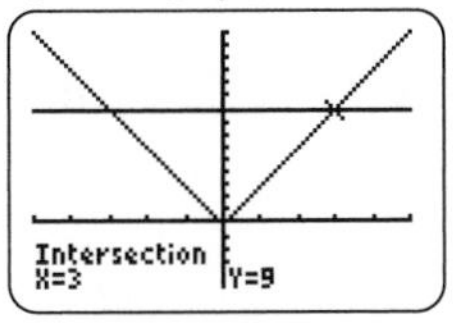

Figure 89b

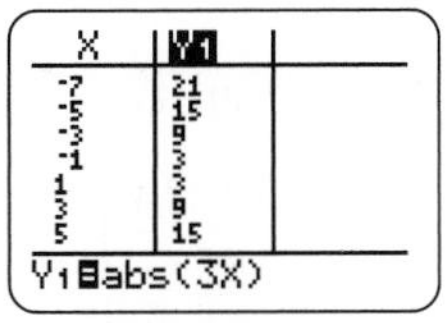

Figure 89c

91. (a) $2x - 5 = 1 \Rightarrow 2x = 6 \Rightarrow x = 3$ or $2x - 5 = -1 \Rightarrow 2x = 4 \Rightarrow x = 2$; $\{x \mid x < 2 \text{ or } x > 3\}$

(b) Graph $Y_1 = \text{abs}(2X - 5)$ and $Y_2 = 1$ in $[0, 5, 1]$ by $[-1, 2, 1]$. See Figures 91a and 91b.

(c) Table $Y_1 = \text{abs}(2X - 5)$ with TblStart = 1 and ΔTbl = 0.5. See Figure 91c.

The solution set is $\{x \mid x < 2 \text{ or } x > 3\}$.

[0, 5, 1] by [–1, 2, 1]

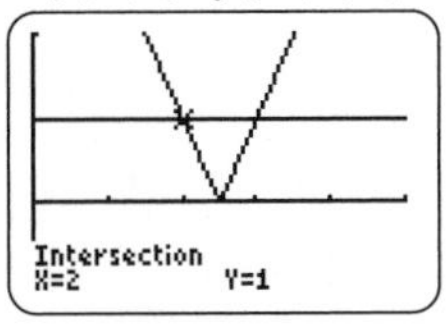

Figure 91a

[0, 5, 1] by [–1, 2, 1]

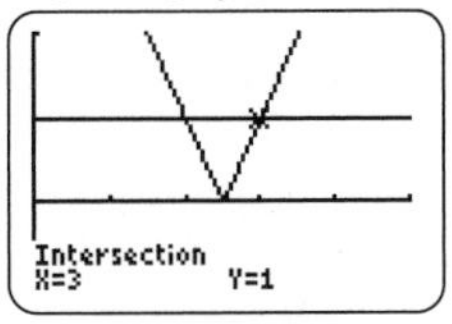

Figure 91b

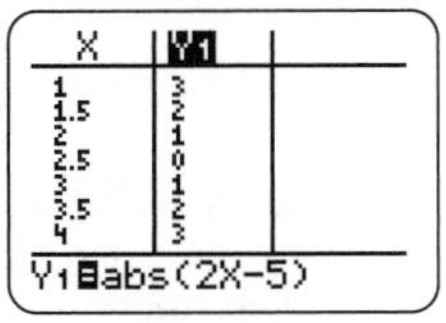

Figure 91c

Applications

93. (a) $T - 43 = 24 \Rightarrow T = 67$ or $T - 43 = -24 \Rightarrow T = 19$; $\{T \mid 19 \le T \le 67\}$

(b) The monthly average temperatures in Marquette, Michigan vary from 19°F to 67°F.

95. (a) $T - 10 = 36 \Rightarrow T = 46$ or $T - 10 = -36 \Rightarrow T = -26$; $\{T \mid -26 \le T \le 46\}$

(b) The monthly average temperatures in Chesterfield, Canada vary from –26°F to 46°F.

97. (a) $A = (29{,}028 + 22{,}834 + 20{,}320 + 19{,}340 + 18{,}510 + 16{,}066 + 7{,}310) \div 7 \approx 19{,}058$ feet

(b) Africa and Europe have elevations within 1000 feet of A.

(c) South America, North America, Africa, Europe and Antarctica have elevations within 5000 feet of A.

99. $d - 2.5 = 0.002 \Rightarrow d = 2.502$ or $d - 2.5 = -0.002 \Rightarrow d = 2.498$; $\{d \mid 2.498 \le d \le 2.502\}$

The diameter can vary from 2.498 inches to 2.502 inches.

101. The solutions to $\left|\frac{x - 20}{20}\right| < 0.05$ satisfy $c < x < d$ where c and d are the solutions to $\left|\frac{x - 20}{20}\right| = 0.05$.

$\left|\frac{x - 20}{20}\right| = 0.05$ is equivalent to $\frac{x - 20}{20} = -0.05 \Rightarrow x = 19$ and $\frac{x - 20}{20} = 0.05 \Rightarrow x = 21$.

The interval is $(19, 21)$. The values must be between 19 and 21, exclusively.

Checking Basic Concepts for Section 8.5

1. $\left|\frac{3}{4}x - 1\right| - 3 = 5 \Rightarrow \left|\frac{3}{4}x - 1\right| = 8$

$\frac{3}{4}x - 1 = -8 \Rightarrow \frac{3}{4}x = -7 \Rightarrow x = -\frac{28}{3}$ or $\frac{3}{4}x - 1 = 8 \Rightarrow \frac{3}{4}x = 9 \Rightarrow x = 12$

2. (a) $3x - 6 = 8 \Rightarrow 3x = 14 \Rightarrow x = \frac{14}{3}$ or $3x - 6 = -8 \Rightarrow 3x = -2 \Rightarrow x = -\frac{2}{3}$

(b) The solutions to $|3x - 6| < 8$ satisfy $c < x < d$ where c and d are the solutions to $|3x - 6| = 8$.

From part (a), the interval is $\left(-\frac{2}{3}, \frac{14}{3}\right)$.

(c) The solutions to $|3x - 6| > 8$ satisfy $x < c$ or $x > d$ where c and d are the solutions to $|3x - 6| = 8$.

From part (a), the interval is $\left(-\infty, -\frac{2}{3}\right) \cup \left(\frac{14}{3}, \infty\right)$.

3. The solutions to $|-2(3 - x)| < 6$ satisfy $c < x < d$ where c and d are the solutions to $|-2(3 - x)| = 6$.

$|-2(3 - x)| = 6$ is equivalent to $-2(3 - x) = -6 \Rightarrow x = 0$ and $-2(3 - x) = 6 \Rightarrow x = 6$.

The interval is $(0, 6)$. Similarly, the solution to $|-2(3 - x)| \geq 6$ is the interval $(-\infty, 0] \cup [6, \infty)$.

4. (a) From the graph $y = 2$ when $x = 1$ or $x = 3$.

(b) $y \leq 2$ when $1 \leq x \leq 3$. The interval is $[1, 3]$.

(c) $y \geq 2$ when $x \leq 1$ or $x \geq 3$. The interval is $(-\infty, 1] \cup [3, \infty)$.

Chapter 8 Review Exercises

Section 8.1

1. $f(-2) = 3(-2) - 1 = -7$; $f\left(\frac{1}{3}\right) = 3\left(\frac{1}{3}\right) - 1 = 0$

2. $f(-3) = 5 - 3(-3)^2 = 5 - 27 = -22$; $f(1) = 5 - 3(1)^2 = 5 - 3 = 2$

3. $f(0) = \sqrt{0} - 2 = -2$; $f(9) = \sqrt{9} - 2 = 3 - 2 = 1$

4. $f(-5) = 5$; $f\left(\frac{7}{5}\right) = 5$

5. (a) Since there are 2 pints in a quart, $P(q) = 2q$.

(b) $P(5) = 2(5) = 10$. There are 10 pints in 5 quarts.

6. (a) Three less than four times a number is written $f(x) = 4x - 3$.

(b) $f(5) = 4(5) - 3 = 17$. Three less than four times five is 17.

7. $(3, -2)$

8. $f(4) = 6$; the answers are 4 and 6.

9. See Figure 9.

10. See Figure 10.

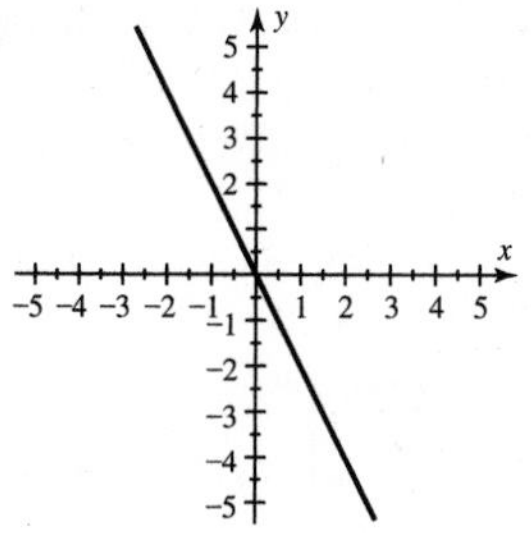
Figure 9

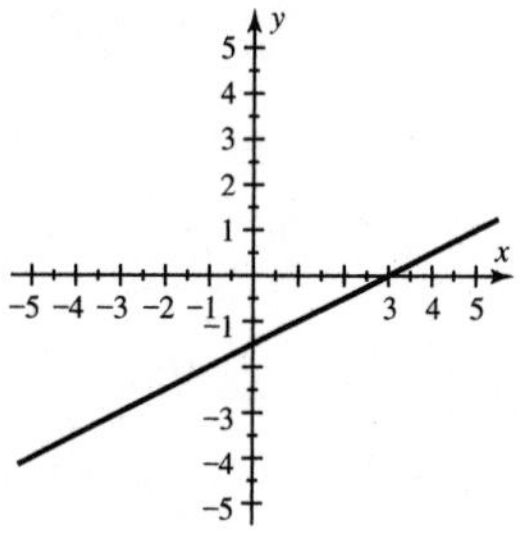
Figure 10

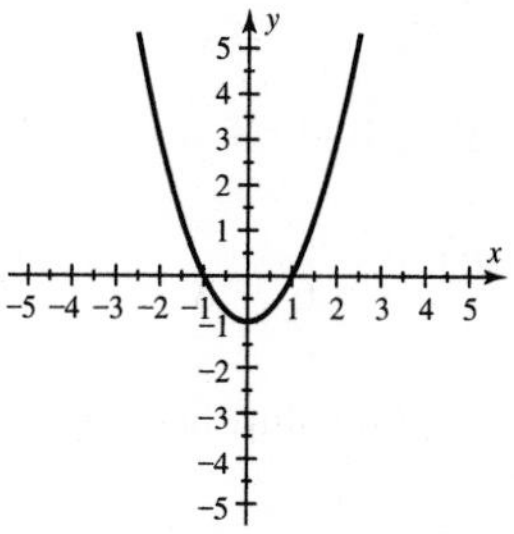
Figure 11

11. See Figure 11.

12. See Figure 12.

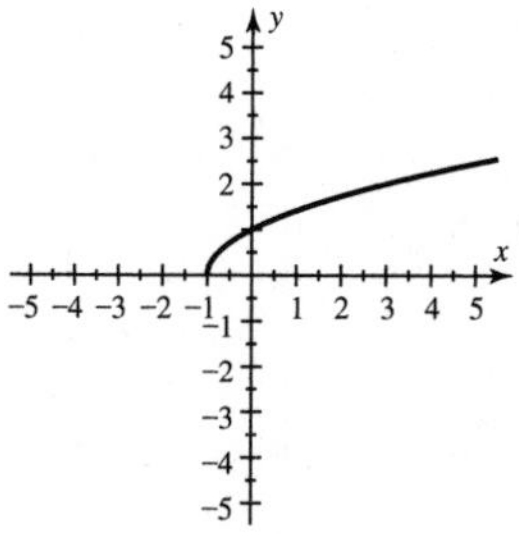
Figure 12

13. $f(0) = 1$; $f(-3) = 4$

14. $f(-2) = 1$; $f(1) = -2$

15. $f(-1) = 7$; $f(3) = -1$

16. Numerical: The table is shown in Figure 16a.

Symbolic: $f(x) = 3x - 2$

Graphical: The graph is shown in Figure 16b.

x	-3	-2	-1	0	1	2	3
$y = f(x)$	-11	-8	-5	-2	1	4	7

Figure 16a

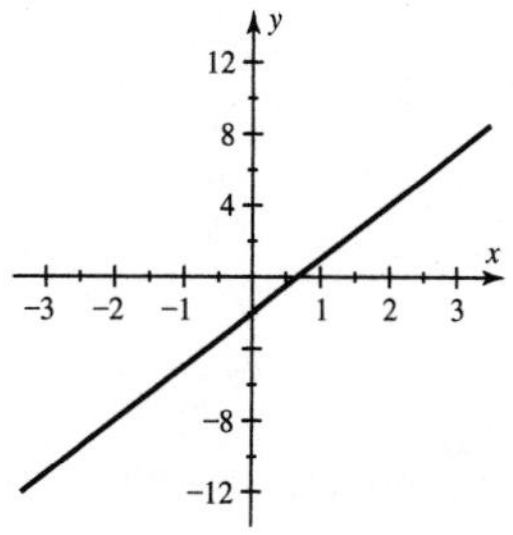
Figure 16b

17. D: all real numbers; R: $y \leq 4$

18. D: $-4 \leq x \leq 4$; R: $-4 \leq y \leq 0$

19. Yes. The graph passes the vertical line test.

20. No. The graph does not pass the vertical line test.

21. $D = \{-3, -1, 2, 4\}$; $R = \{-1, 3, 4\}$; Yes, S is a function since each input has exactly one output.

22. $D = \{-1, 0, 1, 2\}$; $R = \{-2, 2, 3, 4, 5\}$; No, S is not function because the input –1 has more than one output.

23. Any real number is a valid input for this function. D: all real numbers.

24. The radicand must be greater than or equal to zero. D: $x \geq 0$.

25. The denominator of this function cannot equal zero. D: $x \neq 0$.

26. Any real number is a valid input for this function because the variable is squared. D: all real numbers.

Section 8.2

27. No. The graph is not a straight line.

28. Yes. The graph is a straight line.

29. This function is linear because it is in the form $f(x) = ax + b$ with $a = -4$ and $b = 5$.

30. This function is linear because it can be written in the form $f(x) = ax + b$ with $a = -1$ and $b = 7$.

31. This function is not linear because it contains a square root.

32. This function is linear because it can be written in the form $f(x) = ax + b$ with $a = 0$ and $b = 6$.

33. Yes. For each 2-unit increase in x, the values of $f(x)$ increase by 3 units, so $a = \frac{3}{2}$.

    Because $f(x) = -3$ when $x = 0$, the y-intercept is $b = -3$. The function can be written $f(x) = \frac{3}{2}x - 3$.

34. No. For each unit increase in x, the values of $f(x)$ do not increase by a constant amount.

35. $f(-4) = \frac{1}{2}(-4) + 3 = -2 + 3 = 1$

36. $f(-2) = -3$ and $f(1) = 0$

37. See Figure 37.

38. See Figure 38.

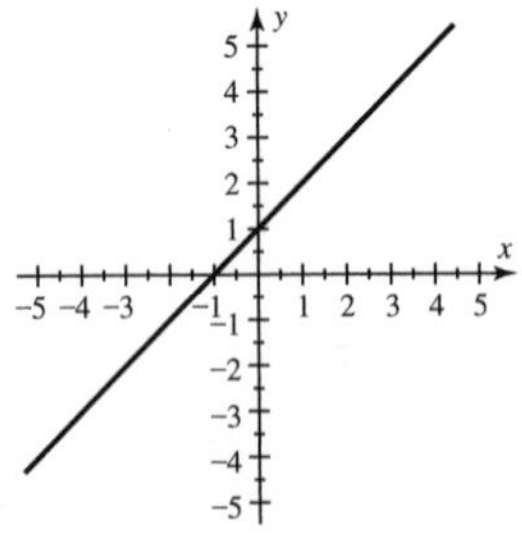

Figure 37

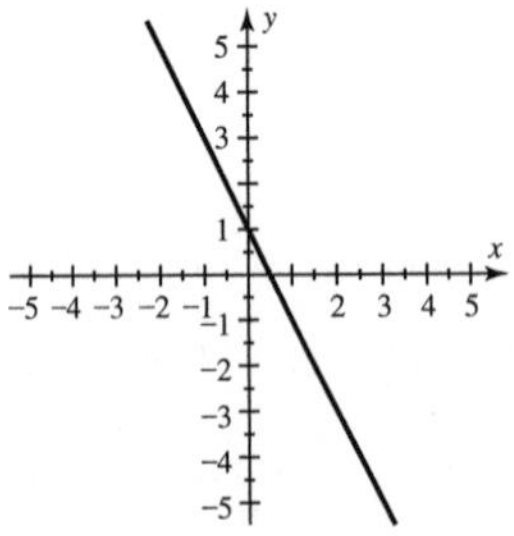

Figure 38

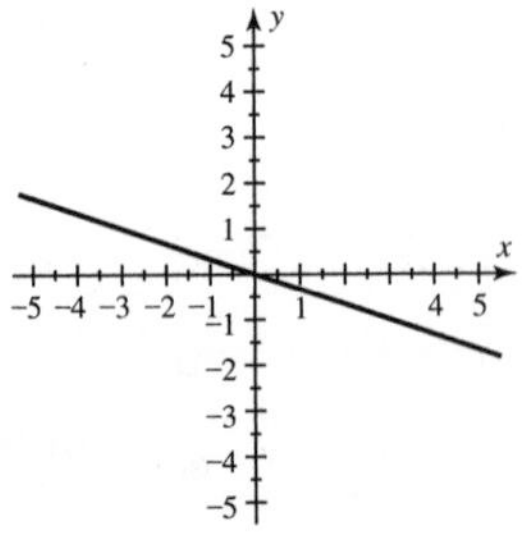

Figure 39

39. See Figure 39.

40. See Figure 40.

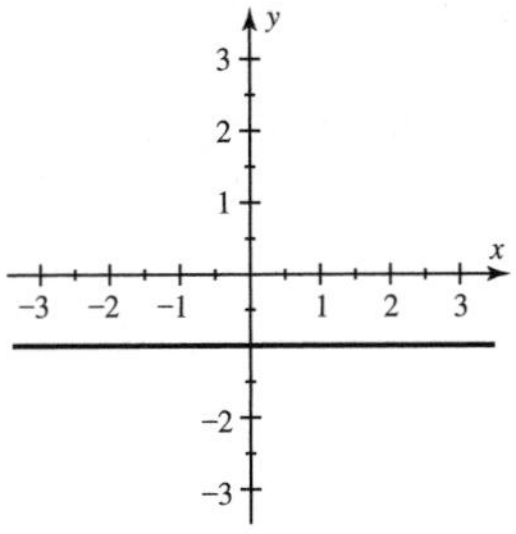

Figure 40

Section 8.3

41. $x + 1 \le 3 \Rightarrow x \le 2$ and $x + 1 \ge -1 \Rightarrow x \ge -2$; $[-2, 2]$. See Figure 41.

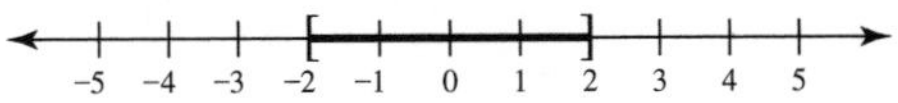

Figure 41

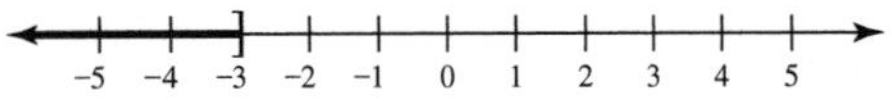

Figure 42

42. $2x + 7 < 5 \Rightarrow 2x < -2 \Rightarrow x < -1$ and $-2x \ge 6 \Rightarrow x \le -3$; $(-\infty, -3]$. See Figure 42.

43. $5x - 1 \le 3 \Rightarrow 5x \le 4 \Rightarrow x \le \frac{4}{5}$ or $1 - x < -1 \Rightarrow 2 < x$; $\left(-\infty, \frac{4}{5}\right] \cup (2, \infty)$. See Figure 43.

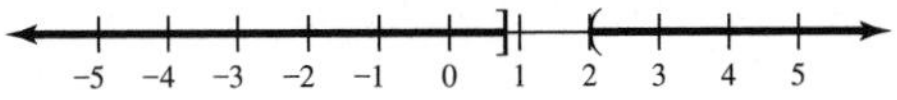

Figure 43

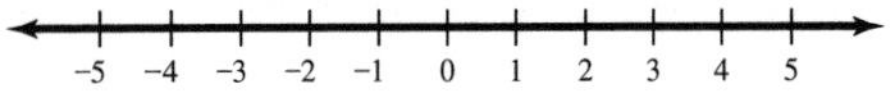

Figure 44

44. $3x + 1 > -1 \Rightarrow 3x > -2 \Rightarrow x > -\frac{2}{3}$ or $3x + 1 < 10 \Rightarrow 3x < 9 \Rightarrow x < 3$; $(-\infty, \infty)$. See Figure 44.

45. $2x + 2$ is between -2 and 4 when $-2 \le x \le 1$; $[-2, 1]$

46. (a) The intersection point of y_1 and y_2 is $(-4, -100)$. The solution is $x = -4$.

(b) The intersection point of y_2 and y_3 is $(2, 50)$. The solution is $x = 2$.

(c) y_2 is between y_1 and y_3 when $-4 \le x \le 2$; $[-4, 2]$

(d) y_2 is below y_3 when $x < 2$; $(-\infty, 2)$

47. (a) The intersection point of y_1 and y_2 is $(2, 2)$. The solution is $x = 2$.

(b) y_1 is below y_2 when $x > 2$; $(2, \infty)$

(c) y_1 is above y_2 when $x < 2$; $(-\infty, 2)$

48. (a) The intersection point of $f(x)$ and $g(x)$ is $(4, 20)$. The solution is $x = 4$.

(b) The intersection point of $g(x)$ and $h(x)$ is $(2, 40)$. The solution is $x = 2$.

(c) $g(x)$ is between $f(x)$ and $h(x)$ when $2 < x < 4$; $(2, 4)$

49. $\left[-3, \frac{2}{3}\right]$

50. $(-6, 45]$

51. $\left(-\infty, \frac{7}{2}\right)$

52. $[1.8, \infty)$

53. $(-3, 4)$

54. $(-\infty, 4) \cup (10, \infty)$

55. $-4 < x + 1 < 6 \Rightarrow -5 < x < 5$; The solution set is $(-5, 5)$.

56. $20 \le 2x + 4 \le 60 \Rightarrow 16 \le 2x \le 56 \Rightarrow 8 \le x \le 28$; The solution set is $[8, 28]$.

57. $-3 < 4 - \frac{1}{3}x < 7 \Rightarrow -7 < -\frac{1}{3}x < 3 \Rightarrow 21 > x > -9 \Rightarrow -9 < x < 21$; The solution set is $(-9, 21)$.

58. $2 \le \frac{1}{2}x - 2 \le 12 \Rightarrow 4 \le \frac{1}{2}x \le 14 \Rightarrow 8 \le x \le 28$; The solution set is $[8, 28]$.

59. $-3 \le \frac{4 - 5x}{3} - 2 < 3 \Rightarrow -9 \le 4 - 5x - 6 < 9 \Rightarrow -9 \le -5x - 2 < 9 \Rightarrow -7 \le -5x < 11 \Rightarrow$

$\frac{7}{5} \ge x > -\frac{11}{5} \Rightarrow -\frac{11}{5} < x \le \frac{7}{5}; \left(-\frac{11}{5}, \frac{7}{5}\right]$

60. $30 \le \frac{2x - 6}{5} - 4 < 50 \Rightarrow 150 \le 2x - 6 - 20 < 250 \Rightarrow 150 \le 2x - 26 < 250 \Rightarrow$

$176 \le 2x < 276 \Rightarrow 88 \le x < 138; [88, 138)$

Section 8.4

61. All real number inputs valid and since $t^2 \ge 0$ for all possible real outputs $\frac{1}{2}t^2 \ge 0$, $D = (-\infty, \infty)$; $R = [0, \infty)$.

62. All real number inputs valid and since absolute value outputs will be positive, $D = (-\infty, \infty)$; $R = [0, \infty)$.

63. The function will only be undefined when the denominator $2x - 8 = 0 \Rightarrow 2x - 8 \ne 0 \Rightarrow 2x \ne 8 \Rightarrow x \ne 4$.

Therefore $D = (-\infty, 4) \cup (4, \infty)$

64. $D = [-3, 1]$; $R = [-3, 6]$

65. Yes, the function is a polynomial; highest exponent on the variable is the second power, so 2nd degree; second degree polynomials are quadratic functions.

66. Yes, the function is a polynomial; highest exponent on the variable is the first power, so 1st degree; first degree polynomials are linear functions.

67. Yes, the function is a polynomial; highest exponent on the variable is the third power, so 3rd degree; third degree polynomials are cubic functions.

68. No, functions with absolute values are not polynomial functions.

69. $|1 - 4t|$ for $t = 3 \Rightarrow |1 - 4(3)| = |1 - 12| = |-11| = 11$

$|1 - 4t|$ for $t = -\frac{1}{4} \Rightarrow \left|1 - 4\left(-\frac{1}{4}\right)\right| = |1 - (-1)| = |2| = 2$

70. $\dfrac{4}{4-t^2}$ for $t = 3 \Rightarrow \dfrac{4}{4-(3)^2} = \dfrac{4}{4-9} = \dfrac{4}{-5} = -\dfrac{4}{5}$;

$\dfrac{4}{4-t^2}$ for $t = -2 \Rightarrow \dfrac{4}{4-(-2)^2} = \dfrac{4}{4-4} = \dfrac{4}{0}$ = undefined

71. See Figure 71.

72. See Figure 72.

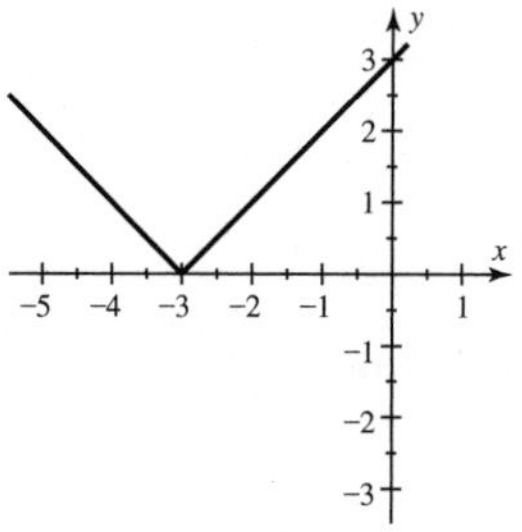

Figure 71

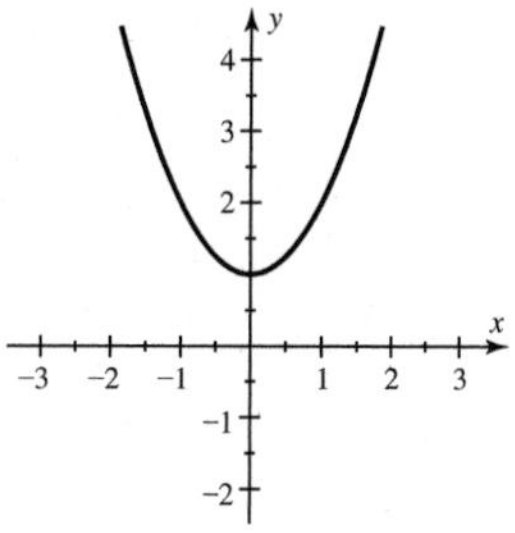

Figure 72

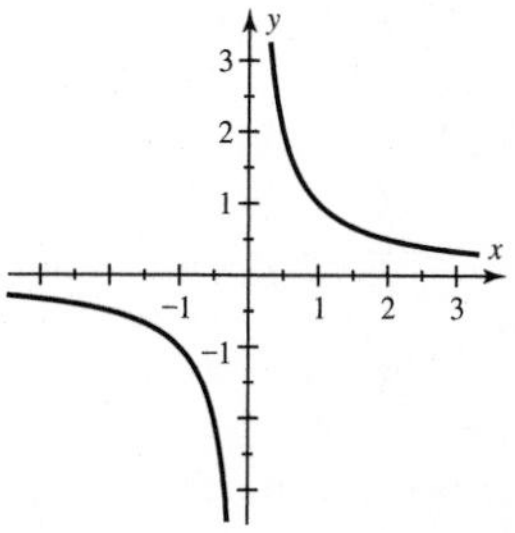

Figure 73

73. See Figure 73.

74. See Figure 74.

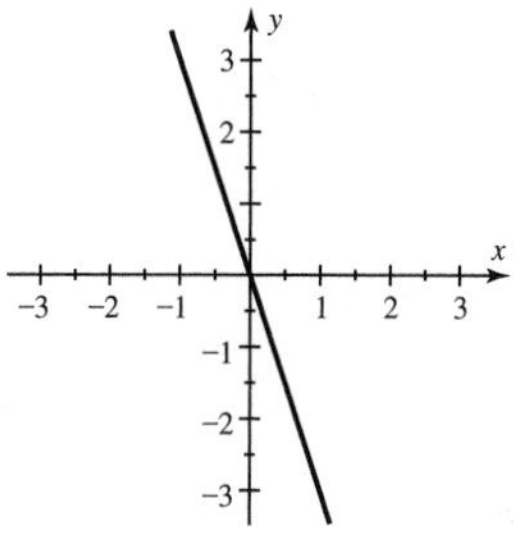

Figure 74

Section 8.5

75. (a) From the table, $y_1 = 2$ when $x = 0$ or $x = 4$.

(b) From the table, $y_1 < 2$ when $0 < x < 4$; $(0, 4)$.

(c) From the table, $y_1 > 2$ when $x < 0$ or $x > 4$; $(-\infty, 0) \cup (4, \infty)$.

76. (a) From the graph, $|2x + 2| = 4$ when $x = -3$ or $x = 1$.

(b) From the graph, $|2x + 2| \le 4$ when $-3 \le x \le 1$; $[-3, 1]$.

(c) From the graph, $|2x + 2| \ge 4$ when $x \le -3$ or $x \ge 1$; $(-\infty, -3] \cup [1, \infty)$.

77. $x = -22$ or $x = 22$

78. $2x - 9 = 7 \Rightarrow 2x = 16 \Rightarrow x = 8$ or $2x - 9 = -7 \Rightarrow 2x = 2 \Rightarrow x = 1$

79. $4 - \dfrac{1}{2}x = 17 \Rightarrow -\dfrac{1}{2}x = 13 \Rightarrow x = -26$ or $4 - \dfrac{1}{2}x = -17 \Rightarrow -\dfrac{1}{2}x = -21 \Rightarrow x = 42$

80. First note that $\frac{1}{3}|3x - 1| + 1 = 9 \Rightarrow \frac{1}{3}|3x - 1| = 8 \Rightarrow |3x - 1| = 24.$

$3x - 1 = 24 \Rightarrow 3x = 25 \Rightarrow x = \frac{25}{3}$ or $3x - 1 = -24 \Rightarrow 3x = -23 \Rightarrow x = -\frac{23}{3}$

81. $2x - 5 = 5 - 3x \Rightarrow 5x = 10 \Rightarrow x = 2$ or $2x - 5 = -5 + 3x \Rightarrow -x = 0 \Rightarrow x = 0$

82. $-3 + 3x = -2x + 6 \Rightarrow 5x = 9 \Rightarrow x = \frac{9}{5}$ or $-3 + 3x = 2x - 6 \Rightarrow x = -3$

83. (a) $x + 1 = 7 \Rightarrow x = 6$ or $x + 1 = -7 \Rightarrow x = -8$

(b) The solutions to $|x + 1| \le 7$ satisfy $c \le x \le d$ where c and d are the solutions to $|x + 1| = 7$.

From part (a), the interval is $[-8, 6]$.

(c) The solutions to $|x + 1| \ge 7$ satisfy $x \le c$ or $x \ge d$ where c and d are the solutions to $|x + 1| = 7$.

From part (a), the interval is $(-\infty, -8] \cup [6, \infty)$.

84. (a) $1 - 2x = 6 \Rightarrow -2x = 5 \Rightarrow x = -\frac{5}{2}$ or $1 - 2x = -6 \Rightarrow -2x = -7 \Rightarrow x = \frac{7}{2}$

(b) The solutions to $|1 - 2x| \le 6$ satisfy $c \le x \le d$ where c and d are the solutions to $|1 - 2x| = 6$.

From part (a), the interval is $\left[-\frac{5}{2}, \frac{7}{2}\right]$.

(c) The solutions to $|1 - 2x| \ge 6$ satisfy $x \le c$ or $x \ge d$ where c and d are the solutions to $|1 - 2x| = 6$.

From part (a), the interval is $\left(-\infty, -\frac{5}{2}\right] \cup \left[\frac{7}{2}, \infty\right)$.

85. The solutions to $|x| > 3$ satisfy $x < c$ or $x > d$ where c and d are the solutions to $|x| = 3$.

$|x| = 3$ is equivalent to $x = -3$ and $x = 3$. The interval is $(-\infty, -3) \cup (3, \infty)$.

86. The solutions to $|-5x| < 20$ satisfy $c < x < d$ where c and d are the solutions to $|-5x| = 20$.

$|-5x| = 20$ is equivalent to $-5x = -20 \Rightarrow x = 4$ and $-5x = 20 \Rightarrow x = -4$. The interval is $(-4, 4)$.

87. The solutions to $|4x - 2| \le 14$ satisfy $c \le x \le d$ where c and d are the solutions to $|4x - 2| = 14$.

$|4x - 2| = 14$ is equivalent to $4x - 2 = -14 \Rightarrow x = -3$ and $4x - 2 = 14 \Rightarrow x = 4$. The interval is $[-3, 4]$.

88. The solutions to $\left|1 - \frac{4}{5}x\right| \ge 3$ satisfy $x \le c$ or $x \ge d$ where c and d are the solutions to $\left|1 - \frac{4}{5}x\right| = 3$.

$\left|1 - \frac{4}{5}x\right| = 3$ is equivalent to $1 - \frac{4}{5}x = -3 \Rightarrow x = 5$ and $1 - \frac{4}{5}x = 3 \Rightarrow x = -\frac{5}{2}$.

The interval is $\left(-\infty, -\frac{5}{2}\right] \cup [5, \infty)$.

89. The solutions to $|t - 4.5| \le 0.1$ satisfy $c \le t \le d$ where c and d are the solutions to $|t - 4.5| = 0.1$.

$|t - 4.5| = 0.1$ is equivalent to $t - 4.5 = -0.1 \Rightarrow t = 4.4$ and $t - 4.5 = 0.1 \Rightarrow t = 4.6$.

The interval is $[4.4, 4.6]$.

90. First divide each side of $-2|13t - 5| \geq -4$ by -2 to obtain $|13t - 5| \leq 2$.

The solutions to $|13t - 5| \leq 2$ satisfy $c \leq t \leq d$ where c and d are the solutions to $|13t - 5| = 2$.

$|13t - 5| = 2$ is equivalent to $13t - 5 = -2 \Rightarrow t = \frac{3}{13}$ and $13t - 5 = 2 \Rightarrow t = \frac{7}{13}$.

The interval is $\left[\frac{3}{13}, \frac{7}{13}\right]$.

91. The inequality $|5 - 4x| > -5$ is true for all values of x because absolute value is never negative.

The interval is $(-\infty, \infty)$.

92. Since absolute value can never be negative, $|2t - 3| \leq 0$ is equivalent to $|2t - 3| = 0$.

$|2t - 3| = 0$ is equivalent to $2t - 3 = 0 \Rightarrow t = \frac{3}{2}$. The only solution is $\frac{3}{2}$.

93. Graph $Y_1 = \text{abs}(2X)$ and $Y_2 = 3$ in $[-3, 3, 1]$ by $[0, 5, 1]$. See Figures 93a and 93b.

From the graph, $|2x| \geq 3$ in the interval $(-\infty, -1.5] \cup [1.5, \infty)$.

[−3, 3, 1] by [0, 5, 1]

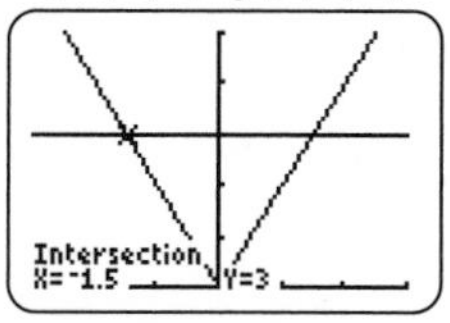

Figure 93a

[−3, 3, 1] by [0, 5, 1]

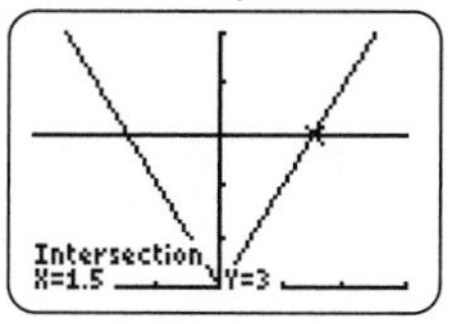

Figure 93b

[−7, 7, 1] by [0, 4, 1]

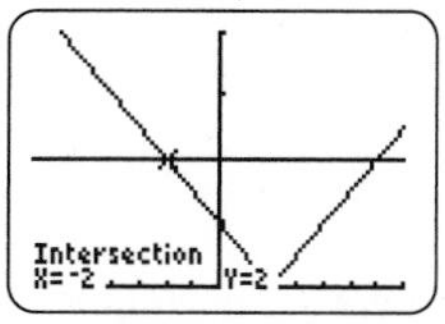

Figure 94a

[−7, 7, 1] by [0, 4, 1]

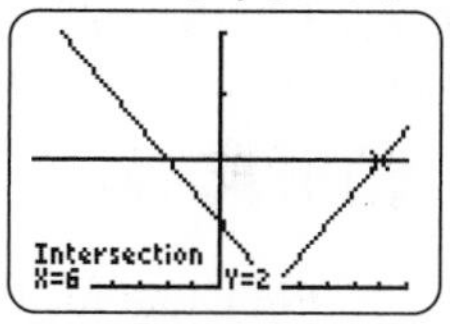

Figure 94b

94. Graph $Y_1 = \text{abs}((1/2)X - 1)$ and $Y_2 = 2$ in $[-7, 7, 1]$ by $[0, 4, 1]$. See Figures 94a and 94b.

From the graph, $\left|\frac{1}{2}x - 1\right| \leq 2$ in the interval $[-2, 6]$.

Applications

95. (a) $f(1910) = -0.0492(1910) + 119.1 \approx 25.1$ years

(b) Graph $Y_1 = -0.0492X + 119.1$ in $[1885, 1965, 10]$ by $[22, 26, 1]$. See Figure 95.

The median age at first marriage for males has decreased over this time period.

(c) The slope is -0.0492. The median age decreased by about 0.0492 year per year.

[1885, 1965, 10] by [22, 26, 1]

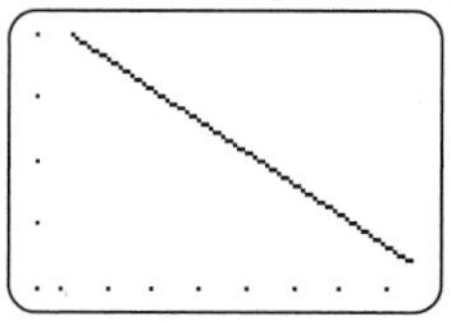

Figure 95

96. (a) $f(1991) = 2.4$ million

(b) The number of marriages each year did not change over this time period.

97. (a) $f(x) = 8x$

(b) The slope of the graph of f is 8.

(c) The total fat changes at a rate of 8 grams per cup of milk.

98. (a) See Figure 98.

(b) Using the first and last data points to find the linear function results in $f(x) = -0.31x + 633.6$.

(c) $f(2000) = -0.31(2000 - 1990) + 16.7 = -0.31(10) + 16.7 = -3.1 + 16.7 = 13.6$

The birth rate is about 13.6 per 1000 people. *Answers may vary.*

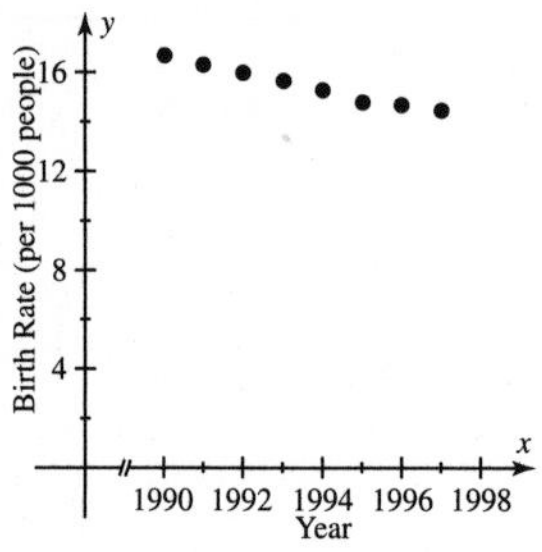

Figure 98

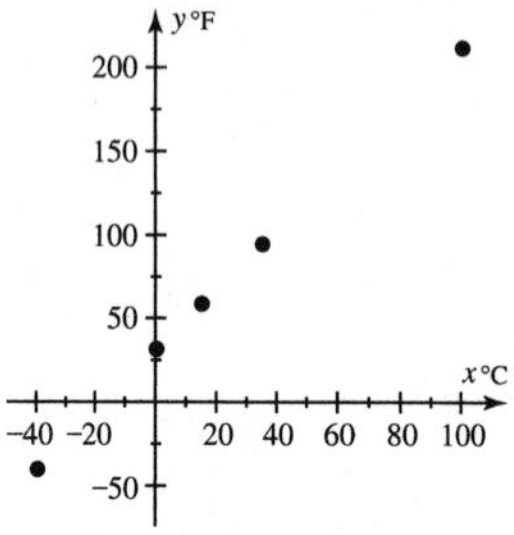

Figure 100

99. (a) From the table $f(1995) = 113$. In 1995 there were 113 unhealthy days.

(b) $D = \{1995, 1996, 1997, 1998, 1999\}$; $R = \{27, 56, 60, 94, 113\}$

(c) The number of unhealthy days has decreased over this time period.

100. (a) See Figure 100. There is a linear relationship.

(b) Using the points (0, 32) and (100, 212) the slope is $m = \dfrac{212 - 32}{100 - 0} = \dfrac{180}{100} = \dfrac{9}{5}$. The y-intercept is 32.

The function is given by $f(x) = \dfrac{9}{5}x + 32$. The slope of $\dfrac{9}{5}$ means that a 1°C change equals a $\dfrac{9^\circ}{5}$ F change.

(c) $f(20) = \dfrac{9}{5}(20) + 32 = 36 + 32 = 68°F$.

101. Let x be the width of the rectangle. Then its length is $2x + 5$ and its perimeter is $2x + 2(2x + 5)$.

$2x + 2(2x + 5) = 88 \Rightarrow 2x + 4x + 10 = 88 \Rightarrow 6x = 78 \Rightarrow x = 13$

The width is 13 feet and the length is $2(13) + 5 = 31$ feet. The rectangle is 13 ft by 31 ft.

102. $-48 \le \dfrac{9}{5}C + 32 \le 107 \Rightarrow -80 \le \dfrac{9}{5}C \le 75 \Rightarrow -80\left(\dfrac{5}{9}\right) \le C \le 75\left(\dfrac{5}{9}\right) \Rightarrow -44.\overline{4} \le C \le 41.\overline{6}$

The temperature range in Celsius is $-44.\overline{4}$°C to $41.\overline{6}$°C.

103. $|L - 160| \le 1$; $L - 160 = 1 \Rightarrow L = 161$ or $L - 160 = -1 \Rightarrow L = 159$; $\{L \mid 159 \le L \le 161\}$

104. (a) $|A - 3.9| \le 1.7$

(b) $A - 3.9 = 1.7 \Rightarrow A = 5.6$ or $A - 3.9 = -1.7 \Rightarrow A = 2.2$; $\{A \mid 2.2 \le A \le 5.6\}$

105. The solutions to $\left|\dfrac{T - 35}{35}\right| < 0.08$ satisfy $c < T < d$ where c and d are the solutions to $\left|\dfrac{T - 35}{35}\right| = 0.08$.

$\left|\dfrac{T - 35}{35}\right| = 0.08$ is equivalent to $\dfrac{T - 35}{35} = -0.08 \Rightarrow x = 32.2$ and $\dfrac{T - 35}{35} = 0.08 \Rightarrow x = 37.8$.

The interval is (32.2, 37.8). The values must be between 32.2 and 37.8, exclusively.

Chapter 8 Test

1. $f(4) = 3(4)^2 - \sqrt{4} = 3(16) - 2 = 48 - 2 = 46$
2. (a) See Figure 2a.

   (b) See Figure 2b.

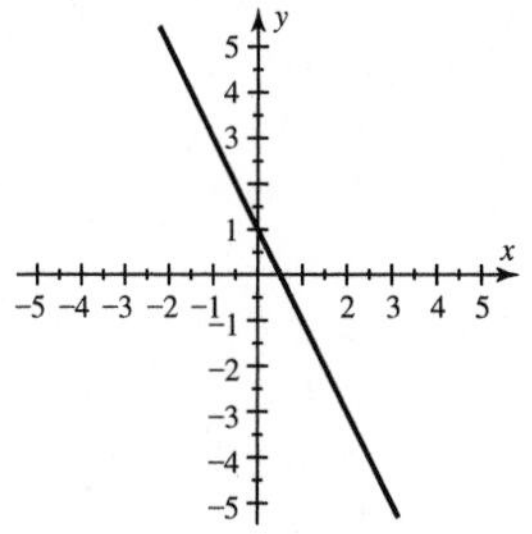

Figure 2a

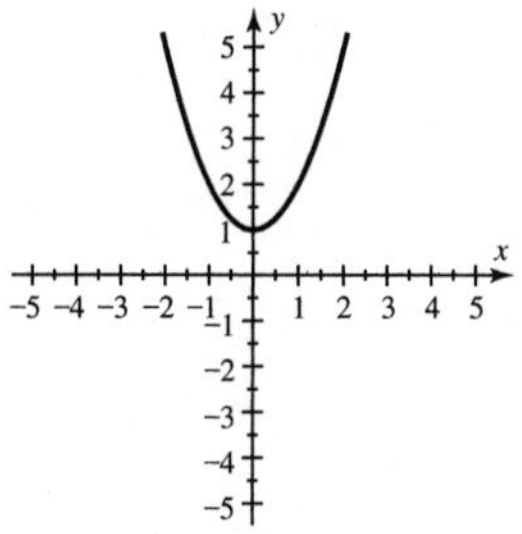

Figure 2b

3. $f(-3) = 0$; $f(0) = -3$; $D{:}\{x\,|\,-3 \le x \le 3\}$ and $R{:}\{x\,|\,-3 \le y \le 0\}$
4. Symbolic: $f(x) = x^2 - 5$

   Numerical: The table is shown in Figure 4a.

   Graphical: The graph is shown in Figure 4b.

x	−3	−2	−1	0	1	2	3
$y = f(x)$	4	−1	−4	−5	−4	−1	4

Figure 4a

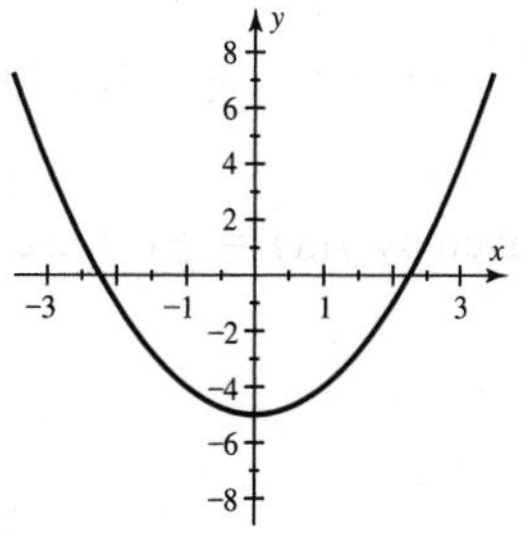

Figure 4b

5. No. It does not pass the vertical line test.
6. $2x + 6 < 2$ and $-3x \ge 3 \Rightarrow 2x < -4$ and $x \le -1 \Rightarrow x < -2$ and $x \le -1$. See Figure 6.

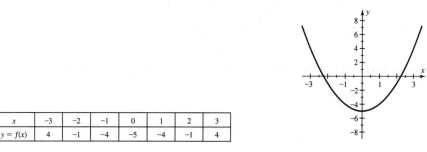

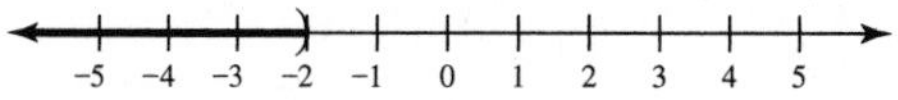

Figure 6

7. From the table, $-3x < -3$ when $x > 1$ and $-3x > 6$ when $x < -2$. The interval is $(-\infty, -2) \cup (1, \infty)$.
8. (a) The intersection point of y_1 and y_2 is $(-5, -300)$. The solution is $x = -5$.

   (b) The intersection point of y_2 and y_3 is $(5, 100)$. The solution is $x = 5$.

   (c) y_2 is between y_1 and y_3 when $-5 \le x \le 5$. The interval is $[-5, 5]$.

   (d) y_2 is below y_3 when $x < 5$. The interval is $(-\infty, 5)$.
9. $-2 < 2 + \frac{1}{2}x < 2 \Rightarrow -4 < \frac{1}{2}x < 0 \Rightarrow -8 < x < 0$; $(-8, 0)$
10. All real number inputs are valid and any absolute value output will be positive, $D = (-\infty, \infty)$; $R = [0, \infty)$.

11. Yes, the function is a polynomial. The highest exponent on the variable is three, so it is 3rd degree. Third degree polynomials are cubic functions.

12. $-\dfrac{4t}{5-t}$ for $t = -2 \Rightarrow -\dfrac{4(-2)}{5-(-2)} = -\dfrac{-8}{7} = \dfrac{8}{7}$; The function will only be undefined when the denominator $5 - t = 0 \Rightarrow 5 - t \neq 0 \Rightarrow -t \neq -5 \Rightarrow t \neq 5 \Rightarrow D = (-\infty, 5) \cup (5, \infty)$.

13. $2 - \dfrac{1}{3}x = 6 \Rightarrow -\dfrac{1}{3}x = 4 \Rightarrow x = -12$ or $2 - \dfrac{1}{3}x = -6 \Rightarrow -\dfrac{1}{3}x = -8 \Rightarrow x = 24$

14. (a) $1 - 5x = 3 \Rightarrow -5x = 2 \Rightarrow x = -\dfrac{2}{5}$ or $1 - 5x = -3 \Rightarrow -5x = -4 \Rightarrow x = \dfrac{4}{5}$

(b) The solutions to $|1 - 5x| \leq 3$ satisfy $c \leq x \leq d$ where c and d are the solutions to $|1 - 5x| = 3$.

From part (a), the interval is $\left[-\dfrac{2}{5}, \dfrac{4}{5}\right]$.

(c) The solutions to $|1 - 5x| \geq 3$ satisfy $x \leq c$ or $x \geq d$ where c and d are the solutions to $|1 - 5x| = 3$.

From part (a), the interval is $\left(-\infty, -\dfrac{2}{5}\right] \cup \left[\dfrac{4}{5}, \infty\right)$.

15. (a) First divide the weight 150 by 2 to get 75. The function is $f(x) = 0.4x + 75$.

(b) $0.4x + 75 = 89 \Rightarrow 0.4x = 14 \Rightarrow x = \dfrac{14}{0.4} \Rightarrow x = 35$ minutes

16. (a) Yes; $P(0) = 100$, $P(20) = 134$, $P(30) = 150$ and $P(50) = 180$

(b) Probably not, because the race is over in 50 seconds; $D = [0, 50]$.

Chapter 8 Extended and Discovery Exercises

1. (a) The graph for tank A is linear. See Figures 1a. The graph for tank B is nonlinear. See Figure 1b.

(b) Tank B flows faster at first so it is the first to be half empty.

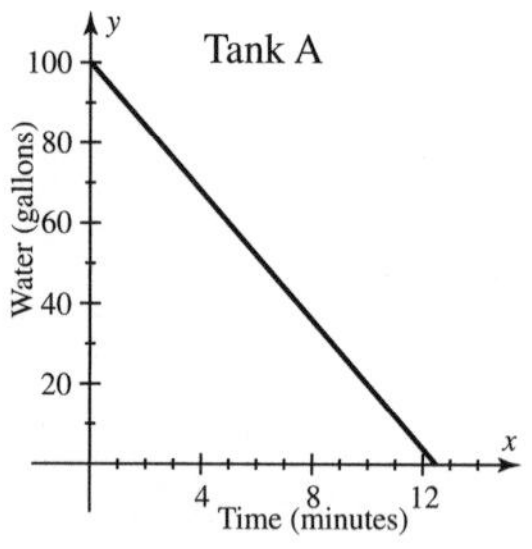

Figure 1a

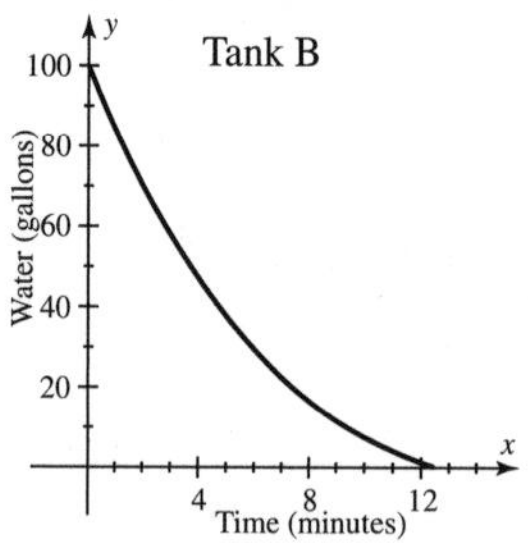

Figure 1b

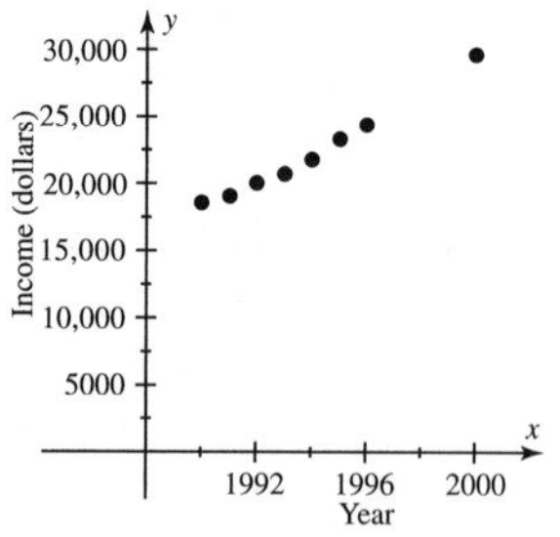

Figure 2

2. (a) See Figure 2.

(b) Since the data appears to be nearly linear with an annual increase of about \$1100 per year we may find a point-slope form of a linear equation using the point (1990, 18,666) and slope $m = 1100$.

The equation is $f(x) = 1100(x - 1990) + 18{,}666$. *Answers may vary.*

(c) $f(1998) = 1100(1998 - 1990) + 18{,}666 = 8800 + 18{,}666 = \$27{,}466$

3. (a) When the fish hatches it weighs about 7 mg. It weighs about 105 mg at 6 weeks of age and about 158 mg at 12 weeks of age. *Answers may vary.*

(b) From hatching to 6 weeks: $\frac{105 - 7}{6 - 0} = \frac{98}{6} \approx 16.3$ mg/week.

From 6 weeks to 12 weeks: $\frac{158 - 105}{12 - 6} = \frac{53}{6} \approx 8.8$ mg/week.

(c) On average the fish gains about 16.3 mg per week during the first 6 weeks of its life and about 8.8 mg per week during the second 6 weeks of its life.

(d) The fish gains weight the fastest during the first 6 weeks of its life.

4. (a) The scatterplot is shown in Figure 4a.

(b) The relationship appears to be linear. This seems reasonable if one considers that when the number of megabytes doubles, the number of seconds should also double.

(c) Using the points (0.129, 6.010) and (1.260, 60.18) $m = \frac{60.18 - 6.010}{1.260 - 0.129} \approx 47.9$, $h = 0.129$ and $k = 6.010$.

The equation is $y \approx 47.9(x - 0.129) + 6.010 \Rightarrow y \approx 47.9x - 0.1691$.

Each additional megabyte of memory can record approximately 47.9 seconds of music.

(d) The scatterplot and the line are shown in Figure 4d.

(e) $47.9x - 0.1691 = 120$

(f) Symbolic: $47.9x - 0.1691 = 120 \Rightarrow 47.9x = 120.1691 \Rightarrow x \approx 2.5$ Mb

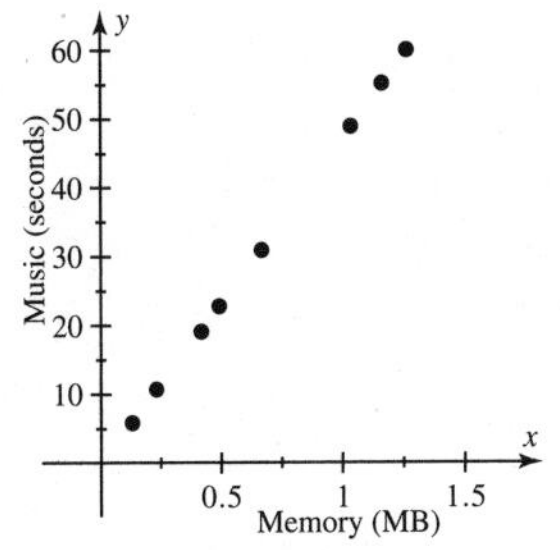

Figure 4a

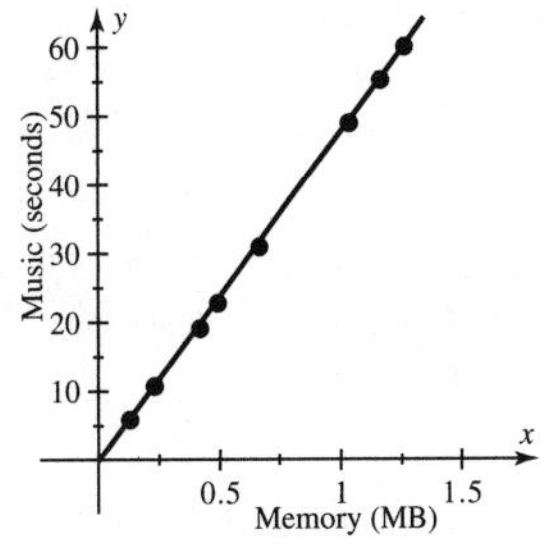

Figure 4d

Critical Thinking Solutions for Chapter 8

Section 8.1

- The graph is shown in Figure 8.1. Here the domain and range are given by $D\colon 0 \le x \le 5$ and $R\colon 0 \le y \le 250$.

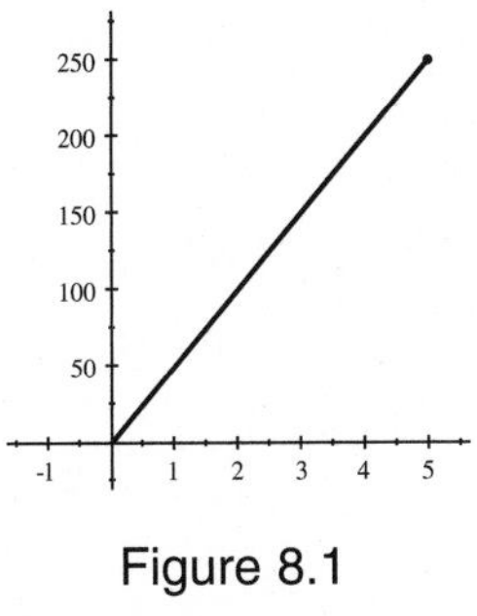

Figure 8.1

Section 8.2

- A third point will verify that the first two points are plotted correctly.

Section 8.3

- 1. See Figure 8.3a. There are no numbers that satisfy *both* inequalities.

  2. See Figure 8.3b. Every real number is *either* greater than 2 *or* less than 5.

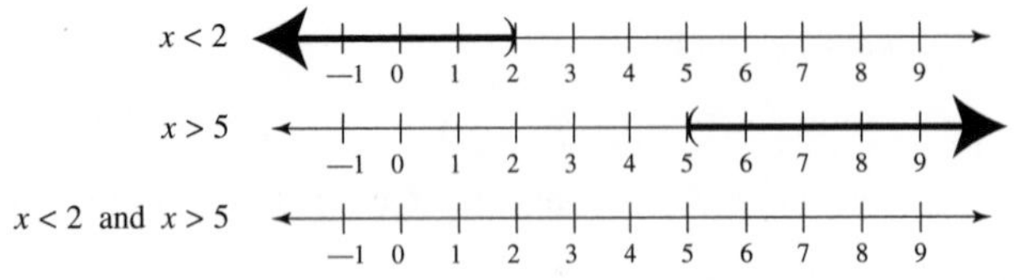

Figure 8.3a

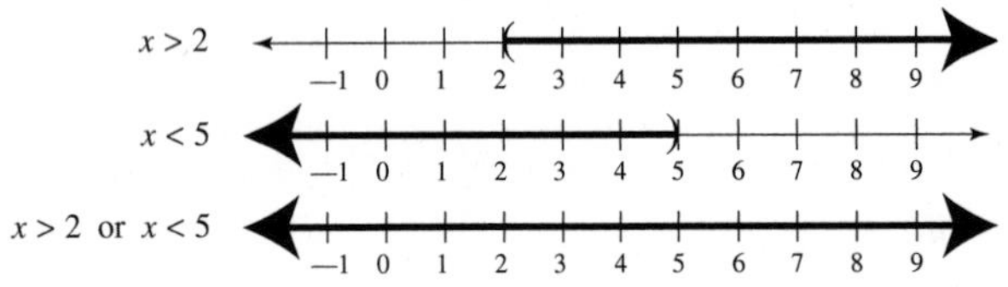

Figure 8.3b

- Students exhale more carbon dioxide during an exam than they do during a lecture. This increase may be due to anxiety experienced during examinations

Section 8.5

- 1. The solution set includes all real numbers since an absolute value is always greater than –3.

  An absolute value is always nonnegative.

  2. There are no solutions since an absolute value is never less than –3.

Chapter 9: Systems of Linear Equations

9.1: Systems of Linear Equations in Three Variables

Concepts

1. No, three planes cannot intersect at exactly 2 points.

3. Yes, since $1 + 2 + 3 = 6$.

5. Two

Solving Linear Systems

7. (1, 2, 3) satisfies all three inequalities.

9. (–1, 1, 2) satisfies all three inequalities.

11. Substitute $z = 1$ into the second equation: $2y + (1) = -1 \Rightarrow 2y = -2 \Rightarrow y = -1$

    Substitute $z = 1$ and $y = -1$ into the first equation: $x + (-1) - (1) = 1 \Rightarrow x - 2 = 1 \Rightarrow x = 3$

    The solution is (3, –1, 1).

13. Substitute $z = 2$ into the second equation: $2y + 3(2) = 3 \Rightarrow 2y = -3 \Rightarrow y = -\frac{3}{2}$

    Substitute $z = 2$ and $y = -\frac{3}{2}$ into the first equation: $-x - 3\left(-\frac{3}{2}\right) + (2) = -2 \Rightarrow -x = -\frac{17}{2} \Rightarrow x = \frac{17}{2}$

    The solution is $\left(\frac{17}{2}, -\frac{3}{2}, 2\right)$.

15. Substitute $c = -2$ into the second equation: $-3b + (-2) = 4 \Rightarrow -3b = 6 \Rightarrow b = -2$

    Substitute $c = -2$ and $b = -2$ into the first equation: $a - (-2) + 2(-2) = 3 \Rightarrow a - 2 = 3 \Rightarrow a = 5$

    The solution is (5, –2, –2).

17. Add the first two equations together to eliminate the variable x.

$$\begin{array}{r} x + y - z = 11 \\ -x + 2y + 3z = -1 \\ \hline 3y + 2z = 10 \end{array}$$

    From the third equation, $2z = 4 \Rightarrow z = 2$. And so $3y + 2(2) = 10 \Rightarrow 3y = 6 \Rightarrow y = 2$.

    Substitute $z = 2$ and $y = 2$ into the first equation: $x + (2) - (2) = 11 \Rightarrow x = 11$

    The solution is (11, 2, 2).

19. Add the first two equations together to eliminate both of the variables x and z.

$$\begin{array}{r} x + y - z = -2 \\ -x \qquad + z = 1 \\ \hline y = -1 \end{array}$$

    Substitute $y = -1$ into the third equation, $(-1) + 2z = 3 \Rightarrow 2z = 4 \Rightarrow z = 2$.

    Substitute $z = 2$ and $y = -1$ into the first equation: $x + (-1) - (2) = -2 \Rightarrow x = 1$

    The solution is (1, –1, 2).

21. Add the second and third equations together to eliminate the variable y.

$$\begin{array}{r} y + z = -1 \\ -y + 3z = 9 \\ \hline 4z = 8 \end{array}$$

And so $z = 2$. Substitute $z = 2$ into the second equation, $y + (2) = -1 \Rightarrow y = -3$.

Substitute $z = 2$ and $y = -3$ into the first equation: $x + (-3) - 2(2) = -7 \Rightarrow x = 0$

The solution is $(0, -3, 2)$.

23. Multiply the second equation by -2 and add the first and second equations to eliminate the variables y and z.

$$\begin{array}{r} x + 2y + 2z = 1 \\ -2x - 2y - 2z = 0 \\ \hline -x = 1 \end{array}$$

And so $x = -1$. Add the first and third equations together to eliminate the variables x and y.

$$\begin{array}{r} x + 2y + 2z = 1 \\ -x - 2y + 3z = -11 \\ \hline 5z = -10 \end{array}$$

And so $z = -2$. Substitute $x = -1$ and $z = -2$ into the second equation: $(-1) + y + (-2) = 0 \Rightarrow y = 3$

The solution is $(-1, 3, -2)$.

25. Multiply the second equation by -1 and add the first and second equations to eliminate the variables y and z.

$$\begin{array}{r} x + y + z = 5 \\ -y - z = -6 \\ \hline x = -1 \end{array}$$

And so $x = -1$. Substitute $x = -1$ into the third equation: $(-1) + z = 3 \Rightarrow z = 4$

Substitute $x = -1$ and $z = 4$ into the first equation: $(-1) + y + (4) = 5 \Rightarrow y = 2$

The solution is $(-1, 2, 4)$.

27. Add the second and third equations to eliminate the variables x and z.

$$\begin{array}{r} -x + y + 2z = 1 \\ x + y - 2z = 9 \\ \hline 2y = 10 \end{array}$$

And so, $y = 5$. Now add the first and second equations to eliminate the variable x.

$$\begin{array}{r} x + 2y + 3z = 24 \\ -x + y + 2z = 1 \\ \hline 3y + 5z = 25 \end{array}$$

Now substitute $y = 5$ in this new equation: $3(5) + 5z = 25 \Rightarrow 5z = 10 \Rightarrow z = 2$

Finally substitute $y = 5$ and $z = 2$ in the first equation: $x + 2(5) + 3(2) = 24 \Rightarrow x = 8$

The solution is $(8, 5, 2)$.

29. Add the first and second equations to eliminate the variables y and z.

$$\begin{array}{r} 2x + y + z = 3 \\ 2x - y - z = 9 \\ \hline 4x = 12 \end{array}$$

And so, $x = 3$. Add the second and third equations together to eliminate the variable y.

$$\begin{array}{r} 2x - y - z = 9 \\ x + y - z = 0 \\ \hline 3x - 2z = 9 \end{array}$$

Now substitute $x = 3$ in this new equation: $3(3) - 2z = 9 \Rightarrow -2z = 0 \Rightarrow z = 0$

Finally substitute $x = 0$ and $z = 0$ in the third equation: $(3) + y - (0) = 0 \Rightarrow y = -3$

The solution is $(3, -3, 0)$.

31. Multiply the first equation by –1 and add the first and second equations to eliminate the variable x.

$$\begin{array}{r} -2x - 6y + 2z = -47 \\ 2x + y + 3z = -28 \\ \hline -5y + 5z = -75 \end{array}$$

Multiply the third equation by 2 and add the first and third equations to eliminate the variables x and z.

$$\begin{array}{r} 2x + 6y - 2z = 47 \\ -2x + 2y + 2z = -7 \\ \hline 8y = 40 \end{array}$$

And so $y = 5$. Substitute $y = 5$ into the first *new* equation: $-5(5) + 5z = -75 \Rightarrow 5z = -50 \Rightarrow z = -10$

Substitute $y = 5$ and $z = -10$ into the *original* third equation: $-x + (5) + (-10) = -\frac{7}{2} \Rightarrow x = -\frac{3}{2}$

The solution is $\left(-\frac{3}{2}, 5, -10\right)$.

33. Multiply the second equation by –1 and add the first and second equations to eliminate the variable y.

$$\begin{array}{r} x + 3y - 4z = \frac{13}{2} \\ 2x - 3y + z = -\frac{1}{2} \\ \hline 3x - 3z = 6 \end{array}$$

Multiply this *new* equation by –1 and add it to the third equation to eliminate the variable x.

$$\begin{array}{r} -3x + 3z = -6 \\ 3x + z = 4 \\ \hline 4z = -2 \end{array}$$

And so $z = -\frac{1}{2}$. Substitute $z = -\frac{1}{2}$ into the first *new* equation: $3x - 3\left(-\frac{1}{2}\right) = 6 \Rightarrow 3x = \frac{9}{2} \Rightarrow x = \frac{3}{2}$

Substitute $x = \frac{3}{2}$ and $z = -\frac{1}{2}$ into the *original* first equation: $\left(\frac{3}{2}\right) + 3y - 4\left(-\frac{1}{2}\right) = \frac{13}{2} \Rightarrow y = 1$

The solution is $\left(\frac{3}{2}, 1, -\frac{1}{2}\right)$.

Applications

35. (a) $x + 2y + 4z = 10$

$x + 4y + 6z = 15$

$3y + 2z = 6$

(b) Using techniques similar to those used in exercises 17 - 34, the solution is (2, 1, 1.5).

A hamburger costs \$2.00, fries cost \$1.00 and a soft drink costs \$1.50.

37. (a) $x + y + z = 180$

$x - z = 55$

$x - y - z = -10$

(b) Using techniques similar to those used in exercises 17 - 34, the solution is (85, 65, 30).

The angles are $x = 85°$, $y = 65°$, and $z = 30°$.

(c) These values check.

39. (a) $N + P + K = 80$

$N + P - K = 8$

$9P - K = 0$

(b) Using techniques similar to those used in exercises 17 - 34, the solution is (40, 4, 36).

The sample contains 40 pounds of nitrogen, 4 pounds of phosphorus and 36 pounds of potassium.

41. (a) $a + 600b + 4c = 525$

$a + 400b + 2c = 365$

$a + 900b + 5c = 805$

(b) Using techniques similar to those used in exercises 17 - 34, the solution is (5, 1, –20).

That is, $a = 5$, $b = 1$, and $c = -20$ and so the equation is $F = 5 + A - 20W$.

(c) When $A = 500$ and $W = 3$, $F = 5 + (500) - 20(3) = 445$ fawns.

43. Let x, y and z represent the amounts invested at 8%, 10% and 15% respectively. The system needed is:

$$x + y + z = 30{,}000$$
$$0.08x + 0.10y + 0.15z = 3550$$
$$x + y - z = 2000$$

Using techniques similar to those used in exercises 17 - 34, the solution is (7500, 8500, 14,000).

There was \$7500 invested at 8%, \$8500 invested at 10% and \$14,000 invested at 15%.

9.2: Matrix Solutions of Linear Systems

Concepts

1. A rectangular array of numbers.

3. $\left[\begin{array}{cc|c} 1 & 3 & 10 \\ 2 & -6 & 4 \end{array}\right]$; 2×3; *Answers may vary.*

5. $\left[\begin{array}{cc|c} 1 & 0 & -3 \\ 0 & 1 & 5 \end{array}\right]$; *Answers may vary.*

Dimensions of Matrices and Augmented Matrices

7. 3×3

9. 3×2

11. $\left[\begin{array}{cc|c} 1 & -3 & 1 \\ -1 & 3 & -1 \end{array}\right]$

13. $\left[\begin{array}{ccc|c} 2 & -1 & 2 & -4 \\ 1 & -2 & 0 & 2 \\ -1 & 1 & -2 & -6 \end{array}\right]$

15. $\begin{aligned} x + 2y &= -6 \\ 5x - y &= 4 \end{aligned}$

17. $\begin{aligned} x - y + 2z &= 6 \\ 2x + y - 2z &= 1 \\ -x + 2y - z &= 3 \end{aligned}$

19. $\begin{aligned} x &= 4 \\ y &= -2 \\ z &= 7 \end{aligned}$

Gaussian Elimination

21. $\left[\begin{array}{cc|c} 1 & 1 & 4 \\ 1 & 3 & 10 \end{array}\right] \begin{array}{c} \\ R_2 - R_1 \to \end{array} \left[\begin{array}{cc|c} 1 & 1 & 4 \\ 0 & 2 & 6 \end{array}\right] \begin{array}{c} \\ (1/2)R_2 \to \end{array} \left[\begin{array}{cc|c} 1 & 1 & 4 \\ 0 & 1 & 3 \end{array}\right] \begin{array}{c} R_1 - R_2 \to \\ \end{array} \left[\begin{array}{cc|c} 1 & 0 & 1 \\ 0 & 1 & 3 \end{array}\right]$

The solution is (1, 3).

23. $\left[\begin{array}{cc|c} 2 & 3 & 3 \\ -2 & 2 & 7 \end{array}\right] \begin{array}{c} \\ R_2 + R_1 \to \end{array} \left[\begin{array}{cc|c} 2 & 3 & 3 \\ 0 & 5 & 10 \end{array}\right] \begin{array}{c} \\ (1/5)R_2 \to \end{array} \left[\begin{array}{cc|c} 2 & 3 & 3 \\ 0 & 1 & 2 \end{array}\right] \begin{array}{c} R_1 - 3R_2 \to \\ \end{array} \left[\begin{array}{cc|c} 2 & 0 & -3 \\ 0 & 1 & 2 \end{array}\right]$

$\begin{array}{c} (1/2)R_2 \to \\ \end{array} \left[\begin{array}{cc|c} 1 & 0 & -\frac{3}{2} \\ 0 & 1 & 2 \end{array}\right]$

The solution is $\left(-\dfrac{3}{2}, 2\right)$.

25. $\left[\begin{array}{cc|c} 1 & -1 & 5 \\ 1 & 3 & -1 \end{array}\right] \begin{array}{c} \\ R_2 - R_1 \to \end{array} \left[\begin{array}{cc|c} 1 & -1 & 5 \\ 0 & 4 & -6 \end{array}\right] \begin{array}{c} \\ (1/4)R_2 \to \end{array} \left[\begin{array}{cc|c} 1 & -1 & 5 \\ 0 & 1 & -\frac{3}{2} \end{array}\right] \begin{array}{c} R_1 + R_2 \to \\ \end{array} \left[\begin{array}{cc|c} 1 & 0 & \frac{7}{2} \\ 0 & 1 & -\frac{3}{2} \end{array}\right]$

The solution is $\left(\dfrac{7}{2}, -\dfrac{3}{2}\right)$.

27. $\left[\begin{array}{cc|c} 4 & -8 & -10 \\ 1 & 1 & 2 \end{array}\right] \begin{array}{c} \textit{Exchange} \\ R_2 \leftrightarrow R_1 \end{array} \left[\begin{array}{cc|c} 1 & 1 & 2 \\ 4 & -8 & -10 \end{array}\right] \begin{array}{c} \\ (-1/2)R_2 \to \end{array} \left[\begin{array}{cc|c} 1 & 1 & 2 \\ -2 & 4 & 5 \end{array}\right] \begin{array}{c} \\ R_2 + 2R_1 \to \end{array} \left[\begin{array}{cc|c} 1 & 1 & 2 \\ 0 & 6 & 9 \end{array}\right]$

$\begin{array}{c} \\ (1/6)R_2 \to \end{array} \left[\begin{array}{cc|c} 1 & 1 & 2 \\ 0 & 1 & \frac{3}{2} \end{array}\right] \begin{array}{c} R_1 - R_2 \to \\ \end{array} \left[\begin{array}{cc|c} 1 & 0 & \frac{1}{2} \\ 0 & 1 & \frac{3}{2} \end{array}\right]$

The solution is $\left(\dfrac{1}{2}, \dfrac{3}{2}\right)$.

29. $$\left[\begin{array}{ccc|c} 1 & 1 & 1 & 6 \\ 0 & 2 & -1 & 1 \\ 0 & 1 & 1 & 5 \end{array}\right] \begin{array}{l} R_1 - R_3 \to \\ R_2 - 2R_3 \to \\ \end{array} \left[\begin{array}{ccc|c} 1 & 0 & 0 & 1 \\ 0 & 0 & -3 & -9 \\ 0 & 1 & 1 & 5 \end{array}\right] \begin{array}{l} \\ \textit{Exchange} \\ R_2 \leftrightarrow R_3 \end{array} \left[\begin{array}{ccc|c} 1 & 0 & 0 & 1 \\ 0 & 1 & 1 & 5 \\ 0 & 0 & -3 & -9 \end{array}\right] \begin{array}{l} \\ \\ (-1/3)R_3 \to \end{array} \left[\begin{array}{ccc|c} 1 & 0 & 0 & 1 \\ 0 & 1 & 1 & 5 \\ 0 & 0 & 1 & 3 \end{array}\right]$$

$$R_2 - R_3 \to \left[\begin{array}{ccc|c} 1 & 0 & 0 & 1 \\ 0 & 1 & 0 & 2 \\ 0 & 0 & 1 & 3 \end{array}\right]$$

The solution is (1, 2, 3).

31. $$\left[\begin{array}{ccc|c} 1 & 2 & 3 & 6 \\ -1 & 3 & 4 & 0 \\ 1 & 1 & -2 & -6 \end{array}\right] \begin{array}{l} \\ R_2 + R_1 \to \\ R_3 - R_1 \to \end{array} \left[\begin{array}{ccc|c} 1 & 2 & 3 & 6 \\ 0 & 5 & 7 & 6 \\ 0 & -1 & -5 & -12 \end{array}\right] \begin{array}{l} \\ \\ (-1)R_3 \to \end{array} \left[\begin{array}{ccc|c} 1 & 2 & 3 & 6 \\ 0 & 5 & 7 & 6 \\ 0 & 1 & 5 & 12 \end{array}\right]$$

$$\begin{array}{l} R_1 - 2R_3 \to \\ R_2 - 5R_3 \to \\ \end{array} \left[\begin{array}{ccc|c} 1 & 0 & -7 & -18 \\ 0 & 0 & -18 & -54 \\ 0 & 1 & 5 & 12 \end{array}\right] \begin{array}{l} \\ \textit{Exchange} \\ R_2 \leftrightarrow R_3 \end{array} \left[\begin{array}{ccc|c} 1 & 0 & -7 & -18 \\ 0 & 1 & 5 & 12 \\ 0 & 0 & -18 & -54 \end{array}\right] \begin{array}{l} \\ \\ (-1/18)R_3 \to \end{array} \left[\begin{array}{ccc|c} 1 & 0 & -7 & -18 \\ 0 & 1 & 5 & 12 \\ 0 & 0 & 1 & 3 \end{array}\right]$$

$$\begin{array}{l} R_1 + 7R_3 \to \\ R_2 - 5R_3 \to \\ \end{array} \left[\begin{array}{ccc|c} 1 & 0 & 0 & 3 \\ 0 & 1 & 0 & -3 \\ 0 & 0 & 1 & 3 \end{array}\right]$$

The solution is (3, –3, 3).

33. $$\left[\begin{array}{ccc|c} 1 & 1 & 1 & 0 \\ 2 & 1 & 2 & -1 \\ 1 & 1 & 0 & 0 \end{array}\right] \begin{array}{l} \\ R_2 - 2R_1 \to \\ R_3 - R_1 \to \end{array} \left[\begin{array}{ccc|c} 1 & 1 & 1 & 0 \\ 0 & -1 & 0 & -1 \\ 0 & 0 & -1 & 0 \end{array}\right] \begin{array}{l} \\ (-1)R_2 \to \\ (-1)R_3 \to \end{array} \left[\begin{array}{ccc|c} 1 & 1 & 1 & 0 \\ 0 & 1 & 0 & 1 \\ 0 & 0 & 1 & 0 \end{array}\right] \begin{array}{l} R_1 - R_2 \to \\ \\ \end{array} \left[\begin{array}{ccc|c} 1 & 0 & 1 & -1 \\ 0 & 1 & 0 & 1 \\ 0 & 0 & 1 & 0 \end{array}\right]$$

$$\begin{array}{l} R_1 - R_3 \to \\ \\ \end{array} \left[\begin{array}{ccc|c} 1 & 0 & 0 & -1 \\ 0 & 1 & 0 & 1 \\ 0 & 0 & 1 & 0 \end{array}\right]$$

The solution is (–1, 1, 0).

35. $$\left[\begin{array}{ccc|c} 1 & 1 & 1 & 3 \\ -1 & 0 & -1 & -2 \\ 1 & 1 & 2 & 4 \end{array}\right] \begin{array}{l} \\ R_2 + R_1 \to \\ R_3 - R_1 \to \end{array} \left[\begin{array}{ccc|c} 1 & 1 & 1 & 3 \\ 0 & 1 & 0 & 1 \\ 0 & 0 & 1 & 1 \end{array}\right] \begin{array}{l} R_1 - R_2 \to \\ \\ \end{array} \left[\begin{array}{ccc|c} 1 & 0 & 1 & 2 \\ 0 & 1 & 0 & 1 \\ 0 & 0 & 1 & 1 \end{array}\right] \begin{array}{l} R_1 - R_3 \to \\ \\ \end{array} \left[\begin{array}{ccc|c} 1 & 0 & 0 & 1 \\ 0 & 1 & 0 & 1 \\ 0 & 0 & 1 & 1 \end{array}\right]$$

The solution is (1, 1, 1).

37. $$\left[\begin{array}{ccc|c} 1 & 2 & 1 & 3 \\ 2 & 1 & -1 & -6 \\ -1 & -1 & 2 & 5 \end{array}\right] \begin{array}{l} \\ R_2 - 2R_1 \to \\ R_3 + R_1 \to \end{array} \left[\begin{array}{ccc|c} 1 & 2 & 1 & 3 \\ 0 & -3 & -3 & -12 \\ 0 & 1 & 3 & 8 \end{array}\right] \begin{array}{l} \\ (-1/3)R_2 \to \\ \end{array} \left[\begin{array}{ccc|c} 1 & 2 & 1 & 3 \\ 0 & 1 & 1 & 4 \\ 0 & 1 & 3 & 8 \end{array}\right]$$

$$\begin{array}{l} \\ \\ R_3 - R_2 \to \end{array} \left[\begin{array}{ccc|c} 1 & 2 & 1 & 3 \\ 0 & 1 & 1 & 4 \\ 0 & 0 & 2 & 4 \end{array}\right] \begin{array}{l} R_1 - 2R_2 \to \\ \\ (1/2)R_3 \to \end{array} \left[\begin{array}{ccc|c} 1 & 0 & -1 & -5 \\ 0 & 1 & 1 & 4 \\ 0 & 0 & 1 & 2 \end{array}\right] \begin{array}{l} R_1 + R_3 \to \\ R_2 - R_3 \to \\ \end{array} \left[\begin{array}{ccc|c} 1 & 0 & 0 & -3 \\ 0 & 1 & 0 & 2 \\ 0 & 0 & 1 & 2 \end{array}\right]$$

The solution is (–3, 2, 2).

39. See example 6 in the text for graphing calculator instructions.

$$[A] = \left[\begin{array}{cc|c} 1 & 4 & 13 \\ 5 & -3 & -50 \end{array}\right]; \ \text{rref}([A]) = \left[\begin{array}{cc|c} 1 & 0 & -7 \\ 0 & 1 & 5 \end{array}\right];$$ The solution is (–7, 5).

41. See example 6 in the text for graphing calculator instructions.

$$[A] = \left[\begin{array}{ccc|c} 2 & -1 & 3 & 9 \\ -4 & 5 & 2 & 12 \\ 2 & 0 & 7 & 23 \end{array}\right]; \ \text{rref}([A]) = \left[\begin{array}{ccc|c} 1 & 0 & 0 & 1 \\ 0 & 1 & 0 & 2 \\ 0 & 0 & 1 & 3 \end{array}\right];$$ The solution is (1, 2, 3).

43. See example 6 in the text for graphing calculator instructions.

$$[A] = \left[\begin{array}{ccc|c} 6 & 2 & 1 & 4 \\ -2 & 4 & 1 & -3 \\ 2 & -8 & 0 & -2 \end{array}\right]; \ \text{rref}([A]) = \left[\begin{array}{ccc|c} 1 & 0 & 0 & 1 \\ 0 & 1 & 0 & 0.5 \\ 0 & 0 & 1 & -3 \end{array}\right];$$ The solution is (1, 0.5, –3).

45. See example 6 in the text for graphing calculator instructions.

$$[A] = \left[\begin{array}{ccc|c} 4 & 3 & 12 & -9.25 \\ -1 & 15 & 8 & -4.75 \\ 0 & 6 & 7 & -5.5 \end{array}\right]; \ \text{rref}([A]) = \left[\begin{array}{ccc|c} 1 & 0 & 0 & 0.5 \\ 0 & 1 & 0 & 0.25 \\ 0 & 0 & 1 & -1 \end{array}\right];$$ The solution is (0.5, 0.25, –1).

47. See example 6 in the text for graphing calculator instructions.

$$[A] = \left[\begin{array}{ccc|c} 1.2 & -0.9 & 2.7 & 5.37 \\ 3.1 & -5.1 & 7.2 & 14.81 \\ 0.2 & 1.8 & -3.6 & -6.38 \end{array}\right]; \ \text{rref}([A]) = \left[\begin{array}{ccc|c} 1 & 0 & 0 & 0.5 \\ 0 & 1 & 0 & -0.2 \\ 0 & 0 & 1 & 1.7 \end{array}\right];$$ The solution is (0.5, –0.2, 1.7).

49. $$\left[\begin{array}{cc|c} 1 & 2 & 4 \\ -2 & -4 & -8 \end{array}\right] \begin{array}{l} \\ R_2 + 2R_1 \rightarrow \end{array} \left[\begin{array}{cc|c} 1 & 2 & 4 \\ 0 & 0 & 0 \end{array}\right]$$

Row 2 represents the equation 0 = 0. The system is dependent.

51. $$\left[\begin{array}{ccc|c} 1 & 1 & 1 & 3 \\ 1 & 1 & -1 & 1 \\ 1 & 1 & 0 & 3 \end{array}\right] \begin{array}{l} \\ R_2 - R_1 \rightarrow \\ R_3 - R_1 \rightarrow \end{array} \left[\begin{array}{ccc|c} 1 & 1 & 1 & 3 \\ 0 & 0 & -2 & -2 \\ 0 & 0 & -1 & 0 \end{array}\right] \begin{array}{l} \\ R_2 - 2R_3 \rightarrow \\ \end{array} \left[\begin{array}{ccc|c} 1 & 1 & 1 & 3 \\ 0 & 0 & 0 & -2 \\ 0 & 0 & -1 & 0 \end{array}\right]$$

Row 2 represents the equation 0 = –2. The system is inconsistent.

53. $$\left[\begin{array}{ccc|c} 1 & 2 & 3 & 14 \\ 2 & -3 & -2 & -10 \\ 3 & -1 & 1 & 4 \end{array}\right] \begin{array}{l} \\ R_2 - 2R_1 \rightarrow \\ R_3 - 3R_1 \rightarrow \end{array} \left[\begin{array}{ccc|c} 1 & 2 & 3 & 14 \\ 0 & -7 & -8 & -38 \\ 0 & -7 & -8 & -38 \end{array}\right] \begin{array}{l} \\ \\ R_3 - R_2 \rightarrow \end{array} \left[\begin{array}{ccc|c} 1 & 2 & 3 & 14 \\ 0 & -7 & -8 & -38 \\ 0 & 0 & 0 & 0 \end{array}\right]$$

Row 3 represents the equation 0 = 0. The system is dependent.

Applications

55. The equation found in example 7 is $W = -374 + 19H + 6L$. When $H = 12$ and $L = 60$,

$W = -374 + 19(12) + 6(60) = 214$ lb.

57. (a)
$$\begin{aligned} a \quad + 2b \quad + 1.4c &= 3 \\ a + 1.5b + 0.65c &= 2 \\ a \quad + 4b \quad + 3.4c &= 6 \end{aligned}$$

(b) Using the graphing calculator to solve the system, the solution is $a = 0.6$, $b = 0.5$, $c = 1$.

So the equation is $H = 0.6 + 0.5M + P$.

(c) When $M = 3$ and $P = 2$, $H \approx 0.6 + 0.5(3) + (2) = 4.1 \approx 4$ people.59. Let x, y and z represent the time spent running at 5, 6 and 8 mph respectively. The system needed is:

$$\begin{aligned} x + y + z &= 2 \\ 5x + 6y + 8z &= 12.5 \\ x \qquad - z &= 0 \end{aligned} \quad \text{and so } [A] = \left[\begin{array}{ccc|c} 1 & 1 & 1 & 2 \\ 5 & 6 & 8 & 12.5 \\ 1 & 0 & -1 & 0 \end{array}\right]; \ \text{rref}([A]) = \left[\begin{array}{ccc|c} 1 & 0 & 0 & 0.5 \\ 0 & 1 & 0 & 1 \\ 0 & 0 & 1 & 0.5 \end{array}\right]$$

The solution is (0.5, 1, 0.5). The runner ran 0.5 hr at 5 mph, 1 hr at 6 mph and 0.5 hr at 8 mph.

61. Let x, y and z represent the amount invested at 5%, 8% and 12% respectively. The system needed is:

$$\begin{aligned} x \quad + y \quad + z &= 3000 \\ 0.05x + 0.08y + 0.12z &= 285 \\ 3x \qquad - z &= 0 \end{aligned} \quad \text{and so } [A] = \left[\begin{array}{ccc|c} 1 & 1 & 1 & 3000 \\ 0.05 & 0.08 & 0.12 & 285 \\ 3 & 0 & -1 & 0 \end{array}\right]; \ \text{rref}([A]) = \left[\begin{array}{ccc|c} 1 & 0 & 0 & 500 \\ 0 & 1 & 0 & 1000 \\ 0 & 0 & 1 & 1500 \end{array}\right]$$

The solution is (500, 1000, 1500). There was \$500 invested at 5%, \$1000 at 8% and \$1500 at 12%.

Checking Basic Concepts for Sections 9.1 & 9.2

1. (1, 3, –1) satisfies all three equations.

2. Multiply the first equation by –2 and add the first and second equations to eliminate the variable x.

$$\begin{aligned} -2x + 2y - 2z &= -4 \\ 2x - 3y + z &= -1 \\ \hline -y - z &= -5 \end{aligned}$$

Add the first and third equations to eliminate the variables x and y.

$$\begin{aligned} x - y + z &= 2 \\ -x + y + z &= 4 \\ \hline 2z &= 6 \end{aligned}$$

And so $z = 3$. Substitute $z = 3$ into the first *new* equation: $-y - (3) = -5 \Rightarrow -y = -2 \Rightarrow y = 2$

Substitute $y = 2$ and $z = 3$ into the *original* first equation: $x - (2) + (3) = 2 \Rightarrow x = 1$

The solution is (1, 2, 3).

3. (a)
$$\left[\begin{array}{ccc|c} 1 & 2 & 1 & 1 \\ 1 & 1 & 1 & -1 \\ 0 & 1 & 1 & 1 \end{array}\right] \begin{array}{l} \\ R_2 - R_1 \rightarrow \\ \\ \end{array} \left[\begin{array}{ccc|c} 1 & 2 & 1 & 1 \\ 0 & -1 & 0 & -2 \\ 0 & 1 & 1 & 1 \end{array}\right] \begin{array}{r} R_1 + 2R_2 \rightarrow \\ -1R_2 \rightarrow \\ R_3 + R_2 \rightarrow \end{array} \left[\begin{array}{ccc|c} 1 & 0 & 1 & -3 \\ 0 & 1 & 0 & 2 \\ 0 & 0 & 1 & -1 \end{array}\right]$$

$$\begin{array}{r} R_1 - R_3 \rightarrow \\ \\ \\ \end{array} \left[\begin{array}{ccc|c} 1 & 0 & 0 & -2 \\ 0 & 1 & 0 & 2 \\ 0 & 0 & 1 & -1 \end{array}\right]; \text{ The solution is } (-2, 2, -1).$$

(b)
$$[A] = \left[\begin{array}{ccc|c} 1 & 2 & 1 & 1 \\ 1 & 1 & 1 & -1 \\ 0 & 1 & 1 & 1 \end{array}\right]; \ \text{rref}([A]) = \left[\begin{array}{ccc|c} 1 & 0 & 0 & -2 \\ 0 & 1 & 0 & 2 \\ 0 & 0 & 1 & -1 \end{array}\right]; \text{ The solution is } (-2, 2, -1).$$

9.3: Determinants

Calculating Determinants

1. $\det A = 1(-8) - 3(-2) = -8 + 6 = -2$

3. $\det A = -3(-1) - 8(7) = 3 - 56 = -53$

5. $\det A = 23(-13) - 6(4) = -299 - 24 = -323$

7. $\det A = 1[(1)(7) - (-4)(-3)] - 0[(-1)(7) - (-4)(2)] + 0[(-1)(-3) - (1)(2)] = -5 - 0 + 0 = -5$

9. $\det A = 2[(-2)(8) - (1)(6)] - 1[(-1)(8) - (1)(0)] + 0[(-1)(6) - (-2)(0)] = -44 + 8 + 0 = -36$

11. $\det A = (-1)[(-3)(7) - (-3)(5)] - 3[(3)(7) - (-3)(5)] + 2[(3)(5) - (-3)(5)] = 6 - 108 + 60 = -42$

13. $\det A = 5[(-2)(5) - (0)(0)] - 0[(0)(5) - (0)(0)] + 0[(0)(0) - (-2)(0)] = -50 - 0 + 0 = -50$

15. $\det A = 0[(3)(9) - (5)(-9)] - 0[(2)(9) - (5)(-3)] + 0[(2)(-9) - (3)(-3)] = 0 - 0 + 0 = 0$

17. Using the calculator we find det $([A]) = -3555$

19. Using the calculator we find det $([A]) = -7466.5$

Calculating Area

21. The triangle has vertices (3, 2), (5, 8) and (9, 5). The matrix needed is $A = \begin{bmatrix} 3 & 5 & 9 \\ 2 & 8 & 5 \\ 1 & 1 & 1 \end{bmatrix}$.

    The area is $D = \left|\frac{1}{2}\det([A])\right| = 15 \text{ ft}^2$.

23. The triangle has vertices $(-6, -4)$, (2, 6) and $(6, -2)$. The matrix needed is $A = \begin{bmatrix} -6 & 2 & 6 \\ -4 & 6 & -2 \\ 1 & 1 & 1 \end{bmatrix}$.

    The area is $D = \left|\frac{1}{2}\det([A])\right| = 52 \text{ ft}^2$.

25. Split the figure into two triangles with vertices (2, 1), (3, 6), (9, 3) and vertices (3, 6), (7, 7), (9, 3).

    The matrices needed are $A = \begin{bmatrix} 2 & 3 & 9 \\ 1 & 6 & 3 \\ 1 & 1 & 1 \end{bmatrix}$ and $B = \begin{bmatrix} 3 & 7 & 9 \\ 6 & 7 & 3 \\ 1 & 1 & 1 \end{bmatrix}$.

    The area is $D = \left|\frac{1}{2}\det([A])\right| + \left|\frac{1}{2}\det([B])\right| = 16.5 + 9 = 25.5 \text{ ft}^2$.

Cramer's Rule

27. $E = \det\begin{bmatrix} 4 & 3 \\ 20 & -4 \end{bmatrix} = -16 - 60 = -76$; $F = \det\begin{bmatrix} 5 & 4 \\ 6 & 20 \end{bmatrix} = 100 - 24 = 76$

    $D = \det\begin{bmatrix} 5 & 3 \\ 6 & -4 \end{bmatrix} = -20 - 18 = -38$; The solution is $x = \frac{E}{D} = \frac{-76}{-38} = 2$ and $y = \frac{F}{D} = \frac{76}{-38} = -2$.

29. $E = \det\begin{bmatrix} -3 & -5 \\ -8 & 6 \end{bmatrix} = -18 - 40 = -58$; $F = \det\begin{bmatrix} 7 & -3 \\ -4 & -8 \end{bmatrix} = -56 - 12 = -68$

    $D = \det\begin{bmatrix} 7 & -5 \\ -4 & 6 \end{bmatrix} = 42 - 20 = 22$; The solution is $x = \frac{E}{D} = \frac{-58}{22} = -\frac{29}{11}$ and $y = \frac{F}{D} = \frac{-68}{22} = -\frac{34}{11}$.

31. $E = \det\begin{bmatrix} -61 & -3 \\ -23 & -4 \end{bmatrix} = 244 - 69 = 175$; $F = \det\begin{bmatrix} 8 & -61 \\ -1 & -23 \end{bmatrix} = -184 - 61 = -245$

$D = \det\begin{bmatrix} 8 & -3 \\ -1 & -4 \end{bmatrix} = -32 - 3 = -35$; The solution is $x = \frac{E}{D} = \frac{175}{-35} = -5$ and $y = \frac{F}{D} = \frac{-245}{-35} = 7$.

Checking Basic Concepts for Section 9.3

1. (a) $\det A = -3(3) - (-2)(4) = -9 + 8 = -1$

   (b) $\det A = 1[(1)(-1) - (2)(1)] - 5[(-2)(-1) - (2)(3)] + 0[(-2)(1) - (1)(3)] = -3 + 20 + 0 = 17$

2. $E = \det\begin{bmatrix} -14 & -1 \\ -36 & -4 \end{bmatrix} = 56 - 36 = 20$; $F = \det\begin{bmatrix} 2 & -14 \\ 3 & -36 \end{bmatrix} = -72 - (-42) = -30$

   $D = \det\begin{bmatrix} 2 & -1 \\ 3 & -4 \end{bmatrix} = -8 - (-3) = -5$; The solution is $x = \frac{E}{D} = \frac{20}{-5} = -4$ and $y = \frac{F}{D} = \frac{-30}{-5} = 6$.

3. The triangle has vertices (–1, 2), (5, 6) and (2, –3). The matrix needed is $A = \begin{bmatrix} -1 & 5 & 2 \\ 2 & 6 & -3 \\ 1 & 1 & 1 \end{bmatrix}$.

   The area is $D = \left|\frac{1}{2}\det([A])\right| = 21$ square units.

Chapter 9 Review Exercises

Section 9.1

1. Yes, since $3 + (-4) + 5 = 4$.

2. (1, –1, 2) is a solution since it satisfies all three of the equations.

3. Add the first two equations together to eliminate the variable x.

$$\begin{array}{r} x - y - 2z = -11 \\ -x + 2y + 3z = 16 \\ \hline y + z = 5 \end{array}$$

   From the third equation, $3z = 6 \Rightarrow z = 2$. And so $y + (2) = 5 \Rightarrow y = 3$.

   Substitute $z = 2$ and $y = 3$ into the first equation: $x - (3) - 2(2) = -11 \Rightarrow x = -4$

   The solution is (–4, 3, 2).

4. Multiply the second equation by –5 and the third equation by 3. Add these equations to eliminate the variable z.

$$\begin{array}{r} 10x - 5y - 15z = 10 \\ 3x - 6y + 15z = -78 \\ \hline 13x - 11y = -68 \end{array}$$

Multiply the first equation by 11 and add it to this *new* equation to eliminate the variable y.

$$\begin{array}{r} 11x + 11y = 44 \\ 13x - 11y = -68 \\ \hline 24x = -24 \end{array}$$

And so $x = -1$. Substitute $x = -1$ into the first equation: $(-1) + y = 4 \Rightarrow y = 5$

Substitute $x = -1$ and $y = 5$ into the second equation: $-2(-1) + (5) + 3z = -2 \Rightarrow 3z = -9 \Rightarrow z = -3$

The solution is $(-1, 5, -3)$.

5. Multiply the second equation by –1 and add it to the third equation to eliminate the variable z.

$$\begin{array}{r} -x - 2y - z = -7 \\ -2x + y + z = 7 \\ \hline -3x - y = 0 \end{array}$$

Multiply the first equation by –1 and add it to this *new* equation to eliminate the variable y.

$$\begin{array}{r} -2x + y = 5 \\ -3x - y = 0 \\ \hline -5x = 5 \end{array}$$

And so $x = -1$. Substitute $x = -1$ into the first equation: $2(-1) - y = -5 \Rightarrow y = 3$

Substitute $x = -1$ and $y = 3$ into the second equation: $-2(-1) + (3) + z = 7 \Rightarrow z = 2$

The solution is $(-1, 3, 2)$.

6. Multiply the second equation by 2 and add the first and second equations to eliminate the variable x.

$$\begin{array}{r} 2x + 3y + z = 6 \\ -2x + 4y + 4z = 6 \\ \hline 7y + 5z = 12 \end{array}$$

Add the second and third equations together to eliminate the variable x.

$$\begin{array}{r} -x + 2y + 2z = 3 \\ x + y + 2z = 4 \\ \hline 3y + 4z = 7 \end{array}$$

Multiply the first *new* equation by 4 and the second *new* equation by –5. Add these to eliminate the variable z.

$$\begin{array}{r} 28y + 20z = 48 \\ -15y - 20z = -35 \\ \hline 13y = 13 \end{array}$$

And so $y = 1$. Substitute $y = 1$ into the second *new* equation: $3(1) + 4z = 7 \Rightarrow 4z = 4 \Rightarrow z = 1$

Substitute $y = 1$ and $z = 1$ into the *original* third equation: $x + (1) + 2(1) = 4 \Rightarrow x = 1$

The solution is $(1, 1, 1)$.

Section 9.2

7. $$\left[\begin{array}{ccc|c}1&1&1&-6\\1&2&1&-8\\0&1&1&-5\end{array}\right]\begin{array}{l}\\R_2-R_1\rightarrow\\ \\\end{array}\left[\begin{array}{ccc|c}1&1&1&-6\\0&1&0&-2\\0&1&1&-5\end{array}\right]\begin{array}{l}R_1-R_3\rightarrow\\ \\R_3-R_2\rightarrow\end{array}\left[\begin{array}{ccc|c}1&0&0&-1\\0&1&0&-2\\0&0&1&-3\end{array}\right]$$; The solution is (–1, –2, –3).

8. $$\left[\begin{array}{ccc|c}1&1&1&-3\\-1&1&0&5\\0&1&1&-1\end{array}\right]\begin{array}{l}R_1-R_3\rightarrow\\R_2+R_1\rightarrow\\ \\\end{array}\left[\begin{array}{ccc|c}1&0&0&-2\\0&2&1&2\\0&1&1&-1\end{array}\right]\begin{array}{l}\\R_2-R_3\rightarrow\\ \\\end{array}\left[\begin{array}{ccc|c}1&0&0&-2\\0&1&0&3\\0&1&1&-1\end{array}\right]\begin{array}{l}\\ \\R_3-R_2\rightarrow\end{array}\left[\begin{array}{ccc|c}1&0&0&-2\\0&1&0&3\\0&0&1&-4\end{array}\right]$$

The solution is (–2, 3, –4).

9. $$\left[\begin{array}{ccc|c}1&2&-1&1\\-1&1&-2&5\\0&2&1&10\end{array}\right]\begin{array}{l}R_1-R_3\rightarrow\\R_2+R_1\rightarrow\\ \\\end{array}\left[\begin{array}{ccc|c}1&0&-2&-9\\0&3&-3&6\\0&2&1&10\end{array}\right]\begin{array}{l}\\(1/3)R_2\rightarrow\\ \\\end{array}\left[\begin{array}{ccc|c}1&0&-2&-9\\0&1&-1&2\\0&2&1&10\end{array}\right]$$

$$\begin{array}{l}\\ \\R_3-2R_2\rightarrow\end{array}\left[\begin{array}{ccc|c}1&0&-2&-9\\0&1&-1&2\\0&0&3&6\end{array}\right]\begin{array}{l}\\ \\(1/3)R_3\rightarrow\end{array}\left[\begin{array}{ccc|c}1&0&-2&-9\\0&1&-1&2\\0&0&1&2\end{array}\right]\begin{array}{l}R_1+2R_3\rightarrow\\R_2+R_3\rightarrow\\ \\\end{array}\left[\begin{array}{ccc|c}1&0&0&-5\\0&1&0&4\\0&0&1&2\end{array}\right]$$

The solution is (–5, 4, 2).

10. $$\left[\begin{array}{ccc|c}2&2&-2&-14\\-2&-3&2&12\\1&1&-4&-22\end{array}\right]\begin{array}{r}(1/2)R_1\rightarrow\\R_2+R_1\rightarrow\\R_3-(1/2)R_1\rightarrow\end{array}\left[\begin{array}{ccc|c}1&1&-1&-7\\0&-1&0&-2\\0&0&-3&-15\end{array}\right]\begin{array}{r}R_1+R_2\rightarrow\\-1R_2\rightarrow\\(-1/3)R_3\rightarrow\end{array}\left[\begin{array}{ccc|c}1&0&-1&-9\\0&1&0&2\\0&0&1&5\end{array}\right]$$

$$\begin{array}{l}R_1+R_3\rightarrow\\ \\ \\\end{array}\left[\begin{array}{ccc|c}1&0&0&-4\\0&1&0&2\\0&0&1&5\end{array}\right]$$; The solution is (–4, 2, 5).

11. See example 6 in section 4.6 in the text for graphing calculator instructions.

$$[A]=\left[\begin{array}{ccc|c}3&-2&6&-17\\-2&-1&5&20\\0&4&7&30\end{array}\right];\ \text{rref}([A])=\left[\begin{array}{ccc|c}1&0&0&-7\\0&1&0&4\\0&0&1&2\end{array}\right]$$; The solution is (–7, 4, 2).

12. See example 6 in section 4.6 in the text for graphing calculator instructions.

$$[A]=\left[\begin{array}{ccc|c}19&-13&-7&7.4\\22&33&-8&110.5\\10&-56&9&23.7\end{array}\right];\ \text{rref}([A])=\left[\begin{array}{ccc|c}1&0&0&5.4\\0&1&0&2.1\\0&0&1&9.7\end{array}\right]$$; The solution is (5.4, 2.1, 9.7)

Section 9.3

13. $\det A = 6(2) - (-4)(-5) = 12 - 20 = -8$

14. $\det A = 0(9) - 5(-6) = 0 + 30 = 30$

15. $\det A = 3[(4)(1) - (-3)(7)] - 1[(-5)(1) - (-3)(-3)] + 0[(-5)(7) - (4)(-3)] = 75 - (-14) + 0 = 89$

16. $\det A = -2[(1)(8) - (-5)(-3)] - 2[(-1)(8) - (-5)(-7)] + 3[(-1)(-3) - (1)(-7)] = 14 - (-86) + 30 = 130$

17. Using the calculator we find $\det([A]) = 181{,}845$

18. Using the calculator we find $\det([A]) = 67.688$

19. The triangle has vertices (–4, 6), (–2, –4) and (6, 2). The matrix needed is $A = \begin{bmatrix} -4 & -2 & 6 \\ 6 & -4 & 2 \\ 1 & 1 & 1 \end{bmatrix}$.

The area is $D = \left|\frac{1}{2}\det([A])\right| = 46 \text{ ft}^2$.

20. The triangle has vertices (–12, –8), (4, 8) and (8, –4). The matrix needed is $A = \begin{bmatrix} -12 & 4 & 8 \\ -8 & 8 & -4 \\ 1 & 1 & 1 \end{bmatrix}$.

The area is $D = \left|\frac{1}{2}\det([A])\right| = 128 \text{ ft}^2$.

21. $E = \det\begin{bmatrix} 8 & 6 \\ 18 & -8 \end{bmatrix} = -64 - 108 = -172$; $F = \det\begin{bmatrix} 7 & 8 \\ 5 & 18 \end{bmatrix} = 126 - 40 = 86$

$D = \det\begin{bmatrix} 7 & 6 \\ 5 & -8 \end{bmatrix} = -56 - 30 = -86$; The solution is $x = \frac{E}{D} = \frac{-172}{-86} = 2$ and $y = \frac{F}{D} = \frac{86}{-86} = -1$.

22. $E = \det\begin{bmatrix} 25 & 5 \\ -3 & 4 \end{bmatrix} = 100 + 15 = 115$; $F = \det\begin{bmatrix} -2 & 25 \\ 3 & -3 \end{bmatrix} = 6 - 75 = -69$

$D = \det\begin{bmatrix} -2 & 5 \\ 3 & 4 \end{bmatrix} = -8 - 15 = -23$; The solution is $x = \frac{E}{D} = \frac{115}{-23} = -5$ and $y = \frac{F}{D} = \frac{-69}{-23} = 3$.

23. $E = \det\begin{bmatrix} 1.5 & -6 \\ 8 & -5 \end{bmatrix} = -7.5 + 48 = 40.5$; $F = \det\begin{bmatrix} 3 & 1.5 \\ 7 & 8 \end{bmatrix} = 24 - 10.5 = 13.5$

$D = \det\begin{bmatrix} 3 & -6 \\ 7 & -5 \end{bmatrix} = -15 + 42 = 27$; The solution is $x = \frac{E}{D} = \frac{40.5}{27} = \frac{3}{2}$ and $y = \frac{F}{D} = \frac{13.5}{27} = \frac{1}{2}$.

24. $E = \det\begin{bmatrix} -47 & 4 \\ 63 & -7 \end{bmatrix} = 329 - 252 = 77$; $F = \det\begin{bmatrix} -5 & -47 \\ 6 & 63 \end{bmatrix} = -315 + 282 = -33$

$D = \det\begin{bmatrix} -5 & 4 \\ 6 & -7 \end{bmatrix} = 35 - 24 = 11$; The solution is $x = \frac{E}{D} = \frac{77}{11} = 7$ and $y = \frac{F}{D} = \frac{-33}{11} = -3$.

Applications

25. Let x and y represent pedestrian fatalities for 1988 and 1998 respectively. Then the system needed is $x + y = 12{,}090$ and $x - y = 1650$. Adding the two equations will eliminate the variable y.

$$\begin{aligned} x + y &= 12{,}090 \\ x - y &= 1650 \\ \hline 2x &= 13{,}740 \end{aligned}$$

Thus, $x = 6870$. And so $(6870) + y = 12{,}090 \Rightarrow y = 5220$.

There were 6870 pedestrian fatalities in 1988 and 5220 in 1998.

26. Let x and y represent the number of \$8 and \$12 tickets respectively. Then the system needed is $x + y = 480$ and $8x + 12y = 4620$. Note that $x + y = 480 \Rightarrow y = -x + 480$ and $8x + 12y = 4620 \Rightarrow y = -\frac{2}{3}x + 385$.

Multiplying the first equation by –8 and adding the two equations will eliminate the variable x.

$$\begin{aligned} -8x - 8y &= -3840 \\ 8x + 12y &= 4620 \\ \hline 4y &= 780 \end{aligned}$$

Thus, $y = 195$. And so $x + (195) = 480 \Rightarrow x = 285$. The solution is (285, 195).

There were 285 tickets sold costing \$8 each and 195 tickets sold costing \$12 each.

27. (a)
$$\begin{aligned} m + 3c + 5b &= 14 \\ m + 2c + 4b &= 11 \\ c + 3b &= 5 \end{aligned}$$

(b) Using a graphing calculator to solve the system, the solution is (3, 2, 1).

A malt costs \$3.00, cones cost \$2.00 and an ice cream bar costs \$1.00.

28. Let x, y and z represent the measure of the largest, middle and smallest angle respectively. The system needed is:

$$\begin{aligned} x + y + z &= 180 \\ x - y - z &= 20 \\ x \qquad - z &= 85 \end{aligned}$$

Using a graphing calculator to solve the system, the solution is (100, 65, 15).

The measures of the three angles are 100°, 65° and 15°.

29. Let x, y and z represent the amount of \$1.50, \$2.00 and \$2.50 candy respectively. The system needed is:

$$\begin{aligned} x + y + z &= 12 \\ 1.50x + 2.00y + 2.50z &= 26 \\ -y + z &= 2 \end{aligned}$$

Using a graphing calculator to solve the system, the solution is (2, 4, 6).

There should be 2 lb of \$1.50 candy, 4 lb of \$2.00 candy and 6 lb of \$2.50 candy.

30. (a)
$$\begin{aligned} a + 202b + 63c &= 40 \\ a + 365b + 70c &= 50 \\ a + 446b + 77c &= 55 \end{aligned}$$

(b) Using the graphing calculator to solve the system, the solution is $a \approx 27.134$, $b \approx 0.061$, $c \approx 0.009$.

So the equation is $C \approx 27.134 + 0.061W + 0.009L$.

(c) When $W = 300$ and $L = 68$, $C \approx 27.134 + 0.061(300) + 0.009(68) = 46.046 \approx 46$ inches.

Chapter 9 Test

1. No, three planes cannot intersect at exactly three points.

2. Using $(-4, 3, 3)$ we get $(-4) - 3(3) + 4(3) = -1 \Rightarrow -1 = -1$, which is true. We also get $2(-4) + 3 - 3(3) = 6 \Rightarrow -14 = 6$, which is false. Therefore $(-4, 3, 3)$ is not a solution.

   Using $(1, -2, -2)$ we get $(1) - 3(-2) + 4(-2) = -1 \Rightarrow -1 = -1$, which is true. We also get $2(1) + (-2) - 3(-2) = 6 \Rightarrow 6 = 6$, which is true. We also get $(1) - (-2) + (-2) = 1 \Rightarrow 1 = 1$, which is true. Therefore $(1, -2, -2)$ is a solution.

3. Using elimination on the first two equations and adding gives:

$$\begin{array}{r} x - y + 2z = 5 \\ -3x + y - 3z = -8 \\ \hline 0 + 0 - z = -3 \Rightarrow z = 3 \end{array}$$

Using elimination on the top and bottom equations and subtracting gives:

$$\begin{array}{r} x - y + 2z = 5 \\ x - 2y + 2z = 3 \\ \hline 0 + y + 0 = 2 \Rightarrow y = 2 \end{array}$$

Substituting $z = 3$ and $y = 2$ into the first equation gives: $x - 2 + 2(3) = 5 \Rightarrow x + 4 = 5 \Rightarrow x = 1$.

Therefore (1, 2, 3).

4. (a) $\left[\begin{array}{cc|c} 2 & -4 & -10 \\ -3 & -2 & 7 \end{array}\right]$

(b) $\left[\begin{array}{cc|c} 2 & -4 & -10 \\ -3 & -2 & 7 \end{array}\right] \begin{array}{l} \\ 3R_1 + 2R_2 \rightarrow \end{array} \left[\begin{array}{cc|c} 2 & -4 & -10 \\ 0 & -16 & -16 \end{array}\right] \begin{array}{l} (1/2)R_1 \rightarrow \\ (-1/16)R_2 \rightarrow \end{array} \left[\begin{array}{cc|c} 1 & -2 & -5 \\ 0 & 1 & 1 \end{array}\right] \begin{array}{l} R_1 + 2R_2 \rightarrow \\ \end{array} \left[\begin{array}{cc|c} 1 & 0 & -3 \\ 0 & 1 & 1 \end{array}\right]$

The solution is (−3, 1).

5. (a) $\left[\begin{array}{ccc|c} 1 & 1 & 1 & 2 \\ 1 & -1 & -1 & 3 \\ 2 & 2 & 1 & 6 \end{array}\right]$

(b) $\left[\begin{array}{ccc|c} 1 & 1 & 1 & 2 \\ 1 & -1 & -1 & 3 \\ 2 & 2 & 1 & 6 \end{array}\right] \begin{array}{l} \\ R_2 - R_1 \rightarrow \\ R_3 - 2R_1 \rightarrow \end{array} \left[\begin{array}{ccc|c} 1 & 1 & 1 & 2 \\ 0 & -2 & -2 & 1 \\ 0 & 0 & -1 & 2 \end{array}\right] \begin{array}{l} R_1 + R_3 \rightarrow \\ R_2 + (-2)R_3 \rightarrow \\ (-1)R_3 \rightarrow \end{array} \left[\begin{array}{ccc|c} 1 & 1 & 0 & 4 \\ 0 & -2 & 0 & -3 \\ 0 & 0 & 1 & -2 \end{array}\right]$

$\begin{array}{l} R_1 + (1/2)R_2 \rightarrow \\ (-1/2)R_2 \rightarrow \\ \end{array} \left[\begin{array}{ccc|c} 1 & 0 & 0 & \frac{5}{2} \\ 0 & 1 & 0 & \frac{3}{2} \\ 0 & 0 & 1 & -2 \end{array}\right]$; The solution is $\left(\frac{5}{2}, \frac{3}{2}, -2\right)$.

6. $\det A = \det \begin{bmatrix} a_1 & b_1 & c_1 \\ a_2 & b_2 & c_2 \\ a_3 & b_3 & c_3 \end{bmatrix}$ if $\begin{bmatrix} 3 & 2 & -1 \\ 6 & 2 & -6 \\ 0 & 8 & -3 \end{bmatrix}$ then

$\det A = 3 \cdot \det \begin{bmatrix} 2 & -6 \\ 8 & -3 \end{bmatrix} - 6 \cdot \det \begin{bmatrix} 2 & -1 \\ 8 & -3 \end{bmatrix} + 0 \cdot \det \begin{bmatrix} 2 & -1 \\ 2 & -6 \end{bmatrix}$;

and so $\det A = 3 \cdot [(2)(-3) - (8)(-6)] - 6 \cdot [(2)(-3) - (8)(-1)] + 0$,

$\det A = (3 \cdot 42) - (6 \cdot 2) + 0 \Rightarrow \det A = 114$.

7. By cramer's rule: $5x - 3y = 7$ and $-4x + 2y = 11$ then

$E = \det \begin{bmatrix} 7 & -3 \\ 11 & 2 \end{bmatrix} = (7)(2) - (11)(-3) \Rightarrow E = 47$; $F = \det \begin{bmatrix} 5 & 7 \\ -4 & 11 \end{bmatrix} = (5)(11) - (-4)(7) \Rightarrow F = 83$;

$D = \det \begin{bmatrix} 5 & -3 \\ -4 & 2 \end{bmatrix} = (5)(2) - (-4)(-3) \Rightarrow D = -2$ if $x = \dfrac{E}{D}$ and $y = \dfrac{F}{D}$ then $\left(-\dfrac{47}{2}, -\dfrac{83}{2}\right)$.

8. Let x = hours jogged at 6 mph, y = hours jogged at 7 mph, and z = hours jogged at 9 mph. Then $6x + 7y + 9z = 7.1$, $x + y + z = 1$, and $x = z + 0.2 \Rightarrow x - z = 0.2$. Adding $x + y + z = 1$ and $x - z = 0.2$ yields $2x + y = 1.2$. Multiplying $x + y + z = 1$ by -9 and adding to $6x + 7y + 9z = 7.1$ yields $-3x - 2y = -1.9$. Now multiplying $2x + y = 1.2$ by 2 and adding to $-3x - 2y = -1.9$ yields $x = 0.5$. Then $2(0.5) + y = 1.2 \Rightarrow 1 + y = 1.2 \Rightarrow y = 0.2$ and $0.5 + 0.2 + z = 1 \Rightarrow z = 0.3$. Therefore $x = 0.5$ hr, $y = 0.2$ hr, and $z = 0.3$ hr $\Rightarrow x = 30$ min. at 6mph, $y = 12$ min. at 7 mph, and $z = 18$ min. at 9 mph.

9. Let x = the degree measure of the smallest angle of the triangle, y = the degree measure of the middle sized angle of the triangle, and z = the degree measure of the largest angle of the triangle. Then $x + y + z = 180$, $z = x + 50 \Rightarrow -x + z = 50$, and $x + y = z + 10 \Rightarrow x + y - z = 10$. Adding $-x + z = 50$ to $x + y - z = 10$ yields $y = 60$. Then adding $x + y + z = 180$ to $x + y - z = 10$ yields $2x + 2y = 190$. Substituting $y = 60$ into $2x + 2y = 190$ yields $2x + 2(60) = 190 \Rightarrow 2x + 120 = 190 \Rightarrow 2x = 70 \Rightarrow x = 35$. Now substituting $x = 35$ and $y = 60$ into $x + y + z = 180$ yields $35 + 60 + z = 180 \Rightarrow z = 85$. Therefore $x = 35$, $y = 60$, and $z = 85$ are the measures of each angle in the triangle.

10. (a) $a + 20b + 25c = 168$

$a + 24b + 40c = 270$

$a + 30b + 50c = 405$

(b) Multiplying equation one by -1 and adding to equation two yields: $4b + 15c = 102$. Multiplying equation two by -1 and adding to equation three yields: $6b + 10c = 135$. Now multiplying equation $4b + 15c = 102$ by 3 and equation $6b + 10c = 135$ by -2 and adding the results yields: $25c = 36 \Rightarrow c = 1.44$. Substituting $c = 1.44$ into $6b + 10c = 135$ yields: $6b + 14.4 = 135 \Rightarrow 6b = 120.6 \Rightarrow b = 20.1$. Now substituting $b = 20.1$ and $c = 1.44$ into $a + 20b + 25c = 168$ yields: $a + 20(20.1) + 25(1.44) = 168 \Rightarrow a + 402 + 36 = 168 \Rightarrow a = -270$. Therefore $a = -270$, $b = 20.1$, and $c = 1.44$.

(c) $w = -270 + 20.1(26) + 1.44(44) \Rightarrow w = -270 + 522.6 + 63.36 \Rightarrow w = 315.96$. Therefore $w \approx 316$ lbs., the weight of the bear.

Chapter 9 Extended and Discovery Exercises

1. $D = 1[(1)(3) - (1)(2)] - 2[(1)(3) - (1)(1)] + 0[(1)(2) - (1)(1)] = 1 - 4 + 0 = -3$

$E = 6[(1)(3) - (1)(2)] - 9[(1)(3) - (1)(1)] + 9[(1)(2) - (1)(1)] = 6 - 18 + 9 = -3$

$F = 1[(9)(3) - (9)(2)] - 2[(6)(3) - (9)(1)] + 0[(6)(1) - (9)(1)] = 9 - 18 + 0 = -9$

$G = 1[(1)(9) - (1)(9)] - 2[(1)(9) - (1)(6)] + 0[(1)(9) - (1)(6)] = 0 - 6 + 0 = -6$

$x = \dfrac{E}{D} = \dfrac{-3}{-3} = 1,\ y = \dfrac{F}{D} = \dfrac{-9}{-3} = 3,\ z = \dfrac{G}{D} = \dfrac{-6}{-3} = 2$. The solution is $(1, 3, 2)$.

2. $D = 0[(-1)(-1) - (1)(-1)] - 2[(1)(-1) - (1)(1)] + 1[(1)(-1) - (-1)(1)] = 0 + 4 + 0 = 4$

$E = 1[(-1)(-1) - (1)(-1)] - (-1)[(1)(-1) - (1)(1)] + 3[(1)(-1) - (-1)(1)] = 2 - 2 + 0 = 0$

$F = 0[(-1)(-1) - (3)(-1)] - 2[(1)(-1) - (3)(1)] + 1[(1)(-1) - (-1)(1)] = 0 + 8 + 0 = 8$

$G = 0[(-1)(3) - (1)(-1)] - 2[(1)(3) - (1)(1)] + 1[(1)(-1) - (-1)(1)] = 0 - 4 + 0 = -4$

$x = \frac{E}{D} = \frac{0}{4} = 0,\ y = \frac{F}{D} = \frac{8}{4} = 2,\ z = \frac{G}{D} = \frac{-4}{4} = -1$. The solution is $(0, 2, -1)$.

3. $D = 1[(1)(2) - (1)(0)] - 1[(0)(2) - (1)(1)] + 0[(0)(0) - (1)(1)] = 2 + 1 + 0 = 3$

$E = 2[(1)(2) - (1)(0)] - 0[(0)(2) - (1)(1)] + 1[(0)(0) - (1)(1)] = 4 + 0 - 1 = 3$

$F = 1[(0)(2) - (1)(0)] - 1[(2)(2) - (1)(1)] + 0[(0)(2) - (1)(0)] = 0 - 3 + 0 = -3$

$G = 1[(1)(1) - (1)(0)] - 1[(0)(1) - (1)(2)] + 0[(0)(0) - (1)(2)] = 1 + 2 + 0 = 3$

$x = \frac{E}{D} = \frac{3}{3} = 1,\ y = \frac{F}{D} = \frac{-3}{3} = -1,\ z = \frac{G}{D} = \frac{3}{3} = 1$. The solution is $(1, -1, 1)$.

4. $D = 1[(-2)(-3) - (1)(-3)] - (-1)[(1)(-3) - (1)(2)] + 0[(1)(-3) - (-2)(2)] = 9 - 5 + 0 = 4$

$E = 1[(-2)(-3) - (1)(-3)] - (-2)[(1)(-3) - (1)(2)] + 5[(1)(-3) - (-2)(2)] = 9 - 10 + 5 = 4$

$F = 1[(-2)(-3) - (5)(-3)] - (-1)[(1)(-3) - (5)(2)] + 0[(1)(-3) - (-2)(2)] = 21 - 13 + 0 = 8$

$G = 1[(-2)(5) - (1)(-2)] - (-1)[(1)(5) - (1)(1)] + 0[(1)(-2) - (-2)(1)] = -8 + 4 + 0 = -4$

$x = \frac{E}{D} = \frac{4}{4} = 1,\ y = \frac{F}{D} = \frac{8}{4} = 2,\ z = \frac{G}{D} = \frac{-4}{4} = -1$. The solution is $(1, 2, -1)$.

5. $D = 1[(1)(2) - (-1)(1)] - (-1)[(0)(2) - (-1)(2)] + 2[(0)(1) - (1)(2)] = 3 + 2 - 4 = 1$

$E = 7[(1)(2) - (-1)(1)] - 5[(0)(2) - (-1)(2)] + 6[(0)(1) - (1)(2)] = 21 - 10 - 12 = -1$

$F = 1[(5)(2) - (6)(1)] - (-1)[(7)(2) - (6)(2)] + 2[(7)(1) - (5)(2)] = 4 + 2 - 6 = 0$

$G = 1[(1)(6) - (-1)(5)] - (-1)[(0)(6) - (-1)(7)] + 2[(0)(5) - (1)(7)] = 11 + 7 - 14 = 4$

$x = \frac{E}{D} = \frac{-1}{1} = -1,\ y = \frac{F}{D} = \frac{0}{1} = 0,\ z = \frac{G}{D} = \frac{4}{1} = 4$. The solution is $(-1, 0, 4)$.

6. $D = 1[(-3)(-2) - (4)(-1)] - 2[(2)(-2) - (4)(3)] + 1[(2)(-1) - (-3)(3)] = 10 + 32 + 7 = 49$

$E = -1[(-3)(-2) - (4)(-1)] - 12[(2)(-2) - (4)(3)] + (-12)[(2)(-1) - (-3)(3)] = -10 + 192 - 84 = 98$

$F = 1[(12)(-2) - (-12)(-1)] - 2[(-1)(-2) - (-12)(3)] + 1[(-1)(-1) - (12)(3)] = -36 - 76 - 35 = -147$

$G = 1[(-3)(-12) - (4)(12)] - 2[(2)(-12) - (4)(-1)] + 1[(2)(12) - (-3)(-1)] = -12 + 40 + 21 = 49$

$x = \frac{E}{D} = \frac{98}{49} = 2,\ y = \frac{F}{D} = \frac{-147}{49} = -3,\ z = \frac{G}{D} = \frac{49}{49} = 1$. The solution is $(2, -3, 1)$.

7. (a) The system is correct.

(b)
$$\begin{aligned} x + y \quad &= 20 \\ z &= 1 \\ y - z &= 3 \end{aligned} \quad \text{and so } [A] = \left[\begin{array}{ccc|c} 1 & 1 & 0 & 20 \\ 0 & 0 & 1 & 9 \\ 0 & 1 & -1 & 3 \end{array}\right]$$

(c) $\text{rref}([A]) = \left[\begin{array}{ccc|c} 1 & 0 & 0 & 8 \\ 0 & 1 & 0 & 12 \\ 0 & 0 & 1 & 9 \end{array}\right]$ The solution is (8, 12, 9).

The traffic flow in the x-direction is 8 cars per minute, the flow in the y-direction is 12 cars per minute and the flow in the z-direction is 9 cars per minutes.

8. (a) The system is correct.

(b)
$$\begin{aligned} x + y \quad &= 9 \\ z &= 5 \\ y - z &= -2 \end{aligned} \quad \text{and so } [A] = \left[\begin{array}{ccc|c} 1 & 1 & 0 & 9 \\ 0 & 0 & 1 & 5 \\ 0 & 1 & -1 & -2 \end{array}\right]$$

(c) $\text{rref}([A]) = \left[\begin{array}{ccc|c} 1 & 0 & 0 & 6 \\ 0 & 1 & 0 & 3 \\ 0 & 0 & 1 & 5 \end{array}\right]$ The solution is (6, 3, 5).

The traffic flow in the x-direction is 6 cars per minute, the flow in the y-direction is 3 cars per minute and the flow in the z-direction is 5 cars per minutes.

9. Since Denver is city 1 and Las Vegas is city 4, we look at either entry a_{14} or a_{41}. The distance is 760 miles.

10. Add entry a_{12} to entry a_{23}. The distance is 360 miles.

11. The dimension would be 20×20 and the matrix would contain 400 elements.

12. The elements on the main diagonal represent the distance from a city to itself, which is always zero.

13. See Figure 13.

$$\begin{bmatrix} 0 & 130 & 95 & 75 \\ 130 & 0 & 186 & \bigstar \\ 95 & 186 & 0 & 57 \\ 75 & \bigstar & 57 & 0 \end{bmatrix}$$

Figure 13

$$\begin{bmatrix} 0 & 97 & \bigstar & \bigstar & 59 \\ 97 & 0 & 113 & 118 & \bigstar \\ \bigstar & 113 & 0 & 94 & \bigstar \\ \bigstar & 118 & 94 & 0 & 177 \\ 59 & \bigstar & \bigstar & 177 & 0 \end{bmatrix}$$

Figure 14

14. See Figure 14.

15. All maps for adjacency matrix A must have the same distances between cities, but the location of each city may vary. The solution is not unique. One possible solution is shown in Figure 15.

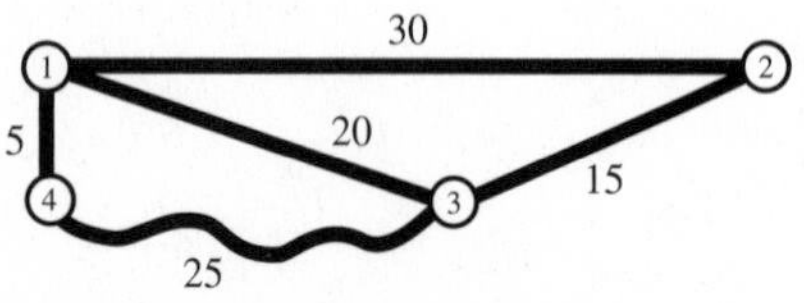

Figure 15

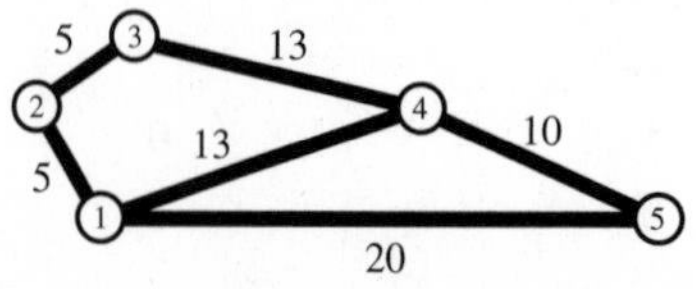

Figure 16

16. All maps for adjacency matrix A must have the same distances between cities, but the location of each city may vary. The solution is not unique. One possible solution is shown in Figure 16.

17. (a) $\left[\begin{array}{cccc|c} 1 & 19 & 57.5 & 32 & 125 \\ 1 & 26 & 65 & 42 & 316 \\ 1 & 30 & 72 & 48 & 436 \\ 1 & 30.5 & 75 & 54 & 514 \end{array}\right]$

(b) $a \approx -552.272$, $b \approx 8.733$, $c \approx 2.859$, $d \approx 10.843$

(c) $N = 24$, $L = 63$ and $C = 39$, $W \approx -552.272 + 8.733(24) + 2.859(63) + 10.843(39) \approx 260$

A bear with a 24-inch neck, 63-inch length and 39-inch chest weighs approximately 260 pounds.

Cumulative Review Exercises for Chapters 1-9

1. Prime factors of $360 = 2 \cdot 2 \cdot 2 \cdot 3 \cdot 3 \cdot 5 \Rightarrow 2^3 \cdot 3^2 \cdot 5$.

2. $2n + 7 = n - 2$, then $2n + 7 = n - 2 \Rightarrow n + 7 = -2 \Rightarrow n = -9$

3. $\frac{2}{3} + \frac{4}{7} \cdot \frac{21}{28} = \frac{2}{3} + \frac{84}{196} = \frac{392}{588} + \frac{252}{588} = \frac{644}{588} = \frac{23}{21}$

4. $\frac{3}{5} \div \frac{6}{5} - \frac{2}{3} = \frac{3}{5} \times \frac{5}{6} - \frac{2}{3} = \frac{1}{2} - \frac{2}{3} = \frac{3}{6} - \frac{4}{6} = -\frac{1}{6}$

5. $30 - 4 \div 2 \cdot 6 = 30 - (4 \div 2) \cdot 6 = 30 - (2) \cdot 6 = 30 - (2 \cdot 6) = 30 - 12 = 18$

6. $\frac{3^2 - 2^3}{20 - 5 \cdot 2} = \frac{9 - 8}{20 - 10} \Rightarrow \frac{1}{10}$

7. $2(x + 1) - 6x = x - 4 \Rightarrow 2x + 2 - 6x = x - 4 \Rightarrow -5x + 2 = -4 \Rightarrow -5x = -6 \Rightarrow x = \frac{6}{5}$

8. $x = 2$. See Figure 8. Checking: $4 - 3(2) = -2 \Rightarrow 4 - 6 = -2 \Rightarrow -2 = -2$, yes.

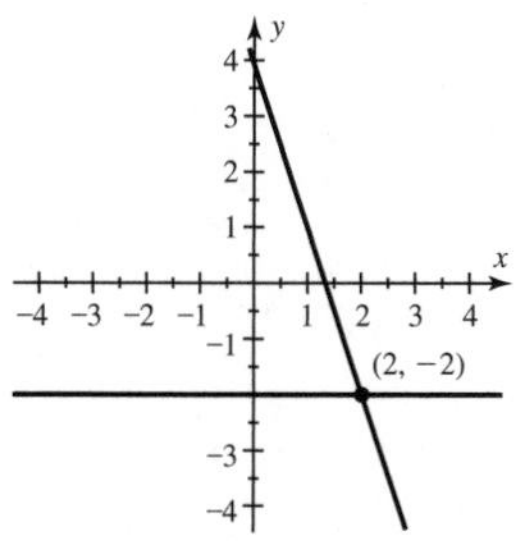

Figure 8

9. $124\% = \frac{124}{100}$, which reduced $= \frac{31}{25}$ and 1.24.

10. When $A = 30$ miles^2 and $h = 10$ miles then for $A = \frac{1}{2}bh$, $30 = \frac{1}{2}b(10) \Rightarrow 30 = 5b \Rightarrow b = 6$ miles.

11. $A = \frac{h}{2}(a + b)$ then $A = \frac{h}{2}a + \frac{h}{2}b \Rightarrow A - \frac{h}{2}a = \frac{h}{2}b \Rightarrow \frac{2}{h}\left(A - \frac{ha}{2}\right) = b \Rightarrow b = \frac{2a}{h} - a$

12. $bt - 1 < 3 - t$, $7t < 4 \Rightarrow t < \frac{4}{7} \Rightarrow \left\{t \,\middle|\, t < \frac{4}{7}\right\}$

13. See Figure 13.

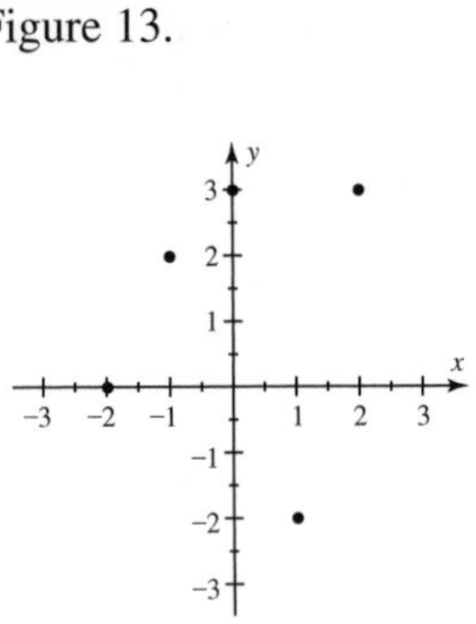

Figure 13

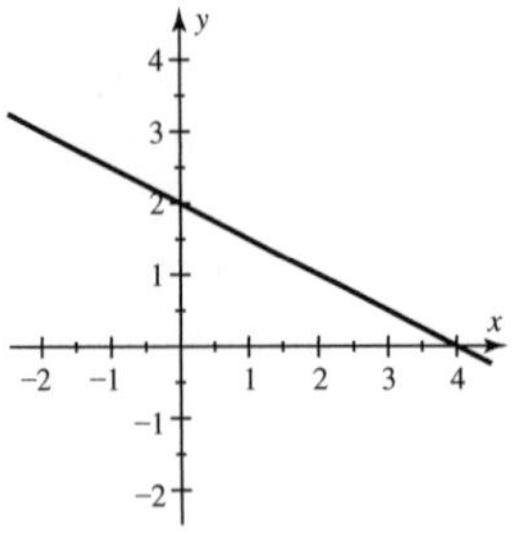

Figure 14

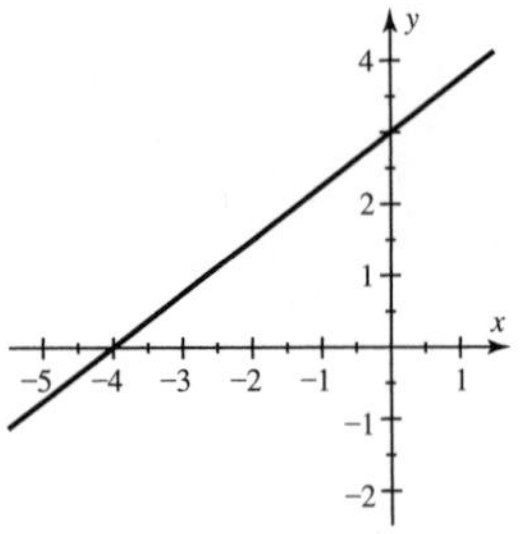

Figure 15

14. See Figure 14. x-intercept: 4; y-intercept: 2.

15. See Figure 15. x-intercept: -4; y-intercept: 3.

16. See Figure 16. x-intercept: -2; y-intercept: none.

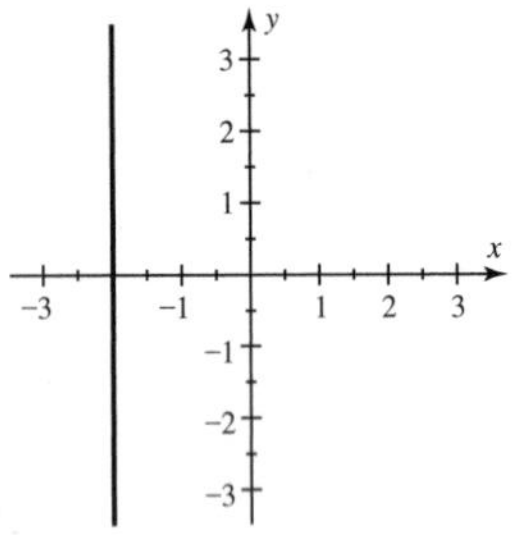

Figure 16

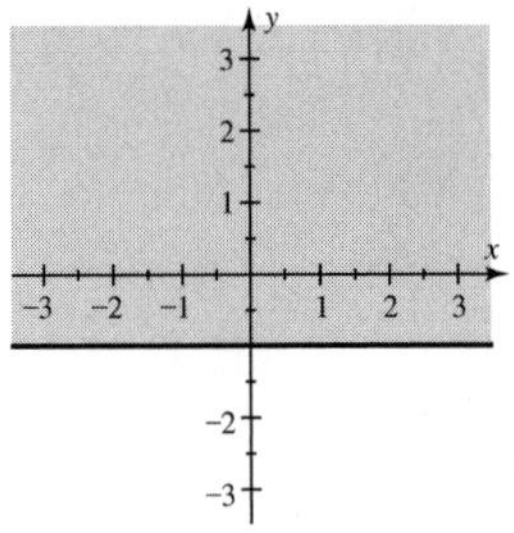

Figure 23

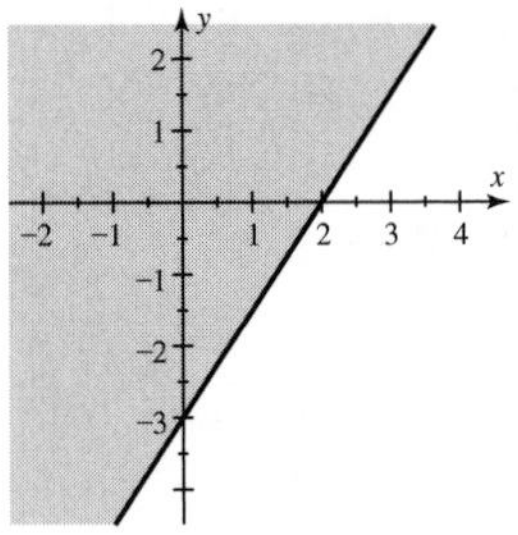

Figure 24

17. x-intercept: 2; y-intercept: 4; Therefore $m = \dfrac{4 - 0}{0 - 2} \Rightarrow m = -2 \Rightarrow y = -2x + 4$.

18. Using point-slope form: $y - 3 = -2(x + 1) \Rightarrow y - 3 = -2x - 2 \Rightarrow y = -2x + 1$

19. First find slope: $m = \dfrac{8 - 5}{2 - (-3)} = \dfrac{3}{5}$. Now use point-slope form: $y - 8 = \dfrac{3}{5}(x - 2) \Rightarrow y - 8 = \dfrac{3}{5}x - \dfrac{6}{5} \Rightarrow$

$y = \dfrac{3}{5}x + \dfrac{34}{5}$.

20. First put $x + 2y = 5$ into slope-intercept form: $x + 2y = 5 \Rightarrow 2y = -x + 5 \Rightarrow y = -\dfrac{1}{2}x + \dfrac{5}{2} \Rightarrow m = -\dfrac{1}{2}$.

The slope of a line perpendicular to this would be $\dfrac{2}{1}$ or 2. Now using slope-intercept form

$y - 1 = 2(x + 1) \Rightarrow y - 1 = 2x + 2 \Rightarrow y = 2x + 3$.

21. $P = 500x + 4000$

22. Using substitution; $-2a + b = -5 \Rightarrow b = 2a - 5$ and so $4a - 3(2a - 5) = 0$, $4a - 6a + 15 = 0$,

$-2a + 15 = 0 \Rightarrow a = 7.5$, and $-2(7.5) + b = -5 \Rightarrow b = 10 \Rightarrow (7.5, 10)$.

23. See Figure 23.

24. See Figure 24.

25. See Figure 25.

26. See Figure 26.

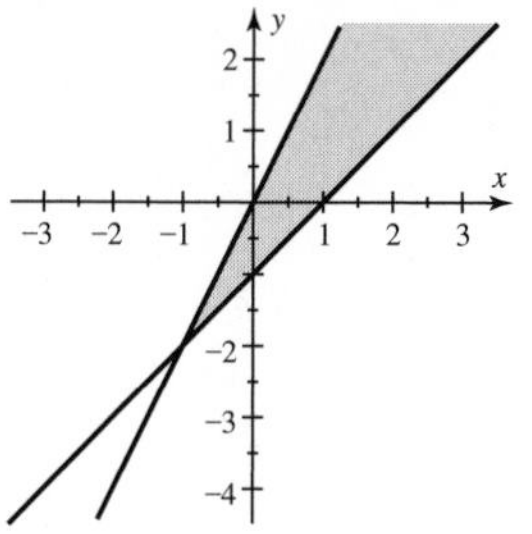

Figure 25

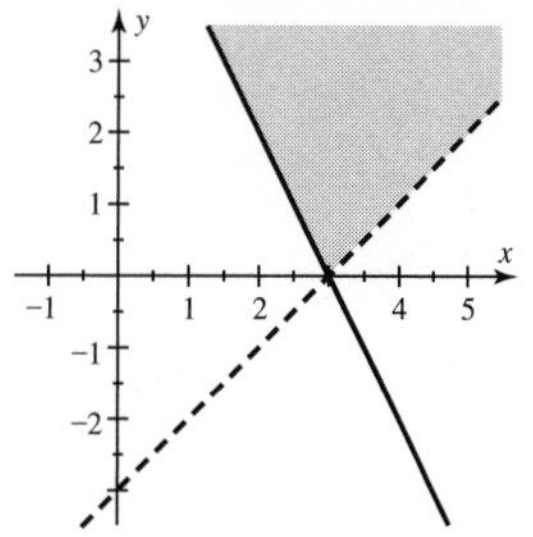

Figure 26

27. $(ab - bb^2) - (4b^2 + 8ab + 2) \Rightarrow -7ab - 10b^2 - 2$

28. $5 - 3^4 = 5 - 81 \Rightarrow -76$

29. $4(4^{-2})(3^{-1})(3^4) = \frac{4}{1} \cdot \frac{1}{4^2} \cdot \frac{1}{3} \cdot \frac{3^4}{1} = \frac{4}{1} \cdot \frac{1}{16} \cdot \frac{1}{3} \cdot \frac{81}{1} = \frac{27}{4}$

30. $\frac{2^{-4}}{4^{-2}} = \frac{4^2}{2^4} = \frac{16}{16} = 1$

31. $(8t^{-3})(3t^2)(t^5) = (8 \cdot 3)(t^{-3+2+5}) = 24t^4$

32. $2(rt)^4 \Rightarrow 2r^4t^4$

33. $(2t^3)^{-2} = \frac{1}{(2t^3)^2} \Rightarrow \frac{1}{2^2 \cdot t^{3 \cdot 2}} = \frac{1}{4t^6}$

34. $(4a^2b^3)^2(2ab)^{-3} = (4^2 \cdot a^{2 \cdot 2} \cdot b^{3 \cdot 2})\left(\frac{1}{2^3a^3b^3}\right) = \frac{16a^4b^6}{8a^3b^3} = 2a^{4-3}b^{6-3} = 2ab^3$

35. $\left(\frac{2rt^{-1}}{3r^{-2}t^3}\right)^4 = \frac{2^4 \cdot r^4 \cdot t^{-1 \cdot 4}}{3^4 \cdot r^{-2 \cdot 4} \cdot t^{3 \cdot 4}} = \frac{16r^4y^{-4}}{81r^{-8}t^{12}} = \frac{16r^{4-(-8)}t^{-4-12}}{81} = \frac{16r^{12}t^{-16}}{81} = \frac{16r^{12}}{81t^{16}}$

36. $\left(\frac{2a^{-1}}{ab^{-2}}\right)^{-3} = \frac{2^{-3} \cdot a^{-1 \cdot (-3)}}{a^{-3}b^{-2 \cdot (-3)}} = \frac{2^{-3}a^3}{a^{-3}b^6} = \frac{a^{3-(-3)}}{2^3b^6} = \frac{a^6}{8b^6}$

37. $2a^2(a^2 - 2a + 3) = 2a^4 - 4a^3 + 6a^2$

38. $(a + b)(a^2 - ab + b^2) = a^3 - a^2b + ab^2 + a^2b - ab^2 + b^3 = a^3 + b^3$

39. $(5x + 1)(x - 7) = 5x^2 - 35x + x - 7 = 5x^2 - 34x - 7$

40. $(y - 3)(2y + 3) = 2y^2 + 3y - 6y - 9 = 2y^2 - 3y - 9$

41. $(a + b)(a - b) = a^2 - ab + ab - b^2 = a^2 - b^2$

42. $(2x + 3y)^2 = 4x^2 + 6xy + 6xy + 9y^2 = 4x^2 + 12xy + 9y^2$

43. Move the decimal point five places to the left, $1.5 \times 10^{-5} = 0.000015$.

44. Move the decimal point six places to the left, $2{,}130{,}000 = 2.13 \times 10^6$.

45. $\frac{4x^3 - 8x^2 + 6x}{2x} = \frac{4x^3}{2x} - \frac{8x^2}{2x} + \frac{6x}{2x} = 2x^2 - 4x + 3$

46.

$$\begin{array}{r} x^3 - 4x^2 + 3x - 2 + \dfrac{1}{x-5} \\ x - 5\overline{)x^4 - 9x^3 + 23x^2 - 17x + 11} \\ \underline{x^4 - 5x^3} \qquad\qquad\qquad\qquad \\ -4x^3 + 23x^2 \qquad\qquad \\ \underline{-4x^3 + 20x^2} \qquad\qquad \\ 3x^2 - 17x \qquad \\ \underline{3x^2 - 15x} \qquad \\ -2x + 11 \\ \underline{-2x + 10} \\ 1 \end{array}$$

47. $10ab^2 - 25a^3b^5 = 5ab^2(2 - 5a^2b^3)$

48. $y^3 - 3y^2 + 2y - 6 = (y^3 - 3y^2) + (2y - 6) = y^2(y - 3) + 2(y - 3) = (y - 3)(y^2 + 2)$

49. $6z^2 + 7z - 3 = (2z + 3)(3z - 1)$

50. $4z^2 - 9 = (2z)^2 - 3^2 = (2z - 3)(2z + 3)$

51. $4y^2 - 20y + 25 = (2y - 5)(2y - 5) = (2y - 5)^2$

52. $a^3 - 27 = a^3 - 3^3 = (a - 3)(a^2 + 3a + 9)$

53. $4z^4 - 17z + 15 = (z^2 - 3)(4z^2 - 5)$

54. $2a^3b + a^2b^2 - ab^3 = ab(2a^2 + ab - b^2) = ab(2a - b)(a + b)$

55. $x - 1 = 0 \Rightarrow x = 1$ and $x + 2 = 0 \Rightarrow x = -2$. Therefore $x = -2, 1$.

56. Factor $x^2 - 9x = 0 \Rightarrow x(x - 9) = 0$, so $x = 0$ and $x - 9 = 0 \Rightarrow x = 9$. Therefore $x = 0, 9$.

57. Set $6y^2 - 7y = 3$ equal to zero $\Rightarrow 6y^2 - 7y - 3 = 0$. Now factor: $6y^2 - 7y - 3 = 0 \Rightarrow$

$(3y + 1)(2y - 3) = 0$. So $3y + 1 = 0 \Rightarrow 3y = -1 \Rightarrow y = -\frac{1}{3}$ and $2y - 3 = 0 \Rightarrow 2y = 3 \Rightarrow y = \frac{3}{2}$.

Therefore $y = -\frac{1}{3}, \frac{3}{2}$.

58. Set $x^3 = 4x$ equal to zero $\Rightarrow x^3 - 4x = 0$. Now factor: $x^3 - 4x = 0 \Rightarrow x(x^2 - 4) \Rightarrow$

$x(x + 2)(x - 2) = 0$. So $x + 2 = 0 \Rightarrow x = -2$, and $x - 2 = 0 \Rightarrow x = 2$. Therefore $x = -2, 0, 2$.

59. $\dfrac{x^2 - 16}{x + 4} = \dfrac{(x + 4)(x - 4)}{x + 4} = x - 4$

60. $\dfrac{2x^2 - 11x - 6}{6x^2 - 5x - 4} = \dfrac{(2x + 1)(x - 6)}{(2x + 1)(3x - 4)} = \dfrac{x - 6}{3x - 4}$

61. $\dfrac{x - 3}{16 - x^2}$ will be undefined when $16x^2 = 0$. $x^2 - 16 = 0 \Rightarrow (x + 4)(x - 4) = 0$. So $x + 4 = 0 \Rightarrow$

$x = -4$ and $x - 4 = 0 \Rightarrow x = 4$. Therefore it will be undefined when $x = -4, 4$.

62. $\dfrac{4(-2) + 1}{(-2) - 1} = \dfrac{-8 + 1}{-3} = \dfrac{-7}{-3} = \dfrac{7}{3}$

63. $\dfrac{x^2 - 3x + 2}{x + 7} \div \dfrac{x - 2}{2x + 14} = \dfrac{(x - 2)(x - 1)}{x + 7} \div \dfrac{x - 2}{2(x + 7)} = \dfrac{(x - 2)(x - 1)}{x + 7} \cdot \dfrac{2(x + 7)}{x - 2} = \dfrac{2(x - 1)}{1} = 2(x - 1)$

64. $\dfrac{x}{2x + 3} + \dfrac{x + 3}{2x + 3} = \dfrac{x + x + 3}{2x + 3} = \dfrac{2x + 3}{2x + 3} = 1$

65. $\frac{5x}{x^2-1} - \frac{3}{x+1} = \frac{5x}{(x+1)(x-1)} - \frac{3}{x+1} = \frac{5x}{(x+1)(x-1)} - \frac{3(x-1)}{(x+1)(x-1)} = \frac{5x-3x+3}{(x+1)(x-1)} = \frac{2x+3}{(x-1)(x+1)}$

66. $\frac{\frac{2}{x}-\frac{2}{y}}{\frac{2}{x}+\frac{2}{y}} = \frac{\frac{2y}{xy}-\frac{2x}{xy}}{\frac{2y}{xy}+\frac{2x}{xy}} = \frac{\frac{2y-2x}{xy}}{\frac{2y+2x}{xy}} = \frac{2y-2x}{xy} \cdot \frac{xy}{2y+2x} = \frac{2y-2x}{2y+2x} = \frac{2(y-x)}{2(y+x)} = \frac{y-x}{y+x}$

67. $\frac{x+2}{5} = \frac{x}{4} \Rightarrow 4(x+2) = 5x \Rightarrow 4x+8 = 5x \Rightarrow x = 8$

68. $\frac{1}{3x} + \frac{5}{2x} = 2 \Rightarrow \frac{2}{6x} + \frac{15}{6x} = \frac{12x}{6x}$, so $2 + 15 = 12x \Rightarrow 17 = 12x \Rightarrow x = \frac{17}{12}$

69. $\frac{1}{x-2} + \frac{2}{x+2} = \frac{1}{x^2-4} \Rightarrow \frac{1}{x-2} + \frac{2}{x+2} = \frac{1}{(x+2)(x-2)} \Rightarrow \frac{x+2}{(x+2)(x-2)} + \frac{2(x-2)}{(x+2)(x-2)} = \frac{1}{(x+2)(x-2)}$, so $x + 2 + 2(x-2) = 1 \Rightarrow x + 2 + 2x - 4 = 1 \Rightarrow 3x - 2 = 1 \Rightarrow 3x = 3 \Rightarrow x = 1$

70. If y is inversely proportional to x then $y = \frac{k}{x}$. If $y = 25$ when $x = 4$ then $25 = \frac{k}{4} \Rightarrow k = 100$.

So if $x = 10$ then $y = \frac{100}{10} \Rightarrow y = 10$.

71. $f(-3) = 1 - 4(-3) \Rightarrow f(-3) = 1 - (-12) \Rightarrow f(-3) = 13$

72. See Figure 72. $D = (-\infty, \infty)$, $R = (-2, \infty)$.

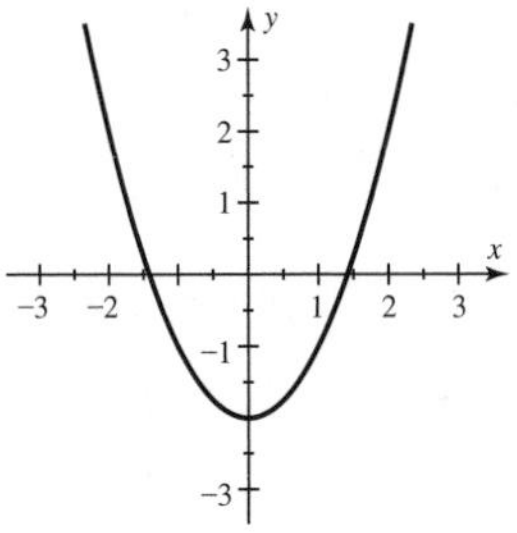

Figure 72

Figure 79

73. $f(0) = 2, f(-2) = -2$.

74. $f(0) = 2, f(-2) = -4$.

75. Because as x increases 1, $f(x)$ decreases -4 for every given case it is a linear function. Using $f(x)$ = constant change (x) + value at $x = 0$, we get $f(x) = -4x + 3$.

76. Here y_1 is below y_2 when $x \le -3$. The interval is $(-\infty, -3]$

77. $\frac{4x-9}{6} > \frac{1}{2} \Rightarrow 4x - 9 > 3 \Rightarrow 4x > 12 \Rightarrow x > 3$. The interval is $(3, \infty)$.

78. $\frac{2}{3}z - 2 \le \frac{1}{4}z - (2z+2) \Rightarrow 8z - 24 \le 3z - 24z - 24 \Rightarrow 8z - 24 \le -21z - 24 \Rightarrow$ $29z \le 0 \Rightarrow z \le 0$. The interval is $(-\infty, 0]$.

79. $x + 2 > 1 \Rightarrow x > -1$ and $2x - 1 \le 9 \Rightarrow 2x \le 10 \Rightarrow x \le 5$

The solutions must satisfy both of these inequalities. The interval is $(-1, 5]$. See Figure 79.

80. $4x + 7 < 1 \Rightarrow 4x < -6 \Rightarrow x < -\frac{3}{2}$ or $3x + 2 \geq 11 \Rightarrow 3x \geq 9 \Rightarrow x \geq 3$ The solutions may satisfy only one (or both) of these inequalities. The interval is $\left(-\infty, -\frac{3}{2}\right) \cup [3, \infty)$. See Figure 80.

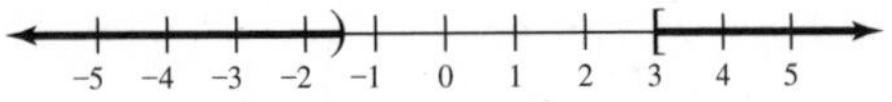

Figure 80

81. $-7 \leq 2x - 3 \leq 5 \Rightarrow -4 \leq 2x \leq 8 \Rightarrow -2 \leq x \leq 4$. The interval is $[-2, 4]$.

82. $-8 \leq -\frac{1}{2}x - 3 \leq 5 \Rightarrow -5 \leq -\frac{1}{2}x \leq 8 \Rightarrow 10 \geq x \geq -16 \Rightarrow -16 \leq x \leq 10$. The interval is $[-16, 10]$.

83. (a) $y_1 = 2$ when $x = -3$ or when $x = 1$

(b) $y_1 \leq 2$ when $-3 \leq x \leq 1$. $[-3, 1]$

(c) $y_1 \geq 2$ when $x \leq -3$ or $x \geq 1$. $(-\infty, -3] \cup [1, \infty)$

84. $\frac{2}{3}x - 4 = -8 \Rightarrow \frac{2}{3}x = -4 \Rightarrow x = -6$ or $\frac{2}{3}x - 4 = 8 \Rightarrow \frac{2}{3}x = 12 \Rightarrow x = 18$

85. The solutions to $|3x + 5| > 13$ satisfy $x < c$ or $x > d$ where c and d are the solutions to $|3x + 5| = 13$.

$|3x + 5| = 13$ is equivalent to $3x + 5 = -13 \Rightarrow x = -6$ and $3x + 5 = 13 \Rightarrow x = \frac{8}{3}$.

The interval is $(-\infty, -6) \cup \left(\frac{8}{3}, \infty\right)$.

86. First divide each side of $-3|2t - 11| \geq -9$ by -3 to obtain $|2t - 11| \leq 3$.

The solutions to $|2t - 11| \leq 3$ satisfy $c \leq t \leq d$ where c and d are the solutions to $|2t - 11| = 3$.

$|2t - 11| = 3$ is equivalent to $2t - 11 = -3 \Rightarrow t = 4$ and $2t - 11 = 3 \Rightarrow t = 7$. The interval is $[4, 7]$.

87. Multiply the second equation by 3 and add the first and second equations to eliminate the variable y.

$$\begin{array}{r} 2x + 3y - z = 3 \\ 9x - 3y + 12z = 30 \\ \hline 11x + 11z = 33 \end{array} \quad \text{or } x + z = 3$$

Add the second and third equations together to eliminate the variable y.

$$\begin{array}{r} 3x - y + 4z = 10 \\ 2x + y - 2z = -1 \\ \hline 5x + 2z = 9 \end{array}$$

Multiply the first *new* equation by –2 and add the first *new* equation and second *new* equation to eliminate z.

$$\begin{array}{r} -2x - 2z = -6 \\ 5x + 2z = 9 \\ \hline 3x = 3 \end{array}$$

And so $x = 1$. Substitute $x = 1$ into the first *new* equation: $(1) + z = 3 \Rightarrow z = 2$

Substitute $x = 1$ and $z = 2$ into the *original* first equation: $2(1) + 3y - (2) = 3 \Rightarrow y = 1$

The solution is $(1, 1, 2)$.

88. $\left[\begin{array}{ccc|c} 1 & 1 & -1 & 4 \\ -1 & -1 & -1 & 0 \\ 1 & -2 & 1 & -9 \end{array}\right] \begin{array}{l} \\ R_2 + R_1 \rightarrow \\ R_3 - R_1 \rightarrow \end{array} \left[\begin{array}{ccc|c} 1 & 1 & -1 & 4 \\ 0 & 0 & -2 & 4 \\ 0 & -3 & 2 & -13 \end{array}\right] \begin{array}{l} \\ \textit{Exchange} \\ R_2 \leftrightarrow R_3 \end{array} \left[\begin{array}{ccc|c} 1 & 1 & -1 & 4 \\ 0 & -3 & 2 & -13 \\ 0 & 0 & -2 & 4 \end{array}\right]$

$\begin{array}{l} \\ \\ (-1/2)R_3 \rightarrow \end{array} \left[\begin{array}{ccc|c} 1 & 1 & -1 & 4 \\ 0 & -3 & 2 & -13 \\ 0 & 0 & 1 & -2 \end{array}\right] \begin{array}{l} R_1 + R_3 \rightarrow \\ R_2 - 2R_3 \rightarrow \\ \end{array} \left[\begin{array}{ccc|c} 1 & 1 & 0 & 2 \\ 0 & -3 & 0 & -9 \\ 0 & 0 & 1 & -2 \end{array}\right] \begin{array}{l} R_1 + (1/3)R_2 \rightarrow \\ (-1/3)R_2 \rightarrow \\ \end{array} \left[\begin{array}{ccc|c} 1 & 0 & 0 & -1 \\ 0 & 1 & 0 & 3 \\ 0 & 0 & 1 & -2 \end{array}\right]$

The solution is $(-1, 3, -2)$.

89. $\det A = 4(3) - 1(-2) = 12 + 2 = 14$

90. Since the constant change is 325 and since when $t = 0$, $d = 0$. Then $d = 325t$.

91. (a) $f(x) = \frac{1}{2}x + 4$

(b) $\frac{1}{2}$

(c) Snow is falling at the rate of $\frac{1}{2}$ inch per hour.

(d) $f(4) = \frac{1}{2}(4) + 4 \Rightarrow f(4) = 2 + 4 \Rightarrow f(4) = 6$ inches of snow.

92. See Figure 92.

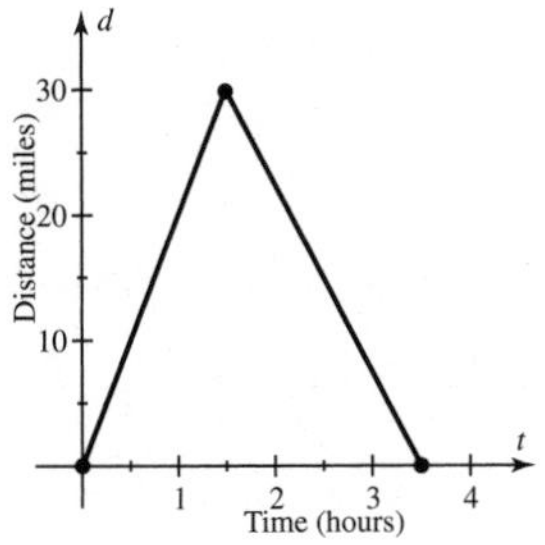

Figure 92

93. Let x = number of adults and let y = number of children. Then $x + y = 8$ and $25x + 15y = 170$. Multiplying the first equation by (-15) and adding it to the second equation yields: $10x = 50 \Rightarrow x = 5$, so $5 + y = 8 \Rightarrow y = 3$. Therefore there are 5 adults and 3 children.

94. If rate $\cdot$ time $= 1$ job, then the two rates are: $r \cdot 2 = 1 \Rightarrow r = \frac{1}{2}$ and $r \cdot (1.5) = 1 \Rightarrow r = \frac{2}{3}$. Now working together we add the rates so, $\frac{1}{2}t + \frac{2}{3}t = 1 \Rightarrow \frac{7}{6}t = 1 \Rightarrow t = \frac{6}{7}$. Therefore they can do the job together in $\frac{6}{7}$ hour.

95. (a) $h(t) = 88(2) - 16(2)^2 \Rightarrow h(t) = 176 - 16(4) \Rightarrow h(t) = 176 - 64 \Rightarrow h(t) = 112$ feet.

(b) $0 = 88t - 16t^2 \Rightarrow 16t^2 - 88t = 0 \Rightarrow 8t(2t - 11) = 0$. So $8t = 0 \Rightarrow t = 0$ at contact and

$2t - 11 = 0 \Rightarrow 2t = 11 \Rightarrow t = \frac{11}{2} \Rightarrow t = 5.5$ seconds.

96. $\frac{7}{4} = \frac{x}{35} \Rightarrow 4x = 245 \Rightarrow x = 61.25$ feet.

97. (a) $T = \frac{1}{20 - 15} \Rightarrow T = \frac{1}{5}$. $\frac{1}{5}$ min.; the average wait is $\frac{1}{5}$ min. or 12 sec. when vehicles arrive at 15/min.

(b) See Figure 97.

x	5	10	15	19	19.9
T	$\frac{1}{15}$	$\frac{1}{10}$	$\frac{1}{5}$	1	10

Figure 97

(c) The wait time increases dramatically.

98. For $A = 74, -0.005 \le \frac{L - A}{A} \le 0.005 \Rightarrow -0.37 \le L - 74 \le 0.37 \Rightarrow 73.63 \le L \le 74.37$.

99. (a) $4b + 3f + 4m = 23$

$b + 2f + m = 7$

$3b + f + 2m = 13$

(b) Multiplying the second equation by (-4) and adding it to the first equation yields: $-5f = -5 \Rightarrow f = 1$. Multiplying the second equation by (-2) and adding it to the third equation yields: $b - 3f = -1 \Rightarrow b - 3(1) = -1 \Rightarrow b - 3 = -1 \Rightarrow b = 2$. Substituting $b = 2$ and $f = 1$ into $b + 2f + m = 7 \Rightarrow 2 + 2(1) + m = 7 \Rightarrow 2 + 2 + m = 7 \Rightarrow 4 + m = 7 \Rightarrow m = 3$. Therefore burger: \$2; fries: \$1; malt: \$3.

Critical Thinking Solutions for Chapter 9

Section 9.1

- There are no solutions. The planes are parallel.
- Hunting, predators, etc. The number of variables would increase.
- The number of adults would positively affect (increase) the number of fawns and the severity of the winter would negatively affect (decrease) the number of fawns.

Section 9.2

- The first matrix represents an inconsistent system and the second matrix represents a dependent system.

Section 9.3

- The points are colinear; they all lie on the same line.

Chapter 10: Radical Expressions and Functions

10.1: Radical Expressions and Rational Exponents

Concepts

1. ± 3

3. 2

5. b

7. $(\sqrt[\Box]{a})^m$ or $\sqrt[\Box]{a^m}$

Radical Expressions

9. $\sqrt{9} = 3$

11. $-\sqrt{5} \approx -2.24$

13. $\sqrt{z^2} = |z|$

15. $\sqrt[3]{27} = 3$

17. $\sqrt[3]{-64} = -4$

19. $\sqrt[3]{5} \approx 1.71$

21. $-\sqrt[3]{x^9} = -\sqrt[3]{(x^3)^3} = -x^3$

23. $\sqrt[3]{(2x)^6} = \sqrt[3]{((2x)^2)^3} = (2x)^2 = 4x^2$

25. $\sqrt[\Box]{81} = 3$

27. $\sqrt[5]{-7} \approx -1.48$

Rational Exponents

29. $6^{1/2} = \sqrt{6}$

31. $(xy)^{1/2} = \sqrt{xy}$

33. $y^{-1/5} = \dfrac{1}{\sqrt[5]{y}}$

35. $16^{1/2} = \sqrt{16} = 4$

37. $256^{1/4} = \sqrt[\Box]{256} = 4$

39. $32^{1/5} = \sqrt[5]{32} = 2$

41. $(-8)^{4/3} = (\sqrt[3]{-8})^4 = (-2)^4 = 16$

43. $2^{1/2} \cdot 2^{2/3} = 2^{1/2+2/3} = 2^{7/6} \approx 2.24$

45. $\left(\dfrac{4}{9}\right)^{1/2} = \dfrac{4^{1/2}}{9^{1/2}} = \dfrac{\sqrt{4}}{\sqrt{9}} = \dfrac{2}{3}$

47. $\dfrac{4^{2/3}}{4^{1/2}} = 4^{2/3-1/2} = 4^{1/6} \approx 1.26$

49. $4^{-1/2} = \dfrac{1}{4^{1/2}} = \dfrac{1}{\sqrt{4}} = \dfrac{1}{2}$

51. $(-8)^{-1/3} = \dfrac{1}{(-8)^{1/3}} = \dfrac{1}{\sqrt[3]{-8}} = \dfrac{1}{-2} = -\dfrac{1}{2}$

53. $\left(\dfrac{1}{16}\right)^{-1/4} = 16^{1/4} = \sqrt{16} = 2$

55. $(2^{1/2})^3 = 2^{1/2 \cdot 3} = 2^{3/2} \approx 2.83$

57. $(x^2)^{3/2} = x^{2 \cdot 3/2} = x^3$

59. $(x^2y^8)^{1/2} = x^{2 \cdot 1/2} \cdot y^{8 \cdot 1/2} = xy^4$

61. $\sqrt[3]{x^3y^6} = (x^3y^6)^{1/3} = x^{3 \cdot 1/3} \cdot y^{6 \cdot 1/3} = xy^2$

63. $\sqrt{\dfrac{y^4}{x^2}} = \left(\dfrac{y^4}{x^2}\right)^{1/2} = \dfrac{y^{4 \cdot 1/2}}{x^{2 \cdot 1/2}} = \dfrac{y^2}{x}$

65. $\sqrt{y^3} \cdot \sqrt[3]{y^2} = (y^3)^{1/2} \cdot (y^2)^{1/3} = y^{3 \cdot 1/2} \cdot y^{2 \cdot 1/3} = y^{3/2} \cdot y^{2/3} = y^{3/2 + 2/3} = y^{13/6}$

67. $\left(\dfrac{x^6}{27}\right)^{2/3} = \dfrac{x^{6 \cdot 2/3}}{27^{2/3}} = \dfrac{x^4}{(\sqrt[3]{27})^2} = \dfrac{x^4}{3^2} = \dfrac{x^4}{9}$

69. $\left(\dfrac{x^2}{y^6}\right)^{-1/2} = \left(\dfrac{y^6}{x^2}\right)^{1/2} = \dfrac{y^{6 \cdot 1/2}}{x^{2 \cdot 1/2}} = \dfrac{y^3}{x}$

71. $\sqrt{\sqrt{y}} = (y^{1/2})^{1/2} = y^{1/2 \cdot 1/2} = y^{1/4}$

73. $(a^{-1/2})^{4/3} = a^{-1/2 \cdot 4/3} = a^{-2/3} = \dfrac{1}{a^{2/3}}$

75. $(a^3b^6)^{1/3} = a^{3 \cdot 1/3} \cdot b^{6 \cdot 1/3} = ab^2$

77. $\dfrac{(k^{1/2})^{-3}}{(k^2)^{1/4}} = \dfrac{k^{-3/2}}{k^{1/2}} = k^{-3/2 - 1/2} = k^{-4/2} = k^{-2} = \dfrac{1}{k^2}$

79. $\sqrt{b} \cdot \sqrt[4]{b} = b^{1/2} \cdot b^{1/4} = b^{1/2 + 1/4} = b^{3/4}$

81. $\sqrt{z} \cdot \sqrt[3]{z^2} \cdot \sqrt[4]{z^3} = z^{1/2} \cdot z^{2/3} \cdot z^{3/4} = z^{1/2 + 2/3 + 3/4} = z^{23/12}$

83. $p^{1/2}(p^{3/2} + p^{1/2}) = p^{1/2 + 3/2} + p^{1/2 + 1/2} = p^2 + p$

85. $\sqrt[3]{x}(\sqrt{x} - \sqrt[3]{x^2}) = x^{1/3}(x^{1/2} - x^{2/3}) = x^{1/3 + 1/2} - x^{1/3 + 2/3} = x^{5/6} - x$

87. $\sqrt{(-4)^2} = \sqrt{16} = 4$

89. $\sqrt{y^2} = |y|$

91. $\sqrt{(a + 3)^2} = |a + 3|$

93. $\sqrt{(x - 5)^2} = |x - 5|$

95. $\sqrt{x^2 - 2x + 1} = \sqrt{(x - 1)^2} = |x - 1|$

97. $\sqrt[4]{y^4} = (y^4)^{1/4} = y^{4 \cdot 1/4} = |y|$

99. $\sqrt[4]{x^{12}} = (x^{12})^{1/4} = x^{12 \cdot 1/4} = |x^3|$

101. $\sqrt[5]{x^5y^{10}} = (x^5y^{10})^{1/5} = x^{5 \cdot 1/5}y^{10 \cdot 1/5} = xy^2$

Applications

103. $15\pi R^2 = 65 \Rightarrow R^2 = \dfrac{65}{15\pi} \Rightarrow R = \sqrt{\dfrac{65}{15\pi}} \approx 1.17$ miles

105. $s = \frac{1}{2}(3 + 4 + 5) = 6 \Rightarrow A = \sqrt{6(6-3)(6-4)(6-5)} = \sqrt{6(3)(2)(1)} = \sqrt{36} = 6$

10.2: Simplifying Radical Expressions

Concepts

1. Yes
3. $\sqrt[3]{ab}$
5. $\frac{a}{b}$
7. No, because $1^3 \neq 3$.

Multiplying and Dividing

9. $\sqrt{3} \cdot \sqrt{3} = \sqrt{3 \cdot 3} = \sqrt{9} = 3$
11. $\sqrt{2} \cdot \sqrt{50} = \sqrt{2 \cdot 50} = \sqrt{100} = 10$
13. $\sqrt[3]{4} \cdot \sqrt[3]{16} = \sqrt[3]{4 \cdot 16} = \sqrt[3]{64} = 4$
15. $\sqrt{\frac{9}{25}} = \frac{\sqrt{9}}{\sqrt{25}} = \frac{3}{5}$
17. $\sqrt{\frac{1}{2}} \cdot \sqrt{\frac{1}{8}} = \sqrt{\frac{1 \cdot 1}{2 \cdot 8}} = \sqrt{\frac{1}{16}} = \frac{\sqrt{1}}{\sqrt{16}} = \frac{1}{4}$
19. $\sqrt{\frac{x}{2}} \cdot \sqrt{\frac{x}{8}} = \sqrt{\frac{x \cdot x}{2 \cdot 8}} = \sqrt{\frac{x^2}{16}} = \frac{\sqrt{x^2}}{\sqrt{16}} = \frac{x}{4}$
21. $\frac{\sqrt{45}}{\sqrt{5}} = \sqrt{\frac{45}{5}} = \sqrt{9} = 3$
23. $\sqrt[3]{-4} \cdot \sqrt[3]{-16} = \sqrt[3]{-4 \cdot (-16)} = \sqrt[3]{64} = 4$
25. $\sqrt[4]{9} \cdot \sqrt[4]{9} = \sqrt[4]{9 \cdot 9} = \sqrt[4]{81} = 3$
27. $\frac{\sqrt[5]{64}}{\sqrt[5]{-2}} = \sqrt[5]{\frac{64}{-2}} = \sqrt[5]{-32} = -2$
29. $\frac{\sqrt{a^2b}}{\sqrt{b}} = \sqrt{\frac{a^2b}{b}} = \sqrt{a^2} = a$
31. $\frac{\sqrt[3]{54}}{\sqrt[3]{2}} = \sqrt[3]{\frac{54}{2}} = \sqrt[3]{27} = 3$
33. $\sqrt{4x^4} = \sqrt{4} \cdot \sqrt{(x^2)^2} = 2x^2$
35. $\sqrt[3]{-5a^6} = \sqrt[3]{-5} \cdot \sqrt[3]{(a^2)^3} = \sqrt[3]{-5} \cdot a^2 = -a^2\sqrt[3]{5}$
37. $\sqrt{16x^4y} = \sqrt{16} \cdot \sqrt{x^4} \cdot \sqrt{y} = 2x\sqrt{y}$
39. $\sqrt{3x} \cdot \sqrt{12x} = \sqrt{3 \cdot 12 \cdot x \cdot x} = \sqrt{36x^2} = \sqrt{36} \cdot \sqrt{x^2} = 6x$
41. $\sqrt[3]{8x^6y^3z^9} = \sqrt[3]{8} \cdot \sqrt[3]{(x^2)^3} \cdot \sqrt[3]{y^3} \cdot \sqrt[3]{(z^3)^3} = 2x^2yz^3$

43. $\sqrt[4]{\frac{3}{4}} \cdot \sqrt[4]{\frac{27}{4}} = \sqrt[4]{\frac{3}{4} \cdot \frac{27}{4}} = \sqrt[4]{\frac{81}{16}} = \;= \frac{3}{2}$

45. $\sqrt[3]{12} \cdot \sqrt[3]{ab} = \sqrt[3]{12ab}$

47. $\sqrt[4]{25z} \cdot \sqrt[4]{25z} = \sqrt[4]{625z^2} = \sqrt[4]{625} \cdot \sqrt[4]{z^2} = 5\sqrt{z}$

49. $\sqrt[5]{\frac{7a}{b^2}} \cdot \sqrt[5]{\frac{b^2}{7a^6}} = \sqrt[5]{\frac{7ab^2}{7a^6b^2}} = \sqrt[5]{\frac{1}{a^5}} = \frac{1}{a}$

51. $\sqrt{x+4} \cdot \sqrt{x-4} = \sqrt{(x+4)(x-4)} = \sqrt{x^2 - 16}$

53. $\sqrt[3]{a+1} \cdot \sqrt[3]{a^2 - a + 1} = \sqrt[3]{(a+1)(a^2 - a + 1)} = \sqrt[3]{a^3 + 1}$

55. $\frac{\sqrt{x^2 + 2x + 1}}{\sqrt{x+1}} = \sqrt{\frac{x^2 + 2x + 1}{x+1}} = \sqrt{\frac{(x+1)(x+1)}{x+1}} = \sqrt{x+1}$

57. $\sqrt{500} = \sqrt{100 \cdot 5} = \sqrt{100} \cdot \sqrt{5} = 10\sqrt{5}$; the answer is 10.

59. $\sqrt{8} = \sqrt{4 \cdot 2} = \sqrt{4} \cdot \sqrt{2} = 2\sqrt{2}$; the answer is 2.

61. $\sqrt{45} = \sqrt{9 \cdot 5} = \sqrt{9} \cdot \sqrt{5} = 3\sqrt{5}$; the answer is 3.

63. $\sqrt{200} = \sqrt{100 \cdot 2} = \sqrt{100} \cdot \sqrt{2} = 10\sqrt{2}$

65. $\sqrt[3]{81} = \sqrt[3]{27 \cdot 3} = \sqrt[3]{27} \cdot \sqrt[3]{3} = 3\sqrt[3]{3}$

67. $\sqrt[4]{64} = \sqrt[4]{16 \cdot 4} = \sqrt[4]{16} \cdot \sqrt[4]{4} = 2\sqrt[4]{4} = 2\sqrt[4]{2^2} = 2\sqrt{2}$

69. $\sqrt[5]{-64} = \sqrt[5]{-2^6} = \sqrt[5]{-2^5 \cdot 2} = \sqrt[5]{-2^5} \cdot \sqrt[5]{2} = -2\sqrt[5]{2}$

71. $\sqrt{b^5} = \sqrt{(b^2)^2 \cdot b} = \sqrt{(b^2)^2} \cdot \sqrt{b} = b^2\sqrt{b}$

73. $\sqrt{8n^3} = \sqrt{(2n)^2 \cdot 2n} = \sqrt{(2n)^2} \cdot \sqrt{2n} = 2n\sqrt{2n}$

75. $\sqrt{12a^2b^5} = \sqrt{(2ab^2)^2 \cdot 3b} = \sqrt{(2ab^2)^2} \cdot \sqrt{3b} = 2ab^2\sqrt{3b}$

77. $\sqrt[3]{125x^4y^5} = \sqrt[3]{(5xy)^3 \cdot xy^2} = \sqrt[3]{(5xy)^3} \cdot \sqrt[3]{xy^2} = 5xy\sqrt[3]{xy^2}$

79. $\sqrt[3]{5t} \cdot \sqrt[3]{125t} = \sqrt[3]{625t^2} = \sqrt[3]{5^4t^2} = \sqrt[3]{5^3 \cdot 5t^2} = \sqrt[3]{5^3} \cdot \sqrt[3]{5t^2} = 5\sqrt[3]{rt^2}$

81. $\sqrt[4]{\frac{9t^5}{r^8}} \cdot \sqrt[4]{\frac{9r}{5t}} = \sqrt[4]{\frac{81rt^5}{5r^8t}} = \sqrt[4]{\frac{81t^4}{5r^7}} = \frac{\sqrt[4]{(3t)^4}}{\sqrt[4]{r^4 \cdot 5r^3}} = \frac{3t}{r\sqrt[4]{5r^3}}$

83. $\sqrt{3} \cdot \sqrt[3]{3} = 3^{1/2} \cdot 3^{1/3} = 3^{1/2+1/3} = 3^{5/6} = \sqrt[6]{3^5}$

85. $\sqrt[4]{8} \cdot \sqrt[3]{4} = \sqrt[4]{2^3} \cdot \sqrt[3]{2^2} = 2^{3/4} \cdot 2^{2/3} = 2^{3/4+2/3} = 2^{17/12} = 2^{12/12+5/12} = 2 \cdot 2^{5/12} = 2\sqrt[12]{2^5}$

87. $\sqrt[4]{27} \cdot \sqrt[3]{9} \cdot \sqrt{3} = \sqrt[4]{3^3} \cdot \sqrt[3]{3^2} \cdot \sqrt{3} = 3^{3/4} \cdot 3^{2/3} \cdot 3^{1/2} = 3^{3/4+2/3+1/2} = 3^{23/12} = 3^{12/12} \cdot 3^{11/12} = 3\sqrt[12]{3^{11}}$

89. $\sqrt[4]{x^3} \cdot \sqrt[3]{x} = x^{3/4} \cdot x^{1/3} = x^{3/4+1/3} = x^{13/12} = x^{12/12} \cdot x^{1/12} = x\sqrt[12]{x}$

91. $\sqrt[4]{rt} \cdot \sqrt[3]{r^2t} = (rt)^{1/4} \cdot (r^2t)^{1/3} = r^{1/4}t^{1/4} \cdot r^{2/3}t^{1/3} = r^{1/4+2/3}t^{1/4+1/3} = r^{11/12}t^{7/12} = \sqrt[12]{r^{11}t^7}$

93. $\frac{1}{\sqrt{7}} = \frac{1}{\sqrt{7}} \cdot \frac{\sqrt{7}}{\sqrt{7}} = \frac{\sqrt{7}}{7}$

95. $\frac{4}{\sqrt{3}} = \frac{4}{\sqrt{3}} \cdot \frac{\sqrt{3}}{\sqrt{3}} = \frac{4\sqrt{3}}{3}$

97. $\frac{5}{3\sqrt{5}} = \frac{5}{3\sqrt{5}} \cdot \frac{\sqrt{5}}{\sqrt{5}} = \frac{5\sqrt{5}}{3 \cdot 5} = \frac{5\sqrt{5}}{15} = \frac{\sqrt{5}}{3}$

99. $\sqrt{\frac{b}{12}} = \frac{\sqrt{b}}{\sqrt{12}} = \frac{\sqrt{b}}{\sqrt{12}} \cdot \frac{\sqrt{12}}{\sqrt{12}} = \frac{\sqrt{12b}}{12} = \frac{\sqrt{4 \cdot 3b}}{12} = \frac{2\sqrt{3b}}{12} = \frac{\sqrt{3b}}{6}$

101. $\frac{rt}{2\sqrt{r^3}} = \frac{rt}{2\sqrt{r^3}} \cdot \frac{\sqrt{r^3}}{\sqrt{r^3}} = \frac{rt\sqrt{r^3}}{2r^3} = \frac{rt\sqrt{r^2 \cdot r}}{2r^3} = \frac{r^2t\sqrt{r}}{2r^3} = \frac{t\sqrt{r}}{2r}$

Applications

103. (a) $A = 100\sqrt[3]{8^2} = 100\sqrt[3]{64} = 100 \cdot 4 = 400$ square inches

(b) $A = 100\sqrt[3]{W^2} \Rightarrow A = 100W^{2/3}$

Checking Basic Concepts for Sections 10.1 & 10.2

1. (a) ± 7

(b) 7

(c) $x^2 = 49 \Rightarrow x = \pm\sqrt{49} \Rightarrow x = \pm 7$

2. (a) $\sqrt[3]{-8} = -2$

(b) $-\sqrt[4]{81} = -3$

3. (a) $x^{3/2} = \sqrt{x^3}$ or $(\sqrt{x})^3$

(b) $x^{2/3} = \sqrt[3]{x^2}$ or $(\sqrt[3]{x})^2$

(c) $x^{-2/5} = \frac{1}{\sqrt[5]{x^2}}$ or $\frac{1}{(\sqrt[5]{x})^2}$

4. $\sqrt{(x-1)^2} = |x - 1|$

5. (a) $(64^{-3/2})^{1/3} = 64^{-3/2 \cdot 1/3} = 64^{-1/2} = \frac{1}{64^{1/2}} = \frac{1}{\sqrt{64}} = \frac{1}{8}$

(b) $\sqrt{5} \cdot \sqrt{20} = \sqrt{5 \cdot 20} = \sqrt{100} = 10$

(c) $\sqrt[3]{-8x^4y} = \sqrt[3]{(-2x)^3 \cdot xy} = -2x\sqrt[3]{xy}$

(d) $\sqrt{\frac{4b}{5}} \cdot \sqrt{\frac{4b^3}{5}} = \sqrt{\frac{4b \cdot 4b^3}{5 \cdot 5}} = \frac{\sqrt{16b^4}}{\sqrt{25}} = \frac{4b^2}{5}$

6. $\sqrt[3]{7} \cdot \sqrt{7} = 7^{1/3} \cdot 7^{1/2} = 7^{1/3+1/2} = 7^{5/6} = \sqrt[6]{7^5}$

7. $\frac{6}{2\sqrt{6}} = \frac{6}{2\sqrt{6}} \cdot \frac{\sqrt{6}}{\sqrt{6}} = \frac{6\sqrt{6}}{2 \cdot 6} = \frac{\sqrt{6}}{2}$

10.3: Operations on Radical Expressions

Concepts

1. $2\sqrt{a}$

3. like

5. $\sqrt{t} + 5$

Like Radicals

7. Not possible, since $\sqrt{12} = 2\sqrt{3}$ and $\sqrt{24} = 2\sqrt{6}$.

9. Since $\sqrt{28} = \sqrt{4 \cdot 7} = \sqrt{4} \cdot \sqrt{7} = 2\sqrt{7}$ and $\sqrt{63} = \sqrt{9 \cdot 7} = \sqrt{9} \cdot \sqrt{7} = 3\sqrt{7}$,

   the like radicals are $\sqrt{7}, 2\sqrt{7}$, and $3\sqrt{7}$.

11. Since $\sqrt[3]{16} = \sqrt[3]{8 \cdot 2} = \sqrt[3]{8} \cdot \sqrt[3]{2} = 2\sqrt[3]{2}$ and $\sqrt[3]{-54} = \sqrt[3]{-27 \cdot 2} = \sqrt[3]{-27} \cdot \sqrt[3]{2} = -3\sqrt[3]{2}$,

    the like radicals are $2\sqrt[3]{2}$ and $-3\sqrt[3]{2}$.

13. Not possible, since $\sqrt{x^2y} = x\sqrt{y}$ and $\sqrt{4y^2} = 2y$.

15. Since $\sqrt[3]{8xy} = \sqrt[3]{8} \cdot \sqrt[3]{xy} = 2\sqrt[3]{xy}$ and $\sqrt[3]{x^4y^4} = \sqrt[3]{(xy)^3 \cdot xy} = \sqrt[3]{(xy)^3} \cdot \sqrt[3]{xy} = xy\sqrt[3]{xy}$,

    the like radicals are $2\sqrt[3]{xy}$ and $xy\sqrt[3]{xy}$.

17. $2\sqrt{3} + 7\sqrt{3} = 9\sqrt{3}$

19. $9\sqrt{5} + \sqrt{2} - \sqrt{5} = 8\sqrt{5} + \sqrt{2}$

21. $\sqrt{x} + \sqrt{x} - \sqrt{y} = 2\sqrt{x} - \sqrt{y}$

23. $\sqrt[3]{z} + \sqrt[3]{z} = 2\sqrt[3]{z}$

25. $2\sqrt[3]{6} - 7\sqrt[3]{6} = -5\sqrt[3]{6}$

27. $\sqrt[3]{y^6} - \sqrt[3]{y^3} = \sqrt[3]{(y^2)^3} - \sqrt[3]{y^3} = y^2 - y$

29. $3\sqrt{28} + 3\sqrt{7} = 3\sqrt{4 \cdot 7} + 3\sqrt{7} = 3 \cdot 2\sqrt{7} + 3\sqrt{7} = 9\sqrt{7}$

31. $\sqrt{44} - 4\sqrt{11} = \sqrt{4 \cdot 11} - 4\sqrt{11} = 2\sqrt{11} - 4\sqrt{11} = -2\sqrt{11}$

33. $2\sqrt[3]{16} + \sqrt[3]{2} - \sqrt{2} = 2\sqrt[3]{8 \cdot 2} + \sqrt[3]{2} - \sqrt{2} = 2 \cdot 2\sqrt[3]{2} + \sqrt[3]{2} - \sqrt{2} = 5\sqrt[3]{2} - \sqrt{2}$

35. $\sqrt[3]{xy} - 2\sqrt[3]{xy} = -\sqrt[3]{xy}$

37. $\sqrt{4x + 8} + \sqrt{x + 2} = \sqrt{4(x + 2)} + \sqrt{x + 2} = 2\sqrt{x + 2} + \sqrt{x + 2} = 3\sqrt{x + 2}$

39. $\dfrac{4\sqrt{3}}{3} + \dfrac{\sqrt{3}}{6} = \dfrac{4\sqrt{3}}{3} \cdot \dfrac{2}{2} + \dfrac{\sqrt{3}}{6} = \dfrac{8\sqrt{3}}{6} + \dfrac{\sqrt{3}}{6} = \dfrac{8\sqrt{3} + \sqrt{3}}{6} = \dfrac{9\sqrt{3}}{6} = \dfrac{3\sqrt{3}}{2}$

41. $\dfrac{15\sqrt{8}}{4} - \dfrac{2\sqrt{2}}{5} = \dfrac{15 \cdot 2\sqrt{2}}{4} \cdot \dfrac{5}{5} - \dfrac{2\sqrt{2}}{5} \cdot \dfrac{4}{4} = \dfrac{150\sqrt{2}}{20} - \dfrac{8\sqrt{2}}{20} = \dfrac{150\sqrt{2} - 8\sqrt{2}}{20} = \dfrac{142\sqrt{2}}{20} = \dfrac{71\sqrt{2}}{10}$

43. $2\sqrt[4]{64} - \sqrt[4]{324} + \sqrt[4]{4} = 2\sqrt[4]{16 \cdot 4} - \sqrt[4]{81 \cdot 4} + \sqrt[4]{4} = 4\sqrt[4]{4} - 3\sqrt[4]{4} + \sqrt[4]{4} = 2\sqrt[4]{4} = 2\sqrt{2}$

45. $5\sqrt[4]{x^5} - \sqrt[4]{x} = 5\sqrt[4]{x^4 \cdot x} - \sqrt[4]{x} = 5x\sqrt[4]{x} - \sqrt[4]{x} = (5x - 1)\sqrt[4]{x}$

47. $\sqrt{64x^3} - \sqrt{x} + 3\sqrt{x} = \sqrt{(8x)^2 \cdot x} - \sqrt{x} + 3\sqrt{x} = 8x\sqrt{x} - \sqrt{x} + 3\sqrt{x} = 2\sqrt{x}(4x + 1)$

49. $\sqrt[4]{81a^5b^5} - \sqrt[4]{ab} = \sqrt[4]{(3ab)^4 \cdot ab} - \sqrt[4]{ab} = 3ab\sqrt[4]{ab} - \sqrt[4]{ab} = (3ab - 1)\sqrt[4]{ab}$

51. $5\sqrt[3]{\dfrac{n^4}{125}} - 2\sqrt[3]{n} = 5\sqrt[3]{\dfrac{n^3}{125}} \cdot n - 2\sqrt[3]{n} = 5 \cdot \dfrac{n}{5}\sqrt[3]{n} - 2\sqrt[3]{n} = n\sqrt[3]{n} - 2\sqrt[3]{n} = (n - 2)\sqrt[3]{n}$

53. $(3 + \sqrt{7})(3 - \sqrt{7}) = 3^2 - (\sqrt{7})^2 = 9 - 7 = 2$

55. $(11 - \sqrt{2})(11 + \sqrt{2}) = 11^2 - (\sqrt{2})^2 = 121 - 2 = 119$

57. $(\sqrt{x} + 8)(\sqrt{x} - 8) = (\sqrt{x})^2 - 8^2 = x - 64$

59. $(\sqrt{ab} - \sqrt{c})(\sqrt{ab} + \sqrt{c}) = (\sqrt{ab})^2 - (\sqrt{c})^2 = ab - c$

61. $(\sqrt{x} - 7)(\sqrt{x} + 8) = (\sqrt{x})^2 + 8\sqrt{x} - 7\sqrt{x} - 56 = x + \sqrt{x} - 56$

63. $\dfrac{1}{3 - \sqrt{2}} = \dfrac{1}{3 - \sqrt{2}} \cdot \dfrac{3 + \sqrt{2}}{3 + \sqrt{2}} = \dfrac{3 + \sqrt{2}}{9 - 2} = \dfrac{3 + \sqrt{2}}{7}$

65. $\dfrac{\sqrt{2}}{\sqrt{5} + 2} = \dfrac{\sqrt{2}}{\sqrt{5} + 2} \cdot \dfrac{\sqrt{5} - 2}{\sqrt{5} - 2} = \dfrac{\sqrt{10} - 2\sqrt{2}}{5 - 4} = \dfrac{\sqrt{10} - 2\sqrt{2}}{1} = \sqrt{10} - 2\sqrt{2}$

67. $\dfrac{\sqrt{7} - 2}{\sqrt{7} + 2} = \dfrac{\sqrt{7} - 2}{\sqrt{7} + 2} \cdot \dfrac{\sqrt{7} - 2}{\sqrt{7} - 2} = \dfrac{7 - 4\sqrt{7} + 4}{7 - 4} = \dfrac{11 - 4\sqrt{7}}{3}$

69. $\dfrac{1}{\sqrt{7} - \sqrt{6}} = \dfrac{1}{\sqrt{7} - \sqrt{6}} \cdot \dfrac{\sqrt{7} + \sqrt{6}}{\sqrt{7} + \sqrt{6}} = \dfrac{\sqrt{7} + \sqrt{6}}{7 - 6} = \dfrac{\sqrt{7} + \sqrt{6}}{1} = \sqrt{7} + \sqrt{6}$

71. $\dfrac{\sqrt{z}}{\sqrt{z} - 3} = \dfrac{\sqrt{z}}{\sqrt{z} - 3} \cdot \dfrac{\sqrt{z} + 3}{\sqrt{z} + 3} = \dfrac{z + 3\sqrt{z}}{z - 9}$

73. $\dfrac{\sqrt{a} + \sqrt{b}}{\sqrt{a} - \sqrt{b}} = \dfrac{\sqrt{a} + \sqrt{b}}{\sqrt{a} - \sqrt{b}} \cdot \dfrac{\sqrt{a} + \sqrt{b}}{\sqrt{a} + \sqrt{b}} = \dfrac{a + 2\sqrt{ab} + b}{a - b}$

75. $\dfrac{1}{\sqrt{x + 1} - \sqrt{x}} = \dfrac{1}{\sqrt{x + 1} - \sqrt{x}} \cdot \dfrac{\sqrt{x + 1} + \sqrt{x}}{\sqrt{x + 1} + \sqrt{x}} = \dfrac{\sqrt{x + 1} + \sqrt{x}}{x + 1 - x} = \dfrac{\sqrt{x + 1} + \sqrt{x}}{1} = \sqrt{x + 1} + \sqrt{x}$

Geometry

77. $\sqrt{27} + \sqrt{48} + \sqrt{75} = \sqrt{9 \cdot 3} + \sqrt{16 \cdot 3} + \sqrt{25 \cdot 3} = 3\sqrt{3} + 4\sqrt{3} + 5\sqrt{3} = 12\sqrt{3} \approx 20.8$ cm

10.4: Radical Functions

Concepts

1. See Figure 1.

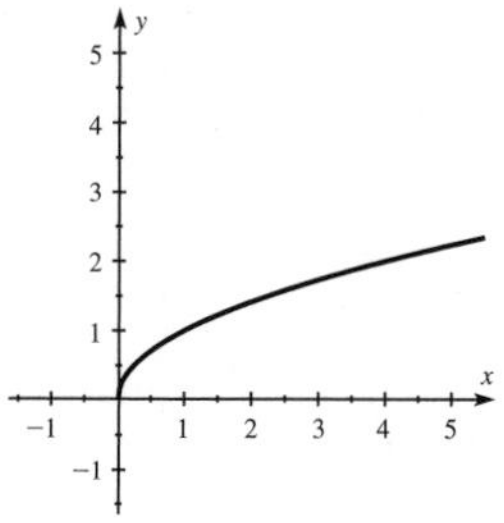

Figure 1

3. $\{x \mid x \geq 0\}$

5. $f(x) = x^p$, where p is rational

7. The variable cannot be negative. The domain is $\{x \mid x \geq 0\}$.

Root Functions

9. $T(100) = \dfrac{\sqrt{100}}{2} = \dfrac{10}{2} = 5$

11. $f(4) = \sqrt{4 + 5} + \sqrt{4} = \sqrt{9} + \sqrt{4} = 3 + 2 = 5$

13. $x + 1 \geq 0 \Rightarrow x \geq -1 \Rightarrow$ Domain: $[-1, \infty)$

15. $2x - 4 \geq 0 \Rightarrow 2x \geq 4 \Rightarrow x \geq 2 \Rightarrow$ Domain: $[2, \infty)$

17. $1 - x \geq 0 \Rightarrow -x \geq -1 \Rightarrow x \leq 1 \Rightarrow$ Domain: $(-\infty, 1]$

19. $8 - 5x \geq 0 \Rightarrow -5x \geq -8 \Rightarrow x \leq \dfrac{8}{5} \Rightarrow$ Domain: $\left(-\infty, \dfrac{5}{8}\right]$

21. $3x^2 + 4 \geq 0 \Rightarrow 3x^2 \geq -4 \Rightarrow x^2 \geq -\dfrac{4}{3} \Rightarrow$ Domain: $(-\infty, \infty)$

23. $2x + 1 > 0 \Rightarrow 2x > -1 \Rightarrow x > -\dfrac{1}{2} \Rightarrow$ Domain: $\left(-\dfrac{1}{2}, \infty\right)$

Equations and Graphs

25. $x^2 = 49 \Rightarrow x = \pm\sqrt{49} \Rightarrow x = \pm 7$

27. $2z^2 = 200 \Rightarrow z^2 = 100 \Rightarrow z = \pm\sqrt{100} \Rightarrow z = \pm 10$

29. $(t + 1)^2 = 16 \Rightarrow t + 1 = \pm\sqrt{16} \Rightarrow t = -1 \pm 4 \Rightarrow t = -5$ or 3

31. $(4 - 2x)^2 = 100 \Rightarrow 4 - 2x = \pm\sqrt{100} \Rightarrow -2x = -4 \pm 10 \Rightarrow x = \dfrac{-4 \pm 10}{-2} \Rightarrow x = -3$ or 7

33. $b^3 = 64 \Rightarrow b = \sqrt[3]{64} \Rightarrow b = 4$

35. $2t^3 = -128 \Rightarrow t^3 = -64 \Rightarrow t = \sqrt[3]{-64} \Rightarrow t = -4$

37. $(x + 1)^3 = 8 \Rightarrow x + 1 = \sqrt[3]{8} \Rightarrow x + 1 = 2 \Rightarrow x = 1$

39. $(2 - 5z)^3 = -125 \Rightarrow 2 - 5z = \sqrt[3]{-125} \Rightarrow 2 - 5z = -5 \Rightarrow -5z = -7 \Rightarrow z = \dfrac{7}{5}$

41. See Figure 41. This graph is shifted 2 units left.

43. See Figure 43. This graph is shifted 2 units upward.

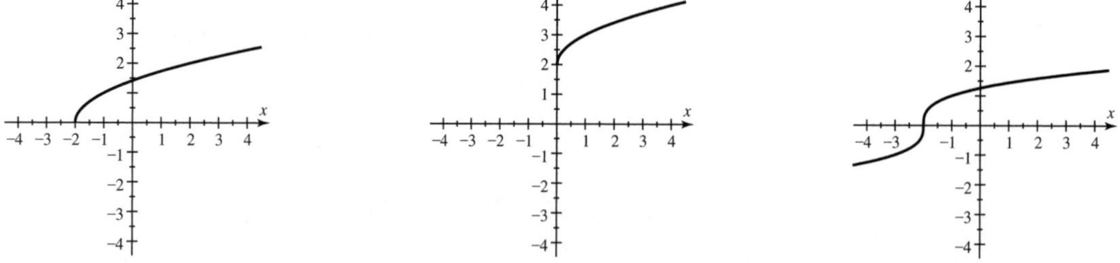

Figure 41 Figure 43 Figure 45

45. See Figure 45. This graph is shifted 2 units left.

Power Functions

47. $f(4) = 4^{5/2} = (\sqrt{4})^5 = 2^5 = 32; f(5) = 5^{5/2} \approx 55.90$

49. $f(-32) = (-32)^{-7/5} = \dfrac{1}{(-32)^{7/5}} = \dfrac{1}{(\sqrt[5]{-32})^7} = \dfrac{1}{(-2)^7} = -\dfrac{1}{128} \approx -0.01; f(10) = 10^{-7/5} = \dfrac{1}{10^{7/5}} \approx 0.04$

51. $f(256) = 256^{1/4} = \sqrt[4]{256} = 4; f(-10) = (-10)^{1/4} = \sqrt[4]{-10} \Rightarrow$ Not possible

53. $f(32) = 32^{2/5} = (\sqrt[5]{32})^2 = 2^2 = 4;\ f(-32) = (-32)^{2/5} = (\sqrt[5]{-32})^2 = (-2)^2 = 4$

55. Graph $Y_1 = $ X^(1/5) and $Y_2 = $ X^(1/3) in [0, 6, 1] by [0, 6, 1]. See Figure 55. Function $g(x)$ increases faster.

[0, 6, 1] by [0, 6, 1]

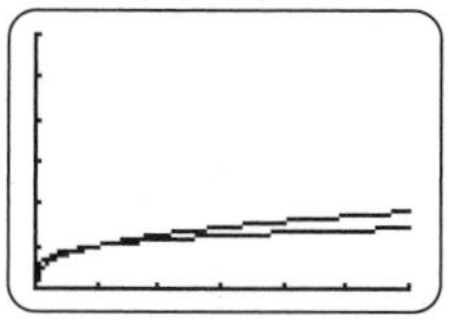

Figure 55

[0, 6, 1] by [0, 6, 1]

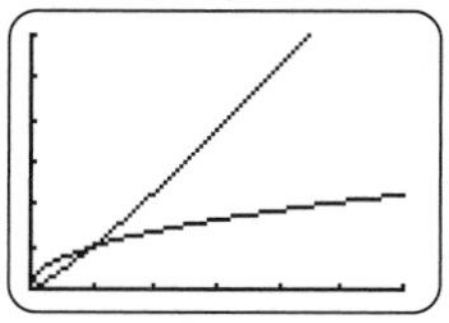

Figure 57

[0, 1600, 400] by [0, 220, 20]

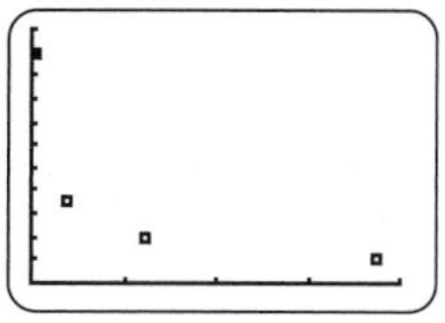

Figure 65

57. Graph $Y_1 = $ X^1.2 and $Y_2 = $ X^0.45 in [0, 6, 1] by [0, 6, 1]. See Figure 57. Function $f(x)$ increases faster.

Applications

59. $T(4) = \dfrac{\sqrt{4}}{2} = \dfrac{2}{2} = 1$ second

61. (a) $T(0.8c) = 10\sqrt{1 - (0.8c/c)^2} = 10\sqrt{1 - 0.8^2} = 10\sqrt{1 - 0.64} = 10\sqrt{0.36} = 10 \cdot 0.6 = 6$ years

(b) The twin in the spaceship will be 4 years younger than the twin on Earth.

63. (a) $W(2v) = 3.8(2v)^3 = 3.8 \cdot 8v^3 = 8(3.8v^3) = 8 \cdot W(v)$. It increases by a factor of 8.

(b) $W = 3.8v^3 \Rightarrow v^3 = \dfrac{W}{3.8} \Rightarrow v = \sqrt[3]{\dfrac{W}{3.8}}$

(c) $v = \sqrt[3]{\dfrac{30{,}400}{3.8}} = \sqrt[3]{8000} = 20$ mph

65. (a) As animal size increases, the pulse rate decreases.

(b) Plot the data in [0, 1600, 400] by [0, 220, 20]. See Figure 65.

(c) $R = kW^{-1/2} \Rightarrow 198 = k \cdot 20^{-1/2} \Rightarrow 198 = \dfrac{k}{20^{1/2}} \Rightarrow k = 198 \cdot 20^{1/2} \approx 885$

(d) $R = 885(700)^{-1/2} \approx 33$; A 700-pound animal will have a pulse rate of about 33 bpm.

Checking Basic Concepts for Sections 10.3 & 10.4

1. (a) $\sqrt{3} \cdot \sqrt{12} = \sqrt{3 \cdot 12} = \sqrt{36} = 6$

(b) $\dfrac{\sqrt[3]{81}}{\sqrt[3]{3}} = \sqrt[3]{\dfrac{81}{3}} = \sqrt[3]{27} = 3$

(c) $\sqrt{36x^6} = \sqrt{36} \cdot \sqrt{(x^3)^2} = 6x^3$

3. (a) $\sqrt[3]{xy^4} - \sqrt[3]{x^4y} = \sqrt[3]{y^3 \cdot xy} - \sqrt[3]{x^3 \cdot xy} = y\sqrt[3]{xy} - x\sqrt[3]{xy} = (y - x)\sqrt[3]{xy}$

(b) $(4 - \sqrt{2})(4 + \sqrt{2}) = 4^2 - (\sqrt{2})^2 = 16 - 2 = 14$

5. (a) See Figure 5a. $f(-1)$ is undefined

(b) See Figure 5b. $f(-1) = -1$

(c) See Figure 5c. $f(-1) = 1$

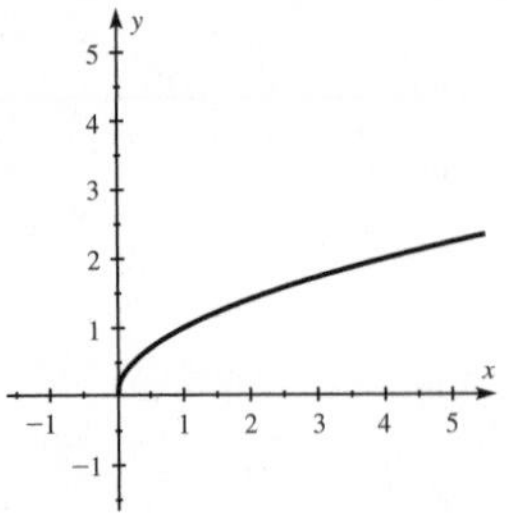

Figure 5a

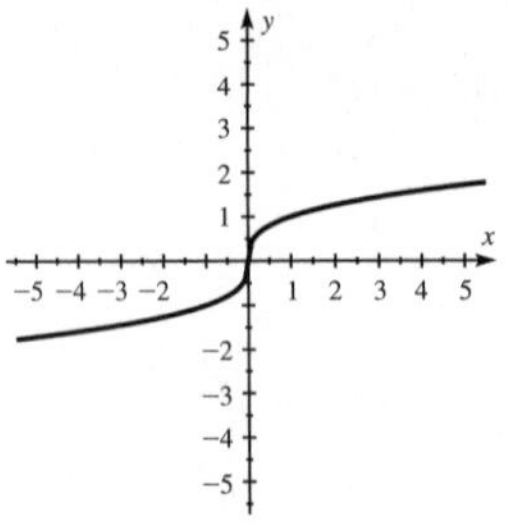

Figure 5b

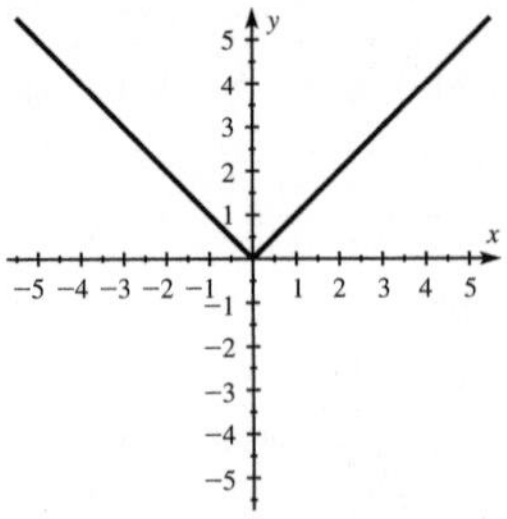

Figure 5c

7. $x - 4 \geq 0 \Rightarrow x \geq 4 \Rightarrow$ Domain: $[4, \infty)$

10.5: Equations Involving Radical Expressions

Concepts

1. Square each side.

3. Yes

5. The Pythagorean theorem is used to find an unknown side of a right tringle.

7. $d = \sqrt{(x_2 - x_1)^2 + (y_2 - y_1)^2}$

Symbolic Solutions

9. $\sqrt{x} = 8 \Rightarrow (\sqrt{x})^2 = 8^2 \Rightarrow x = 64$

11. $\sqrt[4]{x} = 3 \Rightarrow (\sqrt[4]{x})^4 = 3^4 \Rightarrow x = 81$

13. $\sqrt{2t + 4} = 4 \Rightarrow (\sqrt{2t + 4})^2 = 4^2 \Rightarrow 2t + 4 = 16 \Rightarrow 2t = 12 \Rightarrow t = 6$

15. $\sqrt{x + 6} = x \Rightarrow (\sqrt{x + 6})^2 = x^2 \Rightarrow x + 6 = x^2 \Rightarrow x^2 - x - 6 = 0 \Rightarrow (x + 2)(x - 3) = 0 \Rightarrow$

$x = -2$ or $x = 3$. The solution $x = -2$ does not check. The solution is $x = 3$.

17. $\sqrt[3]{x} = 3 \Rightarrow (\sqrt[3]{x})^3 = 3^3 \Rightarrow x = 27$

19. $\sqrt[3]{2z - 4} = -2 \Rightarrow 2z - 4 = (-2)^3 \Rightarrow 2z - 4 = -8 \Rightarrow 2z = -4 \Rightarrow z = -2$

21. $\sqrt[4]{t + 1} = 2 \Rightarrow t + 1 = 2^4 \Rightarrow t + 1 = 16 \Rightarrow t = 15$

23. $\sqrt{5z - 1} = \sqrt{z + 1} \Rightarrow (\sqrt{5z - 1})^2 = (\sqrt{z + 1})^2 \Rightarrow 5z - 1 = z + 1 \Rightarrow 4z = 2 \Rightarrow z = \dfrac{1}{2}$

25. $\sqrt{1 - x} = 1 - x \Rightarrow (\sqrt{1 - x})^2 = (1 - x)^2 \Rightarrow 1 - x = 1 - 2x + x^2 \Rightarrow x^2 - x = 0 \Rightarrow$

$x(x - 1) = 0 \Rightarrow x = 0$ or $x = 1$

27. $\sqrt{b^2 - 4} = b - 2 \Rightarrow (\sqrt{b^2 - 4})^2 = (b - 2)^2 \Rightarrow b^2 - 4 = b^2 - 4b + 4 \Rightarrow 4b = 8 \Rightarrow b = 2$

29. $\sqrt{1-2x} = x+7 \Rightarrow (\sqrt{1-2x})^2 = (x+7)^2 \Rightarrow 1 - 2x = x^2 + 14x + 49 \Rightarrow x^2 + 16x + 48 = 0 \Rightarrow$
$(x+12)(x+4) = 0 \Rightarrow x = -12$ or $x = -4$. The solution $x = -12$ does not check. The solution is $x = -4$.

31. $\sqrt{x} = \sqrt{x-5} + 1 \Rightarrow (\sqrt{x})^2 = (\sqrt{x-5}+1)^2 \Rightarrow x = (x-5) + 2\sqrt{x-5} + 1 \Rightarrow$
$2\sqrt{x-5} = 4 \Rightarrow (2\sqrt{x-5})^2 = 4^2 \Rightarrow 4(x-5) = 16 \Rightarrow 4x - 20 = 16 \Rightarrow 4x = 36 \Rightarrow x = 9$

33. $\sqrt{2t-2} + \sqrt{t} = 7 \Rightarrow \sqrt{2t-2} = 7 - \sqrt{t} \Rightarrow (\sqrt{2t-2})^2 = (7-\sqrt{t})^2 \Rightarrow 2t - 2 = 49 - 14\sqrt{t} + t \Rightarrow$
$14\sqrt{t} = 51 - t \Rightarrow (14\sqrt{t})^2 = (51-t)^2 \Rightarrow 196t = 2601 - 102t + t^2 \Rightarrow t^2 - 298t + 2601 = 0 \Rightarrow$
$(t-9)(t-289) = 0 \Rightarrow t = 9$ or $t = 289$. The solution $t = 289$ does not check. The solution is $t = 9$.

Graphical Solutions

35. Graphical: Graph $Y_1 = {}^3\sqrt{}(X+5)$ and $Y_2 = 2$ in [−7, 7, 1] by [0, 4, 1]. See Figure 35. The solution is $x = 3$.

37. Graphical: Graph $Y_1 = \sqrt{}(2X-3)$ and $Y_2 = \sqrt{}(X) - (1/2)$ in [0, 3, 1] by [−2, 2, 1]. See Figure 37.
The solution is $x \approx 1.88$.

[−7, 7, 1] by [0, 4, 1]

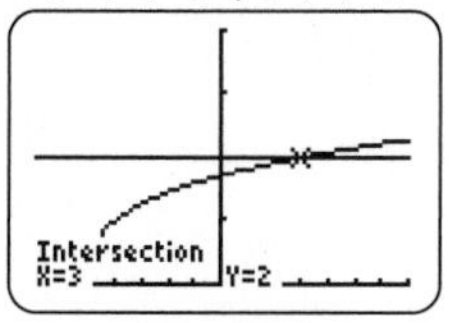

Figure 35

[0, 3, 1] by [−2, 2, 1]

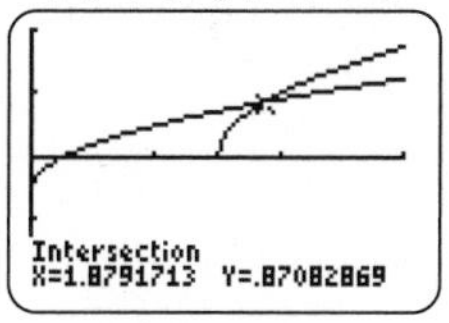

Figure 37

[−4, 4, 1] by [−4, 4, 1]

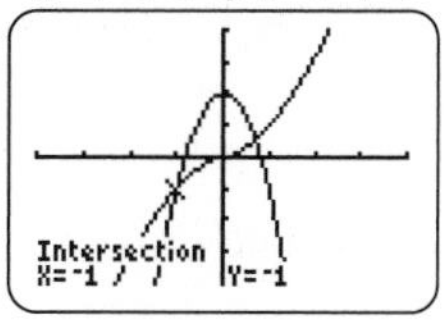

Figure 39a

[−4, 4, 1] by [−4, 4, 1]

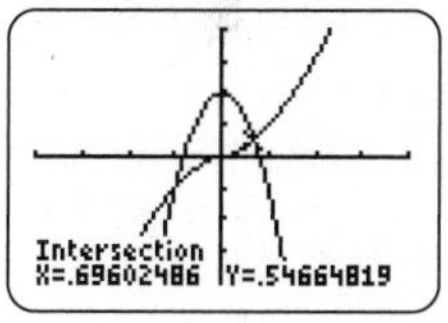

Figure 39b

39. Graphical: Graph $Y_1 = X\wedge(5/3)$ and $Y_2 = 2 - 3X^2$ in [−4, 4, 1] by [−4, 4, 1]. See Figures 39a & 39b.
The solutions are $x = -1$ or $x \approx 0.70$.

41. Graphical: Graph $Y_1 = X\wedge(1/3) - 1$ and $Y_2 = 2 - X$ in [−3, 3, 1] by [−3, 3, 1]. See Figure 41.
The solution is $z \approx 1.79$.

43. Graphical: Graph $Y_1 = \sqrt{}(X+2) + \sqrt{}(3X+2)$ and $Y_2 = 2$ in [−2, 2, 1] by [0, 5, 1]. See Figure 43.
The solution is $y \approx -0.47$.

[−3, 3, 1] by [−3, 3, 1]

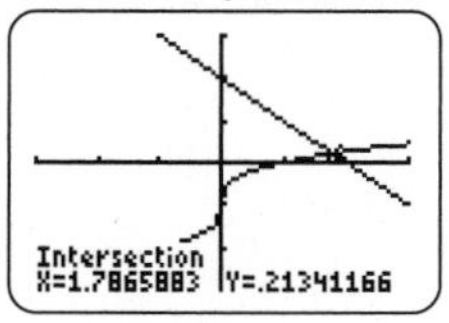

Figure 41

[−2, 2, 1] by [0, 5, 1]

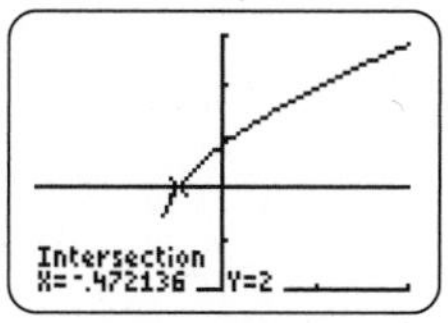

Figure 43

[0, 30, 5] by [0, 10, 1]

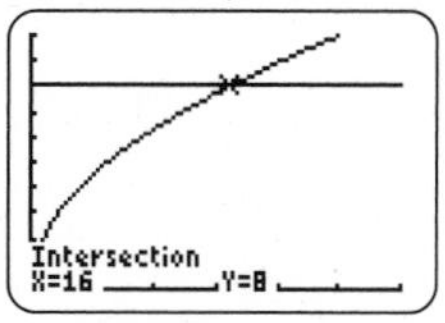

Figure 45b

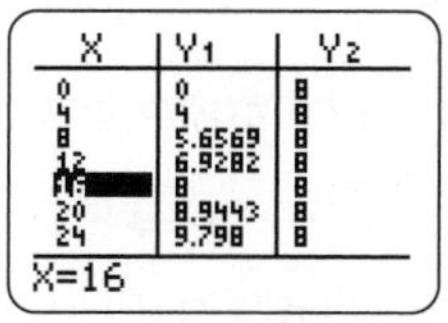

Figure 45c

Using More Than One Method

45. (a) $2\sqrt{x} = 8 \Rightarrow (2\sqrt{x})^2 = 8^2 \Rightarrow 4x = 64 \Rightarrow x = 16$

(b) Graph $Y_1 = 2\sqrt{}(X)$ and $Y_2 = 8$ in [0, 30, 5] by [0, 10, 1]. See Figure 45b. The solution is $x = 16$.

(c) Table $Y_1 = 2\sqrt{}(X)$ and $Y_2 = 8$ with TblStart = 0 and ΔTbl = 4. See Figure 45c. The solution is $x = 16$.

47. (a) $\sqrt{6z - 2} = 8 \Rightarrow (\sqrt{6z - 2})^2 = 8^2 \Rightarrow 6z - 2 = 64 \Rightarrow 6z = 66 \Rightarrow z = 11$

(b) Graph $Y_1 = \sqrt{}(6X - 2)$ and $Y_2 = 8$ in [0, 20, 2] by [0, 10, 1]. See Figure 47b. The solution is $z = 11$.

(c) Table $Y_1 = \sqrt{}(6X - 2)$ and $Y_2 = 8$ with TblStart = 7 and ΔTbl = 1. See Figure 47c. The solution is $z = 11$.

[0, 20, 2] by [0, 10, 1]

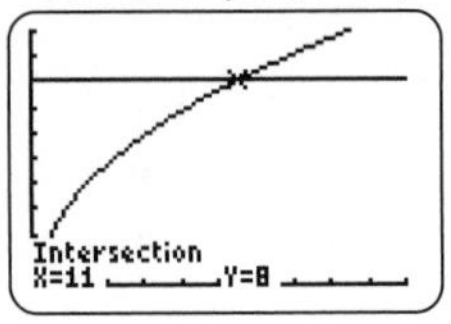

Figure 47b

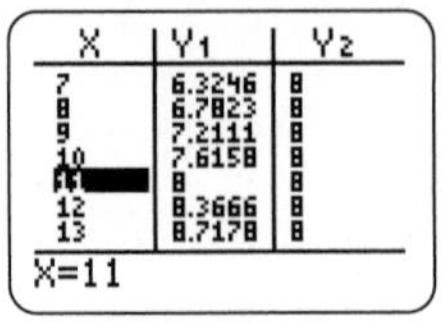

Figure 47c

Solving an Equation for a Variable

49. $T = 2\pi\sqrt{\frac{L}{32}} \Rightarrow \frac{T}{2\pi} = \sqrt{\frac{L}{32}} \Rightarrow \left(\frac{T}{2\pi}\right)^2 = \frac{L}{32} \Rightarrow \frac{T^2}{4\pi^2} = \frac{L}{32} \Rightarrow 32 \cdot \frac{T^2}{4\pi^2} = L \Rightarrow L = \frac{8T^2}{\pi^2}$

51. $r = \sqrt{\frac{A}{\pi}} \Rightarrow r^2 = \frac{A}{\pi} \Rightarrow \pi r^2 = A \Rightarrow A = \pi r^2$

Pythagorean Theorem

53. Yes, since $6^2 + 8^2 = 10^2$. That is $36 + 64 = 100$.

55. Yes, since $(\sqrt{5})^2 + (\sqrt{9})^2 = (\sqrt{14})^2$. That is $5 + 9 = 14$.

57. Yes, since $7^2 + 24^2 = 25^2$. That is $49 + 576 = 625$.

59. No, since $8^2 + 8^2 \neq 16^2$. That is $64 + 64 \neq 256$.

61. $4^2 + 4^2 = c^2 \Rightarrow c^2 = 16 + 16 \Rightarrow c^2 = 32 \Rightarrow c = \sqrt{32} = 4\sqrt{2}$

63. $24^2 + b^2 = 25^2 \Rightarrow 576 + b^2 = 625 \Rightarrow b^2 = 49 \Rightarrow b = \sqrt{49} = 7$

65. $3^2 + 4^2 = c^2 \Rightarrow c^2 = 9 + 16 \Rightarrow c^2 = 25 \Rightarrow c = \sqrt{25} = 5$

67. $(\sqrt{3})^2 + b^2 = 8^2 \Rightarrow 3 + b^2 = 64 \Rightarrow b^2 = 61 \Rightarrow b = \sqrt{61}$

69. $a^2 + 48^2 = 50^2 \Rightarrow a^2 + 2304 = 2500 \Rightarrow a^2 = 196 \Rightarrow a = \sqrt{196} = 14$

Distance Formula

71. From (–2, 1) to (2, 3), $d = \sqrt{(2 - (-2))^2 + (3 - 1)^2} = \sqrt{4^2 + 2^2} = \sqrt{16 + 4} = \sqrt{20} = 2\sqrt{5}$.

73. From (10, 40) to (30, –20),

$d = \sqrt{(30 - 10)^2 + (-20 - 40)^2} = \sqrt{20^2 + (-60)^2} = \sqrt{400 + 3600} = \sqrt{4000} = 20\sqrt{10}$.

75. $d = \sqrt{(4 - (-1))^2 + (10 - 2)^2} = \sqrt{5^2 + 8^2} = \sqrt{25 + 64} = \sqrt{89}$.

77. $d = \sqrt{(4 - 0)^2 + (0 - (-3))^2} = \sqrt{4^2 + 3^2} = \sqrt{16 + 9} = \sqrt{25} = 5$.

79. $\sqrt{(0 - x)^2 + (6 - 3)^2} = 5 \Rightarrow \sqrt{(-x)^2 + 3^2} = 5 \Rightarrow \sqrt{x^2 + 9} = 5 \Rightarrow (\sqrt{x^2 + 9})^2 = 5^2 \Rightarrow$

$x^2 + 9 = 25 \Rightarrow x^2 = 16 \Rightarrow x = \sqrt{16} = \pm 4$. Since x is positive, $x = 4$.

81. $\sqrt{(62-x)^2+(6-(-5))^2}=61 \Rightarrow \sqrt{(62-x)^2+11^2}=61 \Rightarrow \sqrt{(3844-124x+x^2)+121}=61 \Rightarrow$
$\sqrt{x^2-124x+3965}=61 \Rightarrow (\sqrt{x^2-124x+3965})^2=61^2 \Rightarrow x^2-124x+3965=3721 \Rightarrow$
$x^2-124x+244=0 \Rightarrow (x-2)(x-122)=0 \Rightarrow x=2$ or $x=122$

Applications

83. $400=100\sqrt[3]{W^2} \Rightarrow \dfrac{400}{100}=\sqrt[3]{W^2} \Rightarrow 4=\sqrt[3]{W^2} \Rightarrow 4^3=(\sqrt[3]{W^2})^3 \Rightarrow 64=W^2 \Rightarrow W=8$ lb

85. $D(6)=1.22\sqrt{6}\approx 2.988 \approx 3$ miles

87. $1.22\sqrt{h}=20 \Rightarrow \sqrt{h}=\dfrac{20}{1.22} \Rightarrow (\sqrt{h})^2=\left(\dfrac{20}{1.22}\right)^2 \Rightarrow h\approx 268.745 \approx 269$ feet

89. $d^2=11.4^2+15.2^2 \Rightarrow d^2=129.96+231.04 \Rightarrow d^2=361 \Rightarrow d=\sqrt{361}=19$ inches

91. The height can be found using proportions: $\dfrac{16}{9}=\dfrac{29}{x} \Rightarrow 16x=261 \Rightarrow x=\dfrac{261}{16}\approx 16.3$ inches.

Then $d^2=29^2+16.3^2 \Rightarrow d^2=841+265.69 \Rightarrow d^2=1106.69 \Rightarrow d=\sqrt{1106.69}\approx 33.3$ inches.

93. (a) $\dfrac{60}{11}\sqrt{d}=60 \Rightarrow \sqrt{d}=60\left(\dfrac{11}{60}\right) \Rightarrow \sqrt{d}=11 \Rightarrow (\sqrt{d})^2=11^2 \Rightarrow d=121$ feet

(b) $\dfrac{60}{11}\sqrt{d}=100 \Rightarrow \sqrt{d}=100\left(\dfrac{11}{60}\right) \Rightarrow \sqrt{d}=\dfrac{55}{3} \Rightarrow (\sqrt{d})^2=\left(\dfrac{55}{3}\right)^2 \Rightarrow d\approx 336$ feet

95. (a) $V=30\sqrt{\dfrac{285}{178}}\approx 38$ mph. The accident vehicle was traveling about 38 mph.

(b) $45\sqrt{\dfrac{D}{255}}=60 \Rightarrow \sqrt{\dfrac{D}{255}}=\dfrac{60}{45} \Rightarrow \left(\sqrt{\dfrac{D}{255}}\right)^2=\left(\dfrac{4}{3}\right)^2 \Rightarrow \dfrac{D}{255}=\dfrac{16}{9} \Rightarrow D=255\left(\dfrac{16}{9}\right)\approx 453$ feet

97. $c^2=a^2+a^2 \Rightarrow c^2=2a^2 \Rightarrow c=\sqrt{2a^2}=a\sqrt{2}$

10.6 Complex Numbers

Concepts

1. $2+3i$; *Answers may vary.*
3. i
5. $i\sqrt{a}$
7. $a+bi$
9. 4

Complex Numbers

11. $\sqrt{-5}=i\sqrt{5}$
13. $\sqrt{-100}=i\sqrt{100}=i\cdot 10=10i$
15. $\sqrt{-144}=i\sqrt{144}=i\cdot 12=12i$
17. $\sqrt{-12}=i\sqrt{12}=i\cdot\sqrt{4\cdot 3}=i\cdot\sqrt{4}\cdot\sqrt{3}=i\cdot 2\cdot\sqrt{3}=2i\sqrt{3}$

19. $\sqrt{-18} = i\sqrt{18} = i \cdot \sqrt{9 \cdot 2} = i \cdot \sqrt{9} \cdot \sqrt{2} = i \cdot 3 \cdot \sqrt{2} = 3i\sqrt{2}$

21. $(5 + 3i) + (-2 - 3i) = (5 + (-2)) + (3 + (-3))i = 3 + 0i = 3$

23. $(2i) + (-8 + 5i) = (0 + (-8)) + (2 + 5)i = -8 + 7i$

25. $(2 - 7i) - (1 + 2i) = (2 - 1) + (-7 - 2)i = 1 - 9i$

27. $(5i) - (10 - 2i) = (0 - 10) + (5 - (-2))i = -10 + 7i$

29. $4(5 - 3i) = 20 - 12i$

31. $(-3 - 4i)(5 - 4i) = -15 + 12i - 20i + 16i^2 = -15 - 8i + 16(-1) = -15 - 8i - 16 = -31 - 8i$

33. $(-4i)(5i) = -4 \cdot 5 \cdot i^2 = -20(-1) = 20$

35. $3i + (2 - 3i) - (1 - 5i) = 3i + 2 - 3i - 1 + 5i = 1 + 5i$

37. $(2 + i)^2 = 4 + 4i + i^2 = 4 + 4i - 1 = 3 + 4i$

39. $2i(-3 + i) = -6i + 2i^2 = -6i + 2(-1) = -2 - 6i$

41. $i(1 + i)^2 = i(1 + 2i + i^2) = i(1 + 2i - 1) = i(2i) = 2i^2 = 2(-1) = -2$

43. When 11 is divided by 4, the result is 2 with remainder 3. Thus $i^{11} = i^3 = -i$.

45. When 21 is divided by 4, the result is 5 with remainder 1. Thus $i^{21} = i^1 = i$.

47. When 58 is divided by 4, the result is 14 with remainder 2. Thus $i^{58} = i^2 = -1$.

49. When 64 is divided by 4, the result is 16 with remainder 0. Thus $i^{64} = i^0 = 1$.

51. $3 - 4i$

53. Since $-6i = 0 - 6i$, the complex conjugate is $0 + 6i = 6i$.

55. $5 + 4i$

57. Since $-1 = -1 + 0i$, the complex conjugate is $-1 - 0i = -1$.

59. $\dfrac{2}{1+i} = \dfrac{2}{1+i} \cdot \dfrac{1-i}{1-i} = \dfrac{2(1-i)}{1^2 - i^2} = \dfrac{2-2i}{1+1} = \dfrac{2-2i}{2} = \dfrac{2}{2} - \dfrac{2}{2}i = 1 - i$

61. $\dfrac{3i}{5-2i} = \dfrac{3i}{5-2i} \cdot \dfrac{5+2i}{5+2i} = \dfrac{3i(5+2i)}{5^2 - 4i^2} = \dfrac{15i + 6i^2}{25+4} = \dfrac{15i - 6}{29} = -\dfrac{6}{29} + \dfrac{15}{29}i$

63. $\dfrac{8+9i}{5+2i} = \dfrac{8+9i}{5+2i} \cdot \dfrac{5-2i}{5-2i} = \dfrac{40 - 16i + 45i - 18i^2}{5^2 - 4i^2} = \dfrac{40 + 29i - 18(-1)}{25+4} = \dfrac{58 + 29i}{29} = 2 + i$

65. $\dfrac{5+7i}{1-i} = \dfrac{5+7i}{1-i} \cdot \dfrac{1+i}{1+i} = \dfrac{5 + 5i + 7i + 7i^2}{1^2 - i^2} = \dfrac{5 + 12i + 7(-1)}{1+1} = \dfrac{-2 + 12i}{2} = -1 + 6i$

67. $\dfrac{2-i}{i} = \dfrac{2-i}{i} \cdot \dfrac{-i}{-i} = \dfrac{-2i + i^2}{-i^2} = \dfrac{-2i + (-1)}{-(-1)} = \dfrac{-2i - 1}{1} = -1 - 2i$

69. $\dfrac{1}{i} + \dfrac{1}{2i} = \dfrac{2}{2i} + \dfrac{1}{2i} = \dfrac{3}{2i} = \dfrac{3}{2i} \cdot \dfrac{-2i}{-2i} = \dfrac{-6i}{-4i^2} = \dfrac{-6i}{-4(-1)} = \dfrac{-6i}{4} = -\dfrac{3}{2}i$

71. $\dfrac{1}{-1+i} - \dfrac{2}{i} = \dfrac{i}{i(-1+i)} - \dfrac{2(-1+i)}{i(-1+i)} = \dfrac{i}{-1-i} - \dfrac{-2+2i}{-1-i} = \dfrac{i + 2 - 2i}{-1-i} = \dfrac{2-i}{-1-i}$

$= \dfrac{2-i}{-1-i} \cdot \dfrac{-1+i}{-1+i} = \dfrac{-2 + 2i + i - i^2}{1 - i^2} = \dfrac{-2 + 3i - (-1)}{1 - (-1)} = \dfrac{-1 + 3i}{2} = -\dfrac{1}{2} + \dfrac{3}{2}i$

Applications

73. $Z = \frac{40 + 70i}{2 + 3i} = \frac{40 + 70i}{2 + 3i} \cdot \frac{2 - 3i}{2 - 3i} = \frac{80 - 120i + 140i - 210i^2}{2^2 - 9i^2} = \frac{290 + 20i}{13} = \frac{290}{13} + \frac{20}{13}i$

Checking Basic Concepts for Sections 10.5 & 10.6

1. (a) $\sqrt{2x - 4} = 2 \Rightarrow (\sqrt{2x - 4})^2 = 2^2 \Rightarrow 2x - 4 = 4 \Rightarrow 2x = 8 \Rightarrow x = 4$

   (b) $\sqrt[3]{x - 1} = 3 \Rightarrow (\sqrt[3]{x - 1})^3 = 3^3 \Rightarrow x - 1 = 27 \Rightarrow x = 28$

   (c) $\sqrt{3x} = 1 + \sqrt{x + 1} \Rightarrow (\sqrt{3x})^2 = (1 + \sqrt{x + 1})^2 \Rightarrow 3x = 1 + 2\sqrt{x + 1} + x + 1 \Rightarrow$

   $3x = x + 2 + 2\sqrt{x + 1} \Rightarrow 2x - 2 = 2\sqrt{x + 1} \Rightarrow x - 1 = \sqrt{x + 1} \Rightarrow (x - 1)^2 = (\sqrt{x + 1})^2 \Rightarrow$

   $x^2 - 2x + 1 = x + 1 \Rightarrow x^2 - 3x = 0 \Rightarrow x(x - 3) = 0 \Rightarrow x = 0$ or $x = 3$

   The solution $x = 0$ does not check. The solution is $x = 3$.

2. $d = \sqrt{(2 - (-3))^2 + (-7 - 5)^2} = \sqrt{5^2 + (-12)^2} = \sqrt{25 + 144} = \sqrt{169} = 13$

3. $h^2 + 12.8^2 = 16^2 \Rightarrow h^2 + 163.84 = 256 \Rightarrow h^2 = 92.16 \Rightarrow h = \sqrt{92.16} = 9.6$ inches

4. (a) $\sqrt{-64} = i\sqrt{64} = i(8) = 8i$

   (b) $\sqrt{-17} = i\sqrt{17}$

5. (a) $(2 - 3i) + (1 - i) = (2 + 1) + (-3 + (-1))i = 3 - 4i$

   (b) $4i - (2 + i) = (0 - 2) + (4 - 1)i = -2 + 3i$

   (c) $(3 - 2i)(1 + i) = 3 + 3i - 2i - 2i^2 = 3 + i - 2(-1) = 3 + i + 2 = 5 + i$

   (d) $\frac{3}{2 - 2i} = \frac{3}{2 - 2i} \cdot \frac{2 + 2i}{2 + 2i} = \frac{3(2 + 2i)}{2^2 - 4i^2} = \frac{6 + 6i}{4 + 4} = \frac{6 + 6i}{8} = \frac{6}{8} + \frac{6}{8}i = \frac{3}{4} + \frac{3}{4}i$

Chapter 10 Review Exercises

Section 10.1

1. $\sqrt{4} = 2$
2. $\sqrt{36} = 6$
3. $\sqrt{9x^2} = \sqrt{9} \cdot \sqrt{x^2} = 3|x|$
4. $\sqrt{(x - 1)^2} = |x - 1|$
5. $\sqrt[3]{-64} = -4$
6. $\sqrt[3]{-125} = -5$
7. $\sqrt[3]{x^6} = \sqrt[3]{(x^2)^3} = x^2$
8. $\sqrt[3]{27x^3} = \sqrt[3]{27} \cdot \sqrt[3]{x^3} = 3x$
9. $\sqrt[4]{16} = 2$
10. $\sqrt[5]{-1} = -1$
11. $\sqrt[4]{x^8} = \sqrt[4]{(x^2)^4} = x^2$
12. $\sqrt[5]{(x + 1)^5} = x + 1$

13. $14^{1/2} = \sqrt{14}$

14. $(-5)^{1/3} = \sqrt[3]{-5}$

15. $\left(\frac{x}{y}\right)^{3/2} = \left(\sqrt{\frac{x}{y}}\right)^3$ or $\sqrt{\left(\frac{x}{y}\right)^3}$

16. $(xy)^{-2/3} = \frac{1}{(xy)^{2/3}} = \frac{1}{\sqrt[3]{(xy)^2}}$ or $\frac{1}{(\sqrt[3]{xy})^2}$

17. $(-27)^{2/3} = (\sqrt[3]{-27})^2 = (-3)^2 = 9$

18. $16^{1/4} = \sqrt[4]{16} = 2$

19. $16^{3/2} = (\sqrt{16})^3 = 4^3 = 64$

20. $81^{3/4} = (\sqrt[4]{81})^3 = 3^3 = 27$

21. $(z^3)^{2/3} = z^{3 \cdot 2/3} = z^2$

22. $(x^2y^4)^{1/2} = x^{2 \cdot 1/2} \cdot y^{4 \cdot 1/2} = xy^2$

23. $\left(\frac{x^2}{y^6}\right)^{3/2} = \frac{x^{2 \cdot 3/2}}{y^{6 \cdot 3/2}} = \frac{x^3}{y^9}$

24. $\left(\frac{x^3}{y^6}\right)^{-1/3} = \frac{x^{3 \cdot (-1/3)}}{y^{6 \cdot (-1/3)}} = \frac{x^{-1}}{y^{-2}} = \frac{y^2}{x}$

Section 10.2

25. $\sqrt{2} \cdot \sqrt{32} = \sqrt{64} = 8$

26. $\sqrt[3]{-4} \cdot \sqrt[3]{2} = \sqrt[3]{-8} = -2$

27. $\sqrt[3]{x^4} \cdot \sqrt[3]{x^2} = \sqrt[3]{x^6} = \sqrt[3]{(x^2)^3} = x^2$

28. $\frac{\sqrt{80}}{\sqrt{20}} = \sqrt{\frac{80}{20}} = \sqrt{4} = 2$

29. $\sqrt[3]{-\frac{x}{8}} = -\frac{\sqrt[3]{x}}{\sqrt[3]{8}} = -\frac{\sqrt[3]{x}}{2}$

30. $\sqrt{\frac{1}{3}} \cdot \sqrt{\frac{1}{3}} = \left(\sqrt{\frac{1}{3}}\right)^2 = \frac{1}{3}$

31. $\sqrt{48} = \sqrt{16 \cdot 3} = \sqrt{16} \cdot \sqrt{3} = 4\sqrt{3}$

32. $\sqrt{54} = \sqrt{9 \cdot 6} = \sqrt{9} \cdot \sqrt{6} = 3\sqrt{6}$

33. $\sqrt[3]{\frac{3}{x}} \cdot \sqrt[3]{\frac{9}{x^2}} = \sqrt[3]{\frac{3 \cdot 9}{x \cdot x^2}} = \sqrt[3]{\frac{27}{x^3}} = \frac{\sqrt[3]{27}}{\sqrt[3]{x^3}} = \frac{3}{x}$

34. $\sqrt{32a^3b^2} = \sqrt{(4ab)^2 \cdot 2a} = \sqrt{(4ab)^2} \cdot \sqrt{2a} = 4ab\sqrt{2a}$

35. $\sqrt{3xy} \cdot \sqrt{27xy} = \sqrt{3 \cdot 27 \cdot xy \cdot xy} = \sqrt{81(xy)^2} = \sqrt{(9xy)^2} = 9xy$

36. $\sqrt[3]{-25z^2} \cdot \sqrt[3]{-5z^2} = \sqrt[3]{-25 \cdot (-5) \cdot z^2 \cdot z^2} = \sqrt[3]{125z^4} = \sqrt[3]{(5z)^3 \cdot z} = \sqrt{(5z)^3} \cdot \sqrt[3]{z} = 5z\sqrt[3]{z}$

37. $\sqrt{x^2 + 2x + 1} = \sqrt{(x + 1)^2} = x + 1$

38. $\sqrt[4]{\frac{2a^2}{b}} \cdot \; = \sqrt[4]{\frac{8a^3}{b^3}} = \sqrt[4]{\frac{16a^5}{b^4}} = \sqrt[4]{\left(\frac{2a}{b}\right)^4 \cdot a} = \sqrt[4]{\left(\frac{2a}{b}\right)^4} \cdot \sqrt[4]{a} = \frac{2a\sqrt[4]{a}}{b}$

39. $2\sqrt{x} \cdot \sqrt[3]{x} = 2x^{1/2} \cdot x^{1/3} = 2x^{1/2+1/3} = 2x^{5/6} = 2\sqrt[6]{x^5}$

40. $\sqrt[3]{rt} \cdot \sqrt[4]{r^2t^4} = (rt)^{1/3} \cdot (r^2t^4)^{1/4} = r^{1/3}t^{1/3} \cdot r^{1/2}t = r^{1/3+1/2}t^{1/3+1} = r^{5/6}t^{4/3} = r^{5/6}t^{8/6} = \sqrt[6]{r^5t^8}$ or $t\sqrt[6]{r^5t^2}$

41. $\frac{4}{\sqrt{5}} = \frac{4}{\sqrt{5}} \cdot \frac{\sqrt{5}}{\sqrt{5}} = \frac{4\sqrt{5}}{5}$

42. $\frac{r}{2\sqrt{t}} = \frac{r}{2\sqrt{t}} \cdot \frac{\sqrt{t}}{\sqrt{t}} = \frac{r\sqrt{t}}{2t}$

Section 10.3

43. $3\sqrt{3} + \sqrt{3} = 4\sqrt{3}$

44. $\sqrt[3]{x} + 2\sqrt[3]{x} = 3\sqrt[3]{x}$

45. $3\sqrt[3]{5} - 6\sqrt[3]{5} = -3\sqrt[3]{5}$

46. $\sqrt[\square]{y} - 2\sqrt[\square]{y} = -\sqrt[\square]{y}$

47. $2\sqrt{12} + 7\sqrt{3} = 2\sqrt{4 \cdot 3} + 7\sqrt{3} = 2\sqrt{4} \cdot \sqrt{3} + 7\sqrt{3} = 4\sqrt{3} + 7\sqrt{3} = 11\sqrt{3}$

48. $3\sqrt{18} - 2\sqrt{2} = 3\sqrt{9 \cdot 2} - 2\sqrt{2} = 3\sqrt{9} \cdot \sqrt{2} - 2\sqrt{2} = 9\sqrt{2} - 2\sqrt{2} = 7\sqrt{2}$

49. $7\sqrt[3]{16} - \sqrt[3]{2} = 7\sqrt[3]{8 \cdot 2} - \sqrt[3]{2} = 7\sqrt[3]{8} \cdot \sqrt[3]{2} - \sqrt[3]{2} = 14\sqrt[3]{2} - \sqrt[3]{2} = 13\sqrt[3]{2}$

50. $\sqrt{4x+4} + \sqrt{x+1} = \sqrt{4(x+1)} + \sqrt{x+1} = \sqrt{4} \cdot \sqrt{x+1} + \sqrt{x+1} = 3\sqrt{x+1}$

51. $\sqrt{4x^3} - \sqrt{x} = \sqrt{(2x)^2 \cdot x} - \sqrt{x} = \sqrt{(2x)^2} \cdot \sqrt{x} - \sqrt{x} = 2x\sqrt{x} - \sqrt{x} = (2x-1)\sqrt{x}$

52. $\sqrt[3]{ab^4} + 2\sqrt[3]{a^4b} = \sqrt{b^3 \cdot ab} + 2\sqrt[3]{a^3 \cdot ab} = \sqrt[3]{b^3} \cdot \sqrt[3]{ab} + 2\sqrt[3]{a^3} \cdot \sqrt[3]{ab} = (b+2a)\sqrt[3]{ab}$

53. $(3+\sqrt{6})(3-\sqrt{6}) = 3^2 - (\sqrt{6})^2 = 9 - 6 = 3$

54. $(10-\sqrt{5})(10+\sqrt{5}) = 10^2 - (\sqrt{5})^2 = 100 - 5 = 95$

55. $(\sqrt{a}+\sqrt{2b})(\sqrt{a}-\sqrt{2b}) = (\sqrt{a})^2 - (\sqrt{2b})^2 = a - 2b$

56. $(\sqrt{xy}-1)(\sqrt{xy}+2) = (\sqrt{xy})^2 + 2\sqrt{xy} - \sqrt{xy} - 2 = xy + \sqrt{xy} - 2$

57. $\frac{1}{\sqrt{2}+3} = \frac{1}{\sqrt{2}+3} \cdot \frac{\sqrt{2}-3}{\sqrt{2}-3} = \frac{\sqrt{2}-3}{2-9} = \frac{\sqrt{2}-3}{-7} = \frac{3-\sqrt{2}}{7}$

58. $\frac{2}{5-\sqrt{7}} = \frac{2}{5-\sqrt{7}} \cdot \frac{5+\sqrt{7}}{5+\sqrt{7}} = \frac{10+2\sqrt{7}}{25-7} = \frac{10-2\sqrt{7}}{18} = \frac{5-\sqrt{7}}{9}$

59. $\frac{1}{\sqrt{8}-\sqrt{7}} = \frac{1}{\sqrt{8}-\sqrt{7}} \cdot \frac{\sqrt{8}+\sqrt{7}}{\sqrt{8}+\sqrt{7}} = \frac{\sqrt{8}+\sqrt{7}}{8-7} = \frac{\sqrt{8}+\sqrt{7}}{1} = \sqrt{8}+\sqrt{7}$

60. $\frac{\sqrt{a}-\sqrt{b}}{\sqrt{a}+\sqrt{b}} = \frac{\sqrt{a}-\sqrt{b}}{\sqrt{a}+\sqrt{b}} \cdot \frac{\sqrt{a}-\sqrt{b}}{\sqrt{a}-\sqrt{b}} = \frac{a-2\sqrt{ab}+b}{a-b}$

Section 10.4

61. See Figure 61.

62. See Figure 62.

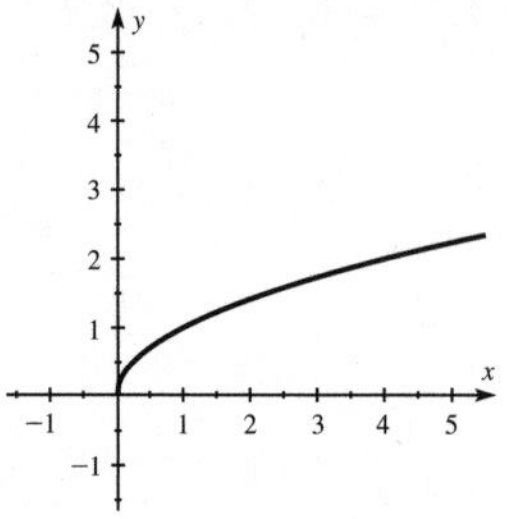

Figure 61

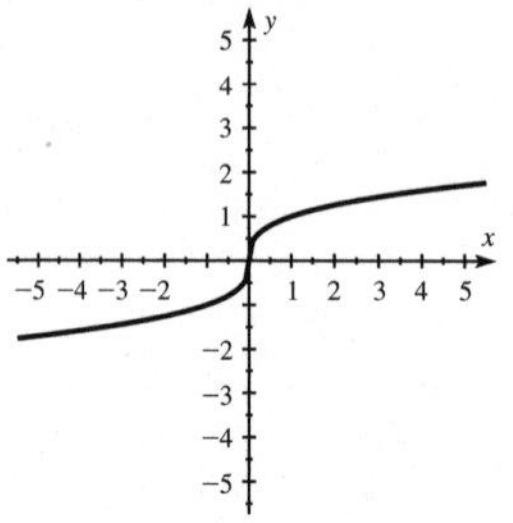

Figure 62

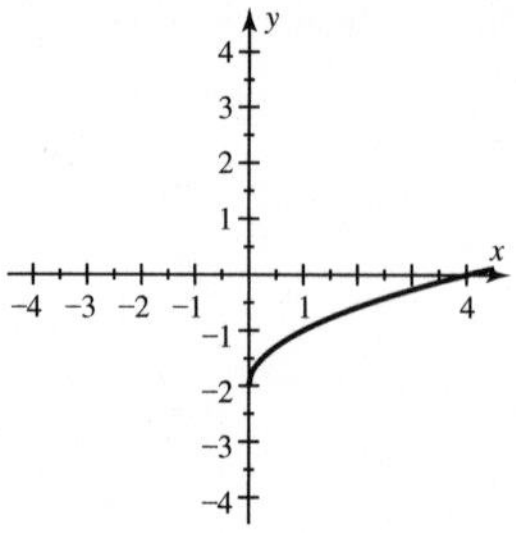

Figure 63

63. See Figure 63. This graph is shifted 2 units downward.

64. See Figure 64. This graph is shifted 1 unit to the right.

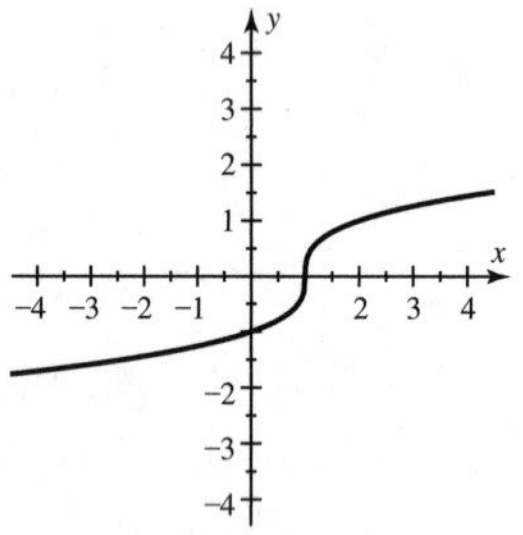

Figure 64

65. $x - 1 \geq 0 \Rightarrow x \geq 1 \Rightarrow$ Domain: $[1, \infty)$

66. $6 - 2x \geq 0 \Rightarrow -2x \geq -6 \Rightarrow x \leq 3 \Rightarrow$ Domain: $(-\infty, 3]$

67. $x^2 + 1 \geq 0 \Rightarrow x^2 \geq -1 \Rightarrow$ Domain: $(-\infty, \infty)$

68. $x + 2 > 0 \Rightarrow x > -2 \Rightarrow$ Domain: $(-2, \infty)$

69. $x^2 = 121 \Rightarrow x = \pm\sqrt{121} \Rightarrow x = \pm 11$

70. $2z^2 = 32 \Rightarrow z^2 = 16 \Rightarrow z = \pm\sqrt{16} \Rightarrow z = \pm 4$

71. $(x - 1)^2 = 16 \Rightarrow x - 1 = \pm\sqrt{16} \Rightarrow x - 1 = \pm 4 \Rightarrow x = 1 \pm 4 \Rightarrow x = -3$ or $x = 5$

72. $x^3 = 64 \Rightarrow x = \sqrt[3]{64} \Rightarrow x = 4$

73. $(x - 1)^3 = 8 \Rightarrow x - 1 = \sqrt[3]{8} \Rightarrow x - 1 = 2 \Rightarrow x = 3$

74. $(2x - 1)^3 = 27 \Rightarrow 2x - 1 = \sqrt[3]{27} \Rightarrow 2x - 1 = 3 \Rightarrow 2x = 4 \Rightarrow x = 2$

Section 10.5

75. $\sqrt{x + 2} = x \Rightarrow (\sqrt{x + 2})^2 = x^2 \Rightarrow x + 2 = x^2 \Rightarrow x^2 - x - 2 = 0 \Rightarrow (x - 2)(x + 1) = 0 \Rightarrow$ $x = 2$ or $x = -1$. The solution $x = -1$ does not check. The solution is $x = 2$.

76. $\sqrt{2x - 1} = \sqrt{x + 3} \Rightarrow (\sqrt{2x - 1})^2 = (\sqrt{x + 3})^2 \Rightarrow 2x - 1 = x + 3 \Rightarrow x = 4$

77. $\sqrt[3]{x - 1} = 2 \Rightarrow (\sqrt[3]{x - 1})^3 = 2^3 \Rightarrow x - 1 = 8 \Rightarrow x = 9$

78. $\sqrt[3]{3x} = 3 \Rightarrow (\sqrt[3]{3x})^3 = 3^3 \Rightarrow 3x = 27 \Rightarrow x = 9$

79. $\sqrt{2x} = x - 4 \Rightarrow (\sqrt{2x})^2 = (x - 4)^2 \Rightarrow 2x = x^2 - 8x + 16 \Rightarrow x^2 - 10x + 16 = 0 \Rightarrow$
$(x - 2)(x - 8) = 0 \Rightarrow x = 2$ or $x = 8$. The solution $x = 2$ does not check. The solution is $x = 8$.

80. $\sqrt{x} + 1 = \sqrt{x + 2} \Rightarrow (\sqrt{x} + 1)^2 = (\sqrt{x + 2})^2 \Rightarrow x + 2\sqrt{x} + 1 = x + 2 \Rightarrow 2\sqrt{x} = 1 \Rightarrow$
$(2\sqrt{x})^2 = 1^2 \Rightarrow 4x = 1 \Rightarrow x = \frac{1}{4}$

81. Graph $Y_1 = (2X - 1)$^(1/3) and $Y_2 = 2$ in [−4, 6, 1] by [−3, 3, 1]. See Figure 81. The solution is $x = 4.5$.

[−4, 6, 1] by [−3, 3, 1]

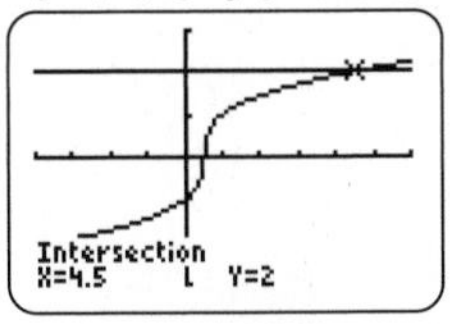

Figure 81

[−5, 5, 1] by [−5, 5, 1]

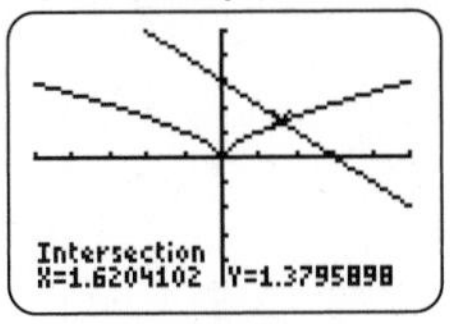

Figure 82

82. Graph $Y_1 = X$^(2/3) and $Y_2 = 3 - X$ in [−5, 5, 1] by [−5, 5, 1]. See Figure 82. The solution is $x \approx 1.62$.

83. $c^2 = 4^2 + 7^2 \Rightarrow c^2 = 16 + 49 \Rightarrow c^2 = 65 \Rightarrow c = \sqrt{65}$

84. $5^2 + b^2 = 8^2 \Rightarrow 25 + b^2 = 64 \Rightarrow b^2 = 39 \Rightarrow b = \sqrt{39}$

85. $d = \sqrt{(2 - (-2))^2 + (-2 - 3)^2} = \sqrt{4^2 + (-5)^2} = \sqrt{16 + 25} = \sqrt{41}$

86. $d = \sqrt{(-4 - 2)^2 + (1 - (-3))^2} = \sqrt{(-6)^2 + 4^2} = \sqrt{36 + 16} = \sqrt{52} = 2\sqrt{13}$

Section 10.6

87. $(1 - 2i) + (-3 + 2i) = (1 + (-3)) + (-2 + 2)i = -2 + 0i = -2$

88. $(1 + 3i) - (3 - i) = (1 - 3) + (3 - (-1))i = -2 + 4i$

89. $(1 - i)(2 + 3i) = 2 + 3i - 2i - 3i^2 = 2 + i - 3(-1) = 2 + i + 3 = 5 + i$

90. $\frac{3 + i}{1 - i} = \frac{3 + i}{1 - i} \cdot \frac{1 + i}{1 + i} = \frac{3 + 3i + i + i^2}{1^2 - i^2} = \frac{3 + 4i - 1}{1 + 1} = \frac{2 + 4i}{2} = \frac{2}{2} + \frac{4}{2}i = 1 + 2i$

91. $\frac{i(4 + i)}{2 - 3i} = \frac{4i + i^2}{2 - 3i} = \frac{-1 + 4i}{2 - 3i} = \frac{-1 + 4i}{2 - 3i} \cdot \frac{2 + 3i}{2 + 3i} = \frac{-2 - 3i + 8i + 12i^2}{4 - 9i^2} = \frac{-2 + 5i + 12(-1)}{4 - 9(-1)}$
$= \frac{-14 + 5i}{13} = -\frac{14}{13} + \frac{5}{13}i$

92. $(1 - i)^2(1 + i) = (1 - 2i + i^2)(1 + i) = (1 - 2i - 1)(1 + i) = -2i(1 + i) = -2i - 2i^2 = 2 - 2i$

Applications

93. $\frac{\sqrt{h}}{2} = 4.6 \Rightarrow \sqrt{h} = 9.2 \Rightarrow (\sqrt{h})^2 = 9.2^2 \Rightarrow h = 84.64 \approx 85$ feet

94. $d^2 = 90^2 + 90^2 \Rightarrow d^2 = 8100 + 8100 \Rightarrow d^2 = 16{,}200 \Rightarrow d = \sqrt{16{,}200} \approx 127.3$ feet

95. $T = \frac{1}{4}\sqrt{10} \approx 0.79$ seconds

96. (a) $L = \sqrt{3.75(500)} = \sqrt{1875} \approx 43$ mph
(b) $L = 1.5\sqrt{500} \approx 34$ mph. A steeper bank allows for a higher speed limit. This agrees with intuition.

97. $x^2 = 7 \Rightarrow x = \sqrt{7} \approx 2.65$ feet

98. (a) $A = s^2 = (\sqrt{5})^2 = 5$ square units

(b) $V = s^3 = (\sqrt{5})^3 = 5\sqrt{5}$ cubic units

(c) $d^2 = (\sqrt{5})^2 + (\sqrt{5})^2 \Rightarrow d^2 + 5 + 5 \Rightarrow d^2 = 10 \Rightarrow d = \sqrt{10}$ units

(d) $d^2 = (\sqrt{5})^2 + (\sqrt{10})^2 \Rightarrow d^2 = 5 + 10 \Rightarrow d^2 = 15 \Rightarrow d = \sqrt{15}$ units

99. $2\pi\sqrt{\dfrac{L}{32.2}} = 1 \Rightarrow \sqrt{\dfrac{L}{32.2}} = \dfrac{1}{2\pi} \Rightarrow \left(\sqrt{\dfrac{L}{32.2}}\right)^2 = \left(\dfrac{1}{2\pi}\right)^2 \Rightarrow \dfrac{L}{32.2} = \dfrac{1}{4\pi^2} \Rightarrow L = \dfrac{32.2}{4\pi^2} \approx 0.82$ feet

100. $2\pi\sqrt{\dfrac{L}{5.1}} = 1 \Rightarrow \sqrt{\dfrac{L}{5.1}} = \dfrac{1}{2\pi} \Rightarrow \left(\sqrt{\dfrac{L}{5.1}}\right)^2 = \left(\dfrac{1}{2\pi}\right)^2 \Rightarrow \dfrac{L}{5.1} = \dfrac{1}{4\pi^2} \Rightarrow L = \dfrac{5.1}{4\pi^2} \approx 0.13$ feet. It is shorter.

101. $4(1 + r)^{210} = 281 \Rightarrow (1 + r)^{210} = \dfrac{281}{4} \Rightarrow ((1 + r)^{210})^{1/210} = \left(\dfrac{281}{4}\right)^{1/210} \Rightarrow 1 + r = \left(\dfrac{281}{4}\right)^{1/210} \Rightarrow$

$r = \left(\dfrac{281}{4}\right)^{1/210} - 1 \approx 0.02$. From 1790 to 2000 the annual percentage growth rate was about 2%.

102. $S = \pi(11)\sqrt{11^2 + 60^2} = 11\pi\sqrt{121 + 3600} = 11\pi\sqrt{3721} \approx 2108 \text{ in}^2$

103. (a) $2^{-5700/5700} = 2^{-1} = \dfrac{1}{2}$

(b) $2^{-20{,}000/5700} = 2^{-200/57} \approx 0.09 = \dfrac{9}{100}$

Chapter 10 Test

1. $\sqrt{25x^4} = \sqrt{25} \cdot \sqrt{(x^2)^2} = 5x^2$

2. $\sqrt[3]{8z^6} = \sqrt[3]{8} \cdot \sqrt[3]{(z^2)^3} = 2z^2$

3. $\sqrt[4]{16x^4y^5} = \sqrt[4]{(2xy)^4 \cdot y} = \sqrt[4]{(2xy)^4} \cdot \sqrt[4]{y} = 2xy\sqrt[4]{y}$

4. $(\sqrt{3} - \sqrt{2})(\sqrt{3} + \sqrt{2}) = (\sqrt{3})^2 - (\sqrt{2})^2 = 3 - 2 = 1$

5. $7^{2/5} = \sqrt[5]{7^2}$ or $(\sqrt[5]{7})^2$

6. $\left(\dfrac{x}{y}\right)^{-2/3} = \left(\dfrac{y}{x}\right)^{2/3} = \sqrt[3]{\left(\dfrac{y}{x}\right)^2}$ or $\left(\sqrt[3]{\dfrac{y}{x}}\right)^2$

7. $(-8)^{4/3} = (\sqrt[3]{-8})^4 = (-2)^4 = 16$

8. $36^{-3/2} = \dfrac{1}{36^{3/2}} = \dfrac{1}{(\sqrt{36})^3} = \dfrac{1}{6^3} = \dfrac{1}{216}$

9. $4 - x \geq 0 \Rightarrow -x \geq -4 \Rightarrow x \leq 4 \Rightarrow$ Domain: $(-\infty, 4]$

10. See Figure 10.

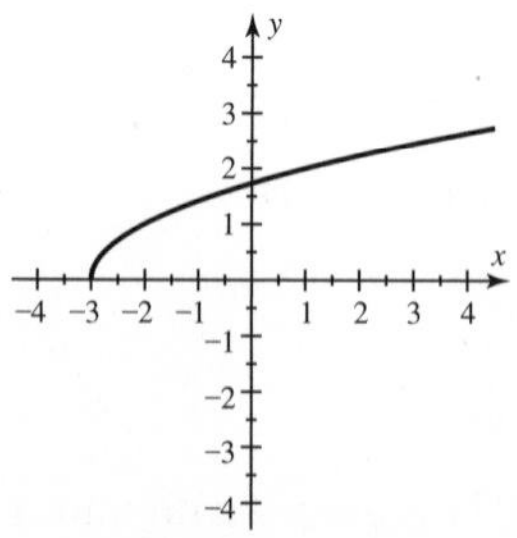

Figure 10

11. $(2z^{1/2})^3 = 2^3 \cdot z^{1/2 \cdot 3} = 8z^{3/2}$

12. $\left(\dfrac{y^2}{z^3}\right)^{-1/3} = \left(\dfrac{z^3}{y^2}\right)^{1/3} = \dfrac{z^{3 \cdot 1/3}}{y^{2 \cdot 1/3}} = \dfrac{z}{y^{2/3}}$

13. $\sqrt{3} \cdot \sqrt{27} = \sqrt{81} = 9$

14. $\dfrac{\sqrt{y^3}}{\sqrt{4y}} = \sqrt{\dfrac{y^3}{4y}} = \sqrt{\dfrac{y^2}{4}} = \dfrac{\sqrt{y^2}}{\sqrt{4}} = \dfrac{y}{2}$

15. $7\sqrt{7} - 3\sqrt{7} + \sqrt{5} = 4\sqrt{7} + \sqrt{5}$

16. $7\sqrt[3]{x} - \sqrt[3]{x} = 6\sqrt[3]{x}$

17. $\sqrt{2x + 2} = x - 11 \Rightarrow (\sqrt{2x + 2})^2 = (x - 11)^2 \Rightarrow 2x + 2 = x^2 - 22x + 121 \Rightarrow$

$x^2 - 24x + 119 = 0 \Rightarrow (x - 7)(x - 17) = 0 \Rightarrow x = 7$ or $x = 17$. The value $x = 7$ does not check. $x = 17$

18. $\dfrac{1}{\sqrt{14} - \sqrt{13}} = \dfrac{1}{\sqrt{14} - \sqrt{13}} \cdot \dfrac{\sqrt{14} + \sqrt{13}}{\sqrt{14} + \sqrt{13}} = \dfrac{\sqrt{14} + \sqrt{13}}{14 - 13} = \dfrac{\sqrt{14} + \sqrt{13}}{1} = \sqrt{14} + \sqrt{13}$

19. $7^2 + b^2 = 13^2 \Rightarrow 49 + b^2 = 169 \Rightarrow b^2 = 120 \Rightarrow b = \sqrt{120} \approx 10.95$

20. $d = \sqrt{(-1 - (-3))^2 + (7 - 5)^2} = \sqrt{2^2 + 2^2} = \sqrt{4 + 4} = \sqrt{8} = 2\sqrt{2}$

21. $(-5 + i) + (7 - 20i) = (-5 + 7) + (1 + (-20))i = 2 - 19i$

22. $(3i) - (6 - 5i) = (0 - 6) + (3 - (-5))i = -6 + 8i$

23. $\left(\dfrac{1}{2} - i\right)\left(\dfrac{1}{2} + i\right) = \dfrac{1}{4} + \dfrac{1}{2}i - \dfrac{1}{2}i - i^2 = \dfrac{1}{4} - (-1) = \dfrac{5}{4}$

24. $\dfrac{2i}{5 + 2i} = \dfrac{2i}{5 + 2i} \cdot \dfrac{5 - 2i}{5 - 2i} = \dfrac{2i(5 - 2i)}{5^2 - 4i^2} = \dfrac{10i - 4i^2}{25 + 4} = \dfrac{4 + 10i}{29} = \dfrac{4}{29} + \dfrac{10}{29}i$

25. (a) $V = \dfrac{4}{3}\pi r^3 \Rightarrow r^3 = \dfrac{3V}{4\pi} \Rightarrow \sqrt[3]{r^3} = \sqrt[3]{\dfrac{3V}{4\pi}} \Rightarrow r = \sqrt[3]{\dfrac{3V}{4\pi}}$

(b) $r = \sqrt[3]{\dfrac{3(50)}{4\pi}} \approx 2.29$ inches

26. $27.4W^{1/3} = 30 \Rightarrow W^{1/3} = \dfrac{30}{27.4} \Rightarrow (W^{1/3})^3 = \left(\dfrac{30}{27.4}\right)^3 \Rightarrow W = \left(\dfrac{30}{27.4}\right)^3 \approx 1.31$ lb

Chapter 10 Extended and Discovery Exercises

1. By trial and error $\dfrac{m}{n} = \dfrac{3}{2}$. Plot the data and graph $Y_1 = 0.0002X$^(3/2) in [0, 2000, 500] by [0, 20, 2]. See Figure 1.

[0, 2000, 500] by [0, 20, 2]

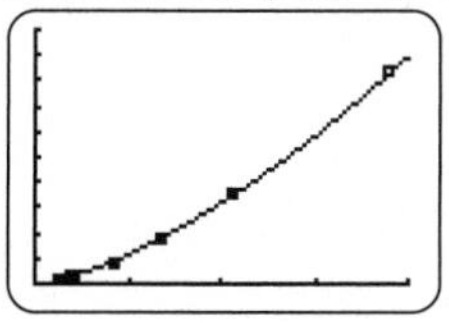

Figure 1

2. (a) $k(47)^{1.12}(11)^{1.98} = 11.4 \Rightarrow k = \dfrac{11.4}{(47)^{1.12}(11)^{1.98}} \approx 0.001325$

(b) $V = 0.001325(105)^{1.12}(20)^{1.98} \approx 91.6$ ft^3

3. (a) $S = 15.7(154)^{0.425}(65)^{0.725} \approx 2753.963261 \approx 2754 \text{ in}^2$

   (b) It increases by a factor of $2^{0.425} \approx 1.34$.

   (c) It increases by a factor of $2^{0.725} \approx 1.65$.

4. (a) Since the segment AB is on land, the expression is $30x$.

   (b) The legs of right triangle BCD have lengths $CB = 1000 - x$ and $CD = 500$. Let $d = BD$.

   $d^2 = (1000 - x)^2 + 500^2 \Rightarrow d = \sqrt{(1000 - x)^2 + 500^2}$

   (c) Since the segment BD is underwater, the expression is $50\sqrt{(1000 - x)^2 + 500^2}$.

   (d) The expression is $30x + 50\sqrt{(1000 - x)^2 + 500^2}$.

   (e) Graph $Y_1 = 30X + 50\sqrt{((100 - X)^2 + 500^2)}$ in [0, 1000, 100] by [40,000, 60,000, 5000]. See Figure 4.

   The minimum cost is \$50,000 when $x = 625$ feet.

[0, 1000, 100] by [40,000, 60,000, 5000]

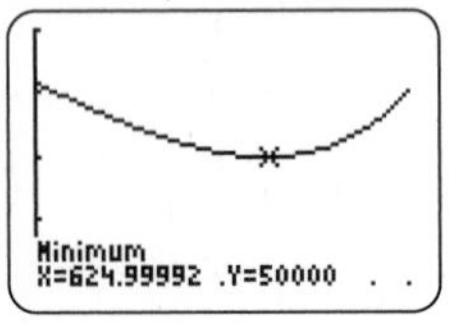

Figure 4

Critical Thinking Solutions for Chapter 10

Section 10.3

- If $\sqrt{a} = c\sqrt{d}$ and $\sqrt{b} = e\sqrt{d}$, then $\sqrt{a} + \sqrt{b} = c\sqrt{d} + e\sqrt{d} = (c + e)\sqrt{d}$. That is, to be able to simplify the expression the following must be true, $a = c^2d$ and $b = e^2d$.

Section 10.4

- Since hang time increases by a factor of $\sqrt{h}$, we would need 4 times the height to double the hang time.

  $4(50) = 200$ feet

- If the wind speed doubles to $2v$, then $W = 2.4(2v)^3 = 2.4 \cdot 8 \cdot v^3 = 8(2.4v^3) = 8W$. That is, the wattage increases by a factor of 8. Conversely, if the wattage doubles to $2W$, then $v = \sqrt[3]{\frac{2W}{2.4}} = \sqrt[3]{2} \cdot \sqrt[3]{\frac{W}{2.4}} = \sqrt[3]{2} \cdot v$.

  That is, the wind speed increases by a factor of $\sqrt[3]{2}$.

Chapter 11: Quadratic Functions and Equations

11.1: Quadratic Functions and Their Graphs

Concepts

1. parabola

3. axis of symmetry)

5. See Figure 5. *Answers may vary.*

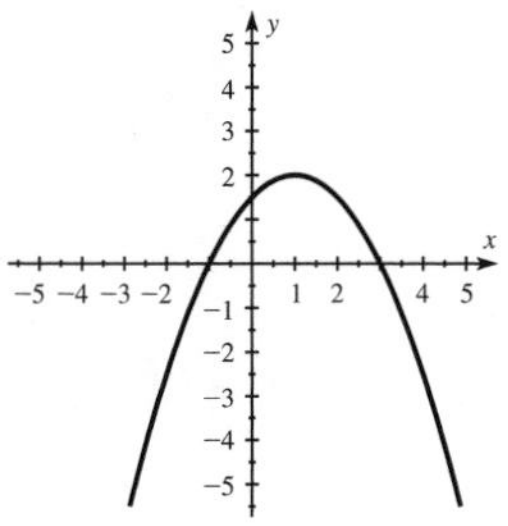

Figure 5

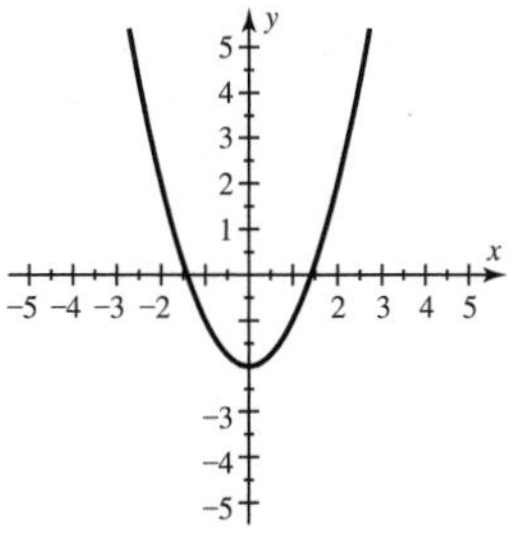

Figure 19

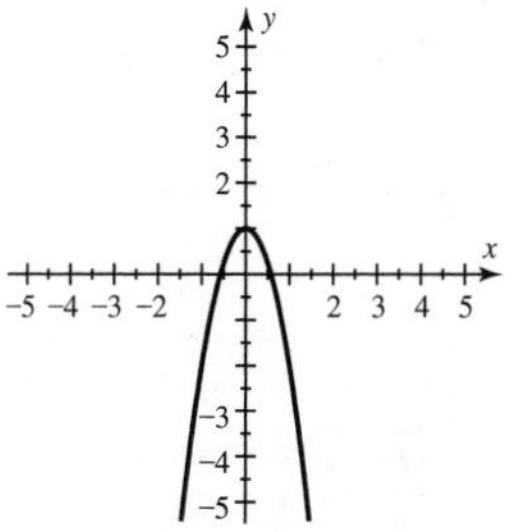

Figure 21

7. narrower

9. $ax^2 + bx + c$ with $a \neq 0$

11. $f(-2) = 0$ and $f(0) = -4$

13. $f(-3) = -2$ and $f(1) = -2$

Graphs of Quadratic Functions

15. The vertex is $(1, -2)$. The axis of symmetry is $x = 1$. The parabola opens upward.

    The graph is increasing when $x \geq 1$ and decreasing when $x \leq 1$.

17. The vertex is $(-2, 3)$. The axis of symmetry is $x = -2$. The parabola opens downward.

    The graph is increasing when $x \leq -2$ and decreasing when $x \geq -2$.

19. (a) See Figure 19.

    (b) The vertex is $(0, -2)$. The axis of symmetry is $x = 0$.

    (c) $f(-2) = (-2)^2 - 2 = 4 - 2 = 2$ and $f(3) = (3)^2 - 2 = 9 - 2 = 7$

21. (a) See Figure 21.

    (b) The vertex is $(0, 1)$. The axis of symmetry is $x = 0$.

    (c) $f(-2) = -3(-2)^2 + 1 = -12 + 1 = -11$ and $f(3) = -3(3)^2 + 1 = -27 + 1 = -26$

23. (a) See Figure 23.

(b) The vertex is $(1, 0)$. The axis of symmetry is $x = 1$.

(c) $f(-2) = ((-2) - 1)^2 = (-3)^2 = 9$ and $f(3) = ((3) - 1)^2 = (2)^2 = 4$

25. (a) See Figure 25.

(b) The vertex is $(-0.5, -2.25)$. The axis of symmetry is $x = -0.5$.

(c) $f(-2) = (-2)^2 + (-2) - 2 = 4 - 2 - 2 = 0$ and $f(3) = (3)^2 + (3) - 2 = 9 + 3 - 2 = 10$

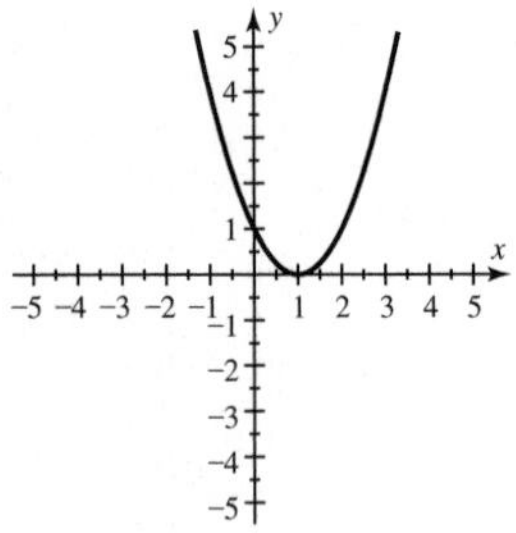

Figure 23

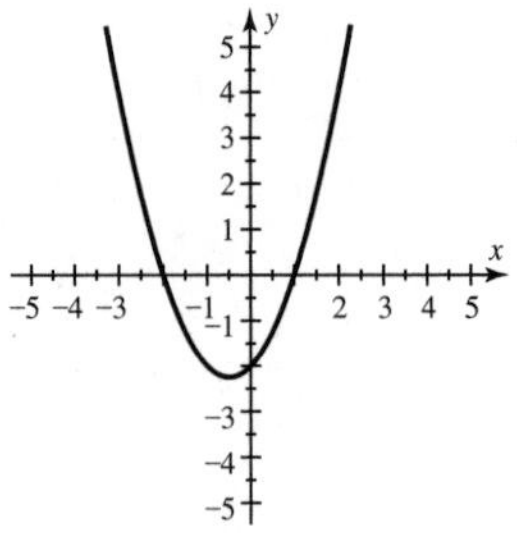

Figure 25

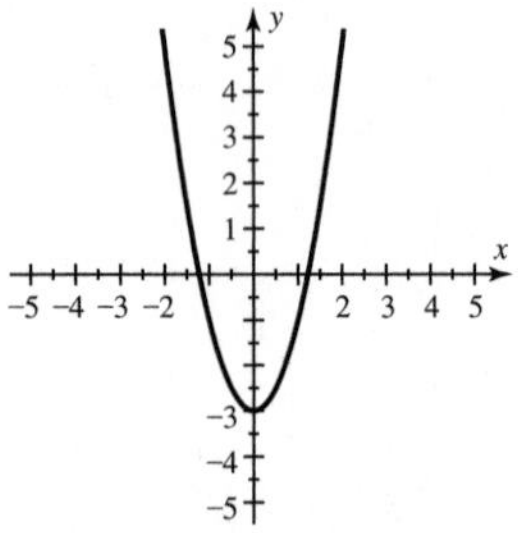

Figure 27

27. (a) See Figure 27.

(b) The vertex is $(0, -3)$. The axis of symmetry is $x = 0$.

(c) $f(-2) = 2(-2)^2 - 3 = 8 - 3 = 5$ and $f(3) = 2(3)^2 - 3 = 18 - 3 = 15$

29. (a) See Figure 29.

(b) The vertex is $(1, 1)$. The axis of symmetry is $x = 1$.

(c) $f(-2) = 2(-2) - (-2)^2 = -4 - 4 = -8$ and $f(3) = 2(3) - (3)^2 = 6 - 9 = -3$

31. (a) See Figure 31.

(b) The vertex is $(1, 1)$. The axis of symmetry is $x = 1$.

(c) $f(-2) = -2(-2)^2 + 4(-2) - 1 = -8 - 8 - 1 = -17$ and $f(3) = -2(3)^2 + 4(3) - 1 = -18 + 12 - 1 = -7$

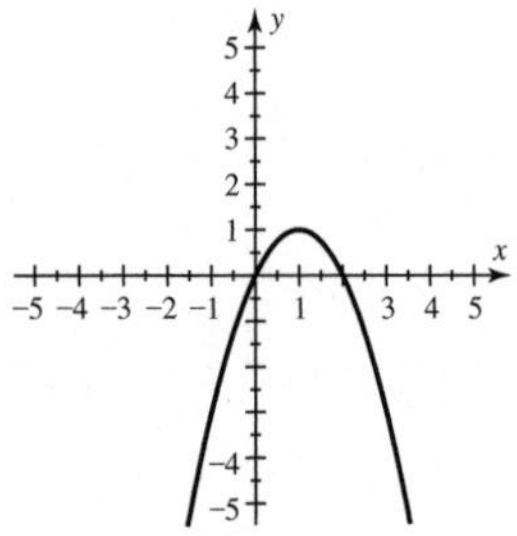

Figure 29

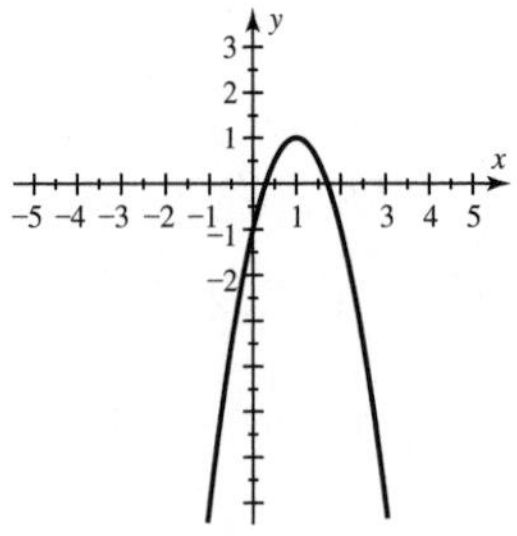

Figure 31

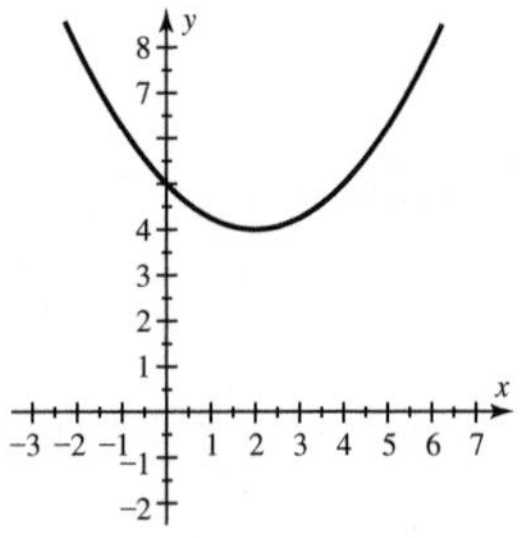

Figure 33

33. (a) See Figure 33.

(b) The vertex is $(2, 4)$. The axis of symmetry is $x = 2$.

(c) $f(-2) = \frac{1}{4}(-2)^2 - (-2) + 5 = 1 + 2 + 5 = 8$ and $f(3) = \frac{1}{4}(3)^2 - (3) + 5 = 2.25 - 3 + 5 = 4.25$

35. $x = -\frac{b}{2a} = -\frac{(-4)}{2(1)} = 2, f(2) = (2)^2 - 4(2) - 2 = 4 - 8 - 2 = -6$; The vertex is $(2, -6)$.

37. $x = -\frac{b}{2a} = -\frac{(-2)}{2(-\frac{1}{3})} = -3, f(-3) = -\frac{1}{3}(-3)^2 - 2(-3) + 1 = -3 + 6 + 1 = 4$; The vertex is $(-3, 4)$.

39. $x = -\frac{b}{2a} = -\frac{(0)}{2(-2)} = 0, f(0) = 3 - 2(0)^2 = 3 - 0 = 3$; The vertex is $(0, 3)$.

41. $x = -\frac{b}{2a} = -\frac{(0.6)}{2(-0.3)} = 1, f(1) = -0.3(1)^2 + 0.6(1) + 1.1 = -0.3 + 0.6 + 1.1 = 1.4$; The vertex is $(1, 1.4)$.

43. See Figure 43. Compared to $y = x^2$, the graph is reflected across the x-axis.

45. See Figure 45. Compared to $y = x^2$, the graph is narrower.

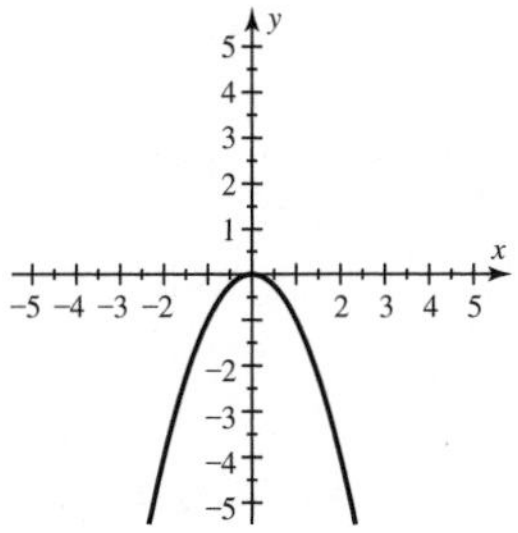

Figure 43

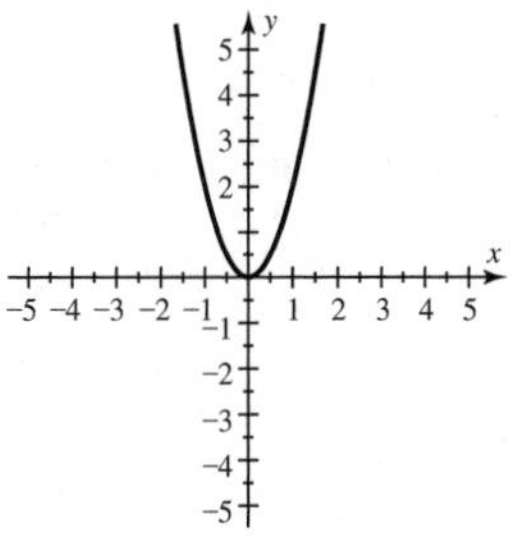

Figure 45

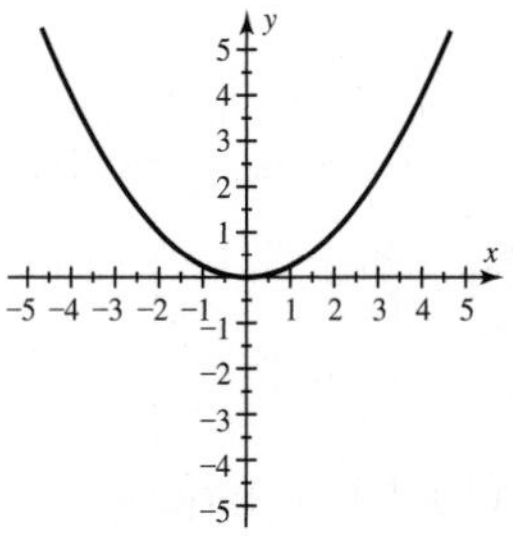

Figure 47

47. See Figure 47. Compared to $y = x^2$, the graph is wider.

49. See Figure 49. Compared to $y = x^2$, the graph is reflected across the x-axis and is wider.

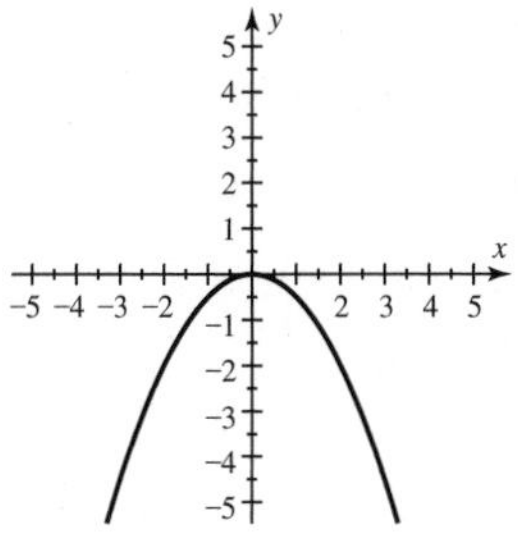

Figure 49

51. Because $-\frac{b}{2a} = -\frac{2}{2(1)} = -1$ and $f(-1) = (-1)^2 + 2(-1) - 1 = -2$, the vertex is $(-1, -2)$.

The minimum y-value on the graph is -2. The graph is increasing when $x \geq -1$ and decreasing when $x \leq -1$.

53. Because $-\frac{b}{2a} = -\frac{-5}{2(1)} = \frac{5}{2}$ and $f\left(\frac{5}{2}\right) = \left(\frac{5}{2}\right)^2 - 5\left(\frac{5}{2}\right) = -\frac{25}{4}$, the vertex is $\left(\frac{5}{2}, -\frac{25}{4}\right)$.

The minimum y-value on the graph is $-\frac{25}{4}$. The graph is increasing when $x \geq \frac{5}{2}$ and decreasing when $x \leq \frac{5}{2}$.

55. Because $-\frac{b}{2a} = -\frac{2}{2(2)} = -\frac{1}{2}$ and $f\left(-\frac{1}{2}\right) = 2\left(-\frac{1}{2}\right)^2 + 2\left(-\frac{1}{2}\right) - 3 = -\frac{7}{2}$, the vertex is $\left(-\frac{1}{2}, -\frac{7}{2}\right)$.

The minimum y-value on the graph is $-\frac{7}{2}$. The graph is increasing when $x \geq -\frac{1}{2}$ and decreasing when $x \leq -\frac{1}{2}$.

57. Because $-\frac{b}{2a} = -\frac{2}{2(-1)} = 1$ and $f(1) = -(1)^2 + 2(1) + 5 = 6$, the vertex is $(1, 6)$.

The maximum y-value on the graph is 6. The graph is increasing when $x \leq 1$ and decreasing when $x \geq 1$.

59. Because $-\dfrac{b}{2a} = -\dfrac{4}{2(-1)} = 2$ and $f(2) = 4(2) - (2)^2 = 4$, the vertex is $(2, 4)$.

The maximum y-value on the graph is 4. The graph is increasing when $x \le 2$ and decreasing when $x \ge 2$.

61. Because $-\dfrac{b}{2a} = -\dfrac{1}{2(-2)} = \dfrac{1}{4}$ and $f\left(\dfrac{1}{4}\right) = -2\left(\dfrac{1}{4}\right)^2 + \left(\dfrac{1}{4}\right) - 5 = -\dfrac{39}{8}$, the vertex is $\left(\dfrac{1}{4}, -\dfrac{39}{8}\right)$.

The maximum y-value on the graph is $-\dfrac{39}{8}$. The graph is increasing when $x \le \dfrac{1}{4}$ and decreasing when $x \ge \dfrac{1}{4}$.

Applications

63. d. The stone's distance from the ground would increase and then decrease.

65. a. The temperature would first decrease but after the repair, it would increase.

67. (a) When the ball is hit, $t = 0$. Then $h(0) = -16(0)^2 + 64(0) + 2 = 2$ feet.

(b) Find the x-coordinate of the vertex. $-\dfrac{b}{2a} = -\dfrac{64}{2(-16)} = 2$ seconds

(c) Find the y-coordinate of the vertex. $h(2) = -16(2)^2 + 64(2) + 2 = 66$ feet.

69. The x-coordinate of the vertex represents the time when the ball reaches its maximum height. Here we have $x = \dfrac{-b}{2a} = \dfrac{-66}{2(-16)} = \dfrac{66}{32} \approx 2$ seconds. The maximum height is $h(2) = -16(2)^2 + 66(2) + 6 \approx 74$ feet.

71. (a) The revenue is increasing when $x \le 50$, and it is decreasing when $x \ge 50$.

(b) From the graph, the maximum revenue is \$2500 when 50 tickets are sold.

(c) If x represents the number of tickets sold, then $100 - x$ represents the price of one ticket.

The total revenue is given by $f(x) = x(100 - x)$.

(d) The number of tickets that should be sold to maximize revenue is $-\dfrac{b}{2a} = -\dfrac{100}{2(-1)} = 50$.

The maximum revenue is $f(50) = 50(100 - 50) = 50(50) = \$2500$.

73. (a) The other two sides have length $\dfrac{1}{2}(60 - 2x) = 30 - x$. The formula is $f(x) = x(30 - x)$.

(b) The function is $f(x) = -x^2 + 30x$. Since the x-coordinate of the vertex is $x = \dfrac{-b}{2a} = \dfrac{-30}{2(-1)} = 15$, one side has length 15 feet. The other side has length $30 - 15 = 15$ feet. The maximum area is $15(15) = 225$ ft^2 when the pen has dimensions 15×15 feet.

75. (a) Graph $Y_1 = -0.095X^2 + 5.4X - 52.2$ in [20, 40, 5] by [0, 30, 5]. See Figure 75a.

(b) Since the x-coordinate of the vertex is $x \approx 28.4$, the temperature resulting in the greatest height for the melon seedling is about 28.4°C. See Figure 75b.

(c) $x = -\dfrac{b}{2a} = -\dfrac{5.4}{2(-0.095)} \approx 28.4$°C

[20, 40, 5] by [0, 30, 5]

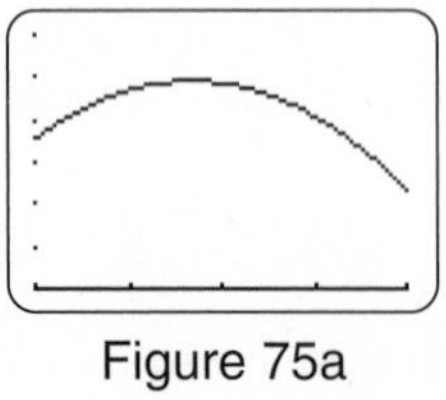

Figure 75a

[20, 40, 5] by [0, 30, 5]

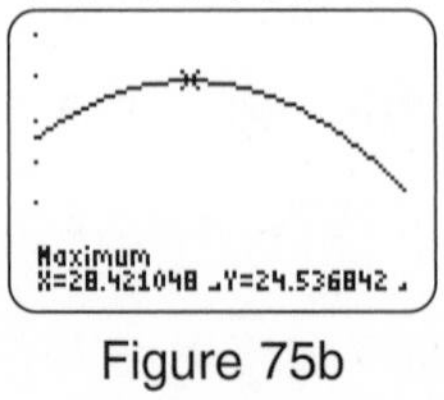

Figure 75b

11.2: Parabolas and Modeling

Concepts

1. $x^2 + 2$

3. $(1, 2)$

5. $f(x) = ax^2 + bx + c$ or $f(x) = a(x - h)^2 + k$

7. downward

Graphs of Parabolas

9. (a) The vertex form of the function is $f(x) = (x - 0)^2 + (-4)$. See Figure 9.

   (b) The vertex is $(0, -4)$.

   (c) Compared to the graph of $y = x^2$, the graph is shifted down 4 units.

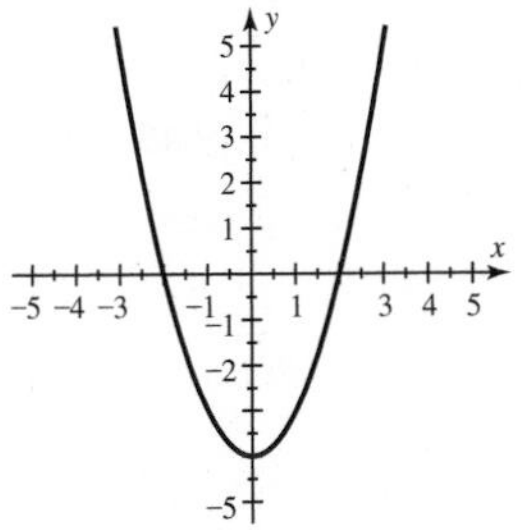

Figure 9

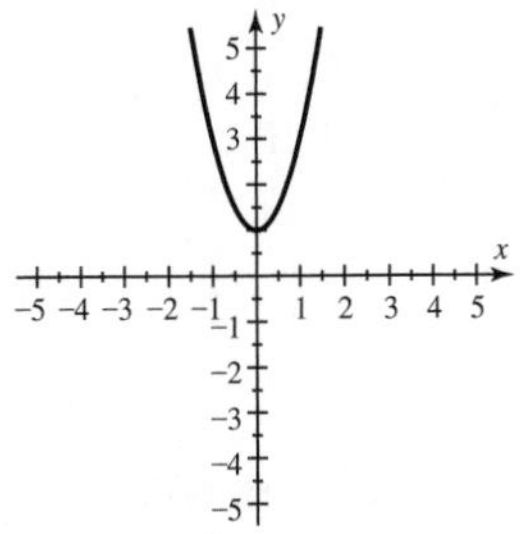

Figure 11

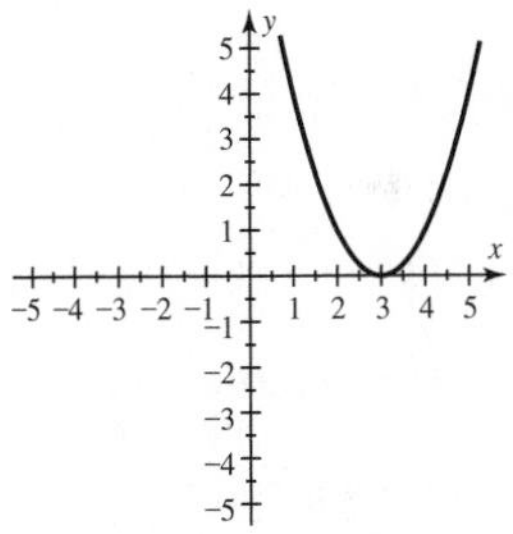

Figure 13

11. (a) The vertex form of the function is $f(x) = 2(x - 0)^2 + 1$. See Figure 11.

    (b) The vertex is $(0, 1)$.

    (c) Compared to the graph of $y = x^2$, the graph is narrower and is shifted up 1 unit.

13. (a) The vertex form of the function is $f(x) = (x - 3)^2 + 0$. See Figure 13.

    (b) The vertex is $(3, 0)$.

    (c) Compared to the graph of $y = x^2$, the graph is shifted right 3 units.

15. (a) The vertex form of the function is $f(x) = -(x - 0)^2 + 0$. See Figure 15.

    (b) The vertex is $(0, 0)$.

    (c) Compared to the graph of $y = x^2$, the graph is reflected across the x-axis.

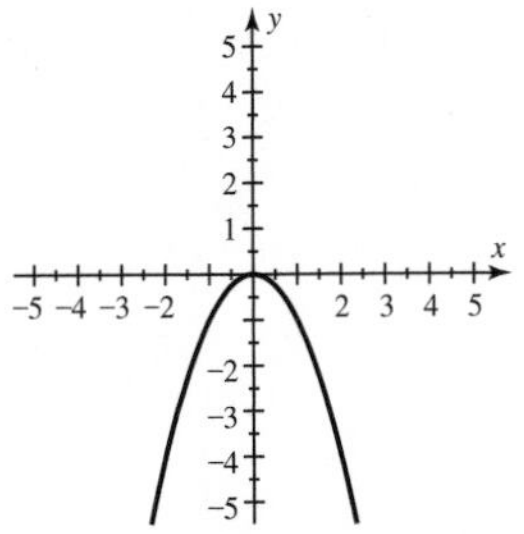

Figure 15

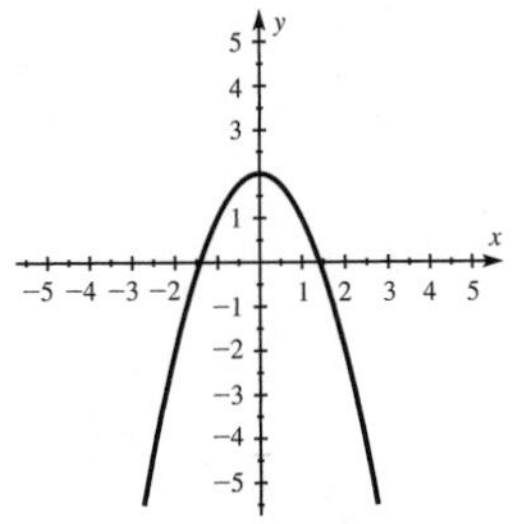

Figure 17

17. (a) The vertex form of the function is $f(x) = -(x - 0)^2 + 2$. See Figure 17.

(b) The vertex is (0, 2).

(c) Compared to the graph of $y = x^2$, the graph is reflected across the x-axis and shifted up 2 units.

19. (a) The vertex form of the function is $f(x) = (x - (-2))^2 + 0$. See Figure 19.

(b) The vertex is (−2, 0).

(c) Compared to the graph of $y = x^2$, the graph is shifted left 2 units.

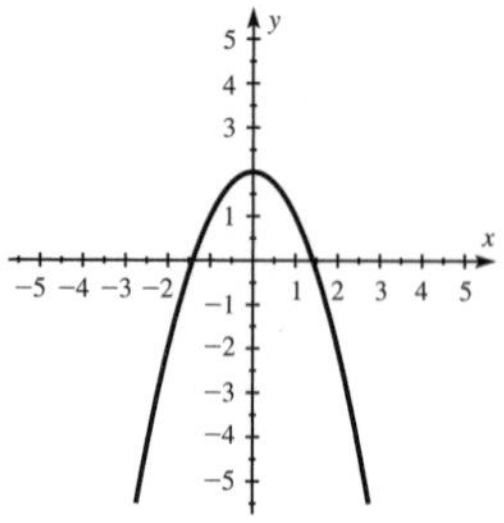

Figure 17

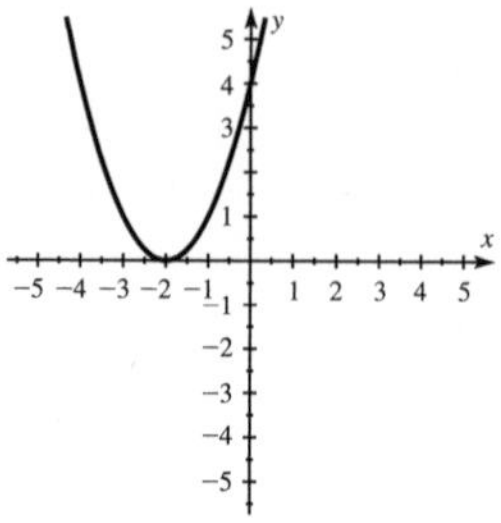

Figure 19

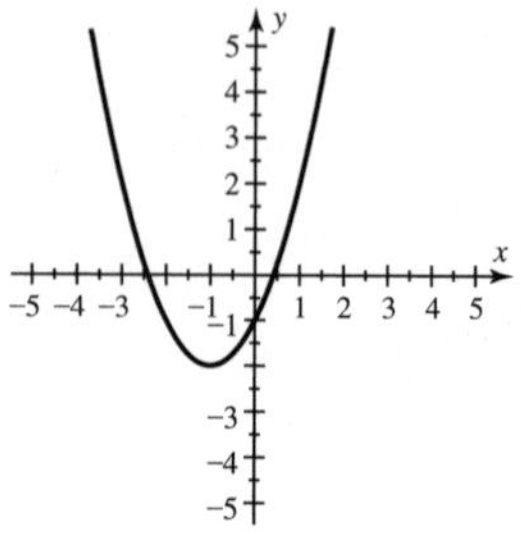

Figure 21

21. (a) The vertex form of the function is $f(x) = (x - (-1))^2 + (-2)$. See Figure 21.

(b) The vertex is (−1, −2).

(c) Compared to the graph of $y = x^2$, the graph is shifted left 1 unit and down 2 units.

23. (a) The vertex form of the function is $f(x) = (x - 1)^2 + 2$. See Figure 23.

(b) The vertex is (1, 2).

(c) Compared to the graph of $y = x^2$, the graph is shifted right 1 unit and up 2 units.

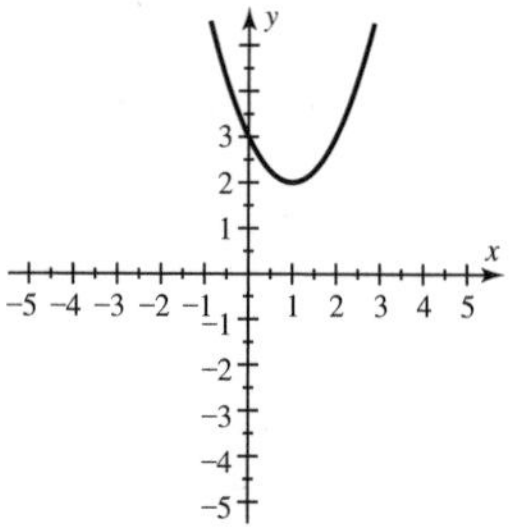

Figure 23

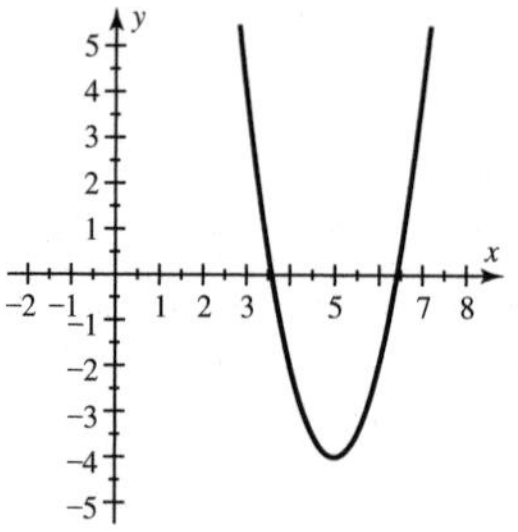

Figure 25

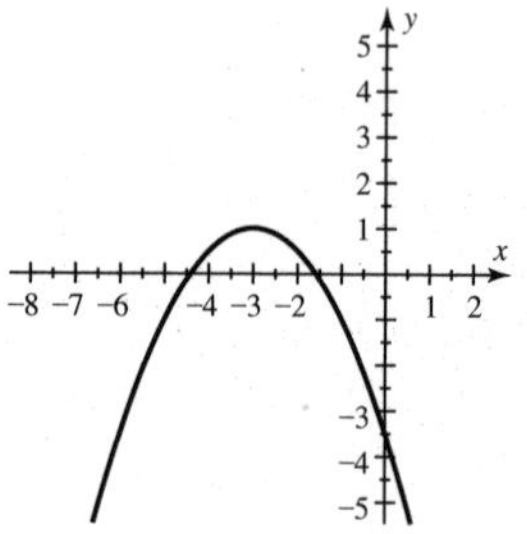

Figure 27

25. (a) The vertex form of the function is $f(x) = 2(x - 5)^2 + (-4)$. See Figure 25.

(b) The vertex is (5, −4).

(c) Compared to the graph of $y = x^2$, the graph is narrower, shifted right 5 units and down 4 units.

27. (a) The vertex form of the function is $f(x) = -\frac{1}{2}(x - (-3))^2 + 1$. See Figure 27.

(b) The vertex is (−3, 1).

(c) Compared to the graph of $y = x^2$, the graph is wider, reflected across the x-axis, left 3 units and up 1 unit.

Vertex Form

29. Since $h = 3$, $k = 4$ and $a = 3$, the equation is $y = 3(x - 3)^2 + 4$. Expand to obtain the other form:

$y = 3(x^2 - 6x + 9) + 4 \Rightarrow y = 3x^2 - 18x + 27 + 4 \Rightarrow y = 3x^2 - 18x + 31$

31. Since $h = 5$, $k = -2$ and $a = -\frac{1}{2}$, the equation is $y = -\frac{1}{2}(x - 5)^2 - 2$. Expand to obtain the other form:

$y = -\frac{1}{2}(x^2 - 10x + 25) - 2 \Rightarrow y = -\frac{1}{2}x^2 + 5x - \frac{25}{2} - 2 \Rightarrow y = -\frac{1}{2}x^2 + 5x - \frac{29}{2}$

33. Since $h = 1$, $k = 2$ and $a = 1$, the equation is $y = (x - 1)^2 + 2$.

35. Since $h = 0$, $k = -3$ and $a = -1$, the equation is $y = -(x - 0)^2 - 3$ or $y = -x^2 - 3$.

37. Since $h = 0$, $k = -3$ and $a = 1$, the equation is $y = (x - 0)^2 - 3$ or $y = x^2 - 3$.

39. Since $h = -1$, $k = 2$ and $a = -1$, the equation is $y = -(x + 1)^2 + 2$.

41. $y = x^2 + 2x - 3 \Rightarrow y = (x^2 + 2x + 1) - 3 - 1 \Rightarrow y = (x + 1)^2 - 4$. The vertex is $(-1, -4)$.

43. $y = x^2 - 4x + 5 \Rightarrow y = (x^2 - 4x + 4) + 5 - 4 \Rightarrow y = (x - 2)^2 + 1$. The vertex is $(2, 1)$.

45. $y = x^2 + 3x - 2 \Rightarrow y = \left(x^2 + 3x + \frac{9}{4}\right) - 2 - \frac{9}{4} \Rightarrow y = \left(x + \frac{3}{2}\right)^2 - \frac{17}{4}$. The vertex is $\left(-\frac{3}{2}, -\frac{17}{4}\right)$.

47. $y = x^2 - 7x + 1 \Rightarrow y = \left(x^2 - 7x + \frac{49}{4}\right) + 1 - \frac{49}{4} \Rightarrow y = \left(x - \frac{7}{2}\right)^2 - \frac{45}{4}$. The vertex is $\left(\frac{7}{2}, -\frac{45}{4}\right)$.

49. $y = 3x^2 + 6x - 1 \Rightarrow y = 3(x^2 + 2x + 1) - 1 - 3 \Rightarrow y = 3(x + 1)^2 - 4$. The vertex is $(-1, -4)$.

51. $y = 2x^2 - 3x \Rightarrow y = 2\left(x^2 - \frac{3}{2}x + \frac{9}{16}\right) - \frac{9}{8} \Rightarrow y = 2\left(x - \frac{3}{4}\right)^2 - \frac{9}{8}$. The vertex is $\left(\frac{3}{4}, -\frac{9}{8}\right)$.

53. $y = -2x^2 - 8x + 5 \Rightarrow y = -2(x^2 + 4x + 4) + 5 + 8 \Rightarrow y = -2(x + 2)^2 + 13$. The vertex is $(-2, 13)$.

Modeling Data

55. Since $y = 2$ when $x = 1$, $2 = a(1)^2 \Rightarrow 2 = 1a \Rightarrow a = 2$.

57. Since $y = 1.2$ when $x = 2$, $1.2 = a(2)^2 \Rightarrow 1.2 = 4a \Rightarrow a = 0.3$.

59. A scatterplot of the data (not shown) indicates that the data point $(1, -3)$ is the vertex of the parabola.

The function has the form $f(x) = a(x - 1)^2 - 3$. By trial and error, $a = 2$. Thus $f(x) = 2(x - 1)^2 - 3$.

61. A scatterplot of the data (not shown) indicates that the data point $(1980, 6)$ is the vertex of the parabola.

The function has the form $f(x) = a(x - 1980)^2 + 6$. By trial and error, $a = 0.5$. So $f(x) = 0.5(x - 1980)^2 + 6$.

63. (a) See Figure 63.

(b) Since $D = 12$ when $x = 12$, we have $12 = a(12)^2 \Rightarrow 12 = 144a \Rightarrow a = \frac{12}{144} \Rightarrow a = \frac{1}{12}$.

The function is $D(x) = \frac{1}{12}x^2$.

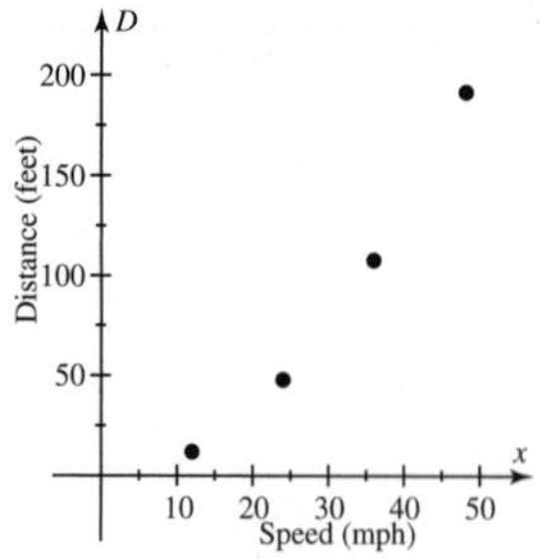

Figure 63

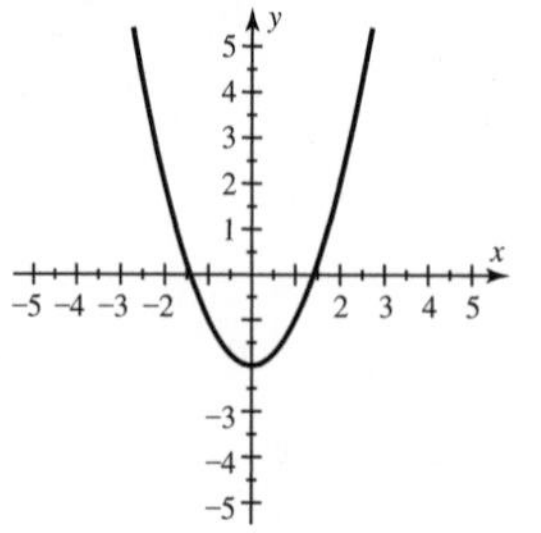
Figure 1a

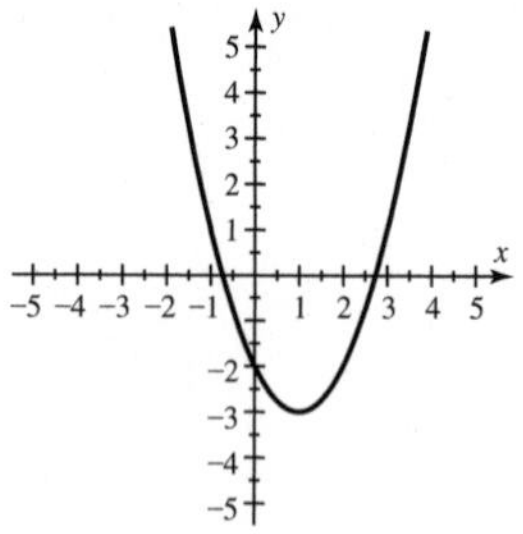
Figure 1b

Checking Basic Concepts for Sections 11.1 & 11.2

1. (a) See Figure 1a. The vertex is $(0, -2)$, and the axis of symmetry is $x = 0$.

   (b) See Figure 1b. The vertex is $(1, -3)$, and the axis of symmetry is $x = 1$.

2. The graph of y_1 opens upward whereas y_2 opens downward. Also, y_1 is narrower than y_2.

3. Because $-\frac{b}{2a} = -\frac{12}{2(-3)} = 2$ and $f(2) = -3(2)^2 + 12(2) - 5 = 7$, the vertex is $(2, 7)$.

   The maximum y-value on the graph is 7. The graph is increasing when $x \le 2$ and decreasing when $x \ge 2$.

4. (a) See Figure 4a. Compared to the graph of $y = x^2$, the graph is shifted right 1 unit and up 2 units.

   (b) See Figure 4b. Compared to the graph of $y = x^2$, the graph is reflected across the x-axis and left 3 units.

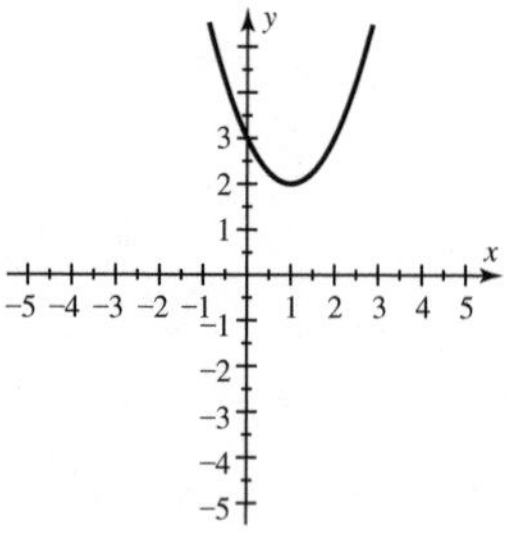
Figure 4a

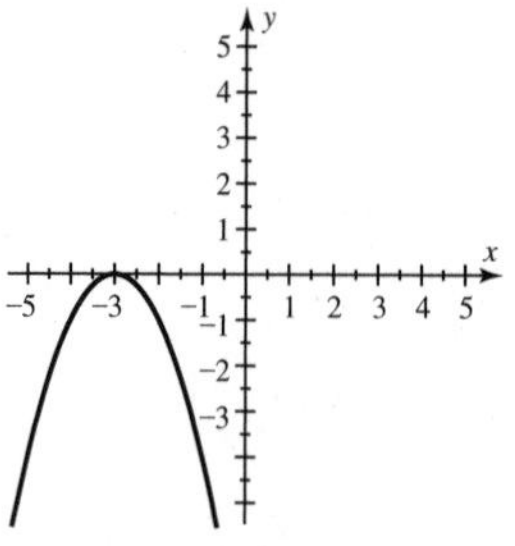
Figure 4b

5. (a) $y = x^2 + 14x - 7 \Rightarrow y = (x^2 + 14x + 49) - 7 - 49 \Rightarrow y = (x + 7)^2 - 56$.

   (b) $y = 4x^2 + 8x - 2 \Rightarrow y = 4(x^2 + 2x + 1) - 2 - 4 \Rightarrow y = 4(x + 1)^2 - 6$.

11.3: Quadratic Equations

Concepts

1. $x^2 + 3x - 2 = 0$; *Answers may vary.* A quadratic equation can have 0, 1 or 2 solutions.

3. Factoring, square root property, completing the square

5. See Figure 5. *Answers may vary.*

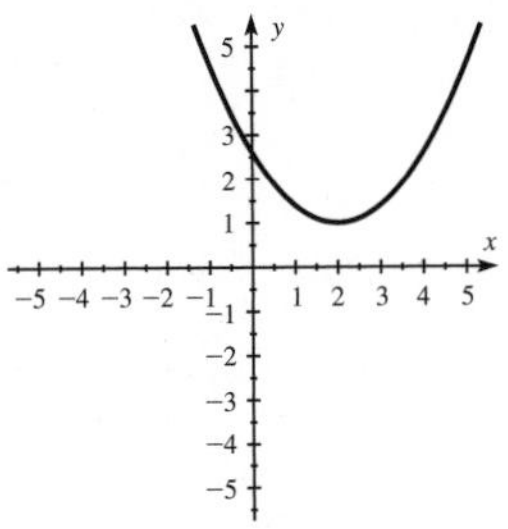

Figure 5

7. $x = \pm 8$; the square root property.

9. Yes

11. No, there is no x^2 term.

13. Yes

15. No, the term $\sqrt{x}$ is not allowed in a quadratic equation.

Solving Quadratic Equations

17. –2, 1

19. No real solutions.

21. –2, 3

23. –0.5

25. $x^2 - 4x - 5 = 0 \Rightarrow (x + 1)(x - 5) = 0 \Rightarrow x + 1 = 0$ or $x - 5 = 0 \Rightarrow x = -1$ or 5

A graph of $y = x^2 - 4x - 5$ (not shown) intersects the x-axis at -1 and 5.

27. $x^2 + 2x = 3 \Rightarrow x^2 + 2x - 3 = 0 \Rightarrow (x + 3)(x - 1) = 0 \Rightarrow x + 3 = 0$ or $x - 1 = 0 \Rightarrow x = -3$ or 1

A graph of $y = x^2 + 2x - 3$ (not shown) intersects the x-axis at -3 and 1.

29. $x^2 = 9 \Rightarrow x^2 - 9 = 0 \Rightarrow (x + 3)(x - 3) = 0 \Rightarrow x + 3 = 0$ or $x - 3 = 0 \Rightarrow x = -3$ or 3

A graph of $y = x^2 - 9$ (not shown) intersects the x-axis at -3 and 3.

31. $4x^2 - 4x - 3 = 0 \Rightarrow (2x + 1)(2x - 3) = 0 \Rightarrow 2x + 1 = 0$ or $2x - 3 = 0 \Rightarrow x = -\frac{1}{2}$ or $\frac{3}{2}$

A graph of $y = 4x^2 - 4x - 3$ (not shown) intersects the x-axis at $-\frac{1}{2}$ and $\frac{3}{2}$.

33. $x^2 + 2x - 35 = 0 \Rightarrow (x + 7)(x - 5) = 0 \Rightarrow$ Either $x + 7 = 0 \Rightarrow x = -7$ or $x - 5 = 0 \Rightarrow x = 5$

35. $6x^2 - x - 1 = 0 \Rightarrow (3x + 1)(2x - 1) = 0 \Rightarrow$ Either $3x + 1 = 0 \Rightarrow x = -\frac{1}{3}$ or $2x - 1 = 0 \Rightarrow x = \frac{1}{2}$

37. $2x^2 - 5x + 3 = 0 \Rightarrow (x - 1)(2x - 3) = 0 \Rightarrow$ Either $x - 1 = 0 \Rightarrow x = 1$ or $2x - 3 = 0 \Rightarrow x = \frac{3}{2}$

39. $10x^2 - 27x + 18 = 0 \Rightarrow (5x - 6)(2x - 3) = 0 \Rightarrow$ Either $5x - 6 = 0 \Rightarrow x = \frac{6}{5}$ or $2x - 3 = 0 \Rightarrow x = \frac{3}{2}$

41. $x^2 = 144 \Rightarrow x = \pm\sqrt{144} \Rightarrow x = \pm 12$

43. $5x^2 - 64 = 0 \Rightarrow 5x^2 = 64 \Rightarrow x^2 = \frac{64}{5} \Rightarrow x = \pm\sqrt{\frac{64}{5}} \Rightarrow x = \pm\frac{8}{\sqrt{5}}$

45. $(x + 1)^2 = 25 \Rightarrow x + 1 = \pm\sqrt{25} \Rightarrow x + 1 = \pm 5 \Rightarrow x = -1 \pm 5 \Rightarrow x = -6$ or 4

47. $(x - 1)^2 = 64 \Rightarrow x - 1 = \pm\sqrt{64} \Rightarrow x - 1 = \pm 8 \Rightarrow x = 1 \pm 8 \Rightarrow x = -7$ or 9

49. $(2x - 1)^2 = 5 \Rightarrow 2x - 1 = \pm\sqrt{5} \Rightarrow 2x = 1 \pm \sqrt{5} \Rightarrow x = \frac{1 \pm \sqrt{5}}{2}$

Completing the Square

51. $\left(\frac{4}{2}\right)^2 = 2^2 = 4$

53. $\left(\frac{-5}{2}\right)^2 = \frac{25}{4}$

55. The term needed to complete the square is $\left(\frac{-8}{2}\right)^2 = (-4)^2 = 16$. The resulting perfect square is $(x - 4)^2$.

57. The term needed to complete the square is $\left(\frac{9}{2}\right)^2 = \frac{81}{4}$. The resulting perfect square is $\left(x + \frac{9}{2}\right)^2$.

59. $x^2 - 2x = 24 \Rightarrow x^2 - 2x + 1 = 24 + 1 \Rightarrow (x - 1)^2 = 25 \Rightarrow x - 1 = \pm\sqrt{25} \Rightarrow x - 1 = \pm 5 \Rightarrow$
$x = 1 \pm 5 \Rightarrow x = -4$ or 6

61. $x^2 + 6x - 2 = 0 \Rightarrow x^2 + 6x + 9 = 2 + 9 \Rightarrow (x + 3)^2 = 11 \Rightarrow x + 3 = \pm\sqrt{11} \Rightarrow x = -3 \pm \sqrt{11}$

63. $x^2 - 3x = 5 \Rightarrow x^2 - 3x + \frac{9}{4} = 5 + \frac{9}{4} \Rightarrow \left(x - \frac{3}{2}\right)^2 = \frac{29}{4} \Rightarrow x - \frac{3}{2} = \pm\sqrt{\frac{29}{4}} \Rightarrow$
$x = \frac{3}{2} \pm \frac{\sqrt{29}}{2} = \frac{3 \pm \sqrt{29}}{2}$

65. $x^2 - 5x + 1 = 0 \Rightarrow x^2 - 5x = -1 \Rightarrow x^2 - 5x + \frac{25}{4} = -1 + \frac{25}{4} \Rightarrow \left(x - \frac{5}{2}\right)^2 = \frac{21}{4} \Rightarrow$
$x - \frac{5}{2} = \pm\sqrt{\frac{21}{4}} \Rightarrow x = \frac{5}{2} \pm \frac{\sqrt{21}}{2} = \frac{5 \pm \sqrt{21}}{2}$

67. $x^2 - 4 = 2x \Rightarrow x^2 - 2x = 4 \Rightarrow x^2 - 2x + 1 = 4 + 1 \Rightarrow (x - 1)^2 = 5 \Rightarrow x - 1 = \pm\sqrt{5} \Rightarrow$
$x = 1 \pm \sqrt{5}$

69. $2x^2 - 3x = 4 \Rightarrow x^2 - \frac{3}{2}x = 2 \Rightarrow x^2 - \frac{3}{2}x + \frac{9}{16} = 2 + \frac{9}{16} \Rightarrow \left(x - \frac{3}{4}\right)^2 = \frac{41}{16} \Rightarrow x - \frac{3}{4} = \pm\sqrt{\frac{41}{16}} \Rightarrow$
$x = \frac{3}{4} \pm \frac{\sqrt{41}}{4} = \frac{3 \pm \sqrt{41}}{4}$

71. $4x^2 - 8x - 7 = 0 \Rightarrow x^2 - 2x - \frac{7}{4} = 0 \Rightarrow x^2 - 2x + 1 = \frac{7}{4} + 1 \Rightarrow (x - 1)^2 = \frac{11}{4} \Rightarrow$
$x - 1 = \pm\sqrt{\frac{11}{4}} \Rightarrow x = 1 \pm \frac{\sqrt{11}}{2} \Rightarrow x = \frac{2 \pm \sqrt{11}}{2}$

73. $36x^2 + 18x + 1 = 0 \Rightarrow 36\left(x^2 + \frac{1}{2}x + \frac{1}{16}\right) = -1 + \frac{36}{16} \Rightarrow 36\left(x + \frac{1}{4}\right)^2 = \frac{20}{16} \Rightarrow$
$\left(x + \frac{1}{4}\right)^2 = \frac{20}{576} \Rightarrow x + \frac{1}{4} = \pm\sqrt{\frac{20}{576}} \Rightarrow x = -\frac{1}{4} \pm \frac{\sqrt{20}}{24} = \frac{-6 \pm 2\sqrt{5}}{24} = \frac{-3 \pm \sqrt{5}}{12}$

Solving Equations by More Than One Method

75. (a) $x^2 - 3x - 18 = 0 \Rightarrow (x + 3)(x - 6) = 0 \Rightarrow$ Either $x + 3 = 0 \Rightarrow x = -3$ or $x - 6 = 0 \Rightarrow x = 6$

(b) Graph $Y_1 = X^2 - 3X - 18$ in [–5, 8, 1] by [–25, 5, 5]. See Figures 75a & 75b.

The solutions are the x-intercepts, $x = -3$ or $x = 6$.

(c) Table $Y_1 = X^2 - 3X - 18$ with TblStart = –6 and ΔTbl = 3. See Figure 75c.

Since $Y_1 = 0$ when $x = -3$ or when $x = 6$, the solutions are $x = -3$ or $x = 6$.

[–5, 8, 1] by [–25, 5, 5]

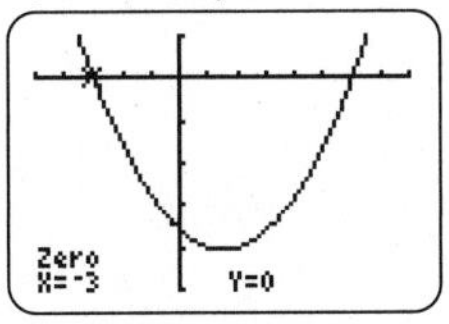

Figure 75a

[–5, 8, 1] by [–25, 5, 5]

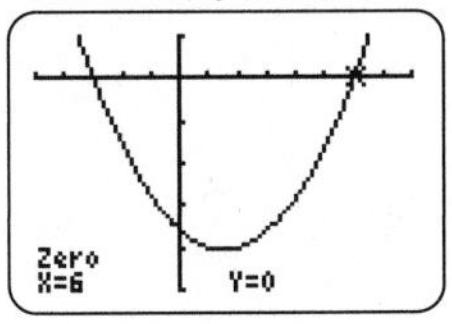

Figure 75b

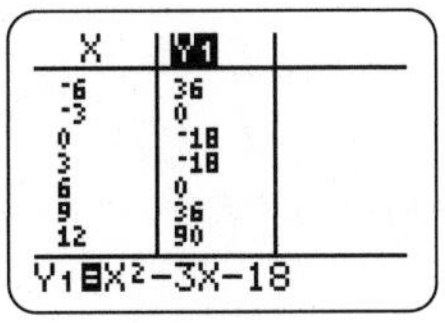

Figure 75c

77. (a) $x^2 - 8x + 15 = 0 \Rightarrow (x - 3)(x - 5) = 0 \Rightarrow$ Either $x - 3 = 0 \Rightarrow x = 3$ or $x - 5 = 0 \Rightarrow x = 5$

(b) Graph $Y_1 = X^2 - 8X + 15$ in [–10, 0, 1] by [–5, 10, 1]. See Figures 77a & 77b.

The solutions are the x-intercepts, $x = 3$ or $x = 5$.

(c) Table $Y_1 = X^2 - 8X + 15$ with TblStart = 1 and ΔTbl = 1. See Figure 77c.

Since $Y_1 = 0$ when $x = 3$ or when $x = 5$, the solutions are $x = 3$ or $x = 5$.

[–10, 0, 1] by [–5, 10, 1]

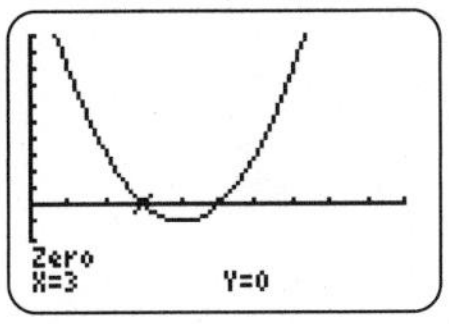

Figure 77a

[–10, 0, 1] by [–5, 10, 1]

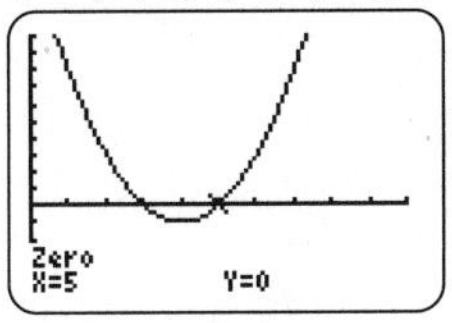

Figure 77b

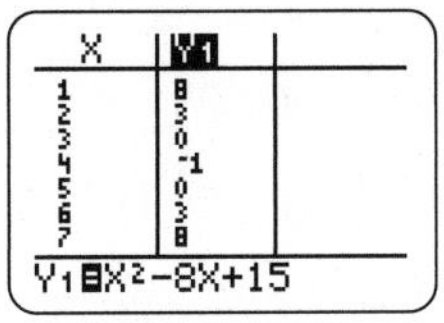

Figure 77c

79. (a) $4(x^2 + 35) = 48x \Rightarrow x^2 + 35 = 12x \Rightarrow x^2 - 12x + 35 = 0 \Rightarrow (x - 5)(x - 7) = 0 \Rightarrow$

Either $x - 5 = 0 \Rightarrow x = 5$ or $x - 7 = 0 \Rightarrow x = 7$

(b) Graph $Y_1 = 4(X^2 + 35) - 48X$ in [–2, 10, 1] by [–6, 6, 1]. See Figures 79a & 79b.

The solutions are the x-intercepts, $x = 5$ or $x = 7$.

(c) Table $Y_1 = 4(X^2 + 35) - 48X$ with TblStart = 3 and ΔTbl = 1. See Figure 79c.

Since $Y_1 = 0$ when $x = 5$ or when $x = 7$, the solutions are $x = 5$ or $x = 7$.

[–3, 3, 1] by [–3, 3, 1]

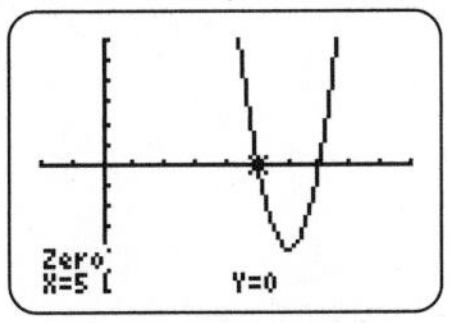

Figure 79a

[–3, 3, 1] by [–3, 3, 1]

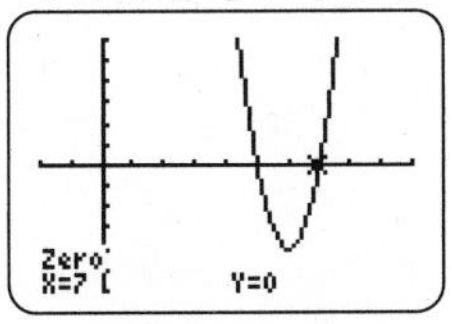

Figure 79b

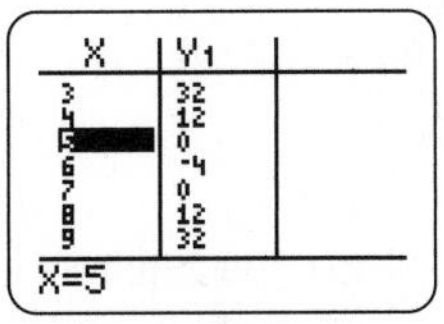

Figure 79c

Solving an Equation for a Variable

81. $x = y^2 - 1 \Rightarrow x + 1 = y^2 \Rightarrow \pm\sqrt{x+1} = y \Rightarrow y = \pm\sqrt{x+1}$

83. $K = \frac{1}{2}mv^2 \Rightarrow 2K = mv^2 \Rightarrow \frac{2K}{m} = v^2 \Rightarrow \pm\sqrt{\frac{2K}{m}} = v \Rightarrow v = \pm\sqrt{\frac{2K}{m}}$

85. $E = \frac{k}{r^2} \Rightarrow Er^2 = k \Rightarrow r^2 = \frac{k}{E} \Rightarrow r = \pm\sqrt{\frac{k}{E}}$

87. $LC = \frac{1}{(2\pi f)^2} \Rightarrow 4\pi^2 f^2 LC = 1 \Rightarrow f^2 = \frac{1}{4\pi^2 LC} \Rightarrow f = \pm\sqrt{\frac{1}{4\pi^2 LC}} \Rightarrow f = \pm\frac{1}{2\pi\sqrt{LC}}$

Applications

89. (a) $\frac{1}{2}x^2 = 450 \Rightarrow x^2 = 900 \Rightarrow x = \pm\sqrt{900} \Rightarrow x = 30$ mph ($x = -30$ has no physical meaning)

(b) $\frac{1}{2}x^2 = 800 \Rightarrow x^2 = 1600 \Rightarrow x = \pm\sqrt{1600} \Rightarrow x = 40$ mph ($x = -40$ has no physical meaning)

91. $60 - 16t^2 = 0 \Rightarrow -16t^2 = -60 \Rightarrow t^2 = \frac{60}{16} \Rightarrow t = \pm\sqrt{\frac{60}{16}} \Rightarrow t = \frac{\sqrt{60}}{4} \approx 1.9$ seconds. The value $t \approx -1.9$ seconds has no physical meaning. The toy takes about 1.9 seconds to hit he ground. This is not twice the time it takes to fall from a height of 30 feet.

93. Let x represent the number of hours the athletes run. The athletes are running along the legs of a right triangle. The distance between them is given by the length of the hypotenuse. One athlete runs $6x$ miles while the other runs $8x$ miles. By the Pythagorean Theorem we have the following

$(6x)^2 + (8x)^2 = 20^2 \Rightarrow 36x^2 + 64x^2 = 400 \Rightarrow 100x^2 = 400 \Rightarrow x^2 = 4 \Rightarrow x = \pm 2.$

The athletes are 20 miles apart after 2 hours.

95. (a) Let x represent the width of the lot. Then $x + 6$ represents the length. So $x(x + 6) = 520$.

The quadratic equation is $x^2 + 6x - 520 = 0$.

(b) $x^2 + 6x - 520 = 0 \Rightarrow (x + 26)(x - 20) = 0 \Rightarrow x = -26$ or 20

Since the value -26 has no physical meaning, the width is 20 feet.

97. The height of the seedling was about 22 centimeters when the temperature was about 23°C and 34°C.

99. (a) The rate of increase each 20-year period is not constant.

(b) The vertex is (1800, 5). In 1800 the population was 5 million.

(c) $0.0066(x - 1800)^2 + 5 = 85 \Rightarrow 0.0066(x - 1800)^2 = 80 \Rightarrow (x - 1800)^2 \approx 12{,}121 \Rightarrow$

$x - 1800 \approx \sqrt{12{,}121} \Rightarrow x - 1800 \approx 110 \Rightarrow x \approx 1910$. The population was 85 million in 1910.

11.4: The Quadratic Formula

Concepts

1. We use the quadratic formula to solve equations of the form $ax^2 + bx + c = 0$.

3. $b^2 - 4ac$

5. Factoring, square root property, completing the square and the quadratic formula.

The Quadratic Formula

7. $x = \dfrac{-11 \pm \sqrt{(11)^2 - 4(2)(-6)}}{2(2)} = \dfrac{-11 \pm \sqrt{169}}{4} = \dfrac{-11 \pm 13}{4} \Rightarrow x = -6 \text{ or } x = \dfrac{1}{2}$

Graph $Y_1 = 2X^2 + 11X - 6$ in [–10, 5, 1] by [–25, 10, 5]. See Figures 7a & 7b. $x = -6$ or $x = \dfrac{1}{2}$

Table $Y_1 = 2X^2 + 11X - 6$ with TblStart = –7.3 and ΔTbl = 1.3. See Figure 7c. $x = -6$ or $x = \dfrac{1}{2}$

[–10, 5, 1] by [–25, 10, 5]

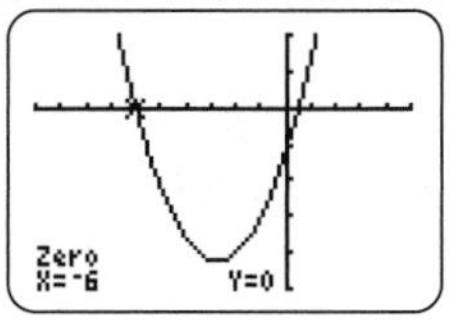

Figure 7a

[–10, 5, 1] by [–25, 10, 5]

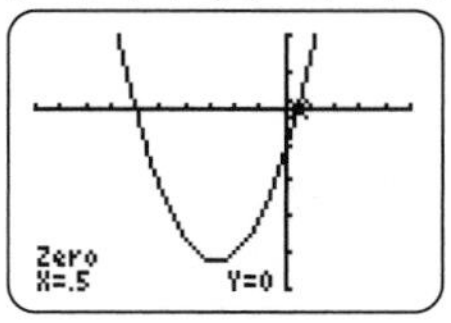

Figure 7b

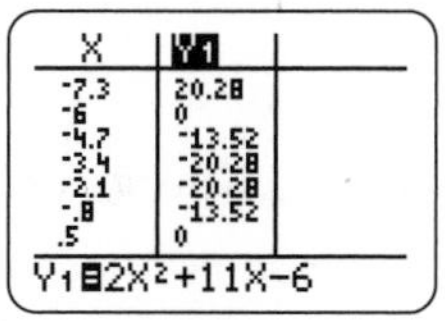

X	Y1
-7.3	20.28
-6	0
-4.7	-13.52
-3.4	-20.28
-2.1	-20.28
-.8	-13.52
.5	0

Y1■2X²+11X-6

Figure 7c

9. $x = \dfrac{-2 \pm \sqrt{(2)^2 - 4(-1)(-1)}}{2(-1)} = \dfrac{-2 \pm \sqrt{0}}{-2} = \dfrac{-2}{-2} \Rightarrow x = 1$

Graph $Y_1 = -X^2 + 2X - 1$ in [–5, 5, 1] by [–5, 5, 1]. See Figure 9a. $x = 1$

Table $Y_1 = -X^2 + 2X - 1$ with TblStart = –2 and ΔTbl = 1. See Figure 9b. $x = 1$

[–5, 5, 1] by [–5, 5, 1]

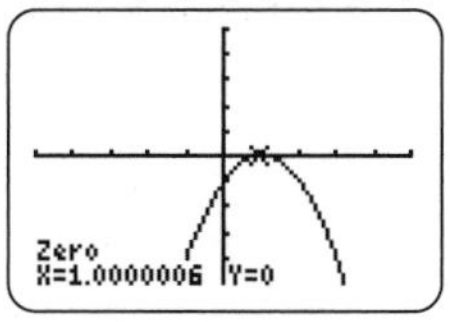

Figure 9a

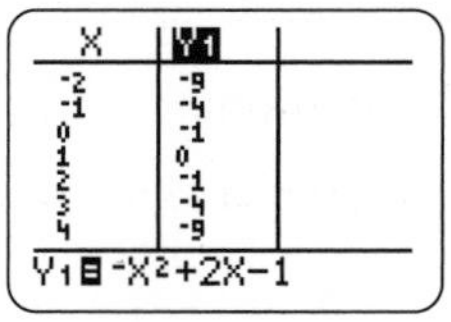

X	Y1
-2	-9
-1	-4
0	-1
1	0
2	-1
3	-4
4	-9

Y1■-X²+2X-1

Figure 9b

11. $x = \dfrac{-(-6) \pm \sqrt{(-6)^2 - 4(1)(-16)}}{2(1)} = \dfrac{6 \pm \sqrt{100}}{2} = \dfrac{6 \pm 10}{2} \Rightarrow x = -2 \text{ or } x = 8$

13. $x = \dfrac{-(-1) \pm \sqrt{(-1)^2 - 4(4)(-1)}}{2(4)} = \dfrac{1 \pm \sqrt{17}}{8}$

15. $x = \dfrac{-2 \pm \sqrt{(2)^2 - 4(-3)(-1)}}{2(-3)} = \dfrac{-2 \pm \sqrt{-8}}{-6} \Rightarrow$ No real solutions.

17. $x = \dfrac{-(-36) \pm \sqrt{(-36)^2 - 4(36)(9)}}{2(36)} = \dfrac{36 \pm \sqrt{0}}{72} = \dfrac{36}{72} = \dfrac{1}{2}$

19. $x = \dfrac{-(-6) \pm \sqrt{(-6)^2 - 4(2)(-2)}}{2(2)} = \dfrac{6 \pm \sqrt{52}}{4} = \dfrac{6 \pm 2\sqrt{13}}{4} = \dfrac{2(3 \pm \sqrt{13})}{2(2)} = \dfrac{3 \pm \sqrt{13}}{2}$

21. $x = \dfrac{-(-4) \pm \sqrt{(-4)^2 - 4(1)(1)}}{2(1)} = \dfrac{4 \pm \sqrt{12}}{2} = \dfrac{4 \pm 2\sqrt{3}}{2} = \dfrac{2(2 \pm \sqrt{3})}{2} = 2 \pm \sqrt{3}$

23. $x = \dfrac{-(-\frac{1}{2}) \pm \sqrt{(-\frac{1}{2})^2 - 4(\frac{3}{2})(-\frac{3}{2})}}{2(\frac{3}{2})} = \dfrac{\frac{1}{2} \pm \sqrt{\frac{37}{4}}}{3} = \dfrac{\frac{1}{2} \pm \frac{\sqrt{37}}{2}}{3} = \dfrac{1 \pm \sqrt{37}}{6}$

25. $x = \dfrac{-(-2) \pm \sqrt{(-2)^2 - 4(2)(-7)}}{2(2)} = \dfrac{2 \pm \sqrt{60}}{4} = \dfrac{2 \pm 2\sqrt{15}}{4} = \dfrac{2(1 \pm \sqrt{15})}{4} = \dfrac{1 \pm \sqrt{15}}{2}$

27. $x = \dfrac{-10 \pm \sqrt{(10)^2 - 4(-3)(-5)}}{2(-3)} = \dfrac{-10 \pm \sqrt{40}}{-6} = \dfrac{-10 \pm 2\sqrt{10}}{-6} = \dfrac{-2(5 \pm \sqrt{10})}{-6} = \dfrac{5 \pm \sqrt{10}}{3}$

The Discriminant

29. (a) Since the parabola opens upward, $a > 0$.

(b) The solutions are the x-intercepts, $x = -1$ or $x = 2$

(c) Since there are two real solutions, the discriminant is positive.

31. (a) Since the parabola opens upward, $a > 0$.

(b) Since there are no x-intercepts, there are no real solutions.

(c) Since there are no real solutions, the discriminant is negative.

33. (a) Since the parabola opens downward, $a < 0$.

(b) The solution is the x-intercept, $x = 2$

(c) Since there is one real solution, the discriminant is zero.

35. (a) $(1)^2 - 4(3)(-2) = 25$

(b) Since the discriminant is positive, there are two real solutions.

(c) Graph $Y_1 = 3X^2 + X - 2$ in [−3, 3, 1] by [−3, 3, 1]. See Figure 35. There are two x-intercepts.

37. (a) $(-4)^2 - 4(1)(4) = 0$

(b) Since the discriminant is zero, there is only one real solution.

(c) Graph $Y_1 = X^2 - 4X + 4$ in [0, 4, 1] by [−3, 3, 1]. See Figure 37. There is one x-intercept.

[−3, 3, 1] by [−3, 3, 1]

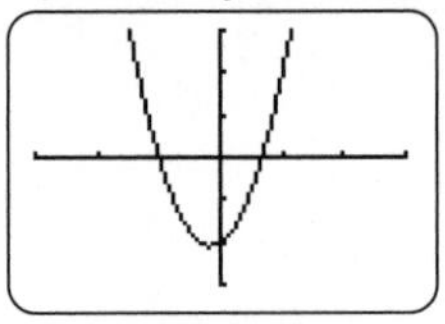

Figure 35

[0, 4, 1] by [−3, 3, 1]

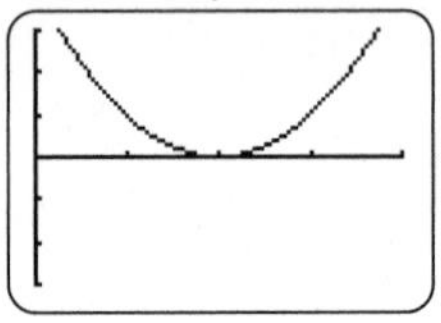

Figure 37

[−10, 10, 1] by [0, 10, 1]

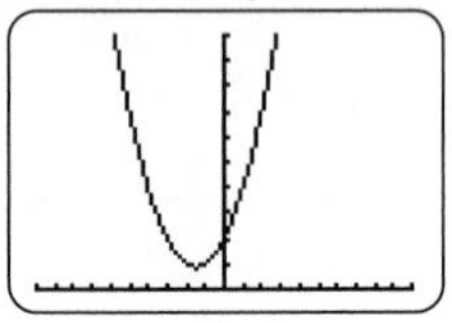

Figure 39

[−5, 5, 1] by [−8, 5, 1]

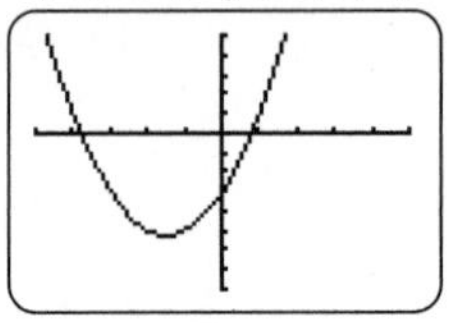

Figure 41

39. (a) $\left(\dfrac{3}{2}\right)^2 - 4\left(\dfrac{1}{2}\right)(2) = -\dfrac{7}{4}$

(b) Since the discriminant is negative, there are no real solutions.

(c) Graph $Y_1 = (1/2)X^2 - (3/2)X + 2$ in [−10, 10, 1] by [0, 10, 1]. See Figure 39. There are no x-intercepts.

41. (a) $(3)^2 - 4(1)(-3) = 21$

(b) Since the discriminant is positive, there are two real solutions.

(c) Graph $Y_1 = X^2 + 3X - 3$ in [−5, 5, 1] by [−8, 5, 1]. See Figure 41. There are two x-intercepts.

43. $x = \dfrac{-(-2) \pm \sqrt{(-2)^2 - 4(1)(-1)}}{2(1)} = \dfrac{2 \pm \sqrt{8}}{2} = \dfrac{2 \pm 2\sqrt{2}}{2} = \dfrac{2(1 \pm \sqrt{2})}{2} = 1 \pm \sqrt{2}$

45. $x = \dfrac{-(-1) \pm \sqrt{(-1)^2 - 4(-2)(3)}}{2(-2)} = \dfrac{1 \pm \sqrt{25}}{-4} = \dfrac{1 \pm 5}{-4} = -\dfrac{3}{2}$ or 1

47. $x = \dfrac{-1 \pm \sqrt{(1)^2 - 4(1)(5)}}{2(1)} = \dfrac{-1 \pm \sqrt{-19}}{2} \Rightarrow$ No real solutions. No x-intercepts.

49. $x = \dfrac{-(0) \pm \sqrt{(0)^2 - 4(1)(9)}}{2(1)} = \dfrac{0 \pm \sqrt{-36}}{2} \Rightarrow$ No real solutions. No x-intercepts.

51. $x = \dfrac{-4 \pm \sqrt{(4)^2 - 4(3)(-2)}}{2(3)} = \dfrac{-4 \pm \sqrt{40}}{6} = \dfrac{-4 \pm 2\sqrt{10}}{6} = \dfrac{2(-2 \pm \sqrt{10})}{6} = \dfrac{-2 \pm \sqrt{10}}{3}$

Complex Solutions

53. $x^2 + 9 = 0 \Rightarrow x^2 = -9 \Rightarrow x = \pm\sqrt{-9} \Rightarrow x = \pm 3i$

55. $x^2 + 80 = 0 \Rightarrow x^2 = -80 \Rightarrow x = \pm\sqrt{-80} \Rightarrow x = \pm\sqrt{-16 \cdot 5} \Rightarrow x = \pm 4i\sqrt{5}$

57. $x^2 + \dfrac{1}{4} = 0 \Rightarrow x^2 = -\dfrac{1}{4} \Rightarrow x = \pm\sqrt{-\dfrac{1}{4}} \Rightarrow x = \pm\dfrac{1}{2}i$

59. $16x^2 + 9 = 0 \Rightarrow 16x^2 = -9 \Rightarrow x^2 = -\dfrac{9}{16} \Rightarrow x = \pm\sqrt{-\dfrac{9}{16}} \Rightarrow x = \pm\dfrac{3}{4}i$

61. $x^2 = -6 \Rightarrow x = \pm\sqrt{-6} \Rightarrow x = \pm i\sqrt{6}$

63. $x^2 - 3 = 0 \Rightarrow x^2 = 3 \Rightarrow x = \pm\sqrt{3}$

65. $x^2 + 2 = 0 \Rightarrow x^2 = -2 \Rightarrow x = \pm\sqrt{-2} \Rightarrow x = \pm i\sqrt{2}$

67. $x = \dfrac{-(-1) \pm \sqrt{(-1)^2 - 4(1)(2)}}{2(1)} = \dfrac{1 \pm \sqrt{-7}}{2} = \dfrac{1 \pm i\sqrt{7}}{2} = \dfrac{1}{2} \pm i\dfrac{\sqrt{7}}{2}$

69. $x = \dfrac{-3 \pm \sqrt{3^2 - 4(2)(4)}}{2(2)} = \dfrac{-3 \pm \sqrt{-23}}{4} = \dfrac{-3 \pm i\sqrt{23}}{4} = -\dfrac{3}{4} \pm i\dfrac{\sqrt{23}}{4}$

71. $x = \dfrac{-(-4) \pm \sqrt{(-4^2) - 4(1)(1)}}{2(1)} = \dfrac{4 \pm \sqrt{12}}{2} = \dfrac{4 \pm 2\sqrt{3}}{2} = 2 \pm \sqrt{3}$

73. $x = \dfrac{-1 \pm \sqrt{1^2 - 4(1)(2)}}{2(1)} = \dfrac{-1 \pm \sqrt{-7}}{2} = \dfrac{-1 \pm i\sqrt{7}}{2} = -\dfrac{1}{2} \pm i\dfrac{\sqrt{7}}{2}$

75. $x = \dfrac{-2 \pm \sqrt{(2)^2 - 4(5)(4)}}{2(5)} = \dfrac{-2 \pm \sqrt{-76}}{10} = \dfrac{-2 \pm 2i\sqrt{19}}{10} = -\dfrac{1}{5} \pm i\dfrac{\sqrt{19}}{5}$

77. $x = \dfrac{-\frac{3}{4} \pm \sqrt{(\frac{3}{4})^2 - 4(\frac{1}{2})(1)}}{2(\frac{1}{2})} = \dfrac{-\frac{3}{4} \pm \sqrt{-\frac{23}{16}}}{1} = -\dfrac{3}{4} \pm \sqrt{\dfrac{-23}{16}} = -\dfrac{3}{4} \pm \dfrac{\sqrt{-23}}{4} = -\dfrac{3}{4} \pm i\dfrac{\sqrt{23}}{4}$

79. $x = \dfrac{-1 \pm \sqrt{(1)^2 - 4(1)(4)}}{2(1)} = \dfrac{-1 \pm \sqrt{-15}}{2} = -\dfrac{1}{2} \pm i\dfrac{\sqrt{15}}{2}$

81. $x = \dfrac{-(-2) \pm \sqrt{(-2)^2 - 4(2)(-1)}}{2(2)} = \dfrac{2 \pm \sqrt{12}}{4} = \dfrac{2 \pm 2\sqrt{3}}{4} = \dfrac{2(1 \pm \sqrt{3})}{4} = \dfrac{1 \pm \sqrt{3}}{2}$

83. $x = \dfrac{-(-1) \pm \sqrt{(-1)^2 - 4(2)(2)}}{2(2)} = \dfrac{1 \pm \sqrt{-15}}{4} = \dfrac{1 \pm i\sqrt{15}}{4} = \dfrac{1}{4} \pm i\dfrac{\sqrt{15}}{4}$

You Decide the Method

85. $x^2 - 3x + 2 = 0 \Rightarrow (x - 1)(x - 2) = 0 \Rightarrow x = 1$ or $x = 2$; *Answers may vary.*

87. Multiply both sides of the equation by 4 to obtain the following result. *Answers may vary.*

$0.5x^2 - 1.75x - 1 = 0 \Rightarrow 2x^2 - 7x - 4 = 0 \Rightarrow (2x + 1)(x - 4) = 0 \Rightarrow x = -\dfrac{1}{2}$ or $x = 4$

89. $x = \dfrac{-(-5) \pm \sqrt{(-5)^2 - 4(1)(2)}}{2(1)} = \dfrac{5 \pm \sqrt{17}}{2}$; Quadratic formula or completing the square.

91. $x = \dfrac{-1 \pm \sqrt{(1)^2 - 4(2)(8)}}{2(2)} = \dfrac{-1 \pm \sqrt{-63}}{4} = \dfrac{-1 \pm 3i\sqrt{7}}{4} = -\dfrac{1}{4} \pm \dfrac{3}{4}i\sqrt{7}$; Quadratic formula.

Applications

93. $\dfrac{1}{9}x^2 + \dfrac{11}{3}x - 42 = 0 \Rightarrow x^2 + 33x - 378 = 0 \Rightarrow x = (x - 9)(x + 42) = 0 \Rightarrow x = 9$ mph

The value $x = -42$ has no physical meaning.

95. $\dfrac{1}{9}x^2 + \dfrac{11}{3}x - 390 = 0 \Rightarrow x^2 + 33x - 3510 = 0 \Rightarrow x = (x - 45)(x + 78) = 0 \Rightarrow x = 45$ mph

The value $x = -78$ has no physical meaning.

97. $2.39x^2 + 5.04x + 5.1 = 200 \Rightarrow 2.39x^2 + 5.04x - 194.9 = 0$

$x = \dfrac{-5.04 \pm \sqrt{(5.04)^2 - 4(2.39)(-194.9)}}{2(2.39)} = \dfrac{-5.04 \pm \sqrt{1888.6456}}{4.78} \Rightarrow x \approx 8.04$; about 1992

The value $x \approx -10.15$ has no meaning in this problem. Our answer agrees with the graph.

99. Let x represent the average speed of the canoe in still water. The trip downstream takes $\dfrac{2}{x+2}$ hours. The trip upstream takes $\dfrac{4}{x-1}$ hours. The total is $\dfrac{2}{x+2} + \dfrac{4}{x-1} = 3$. Solve this equation for x.

$\dfrac{2}{x+2} + \dfrac{4}{x-1} = 3 \Rightarrow 2(x - 1) + 4(x + 2) = 3(x + 2)(x - 1) \Rightarrow 6x + 6 = 3x^2 + 3x - 6 \Rightarrow$

$3x^2 - 3x - 12 = 0 \Rightarrow x^2 - x - 4 = 0 \Rightarrow x = \dfrac{-(-1) \pm \sqrt{(-1)^2 - 4(1)(-4)}}{2(1)} = \dfrac{1 \pm \sqrt{17}}{2} \approx 2.6$ mph

101. (a) The rate of change is not constant.

(b) From the table, the height was 7 centimeters after about 75 seconds. *Answers may vary.*

(c) $x = \dfrac{-(-0.15) \pm \sqrt{(-0.15)^2 - 4(0.0004)(9)}}{2(0.0004)} = \dfrac{0.15 \pm \sqrt{0.0081}}{0.0008} = \dfrac{0.15 \pm 0.09}{0.0008} \Rightarrow x = 75$ seconds

The value $x = 300$ is not possible for this problem.

Checking Basic Concepts for Sections 11.3 & 11.4

1. Symbolical:

$2x^2 - 7x + 3 = 0 \Rightarrow (2x - 1)(x - 3) = 0 \Rightarrow$ Either $2x - 1 = 0 \Rightarrow x = \dfrac{1}{2}$ or $x - 3 = 0 \Rightarrow x = 3$

Graphical: Graph $Y_1 = 2X^2 - 7X + 3$ in [-5, 5, 1] by [-5, 5, 1]. See Figures 1a & 1b. $x = \dfrac{1}{2}$ or $x = 3$

[-5, 5, 1] by [-5, 5, 1]

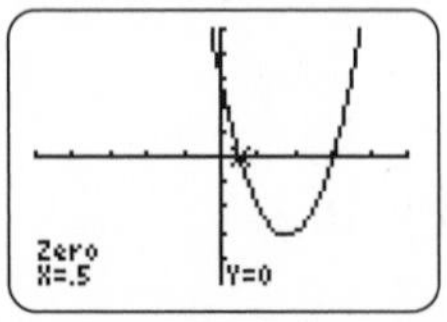

Figure 1a

[-5, 5, 1] by [-5, 5, 1]

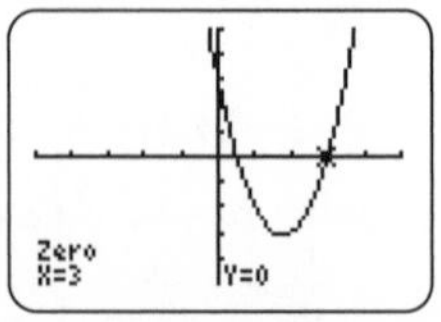

Figure 1b

2. $x^2 = 5 \Rightarrow x = \pm\sqrt{5}$

3. $x^2 - 4x + 1 = 0 \Rightarrow x^2 - 4x + 4 = -1 + 4 \Rightarrow (x - 2)^2 = 3 \Rightarrow x - 2 = \pm\sqrt{3} \Rightarrow x = 2 \pm \sqrt{3}$

4. $x^2 + y^2 = 1 \Rightarrow y^2 = 1 - x^2 \Rightarrow y = \pm\sqrt{1 - x^2}$

5. (a) $2x^2 = 3x + 1 \Rightarrow 2x^2 - 3x - 1 = 0 \Rightarrow x = \dfrac{-(-3) \pm \sqrt{(-3)^2 - 4(2)(-1)}}{2(2)} = \dfrac{3 \pm \sqrt{17}}{4}$

   (b) $9x^2 - 24x + 16 = 0 \Rightarrow x = \dfrac{-(-24) \pm \sqrt{(-24)^2 - 4(9)(16)}}{2(9)} = \dfrac{24 \pm \sqrt{0}}{18} = \dfrac{24}{18} = \dfrac{4}{3}$

   (c) $x = \dfrac{-1 \pm \sqrt{1^2 - 4(1)(2)}}{2(1)} = \dfrac{-1 \pm \sqrt{-7}}{2} = \dfrac{-1 \pm i\sqrt{7}}{2} = -\dfrac{1}{2} \pm i\dfrac{\sqrt{7}}{2}$

6. (a) $(-5)^2 - 4(1)(5) = 5$; Since the discriminant is positive, there are two real solutions.

   (b) $(-5)^2 - 4(2)(4) = -7$; Since the discriminant is negative, there are no real solutions.

   (c) $(-56)^2 - 4(49)(16) = 0$; Since the discriminant is zero, there is one real solution.

11.5: Quadratic Inequalities

Concepts

1. An inequality has an inequality sign rather than an equals sign.

3. No, since $9 \not< 7$.

5. $-2 < x < 4$

7. Yes

9. Yes

11. No, this inequality is linear.

13. Yes, since $2(3)^2 + (3) - 1 = 20$ and $20 > 0$.

15. No, since $(0)^2 + 2 = 2$ and $2 \not\leq 0$.

17. No, since $(-3)^2 - 3(-3) = 18$ and $18 \not\leq 1$.

Solving Quadratic Inequalities

19. (a) The solutions are the x-intercepts, $x = -3$ or $x = 2$.

    (b) $-3 < x < 2$

    (c) $x < -3$ or $x > 2$

21. (a) The solutions are the x-intercepts, $x = -2$ or $x = 2$.

    (b) $-2 < x < 2$

    (c) $x < -2$ or $x > 2$

23. (a) The solutions are the x-intercepts, $x = -10$ or $x = 5$.

    (b) $x < -10$ or $x > 5$

    (c) $-10 < x < 5$

25. (a) The solutions are $x = -2$ or $x = 2$.

(b) $-2 < x < 2$

(c) $x < -2$ or $x > 2$

27. (a) The solutions are $x = -4$ or $x = 0$.

(b) $-4 < x < 0$

(c) $x < -4$ or $x > 0$

29. First replace the inequality symbol with an equals sign and solve the resulting equation.

$x^2 + 4x + 3 = 0 \Rightarrow (x + 3)(x + 1) = 0 \Rightarrow x = -3$ or -1. The parabola given by $y = x^2 + 4x + 3$ lies below the x-axis when $-3 < x < -1$. The interval is $(-3, -1)$.

31. First replace the inequality symbol with an equals sign and solve the resulting equation.

$2x^2 - x - 15 = 0 \Rightarrow (2x + 5)(x - 3) = 0 \Rightarrow x = -2.5$ or 3. The parabola given by $y = 2x^2 - x - 15$ lies above the x-axis when $x \leq -2.5$ or $x \geq 3$. The interval is $(-\infty, -2.5] \cup [3, \infty)$.

33. First replace the inequality symbol with an equals sign and solve the resulting equation.

$2x^2 = 8 \Rightarrow x^2 = 4 \Rightarrow x^2 - 4 = 0 \Rightarrow (x + 2)(x - 2) = 0 \Rightarrow x = -2$ or 2. The parabola given by $y = 2x^2 - 8$ lies below the x-axis when $-2 \leq x \leq 2$. The interval is $[-2, 2]$.

35. The value of x^2 is greater than -5 for all values of x. The parabola given by $y = x^2 + 5$ lies entirely above the x-axis. The interval is $(-\infty, \infty)$.

37. First replace the inequality symbol with an equals sign and solve the resulting equation.

$-x^2 + 3x = 0 \Rightarrow -x(x - 3) = 0 \Rightarrow x = 0$ or 3. The parabola given by $y = -x^2 + 3x$ lies above the x-axis when $0 < x < 3$. The interval is $(0, 3)$.

39. (a) $x^2 - 4 = 0 \Rightarrow x^2 = 4 \Rightarrow x = -2$ or $x = 2$

(b) Since the parabola opens upward, the solution is $-2 < x < 2$.

(c) Since the parabola opens upward, the solution is $x < -2$ or $x > 2$.

41. (a) $x^2 + x - 1 = 0 \Rightarrow x = \dfrac{-1 \pm \sqrt{(1)^2 - 4(1)(-1)}}{2(1)} \Rightarrow x = \dfrac{-1 \pm \sqrt{5}}{2}$

(b) Since the parabola opens upward, the solution is $\dfrac{-1 - \sqrt{5}}{2} < x < \dfrac{-1 + \sqrt{5}}{2}$.

(c) Since the parabola opens upward, the solution is $x < \dfrac{-1 - \sqrt{5}}{2}$ or $x > \dfrac{-1 + \sqrt{5}}{2}$.

43. $x^2 + 10x + 21 = 0 \Rightarrow (x + 7)(x + 3) = 0 \Rightarrow x = -7$ or $x = -3$

Since the parabola opens upward, the solution is $[-7, -3]$.

45. $3x^2 - 9x - 6 = 0 \Rightarrow 3(x - 1)(x - 2) = 0 \Rightarrow x = 1$ or $x = 2$

Since the parabola opens upward, the solution is $(-\infty, 1) \cup (2, \infty)$..

47. $x^2 = 10 \Rightarrow x = -\sqrt{10}$ or $x = \sqrt{10}$

Since the parabola opens upward, the solution is $(-\sqrt{10}, \sqrt{10})$.

49. $x(x - 6) = 0 \Rightarrow x = 0$ or $x = 6$

Since the parabola opens upward, the solution is $(-\infty, 2) \cup (6, \infty)$.

51. $x(4 - x) = 2 \Rightarrow -x^2 + 4x - 2 = 0 \Rightarrow x = \dfrac{-4 \pm \sqrt{(4)^2 - 4(-1)(-2)}}{2(-1)} = 2 \pm \sqrt{2}$

Since the parabola opens downward, the solution is $(-\infty, 2 - \sqrt{2}\,] \cup [2 + \sqrt{2}, \infty)$.

Applications

53. (a) Graph $Y_1 = 0.0000375X^2 - 0.175X + 1000$ and $Y_2 = 850$ in [0, 4000, 1000] by [500, 1200, 100].

See Figures 53a & 53b. The elevation is 850 feet or less from 1131 feet to 3535 feet (approximately).

(b) The elevation is 850 feet or more before 1131 feet or after 3535 feet (approximately).

[0, 4000, 1000] by [500, 1200, 100]

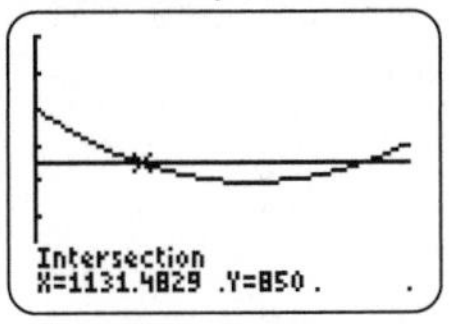

Figure 53a

[0, 4000, 1000] by [500, 1200, 100]

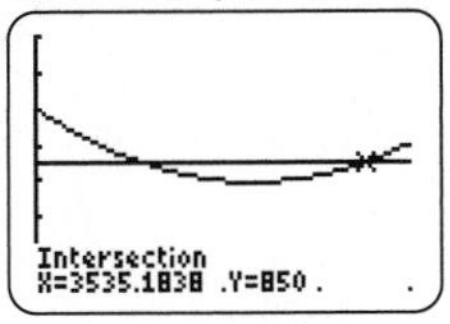

Figure 53b

55. (a) From the formula, $f(1985) = -0.014777(1985)^2 + 54.14(1985) - 49{,}060 \approx 183$.

From the graph $f(1985) \approx 183$.

(b) The death rate was 250 or less about 1970 and after.

(c) $-0.014777x^2 + 54.14x - 49{,}060 = 250 \Rightarrow -0.014777x^2 + 54.14x - 49{,}310 = 0 \Rightarrow$

$$x = \frac{-54.14 \pm \sqrt{(54.14)^2 - 4(-0.014777)(-49{,}310)}}{2(-0.014777)} \approx 1694 \text{ or } 1969.$$

The only valid solution is 1969. The death rate was 250 or less about 1969 or after.

57. Let w represent the width of the pen. Then $w + 5$ represents the length and the area is given by $w(w + 5) = w^2 + 5w$. We want to find w so that $w^2 + 5w \geq 176$ and $w^2 + 5w \leq 500$. $w^2 + 5w - 176 = 0 \Rightarrow (w + 16)(w - 16) = 0 \Rightarrow w = -16$ or $w = 11$, so $w \geq 11$. The values $w \leq -16$ have no meaning. $w^2 + 5w - 500 = 0 \Rightarrow (w + 25)(w - 20) = 0 \Rightarrow w = -25$ or $w = 20$, so $w \leq 20$. The values $w \leq -25$ have no meaning. The width must be from 11 feet to 20 feet

11.6: Equations in Quadratic Form

Concepts

1. $u^2 - 7u + 6 = 0 \Rightarrow (u - 1)(u - 6) = 0 \Rightarrow u = 1$ or 6

When $u = 1, x^2 = 1 \Rightarrow x = \pm 1$. When $u = 6, x^2 = 6 \Rightarrow x = \pm\sqrt{6}$.

3. $3u^2 + u - 10 = 0 \Rightarrow (u + 2)(3u - 5) = 0 \Rightarrow u = -2$ or $\dfrac{5}{3}$

When $u = -2, z^3 = -2 \Rightarrow z = -\sqrt[3]{2}$. When $u = \dfrac{5}{3}, z^3 = \dfrac{5}{3} \Rightarrow z = \sqrt[3]{\dfrac{5}{3}}$.

5. $4u^2 + 17u + 15 = 0 \Rightarrow (u + 3)(4u + 5) = 0 \Rightarrow u = -3 \text{ or } -\frac{5}{4}$

When $u = -3, n^{-1} = -3 \Rightarrow n = -\frac{1}{3}$. When $u = -\frac{5}{4}, n^{-1} = -\frac{5}{4} \Rightarrow n = -\frac{4}{5}$.

7. Let $u = x^2$. Then $u^2 = 8u + 9 \Rightarrow u^2 - 8u - 9 = 0 \Rightarrow (u + 1)(u - 9) = 0 \Rightarrow u = -1 \text{ or } 9$.

When $u = -1, x^2 = -1 \Rightarrow$ no solutions. When $u = 9, x^2 = 9 \Rightarrow x = \pm\sqrt{9} = -3 \text{ or } 3$.

9. Let $u = x^3$. Then $3u^2 - 5u - 2 = 0 \Rightarrow (3u + 1)(u - 2) = 0 \Rightarrow u = -\frac{1}{3} \text{ or } 2$.

When $u = -\frac{1}{3}, x^3 = -\frac{1}{3} \Rightarrow x = -\sqrt[3]{\frac{1}{3}}$. When $u = 2, x^3 = 2 \Rightarrow x = \sqrt[3]{2}$.

11. Let $u = z^{-1}$. Then $2u^2 + 11u = 40 \Rightarrow 2u^2 + 11u - 40 = 0 \Rightarrow (u + 8)(2u - 5) = 0 \Rightarrow u = -8 \text{ or } \frac{5}{2}$.

When $u = -8, z^{-1} = -8 \Rightarrow z = -\frac{1}{8}$. When $u = \frac{5}{2}, z^{-1} = \frac{5}{2} \Rightarrow z = \frac{2}{5}$.

13. Let $u = x^{1/3}$. Then $u^2 - 2u + 1 = 0 \Rightarrow (u - 1)^2 = 0 \Rightarrow u = 1$. When $u = 1, x^{1/3} = 1 \Rightarrow x = 1^3 = 1$.

15. Let $u = x^{1/5}$. Then $u^2 - 33u + 32 = 0 \Rightarrow (u - 1)(u - 32) = 0 \Rightarrow u = 1 \text{ or } 32$.

When $u = 1, x^{1/5} = 1 \Rightarrow x = 1^5 = 1$. When $u = 32, x^{1/5} = 32 \Rightarrow x = 32^5 = 33{,}554{,}432$.

17. Let $u = x^{1/2}$. Then $u^2 - 13u + 36 = 0 \Rightarrow (u - 4)(u - 9) = 0 \Rightarrow u = 4 \text{ or } 9$.

When $u = 4, x^{1/2} = 4 \Rightarrow x = 4^2 = 16$. When $u = 9, x^{1/2} = 9 \Rightarrow x = 9^2 = 81$.

19. Let $u = z^{1/4}$. Then $u^2 - 2u + 1 = 0 \Rightarrow (u - 1)^2 = 0 \Rightarrow u = 1$. When $u = 1, z^{1/4} = 1 \Rightarrow x = 1^4 = 1$.

21. Let $u = x + 1$. Then $u^2 - 5u - 14 = 0 \Rightarrow (u + 2)(u - 7) = 0 \Rightarrow u = -2 \text{ or } 7$.

When $u = -2, x + 1 = -2 \Rightarrow x = -3$. When $u = 7, x + 1 = 7 \Rightarrow x = 6$.

23. Let $u = x^2 - 1$. Then $u^2 - 4 = 0 \Rightarrow (u + 4)(u - 4) = 0 \Rightarrow u = -4 \text{ or } 4$.

When $u = -4, x^2 - 1 = -4 \Rightarrow x^2 = -3 \Rightarrow$ no solutions.

When $u = 4, x^2 - 1 = 4 \Rightarrow x^2 = 3 \Rightarrow x = -\sqrt{3} \text{ or } \sqrt{3}$.

Checking Basic Concepts for Sections 11.5 & 11.6

1. $x^2 - x - 6 = 0 \Rightarrow (x + 2)(x - 3) = 0 \Rightarrow x = -2 \text{ or } x = 3$

Since the parabola opens upward, the solution is $(-\infty, -2) \cup (3, \infty)$.

2. $3x^2 + 5x + 2 = 0 \Rightarrow (x + 1)(3x + 2) = 0 \Rightarrow x = -1 \text{ or } x = -\frac{2}{3}$

Since the parabola opens upward, the solution is $\left[-1, -\frac{2}{3}\right]$.

3. Let $u = x^3$. Then $u^2 + 6u - 16 = 0 \Rightarrow (u + 8)(u - 2) = 0 \Rightarrow u = -8 \text{ or } 2$.

When $u = -8, x^3 = -8 \Rightarrow x = \sqrt[3]{-8} = -2$. When $u = 2, x^3 = 2 \Rightarrow x = \sqrt[3]{2}$.

4. Let $u = x^{1/3}$. Then $u^2 - 7u - 8 = 0 \Rightarrow (u + 1)(u - 8) = 0 \Rightarrow u = -1 \text{ or } 8$.

When $u = -1, x^{1/3} = -1 \Rightarrow x = (-1)^3 = -1$. When $u = 8, x^{1/3} = 8 \Rightarrow x = 8^3 = 512$

Chapter 11 Review Exercises

Section 11.1

1. Vertex: $(-3, 4)$; Axis of symmetry: $x = -3$; Opens downward; Increasing: $x \leq -3$; Decreasing: $x \geq -3$

2. Vertex: $(1, 0)$; Axis of symmetry: $x = 1$; Opens upward; Increasing: $x \geq 1$; Decreasing: $x \leq 1$

3. (a) See Figure 3.

   (b) The vertex is $(0, -2)$. The axis of symmetry is $x = 0$.

   (c) $f(-1) = (-1)^2 - 2 = 1 - 2 = -1$

4. (a) See Figure 4.

   (b) The vertex is $(2, 1)$. The axis of symmetry is $x = 2$.

   (c) $f(3) = -(3)^2 + 4(3) - 3 = -9 + 12 - 3 = 0$

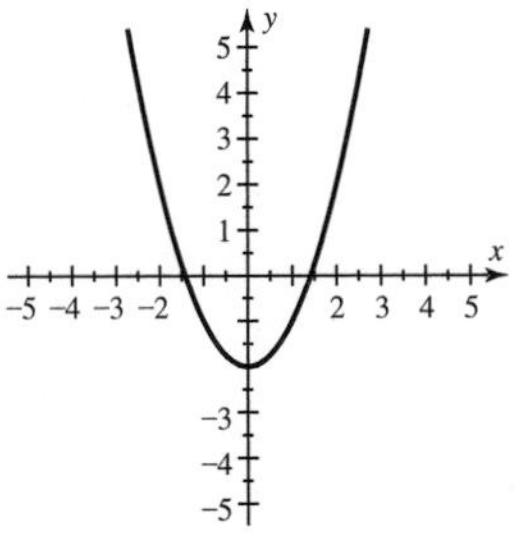

Figure 3

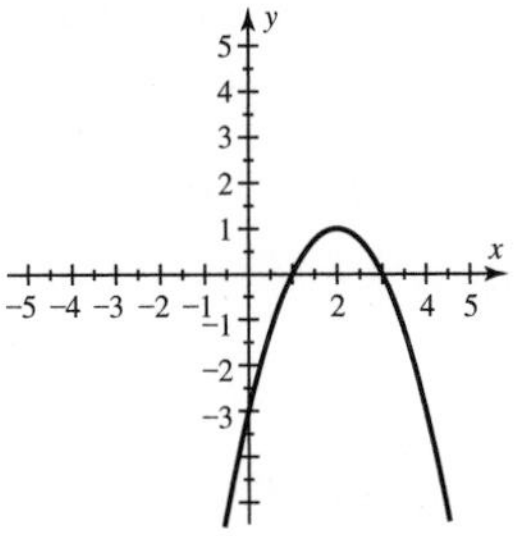

Figure 4

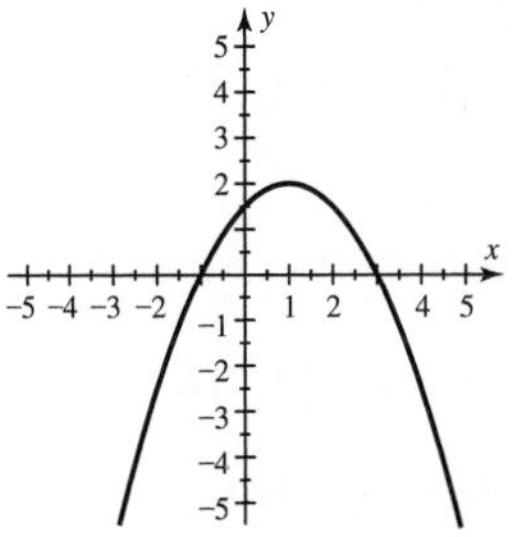

Figure 5

5. (a) See Figure 5.

   (b) The vertex is $(1, 2)$. The axis of symmetry is $x = 1$.

   (c) $f(-2) = -\frac{1}{2}(-2)^2 + (-2) + \frac{3}{2} = -2 - 2 + \frac{3}{2} = -2.5$

6. (a) See Figure 6.

   (b) The vertex is $(-2, -3)$. The axis of symmetry is $x = -2$.

   (c) $f(-3) = 2(-3)^2 + 8(-3) + 5 = 18 - 24 + 5 = -1$

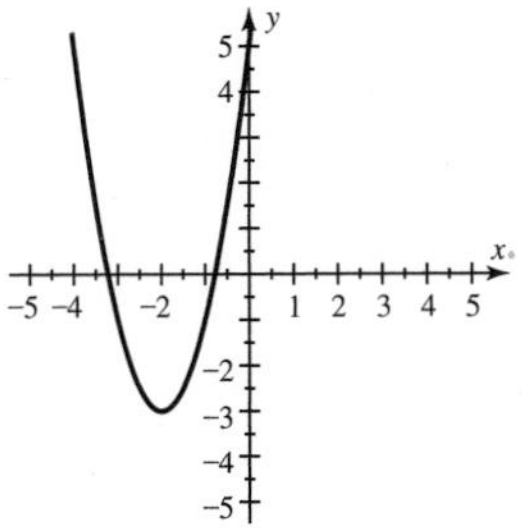

Figure 6

7. Because $-\frac{b}{2a} = -\frac{-6}{2(2)} = \frac{3}{2}$ and $f\left(\frac{3}{2}\right) = 2\left(\frac{3}{2}\right)^2 - 6\left(\frac{3}{2}\right) + 1 = -\frac{7}{2}$, the vertex is $\left(\frac{3}{2}, -\frac{7}{2}\right)$.

The minimum y-value on the graph is $-\frac{7}{2}$.

8. Because $-\frac{b}{2a} = -\frac{2}{2(-3)} = \frac{1}{3}$ and $f\left(\frac{1}{3}\right) = -3\left(\frac{1}{3}\right)^2 + 2\left(\frac{1}{3}\right) - 5 = -\frac{14}{3}$, the vertex is $\left(\frac{1}{3}, -\frac{14}{3}\right)$.

The maximum y-value on the graph is $-\frac{14}{3}$.

9. $x = -\frac{b}{2a} = -\frac{(-4)}{2(1)} = 2, f(2) = (2)^2 - 4(2) - 2 = -6$; The vertex is $(2, -6)$.

10. $x = -\frac{b}{2a} = -\frac{(0)}{2(-1)} = 0, f(0) = 5 - (0)^2 = 5$; The vertex is $(0, 5)$.

11. $x = -\frac{b}{2a} = -\frac{(1)}{2(-\frac{1}{4})} = 2, f(2) = -\frac{1}{4}(2)^2 + (2) + 1 = 2$; The vertex is $(2, 2)$.

12. $x = -\frac{b}{2a} = -\frac{(2)}{2(1)} = -1, f(-1) = 2 + 2(-1) + (-1)^2 = 1$; The vertex is $(-1, 1)$.

Section 11.2

13. (a) See Figure 13.

(b) This graph is a shift of the graph of $y = x^2$ upward 2 units.

14. (a) See Figure 14.

(b) This graph is more narrow than the graph of $y = x^2$.

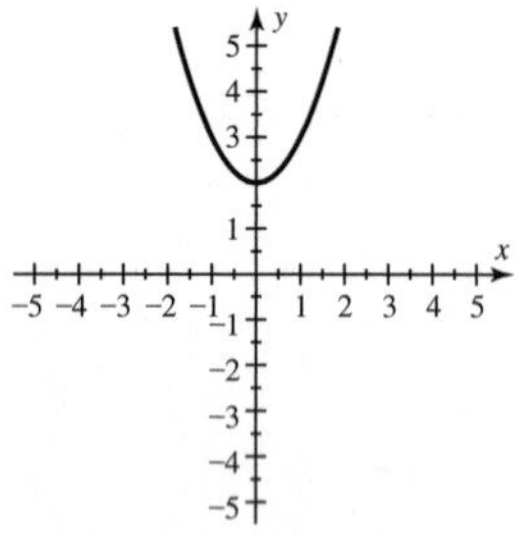
Figure 13

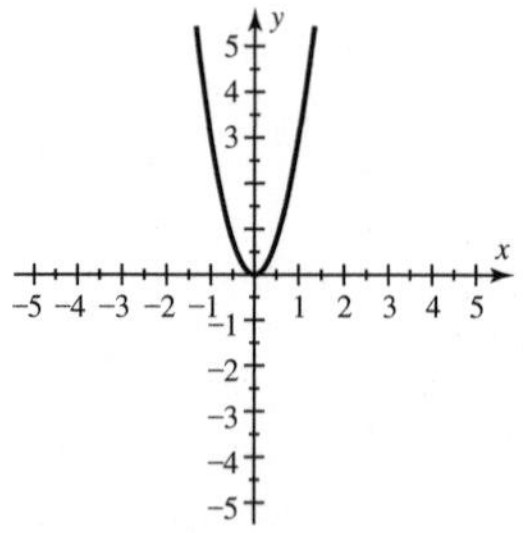
Figure 14

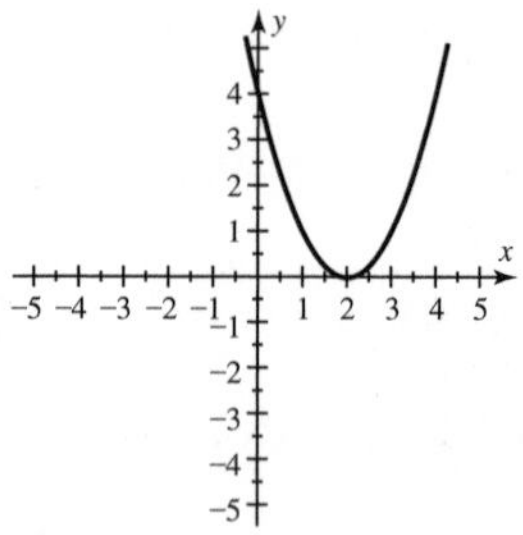
Figure 15

15. (a) See Figure 15.

(b) This graph is a shift of the graph of $y = x^2$ right 2 units.

16. (a) See Figure 16.

(b) This graph is a shift of the graph of $y = x^2$ left 1 unit and downward 3 units.

17. (a) See Figure 17.

(b) This graph is wider than the graph of $y = x^2$ and is shifted left 1 unit and upward 2 units.

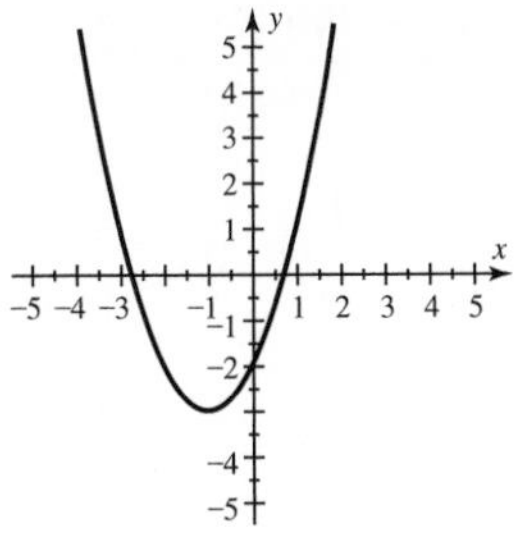

Figure 16

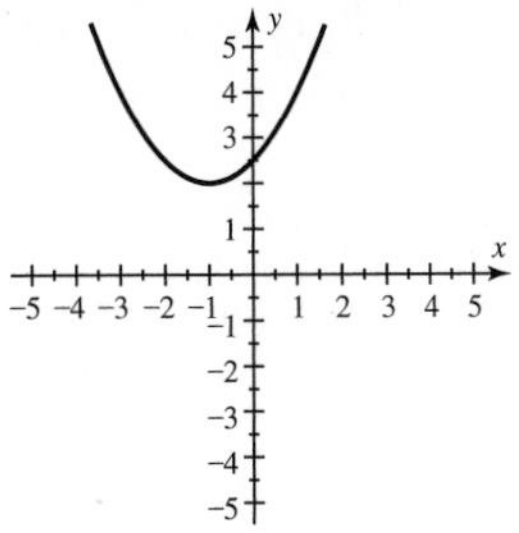

Figure 17

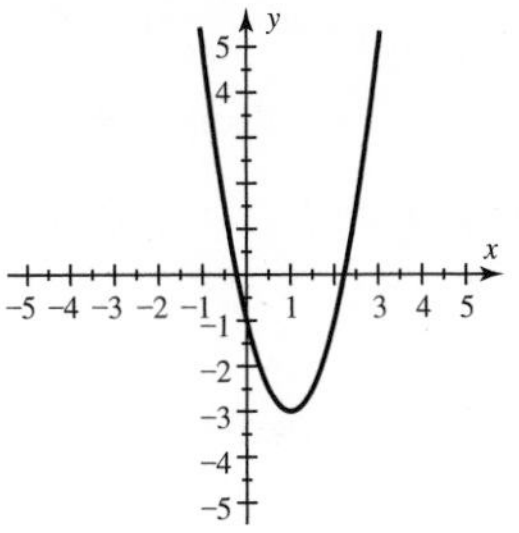

Figure 18

18. (a) See Figure 18.

 (b) This graph is more narrow than the graph of $y = x^2$ and is shifted right 1 unit and downward 3 units.

19. $y = a(x - h)^2 + k$ where (h, k) is the vertex, gives $y = -4(x - 2)^2 - 5$.

20. Opening downward means $a = -1$. $y = a(x - h)^2 + k$ where (h, k) is the vertex, gives $y = -1(x + 4)^2 + 6$.

21. $y = x^2 + 4x - 7 \Rightarrow y = (x^2 + 4x + 4) - 7 - 4 \Rightarrow y = (x + 2)^2 - 11$. The vertex is $(-2, -11)$.

22. $y = x^2 - 7x + 1 \Rightarrow y = \left(x^2 - 7x + \frac{49}{4}\right) + 1 - \frac{49}{4} \Rightarrow y = \left(x - \frac{7}{2}\right)^2 - \frac{45}{4}$. The vertex is $\left(\frac{7}{2}, -\frac{45}{2}\right)$.

23. $y = 2x^2 - 3x - 8 \Rightarrow y = 2\left(x^2 - \frac{3}{2}x + \frac{9}{16}\right) - 8 - \frac{9}{8} \Rightarrow y = 2\left(x - \frac{3}{4}\right)^2 - \frac{73}{8}$. The vertex is $\left(\frac{3}{4}, -\frac{73}{8}\right)$.

24. $y = 3x^2 + 6x - 2 \Rightarrow y = 3(x^2 + 2x + 1) - 2 - 3 \Rightarrow y = 3(x + 1)^2 - 5$. The vertex is $(-1, -5)$.

25. $a(1)^2 - 1 = 2 \Rightarrow a = 3$

26. $a(-1)^2 - 1 = -\frac{3}{4} \Rightarrow a = \frac{1}{4}$

Section 11.3

27. –2, 3

28. –1

29. No real solutions.

30. –4, 6

31. –10, 5

32. –0.5, 0.25

33. (a) Graph $Y_1 = X^2 - 5X - 50$ in [–10, 20, 5] by [–100, 20, 10]. See Figures 33a & 33b.

 The solutions are the x-intercepts, $x = -5$ or $x = 10$.

 (b) Table $Y_1 = X^2 - 5X - 50$ with TblStart = –10 and ΔTbl = 5. See Figure 33c.

 Since $Y_1 = 0$ when $x = -5$ or when $x = 10$, the solutions are $x = -5$ or $x = 10$.

[–10, 20, 5] by [–100, 20, 10]

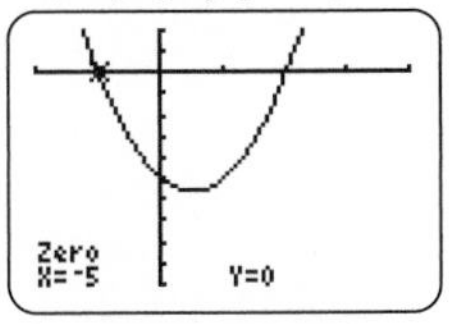

Figure 33a

[–10, 20, 5] by [–100, 20, 10]

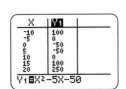

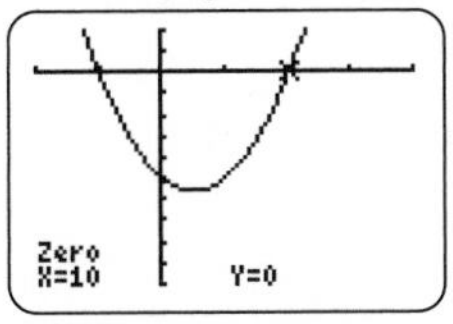

Figure 33b

X	Y1
-10	100
-5	0
0	-50
5	-50
10	0
15	100
20	250

Y1■X²-5X-50

Figure 33c

34. (a) Graph $Y_1 = (1/2)X^2 + X - (3/2)$ in [–5, 5, 1] by [–5, 5, 1]. See Figures 34a & 34b.

The solutions are the x-intercepts, $x = -3$ or $x = 1$.

(b) Table $Y_1 = (1/2)X^2 + X - (3/2)$ with TblStart = –4 and ΔTbl = 1. See Figure 34c.

Since $Y_1 = 0$ when $x = -3$ or when $x = 1$, the solutions are $x = -3$ or $x = 1$.

[–5, 5, 1] by [–5, 5, 1]

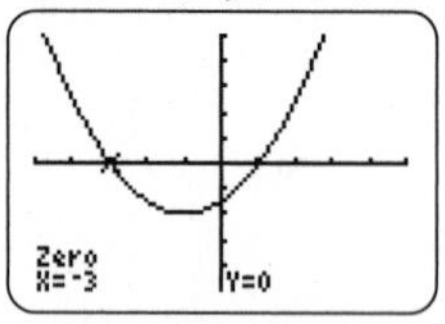

Figure 34a

[–5, 5, 1] by [–5, 5, 1]

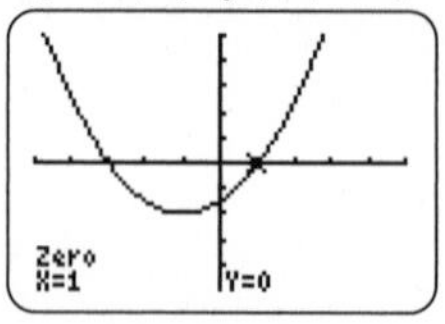

Figure 34b

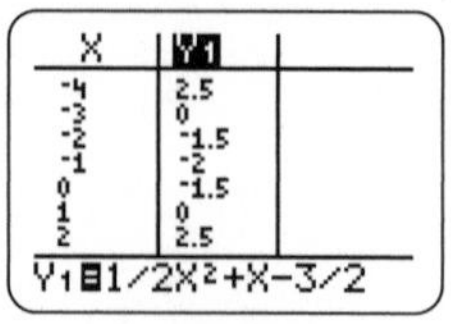

Figure 34c

35. (a) Graph $Y_1 = (1/4)X^2 + (1/2)X - 2$ in [–5, 5, 1] by [–3, 3, 1]. See Figures 35a & 35b.

The solutions are the x-intercepts, $x = -4$ or $x = 2$.

(b) Table $Y_1 = (1/4)X^2 + (1/2)X - 2$ with TblStart = –8 and ΔTbl = 2. See Figure 35c.

Since $Y_1 = 0$ when $x = -4$ or when $x = 2$, the solutions are $x = -4$ or $x = 2$.

[–5, 5, 1] by [–3, 3, 1]

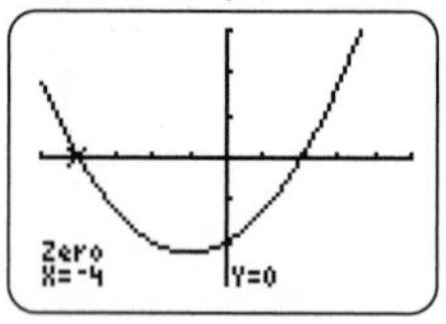

Figure 35a

[–5, 5, 1] by [–3, 3, 1]

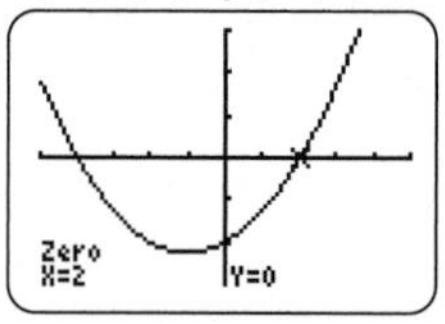

Figure 35b

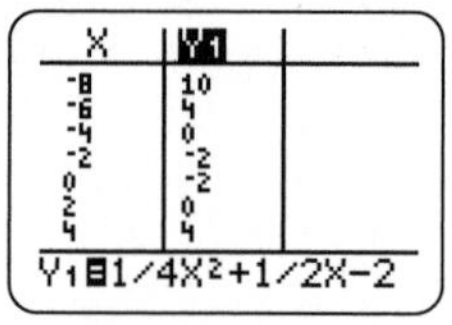

Figure 35c

36. (a) Graph $Y_1 = (1/4)X^2 - (1/2)X - (3/4)$ in [–5, 5, 1] by [–3, 3, 1]. See Figures 36a & 36b.

The solutions are the x-intercepts, $x = -1$ or $x = 3$.

(b) Table $Y_1 = (1/4)X^2 - (1/2)X - (3/4)$ with TblStart = –2 and ΔTbl = 1. See Figure 36c.

Since $Y_1 = 0$ when $x = -1$ or when $x = 3$, the solutions are $x = -1$ or $x = 3$.

[–5, 5, 1] by [–3, 3, 1]

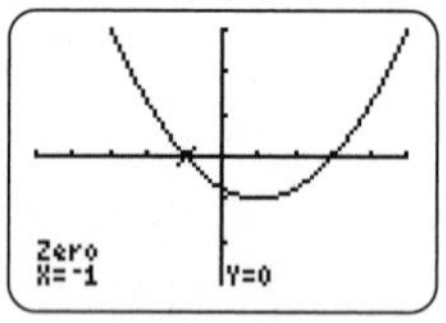

Figure 36a

[–5, 5, 1] by [–3, 3, 1]

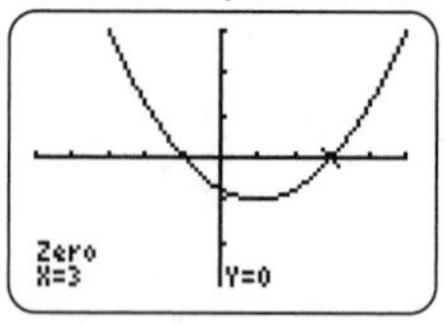

Figure 36b

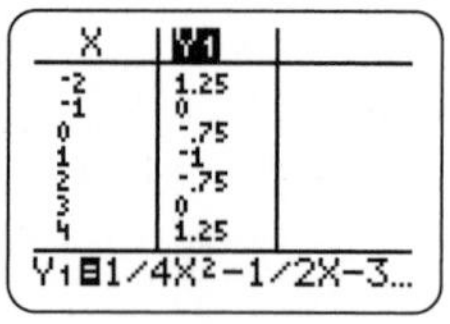

Figure 36c

37. $x^2 + x - 20 = 0 \Rightarrow (x + 5)(x - 4) = 0 \Rightarrow x = -5$ or $x = 4$

38. $x^2 + 11x + 24 = 0 \Rightarrow (x + 8)(x + 3) = 0 \Rightarrow x = -8$ or $x = -3$

39. $15x^2 - 4x - 4 = 0 \Rightarrow (5x + 2)(3x - 2) = 0 \Rightarrow x = -\frac{2}{5}$ or $x = \frac{2}{3}$

40. $7x^2 - 25x + 12 = 0 \Rightarrow (7x - 4)(x - 3) = 0 \Rightarrow x = \frac{4}{7}$ or $x = 3$

41. $x^2 = 100 \Rightarrow x = \pm\sqrt{100} \Rightarrow x = \pm 10$

42. $3x^2 = \frac{1}{3} \Rightarrow x^2 = \frac{1}{9} \Rightarrow x = \pm\sqrt{\frac{1}{9}} \Rightarrow x = \pm\frac{1}{3}$

43. $4x^2 - 6 = 0 \Rightarrow x^2 = \dfrac{6}{4} \Rightarrow x = \pm\sqrt{\dfrac{6}{4}} \Rightarrow x = \pm\dfrac{\sqrt{6}}{2}$

44. $5x^2 = x^2 - 4 \Rightarrow 4x^2 = -4 \Rightarrow x^2 = -1 \Rightarrow x = \pm\sqrt{-1} \Rightarrow$ No real solutions.

45. $x^2 + 6x = -2 \Rightarrow x^2 + 6x + 9 = -2 + 9 \Rightarrow (x + 3)^2 = 7 \Rightarrow x + 3 = \pm\sqrt{7} \Rightarrow x = -3 \pm \sqrt{7}$

46. $x^2 - 4x = 6 \Rightarrow x^2 - 4x + 4 = 6 + 4 \Rightarrow (x - 2)^2 = 10 \Rightarrow x - 2 = \pm\sqrt{10} \Rightarrow x = 2 \pm \sqrt{10}$

47. $x^2 - 2x - 5 = 0 \Rightarrow x^2 - 2x + 1 = 5 + 1 \Rightarrow (x - 1)^2 = 6 \Rightarrow x - 1 = \pm\sqrt{6} \Rightarrow x = 1 \pm \sqrt{6}$

48. $2x^2 + 6x - 1 = 0 \Rightarrow x^2 + 3x + \dfrac{9}{4} = \dfrac{1}{2} + \dfrac{9}{4} \Rightarrow \left(x + \dfrac{3}{2}\right)^2 = \dfrac{11}{4} \Rightarrow x + \dfrac{3}{2} = \pm\sqrt{\dfrac{11}{4}} \Rightarrow x = \dfrac{-3 \pm \sqrt{11}}{2}$

49. $F = \dfrac{k}{(R + r)^2} \Rightarrow F(R + r)^2 = k \Rightarrow (R + r)^2 = \dfrac{k}{F} \Rightarrow R + r = \pm\sqrt{\dfrac{k}{F}} \Rightarrow R = -r \pm \sqrt{\dfrac{k}{F}}$

50. $2x^2 + 3y^2 = 12 \Rightarrow 3y^2 = 12 - 2x^2 \Rightarrow y^2 = \dfrac{12 - 2x^2}{3} \Rightarrow y = \pm\sqrt{\dfrac{12 - 2x^2}{3}}$

Section 11.4

51. $x = \dfrac{-(-9) \pm \sqrt{(-9)^2 - 4(1)(18)}}{2(1)} = \dfrac{9 \pm \sqrt{9}}{2} = \dfrac{9 \pm 3}{2} \Rightarrow x = 3$ or $x = 6$

52. $x = \dfrac{-(-24) \pm \sqrt{(-24)^2 - 4(1)(143)}}{2(1)} = \dfrac{24 \pm \sqrt{4}}{2} = \dfrac{24 \pm 2}{2} \Rightarrow x = 11$ or $x = 13$

53. $x = \dfrac{-1 \pm \sqrt{(1)^2 - 4(6)(-1)}}{2(6)} = \dfrac{-1 \pm \sqrt{25}}{12} = \dfrac{-1 \pm 5}{12} \Rightarrow x = -\dfrac{1}{2}$ or $x = \dfrac{1}{3}$

54. $x = \dfrac{-(-5) \pm \sqrt{(-5)^2 - 4(5)(1)}}{2(5)} = \dfrac{5 \pm \sqrt{5}}{10}$

55. $x = \dfrac{-(-8) \pm \sqrt{(-8)^2 - 4(1)(-5)}}{2(1)} = \dfrac{8 \pm \sqrt{84}}{2} = \dfrac{8 \pm 2\sqrt{21}}{2} = \dfrac{2(4 \pm \sqrt{21})}{2} = 4 \pm \sqrt{21}$

56. $x = \dfrac{-(-6) \pm \sqrt{(-6)^2 - 4(2)(3)}}{2(2)} = \dfrac{6 \pm \sqrt{12}}{4} = \dfrac{6 \pm 2\sqrt{3}}{4} = \dfrac{2(3 \pm \sqrt{3})}{2(2)} = \dfrac{3 \pm \sqrt{3}}{2}$

57. (a) Since the parabola opens upward, $a > 0$.

(b) The solutions are the x-intercepts, $x = -2$ or $x = 3$.

(c) Since there are two unique solutions, the discriminant is positive.

58. (a) Since the parabola opens upward, $a > 0$.

(b) The solution is the x-intercept, $x = 2$.

(c) Since there is one solution, the discriminant is zero.

59. (a) Since the parabola opens downward, $a < 0$.

(b) There are no x-intercepts. No real solutions

(c) Since there are no real solutions, the discriminant is negative.

60. (a) Since the parabola opens downward, $a < 0$.

(b) The solutions are the x-intercepts, $x = -4$ or $x = 2$.

(c) Since there are two unique solutions, the discriminant is positive.

61. (a) $(-3)^2 - 4(2)(1) = 1$

(b) Since the discriminant is positive, there are two real solutions.

(c) Graph $Y_1 = 2X^2 - 3X + 1$ in [0, 2, 1] by [–1, 1, 1]. See Figure 61. There are two x-intercepts.

62. (a) $(2)^2 - 4(7)(-5) = 144$

(b) Since the discriminant is positive, there are two real solutions.

(c) Graph $Y_1 = 7X^2 + 2X - 5$ in [–2, 2, 1] by [–10, 5, 1]. See Figure 62. There are two x-intercepts.

[0, 2, 1] by [–1, 1, 1]

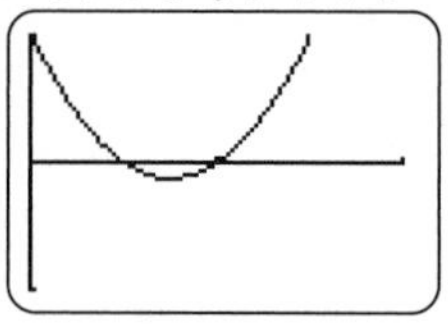

Figure 61

[–2, 2, 1] by [–10, 5, 1]

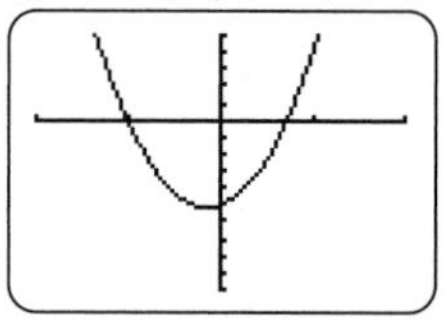

Figure 62

[–3, 3, 1] by [–5, 10, 1]

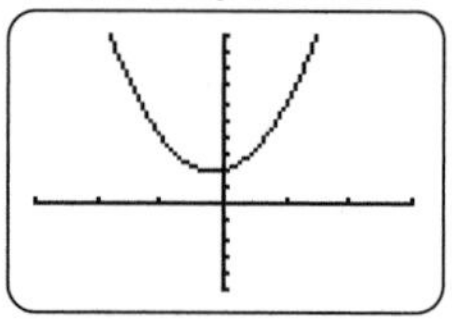

Figure 63

[0, 3, 1] by [–5, 10, 1]

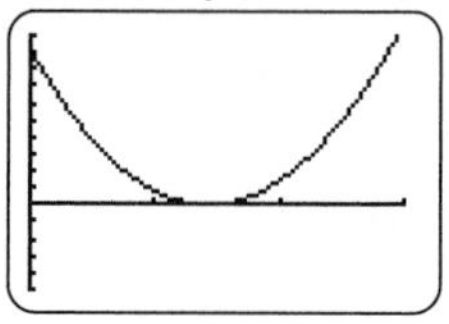

Figure 64

63. (a) $(1)^2 - 4(3)(2) = -23$

(b) Since the discriminant is negative, there are no real solutions.

(c) Graph $Y_1 = 7X^2 + 2X - 5$ in [–3, 3, 1] by [–5, 10, 1]. See Figure 63. There are no x-intercepts.

64. (a) $(-12.6)^2 - 4(4.41)(9) = 0$

(b) Since the discriminant is zero, there is one real solution.

(c) Graph $Y_1 = 7X^2 + 2X - 5$ in [0, 3, 1] by [–5, 10, 1]. See Figure 64. There is one x-intercepts.

65. $x = \dfrac{-1 \pm \sqrt{(1)^2 - 4(1)(5)}}{2(1)} = \dfrac{-1 \pm \sqrt{-19}}{2} = -\dfrac{1}{2} \pm i\dfrac{\sqrt{19}}{2}$

66. $2x^2 + 8 = 0 \Rightarrow 2x^2 = -8 \Rightarrow x^2 = -4 \Rightarrow x = \pm\sqrt{-4} \Rightarrow x = \pm 2i$

67. $x = \dfrac{-(-1) \pm \sqrt{(-1)^2 - 4(2)(1)}}{2(2)} = \dfrac{1 \pm \sqrt{-7}}{4} = \dfrac{1}{4} \pm i\dfrac{\sqrt{7}}{4}$

68. $x = \dfrac{-(-2) \pm \sqrt{(-2)^2 - 4(7)(5)}}{2(7)} = \dfrac{2 \pm \sqrt{-136}}{14} = \dfrac{2 \pm 2\sqrt{-34}}{14} = \dfrac{2(1 \pm \sqrt{-34})}{14} = \dfrac{1}{7} \pm i\dfrac{\sqrt{34}}{7}$

Section 11.5

69. (a) The solutions are the x-intercepts, $x = -2$ or $x = 6$.

(b) $-2 < x < 6$

(c) $x < -2$ or $x > 6$

70. (a) The solutions are the x-intercepts, $x = -2$ or $x = 0$.

(b) $x < -2$ or $x > 0$

(c) $-2 < x < 0$

71. (a) The solutions are $x = -4$ or $x = 4$.

(b) $-4 < x < 4$

(c) $x < -4$ or $x > 4$

72. (a) The solutions are $x = -2$ or $x = 1$.

(b) $-2 < x < 1$

(c) $x < -2$ or $x > 1$

73. (a) $x^2 - 2x - 3 = 0 \Rightarrow (x + 1)(x - 3) = 0 \Rightarrow x = -1$ or $x = 3$

(b) Since the parabola opens upward, the solution is $-1 < x < 3$.

(c) Since the parabola opens upward, the solution is $x < -1$ or $x > 3$.

74. (a) $2x^2 - 7x - 15 = 0 \Rightarrow (2x + 3)(x - 5) = 0 \Rightarrow x = -\frac{3}{2}$ or $x = 5$

(b) Since the parabola opens upward, the solution is $-\frac{3}{2} \le x \le 5$.

(c) Since the parabola opens upward, the solution is $x \le -\frac{3}{2}$ or $x \ge 5$.

75. $x^2 + 4x + 3 = 0 \Rightarrow (x + 3)(x + 1) = 0 \Rightarrow x = -3$ or $x = -1$

Since the parabola opens upward, the solution is $[-3, -1]$.

76. $5x^2 - 16x + 3 = 0 \Rightarrow (5x - 1)(x - 3) = 0 \Rightarrow x = \frac{1}{5}$ or $x = 3$

Since the parabola opens upward, the solution is $\left(\frac{1}{5}, 3\right)$.

77. $6x^2 - 13x + 2 = 0 \Rightarrow (6x - 1)(x - 2) = 0 \Rightarrow x = \frac{1}{6}$ or $x = 2$

Since the parabola opens upward, the solution is $\left(-\infty, \frac{1}{6}\right) \cup (2, \infty)$.

78. $x^2 = 5 \Rightarrow \Rightarrow x = -\sqrt{5}$ or $x = \sqrt{5}$

Since the parabola opens upward, the solution is $(-\infty, \sqrt{5}\,] \cup [\sqrt{5}, \infty)$.

Section 11.6

79. Let $u = x^2$. Then $u^2 - 14u + 45 = 0 \Rightarrow (u - 5)(u - 9) = 0 \Rightarrow u = 5$ or 9.

When $u = 5, x^2 = 5 \Rightarrow x = \pm\sqrt{5}$. When $u = 9, x^2 = 9 \Rightarrow x = \pm\sqrt{9} = \pm 3$.

80. Let $u = z^{-1}$. Then $2u^2 + u - 28 = 0 \Rightarrow (u + 4)(2u - 7) = 0 \Rightarrow u = -4$ or $\frac{7}{2}$.

When $u = -4, z^{-1} = -4 \Rightarrow z = -\frac{1}{4}$. When $u = \frac{7}{2}, z^{-1} = \frac{7}{2} \Rightarrow z = \frac{2}{7}$.

81. Let $u = x^{1/3}$. Then $u^2 - 9u + 8 = 0 \Rightarrow (u - 1)(u - 8) = 0 \Rightarrow u = 1$ or 8.

When $u = 1, x^{1/3} = 1 \Rightarrow x = 1^3 = 1$. When $u = 8, x^{1/3} = 8 \Rightarrow x = 8^3 = 512$.

82. Let $u = x - 1$. Then $u^2 + 2u + 1 = 0 \Rightarrow (u + 1)^2 = 0 \Rightarrow u = -1$. When $u = -1, x - 1 = -1 \Rightarrow x = 0$.

Applications

83. (a) $f(x) = x(12 - 2x)$

(b) Note that $f(x) = x(12 - 2x) \Rightarrow f(x) = -2x^2 + 12 + 0$. Then $-\frac{b}{2a} = -\frac{12}{2(-2)} = 3$.

The maximum area occurs when $x = 3$. The dimensions should be 6 inches by 3 inches.

84. (a) $-16t^2 + 44t + 4 = 32 \Rightarrow -16t^2 + 44t - 28 = 0 \Rightarrow 4x^2 - 11x + 7 = 0 \Rightarrow (x - 1)(4x - 7) = 0 \Rightarrow$

$x = 1$ or $x = \frac{7}{4}$. The height of the stone is 32 feet at 1 second and 1.75 seconds.

(b) Find the vertex. $-\frac{b}{2a} = -\frac{44}{2(-16)} = 1.375; f(1.375) = -16(1.375)^2 + 44(1.375) + 4 = 34.25$

After 1.375 seconds, the stone is at a height of 34.25 feet.

85. (a) $f(x) = x(90 - 3x)$

(b) Graph $Y_1 = X(90 - 3X)$ in [0, 30, 5] by [0, 800, 100]. See Figure 85a.

(c) Graph $Y_1 = X(90 - 3X)$ and $Y_2 = 600$ in [0, 30, 5] by [0, 800, 100]. See Figures 85b & 85c. 10 or 20 rooms.

(d) Graph $Y_1 = X(90 - 3X)$ in [0, 30, 5] by [0, 800, 100]. See Figure 85d. Rent 15 rooms.

(e) $x = -\frac{b}{2a} = -\frac{90}{2(-3)} = 15$. Rent 15 rooms to maximize revenue.

[0, 30, 5] by [0, 800, 100]

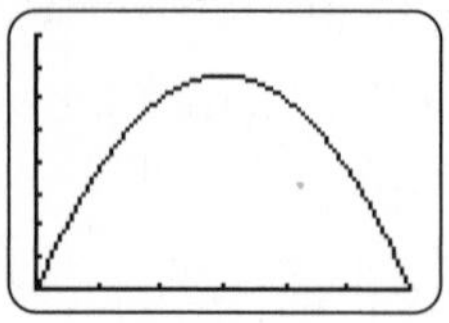

Figure 85a

[0, 30, 5] by [0, 800, 100]

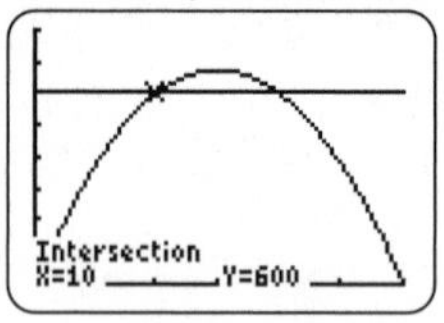

Figure 85b

[0, 30, 5] by [0, 800, 100]

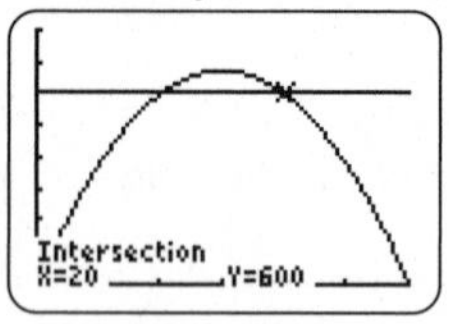

Figure 85c

[0, 30, 5] by [0, 800, 100]

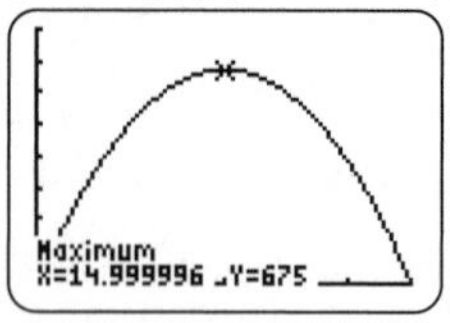

Figure 85d

86. (a) $f(1999) = 0.4(1999 - 1997)^2 + 0.8 = 2.4$; In 1999 there were 2.4 complaints per 100,000 passengers.

(b) Graph $Y_1 = 0.4(X - 1997)^2 + 0.8$ in [1997, 1999, 1] by [0.5, 3, 0.5]. See Figure 86. They have increased.

[1997, 1999, 1] by [0.5, 3, 0.5]

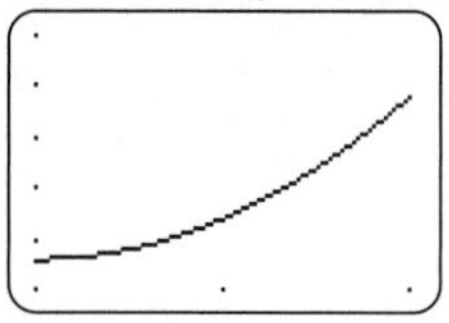

Figure 86

87. (a) $\frac{x^2}{12} = 144 \Rightarrow x^2 = 1728 \Rightarrow x = \sqrt{1728} \approx 41.6$ mph ($-\sqrt{1728}$ mph has no meaning).

(b) $\frac{x^2}{12} = 300 \Rightarrow x^2 = 3600 \Rightarrow x = \sqrt{3600} = 60$ mph (-60 mph has no meaning).

88. (a) $x(x + 2) = 143$ or $x^2 + 2x - 143 = 0$

(b) $x^2 + 2x - 143 = 0 \Rightarrow (x + 13)(x - 11) = 0 \Rightarrow x = -13$ or 11. There are two possible number pairs.

Either $x = -13$, and the other number is -11, or $x = 11$, and the other number is 13.

89. (a) Plot the data in [1935, 1995, 10] by [0, 100, 10]. See Figure 89.

(b) Yes, the data is nearly linear.

(c) Since $m = \dfrac{78 - 25}{1991 - 1940} = \dfrac{53}{51} \approx 1.04$,

The function could be $f(x) = 1.04(x - 1940) + 25$. *Answers may vary.*

[1935, 1995, 10] by [0, 100, 10]

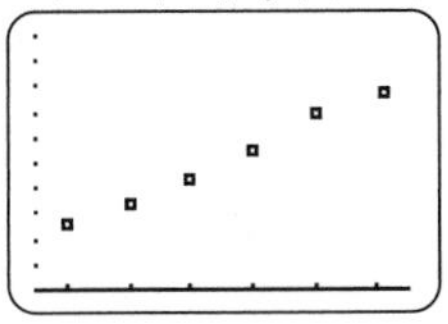

Figure 89

[1950, 1970, 5] by [200, 350, 25]

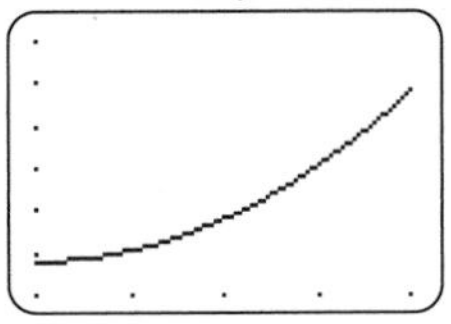

Figure 90

90. (a) The vertex is (1950, 220). In 1950 the per-capita energy consumption was at a low of 220 million Btu.

(b) Graph $Y_1 = (1/4)(X - 1950)^2 + 220$ in [1950, 1970, 5] by [200, 350, 25]. See Figure 90. It Increased.

(c) $f(1996) = \dfrac{1}{4}(1996 - 1950)^2 + 220 = 749$. The function is not a good model for 1996 because the trend represented by the model did not continue after 1970.

91. $\sqrt{123} \approx 11.1$; the screen is about 11.1 inches by 11.1 inches.

92. $x^2 + (x + 70)^2 = 130^2 \Rightarrow x^2 + x^2 + 140x + 4900 = 16{,}900 \Rightarrow 2x^2 + 140x - 12{,}000 = 0 \Rightarrow$

$2(x - 50)(x + 120) = 0 \Rightarrow x = 50$ or $x = -120$. The solution is $x = 50$ feet ($x = -120$ has no meaning).

93. $(30 + 2x)(50 + 2x) - 30(50) = 250 \Rightarrow 1500 + 160x + 4x^2 - 1500 = 250 \Rightarrow 4x^2 + 160x - 250 = 0 \Rightarrow$

$$x = \frac{-160 \pm \sqrt{(160)^2 - 4(4)(-250)}}{2(4)} = \frac{-160 \pm \sqrt{29{,}600}}{8} \Rightarrow x \approx -41.5 \text{ or } x \approx 1.5$$

The width of the strip of grass is about 1.5 feet. The value $x \approx -41.5$ has no physical meaning.

94. We must find r so that $750 \le \dfrac{1}{3}\pi r^2(20) \le 1700$.

$$\frac{1}{3}\pi r^2(20) \ge 750 \Rightarrow r^2 \ge \frac{2250}{20\pi} \Rightarrow r \ge \sqrt{\frac{2250}{20\pi}} \approx 5.98$$

$$\frac{1}{3}\pi r^2(20) \le 1700 \Rightarrow r^2 \ge \frac{5100}{20\pi} \Rightarrow r \ge \sqrt{\frac{5100}{20\pi}} \approx 9.01$$

The values or r can range from about 6 inches to about 9 inches.

Chapter 11 Test

1. $x = -\dfrac{b}{2a} = -\dfrac{1}{2(-\frac{1}{2})} = \dfrac{1}{1} = 1, f(1) = -\dfrac{1}{2}(1)^2 + (1) + 1 = \dfrac{3}{2}$; Vertex: $\left(1, \dfrac{3}{2}\right)$; Axis of symmetry: $x = 1$.

2. Because $-\dfrac{b}{2a} = -\dfrac{3}{2(1)} = -\dfrac{3}{2}$ and $f\left(-\dfrac{3}{2}\right) = \left(-\dfrac{3}{2}\right)^2 + 3\left(-\dfrac{3}{2}\right) - 5 = -\dfrac{29}{4}$, the vertex is $\left(-\dfrac{3}{2}, -\dfrac{29}{4}\right)$.

The minimum y-value on the graph is $-\dfrac{29}{4}$.

3. Since $f(x) = 0$ when $x = -2$, $a(-2)^2 + 2 = 0 \Rightarrow 4a = -2 \Rightarrow a = -\frac{1}{2}$.

4. See Figure 4.

This graph is wider than the graph of $y = x^2$ and is shifted right 3 units and upward 2 units.

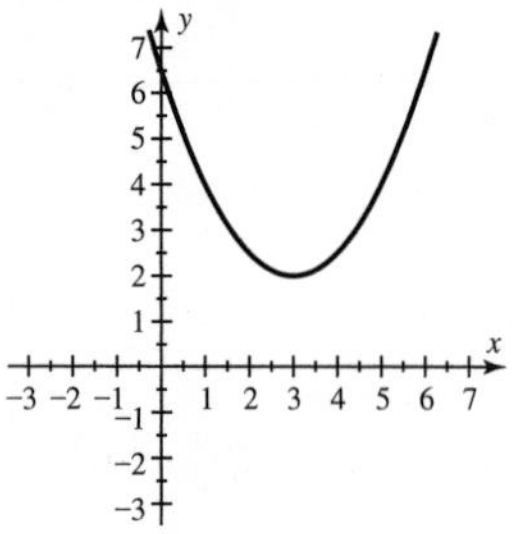

Figure 4

5. $y = x^2 - 6x + 2 \Rightarrow y = (x^2 - 6x + 9) + 2 - 9 \Rightarrow y = (x - 3)^2 - 7$. The vertex is $(3, -7)$.

6. The solutions are the x-intercepts, $x = -1$ or $x = 2$.

7. $3x^2 + 11x - 4 = 0 \Rightarrow (x + 4)(3x - 1) = 0 \Rightarrow x = -4$ or $x = \frac{1}{3}$

8. $2x^2 = 2 - 6x^2 \Rightarrow 8x^2 = 2 \Rightarrow x^2 = \frac{1}{4} \Rightarrow x = \pm\sqrt{\frac{1}{4}} \Rightarrow x = -\frac{1}{2}$ or $x = \frac{1}{2}$

9. $x^2 - 5x = 1 \Rightarrow x^2 - 5x + \frac{25}{4} = 1 + \frac{25}{4} \Rightarrow \left(x - \frac{5}{2}\right)^2 = \frac{29}{4} \Rightarrow x - \frac{5}{2} = \pm\sqrt{\frac{29}{4}} \Rightarrow x = \frac{5 \pm \sqrt{29}}{2}$

10. $x = \frac{-3 \pm \sqrt{(3)^2 - 4(-2)(1)}}{2(-2)} = \frac{-3 \pm \sqrt{17}}{-4} = \frac{3 \pm \sqrt{17}}{4}$

11. (a) Since the parabola opens downward, $a < 0$.

(b) The solutions are the x-intercepts, $x = -3$ or $x = 1$.

(c) Since there are two real solutions, the discriminant is positive.

12. (a) $(4)^2 - 4(-3)(-5) = -44$

(b) Since the discriminant is negative, there are no real solutions.

(c) Graph $Y_1 = -3X^2 + 4X - 5$ in [–5, 5, 1] by [–20, 10, 5]. See Figure 12. It does not intersect the x-axis.

[–5, 5, 1] by [–20, 10, 5]

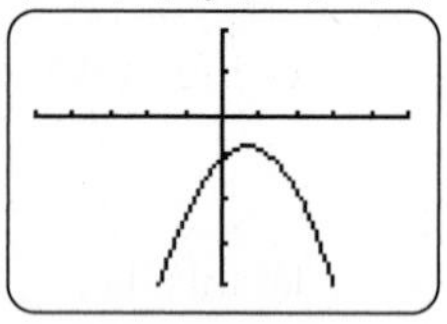

Figure 12

13. (a) The solutions are the x-intercepts, $x = -1$ or $x = 1$.

(b) $-1 < x < 1$

(c) $x < -1$ or $x > 1$

14. (a) The solutions are the x-intercepts, $x = -10$ or $x = 20$.

(b) $x < -10$ or $x > 20$

(c) $-10 < x < 20$

15. (a) $8x^2 - 2x - 3 = 0 \Rightarrow (2x + 1)(4x - 3) = 0 \Rightarrow x = -\frac{1}{2}$ or $x = \frac{3}{4}$

(b) Since the parabola opens upward, the solution is $\left[-\frac{1}{2}, \frac{3}{4}\right]$.

(c) Since the parabola opens upward, the solution is $\left(-\infty, -\frac{1}{2}\right] \cup \left[\frac{3}{4}, \infty\right)$.

16. Let $u = x^3$. Then $u^2 - 3u + 2 = 0 \Rightarrow (u - 1)(u - 2) = 0 \Rightarrow u = 1$ or 2.

When $u = 1$, $x^3 = 1 \Rightarrow x = \sqrt[3]{1} = 1$. When $u = 2$, $x^3 = 2 \Rightarrow x = \sqrt[3]{2}$.

17. $\frac{x^2}{9} = 250 \Rightarrow x^2 = 2250 \Rightarrow x = \sqrt{2250} \approx 47.4$ mph (the value $x \approx -47.4$ mph has no physical meaning).

18. (a) $2y + 2x + 20 = 200 \Rightarrow 2x + 2y = 180 \Rightarrow y = 90 - x$, so the formula is $f(x) = (x + 20)(90 - x)$.

(b) Note that $f(x) = (x + 20)(90 - x) \Rightarrow f(x) = -x^2 + 70x + 1800$. The area is greatest for the value of x at the vertex of the parabola, $x = -\frac{b}{2a} = -\frac{70}{2(-1)} = 35$. The enclosed area is greatest when $x = 35$.

19. (a) Graph $Y_1 = -16X^2 + 88X + 8$ in [0, 6, 1] by [0, 150, 50]. See Figure 19.

(b) $t = \frac{-88 \pm \sqrt{(88)^2 - 4(-16)(8)}}{2(-16)} = \frac{-88 \pm \sqrt{8256}}{-32} \approx 5.6$ seconds (the value $t \approx -0.089$ has no meaning).

(c) The stone reaches a maximum height of 129 feet after 2.75 seconds. See Figure 19.

[0, 6, 1] by [0, 150, 50]

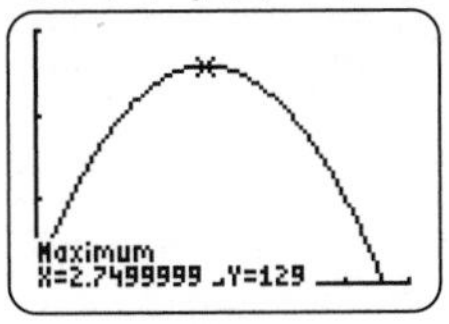

Figure 19

[0, 10, 1] by [0, 75, 5]

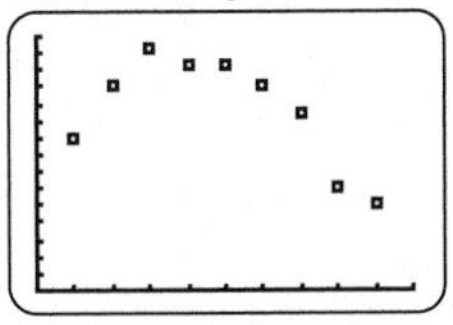

Figure 1b

[0, 10, 1] by [0, 75, 5]

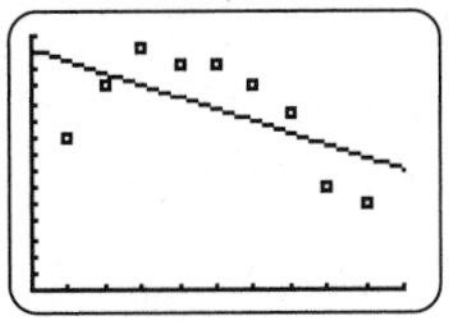

Figure 1c

[0, 10, 1] by [0, 75, 5]

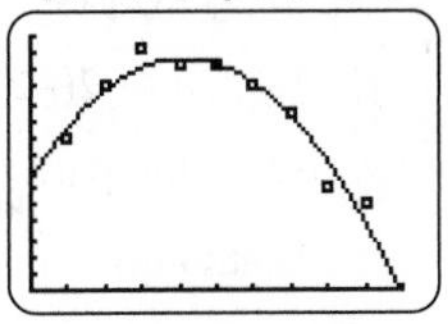

Figure 1d

Chapter 11 Extended and Discovery Exercises

1. (a) For the first 3 years of life, the likelihood of survival increases with age. After 3 years of life, it decreases with age.

(b) Plot the data in [0, 10, 1] by [0, 75, 5]. See Figure 1b. A quadratic function could model this data since the data points form a parabola.

(c) Graph $Y_1 = -3.57X + 71.1$ in [0, 10, 1] by [0, 75, 5]. See Figure 1c.

Graph $Y_1 = -2.07X^2 + 17.1X + 33$ in [0, 10, 1] by [0, 75, 5]. See Figure 1d.

The function f_2 models the data better.

(d) Evaluate f at $x = 6.5$ to find the likelihood of a 5.5-year-old sparrowhawk living 1 more year.

$f_2(6.5) = -2.07(6.5)^2 + 17.1(6.5) + 33 \approx 56.7\%$

2. (a) Plot the data in [–5, 35, 5] by [0, 100, 10]. See Figure 2.

   (b) A quadratic function could model this data since the data points form a parabola.

   (c) Using the data point (12, 95) as the vertex, the function has the form $f(x) = a(x - 12)^2 + 95$.

   By trial and error we find that $a = -0.25$ gives a fairly good fit. The function is given by

   $f(x) = -0.25(x - 12)^2 + 95$. *Answers may vary.*

   (d) The x-coordinate of the vertex, 12°C, represents the the temperature that photosynthesis is most efficient.

[–5, 35, 5] by [0, 100, 10]

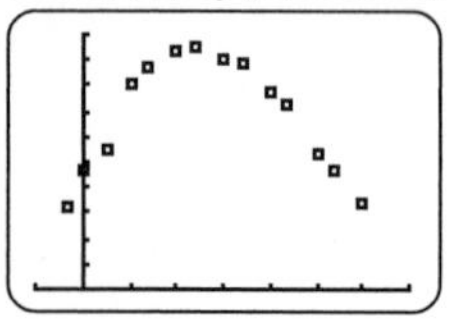

Figure 2

[–4, 4, 1] by [0, 6, 1]

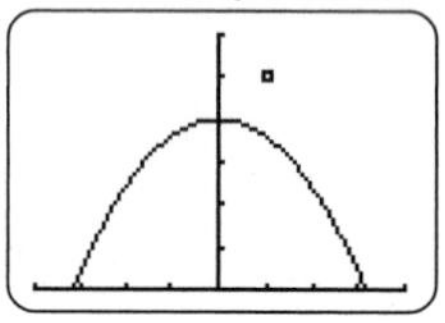

Figure 3a

[–4, 4, 1] by [0, 6, 1]

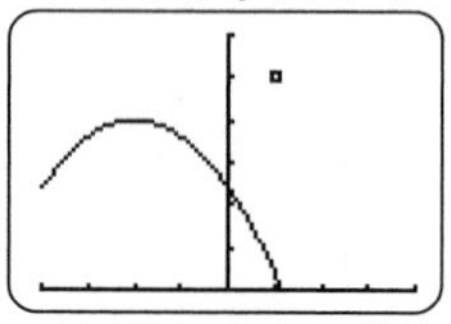

Figure 3b

3. (a) Plot (1, 5) and graph $Y_1 = -0.4X^2 + 4$ in [–4, 4, 1] by [0, 6, 1]. See Figure 3a.

   (b) After 10 seconds the plane would have moved 2 kilometers. We will shift the parabola 2 units left.

   Plot (1, 5) and graph $Y_1 = -0.4(X + 2)^2 + 4$ in [–4, 4, 1] by [0, 6, 1]. See Figure 3b.

4. We would need to translate the mountain both to the right and downward so that the airplane would appear to move to the left and upward. One example could be $f(x) = -0.4(x - 2)^2 + 4 - 2$.

5. The discriminant is $(-1)^2 - 4(10)(-3) = 121 = 11^2$. The trinomial factors as $(2x + 1)(5x - 3)$.

6. The discriminant is $(-3)^2 - 4(4)(-6) = 105$. The trinomial will not factor.

7. The discriminant is $(2)^2 - 4(3)(-2) = 28$. The trinomial will not factor.

8. The discriminant is $(1)^2 - 4(2)(3) = -23$. The trinomial will not factor.

9. $x^3 - x^2 - 6x = 0 \Rightarrow x(x^2 - x - 6) = 0 \Rightarrow x(x - 3)(x + 2) = 0 \Rightarrow x = 0, 3, \text{ or } -2$

   In the interval $(-\infty, -2)$, we test $x = -3$. $f(-3) = (-3)^3 - (-3)^2 - 6(-3) = -18 < 0$

   In the interval $(-2, 0)$, we test $x = -1$. $f(-1) = (-1)^3 - (-1)^2 - 6(-1) = 4 > 0$

   In the interval $(0, 3)$, we test $x = 1$. $f(1) = (1)^3 - (1)^2 - 6(1) = -6 < 0$

   In the interval $(3, \infty)$, we test $x = 4$. $f(4) = (4)^3 - (4)^2 - 6(4) = 24 > 0$

   The solution to the given inequality is $(-2, 0) \cup (3, \infty)$.

10. $x^3 - 3x^2 + 2x = 0 \Rightarrow x(x^2 - 3x + 2) = 0 \Rightarrow x(x - 1)(x - 2) = 0 \Rightarrow x = 0, 1, \text{ or } 2$

    In the interval $(-\infty, 0)$, we test $x = -1$. $f(-1) = (-1)^3 - 3(-1)^2 + 2(-1) = -6 < 0$

    In the interval $(0, 1)$, we test $x = 0.5$. $f(0.5) = (0.5)^3 - 3(0.5)^2 + 2(0.5) = 0.375 > 0$

    In the interval $(1, 2)$, we test $x = 1.5$. $f(1.5) = (1.5)^3 - 3(1.5)^2 + 2(1.5) = -0.375 < 0$

    In the interval $(2, \infty)$, we test $x = 3$. $f(3) = (3)^3 - 3(3)^2 + 2(3) = 6 > 0$

    The solution to the given inequality is $(-\infty, 0) \cup (1, 2)$.

11. $x^3 - 7x^2 + 14x - 8 = 0 \Rightarrow (x^3 - 8) - 7x^2 + 14x = 0 \Rightarrow (x - 2)(x^2 + 2x + 4) - 7x(x - 2) = 0 \Rightarrow$

$(x - 2)((x^2 + 2x + 4) - 7x) = 0 \Rightarrow (x - 2)(x^2 - 5x + 4) = 0 \Rightarrow (x - 2)(x - 1)(x - 4) = 0 \Rightarrow$

$x = 1, 2,$ or 4

In the interval $(-\infty, 1)$, we test $x = 0$. $f(0) = (0)^3 - 7(0)^2 + 14(0) - 8 = -8 \leq 0$

In the interval $(1, 2)$, we test $x = 1.5$. $f(1.5) = (1.5)^3 - 7(1.5)^2 + 14(1.5) - 8 = 0.625 \geq 0$

In the interval $(2, 4)$, we test $x = 3$. $f(3) = (3)^3 - 7(3)^2 + 14(3) - 8 = -2 \leq 0$

In the interval $(4, \infty)$, we test $x = 5$. $f(5) = (5)^3 - 7(5)^2 + 14(5) - 8 = 12 \geq 0$

The solution to the given inequality is $(-\infty, 1] \cup [2, 4]$.

12. $9x - x^3 = 0 \Rightarrow x(9 - x^2) = 0 \Rightarrow x(3 - x)(3 + x) = 0 \Rightarrow x = 0, 3,$ or -3

In the interval $(-\infty, -3)$, we test $x = -4$. $f(-4) = 9(-4) - (-4)^3 = 28 \geq 0$

In the interval $(-3, 0)$, we test $x = -1$. $f(-1) = 9(-1) - (-1)^3 = -8 \leq 0$

In the interval $(0, 3)$, we test $x = 1$. $f(1) = 9(1) - (1)^3 = 8 \geq 0$

In the interval $(3, \infty)$, we test $x = 4$. $f(4) = 9(4) - (4)^3 = -28 \leq 0$

The solution to the given inequality is $(-\infty, -3] \cup [0, 3]$.

13. $x^4 - 5x^2 + 4 = 0 \Rightarrow (x^2 - 1)(x^2 - 4) = 0 \Rightarrow (x - 1)(x + 1)(x - 2)(x + 2) = 0 \Rightarrow x = -2, -1, 1,$ or 2

In the interval $(-\infty, -2)$, we test $x = -3$. $f(-3) = (-3)^4 - 5(-3)^2 + 4 = 40 > 0$

In the interval $(-2, -1)$, we test $x = -1.5$. $f(-1.5) = (-1.5)^4 - 5(-1.5)^2 + 4 = -2.1875 < 0$

In the interval $(-1, 1)$, we test $x = 0$. $f(0) = (0)^4 - 5(0)^2 + 4 = 4 > 0$

In the interval $(1, 2)$, we test $x = 1.5$. $f(1.5) = (1.5)^4 - 5(1.5)^2 + 4 = -2.1875 < 0$

In the interval $(2, \infty)$, we test $x = 3$. $f(3) = (3)^4 - 5(3)^2 + 4 = 40 > 0$

The solution to the given inequality is $(-\infty, -2) \cup (-1, 1) \cup (2, \infty)$.

14. $1 - x^4 = 0 \Rightarrow (1 - x^2)(1 + x^2) = 0 \Rightarrow (1 - x)(1 + x)(1 + x^2) = 0 \Rightarrow x = -1$ or 1

In the interval $(-\infty, -1)$, we test $x = -2$. $f(-2) = 1 - (-2)^4 = -15 < 0$

In the interval $(-1, 1)$, we test $x = 0$. $f(-2) = 1 - (0)^4 = 1 > 0$

In the interval $(1, \infty)$, we test $x = 2$. $f(2) = 1 - (2)^4 = -15 < 0$

The solution to the given inequality is $(-\infty, -1) \cup (1, \infty)$.

15. $\dfrac{3 - x}{3x} = 0 \Rightarrow 3 - x = 0 \Rightarrow x = 3$. The expression is undefined when $3x = 0 \Rightarrow x = 0$.

In the interval $(-\infty, 0)$, we test $x = -1$. $f(-1) = \dfrac{3 - (-1)}{3(-1)} = -\dfrac{4}{3} \leq 0$

In the interval $(0, 3)$, we test $x = 1$. $f(1) = \dfrac{3 - (1)}{3(1)} = \dfrac{2}{3} \geq 0$

In the interval $(3, \infty)$, we test $x = 4$. $f(4) = \dfrac{3 - (4)}{3(4)} = -\dfrac{1}{12} \leq 0$

The solution to the given inequality is $(0, 3]$.

16. $\dfrac{x-2}{x+2} = 0 \Rightarrow x - 2 = 0 \Rightarrow x = 2$. The expression is undefined when $x + 2 = 0 \Rightarrow x = -2$.

In the interval $(-\infty, -2)$, we test $x = -3$. $f(-3) = \dfrac{(-3) - 2}{(-3) + 2} = 5 > 0$

In the interval $(-2, 2)$, we test $x = 0$. $f(0) = \dfrac{(0) - 2}{(0) + 2} = -1 < 0$

In the interval $(2, \infty)$, we test $x = 3$. $f(3) = \dfrac{(3) - 2}{(3) + 2} = \dfrac{1}{5} > 0$

The solution to the given inequality is $(-\infty, -2) \cup (2, \infty)$.

17. $\dfrac{3 - 2x}{1 + x} = 3 \Rightarrow 3 - 2x = 3 + 3x \Rightarrow 5x = 0 \Rightarrow x = 0$.

The expression is undefined when $1 + x = 0 \Rightarrow x = -1$.

In the interval $(-\infty, -1)$, we test $x = -2$. $f(-2) = \dfrac{3 - 2(-2)}{1 + (-2)} - 3 = -10 < 0$

In the interval $(-1, 0)$, we test $x = -0.5$. $f(-0.5) = \dfrac{3 - 2(-0.5)}{1 + (-0.5)} - 3 = 5 > 0$

In the interval $(0, \infty)$, we test $x = 1$. $f(1) = \dfrac{3 - 2(1)}{1 + (1)} - 3 = -\dfrac{5}{2} < 0$

The solution to the given inequality is $(-\infty, -1) \cup (0, \infty)$.

18. $\dfrac{x + 1}{4 - 2x} = 1 \Rightarrow x + 1 = 4 - 2x \Rightarrow 3x = 3 \Rightarrow x = 1$.

The expression is undefined when $4 - 2x = 0 \Rightarrow 2x = 4 \Rightarrow x = 2$.

In the interval $(-\infty, 1]$, we test $x = 0$. $f(0) = \dfrac{(0) + 1}{4 - 2(0)} - 1 = -\dfrac{3}{4} \le 0$

In the interval $(1, 2)$, we test $x = 1.5$. $f(1.5) = \dfrac{(1.5) + 1}{4 - 2(1.5)} - 1 = \dfrac{3}{2} \ge 0$

In the interval $(2, \infty)$, we test $x = 3$. $f(3) = \dfrac{(3) + 1}{4 - 2(3)} - 1 = -3 \le 0$

The solution to the given inequality is $[1, 2)$.

19. The expression is undefined when $x^2 - 4 = 0 \Rightarrow (x + 2)(x - 2) = 0 \Rightarrow x = -2$ or 2.

In the interval $(-\infty, -2)$, we test $x = -3$. $f(-3) = \dfrac{5}{(-3)^2 - 4} = 1 > 0$

In the interval $(-2, 2)$, we test $x = 0$. $f(0) = \dfrac{5}{(0)^2 - 4} = -\dfrac{5}{4} < 0$

In the interval $(2, \infty)$, we test $x = 3$. $f(3) = \dfrac{5}{(3)^2 - 4} = 1 > 0$

The solution to the given inequality is $(-2, 2)$.

20. $\frac{x}{x^2 - 1} = 0 \Rightarrow x = 0$. The expression is undefined when $x^2 - 1 = 0 \Rightarrow (x + 1)(x - 1) = 0 \Rightarrow x = -1$ or 1.

In the interval $(-\infty, -1)$, we test $x = -2$. $f(-2) = \frac{(-2)}{(-2)^2 - 1} = -\frac{2}{3} \leq 0$

In the interval $(-1, 0)$, we test $x = -0.5$. $f(-0.5) = \frac{(-0.5)}{(-0.5)^2 - 1} = \frac{2}{3} \geq 0$

In the interval $(0, 1)$, we test $x = -0.5$. $f(0.5) = \frac{(0.5)}{(0.5)^2 - 1} = -\frac{2}{3} \leq 0$

In the interval $(1, \infty)$, we test $x = 2$. $f(2) = \frac{(2)}{(2)^2 - 1} = \frac{2}{3} \geq 0$

The solution to the given inequality is $(-1, 0] \cup (1, \infty)$.

Critical Thinking Solutions for Chapter 11

Section 11.1

- If the point (x, y) is reflected across the y-axis, the resulting point is $(-x, y)$.

Section 11.2

- When $x = 0$, $y = a(0)^2 + b(0) + c = c$. That is, c is the y-intercept.
- If the speed doubles to $2x$, then $R(2x) = \frac{1}{2}(2x)^2 = \frac{1}{2} \cdot 4x^2 = 4\left(\frac{1}{2}x^2\right) = 4R(x)$. That is, the radius increases by a factor of 4.

Section 11.3

- If we write the equation in $x^2 + kx = d$ form, it would become $x^2 + 0x = 7$. To complete the square we would add zero to both sides of the equation. Completing the square will not work in this case. The square root property should be used for this equation.

Section 11.4

- Both expressions equal zero because these values of x are the solutions to $2x^2 - 3x - 1 = 0$.
- Both expressions equal zero because these values of x are the solutions to $2x^2 + x + 3 = 0$.

Section 11.5

- i. The parabola is above the x-axis for values of x between the intercepts: $(-3, 4)$.

  ii. The parabola is below the x-axis for values of x outside of the intercepts: $(-\infty, -3) \cup (4, \infty)$.

- Graph $Y_1 = X^2 + 1$ in [–5, 5, 1] by [–5, 5, 1]. See Figure 1a.

  i. All real numbers ii. No solutions

  Graph $Y_1 = (X - 1)^2$ in [–5, 5, 1] by [–5, 5, 1]. See Figure 1b.

  iii. All real numbers iv. $x = 1$

[–5, 5, 1] by [–5, 5, 1]

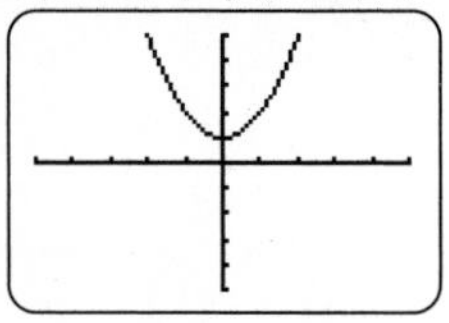

Figure 1a

[–5, 5, 1] by [–5, 5, 1]

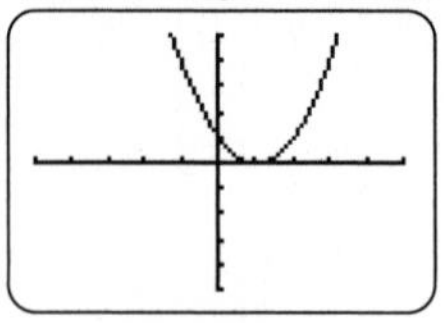

Figure 1b

Chapter 12: Exponential and Logarithmic Functions

12.1: Composite and Inverse Functions

Concepts

1. $g(f(7))$
3. No
5. No
7. adding 10
9. 8; 6
11. one-to-one

Composite Functions

13. (a) $f(-2) = (-2)^2 = 4$, then $(g \circ f)(-2) = g(f(-2)) = g(4) = 4 + 3 = 7$

    (b) $g(4) = 4 + 3 = 7$, then $(f \circ g)(4) = f(g(4)) = f(7) = 7^2 = 49$

    (c) $(g \circ f)(x) = g(f(x)) = g(x^2) = x^2 + 3$

    (d) $(f \circ g)(x) = f(g(x)) = f(x + 3) = (x + 3)^2$

15. (a) $f(-2) = 2(-2) = -4$, then $(g \circ f)(-2) = g(f(-2)) = g(-4) = (-4)^3 - 1 = -65$

    (b) $g(4) = 4^3 - 1 = 63$, then $(f \circ g)(4) = f(g(4)) = f(63) = 2(63) = 126$

    (c) $(g \circ f)(x) = g(f(x)) = g(2x) = (2x)^3 - 1 = 8x^2 - 1$

    (d) $(f \circ g)(x) = f(g(x)) = f(x^3 - 1) = 2(x^3 - 1) = 2x^3 - 2$

17. (a) $f(-2) = \frac{1}{2}(-2) = -1$, then $(g \circ f)(-2) = g(f(-2)) = g(-1) = |(-1) - 2| = 3$

    (b) $g(4) = |4 - 2| = 2$, then $(f \circ g)(4) = f(g(4)) = f(2) = \frac{1}{2}(2) = 1$

    (c) $(g \circ f)(x) = g(f(x)) = g\left(\frac{1}{2}x\right) = \left|\frac{1}{2}x - 2\right|$

    (d) $(f \circ g)(x) = f(g(x)) = f(|x - 2|) = \frac{1}{2}|x - 2|$

19. (a) $f(-2) = \frac{1}{-2} = -\frac{1}{2}$, then $(g \circ f)(-2) = g(f(-2)) = g\left(-\frac{1}{2}\right) = 3 - 5\left(-\frac{1}{2}\right) = \frac{11}{2}$

    (b) $g(4) = 3 - 5(4) = -17$, then $(f \circ g)(4) = f(g(4)) = f(-17) = \frac{1}{-17} = -\frac{1}{17}$

    (c) $(g \circ f)(x) = g(f(x)) = g\left(\frac{1}{x}\right) = 3 - 5\left(\frac{1}{x}\right) = 3 - \frac{5}{x}$

    (d) $(f \circ g)(x) = f(g(x)) = f(3 - 5x) = \frac{1}{3 - 5x}$

21. (a) $f(-2) = 2(-2) = -4$, then $(g \circ f)(-2) = g(f(-2)) = g(-4) = 4(-4)^2 - 2(-4) + 5 = 77$

    (b) $g(4) = 4(4)^2 - 2(4) + 5 = 61$, then $(f \circ g)(4) = f(g(4)) = f(61) = 2(61) = 122$

    (c) $(g \circ f)(x) = g(f(x)) = g(2x) = 4(2x)^2 - 2(2x) + 5 = 16x^2 - 4x + 5$

    (d) $(f \circ g)(x) = f(g(x)) = f(4x^2 - 2x + 5) = 2(4x^2 - 2x + 5) = 8x^2 - 4x + 10$

23. (a) $(f \circ g)(0) = f(g(0)) = f(-1) = 1$

(b) $(g \circ f)(-1) = g(f(-1)) = g(1) = 2$

25. (a) $(f \circ f)(-1) = f(f(-1)) = f(1) = -1$

(b) $(g \circ g)(0) = g(g(0)) = g(-1) = 1$

27. (a) $(f^{-1} \circ g)(-2) = f^{-1}(g(-2)) = f^{-1}(0) = 0$

(b) $(g^{-1} \circ f)(2) = g^{-1}(f(2)) = g^{-1}(-2) = 2$

29. (a) $(f \circ g)(0) = f(g(0)) = f(-1) = 2$

(b) $(g \circ f)(1) = g(f(1)) = g(2) = -3$

(c) $(f \circ f)(-1) = f(f(-1)) = f(2) = -1$

31. $f(1) = f(-1) = 5$; *Answers may vary.*

33. $f(1) = f(-1) = 101$; *Answers may vary.*

35. $f(2) = f(-2) = 4$; *Answers may vary.*

37. This graph passes the horizontal line test. The function is one-to-one.

39. This graph does not pass the horizontal line test. The function is not one-to-one.

41. This graph passes the horizontal line test. The function is one-to-one.

43. Divide x by 7. $f(x) = 7x$; $g(x) = \frac{x}{7}$

45. Multiply x by 2 and then subtract 5. $f(x) = \frac{x + 5}{2}$; $g(x) = 2x - 5$

47. Add 3 to x and then multiply the result by 2. $f(x) = \frac{1}{2}x - 3$; $g(x) = 2(x + 3)$

49. Take the cube root of x and then subtract 5. $f(x) = (x + 5)^3$; $g(x) = \sqrt[3]{x} - 5$

51. $(f \circ f^{-1})(x) = f(f^{-1}(x)) = f\left(\frac{x}{4}\right) = 4\left(\frac{x}{4}\right) = x$ and $(f^{-1} \circ f)(x) = f^{-1}(f(x)) = f^{-1}(4x) = \frac{4x}{4} = x$

53. $(f \circ f^{-1})(x) = f(f^{-1}(x)) = f\left(\frac{x - 5}{3}\right) = 3\left(\frac{x - 5}{3}\right) + 5 = x - 5 + 5 = x$

$(f^{-1} \circ f)(x) = f^{-1}(f(x)) = f^{-1}(3x + 5) = \frac{(3x + 5) - 5}{3} = \frac{3x}{3} = x$

55. $(f \circ f^{-1})(x) = f(f^{-1}(x)) = f(\sqrt[3]{x}) = (\sqrt[3]{x})^3 = x$ and $(f^{-1} \circ f)(x) = f^{-1}(f(x)) = f^{-1}(x^3) = \sqrt[3]{x^3} = x$

57. $(f \circ f^{-1})(x) = f(f^{-1}(x)) = f\left(\frac{1}{x}\right) = \frac{1}{\frac{1}{x}} = x$ and $(f^{-1} \circ f)(x) = f^{-1}(f(x)) = f^{-1}\left(\frac{1}{x}\right) = \frac{1}{\frac{1}{x}} = x$

59. $f(x) = 12x \Rightarrow y = 12x$, interchange x and y and solve for y. $x = 12y \Rightarrow y = \frac{x}{12} \Rightarrow f^{-1}(x) = \frac{x}{12}$

61. $f(x) = x + 8 \Rightarrow y = x + 8$, interchange x and y and solve for y.

$x = y + 8 \Rightarrow y = x - 8 \Rightarrow f^{-1}(x) = x - 8$

63. $f(x) = 5x - 2 \Rightarrow y = 5x - 2$, interchange x and y and solve for y.

$x = 5y - 2 \Rightarrow 5y = x + 2 \Rightarrow y = \frac{x + 2}{5} \Rightarrow f^{-1}(x) = \frac{x + 2}{5}$

65. $f(x) = -\frac{1}{2}x + 1 \Rightarrow y = -\frac{1}{2}x + 1$, interchange x and y and solve for y.

$x = -\frac{1}{2}y + 1 \Rightarrow -\frac{1}{2}y = x - 1 \Rightarrow y = -2(x - 1) \Rightarrow f^{-1}(x) = -2(x - 1)$

67. $f(x) = 8 - x \Rightarrow y = 8 - x$, interchange x and y and solve for y.

$x = 8 - y \Rightarrow y = 8 - x \Rightarrow f^{-1}(x) = 8 - x$

69. $f(x) = \dfrac{x+1}{2} \Rightarrow y = \dfrac{x+1}{2}$, interchange x and y and solve for y.

$x = \dfrac{y+1}{2} \Rightarrow y + 1 = 2x \Rightarrow y = 2x - 1 \Rightarrow f^{-1}(x) = 2x - 1$

71. $f(x) = \sqrt[3]{2x} \Rightarrow y = \sqrt[3]{2x}$, interchange x and y and solve for y.

$x = \sqrt[3]{2y} \Rightarrow 2y = x^3 \Rightarrow y = \dfrac{x^3}{2} \Rightarrow f^{-1}(x) = \dfrac{x^3}{2}$

73. $f(x) = x^3 - 8 \Rightarrow y = x^3 - 8$, interchange x and y and solve for y.

$x = y^3 - 8 \Rightarrow y^3 = x + 8 \Rightarrow y = \sqrt[3]{x+8} \Rightarrow f^{-1}(x) = \sqrt[3]{x+8}$

75. See Figure 75. The domain of f = the range of f^{-1} = {0, 1, 2, 3, 4}.

The range of f = the domain of f^{-1} = {0, 5, 10, 15, 20}.

x	0	5	10	15	20
$f^{-1}(x)$	0	1	2	3	4

Figure 75

x	4	2	0	−2	−4
$f^{-1}(x)$	−5	0	5	10	15

Figure 77

77. See Figure 77. The domain of f = the range of f^{-1} = {−5, 0, 5, 10, 15}.

The range of f = the domain of f^{-1} = {−4, −2, 0, 2, 4}.

79. The graph of f^{-1} is a reflection of the graph of f across the line $y = x$. See Figure 79.

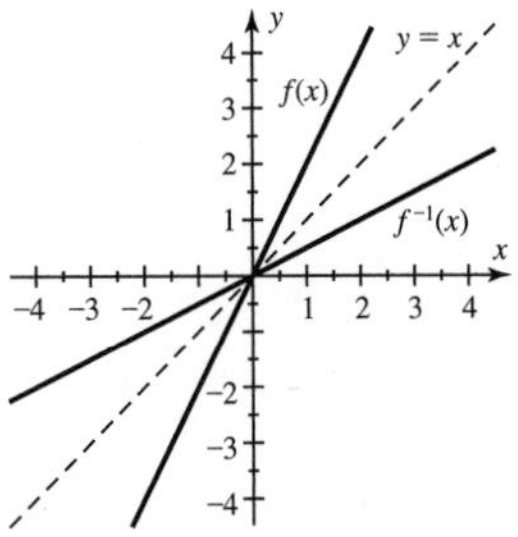

Figure 79

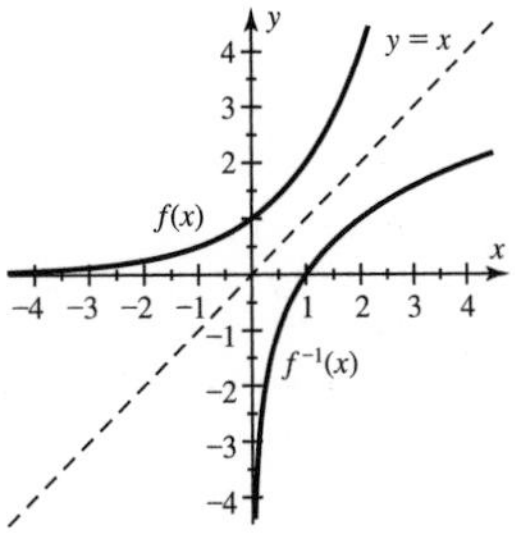

Figure 81

81. The graph of f^{-1} is a reflection of the graph of f across the line $y = x$. See Figure 81.

Applications

83. (a) $(C \circ r)(5) = C(r(5)) = C(2 \cdot 5) = C(10) = 2\pi \cdot 10 = 20\pi$

After 5 seconds, the wave has a circumference of $20\pi \approx 62.8$ feet.

(b) $(C \circ r)(t) = C(r(t)) = C(2t) = 2\pi \cdot 2t = 4\pi t$

85. (a) $T(1) = 75°$ and $M(75) = 150$

(b) $(M \circ T)(1) = M(T(1)) = M(75) = 150$

One hour after midnight there are 150 mosquitoes per 100 square feet.

(c) $(M \circ T)(h)$ calculates the number of mosquitoes per 100 square feet, h hours after midnight.

(d) For $T(h)$, $m = \dfrac{50 - 80}{6 - 0} = \dfrac{-30}{6} = -5$. Since the y-intercept is 80, the equation is $T(h) = -5h + 80$.

For $M(T)$, $m = \dfrac{150 - 100}{75 - 50} = \dfrac{50}{25} = 2$. Since the line passes through (50, 100), the equation is $M(T) = 2T$.

(e) $(M \circ T)(h) = M(T(h)) = M(-5h + 80) = 2(-5h + 80) = -10h + 160$

87. (a) $P(1980) = 16$; In 1980, 16% of people 25 or older completed 4 or more years of college.

(b) See Figure 87.

(c) $P^{-1}(16) = 1980$

x	8	16	27
$P^{-1}(x)$	1960	1980	2000

Figure 87

89. (a) Yes, this is a one-to-one function because different inputs result in different outputs.

(b) $f(x) = \frac{5}{9}x + 32 \Rightarrow y = \frac{5}{9}x + 32$, interchange x and y and solve for y.

$x = \frac{5}{9}y + 32 \Rightarrow \frac{5}{9}y = x - 32 \Rightarrow y = \frac{9}{5}(x - 32) \Rightarrow f^{-1}(x) = \frac{9}{5}(x - 32)$

This formula converts x degrees Fahrenheit to an equivalent temperature in degrees Celsius.

91. Since there are 4 quarts in 1 gallon, the function $f(x) = 4x$ converts x gallons to quarts.

$f(x) = 4x \Rightarrow y = 4x$, interchange x and y and solve for y. $x = 4y \Rightarrow y = \frac{x}{4} \Rightarrow f^{-1}(x) = \frac{x}{4}$

This formula converts x quarts to gallons.

12.2: Exponential Functions

Concepts

1. $f(x) = Ca^x$

3. The graph illustrates growth, since $a > 1$.

5. $e \approx 2.718$

7. Factor

Evaluating and Graphing Exponential Functions

9. $f(-2) = 3^{-2} = \frac{1}{3^2} = \frac{1}{9}$ and $f(2) = 3^2 = 9$

11. $f(0) = 5(2^0) = 5(1) = 5$ and $f(5) = 5(2^5) = 5(32) = 160$

13. $f(-2) = \left(\frac{1}{2}\right)^{-2} = 2^2 = 4$ and $f(3) = \left(\frac{1}{2}\right)^3 = \frac{1}{2^3} = \frac{1}{8}$

15. $f(-1) = 5(3)^{-(-1)} = 5(3)^1 = 15$ and $f(2) = 5(3)^{-2} = 5\left(\frac{1}{3^2}\right) = \frac{5}{9}$

17. $f(-3) = 1.8^{-3} \approx 0.17$ and $f(1.5) = 1.8^{1.5} \approx 2.41$

19. $f(-1) = 3(0.6)^{-1} = 5$ and $f(2) = 3(0.6)^2 = 1.08$

21. (a) Exponential decay. For each unit increase in x, $f(x)$ decreases by a factor of $\frac{1}{4}$.

(b) Since $f(x) = 64$ when $x = 0, f(x) = 64\left(\frac{1}{4}\right)^x$

23. (a) Linear growth. For each unit increase in x, $f(x)$ increases by 3 units.

(b) Since $f(x) = 8$ when $x = 0, f(x) = 3x + 8$

25. (a) Exponential growth. For each unit increase in x, $f(x)$ increases by a factor of 1.25.

(b) Since $f(x) = 4$ when $x = 0, f(x) = 4(1.25)^x$

27. Since $y = 1$ when $x = 0$, $1 = Ca^0 \Rightarrow C = 1$. Since $y = 2$ when $x = 1$, $2 = 1(a)^1 \Rightarrow a = 2$.

29. Since $y = 4$ when $x = 0$, $4 = Ca^0 \Rightarrow C = 4$. Since $y = 1$ when $x = 1$, $1 = 4(a)^1 \Rightarrow a = \frac{1}{4}$.

31. c. This function models exponential growth and passes through the point (0, 1).

33. d. This function models exponential decay and passes through the point (2, 1).

35. See Figure 35. The graph illustrates exponential growth.

37. See Figure 37. The graph illustrates exponential decay.

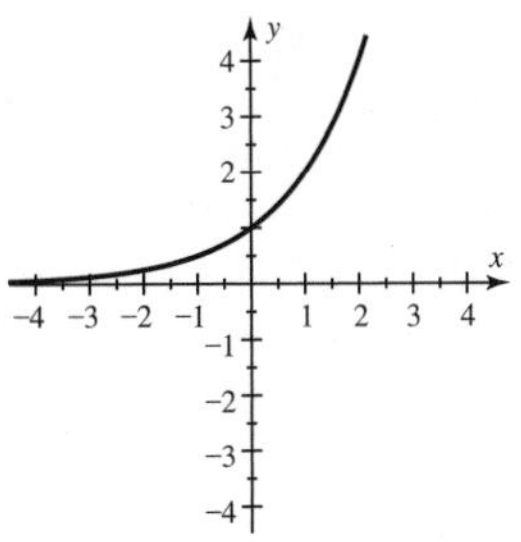

Figure 35

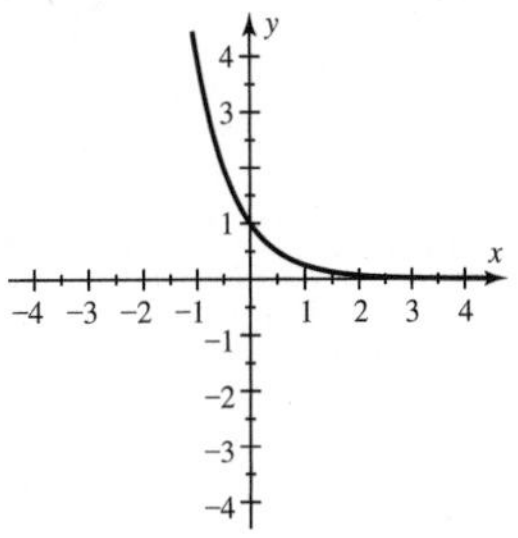

Figure 37

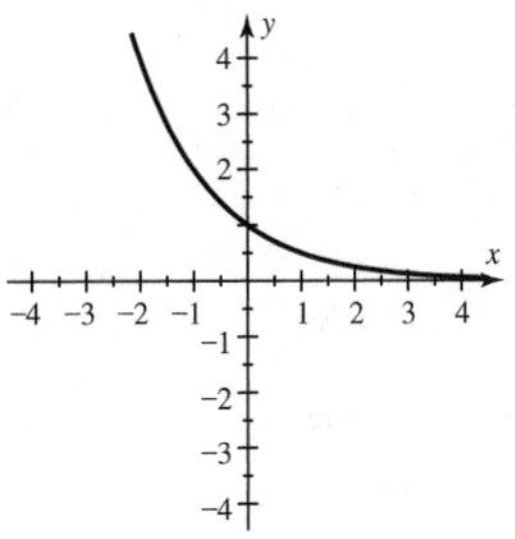

Figure 39

39. See Figure 39. The graph illustrates exponential decay.

41. See Figure 41. The graph illustrates exponential growth.

43. See Figure 43. The graph illustrates exponential growth.

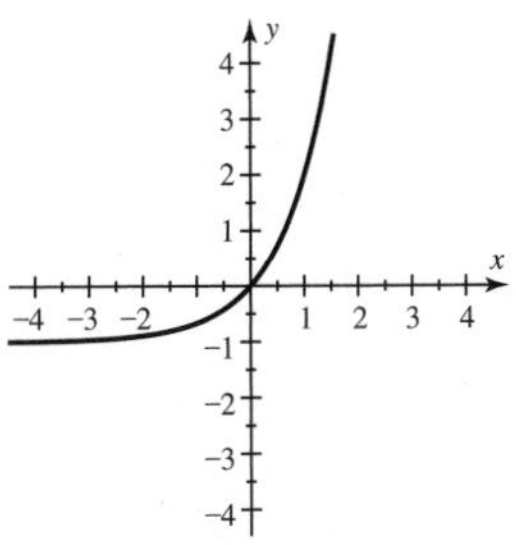

Figure 41

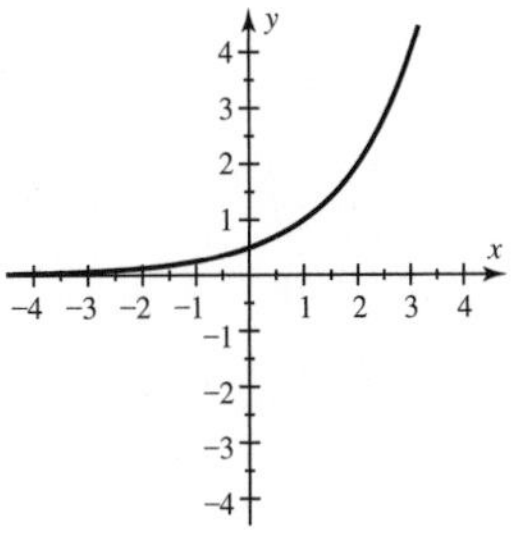

Figure 43

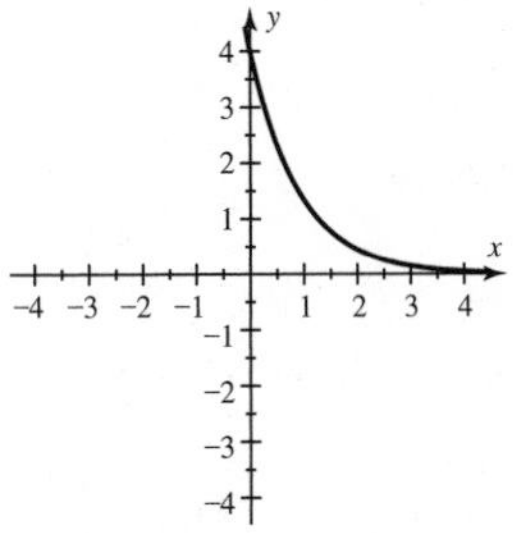

Figure 45

45. See Figure 45. The graph illustrates exponential decay.

47. $e^2e^5 = e^{2+5} = e^7$

49. $\dfrac{a^4a^{-2}}{a^3} = \dfrac{a^{4+(-2)}}{a^3} = \dfrac{a^2}{a^3} = a^{2-3} = a^{-1} = \dfrac{1}{a}$

51. $e^xe^{y-x} = e^{x+(y-x)} = e^y$

53. $\dfrac{2^{x+3}}{2^x} = 2^{x+3-x} = 2^3 = 8$

55. $5^{-y} \cdot 5^{3y} = 5^{-y+3y} = 5^{2y} = 25^y$

Compound Interest

57. $1500(1 + 0.09)^{10} = \$3551.05$

59. $200(1 + 0.20)^{50} = \$1{,}820{,}087.63$

61. $560(1 + 0.014)^{25} = \$792.75$

63. Yes. This is equivalent to having two accounts, each containing \$1000 initially.

65. $A = 300(1 + 0.0495)^{30} \approx \$1278.2$ billion or about \$1.28 trillion

The Natural Exponential Function

67. $f(1.2) = e^{1.2} \approx 3.32$

69. $f(-2) = 1 - e^{-2} \approx 0.86$

71. Graph $Y_1 = e$^(0.5X) in [−4, 4, 1] by [0, 8, 1]. See Figure 71. The graph illustrates exponential growth.

[−4, 4, 1] by [0, 8, 1]

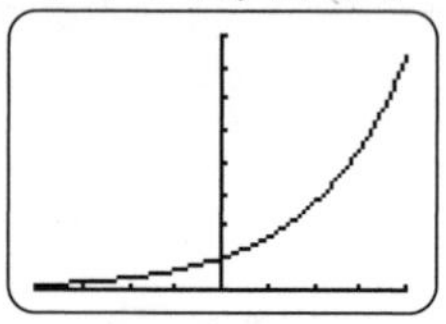

Figure 71

[−4, 4, 1] by [0, 8, 1]

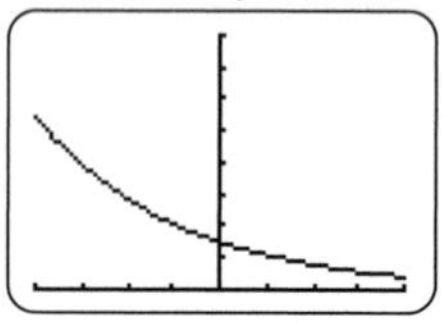

Figure 73

[0, 10, 1] by [4, 7, 1]

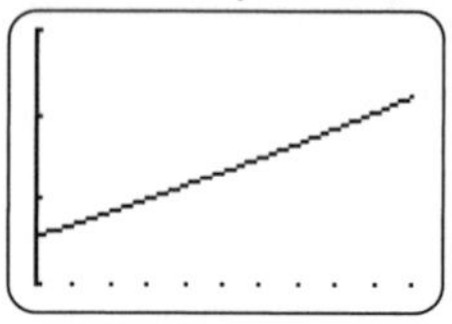

Figure 75

73. Graph $Y_1 = 1.5e$^(−0.32X) in [−4, 4, 1] by [0, 8, 1]. See Figure 73. The graph illustrates exponential decay.

Applications

75. (a) $f(x) = 4.56e^{0.031x}$

 (b) Graph $Y_1 = 4.56e$^(0.031X) in [0, 10, 1] by [4, 7, 1]. See Figure 75.

 (c) Since 2003 is 6 years after 1997, evaluate $f(6) = 4.56e^{0.031(6)} \approx 5.49$ million.

77. (a) Since $f(t) = 500$ when $t = 0$, $500 = Ca^0 \Rightarrow C = 500$. Since $f(t) = 1000$ when $t = 50$,

$$1000 = 500a^{50/50} \Rightarrow a = \frac{1000}{500} = 2$$

 (b) $f(170) = 500(2)^{170/50} \approx 5278$ thousand bacteria per milliliter or 5.278 million bacteria per milliliter

 (c) The growth in the number of bacteria is exponential.

79. (a) $f(1995) = 0.0272(1.495)^{1995-1980} = 0.0272(1.495)^{15} \approx 11.3$ million.

In 1995 there were about 11.3 million cellular phone subscribers.

(b) The growth factor is 1.495. This means that each year from 1985 to 2000 the number of subscribers increases by a factor of 1.495 or by 49.5%.

81. Table $Y_1 = (0.905)$^X with TblStart = 0 and ΔTbl = 10. See Figure 81.

(a) $f(0) = (0.905)^0 = 1$.

The probability that no vehicle will enter the intersection during a period of zero seconds is 1.

(b) Since $f(30) = (0.905)^{30} = 0.05006$ and $f(31) = (0.905)^{31} = 0.04530$, this occurs after about 30 seconds.

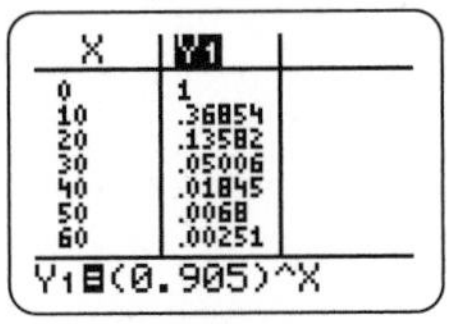

Figure 81

Checking Basic Concepts for Sections 12.1 & 12.2

1. (a) $f(1) = 2(1)^2 + 5(1) - 1 = 6$, and so $(g \circ f)(1) = g(f(1)) = g(6) = 6 + 1 = 7$

(b) $(f \circ g)(x) = f(g(x)) = f(x + 1) = 2(x + 1)^2 + 5(x + 1) - 1 = 2x^2 + 9x + 6$

2. See Figure 2.

(a) No, this is not a one-to-one function because it does not pass the horizontal line test.

(b) No, this function does not have an inverse because it is not one-to-one.

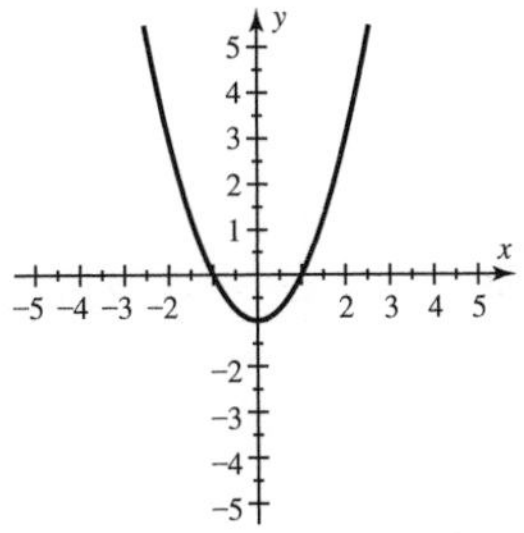

Figure 2

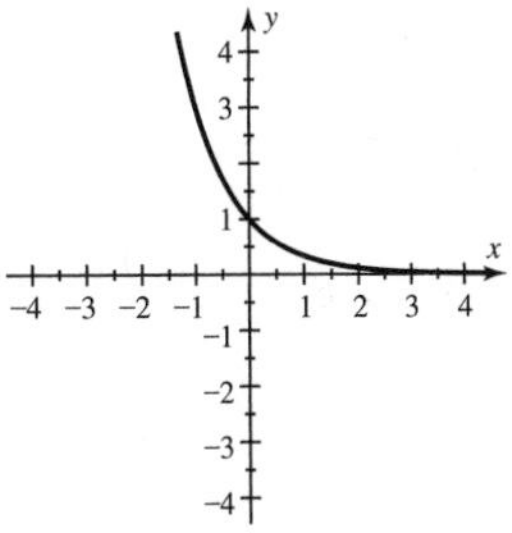

Figure 5

3. $f(x) = 4x - 3 \Rightarrow y = 4x - 3$, interchange x and y and solve for y.

$$x = 4y - 3 \Rightarrow 4y = x + 3 \Rightarrow y = \frac{x+3}{4} \Rightarrow f^{-1}(x) = \frac{x+3}{4}$$

4. $f(-2) = 3(2^{-2}) = 3 \cdot \frac{1}{2^2} = 3 \cdot \frac{1}{4} = \frac{3}{4}$

5. See Figure 5.

6. Since $y = 2$ when $x = 0$, $2 = Ca^0 \Rightarrow C = 2$. Since $y = 1$ when $x = 1$, $1 = 2(a)^1 \Rightarrow a = \frac{1}{2}$.

12.3: Logarithmic Functions

Concepts

1. 10
3. D: $\{x \mid x > 0\}$; R: all real numbers
5. k
7. x
9. log 5

Evaluating and Graphing Logarithmic Functions

11. 5
13. -4
15. $\log 1 = \log 10^0 = 0$
17. $\log \frac{1}{100} = \log 10^{-2} = -2$
19. $\log 10^{4.7} = 4.7.$
21. $\log_5 5^{6x} = 6x.$
23. $\log \sqrt{\frac{1}{1000}} = \log \sqrt{10^{-3}} = \log 10^{-3/2} = -\frac{3}{2}$
25. $\log_2 4 = \log_2 2^2 = 2$
27. $\log_2 \frac{1}{16} = \log_2 2^{-4} = -4$
29. $\log_3 \frac{1}{9} = \log_3 3^{-2} = -2$
31. $\ln 1 = \ln e^0 = 0$
33. $\log 0.001 = \log 10^{-3} = -3$
35. $\log_5 \frac{1}{25} = \log_5 5^{-2} = -2$
37. $10^{\log 2} = 2$
39. $10^{\log x^2} = x^2$
41. $5^{\log_5 17} = 17$
43. $4^{\log_4 (2x)^2} = (2x)^2$
45. $10^{\log 5} = 5$
47. $\ln e^{-5x} = -5x$
49. $\log 10^{(2x-7)} = 2x - 7$
51. $5^{\log_5 0.6z} = 0.6z$
53. $\log 25 \approx 1.398$
55. $\log 1.45 \approx 0.161$
57. $\ln 7 \approx 1.946$
59. $\ln \frac{4}{7} \approx -0.560$

61. Graph $Y_1 = \ln(\text{abs}(X))$ in $[-4, 4, 1]$ by $[-4, 4, 1]$. See Figure 61. The graph is a reflection across the y-axis together with the graph of $y = \ln x$. The domain is $\{x \mid x \neq 0\}$.

[−4, 4, 1] by [−4, 4, 1]

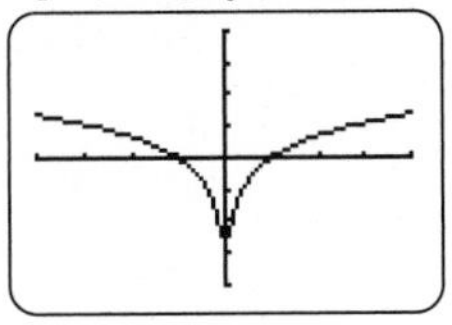

Figure 61

[−4, 4, 1] by [−4, 4, 1]

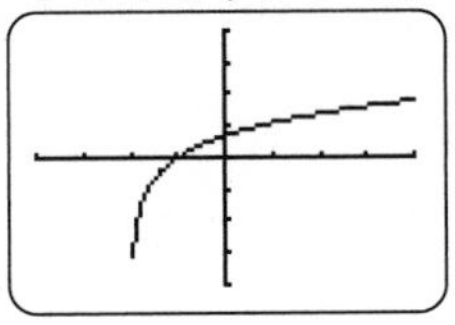

Figure 63

63. Graph $Y_1 = \ln(X + 2)$ in $[-4, 4, 1]$ by $[-4, 4, 1]$. See Figure 63. The graph is shifted 2 units to the left. The domain is $\{x \mid x > -2\}$.

65. d. The graph of this function passes through the point (1, 0) but does not pass through (3, 1).

67. a. The graph of this function is shifted 2 units upward.

69. See Figure 69. Compared to the graph of $y = \log x$, this graph is shifted 1 unit downward.

71. See Figure 71. Compared to the graph of $y = \log x$, this graph is shifted 1 unit to the left.

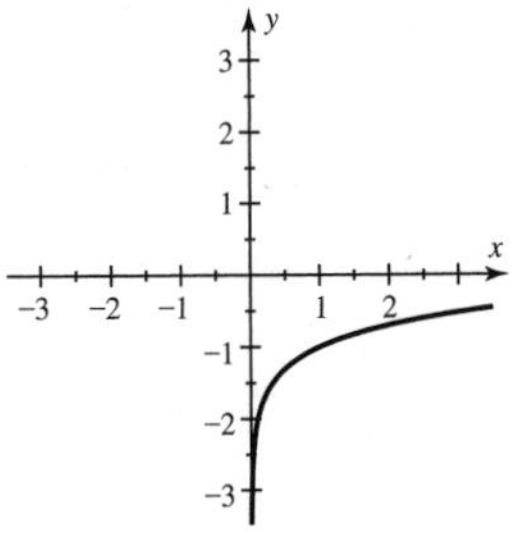

Figure 69

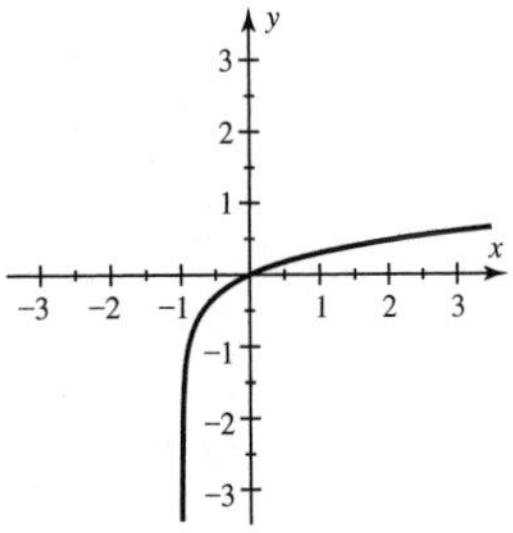

Figure 71

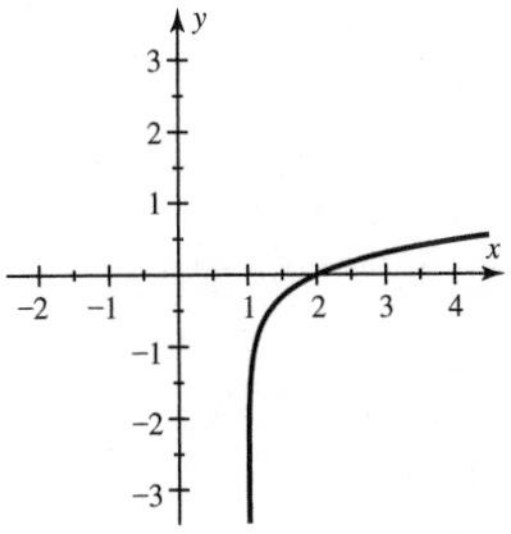

Figure 73

73. See Figure 73. Compared to the graph of $y = \log x$, this graph is shifted 1 unit to the right.

75. See Figure 75. Compared to the graph of $y = \log x$, this graph increases faster.

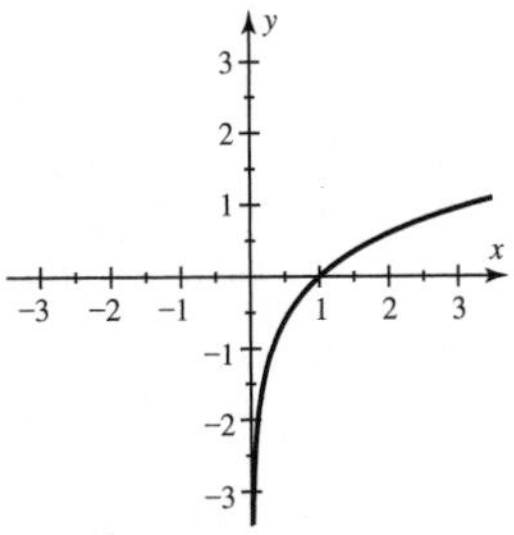

Figure 75

x	$\frac{1}{4}$	$\frac{1}{2}$	1	$\sqrt{2}$	64
$\log_2 x$	−2	−1	0	$\frac{1}{2}$	6

Figure 77

77. See Figure 77.

Applications

79. $f(10^{-4}) = 160 + 10\log(10^{-4}) = 160 + 10(-4) = 160 + (-40) = 120$ db. Yes, this could cause pain.

81. (a) $P(0) = 0.48 \ln(0 + 1) + 27 = 0.48 \ln(1) + 27 = 0.48(0) + 27 = 27$. The air pressure at the eye of the hurricane is 27 inches of mercury. $P(50) = 0.48 \ln(50 + 1) + 27 = 0.48 \ln(51) + 27 \approx 28.9$. The air pressure 50 miles from the eye of the hurricane is about 28.9 inches of mercury.

(b) The pressure increases rapidly at first and then more slowly.

(c) The eye of a hurricane is a low pressure area.

83. (a) $\log \frac{x}{1} = 6.0 \Rightarrow \log x = 6.0 \Rightarrow x = 10^6$ and $\log \frac{x}{1} = 8.0 \Rightarrow \log x = 8.0 \Rightarrow x = 10^8$

(b) $10^8 \div 10^6 = 100$ times

85. (a) $C(1) = 280 \ln(1 + 1) + 1925 = 280 \ln(2) + 1925 \approx 2119$ calories

(b) The caloric intake increases as the amount of land owned increases.

(c) No, the growth levels off and is not linear.

87. (a) $f(50) = 0.338(1.035)^{50} \approx 1.89$; In 2000, the population of less industrialized areas was 1.89 billion. $g(50) = 0.36 + 0.15 \ln(50 + 1) \approx 0.95$; In 2000, the population in industrialized areas was 0.95 billion.

(b) Graph $Y_1 = 280 \ln(X + 1) + 1925$ in [0, 80, 10] by [0, 5, 1]. See Figure 87. The population in less industrialized areas grew faster than the population in industrialized areas.

[0, 80, 10] by [0, 5, 1]

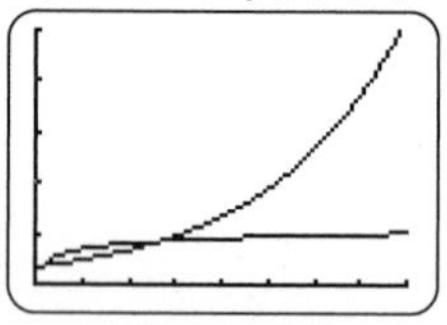

Figure 87

12.4: Properties of Logarithms

Concepts

1. 4

3. 3

5. $\log m - \log n$

7. No

9. $\log_a x = \dfrac{\log x}{\log a}$ or $\log_a x = \dfrac{\ln x}{\ln a}$

Basic Properties of Logarithms

11. $\ln(3 \cdot 5) = \ln 3 + \ln 5$

13. $\log_3 xy = \log_3 x + \log_3 y$

15. $\ln 10z = \ln(2 \cdot 5 \cdot z) = \ln 2 + \ln 5 + \ln z$

17. $\log \frac{7}{3} = \log 7 - \log 3$

19. $\ln \frac{x}{y} = \ln x - \ln y$

21. $\log_2 \frac{45}{x} = \log_2 45 - \log_2 x$

23. $\log 45 + \log 5 = \log(45 \cdot 5) = \log 225$

25. $\ln x + \ln y = \ln xy$

27. $\ln 7x^2 + \ln 2x = \ln(7x^2 \cdot 2x) = \ln 14x^3$

29. $\ln x + \ln y^2 - \ln y = \ln xy^2 - \ln y = \ln \dfrac{xy^2}{y} = \ln xy$

31. $\log 3^6 = 6 \log 3$

33. $\ln 2^x = x \ln 2$

35. $\log_2 5^{1/4} = \dfrac{1}{4} \log_2 5$

37. $\log_4 \sqrt[3]{z} = \log_4 z^{1/3} = \dfrac{1}{3} \log_4 z$

39. $\log x^{y-1} = (y-1) \log x$

41. $4 \log z - \log z^3 = \log z^4 - \log z^3 = \log \dfrac{z^4}{z^3} = \log z$

43. $\log x + 2 \log x + 2 \log y = \log x + \log x^2 + \log y^2 = \log(x \cdot x^2 \cdot y^2) = \log x^3 y^2$

45. $\log x - 2 \log \sqrt{x} = \log x - \log(\sqrt{x})^2 = \log x - \log x = 0$

47. $\ln 2^{x+1} - \ln 2 = \ln \dfrac{2^{x+1}}{2} = \ln 2^x$

49. $2 \log_3 \sqrt{x} - 3 \log_3 x = \log_3(\sqrt{x})^2 - \log_3 x^3 = \log_3 x - \log_3 x^3 = \log_3 \dfrac{x}{x^3} = \log_3 \dfrac{1}{x^2}$

51. $2 \log_a(x+1) - \log_a(x^2-1) = \log_a(x+1)^2 - \log_a(x^2-1) = \log_a \dfrac{(x+1)(x+1)}{(x+1)(x-1)} = \log_a \dfrac{x+1}{x-1}$

53. $\log xy^2 = \log x + \log y^2 = \log x + 2 \log y$

55. $\ln \dfrac{x^4 y}{z} = \ln x^4 y - \ln z = \ln x^4 + \ln y - \ln z = 4 \ln x + \ln y - \ln z$

57. $\log_4 \dfrac{\sqrt[3]{z}}{\sqrt{y}} = \log_4 \dfrac{z^{1/3}}{y^{1/2}} = \log_4 z^{1/3} - \log_4 y^{1/2} = \dfrac{1}{3} \log_4 z - \dfrac{1}{2} \log_4 y$

59. $\log(x^4 y^3) = \log x^4 + \log y^3 = 4 \log x + 3 \log y$

61. $\ln \dfrac{1}{y} - \ln \dfrac{1}{x} = \ln y^{-1} - \ln x^{-1} = -1 \ln y - (-1) \ln x = \ln x - \ln y$

63. $\log_4 \sqrt{\dfrac{x^3 y}{z^2}} = \log_4 \left(\dfrac{x^3 y}{z^2}\right)^{1/2} = \dfrac{1}{2} \log_4 \dfrac{x^3 y}{z^2} = \dfrac{1}{2}(\log_4 x^3 + \log_4 y - \log_4 z^2) = \dfrac{3}{2} \log_4 x + \dfrac{1}{2} \log_4 y - \log_4 z$

65. Graph $Y_1 = \log(X\text{^}3)$ and $Y_2 = 3\log(X)$ in [−6, 6, 1] by [−4, 4, 1]. See Figures 65a & 65b.

By the power rule $\log x^3 = 3 \log x$.

[−6, 6, 1] by [−4, 4, 1]

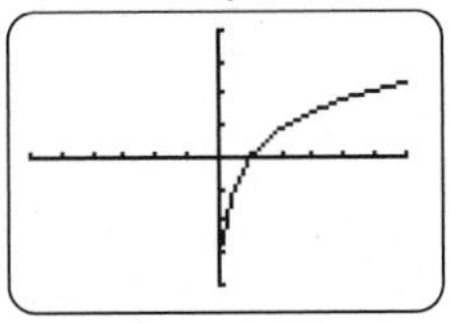

Figure 65a

[−6, 6, 1] by [−4, 4, 1]

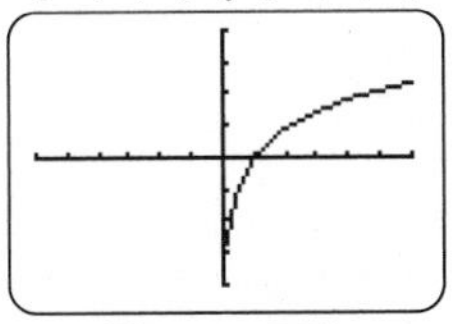

Figure 65b

[−6, 6, 1] by [−4, 4, 1]

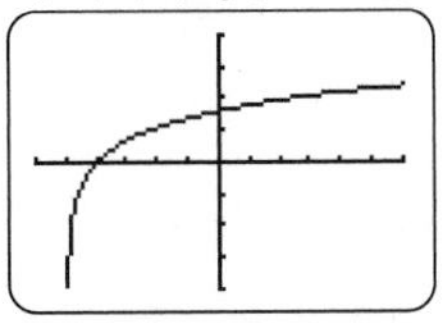

Figure 67a

[−6, 6, 1] by [−4, 4, 1]

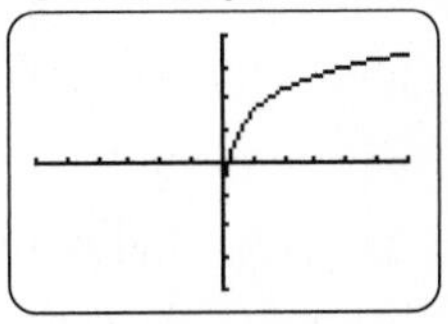

Figure 67b

67. Graph $Y_1 = \ln(X + 5)$ and $Y_2 = \ln(X) + \ln(5)$ in [−6, 6, 1] by [−4, 4, 1]. See Figure 67a & 67b. Not the same.

69. $\log 16 = \log 2^4 = 4 \log 2 = 4(0.3) = 1.2$

71. $\log 65 = \log(5 \cdot 13) = \log 5 + \log 13 = 0.7 + 1.1 = 1.8$

73. $\log 130 = \log(2 \cdot 5 \cdot 13) = \log 2 + \log 5 + \log 13 = 0.3 + 0.7 + 1.1 = 2.1$

75. $\log \frac{5}{2} = \log 5 - \log 2 = 0.7 - 0.3 = 0.4$

77. $\log \frac{1}{13} = \log 13^{-1} = -\log 13 = -1.1$

79. $\log_3 5 = \frac{\log 5}{\log 3} \approx 1.46$

81. $\log_2 25 = \frac{\log 25}{\log 2} \approx 4.64$

83. $\log_9 102 = \frac{\log 102}{\log 9} \approx 2.10$

Applications

85. $f(x) = 10\log(10^{16}x) = 10(\log 10^{16} + \log x) = 10(16 + \log x) = 160 + 10\log x$

Checking Basic Concepts for Sections 12.3 & 12.4

1. (a) $\log 10^4 = 4$

   (b) $\ln e^x = x$

   (c) $\log_2 \frac{1}{8} = \log_2 2^{-3} = -3$

   (d) $\log_5 \sqrt{5} = \log_5 5^{1/2} = \frac{1}{2}$

2. See Figure 2.

   (a) D: $\{x \mid x > 0\}$; R: all real numbers

   (b) $f(1) = 0$

   (c) Yes, for example $\log \frac{1}{10} = -1$.

   (d) No, since negative numbers are not in the domain of $f(x) = \log x$.

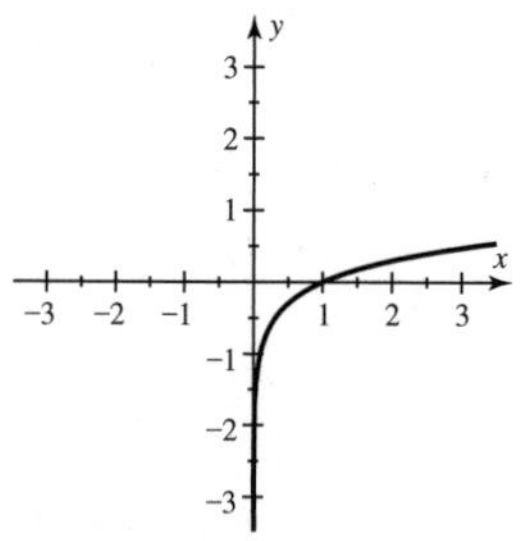

Figure 2

3. (a) $\log xy = \log x + \log y$

   (b) $\ln \frac{x}{yz} = \ln x - \ln yz = \ln x - (\ln y + \ln z) = \ln x - \ln y - \ln z$

   (c) $\ln x^2 = 2\ln x$

   (d) $\log \frac{x^2y^3}{\sqrt{z}} = \log x^2y^3 - \log z^{1/2} = \log x^2 + \log y^3 - \log z^{1/2} = 2\log x + 3\log y - \frac{1}{2}\log z$

4. (a) $\log x + \log y = \log xy$

(b) $\ln 2x - 3\ln y = \ln 2x - \ln y^3 = \ln \frac{2x}{y^3}$

(c) $2\log_2 x + 3\log_2 y - \log_2 z = \log_2 x^2 + \log_2 y^3 - \log_2 z = \log_2 x^2y^3 - \log_2 z = \log_2 \frac{x^2y^3}{z}$

12.5: Exponential and Logarithmic Equations

Concepts

1. Add 5 to both sides..

3. Take the common logarithm of both sides.

5. x

7. $2x$

9. No, $\log \frac{5}{4} = \log 5 - \log 4$

11. One

Exponential Equations

13. $10^x = 1000 \Rightarrow 10^x = 10^3 \Rightarrow x = 3$

15. $2^x = 64 \Rightarrow 2^x = 2^6 \Rightarrow x = 6$

17. $2^{x-3} = 8 \Rightarrow 2^{x-3} = 2^3 \Rightarrow x - 3 = 3 \Rightarrow x = 6$

19. $4^x + 3 = 259 \Rightarrow 4^x = 256 \Rightarrow 4^x = 4^4 \Rightarrow x = 4$

21. $10^{0.4x} = 124 \Rightarrow \log 10^{0.4x} = \log 124 \Rightarrow 0.4x = \log 124 \Rightarrow x = \frac{\log 124}{0.4} \approx 5.23$

23. $e^{-x} = 1 \Rightarrow e^{-x} = e^0 \Rightarrow -x = 0 \Rightarrow x = 0$

25. $e^x - 1 = 6 \Rightarrow e^x = 7 \Rightarrow \ln e^x = \ln 7 \Rightarrow x = \ln 7 \approx 1.95$

27. $2(10)^{x+2} = 35 \Rightarrow 10^{x+2} = \frac{35}{2} \Rightarrow \log 10^{x+2} = \log \frac{35}{2} \Rightarrow x + 2 = \log \frac{35}{2} \Rightarrow x = \log \frac{35}{2} - 2 \approx -0.76$

29. $3.1^{2x} - 4 = 16 \Rightarrow 3.1^{2x} = 20 \Rightarrow \log_{3.1} 3.1^{2x} = \log_{3.1} 20 \Rightarrow 2x = \log_{3.1} 20 \Rightarrow x = \frac{\log 20}{2\log 3.1} \approx 1.32$

31. $e^{3x} = e^{2x-1} \Rightarrow 3x = 2x - 1 \Rightarrow x = -1$

33. $5^{4x} = 5^{x^2-5} \Rightarrow 4x = x^2 - 5 \Rightarrow x^2 - 4x - 5 = 0 \Rightarrow (x + 1)(x - 5) = 0 \Rightarrow x = -1$ or 5

35. $e^{2x} \cdot e^x = 10 \Rightarrow e^{2x+x} = 10 \Rightarrow e^{3x} = 10 \Rightarrow \ln e^{3x} = \ln 10 \Rightarrow 3x = \ln 10 \Rightarrow x = \frac{\ln 10}{3} \approx 0.77$

37. $e^x = 2^{x+2} \Rightarrow \ln e^x = \ln 2^{x+2} \Rightarrow x = (x + 2)\ln 2 \Rightarrow x = x\ln 2 + 2\ln 2 \Rightarrow x - x\ln 2 = 2\ln 2 \Rightarrow$

$x(1 - \ln 2) = 2\ln 2 \Rightarrow x = \frac{2\ln 2}{1 - \ln 2} \approx 4.52$

39. $4^{0.5x} = 5^{x+2} \Rightarrow \log 4^{0.5x} = \log 5^{x+2} \Rightarrow 0.5x\log 4 = (x + 2)\log 5 \Rightarrow 0.5x\log 4 = x\log 5 + 2\log 5 \Rightarrow$

$0.5x\log 4 - x\log 5 = 2\log 5 \Rightarrow x(0.5\log 4 - \log 5) = 2\log 5 \Rightarrow x = \frac{2\log 5}{0.5\log 4 - \log 5} \approx -3.51$

41. (a) The solution is the x-coordinate of the intersection point, $x = 1$.

(b) $0.2(10^x) = 2 \Rightarrow 10^x = 10 \Rightarrow x = 1$

43. (a) The solution is the x-coordinate of the intersection point, $x = -2$.

(b) $2^{-x} = 4 \Rightarrow 2^{-x} = 2^2 \Rightarrow -x = 2 \Rightarrow x = -2$

45. $10^x = 0.1 \Rightarrow 10^x = 10^{-1} \Rightarrow x = -1$

For numerical support, table $Y_1 = 10$^X and $Y_2 = 0.1$ with TblStart = –3 and ΔTbl = 1. See Figure 45.

47. $4e^x + 5 = 9 \Rightarrow 4e^x = 4 \Rightarrow e^x = 1 \Rightarrow e^x = e^0 \Rightarrow x = 0$

For numerical support, table $Y_1 = 4e$^X + 5 and $Y_2 = 9$ with TblStart = –3 and ΔTbl = 1. See Figure 47.

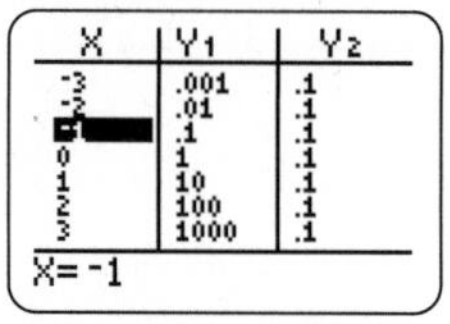

Figure 45

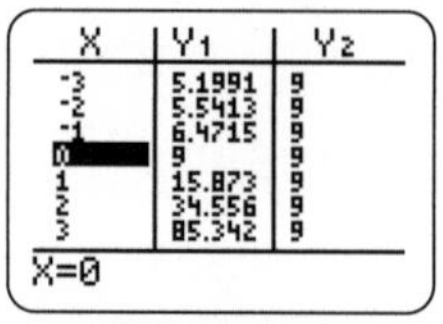

Figure 47

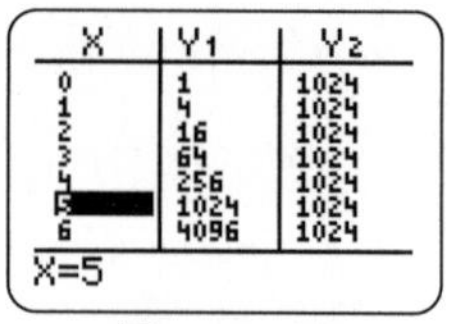

Figure 49

[–1, 1, 1] by [0, 3, 1]

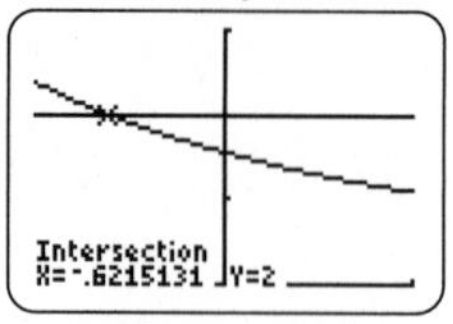

Figure 51

49. $4^x = 1024 \Rightarrow 4^x = 4^5 \Rightarrow x = 5$

For numerical support, table $Y_1 = 4$^X and $Y_2 = 1024$ with TblStart = 0 and ΔTbl = 1. See Figure 49.

51. $(0.55)^x + 0.55 = 2 \Rightarrow 0.55^x = 1.45 \Rightarrow \log_{0.55} 0.55^x = \log_{0.55} 1.45 \Rightarrow x = \dfrac{\log 1.45}{\log 0.55} \approx -0.62$

For graphical support, graph $Y_1 = 0.55$^X + 0.55 and $Y_2 = 2$ in [–1, 1, 1] by [0, 3, 1]. See Figure 51.

53. Graph $Y_1 = e$^X – X and $Y_2 = 2$ in [–5, 5, 1] by [–5, 5, 1]. See Figures 53a & 53b.

The solutions are the x-coordinates of the intersection points, $x \approx -1.84$ and $x \approx 1.15$.

[–5, 5, 1] by [–5, 5, 1]

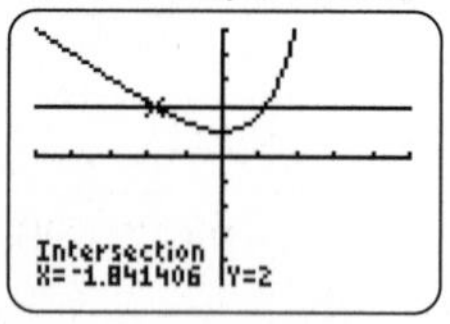

Figure 53a

[–5, 5, 1] by [–5, 5, 1]

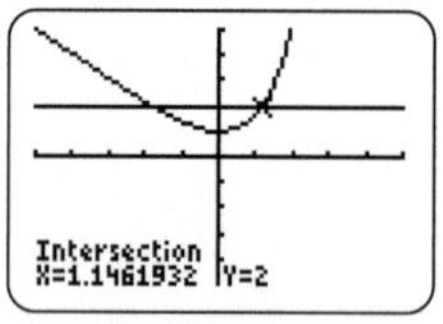

Figure 53b

[–5, 5, 1] by [–5, 5, 1]

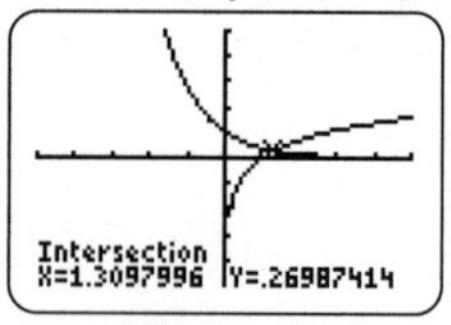

Figure 55

55. Graph $Y_1 = \ln$ (X) and $Y_2 = e$^(–X) in [–5, 5, 1] by [–5, 5, 1]. See Figure 55.

The solution is the x-coordinate of the intersection point, $x \approx 1.31$.

Logarithmic Equations

57. $\log x = 2 \Rightarrow 10^{\log x} = 10^2 \Rightarrow x = 100$

59. $\ln x = 5 \Rightarrow e^{\ln x} = e^5 \Rightarrow x = e^5 \approx 148.41$

61. $\log 2x = 7 \Rightarrow 10^{\log 2x} = 10^7 \Rightarrow 2x = 10{,}000{,}000 \Rightarrow x = 5{,}000{,}000$

63. $\log_2 x = 4 \Rightarrow 2^{\log_2 x} = 2^4 \Rightarrow x = 16$

65. $\log_2 5x = 2.3 \Rightarrow 2^{\log_2 5x} = 2^{2.3} \Rightarrow 5x = 2^{2.3} \Rightarrow x = \dfrac{2^{2.3}}{5} \approx 0.98$

67. $2\log x + 5 = 7.8 \Rightarrow 2\log x = 2.8 \Rightarrow \log x = 1.4 \Rightarrow 10^{\log x} = 10^{1.4} \Rightarrow x = 10^{1.4} \approx 25.12$

69. $5\ln(2x+1) = 55 \Rightarrow \ln(2x+1) = 11 \Rightarrow e^{\ln(2x+1)} = e^{11} \Rightarrow 2x + 1 = e^{11} \Rightarrow x = \dfrac{e^{11} - 1}{2} \approx 29{,}936.57$

71. $\log x^2 = \log x \Rightarrow x^2 = x \Rightarrow x^2 - x = 0 \Rightarrow x(x-1) = 0 \Rightarrow x = 0$ or 1

The solution $x = 0$ causes an undefined expression in the original equation. The only solution is 1.

73. $\ln x + \ln(x+1) = \ln 30 \Rightarrow \ln x(x+1) = \ln 30 \Rightarrow x(x+1) = 30 \Rightarrow x^2 + x - 30 = 0 \Rightarrow$

$(x+6)(x-5) = 0 \Rightarrow x = -6$ or 5

The solution $x = -6$ causes an undefined expression in the original equation. The only solution is 5.

75. $\log_3 3x - \log_3(x+2) = \log_3 2 \Rightarrow \log_3 \dfrac{3x}{x+2} = \log_3 2 \Rightarrow \dfrac{3x}{x+2} = 2 \Rightarrow 3x = 2x + 4 \Rightarrow x = 4$

77. $\log_2(x-1) + \log_2(x+1) = 3 \Rightarrow \log_2(x^2-1) = 3 \Rightarrow 2^{\log_2(x^2-1)} = 2^3 \Rightarrow x^2 - 1 = 8 \Rightarrow$

$x^2 - 9 = 0 \Rightarrow (x+3)(x-3) = 0 \Rightarrow x = -3$ or 3

The solution $x = -3$ causes an undefined expression in the original equation. The only solution is 3.

79. (a) The solution is the x-coordinate of the intersection point, $x = 2$.

(b) $\ln x = 0.7 \Rightarrow e^{\ln x} = e^{0.7} \Rightarrow x = e^{0.7} \approx 2.01$

81. (a) The solution is the x-coordinate of the intersection point, $x = 2$.

(b) $5\log 2x = 3 \Rightarrow \log 2x = 0.6 \Rightarrow 10^{\log 2x} = 10^{0.6} \Rightarrow 2x = 10^{0.6} \Rightarrow x = \dfrac{10^{0.6}}{2} \approx 1.99$

83. $\log x = 1.6 \Rightarrow 10^{\log x} = 10^{1.6} \Rightarrow x = 10^{1.6} \approx 39.81$

For graphical support, graph $Y_1 = \log(X)$ and $Y_2 = 1.6$ in [0, 50, 10] by [−2, 2, 1]. See Figure 83.

85. $\ln(x+1) = 1 \Rightarrow e^{\ln(x+1)} = e^1 \Rightarrow x + 1 = e \Rightarrow x = e - 1 \approx 1.72$

For graphical support, graph $Y_1 = \ln(X+1)$ and $Y_2 = 1$ in [−1, 2, 1] by [−2, 2, 1]. See Figure 85.

87. $17 - 6\log_3 x = 5 \Rightarrow 6\log_3 x = 12 \Rightarrow \log_3 x = 2 \Rightarrow 3^{\log_3 x} = 3^2 \Rightarrow x = 3^2 = 9$

For graphical support, graph $Y_1 = 17 - 6(\ln(X)/\ln(3))$ and $Y_2 = 5$ in [0, 10, 1] by [−3, 3, 1]. See Figure 87.

[0, 50, 10] by [−2, 2, 1]

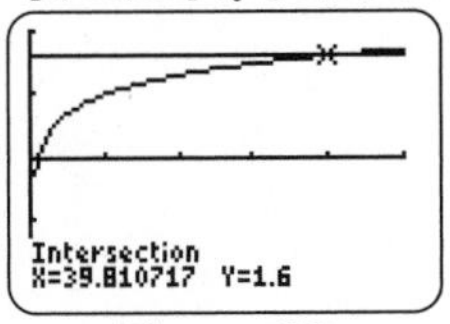

Figure 83

[−1, 2, 1] by [−2, 2, 1]

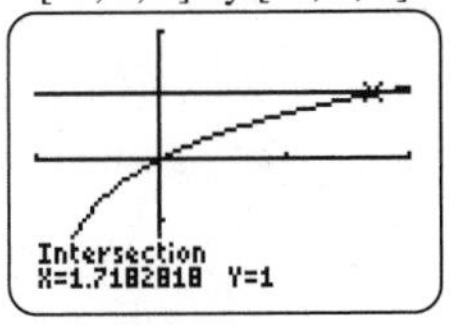

Figure 85

[0, 10, 1] by [−3, 3, 1]

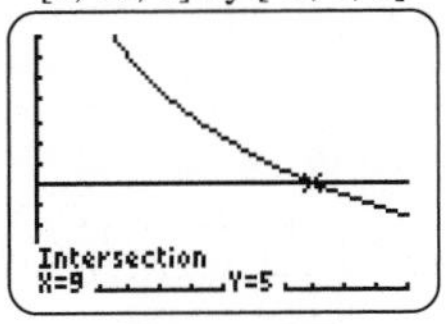

Figure 87

[0, 4, 1] by [0, 3000, 1000]

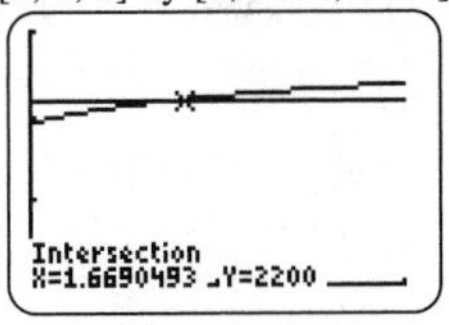

Figure 99

Applications

89. $2000(1+0.15)^t = 6000 \Rightarrow 1.15^t = 3 \Rightarrow \log_{1.15} 1.15^t = \log_{1.15} 3 \Rightarrow t = \dfrac{\log 3}{\log 1.15} \approx 7.86 \approx 8$ years

91. (a) $f(1994) = 2339(1.24)^{(1994-1988)} \approx 8503$; In 1994 there were about 8503 people waiting for liver transplants.

(b) $2339(1.24)^{(x-1988)} = 20{,}000 \Rightarrow 1.24^{(x-1988)} = \dfrac{20{,}000}{2339} \Rightarrow \log_{1.24} 1.24^{(x-1988)} = \log_{1.24}\left(\dfrac{20{,}000}{2339}\right) \Rightarrow$

$x - 1988 = \log_{1.24}\left(\dfrac{20{,}000}{2339}\right) \Rightarrow x = \log_{1.24}\left(\dfrac{20{,}000}{2339}\right) + 1988 = \dfrac{\log\left(\frac{20{,}000}{2339}\right)}{\log 1.24} + 1988 \approx 1998$

93. $3\log x = 3.960 \Rightarrow \log x = 1.320 \Rightarrow 10^{\log x} = 10^{1.320} \Rightarrow x = 10^{1.320} \approx 20.893 = 20{,}893$ lb

95. (a) $f(1) = 230(10^{-0.055 \cdot 1}) \approx 203$; In 1975 there were about 203 thousand bluefin tuna.

(b) About 1979.

(c) $230(10^{-0.055x}) = 115 \Rightarrow 10^{-0.055x} = 0.5 \Rightarrow \log 10^{-0.055x} = \log 0.5 \Rightarrow -0.055x = \log 0.5 \Rightarrow$

$x = \dfrac{\log 0.5}{-0.055} \approx 5.47$ or about 1979.

97. From the data point (1, 25), $25 = a + b\log 1 \Rightarrow 25 = a + b(0) \Rightarrow a = 25$.

Using the data point (10, 28) and the fact that $a = 25$, $28 = 25 + b\log 10 \Rightarrow 28 = 25 + b \Rightarrow b = 3$

99. (a) Graph $Y_1 = 645\log(X+1) + 1925$ and $Y_2 = 2200$ in [0, 4, 1] by [0, 3000, 1000]. See Figure 99.

A person consuming 2200 calories would typically own about 1.67 acres.

(b) $645\log(x+1) + 1925 = 2200 \Rightarrow 645\log(x+1) = 275 \Rightarrow \log(x+1) = \dfrac{275}{645} \Rightarrow$

$10^{\log(x+1)} = 10^{275/645} \Rightarrow x + 1 = 10^{275/645} \Rightarrow x = 10^{275/645} - 1 \approx 1.67$ acres

101. (a) The data is nonlinear. It does not increase at a constant rate.

(b) Each year the amount of fertilizer increases by a factor of 1.06 or 6%.

(c) $5(1.06)^{(x-1950)} = 15 \Rightarrow 1.06^{(x-1950)} = 3 \Rightarrow \log_{1.06} 1.06^{(x-1950)} = \log_{1.06} 3 \Rightarrow x - 1950 = \log_{1.06} 3 \Rightarrow$

$x = \log_{1.06} 3 + 1950 = \dfrac{\log 3}{\log 1.06} + 1950 \approx 1968.85$ or in 1968

103. $160 + 10 \log x = 100 \Rightarrow 10 \log x = -60 \Rightarrow \log x = -6 \Rightarrow 10^{\log x} = 10^{-6} \Rightarrow x = 10^{-6}\ \text{w/cm}^2$

105. $0.48 \ln(x + 1) + 27 = 28 \Rightarrow 0.48 \ln(x + 1) = 1 \Rightarrow \ln(x + 1) = \dfrac{1}{0.48} \Rightarrow e^{\ln(x+1)} = e^{1/0.48} \Rightarrow$

$x + 1 = e^{1/0.48} \Rightarrow x = e^{1/0.48} - 1 \approx 7.03$ or about 7 miles

Checking Basic Concepts for Section 12.5

1. (a) $2(10^x) = 40 \Rightarrow 10^x = 20 \Rightarrow \log 10^x = \log 20 \Rightarrow x = \log 20 \approx 1.30$

(b) $2^{3x} + 3 = 150 \Rightarrow 2^{3x} = 147 \Rightarrow \log_2 2^{3x} = \log_2 147 \Rightarrow 3x = \dfrac{\log 147}{\log 2} \Rightarrow x = \dfrac{\log 147}{3 \log 2} \approx 2.40$

(c) $\ln x = 4.1 \Rightarrow e^{\ln x} = e^{4.1} \Rightarrow x = e^{4.1} \approx 60.34$

(d) $4 \log 2x = 12 \Rightarrow \log 2x = 3 \Rightarrow 10^{\log 2x} = 10^3 \Rightarrow 2x = 1000 \Rightarrow x = 500$

2. $\log(x + 4) + \log(x - 4) = \log 48 \Rightarrow \log(x^2 - 16) = \log 48 \Rightarrow x^2 - 16 = 48 \Rightarrow$

$x^2 - 64 = 0 \Rightarrow (x + 8)(x - 8) = 0 \Rightarrow x = -8$ or 8

The solution $x = -8$ causes an undefined expression in the original equation. The only solution is 8.

3. $500(1.03)^x = 900 \Rightarrow 1.03^x = \dfrac{9}{5} \Rightarrow \log_{1.03} 1.03^x = \log_{1.03}\left(\dfrac{9}{5}\right) \Rightarrow x = \dfrac{\log\left(\frac{9}{5}\right)}{\log 1.03} \approx 19.88$ or about 20 years

Chapter 12 Review Exercises

Section 12.1

1. (a) $f(-2) = 2(-2)^2 - 4(-2) = 16$, then $(g \circ f)(-2) = g(f(-2)) = g(16) = 5(16) + 1 = 81$

(b) $(f \circ g)(x) = f(g(x)) = f(5x + 1) = 2(5x + 1)^2 - 4(5x + 1) = 50x^2 - 2$

2. (a) $f(-2) = \sqrt[3]{-2 - 6} = -2$, then $(g \circ f)(-2) = g(f(-2)) = g(-2) = 4(-2)^3 = -32$

(b) $(f \circ g)(x) = f(g(x)) = f(4x^3) = \sqrt[3]{4x^3 - 6}$

3. (a) $(f \circ g)(2) = f(g(2)) = f(3) = 0$

(b) $(g \circ f)(1) = g(f(1)) = g(2) = 3$

4. (a) $(f \circ g)(-1) = f(g(-1)) = f(2) = 3$

(b) $(g \circ f)(2) = g(f(2)) = g(3) = -2$

(c) $(f \circ f)(1) = f(f(1)) = f(0) = -1$

5. $f(1) = f(-1) = 2$

6. $f(0) = f(2) = 1$

7. This graph does not pass the horizontal line test. The function is not one-to-one.

8. This graph passes the horizontal line test. The function is one-to-one.

9. $(f \circ f^{-1})(x) = f(f^{-1}(x)) = f\left(\frac{x+9}{2}\right) = 2\left(\frac{x+9}{2}\right) - 9 = x + 9 - 9 = x$

$(f^{-1} \circ f)(x) = f^{-1}(f(x)) = f^{-1}(2x - 9) = \frac{(2x-9)+9}{2} = \frac{2x}{2} = x$

10. $(f \circ f^{-1})(x) = f(f^{-1}(x)) = f(\sqrt[3]{x-1}) = (\sqrt[3]{x-1})^3 + 1 = x - 1 + 1 = x$

$(f^{-1} \circ f)(x) = f^{-1}(f(x)) = f^{-1}(x^3 + 1) = \sqrt[3]{(x^3+1) - 1} = \sqrt[3]{x^3} = x$

11. $f(x) = 5x \Rightarrow y = 5x$, interchange x and y and solve for y. $x = 5y \Rightarrow y = \frac{x}{5} \Rightarrow f^{-1}(x) = \frac{x}{5}$

12. $f(x) = x - 11 \Rightarrow y = x - 11$, interchange x and y and solve for y.

$x = y - 11 \Rightarrow y = x + 11 \Rightarrow f^{-1}(x) = x + 11$

13. $f(x) = 2x + 7 \Rightarrow y = 2x + 7$, interchange x and y and solve for y.

$x = 2y + 7 \Rightarrow 2y = x - 7 \Rightarrow y = \frac{x-7}{2} \Rightarrow f^{-1}(x) = \frac{x-7}{2}$

14. $f(x) = \frac{4}{x} \Rightarrow y = \frac{4}{x}$, interchange x and y and solve for y. $x = \frac{4}{y} \Rightarrow xy = 4 \Rightarrow y = \frac{4}{x} \Rightarrow f^{-1}(x) = \frac{4}{x}$

15. See Figure 15. $D = \{3, 7, 8, 10\}$; $R = \{0, 1, 2, 3\}$

x	10	8	7	3
$f^{-1}(x)$	0	1	2	3

Figure 15

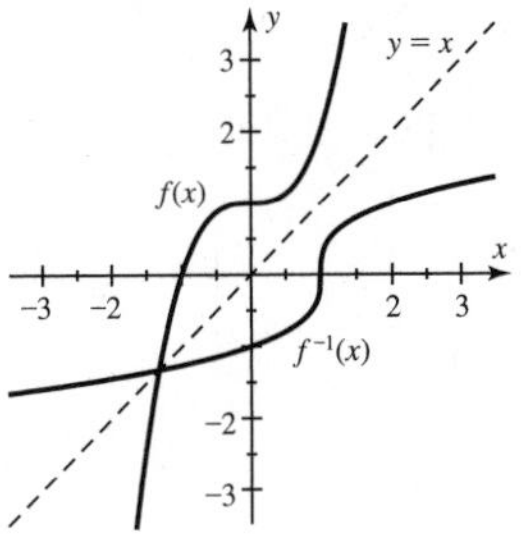

Figure 16

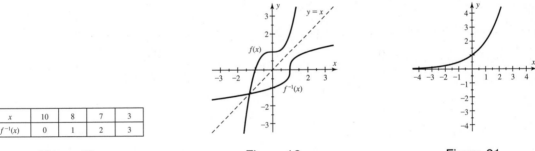

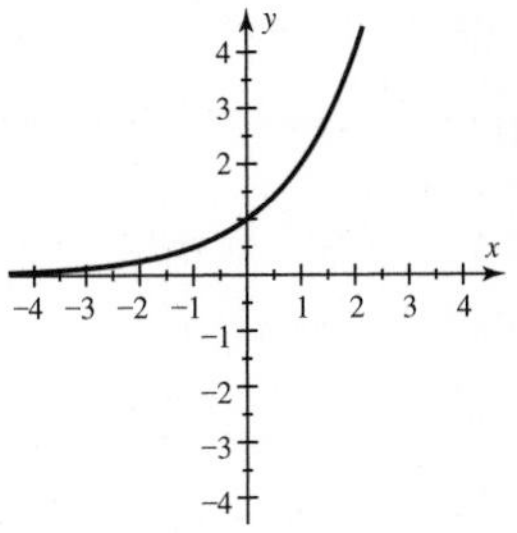

Figure 21

16. The graph of f^{-1} is a reflection of the graph of f across the line $y = x$. See Figure 16.

Sections 12.2 and 12.3

17. $f(-1) = 6^{-1} = \frac{1}{6}$ and $f(2) = 6^2 = 36$

18. $f(0) = 5(2^0) = 5(1) = 5$ and $f(3) = 5(2^{-3}) = 5\left(\frac{1}{8}\right) = \frac{5}{8}$

19. $f(-1) = \left(\frac{1}{3}\right)^{-1} = 3$ and $f(4) = \left(\frac{1}{3}\right)^4 = \frac{1}{3^4} = \frac{1}{81}$

20. $f(0) = 3\left(\frac{1}{6}\right)^0 = 3(1) = 3$ and $f(1) = 3\left(\frac{1}{6}\right)^1 = 3\left(\frac{1}{6}\right) = \frac{3}{6} = \frac{1}{2}$

21. See Figure 21. The graph illustrates exponential growth.

22. See Figure 22. The graph illustrates exponential decay.

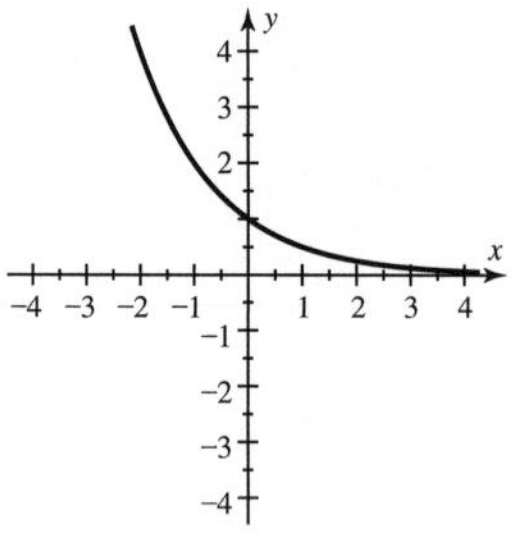

Figure 22

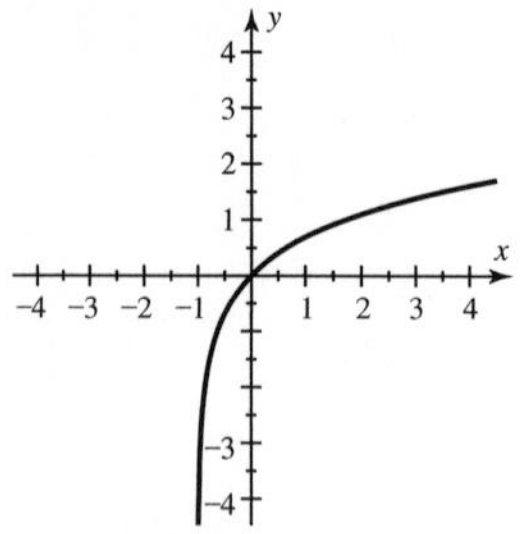

Figure 23

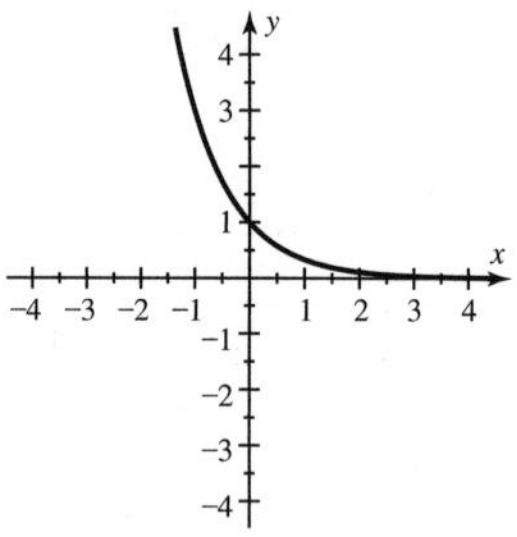

Figure 24

23. See Figure 23. The graph illustrates logarithmic growth.

24. See Figure 24. The graph illustrates exponential decay.

25. (a) Exponential growth. For each unit increase in x, $f(x)$ increases by a factor of 2.

(b) Since $f(x) = 5$ when $x = 0, f(x) = 5(2)^x$

26. (a) Linear growth. For each unit increase in x, $f(x)$ increases by 5 units.

(b) Since $f(x) = 5$ when $x = 0, f(x) = 5x + 5$

27. Since $y = \frac{1}{2}$ when $x = 0, \frac{1}{2} = Ca^0 \Rightarrow C = \frac{1}{2}$. Since $y = 1$ when $x = 1, 1 = \frac{1}{2}(a)^1 \Rightarrow a = 2$.

28. Since $y = 2$ when $x = 2, 2 = k\log_2 2 \Rightarrow 2 = k(1) \Rightarrow k = 2$.

29. $1200(1 + 0.10)^9 = \$2829.54$

30. $900(1 + 0.18)^{40} = \$675{,}340.51$

31. $f(5.3) = 2e^{5.3} - 1 \approx 399.67$

32. $f(2.1) = 0.85^{2.1} \approx 0.71$

33. $f(55) = 2\log 55 \approx 3.48$

34. $f(23) = \ln(2 \cdot 23 + 3) \approx 3.89$

35. $\log 0.001 = \log 10^{-3} = -3$

36. $\log \sqrt{10{,}000} = \log 100 = 2$

37. $\ln e^{-4} = -4$

38. $\log_4 16 = \log_4 4^2 = 2$

39. $\log 65 \approx 1.813$

40. $\ln 0.85 \approx -0.163$

41. $\ln 120 \approx 4.787$

42. $\log_2 \frac{2}{5} \approx -1.322$

43. $10^{\log 7} = 7$

44. $\log_2 2^{5/9} = \frac{5}{9}$

45. $\ln e^{6-x} = 6 - x$

46. $e^{2\ln x} = (e^{\ln x})^2 = x^2$

Section 12.4

47. $\ln xy = \ln x + \ln y$

48. $\log \dfrac{x}{y} = \log x - \log y$

49. $\ln x^2y^3 = \ln x^2 + \ln y^3 = 2\ln x + 3\ln y$

50. $\log \dfrac{\sqrt{x}}{z^3} = \log \dfrac{x^{1/2}}{z^3} = \log x^{1/2} - \log z^3 = \dfrac{1}{2}\log x - 3\log z$

51. $\log_2 \dfrac{x^2y}{z} = \log_2 x^2y - \log_2 z = \log_2 x^2 + \log_2 y - \log_2 z = 2\log_2 x + \log_2 y - \log_2 z$

52. $\log_3 \sqrt[3]{\dfrac{x}{y}} = \log_3 \left(\dfrac{x}{y}\right)^{1/3} = \dfrac{1}{3}\log_3\left(\dfrac{x}{y}\right) = \dfrac{1}{3}(\log_3 x - \log_3 y) = \dfrac{1}{3}\log_3 x - \dfrac{1}{3}\log_3 y$

53. $\log 45 + \log 5 - \log 3 = \log (45 \cdot 5) - \log 3 = \log 225 - \log 3 = \log \dfrac{225}{3} = \log 75$

54. $\log_4 2x + \log_4 5x = \log_4 (2x \cdot 5x) = \log_4 (10x^2)$

55. $2\ln x - 3\ln y = \ln x^2 - \ln y^3 = \ln \dfrac{x^2}{y^3}$

56. $\log x^4 - \log x^3 + \log y = \log \dfrac{x^4}{x^3} + \log y = \log x + \log y = \log xy$

57. $\log 6^3 = 3\log 6$

58. $\ln x^2 = 2\ln x$

59. $\log_2 5^{2x} = (2x)\log_2 5$

60. $\log_4 (0.6)^{x+1} = (x + 1)\log_4 0.6$

Section 12.5

61. $10^x = 100 \Rightarrow 10^x = 10^2 \Rightarrow x = 2$

62. $2^{2x} = 256 \Rightarrow 2^{2x} = 2^8 \Rightarrow 2x = 8 \Rightarrow x = 4$

63. $3e^x + 1 = 28 \Rightarrow 3e^x = 27 \Rightarrow e^x = 9 \Rightarrow \ln e^x = \ln 9 \Rightarrow x = \ln 9 \approx 2.20$

64. $0.85^x = 0.2 \Rightarrow \log_{0.85} 0.85^x = \log_{0.85} 0.2 \Rightarrow x = \log_{0.85} 0.2 = \dfrac{\log 0.2}{\log 0.85} \approx 9.90$

65. $5\ln x = 4 \Rightarrow \ln x = 0.8 \Rightarrow e^{\ln x} = e^{0.8} \Rightarrow x = e^{0.8} \approx 2.23$

66. $\ln 2x = 5 \Rightarrow e^{\ln 2x} = e^5 \Rightarrow 2x = e^5 \Rightarrow x = \dfrac{e^5}{2} \approx 74.21$

67. $2\log x = 80 \Rightarrow \log x = 40 \Rightarrow 10^{\log x} = 10^{40} \Rightarrow x = 10^{40}$

68. $3\log x - 5 = 1 \Rightarrow 3\log x = 6 \Rightarrow \log x = 2 \Rightarrow 10^{\log x} = 10^2 \Rightarrow x = 100$

69. $2^{x+4} = 3^x \Rightarrow \log 2^{x+4} = \log 3^x \Rightarrow (x + 4)\log 2 = x\log 3 \Rightarrow x\log 2 + 4\log 2 = x\log 3 \Rightarrow$

$x\log 3 - x\log 2 = 4\log 2 \Rightarrow x(\log 3 - \log 2) = 4\log 2 \Rightarrow x = \dfrac{4\log 2}{\log 3 - \log 2} \approx 6.84$

70. $\ln (2x + 1) + \ln (x - 5) = \ln 13 \Rightarrow \ln (2x + 1)(x - 5) = \ln 13 \Rightarrow (2x + 1)(x - 5) = 13 \Rightarrow$

$2x^2 - 9x - 5 = 13 \Rightarrow 2x^2 - 9x - 18 = 0 \Rightarrow (2x + 3)(x - 6) = 0 \Rightarrow x = -\dfrac{3}{2}$ or 6

The solution $x = -\dfrac{3}{2}$ causes an undefined expression in the original equation. The only solution is 6.

71. (a) The solution is the x-coordinate of the intersection point, $x = 3$.

(b) $\frac{1}{2}(2^x) = 4 \Rightarrow 2^x = 8 \Rightarrow 2^x = 2^3 \Rightarrow x = 3$

72. (a) The solution is the x-coordinate of the intersection point, $x = 4$.

(b) $\log_2 2x = 3 \Rightarrow 2^{\log_2 2x} = 2^3 \Rightarrow 2x = 8 \Rightarrow x = 4$

Applications

73. (a) $(S \circ r)(8) = S(r(8)) = S(\sqrt{2 \cdot 8}) = S(4) = 4\pi(4)^2 = 64\pi$

After 8 seconds, the balloon has a surface area of $64\pi \approx 201$ square inches.

(b) $(S \circ r)(t) = S(r(t)) = S(\sqrt{2t}) = 4\pi(\sqrt{2t})^2 = 4\pi \cdot 2t = 8\pi t$

74. (a) Yes, this is a one-to-one function because different inputs result in different outputs.

(b) $f(x) = 0.08x \Rightarrow y = 0.08x$, interchange x and y and solve for y.

$x = 0.08y \Rightarrow y = \dfrac{x}{0.08} \Rightarrow f^{-1}(x) = \dfrac{x}{0.08}$

This formula calculates the cost of an item whose sales tax is x dollars.

75. $1500(1 + 0.12)^t = 3000 \Rightarrow 1.12^t = 2 \Rightarrow \log_{1.12} 1.12^t = \log_{1.12} 2 \Rightarrow t = \dfrac{\log 2}{\log 1.12} \approx 6.12 \approx 7$ years

76. $100 = a + b\log 1 \Rightarrow 100 = a + b(0) \Rightarrow a = 100$

$150 = 100 + b\log 10 \Rightarrow 150 = 100 + b(1) \Rightarrow b = 50$

77. $3 = Ca^0 \Rightarrow C = 3$ and $6 = 3a^1 \Rightarrow a = 2$

78. $\log\frac{x}{1} = 7 \Rightarrow 10^{\log x} = 10^7 \Rightarrow x = 10^7$

79. (a) Graph $Y_1 = 1.68e$ ^(0.048X) in [0, 10, 2] by [0, 4, 1]. See Figure 79. This represents exponential growth.

(b) In 2003, $x = 6$ thus $f(6) = 1.68e^{0.048(6)} \approx 2.24$ million

(c) $1.68e^{0.048x} = 3 \Rightarrow e^{0.048x} = \dfrac{3}{1.68} \Rightarrow \ln e^{0.048x} = \ln\left(\dfrac{3}{1.68}\right) \Rightarrow 0.048x = \ln\left(\dfrac{3}{1.68}\right) \Rightarrow$

$x = \dfrac{\ln\left(\frac{3}{1.68}\right)}{0.048} \approx 12.1$. That is 12.1 years after 1997, which corresponds to the year 2009.

[0, 10, 2] by [0, 4, 1]

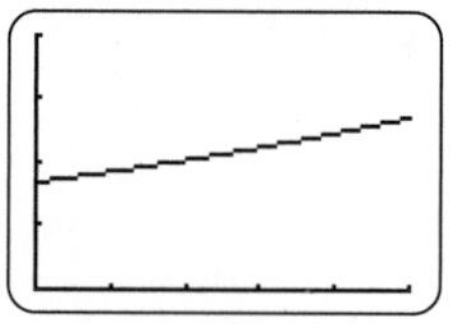

Figure 79

80. (a) $N(0) = 1000e^{0.0014(0)} = 1000$; There were initially 1000 bacteria.

(b) $1000e^{0.0014x} = 2000 \Rightarrow e^{0.0014x} = 2 \Rightarrow \ln e^{0.0014x} = \ln 2 \Rightarrow 0.0014x = \ln 2 \Rightarrow x = \dfrac{\ln 2}{0.0014} \approx 495.11$ min.

81. (a) $f(5) = 1.2\ln 5 + 5 \approx 6.93$ m/sec

(b) $1.2\ln x + 5 = 8 \Rightarrow 1.2\ln x = 3 \Rightarrow \ln x = 2.5 \Rightarrow e^{\ln x} = e^{2.5} \Rightarrow x = e^{2.5} \approx 12.18$ meters

Chapter 12 Test

1. $f(1) = 4(1)^3 - 5(1) = -1$, then $(g \circ f)(1) = g(f(1)) = g(-1) = (-1) + 7 = 6$

   $(f \circ g)(x) = f(g(x)) = f(x + 7) = 4(x + 7)^3 - 5(x + 7)$

2. (a) $(f \circ g)(-1) = f(g(-1)) = f(-1) = 3$

   (b) $(g \circ f)(1) = g(f(1)) = g(1) = 3$

3. Two different inputs result in the same output. For example $-5 \neq 5$, but $f(-5) = f(5) = 0$.

4. $f(x) = 5 - 2x \Rightarrow y = 5 - 2x$, interchange x and y and solve for y.

   $x = 5 - 2y \Rightarrow 2y = 5 - x \Rightarrow y = \dfrac{5 - x}{2} \Rightarrow f^{-1}(x) = \dfrac{5 - x}{2}$

5. The graph of f^{-1} is a reflection of the graph of f across the line $y = x$. See Figure 5.

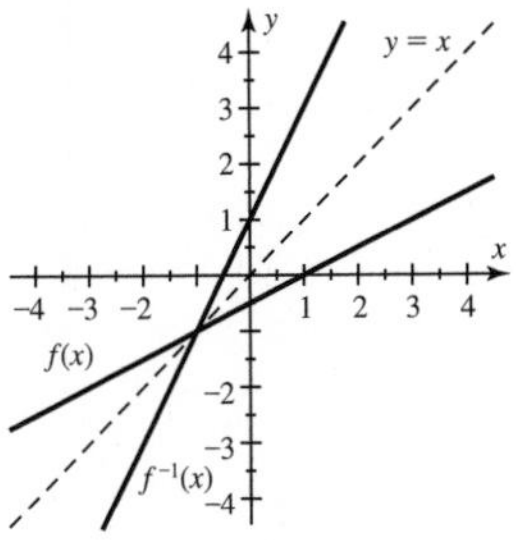

Figure 5

6. See Figure 6. $D = \{2, 4, 6, 8\}$; $R = \{1, 2, 3, 4\}$

x	8	6	4	2
$f^{-1}(x)$	1	2	3	4

Figure 6

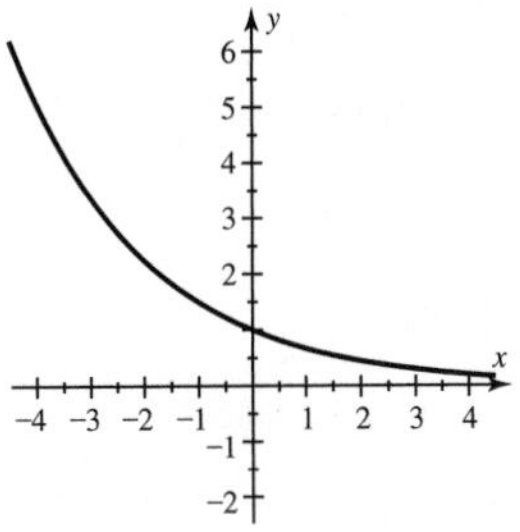

Figure 8

7. $f(2) = 3\left(\dfrac{1}{4}\right)^2 = 3\left(\dfrac{1}{16}\right) = \dfrac{3}{16}$

8. See Figure 8. This graph represents exponential decay.

9. (a) Exponential growth. For each unit increase in x, $f(x)$ increases by a factor of 2.

   (b) Since $f(x) = 3$ when $x = 0$, $f(x) = 3(2)^x$

10. (a) Linear growth. For each unit increase in x, $f(x)$ increases by 1.5 units.

    (b) Since $f(x) = -1$ when $x = 0$, $f(x) = 1.5x - 1$

11. $1 = Ca^0 \Rightarrow C = 1$ and $2 = 1a^{-1} \Rightarrow a = \dfrac{1}{2}$

12. $750(1 + 0.07)^5 = \$1051.91$

13. $f(21) = 1.5 \ln(21 - 5) = 1.5 \ln 16 \approx 4.16$

14. $\log \sqrt{10} = \log 10^{1/2} = \dfrac{1}{2}$

15. $\log_2 43 = \dfrac{\log 43}{\log 2} \approx 5.426$

16. See Figure 16. The graph is shifted 2 units to the right

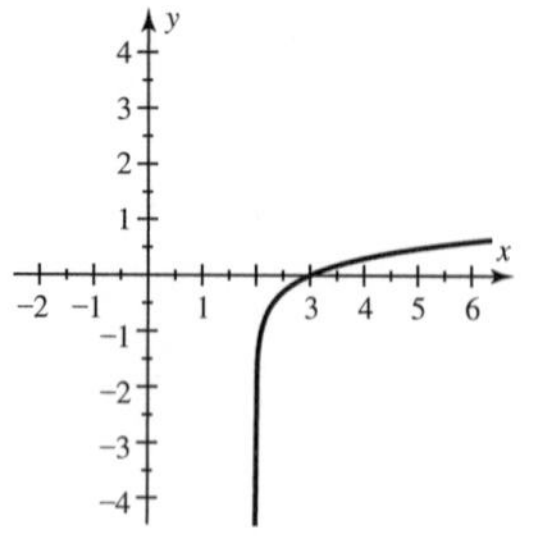

Figure 16

17. $\log \dfrac{x^3y^2}{\sqrt{x}} = \log \dfrac{x^3y^2}{x^{1/2}} = \log x^3 + \log y^2 - \log x^{1/2} = 3 \log x + 2 \log y - \dfrac{1}{2} \log z$

18. $4 \ln x - 5 \ln y + \ln z = \ln x^4 - \ln y^5 + \ln z = \ln \dfrac{x^4}{y^5} + \ln z = \ln \dfrac{x^4 z}{y^5}$

19. $\log 7^{2x} = 2x \log 7$

20. $\ln e^{1-3x} = 1 - 3x$

21. $2e^x = 50 \Rightarrow e^x = 25 \Rightarrow \ln e^x = \ln 25 \Rightarrow x = \ln 25 \approx 3.22$

22. $3(10)^x - 7 = 143 \Rightarrow 3(10)^x = 150 \Rightarrow 10^x = 50 \Rightarrow \log 10^x = \log 50 \Rightarrow x = \log 50 \approx 1.70$

23. $5 \log x = 9 \Rightarrow \log x = 1.8 \Rightarrow 10^{\log x} = 10^{1.8} \Rightarrow x = 10^{1.8} \approx 63.10$

24. $3 \ln 5x = 27 \Rightarrow \ln 5x = 9 \Rightarrow e^{\ln 5x} = e^9 \Rightarrow 5x = e^9 \Rightarrow x = \dfrac{e^9}{5} \approx 1620.62$

25. $5 = a + b \log 1 \Rightarrow 5 = a + b(0) \Rightarrow a = 5$ and $8 = 5 + b \log 10 \Rightarrow 8 = 5 + b(1) \Rightarrow b = 3$

26. (a) $f(0) = 4e^{0.09(0)} = 4e^0 = 4(1) = 4$ million

(b) $f(5) = 4e^{0.09(5)} \approx 6.27$; After 5 hours there were about 6.27 million bacteria.

(c) This represents exponential growth.

(d) $4e^{0.09x} = 6 \Rightarrow e^{0.09x} = 1.5 \Rightarrow \ln e^{0.09x} = \ln 1.5 \Rightarrow 0.09x = \ln 1.5 \Rightarrow x = \dfrac{\ln 1.5}{0.09} \approx 4.51$

There were 6 million bacteria after about 4.51 hours.

Chapter 12 Extended and Discovery Exercises

1. $a^{5730} = 0.5 \Rightarrow (a^{5730})^{1/5730} = 0.5^{1/5730} \Rightarrow a \approx 0.9998790392$

2. $P(10{,}000) = 0.9998790392^{10{,}000} \approx 0.298$ or 29.8%

3. $0.9998790392^x = 0.9 \Rightarrow \log_{0.9998790392} 0.9998790392^x = \log_{0.9998790392} 0.9 \Rightarrow x = \dfrac{\log 0.9}{\log 0.9998790392} \Rightarrow$

$x \approx 871$ years

4. $0.9998790392^x = 0.01 \Rightarrow \log_{0.9998790392} 0.999879^x = \log_{0.9998790392} 0.01 \Rightarrow x = \dfrac{\log 0.01}{\log 0.9998790392} \Rightarrow$

$x \approx 38{,}069$ years (38,100 rounded to the nearest 100 years)

5. Plot the data and graph $Y_1 = 0.133(0.878(0.73\text{^}X) + 0.122(0.92\text{^}X))$ in [0, 25, 5] by [0, 0.11, 0.01].

See Figure 5. The fit is quite good.

[0, 25, 5] by [0, 0.11, 0.01]

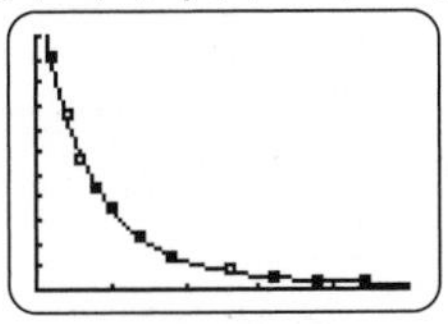

Figure 5

[0, 25, 5] by [0, 0.11, 0.01]

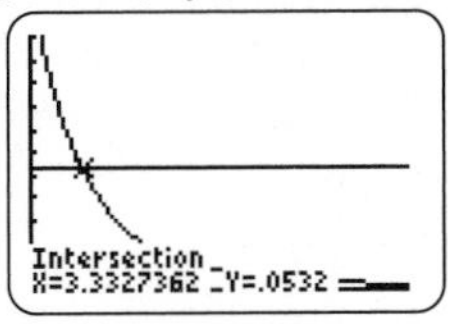

Figure 8

6. $f(0) = 0.133(0.878(0.73^0) + 0.122(0.92^0)) = 0.133(0.878 + 0.122) = 0.133(1) = 0.133$

The initial concentration is 0.133 mg/mL.

7. The concentration decreases to 0 as the body eliminates the dye from the blood stream.

8. Note that 40% of 0.133 is 0.0532.

Graph $Y_1 = 0.133(0.878(0.73\text{^}X) + 0.122(0.92\text{^}X))$ and $Y_2 = 0.0532$ in [0, 25, 5] by [0, 0.11, 0.01].

See Figure 8. This happens after about 3.33 minutes. Solving this problem symbolically would be very difficult.

9. $f(10^{-4.7}) = -\log 10^{-4.7} = -(-4.7) = 4.7$; This rain could cause th pH to drop below 5.6.

10. The ion concentration in sea water is $-\log x = 8.2 \Rightarrow \log x = -8.2 \Rightarrow 10^{\log x} = 10^{-8.2} \Rightarrow x = 10^{-8.2}$.

This is $\dfrac{10^{-4.7}}{10^{-8.2}} \approx 3162$ times greater.

11. $A = 100\left[\dfrac{(1 + \frac{0.09}{26})^{260} - 1}{\frac{0.09}{26}}\right] \approx \$42{,}055.97$

12. A 19-year-old student would have 46 years to deposit money before age 65. *Answers may vary.*

$x\left[\dfrac{(1 + \frac{0.12}{26})^{1196} - 1}{\frac{0.12}{26}}\right] = 1{,}000{,}000 \Rightarrow x = 1{,}000{,}000\left[\dfrac{\frac{0.12}{26}}{(1 + \frac{0.12}{26})^{1196} - 1}\right] = \$18.80$

13. Plot the data in [0, 20, 2] by [0, 700, 100]. See Figure 13.

[0, 20, 2] by [0, 700, 100]

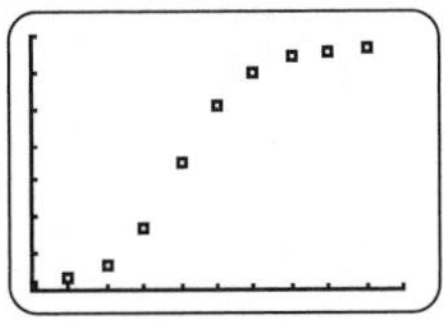

Figure 13

[0, 20, 2] by [0, 700, 100]

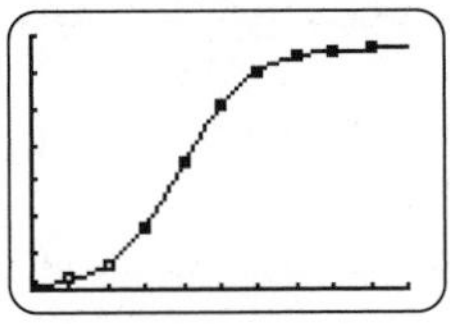

Figure 15

[0, 20, 2] by [0, 700, 100]

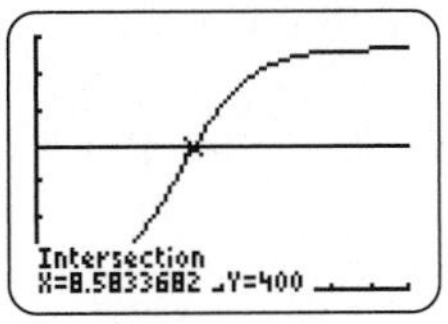

Figure 16

14. The yeast grew slowly at first and then, as more yeast was present, the growth rate increases. Finally, as the yeast began to use up the fixed amount of nourishment, the growth rate slowed.

15. Plot the data and graph $Y_1 = 663/(1 + 71.6(0.579)\text{^}X)$ in [0, 20, 2] by [0, 700, 100]. See Figure 15.

16. Graph $Y_1 = 663/(1 + 71.6(0.579)\text{^}X)$ and $Y_2 = 400$ in [0, 20, 2] by [0, 700, 100]. See Figure 16.

The amount of yeast was equal to 400 units after about 8.6 hours.

17. $400 = \dfrac{663}{1 + 71.6(0.579)^x} \Rightarrow 400(1 + 71.6(0.579)^x) = 663 \Rightarrow 400 + 28{,}640(0.579)^x = 663 \Rightarrow$

$28{,}640(0.579)^x = 263 \Rightarrow 0.579^x = \dfrac{263}{28{,}640} \Rightarrow \log_{0.579} 0.579^x = \log_{0.579} \dfrac{263}{28{,}640} \Rightarrow$

$x = \log_{0.579} \dfrac{263}{28{,}640} = \dfrac{\log\left(\frac{263}{28{,}640}\right)}{\log 0.579} \approx 8.6$ hours

Chapters 1 - 12 Cumulative Review Exercises

1. (a) Because $-\dfrac{11}{7}$ is a fraction in the form $\dfrac{p}{q}$ where p and q are integers and $q \neq 0$, it is a rational number.

   (b) Because the decimal representation for 3π does not terminate or repeat, it is an irrational number.

2. $250 = 10 \times 25 = 2 \times 5 \times 5 \times 5$

3. $2^3 - 7$

4. (a) First find the prime factorizations for 12 and 8. Here $12 = 2^2 \cdot 3$ and $8 = 2^3$. The LCD can be found by multiplying each unique factor raised to its highest power. The LCD is $2^3 \cdot 3 = 24$.

   (b) First find the prime factorizations for 6 and 15. Here $6 = 2 \cdot 3$ and $15 = 3 \cdot 5$. The LCD can be found by multiplying each unique factor raised to its highest power. The LCD is $2 \cdot 3 \cdot 5 = 30$.

5. Because there are five factors of 4, the exponent is 5. The exponential form is 4^5.

6. The order in which the terms $(5 - y)$ and 9 are added on the right side of the equation is reversed on the left side of the equation. This is the commutative property for addition.

7. $\dfrac{2}{3}(x - 3) + 8 = -6 \Rightarrow \dfrac{2}{3}(x - 3) = -14 \Rightarrow x - 3 = -21 \Rightarrow x = -18$

8. Begin by multiplying through by 12 to clear fractions.

   $\dfrac{1}{3}z + 6 < \dfrac{1}{4}z - (5z - 6) \Rightarrow 4z + 72 < 3z - 60z + 72 \Rightarrow 4z < -57z \Rightarrow 61z < 0 \Rightarrow z < 0$

   The solution set is $\{z \mid z < 0\}$.

9. Begin by multiplying through by 3 to clear fractions.

   $\left(\dfrac{t + 2}{3}\right) - 10 = \dfrac{1}{3}t - (5t + 8) \Rightarrow t + 2 - 30 = t - 15t - 24 \Rightarrow 15t = 4 \Rightarrow t = \dfrac{4}{15}$

10. Begin by multiplying through by −5 to clear fractions. Reverse the inequality symbol.

    $-\dfrac{3}{5}x - 4 \leq -1 \Rightarrow 3x + 20 \geq 5 \Rightarrow 3x \geq -15 \Rightarrow x \geq -5$. The solution set is $\{x \mid x \geq -5\}$.

11. $P = \dfrac{J + 2z}{J} \Rightarrow PJ = J + 2z \Rightarrow PJ - J = 2z \Rightarrow J(P - 1) = 2z \Rightarrow J = \dfrac{2z}{P - 1}$

12. $72\% = \dfrac{72}{100} = \dfrac{18}{25}$ and $72\% = 72 \div 100 = 0.72$

13. Because the line passes through the points $(-4, -4)$ and $(0, 1)$, the slope is $m = \dfrac{1 - (-4)}{0 - (-4)} = \dfrac{5}{4}$.

    The line crosses the y-axis at the point $(0, 1)$ so the y-intercept is $b = 1$. The equation is $y = \dfrac{5}{4}x + 1$.

14. A vertical line has an equation of the form $x = k$ where k is the x-coordinate of a point on the line.

Thus, the equation of a vertical line through the point (4, 7) is $x = 4$.

15. $m = \dfrac{-1 - (-3)}{4 - 2} = \dfrac{2}{2} = 1$

16. See Figure 16.

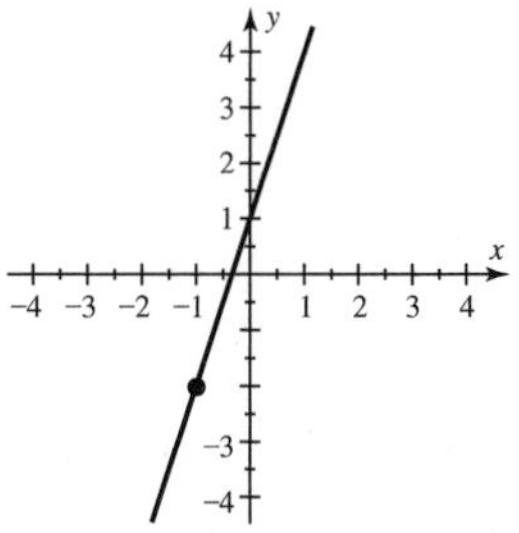

Figure 16

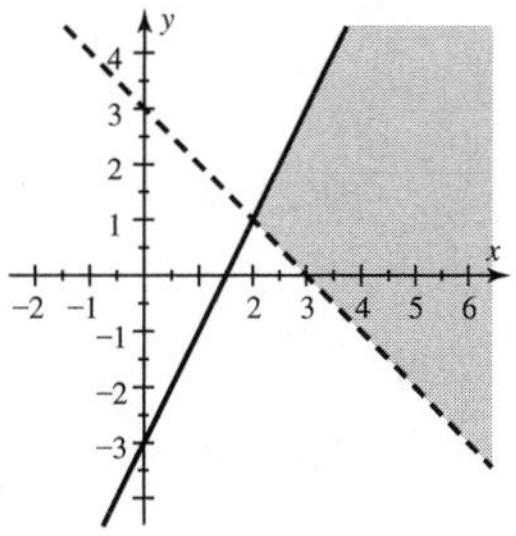

Figure 23

17. Because the line is perpendicular to $y = -\dfrac{1}{7}x - 8$, the slope is the negative reciprocal of $-\dfrac{1}{7}$, or 7.

A line passing through the point (1, 1) with slope 7 has point-slope equation $y = 7(x - 1) + 1$.

This equation in slope-intercept form is $y = 7x - 6$.

18. Because the line is parallel to $y = 3x - 1$, the slope is 3. The point (0, 5) indicates that the y-intercept is $b = 5$.

This equation in slope-intercept form is $y = 3x + 5$.

19. Multiply the first equation by 2, the second equation by 3 and add the equations to eliminate the variable y.

$$\begin{array}{r} 8x - 6y = 2 \\ 15x + 6y = 21 \\ \hline 23x = 23 \end{array}$$

Thus, $x = 1$. And so $4(1) - 3y = 1 \Rightarrow -3y = -3 \Rightarrow y = 1$. The solution is (1, 1).

20. Multiplying the first equation by 3 and adding the two equations will eliminate both variables.

$$\begin{array}{r} 6x - 9y = -6 \\ -6x + 9y = 5 \\ \hline 0 = -1 \end{array}$$

This is always false and the system is inconsistent. No solutions.

21. Multiplying the first equation by 5 and adding the two equations will eliminate the variable y.

$$\begin{array}{r} 10x - 5y = 35 \\ 2x + 5y = 1 \\ \hline 12x = 36 \end{array}$$

Thus, $x = 3$. And so $2(3) - y = 7 \Rightarrow -y = 1 \Rightarrow y = -1$. The solution is (3, −1).

22. Multiply the first equation by 3, the second equation by 2 and add the equations to eliminate both variables.

$$\begin{array}{r} 6x + 24y = -18 \\ -6x - 24y = 18 \\ \hline 0 = 0 \end{array}$$

This is always true and the system is dependent with infinitely many solutions.

23. See Figure 23.

24. Since the lines never intersect, the system has zero solutions.

25. Move the decimal point 4 places to the right. $0.000429 = 4.29 \times 10^{-4}$

26. $\left(\frac{1}{d^2}\right)^{-2} = \left(\frac{d^2}{1}\right)^2 = (d^2)^2 = d^4$

27. $\left(\frac{8a^2}{2b^3}\right)^{-3} = \left(\frac{2b^3}{8a^2}\right)^3 = \left(\frac{b^3}{4a^2}\right)^3 = \frac{(b^3)^3}{(4a^2)^3} = \frac{b^9}{64a^6}$

28. $\frac{(2x^{-2}y^3)^2}{xy^{-2}} = \frac{2^2(x^{-2})^2(y^3)^2}{xy^{-2}} = \frac{4x^{-4}y^6}{xy^{-2}} = 4x^{-4-1}y^{6-(-2)} = 4x^{-5}y^8 = \frac{4y^8}{x^5}$

29. $\frac{x^{-3}y}{4x^2y^{-3}} = \frac{1}{4}x^{-3-2}y^{1-(-3)} = \frac{1}{4}x^{-5}y^4 = \frac{y^4}{4x^5}$

30.
$$\begin{array}{r|l} & 3x^2 + 6x + 10 \\ x - 2 & 3x^3 + 0x^2 - 2x - 15 \\ & 3x^3 - 6x^2 \\ \hline & 6x^2 - 2x - 15 \\ & 6x^2 - 12x \\ \hline & 10x - 15 \\ & 10x - 20 \\ \hline & 5 \end{array}$$

The solution is: $3x^2 + 6x + 10 + \frac{5}{x - 2}$

31. $2x^3 - 4x^2 + 2x = 2x(x^2 - 2x + 1) = 2x(x - 1)(x - 1) = 2x(x - 1)^2$

32. $4a^2 - 25b^2 = (2a)^2 - (5b)^2 = (2a - 5b)(2a + 5b)$

33. $8t^3 - 27 = (2t)^3 - 3^3 = (2t - 3)(4t^2 + 6t + 9)$

34. $4a^3 - 2a^2 + 10a - 5 = 2a^2(2a - 1) + 5(2a - 1) = (2a^2 + 5)(2a - 1)$

35. $6x^2 - 7x - 10 = 0 \Rightarrow (6x + 5)(x - 2) = 0 \Rightarrow 6x + 5 = 0$ or $x - 2 = 0 \Rightarrow x = -\frac{5}{6}$ or 2

36. $9x^2 = 4 \Rightarrow x^2 = \frac{4}{9} \Rightarrow x = \pm\sqrt{\frac{4}{9}} = \pm\frac{2}{3}$

37. $x^4 - 2x^3 = 15x^2 \Rightarrow x^4 - 2x^3 - 15x^2 = 0 \Rightarrow x^2(x^2 - 2x - 15) = 0 \Rightarrow x^2(x - 5)(x + 3) = 0 \Rightarrow$

$x^2 = 0$ or $x - 5 = 0$ or $x + 3 = 0 \Rightarrow x = -3, 0, 5$

38. $5x - 10x^2 = 0 \Rightarrow 5x(1 - 2x) = 0 \Rightarrow 5x = 0$ or $1 - 2x = 0 \Rightarrow x = 0$ or $x = \frac{1}{2}$

39. $\frac{x^2 + 5x + 6}{x^2 - 9} \cdot \frac{x - 3}{x + 2} = \frac{(x + 2)(x + 3)}{(x - 3)(x + 3)} \cdot \frac{x - 3}{x + 2} = \frac{(x + 2)(x + 3)(x - 3)}{(x + 2)(x + 3)(x - 3)} = 1$

40. $\frac{x^2 - 2x - 8}{x^2 + x - 12} \div \frac{(x - 4)^2}{x^2 - 16} = \frac{(x - 4)(x + 2)}{(x + 4)(x - 3)} \cdot \frac{(x - 4)(x + 4)}{(x - 4)(x - 4)} = \frac{(x + 2)(x - 4)(x - 4)(x + 4)}{(x - 3)(x - 4)(x - 4)(x + 4)} = \frac{x + 2}{x - 3}$

41. Multiply each term by the LCD, $(x - 2)(x + 2)$.

$\frac{2}{x + 2} \cdot (x - 2)(x + 2) - \frac{1}{x - 2} \cdot (x - 2)(x + 2) = \frac{-3}{x^2 - 4} \cdot (x - 2)(x + 2) \Rightarrow$

$2(x - 2) - 1(x + 2) = -3 \Rightarrow 2x - 4 - x - 2 = -3 \Rightarrow x - 6 = -3 \Rightarrow x = 3$

42. Multiply each term by the LCD, $(y-1)(y+2)$.

$$\frac{3y}{(y-1)(y+2)}\cdot(y-1)(y+2)=\frac{1}{y-1}\cdot(y-1)(y+2)-2\cdot(y-1)(y+2)\Rightarrow$$

$$3y=1(y+2)-2(y^2+y-2)\Rightarrow 3y=y+2-2y^2-2y+4\Rightarrow 2y^2+4y-6=0\Rightarrow$$

$$2(y+3)(y-1)=0\Rightarrow y+3=0 \text{ or } y-1=0\Rightarrow y=-3 \text{ or } y=1$$

The answer 1 is an extraneous solution. The only solution is -3.

43. Multiply the numerator and the denominator by the LCD, x^2.

$$\frac{\frac{3}{x^2}+x}{x-\frac{3}{x^2}}\cdot\frac{x^2}{x^2}=\frac{\frac{3}{x^2}\cdot x^2+x\cdot x^2}{x\cdot x^2-\frac{3}{x^2}\cdot x^2}=\frac{3+x^3}{x^3-3}=\frac{x^3+3}{x^3-3}$$

44. Since y varies directly as x, $y=kx\Rightarrow 15=3k\Rightarrow k=5$. Then $y=5x\Rightarrow y=5(8)=40$.

45. The denominator cannot equal 0. That is, $x+3\neq 0\Rightarrow x\neq -3$. The domain is $\{x\,|\,x\neq -3\}$.

46. Using the points (2, 5) and (1, 1), $m=\frac{5-1}{2-1}=\frac{4}{1}=4$. The point $(0,-3)$ indicates that the y-intercept is $b=-3$.

The formula is $f(x)=4x-3$.

47. $-10\le -\frac{3}{5}x-4<-1\Rightarrow -6\le -\frac{3}{5}x<3\Rightarrow 10\ge x>-5\Rightarrow -5<x\le 10$. The interval is $(-5, 10]$.

48. First divide each side of $-2|t-4|\ge -12$ by -2 to obtain $|t-4|\le 6$.

The solutions to $|t-4|\le 6$ satisfy $c\le t\le d$ where c and d are the solutions to $|t-4|=6$.

$|t-4|=6$ is equivalent to $t-4=-6\Rightarrow t=-2$ and $t-4=6\Rightarrow t=10$. The interval is $[-2, 10]$.

49. $\det A=-1(4)-3(-2)=-4+6=2$

50. The triangle has vertices $(-2,-3)$, $(-1,2)$ and $(2,1)$. The matrix needed is $A=\begin{bmatrix}-2&-1&2\\-3&2&1\\1&1&1\end{bmatrix}$.

The area is $D=\left|\frac{1}{2}\det([A])\right|=8\text{ in}^2$.

51. $$\left[\begin{array}{ccc|c}2&-1&3&-2\\1&5&-2&-8\\-3&-1&-3&6\end{array}\right]\begin{array}{l}\\\\R_3+R_1\rightarrow\end{array}\left[\begin{array}{ccc|c}2&-1&3&-2\\1&5&-2&-8\\-1&-2&0&4\end{array}\right]\begin{array}{l}\\Exchange\\R_3\rightarrow R_1\end{array}\left[\begin{array}{ccc|c}-1&-2&0&4\\1&5&-2&-8\\2&-1&3&-2\end{array}\right]$$

$$\begin{array}{l}-1R_1\rightarrow\\\\\end{array}\left[\begin{array}{ccc|c}1&2&0&-4\\1&5&-2&-8\\2&-1&3&-2\end{array}\right]\begin{array}{l}\\R_2-R_1\rightarrow\\R_3-2R_1\rightarrow\end{array}\left[\begin{array}{ccc|c}1&2&0&-4\\0&3&-2&-4\\0&-5&3&6\end{array}\right]\begin{array}{l}\\\\R_3+2R_2\rightarrow\end{array}\left[\begin{array}{ccc|c}1&2&0&-4\\0&3&-2&-4\\0&1&-1&-2\end{array}\right]$$

$$\begin{array}{l}\\Exchange\\R_3\rightarrow R_2\end{array}\left[\begin{array}{ccc|c}1&2&0&-4\\0&1&-1&-2\\0&3&-2&-4\end{array}\right]\begin{array}{l}R_1-2R_2\rightarrow\\\\R_3-3R_2\rightarrow\end{array}\left[\begin{array}{ccc|c}1&0&2&0\\0&1&-1&-2\\0&0&1&2\end{array}\right]\begin{array}{l}R_1-2R_3\rightarrow\\R_2+R_3\rightarrow\\\\\end{array}\left[\begin{array}{ccc|c}1&0&0&-4\\0&1&0&0\\0&0&1&2\end{array}\right]$$

The solution is $(-4, 0, 2)$.

52. $\left[\begin{array}{ccc|c} 1 & 1 & -1 & -1 \\ -1 & -1 & -1 & -1 \\ 1 & -2 & 1 & 1 \end{array}\right] \begin{array}{l} \\ R_2 + R_1 \rightarrow \\ R_3 - R_1 \rightarrow \end{array} \left[\begin{array}{ccc|c} 1 & 1 & -1 & -1 \\ 0 & 0 & -2 & -2 \\ 0 & -3 & 2 & 2 \end{array}\right] \begin{array}{l} \\ \textit{Exchange} \\ R_3 \rightarrow R_2 \end{array} \left[\begin{array}{ccc|c} 1 & 1 & -1 & -1 \\ 0 & -3 & 2 & 2 \\ 0 & 0 & -2 & -2 \end{array}\right]$

$\begin{array}{l} \\ \\ -(1/2)R_3 \rightarrow \end{array} \left[\begin{array}{ccc|c} 1 & 1 & -1 & -1 \\ 0 & -3 & 2 & 2 \\ 0 & 0 & 1 & 1 \end{array}\right] \begin{array}{l} R_1 + R_3 \rightarrow \\ R_2 - 2R_3 \rightarrow \\ \\ \end{array} \left[\begin{array}{ccc|c} 1 & 1 & 0 & 0 \\ 0 & -3 & 0 & 0 \\ 0 & 0 & 1 & 1 \end{array}\right] \begin{array}{l} R_1 + (1/3)R_2 \rightarrow \\ -(1/3)R_2 \rightarrow \\ \\ \end{array} \left[\begin{array}{ccc|c} 1 & 0 & 0 & 0 \\ 0 & 1 & 0 & 0 \\ 0 & 0 & 1 & 1 \end{array}\right]$

The solution is (0, 0, 1).

53. $\left(\dfrac{x^6}{y^9}\right)^{2/3} = \dfrac{x^{6\cdot(2/3)}}{y^{9\cdot(2/3)}} = \dfrac{x^4}{y^6}$

54. $\sqrt[3]{-x^4} \cdot \sqrt[3]{-x^5} = -\sqrt[3]{(-x^4)(-x^5)} = \sqrt[3]{x^9} = x^{9/3} = x^3$

55. $\sqrt[3]{a^5b^4} + 3\sqrt[3]{a^5b} = \sqrt[3]{a^3b^3 \cdot a^2b} + 3\sqrt[3]{a^3 \cdot a^2b} = ab\sqrt[3]{a^2b} + 3a\sqrt[3]{a^2b} = (b + 3)a\sqrt[3]{a^2b}$

56. $(5 + \sqrt{5})(5 - \sqrt{5}) = 5^2 - (\sqrt{5})^2 = 25 - 5 = 20$

57. $2(x + 1)^2 = 50 \Rightarrow (x + 1)^2 = 25 \Rightarrow x + 1 = \pm\sqrt{25} \Rightarrow x = -1 \pm 5 \Rightarrow x = -6$ or 4

58. $\sqrt{x + 6} = x \Rightarrow x + 6 = x^2 \Rightarrow x^2 - x - 6 = 0 \Rightarrow (x - 3)(x + 2) = 0 \Rightarrow x - 3 = 0$ or $x + 2 = 0 \Rightarrow$

$x = -2$ or 3. The answer -2 is an extraneous solution. The only solution is 3.

59. $(-2 + 3i) - (-5 - 2i) = -2 + 3i + 5 + 2i = 3 + 5i$

60. $\dfrac{3 - i}{1 + 3i} = \dfrac{3 - i}{1 + 3i} \cdot \dfrac{1 - 3i}{1 - 3i} = \dfrac{3 - 9i - i + 3i^2}{1 - 9i^2} = \dfrac{3 - 10i - 3}{1 + 9} = \dfrac{-10i}{10} = -i$

61. The x-coordinate of the vertex is $x = -\dfrac{b}{2a} = -\dfrac{-12}{2(3)} = 2$. The y-coordinate is $f(2) = 3(2)^2 - 12(2) + 13 = 1$.

The vertex is (2, 1).

62. The maximum y-value located on the graph is found at the vertex.

The x-coordinate of the vertex is $x = -\dfrac{b}{2a} = -\dfrac{6}{2(-2)} = \dfrac{3}{2}$. The y-coordinate of the vertex is

$f\left(\dfrac{3}{2}\right) = -2\left(\dfrac{3}{2}\right)^2 + 6\left(\dfrac{3}{2}\right) - 1 = \dfrac{7}{2}$. The maximum y-value located on the graph is $\dfrac{7}{2}$.

63. $x^2 - 13x + 40 = 0 \Rightarrow (x - 5)(x - 8) = 0 \Rightarrow x - 5 = 0$ or $x - 8 = 0 \Rightarrow x = 5$ or 8

64. First rewrite the equation: $2d^2 - 5 = d \Rightarrow 2d^2 - d - 5 = 0$. Then use the quadratic formula.

$x = \dfrac{1 \pm \sqrt{(-1)^2 - 4(2)(-5)}}{2(2)} = \dfrac{1 \pm \sqrt{41}}{4}$

65. (a) The graph crosses the x-axis at -1 and 3. The solutions are -1, 3.

(b) Because the graph opens downward, $a < 0$.

(c) Because there are two real solutions to the equation, the discriminant is positive.

66. $x^2 + 5x - 14 = 0 \Rightarrow (x + 7)(x - 2) = 0 \Rightarrow x = -7$ or $x = 2$

Since the parabola opens upward, the solution is $(-\infty, -7] \cup [2, \infty)$.

67. (a) Because $g(1) = 2(1) + 1 = 3$ and $f(3) = 3^2 - 2 = 7$, $(f \circ g)(1) = f(g(1)) = f(3) = 7$

(b) $(g \circ f)(x) = g(f(x)) = g(x^2 - 2) = 2(x^2 - 2) + 1 = 2x^2 - 3$

68. $A = 800(1 + 0.075)^{15} \approx \$2367.10$

69. $\log_3 81 = \log_3 3^4 = 4$

70. $e^{\ln(2x)} = 2x$

71. $\log \dfrac{\sqrt{x}}{y^2} = \log \dfrac{x^{1/2}}{y^2} = \log x^{1/2} - \log y^2 = \dfrac{1}{2}\log x - 2\log y$

72. $2\ln x + \ln 5x = \ln x^2 + \ln 5x = \ln(x^2 \cdot 5x) = \ln(5x^3)$

73. $6\log x - 2 = 9 \Rightarrow 6\log x = 11 \Rightarrow \log x = \dfrac{11}{6} \Rightarrow 10^{\log x} = 10^{11/6} \Rightarrow x = 10^{11/6} \approx 68.13$

74. $2^{3x} = 17 \Rightarrow \log 2^{3x} = \log 17 \Rightarrow 3x\log 2 = \log 17 \Rightarrow 3x = \dfrac{\log 17}{\log 2} \Rightarrow x = \dfrac{\log 17}{3\log 2} \approx 1.36$

75. $72 - (-18) = 72 + 18 = 90°F$

76. $\dfrac{87 + 84 + 93 + x}{4} \geq 90 \Rightarrow 264 + x \geq 360 \Rightarrow x \geq 96$. The student must score 96 or more.

77. (a) $m = \dfrac{255 - 450}{4 - 1} = \dfrac{-195}{3} = -65$

(b) Because the slope is negative, the truck is moving *toward* Louisville at a rate of 65 miles per hour.

78. The sum of two complementary angles is 90°. Let x be the smaller angle, then $3x - 14$ represents the larger.

$x + (3x - 14) = 90 \Rightarrow 4x = 104 \Rightarrow x = 26$. The angles are 26° and $3(26) - 14 = 64°$.

79. For the year 2011, let $x = 11$. Then $P = 6(1.014)^{11} \approx 7$ billion.

80. Let x be the number of minutes spent on the elliptical trainer and let y be the number of minutes spent running.

The total number of calories is $12x + 10y = 810$ and the total number of minutes is $x + y = 75$.

Solving the second equation for y gives $y = 75 - x$. Substituting for y in the first equation yields

$12x + 10(75 - x) = 810 \Rightarrow 2x + 750 = 810 \Rightarrow 2x = 60 \Rightarrow x = 30$ and so $y = 75 - 30 = 45$.

The athlete spent 30 minutes on the elliptical trainer and 45 minutes running.

81. Let x be the cost of a ticket and let y be the number of movie-goers. Use $x = 7$ and $y = 400$ to find k.

$y = \dfrac{k}{x} \Rightarrow 400 = \dfrac{k}{7} \Rightarrow k = 2800$. Then when $x = 2$, $y = \dfrac{2800}{2} = 1400$ tickets.

82. $m = \dfrac{15.3 - 16.7}{1994 - 1990} = \dfrac{-1.4}{4} = -0.35$ so $y = -0.35(x - 1990) + 16.7 \Rightarrow y = -0.35x + 713.2$.

83. Let x be the number of double cheeseburgers and let y be the number of orders of jumbo fries.

The total for the first order is $3x + 2y = 6$ and the total for the second order is $5x + 3y = 9.5$.

Solving the first equation for y gives $y = 3 - 1.5x$. Substituting for y in the second equation yields

$5x + 3(3 - 1.5x) = 9.5 \Rightarrow 0.5x + 9 = 9.5 \Rightarrow 0.5x = 0.5 \Rightarrow x = 1$ and so $y = 3 - 1.5(1) = 1.5$.

A double cheeseburger costs \$1.00 and an order of jumbo fries costs \$1.50.

84. $14{,}600 = 12{,}000(1 + r)^5 \Rightarrow \dfrac{14{,}600}{12{,}000} = (1 + r)^5 \Rightarrow \left(\dfrac{14{,}600}{12{,}000}\right)^{1/5} = ((1 + r)^5)^{1/5} \Rightarrow \left(\dfrac{73}{60}\right)^{1/5} = 1 + r \Rightarrow$

$r = \left(\dfrac{73}{60}\right)^{1/5} - 1 \approx 0.04$ or 4%.

85. $36 = 27.4\sqrt[3]{W} \Rightarrow \dfrac{36}{27.4} = \sqrt[3]{W} \Rightarrow \left(\dfrac{36}{27.4}\right)^3 = (\sqrt[3]{W})^3 \Rightarrow W = \left(\dfrac{36}{27.4}\right)^3 \approx 2.27$ pounds

86. (a) The year of the lowest energy consumption is the x-coordinate of the vertex, $x = -\dfrac{b}{2a} = -\dfrac{-975}{2(0.25)} = 1950.$

(b) Find the y-coordinate of the vertex. $f(1950) = 0.25(1950)^2 - 975(1950) + 950{,}845 = 220$ million Btu.

87. $350 = \dfrac{x^2}{12} \Rightarrow x^2 = 4200 \Rightarrow x = \sqrt{4200} \approx 64.8$ mph. Note that $-\sqrt{4200}$ has no physical meaning.

88. $1{,}000{,}000 = 8000(1 + r)^{45} \Rightarrow \dfrac{1{,}000{,}000}{8000} = (1 + r)^{45} \Rightarrow (1 + r)^{45} = 125 \Rightarrow ((1 + r)^{45})^{1/45} = 125^{1/45} \Rightarrow$

$1 + r = 125^{1/45} \Rightarrow r = 125^{1/45} - 1 \approx 0.113$ or 11.3%

89. (a) $f(8) = 1.4\ln(8) + 7 \approx 9.91$ meters per second

(b) $1.4\ln x + 7 = 10 \Rightarrow 1.4\ln x = 3 \Rightarrow \ln x = \dfrac{3}{1.4} \Rightarrow e^{\ln x} = e^{3/1.4} \Rightarrow x \approx 8.52$ meters

Critical Thinking Solutions for Chapter 12

Section 12.2

- Every graph of $y = a^x$ passes through the point $(0, 1)$ because any nonzero base raised to the power 0 equals 1.
- The graph of $y = e^x$ will be between the graphs of $y = 2^x$ and $y = 3^x$ since $2 < e < 3$.

  It is closer to the graph of $y = 3^x$.

Section 12.3

- If the sound level increases by 10 db the intensity increases by a factor of 10.
- $\log_a 1 = 0$ because $a^0 = 1$ for any positive base a.

Section 12.5

- Yes, they are approximately the same since $3\log x = 3\left(\dfrac{\ln x}{\ln 10}\right) = \dfrac{3}{\ln 10} \cdot \ln x \approx 1.3\ln x.$

Chapter 13: Conic Sections

13.1: Parabolas and Circles

Concepts

1. Parabola, ellipse and hyperbola

3. No, it does not pass the vertical line test for functions.

5. No, it does not pass the vertical line test for functions.

7. left

9. circle; (h, k)

Parabolas

11. Since $x = (y - 0)^2 + 0$, the vertex is (0, 0) and the axis of symmetry is $y = 0$. See Figure 11.

13. Since $x = (y - 0)^2 + 1$, the vertex is (1, 0) and the axis of symmetry is $y = 0$. See Figure 13.

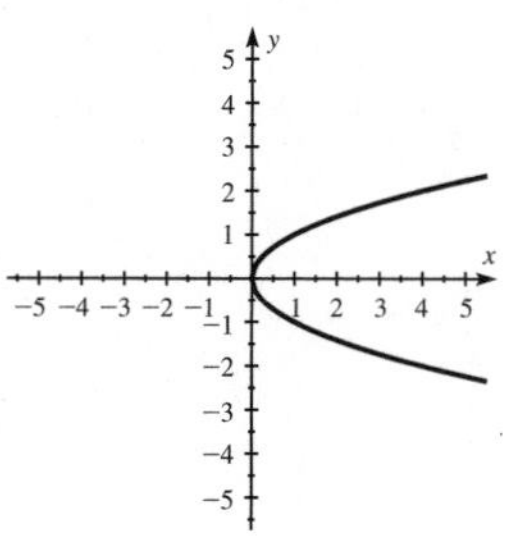

Figure 11

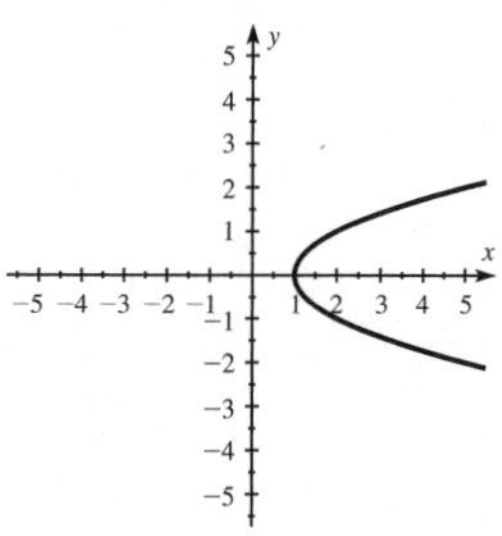

Figure 13

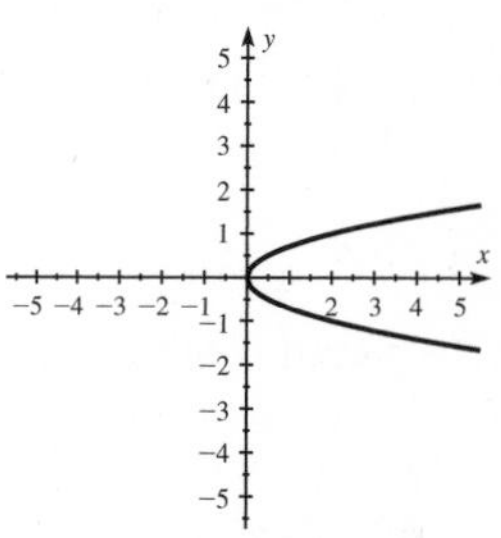

Figure 15

15. Since $x = 2(y - 0)^2 + 0$, the vertex is (0, 0) and the axis of symmetry is $y = 0$. See Figure 15.

17. Since $x = (y - 1)^2 + 2$, the vertex is (2, 1) and the axis of symmetry is $y = 1$. See Figure 17.

19. Since $y = (x + 2)^2 + 1$, the vertex is (–2, 1) and the axis of symmetry is $x = -2$. See Figure 19.

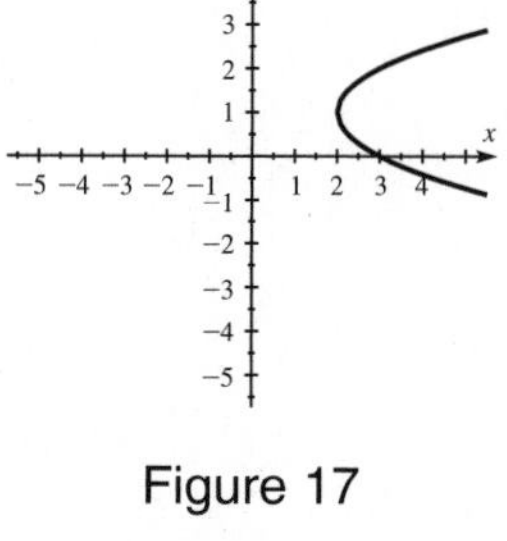

Figure 17

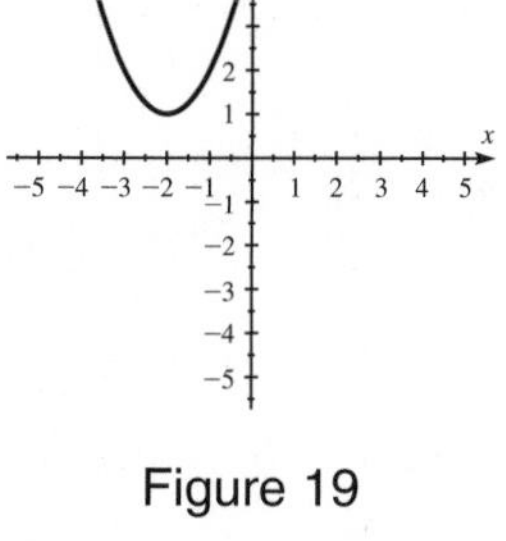

Figure 19

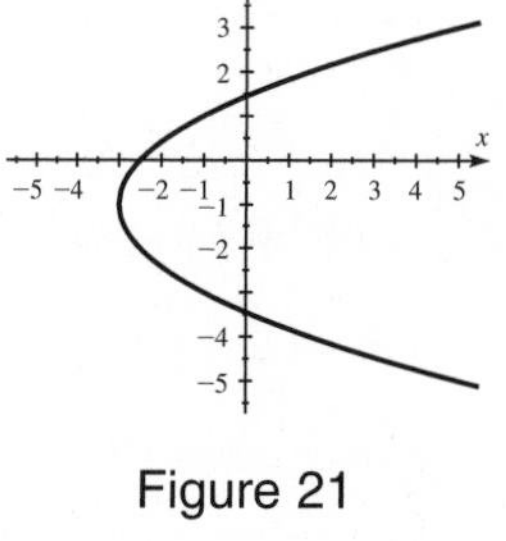

Figure 21

21. Since $x = \frac{1}{2}(y + 1)^2 - 3$, the vertex is (–3, –1) and the axis of symmetry is $y = -1$. See Figure 21.

23. Since $x = -3(y - 1)^2 + 0$, the vertex is (0, 1) and the axis of symmetry is $y = 1$. See Figure 23.

25. See Figure 25.

$$x = -\frac{b}{2a} = -\frac{-1}{2(2)} = \frac{1}{4} \text{ and } y = 2\left(\frac{1}{4}\right)^2 - \left(\frac{1}{4}\right) + 1 = \frac{7}{8}. \text{ Vertex: } \left(\frac{1}{4}, \frac{7}{8}\right). \text{ Axis of symmetry: } x = \frac{1}{4}.$$

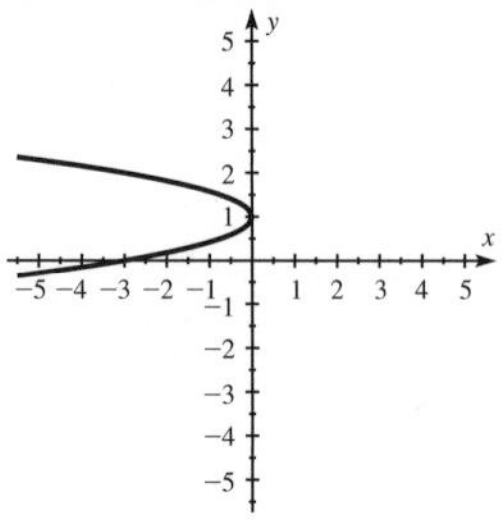

Figure 23

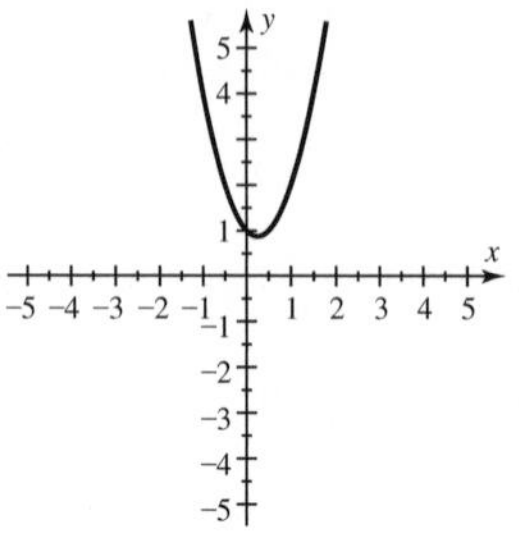

Figure 25

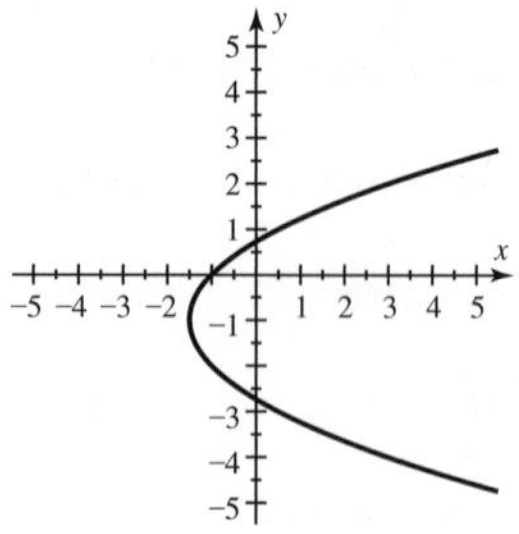

Figure 27

27. See Figure 27.

$$y = -\frac{b}{2a} = -\frac{1}{2(\frac{1}{2})} = -1 \text{ and } x = \frac{1}{2}(-1)^2 + (-1) - 1 = -\frac{3}{2}. \text{ Vertex: } \left(-\frac{3}{2}, -1\right). \text{ Axis of symmetry: } y = -1.$$

29. See Figure 29.

$$y = -\frac{b}{2a} = -\frac{1}{2(3)} = -\frac{1}{6} \text{ and } x = 3\left(-\frac{1}{6}\right)^2 + \left(-\frac{1}{6}\right) = -\frac{1}{12}. \text{ Vertex: } \left(-\frac{1}{12}, -\frac{1}{6}\right). \text{ Axis of symmetry: } y = -\frac{1}{6}.$$

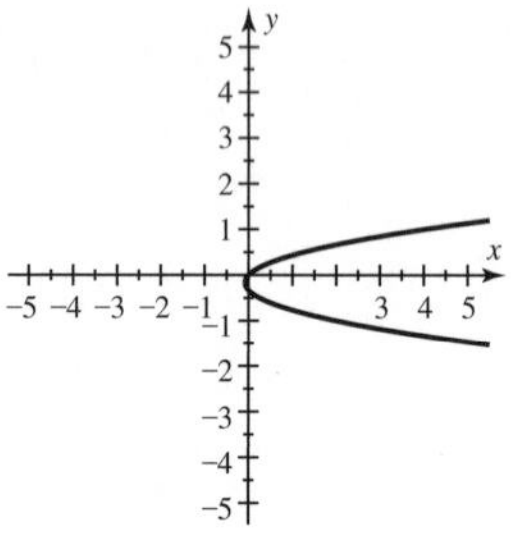

Figure 29

31. Since the parabola opens upward and the vertex is (0, 0), the equation has the form $y = a(x - 0)^2 + 0$.

Since the parabola passes through (1, 1), $1 = a(1 - 0)^2 + 0 \Rightarrow a = 1$. The equation is $y = x^2$.

33. Since the parabola opens to the right and the vertex is (–2, –1), the equation has the form $x = a(y + 1)^2 - 2$.

Since the parabola passes through (–1, 0), $-1 = a(0 + 1)^2 - 2 \Rightarrow a = 1$. The equation is $x = (y + 1)^2 - 2$.

35. By plotting the points by hand, we see that the parabola must open upward.

37. By plotting the points and axis by hand, we see that the parabola must open downward.

39. Since the parabola opens to the left and the vertex is (0, 0), the possible x-values are $x \geq 0$.

41. Since the parabola opens to the right and the vertex is to the left of the y-axis, the parabola has two y-intercepts.

43. $x = 3(0)^2 - (0) + 1 \Rightarrow x = 1$

Circles

45. $(x - 0)^2 + (y - 0)^2 = 1^2 \Rightarrow x^2 + y^2 = 1$

47. $(x - (-1))^2 + (y - 5)^2 = 3^2 \Rightarrow (x + 1)^2 + (y - 5)^2 = 9$

49. $(x - (-4))^2 + (y - (-6))^2 = (\sqrt{2})^2 \Rightarrow (x + 4)^2 + (y + 6)^2 = 2$

51. Since the center is (0, 0) and the radius is 4, the equation is $x^2 + y^2 = 16$.

53. Since the center is (–3, 2) and the radius is 1, the equation is $(x + 3)^2 + (y - 2)^2 = 1$.

55. The radius is 3 and the center is (0, 0). Solving the equation for y results in $y = \pm\sqrt{9 - x^2}$. See Figure 55.

57. The radius is 3 and the center is (1, 3). Solving the equation for y results in $y = 3 \pm \sqrt{9 - (x - 1)^2}$.

See Figure 57.

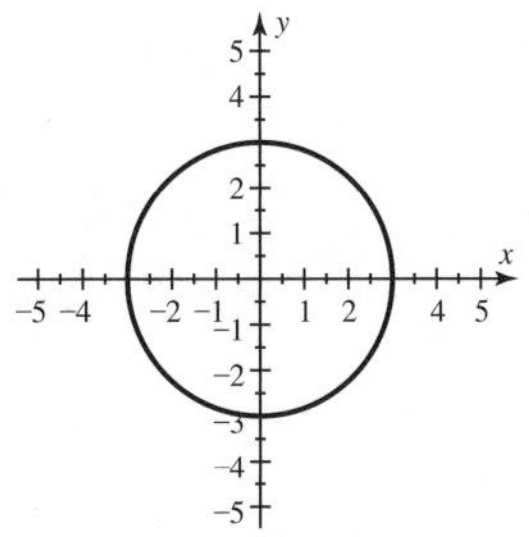

Figure 55

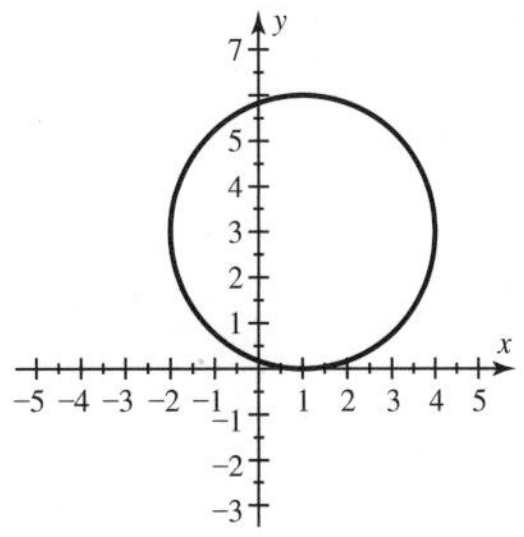

Figure 57

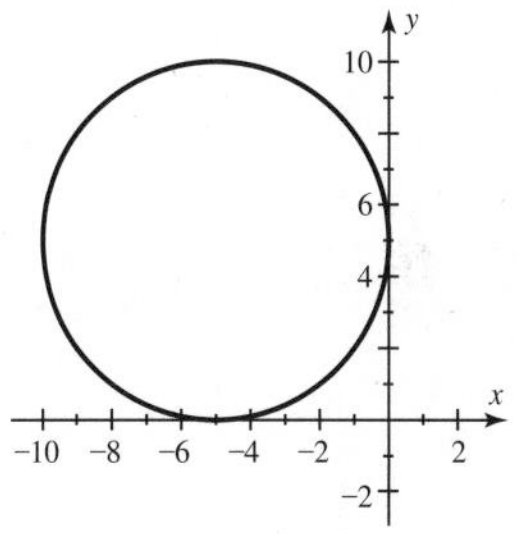

Figure 59

59. The radius is 5 and the center is (–5, 5). Solving the equation for y results in $y = 5 \pm \sqrt{25 - (x + 5)^2}$.

See Figure 59.

61. $x^2 + 6x + y^2 - 2y = -1 \Rightarrow x^2 + 6x + 9 + y^2 - 2y + 1 = -1 + 9 + 1 \Rightarrow (x + 3)^2 + (y - 1)^2 = 9$

The radius is 3 and the center is (–3, 1). Solving the equation for y results in $y = 1 \pm \sqrt{9 - (x + 3)^2}$.

See Figure 61.

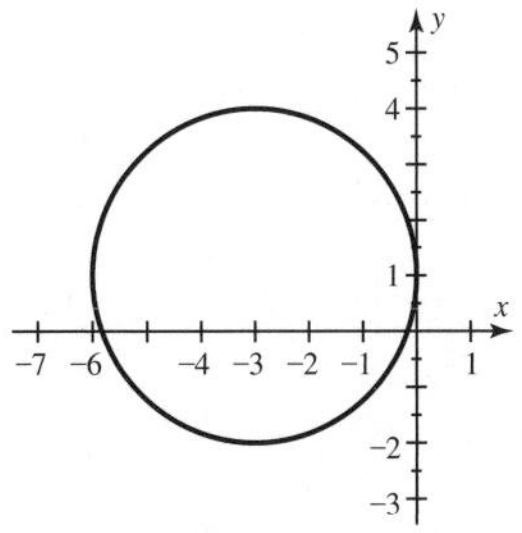

Figure 61

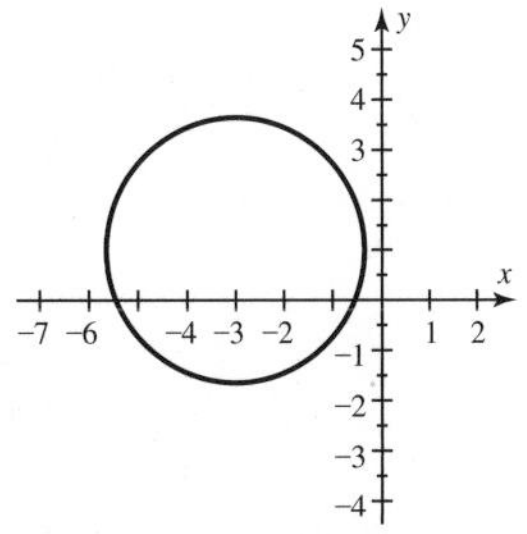

Figure 63

63. $x^2 + 6x + y^2 - 2y + 3 = 0 \Rightarrow x^2 + 6x + 9 + y^2 - 2y + 1 = -3 + 9 + 1 \Rightarrow (x + 3)^2 + (y - 1)^2 = 7$

The radius is $\sqrt{7}$ and the center is (–3, 1). Solving the equation for y results in $y = 1 \pm \sqrt{7 - (x + 3)^2}$.

See Figure 63.

Applications

65. (a) Graph $Y_1 = (32/11025)X^2$ using the DrawInv feature in [−40, 40, 10] by [−120, 120, 20]. See Figure 65.

(b) When $y = 105$, $x = \dfrac{32}{11{,}025}(105)^2 = 32$ feet.

67. (a) Plot (−0.1, 0) and graph $Y_1 = -2.5X^2$ using the DrawInv feature in [−1.5, 1.5, 0.5] by [−1, 1, 0.5]. See Figure 67.

(b) $d = \sqrt{(-2.5 - (-0.1))^2 + (1 - 0)^2} = \sqrt{(-2.4)^2 + 1^2} = \sqrt{6.76} = 2.6$ A.U. or 241,800,000 miles.

[−40, 40, 10] by [−120, 120, 20]

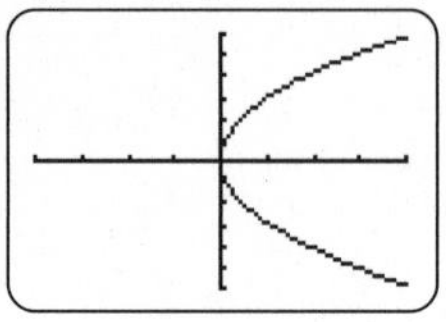

Figure 65

[−1.5, 1.5, 0.5] by [−1, 1, 0.5]

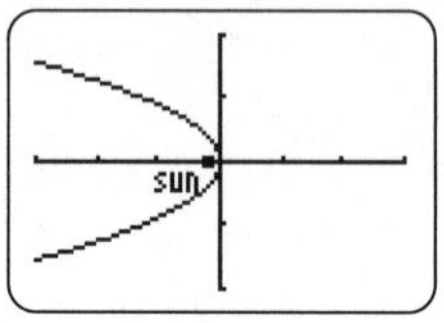

Figure 67

13.2: Ellipses and Hyperbolas

Concepts

1. See Figure 1.

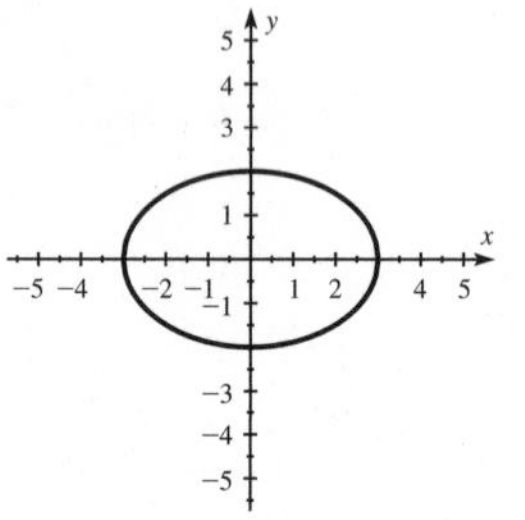

Figure 1

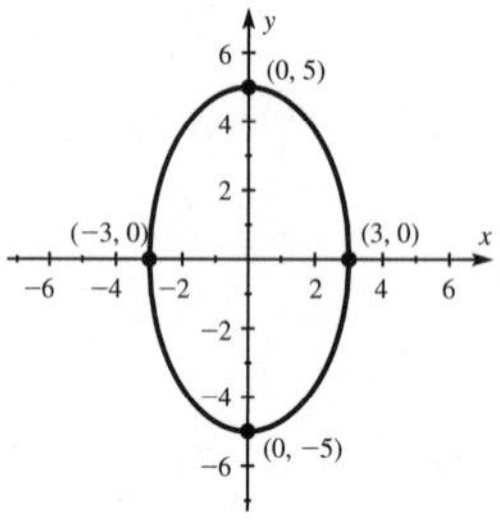

Figure 11

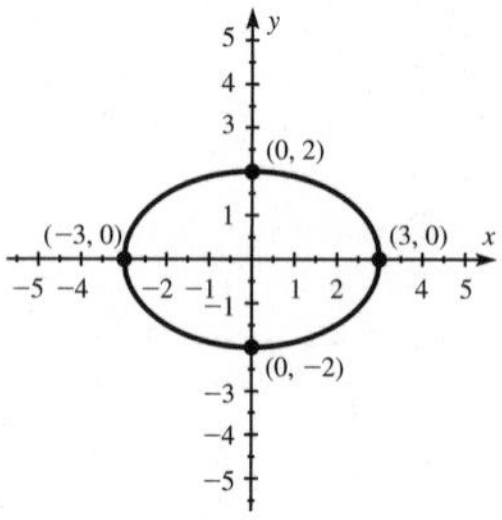

Figure 13

3. horizontal

5. 2

7. left and right

9. They are the diagonals.

Ellipses

11. The ellipse has a vertical major axis with vertices $(0, \pm 5)$ and minor axis endpoints $(\pm 3, 0)$. See Figure 11.

13. The ellipse has a horizontal major axis with vertices $(\pm 3, 0)$ and minor axis endpoints $(0, \pm 2)$. See Figure 13.

15. The ellipse has a vertical major axis with vertices $(0, \pm 2)$ and minor axis endpoints $(\pm 1, 0)$. See Figure 15.

17. The ellipse has a horizontal major axis with vertices $(\pm\sqrt{7}, 0)$ and minor axis endpoints $(0, \pm\sqrt{5})$. See Figure 17.

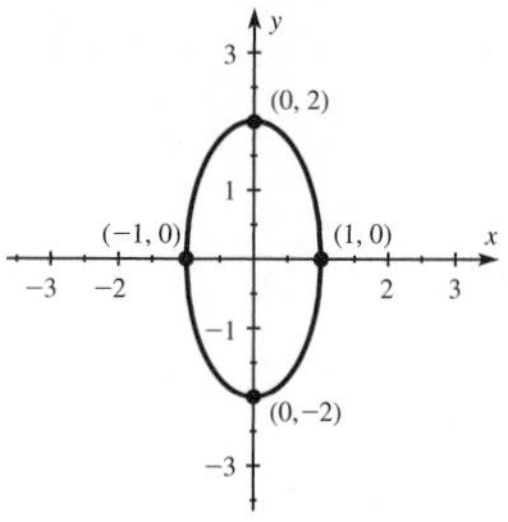

Figure 15

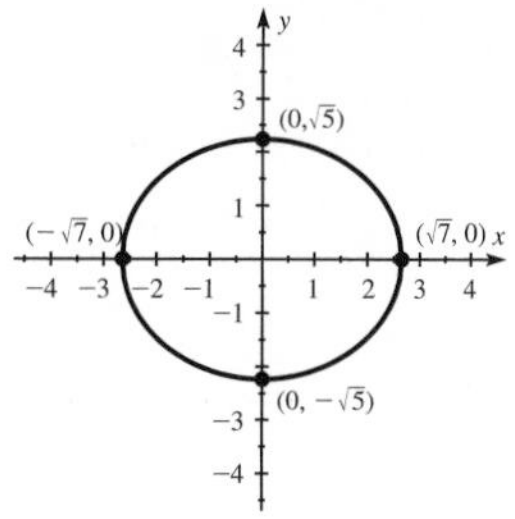

Figure 17

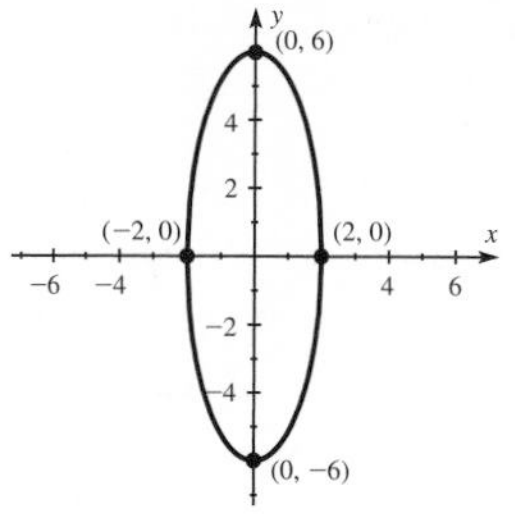

Figure 19

19. $36x^2 + 4y^2 = 144 \Rightarrow \dfrac{36x^2}{144} + \dfrac{4y^2}{144} = 1 \Rightarrow \dfrac{x^2}{4} + \dfrac{y^2}{36} = 1$

The ellipse has a vertical major axis with vertices $(0, \pm 6)$ and minor axis endpoints $(\pm 2, 0)$. See Figure 19.

21. $6y^2 + 7x^2 = 42 \Rightarrow \dfrac{6y^2}{42} + \dfrac{7x^2}{42} = 1 \Rightarrow \dfrac{y^2}{7} + \dfrac{x^2}{6} = 1$

The ellipse has a vertical major axis with vertices $(0, \pm\sqrt{7})$ and minor axis endpoints $(\pm\sqrt{6}, 0)$. See Figure 21.

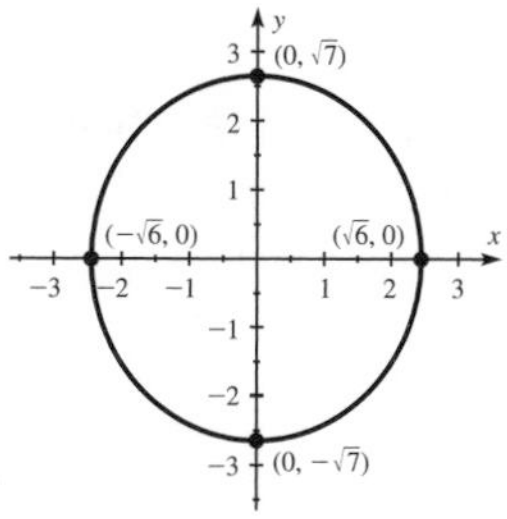

Figure 21

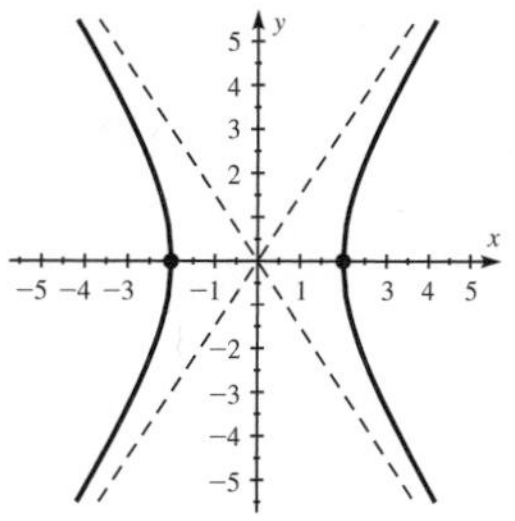

Figure 27

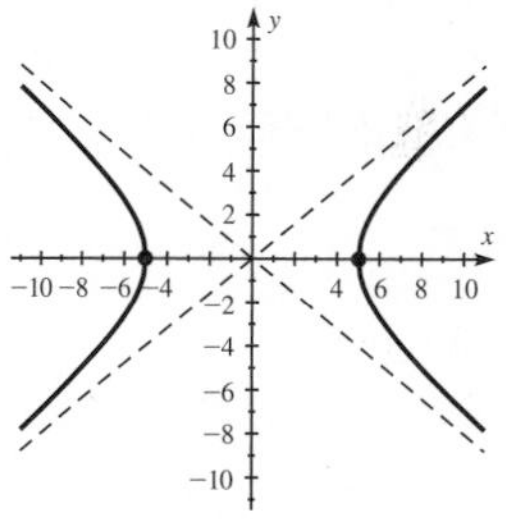

Figure 29

23. Horizontal major axis with vertices $(\pm 3, 0)$ and minor axis endpoints $(0, \pm 2) \Rightarrow \dfrac{x^2}{9} + \dfrac{y^2}{4} = 1$

25. Vertical major axis with vertices $(0, \pm 5)$ and minor axis endpoints $(\pm 4, 0) \Rightarrow \dfrac{y^2}{25} + \dfrac{x^2}{16} = 1$

Hyperbolas

27. The hyperbola has a horizontal transverse axis with vertices $(\pm 2, 0)$ and asymptotes $y = \pm \frac{3}{2}x$. See Figure 27.

29. The hyperbola has a horizontal transverse axis with vertices $(\pm 5, 0)$ and asymptotes $y = \pm \frac{4}{5}x$. See Figure 29.

31. The hyperbola has a horizontal transverse axis with vertices $(\pm 1, 0)$ and asymptotes $y = \pm x$. See Figure 31.

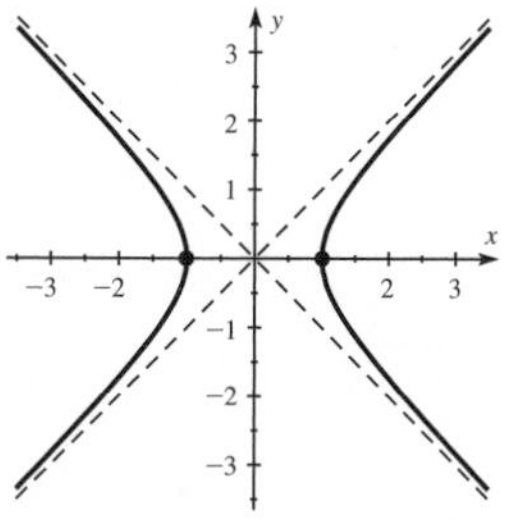

Figure 31

33. The hyperbola has a horizontal transverse axis with vertices $(\pm\sqrt{3}, 0)$ and asymptotes $y = \pm\frac{2}{\sqrt{3}}x$. See Figure 33.

35. $9y^2 - 4x^2 = 36 \Rightarrow \frac{9y^2}{36} - \frac{4x^2}{36} = 1 \Rightarrow \frac{y^2}{4} - \frac{x^2}{9} = 1$

The hyperbola has a vertical transverse axis with vertices $(0, \pm 2)$ and asymptotes $y = \pm\frac{2}{3}x$. See Figure 35.

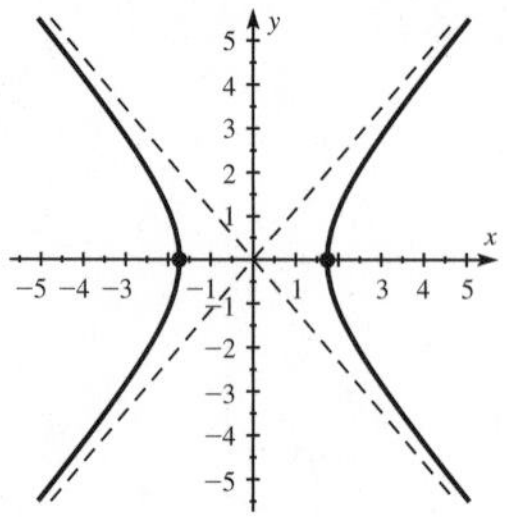

Figure 33

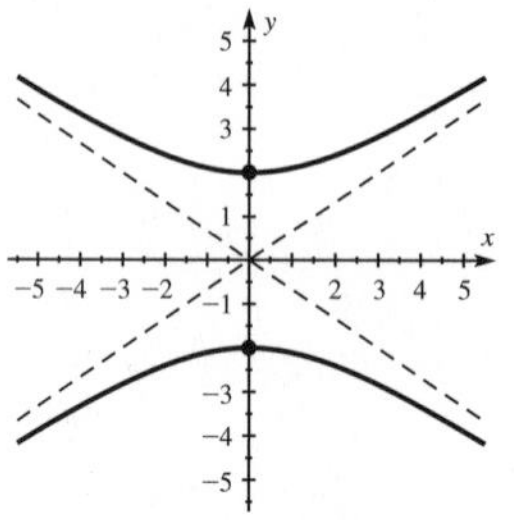

Figure 35

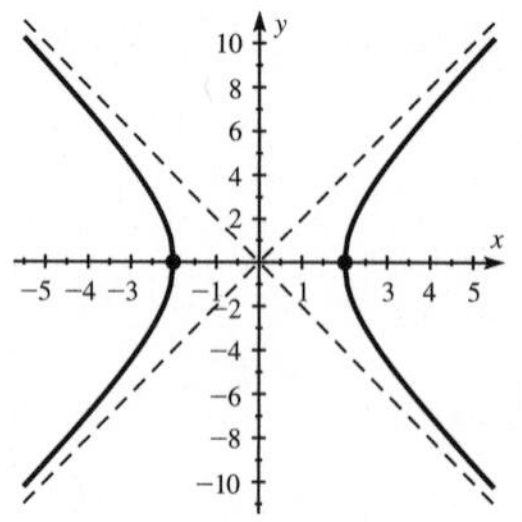

Figure 37

37. $16x^2 - 4y^2 = 64 \Rightarrow \frac{16x^2}{64} - \frac{4y^2}{64} = 1 \Rightarrow \frac{x^2}{4} - \frac{y^2}{16} = 1$

The hyperbola has a horizontal transverse axis with vertices $(\pm 2, 0)$ and asymptotes $y = \pm 2x$. See Figure 37.

39. Horizontal transverse axis with vertices $(\pm 1, 0)$ and asymptotes $y = \pm\frac{1}{1}x \Rightarrow x^2 - y^2 = 1$

41. Vertical transverse axis with vertices $(0, \pm 2)$ and asymptotes $y = \pm\frac{2}{3}x \Rightarrow \frac{y^2}{4} - \frac{x^2}{9} = 1$

Applications

43. (a) $A = \pi(4)(5) \approx 62.83$; $P = 2\pi\sqrt{\frac{4^2 + 5^2}{2}} \approx 28.45$

(b) $A = \pi(\sqrt{7})(\sqrt{2}) \approx 11.75$; $P = 2\pi\sqrt{\frac{(\sqrt{7})^2 + (\sqrt{2})^2}{2}} \approx 13.33$

45. (a) $\frac{x^2}{39.44^2} + \frac{y^2}{38.20^2} = 1 \Rightarrow \frac{y^2}{38.20^2} = 1 - \frac{x^2}{39.44^2} \Rightarrow y = \pm\sqrt{38.20^2\left(1 - \frac{x^2}{39.44^2}\right)}$

Graph $Y_1 = \sqrt{(38.20^2(1 - (X^2/39.44^2)))}$ and $Y_2 = -\sqrt{(38.20^2(1 - (X^2/39.44^2)))}$ and plot the point (9.82,0) in [−60, 60, 10] by [−40, 40, 10]. See Figure 45.

(b) $P = 2\pi\sqrt{\frac{39.44^2 + 38.20^2}{2}} \approx 243.9$ A.U. or about 2.27×10^{10} miles

$A = \pi(39.44)(38.20) \approx 4733$ A.U. or about 4.09×10^{19} square miles

[−60, 60, 10] by [−40, 40, 10]

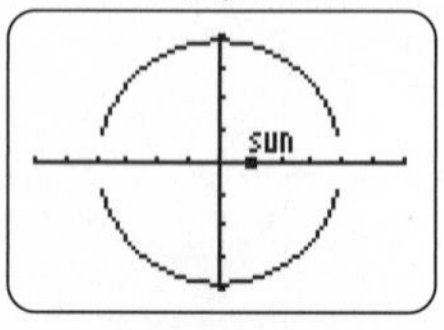

Figure 45

47. The maximum and minimum heights occur when $y = 0$. These values are calculated below.

Earth: $\dfrac{(x-164)^2}{3960^2} + 0 = 1 \Rightarrow (x-164)^2 = 3960^2 \Rightarrow x - 164 = \pm 3960 \Rightarrow x = 4124$ or $x = -3796$.

Explorer VII: $\dfrac{x^2}{4464^2} + 0 = 1 \Rightarrow x^2 = 4464^2 \Rightarrow x = \pm 4464 \Rightarrow x = 4464$ or $x = -4464$.

The maximum height is $-3796 - (-4464) = 668$ miles. The minimum height is $4464 - 4124 = 340$ miles.

49. The height is half the length of the minor axis and the width is the full length of the major axis.

$400x^2 + 10{,}000y^2 = 4{,}000{,}000 \Rightarrow \dfrac{400x^2}{4{,}000{,}000} + \dfrac{10{,}000y^2}{4{,}000{,}000} = 1 \Rightarrow \dfrac{x^2}{10{,}000} + \dfrac{y^2}{400} = 1$

The height is $\sqrt{400} = 20$ feet and the width is $2\sqrt{10{,}000} = 2(100) = 200$ feet.

Checking Basic Concepts for Sections 13.1 & 13.2

1. See Figure 1. Vertex: (1, 2). Axis of symmetry: $y = 2$.

2. The equation is $(x-1)^2 + (y+2)^2 = 4$.

$(x-1)^2 + (y+2)^2 = 4 \Rightarrow (y+2)^2 = 4 - (x-1)^2 \Rightarrow y = -2 \pm \sqrt{4-(x-1)^2}$. See Figure 2.

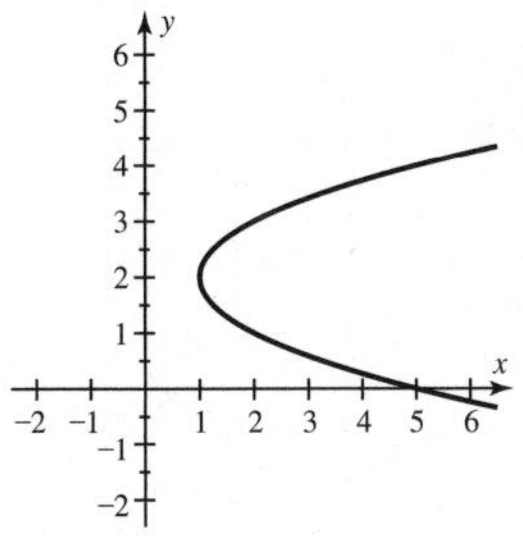

Figure 1

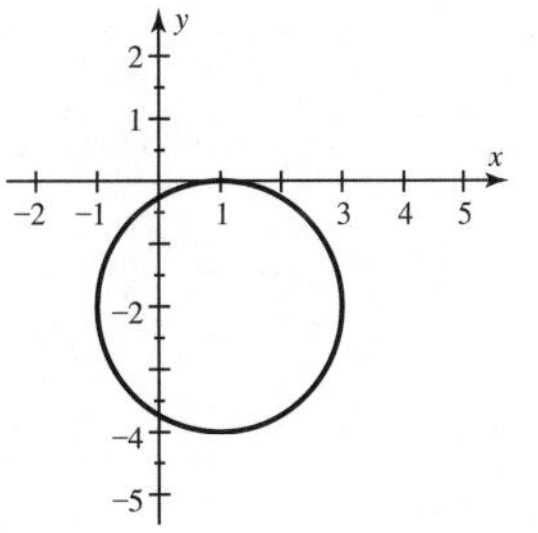

Figure 2

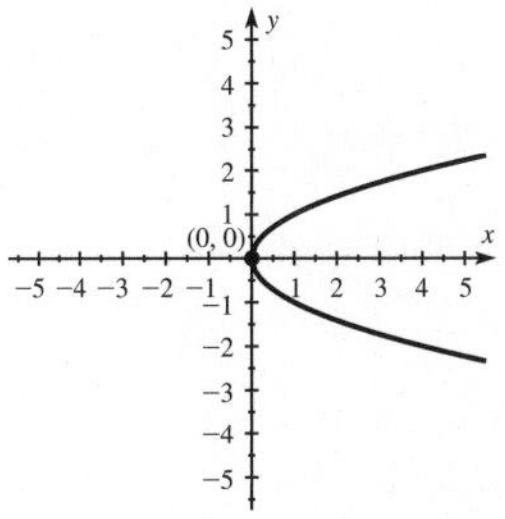

Figure 4a

3. x-intercepts: $\dfrac{x^2}{4} + \dfrac{0^2}{9} = 1 \Rightarrow \dfrac{x^2}{4} = 1 \Rightarrow x^2 = 4 \Rightarrow x = \pm 2$

y-intercepts: $\dfrac{0^2}{4} + \dfrac{y^2}{9} = 1 \Rightarrow \dfrac{y^2}{9} = 1 \Rightarrow y^2 = 9 \Rightarrow y = \pm 3$

4. (a) This parabola has vertex (0, 0) and axis of symmetry $y = 0$. See Figure 4a.

(b) This ellipse has a vertical major axis with vertices $(0, \pm 5)$ and minor axis endpoints $(\pm 4, 0)$. See Figure 4b.

(c) This hyperbola has a horizontal transverse axis with vertices $(\pm 2, 0)$ and asymptotes $y = \pm \dfrac{3}{2}x$. See Figure 4c.

(d) This circle is centered at (1, –2) and has radius 3. See Figure 4d.

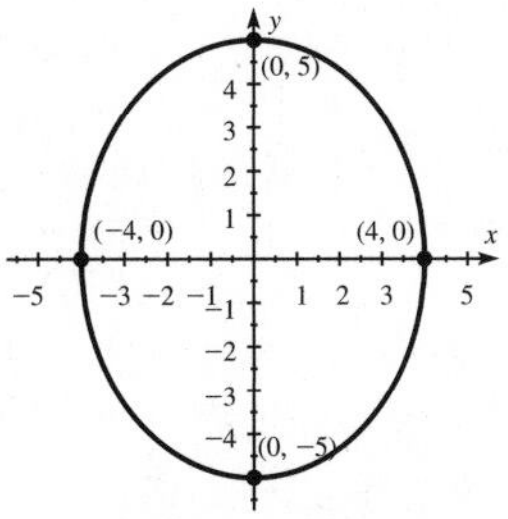

Figure 4b

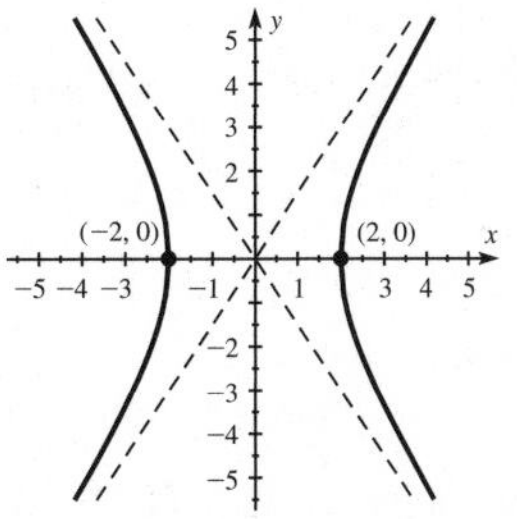

Figure 4c

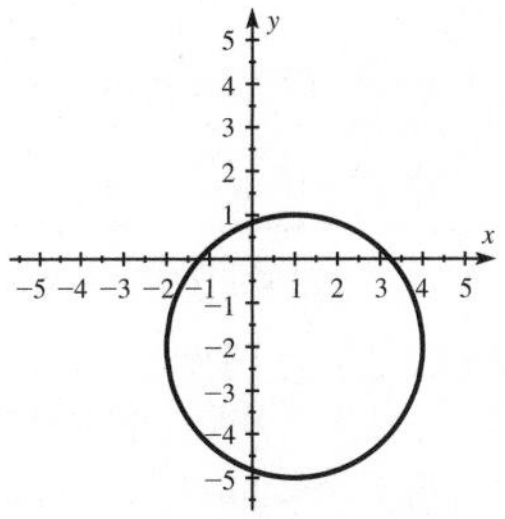

Figure 4d

13.3: Nonlinear Systems of Equations and Inequalities

Concepts

1. Any number.
3. Two, the line intersects the circle twice.
5. No. $5(-2)^2 - 2(-1)^2 = 5(4) - 2(1) = 18 \not> 18$
7. See Figure 7. *Answers may vary.*

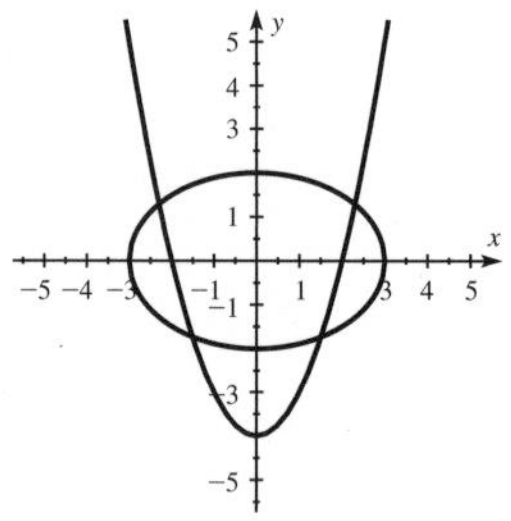

Figure 7

Nonlinear Systems of Equations

9. The solutions are the intersection points (1, 3) and (–1, –3). Both solutions check.
11. The solutions are the intersection points (0, –1) and (0, 1). Both solutions check.
13. Substitute $y = 2x$ into the second equation.

    $x^2 + (2x)^2 = 45 \Rightarrow x^2 + 4x^2 = 45 \Rightarrow 5x^2 = 45 \Rightarrow x^2 = 9 \Rightarrow x = \pm 3$

    When $x = -3$, $y = 2(-3) = -6$. When $x = 3$, $y = 2(3) = 6$. The solutions are (–3, –6) and (3, 6).
15. From the first equation, $y = 1 - x$. Substitute $y = 1 - x$ into the second equation.

    $x^2 - (1 - x)^2 = 3 \Rightarrow x^2 - 1 + 2x - x^2 = 3 \Rightarrow 2x - 1 = 3 \Rightarrow 2x = 4 \Rightarrow x = 2$

    When $x = 2$, $y = 1 - (2) = -1$ The solution is (2, –1).
17. From the first equation, $x^2 = y$. Substitute $x^2 = y$ into the second equation.

    $y + y^2 = 6 \Rightarrow y^2 + y - 6 = 0 \Rightarrow (y + 3)(y - 2) = 0 \Rightarrow$ Either $y = -3$ or $y = 2$

    When $y = -3$, $x = \pm\sqrt{-3}$, (not real numbers). When $y = 2$, $x = \pm\sqrt{2}$. The solutions are $(-\sqrt{2}, 2)$ and $(\sqrt{2}, 2)$.
19. Solve the second equation for y. $x^2 + y = 5 \Rightarrow y = 5 - x^2$

    Graph $Y_1 = 2X$ and $Y_2 = 5 - X^2$ in [–5, 5, 1] by [–5, 5, 1]. See Figures 19a & 19b.

    The solutions are the intersection points (–2, 1) and (–1, –2).

[–5, 5, 1] by [–5, 5, 1]

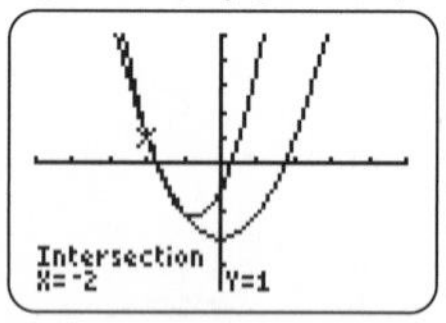

Figure 19a

[–5, 5, 1] by [–5, 5, 1]

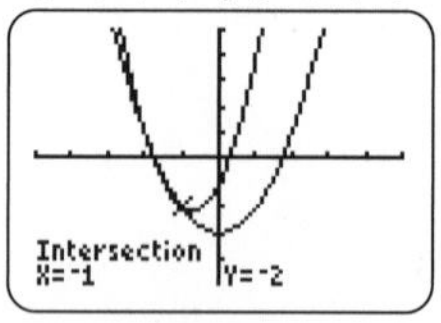

Figure 19b

[–9.4, 9.4, 1] by [–6.2, 6.2, 1]

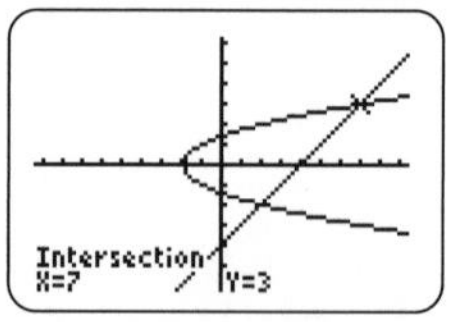

Figure 21a

[–9.4, 9.4, 1] by [–6.2, 6.2, 1]

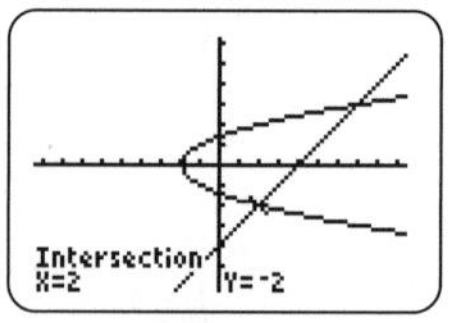

Figure 21b

21. Solve both equations for y. $y - x = -4 \Rightarrow y = x - 4$ and $x - y^2 = -2 \Rightarrow y^2 = x + 2 \Rightarrow y = \pm\sqrt{x + 2}$

    Graph $Y_1 = X - 4$, $Y_2 = \sqrt{(X + 2)}$ and $Y_3 = -\sqrt{(X + 2)}$ in [–9.4, 9.4, 1] by [–6.2, 6.2, 1]. See Figures 21a & 21b.

    The solutions are the intersection points (7, 3) and (2, –2).

23. (a) Substitute $y = -2x$ into the second equation.

$x^2 + (-2x) = 3 \Rightarrow x^2 - 2x - 3 = 0 \Rightarrow (x + 1)(x - 3) = 0 \Rightarrow$ Either $x = -1$ or $x = 3$

When $x = -1$, $y = -2(-1) = 2$. When $x = 3$, $y = -2(3) = -6$. The solutions are $(-1, 2)$ and $(3, -6)$.

(b) Solve the second equation for y. $x^2 + y = 3 \Rightarrow y = 3 - x^2$

Graph $Y_1 = -2X$ and $Y_2 = 3 - X^2$ in [−10, 10, 1] by [−10, 10, 1]. See Figures 23a & 23b.

(c) Table $Y_1 = -2X$ and $Y_2 = 3 - X^2$ with TblStart = −3 and ΔTbl = 1. See Figure 23c.

[−10, 10, 1] by [−10, 10, 1]

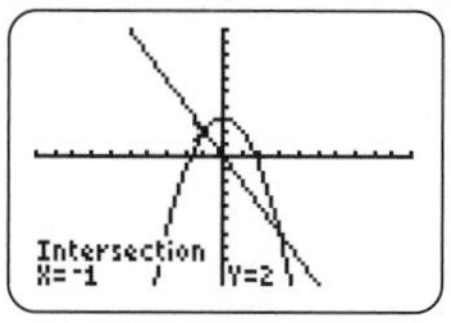

Figure 23a

[−10, 10, 1] by [−10, 10, 1]

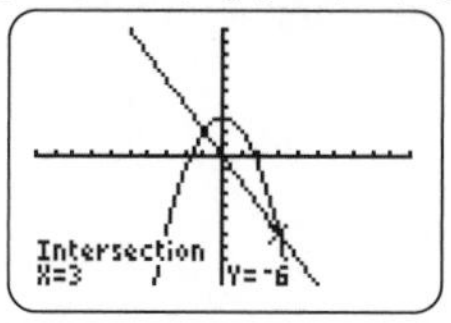

Figure 23b

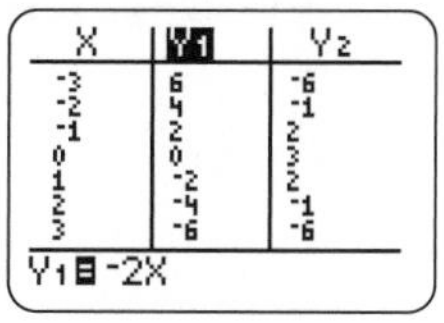

Figure 23c

25. (a) From the second equation, $y = x$. Substitute $y = x$ into the first equation.

$x \cdot x = 1 \Rightarrow x^2 = 1 \Rightarrow x = \pm 1$

When $x = -1$, $y = -1$. When $x = 1$, $y = 1$. The solutions are $(-1, -1)$ and $(1, 1)$.

(b) Solve both equations for y. $xy = 1 \Rightarrow y = \frac{1}{x}$ and $x - y = 0 \Rightarrow y = x$

Graph $Y_1 = 1/X$ and $Y_2 = X$ in [−4.7, 4.7, 1] by [−3.1, 3.1, 1]. See Figures 25a & 25b.

(c) Table $Y_1 = 1/X$ and $Y_2 = X$ with TblStart = −3 and ΔTbl = 1. See Figure 25c.

[−4.7, 4.7, 1] by [−3.1, 3.1, 1]

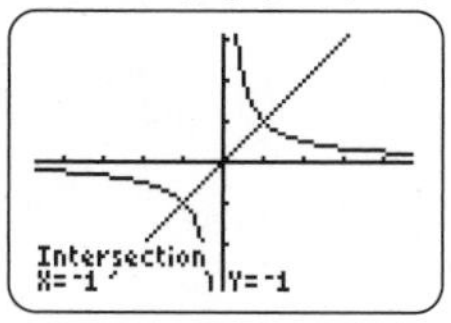

Figure 25a

[−4.7, 4.7, 1] by [−3.1, 3.1, 1]

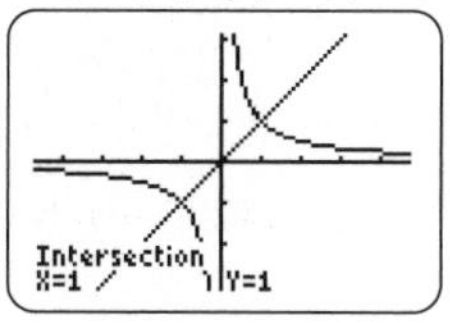

Figure 25b

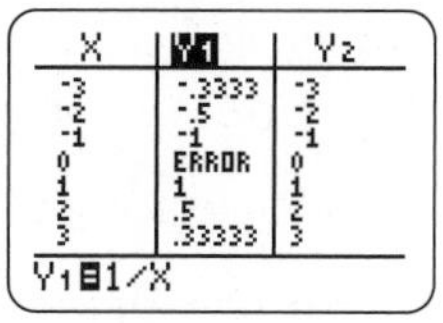

Figure 25c

Nonlinear Systems of Inequalities

27. Sketch the parabola given by $y = x^2$ using a solid line. Try test point (0, 2) to determine shading. Since $2 \geq 0^2$, we shade the portion of the xy-plane containing the point (0, 2). See Figure 27.

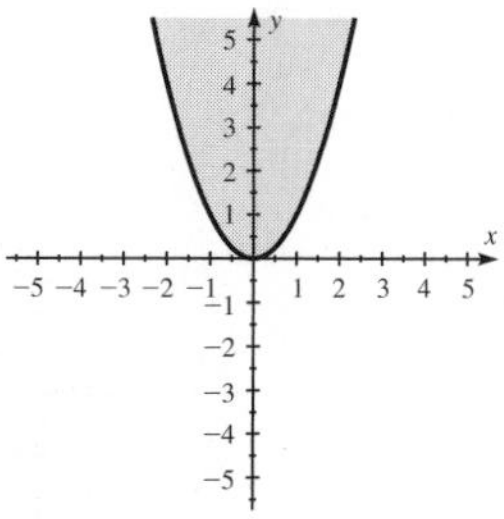

Figure 27

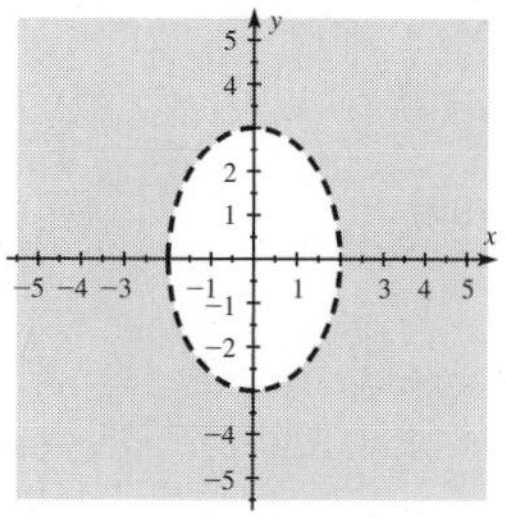

Figure 29

29. Sketch the ellipse given by $\frac{x^2}{4} + \frac{y^2}{9} = 1$ using a dashed line. Try test point (4, 0) to determine shading. Since $\frac{4^2}{4} + \frac{0^2}{9} = 4 > 1$, we shade the portion of the xy-plane containing the point (4, 0). See Figure 29.

31. Sketch the parabola given by $y = x^2 + 1$ using a dashed line and the line given by $y = 3$ using a dashed line. Since the point (0, 2) satisfies both inequalities, we shade the portion of the xy-plane containing the point (0, 2). See Figure 31. One solution is (0, 2). *Answers may vary.*

33. Sketch the circle given by $x^2 + y^2 = 1$ using a solid line and the line given by $y = x$ using a dashed line. Since the point $\left(\frac{1}{2}, -\frac{1}{2}\right)$ satisfies both inequalities, we shade the portion of the xy-plane containing the point $\left(\frac{1}{2}, -\frac{1}{2}\right)$. See Figure 33. One solution is (0.5, –0.5). *Answers may vary.*

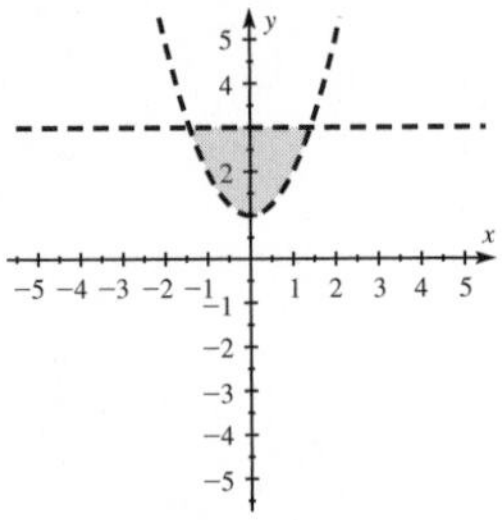

Figure 31

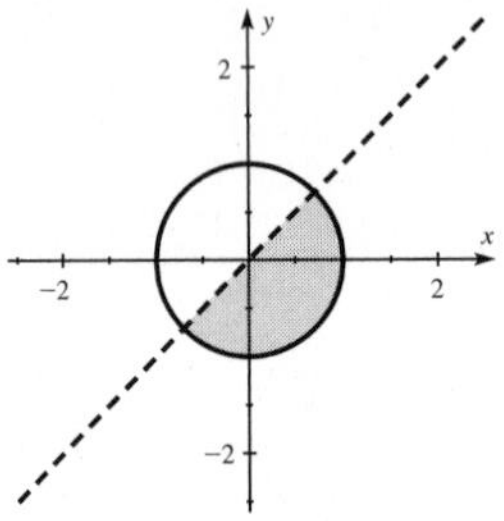

Figure 33

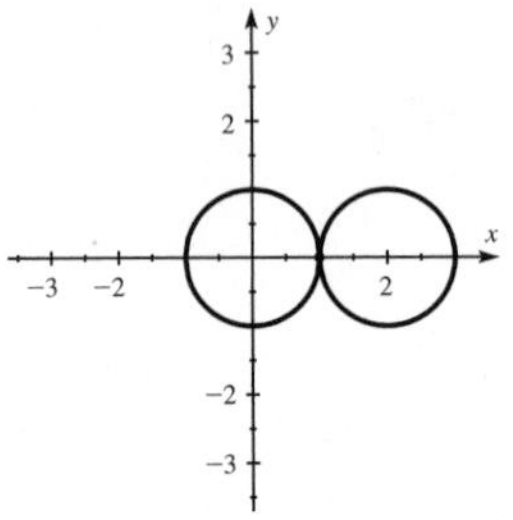

Figure 35

35. Sketch the circle given by $x^2 + y^2 = 1$ using a solid line and the circle given by $(x - 2)^2 + y^2 = 1$ using a solid line. Since the point (1, 0) is the only point that satisfies both inequalities, we mark only the point (1, 0) on the graph. See Figure 35. The only solution is (1, 0)

37. Sketch the hyperbola given by $x^2 - y^2 = 4$ using a solid line and the circle given by $x^2 + y^2 = 9$ using a solid line. Since the point (0, 0) satisfies both inequalities, we shade the portion of the xy-plane containing the point (0, 0). See Figure 37. One solution is (0, 0). *Answers may vary.*

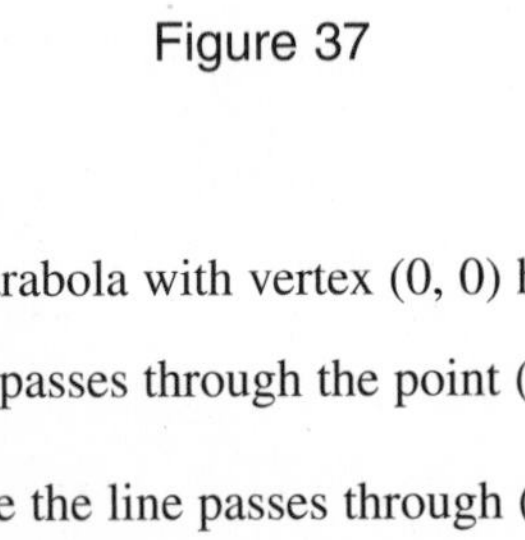

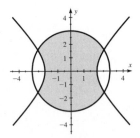

Figure 37

39. a

41. A parabola with vertex (0, 0) has an equation of the form $y = a(x - 0)^2 + 0$ or $y = ax^2$. Since the parabola also passes through the point (1, 1), $1 = a \cdot 1^2 \Rightarrow a = 1$. The equation of the parabola is $y = x^2$. Since the line passes through (0, 4) and (4, 0), its slope is $m = \frac{0 - 4}{4 - 0} = \frac{-4}{4} = -1$. The y-intercept is (0, 4). The equation of the line is $y = -x + 4$ or $y = 4 - x$. Since the line is dashed and the parabola is solid, the system of inequalities is $y \geq x^2$ and $y < 4 - x$.

Applications

43. The necessary equations are $\pi r^2 h = 40$ and $2\pi rh = 50$. Start by solving each of these equations for h.

$\pi r^2 h = 40 \Rightarrow h = \dfrac{40}{\pi r^2}$ and $2\pi rh = 50 \Rightarrow h = \dfrac{50}{2\pi r}$

(a) Graph $Y_1 = 40/(\pi X^2)$ and $Y_2 = 50/(2\pi X)$ in [0, 5, 1] by [0, 10, 1]. See Figure 43.

The graphs intersect near the point (1.6, 4.97). The dimensions are $r = 1.6$ inches and $h \approx 4.97$ inches.

(b) $\dfrac{40}{\pi r^2} = \dfrac{50}{2\pi r} \Rightarrow 80\pi r = 50\pi r^2 \Rightarrow 8r = 5r^2 \Rightarrow 5r^2 - 8r = 0 \Rightarrow r(5r - 8) = 0 \Rightarrow r = 0$ or $r = \dfrac{8}{5}$

Since $r = 0$ has no physical meaning, $r = \dfrac{8}{5} = 1.6$. And so $h = \dfrac{50}{2\pi(\frac{8}{5})} = \dfrac{125}{8\pi} \approx 4.97$.

The dimensions are $r = 1.6$ inches and $h \approx 4.97$ inches.

[0, 5, 1] by [0, 10, 1]

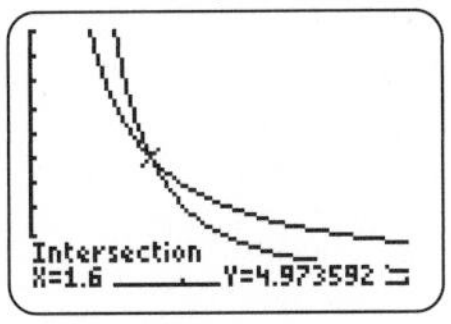

Figure 43

[0, 5, 1] by [0, 10, 1]

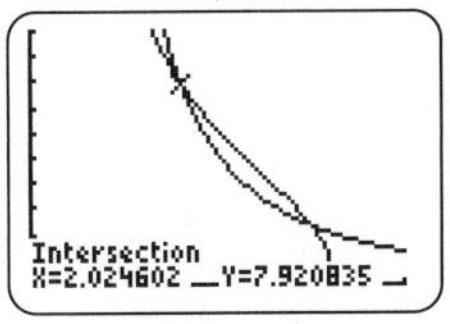

Figure 45a

[0, 5, 1] by [0, 10, 1]

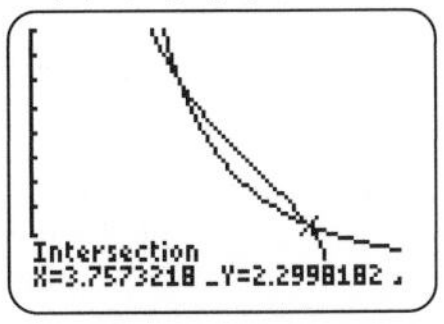

Figure 45b

45. (a) $V = \dfrac{1}{3}\pi r^2 h \Rightarrow h = \dfrac{3V}{\pi r^2}$ and $S = \pi r\sqrt{r^2 + h^2} \Rightarrow r^2 + h^2 = \left(\dfrac{S}{\pi r}\right)^2 \Rightarrow h = \sqrt{\left(\dfrac{S}{\pi r}\right)^2 - r^2}$

(b) Graph $Y_1 = 102/(\pi X^2)$ and $Y_2 = \sqrt{}((52/(\pi X))^2 - X^2)$ in [0, 5, 1] by [0, 10, 1]. See Figures 45a & 45b.

There are two possibilities: $r \approx 2.02$ ft, $h \approx 7.92$ ft or $r \approx 3.76$ ft and $h \approx 2.30$ ft.

Checking Basic Concepts for Section 13.3

1. Symbolically: From the second equation $y = 2x - 3$. Substitute $y = 2x - 3$ into the first equation.

$x^2 - (2x - 3) = 2x \Rightarrow x^2 - 4x + 3 = 0 \Rightarrow (x - 1)(x - 3) = 0 \Rightarrow x = 1$ or $x = 3$

When $x = 1$, $y = 2(1) - 3 = -1$. When $x = 3$, $y = 2(3) - 3 = 3$. The solutions are $(1, -1)$ and $(3, 3)$.

Graphically: Solve each equation for y. $x^2 - y = 2x \Rightarrow y = x^2 - 2x$ and $2x - y = 3 \Rightarrow y = 2x - 3$

Graph $Y_1 = X^2 - 2X$ and $Y_2 = 2X - 3$ in [–5, 5, 1] by [–5, 5, 1]. See Figures 1a & 1b.

[–5, 5, 1] by [–5, 5, 1]

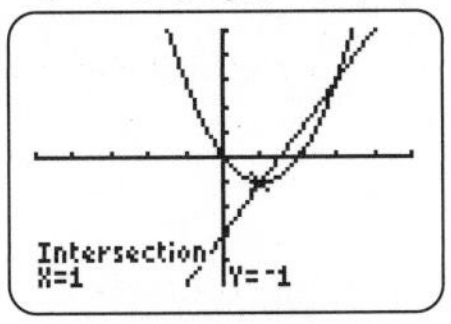

Figure 1a

[–5, 5, 1] by [–5, 5, 1]

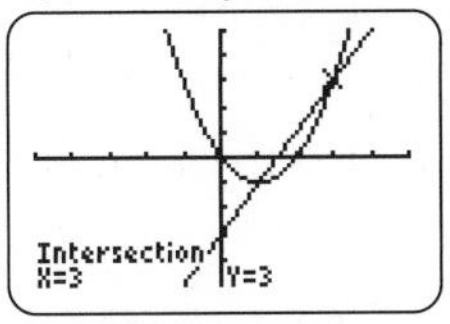

Figure 1b

2. Since graphing these equations would result is a parabola intersected twice by a line, there are two solutions.

3. (a) The point (0, 3) is in the shaded region and is a solution. The point (4, 4) is not in the shaded region and is not a solution. *Answers may vary.*

(b) A parabola with vertex (0, 4) has an equation of the form $y = a(x - 0)^2 + 4$ or $y = ax^2 + 4$. Since the parabola also passes through the point (2, 0), $0 = a \cdot 2^2 + 4 \Rightarrow 4a = -4 \Rightarrow a = -1$. The equation of the parabola is $y = -x^2 + 4$ or $y = 4 - x^2$. Since the line passes through (0, 2) and (2, 0), its slope is $m = \frac{0 - 2}{2 - 0} = \frac{-2}{2} = -1$. The y-intercept is (0, 2). The equation of the line is $y = -x + 2$ or $y = 2 - x$.

Since both the line and the parabola are solid, the system of inequalities is $y \leq 4 - x^2$ and $y \geq 2 - x$.

4. Sketch the circle given by $x^2 + y^2 = 4$ using a solid line and the line given by $y = 1$ using a dashed line. The point (0, 0) satisfies both inequalities. Shade the portion of the xy-plane containing (0, 0). See Figure 4.

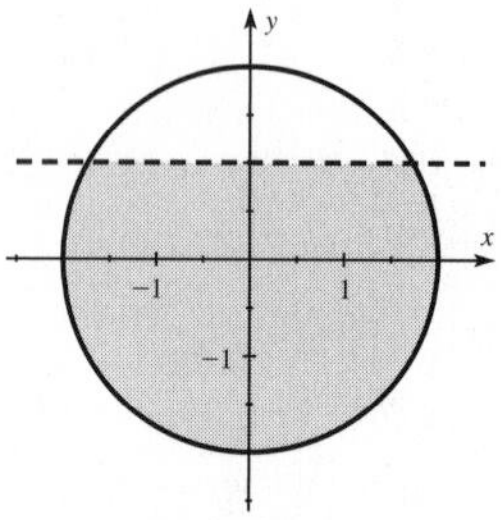

Figure 4

Chapter 13 Review Exercises

Section 13.1

1. Since $x = 2(y + 0)^2 + 0$, the vertex is (0, 0) and the axis of symmetry is $y = 0$. See Figure 1.

2. Since $x = -(y + 1)^2 + 0$, the vertex is (0, −1) and the axis of symmetry is $y = -1$. See Figure 2.

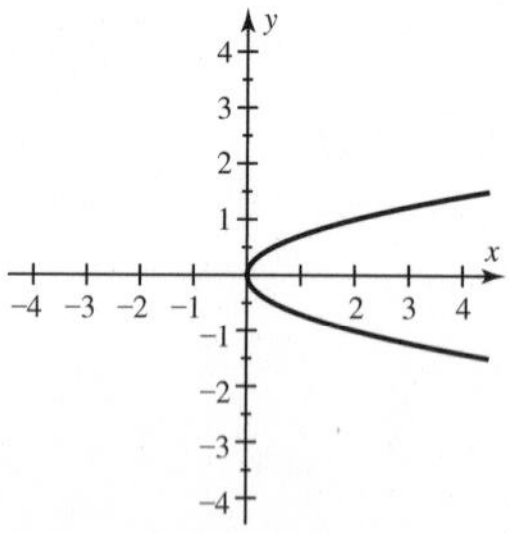

Figure 1

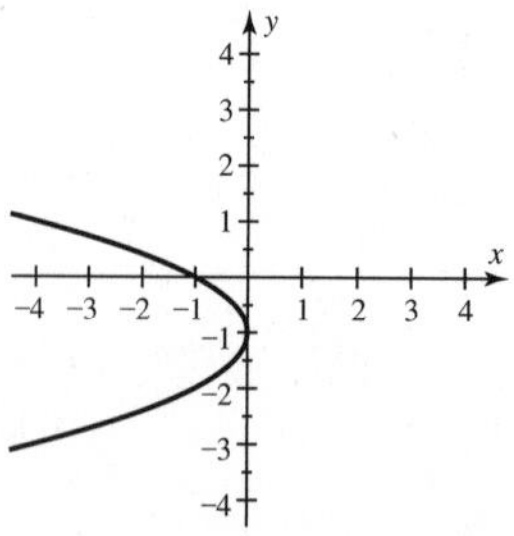

Figure 2

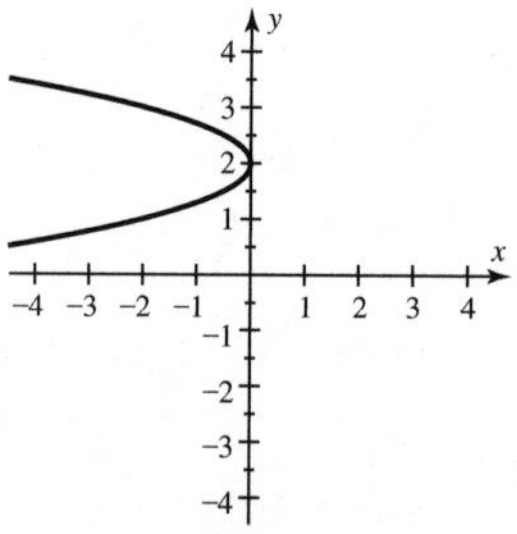

Figure 3

3. Since $x = -2(y - 2)^2 + 0$, the vertex is (0, 2) and the axis of symmetry is $y = 2$. See Figure 3.

4. Since $x = (y + 2)^2 - 1$, the vertex is $(-1, -2)$ and the axis of symmetry is $y = -2$. See Figure 4.

5. Since $x = -3(y - 0)^2 + 1$, the vertex is $(1, 0)$ and the axis of symmetry is $y = 0$. See Figure 5.

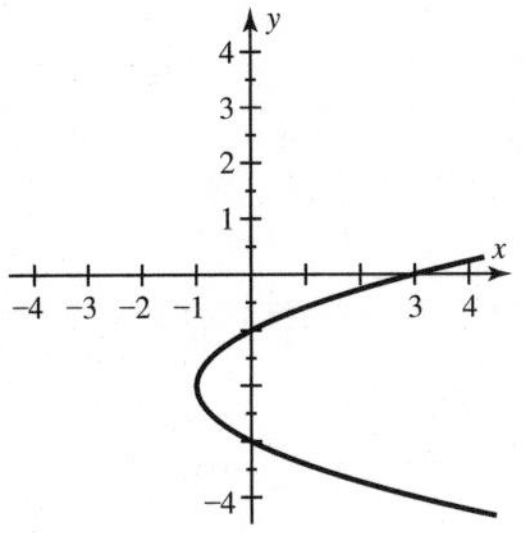

Figure 4

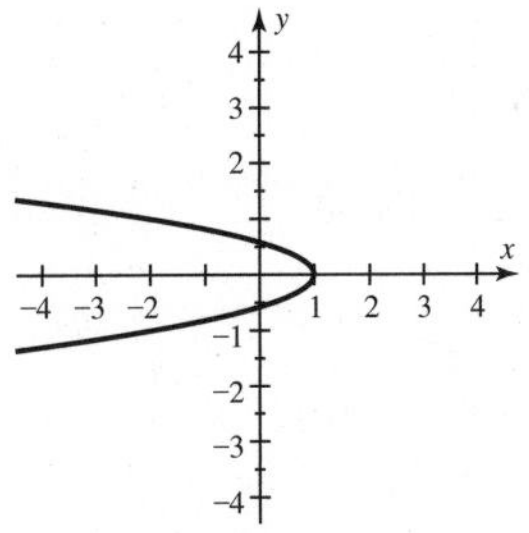

Figure 5

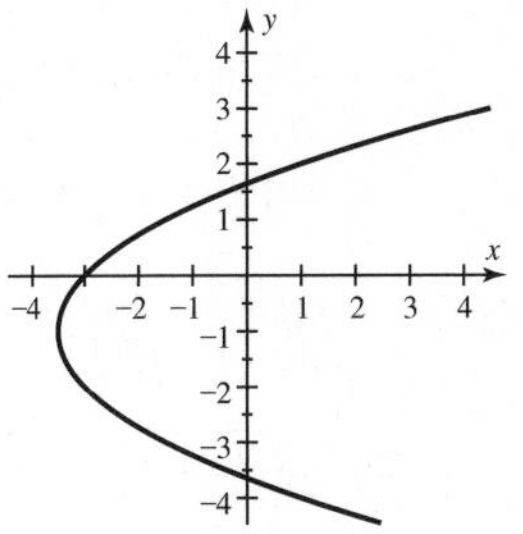

Figure 6

6. Since $x = \frac{1}{2}(y + 1)^2 - \frac{7}{2}$, the vertex is $\left(-\frac{7}{2}, -1\right)$ and the axis of symmetry is $y = -1$. See Figure 6.

7. Since the vertex is $(0, 0)$, the parabola has an equation of the form $x = a(x - 0)^2 + 0$ or $x = ay^2$.

   Since the parabola passes through the point $(1, 1)$, $1 = a(1) \Rightarrow a = 1$. The equation is $x = y^2$.

8. This is a circle of radius 4 centered at $(-2, 2)$. The equation is $(x + 2)^2 + (y - 2)^2 = 16$.

9. $(x - 0)^2 + (y - 0)^2 = 1^2 \Rightarrow x^2 + y^2 = 1$

10. $(x - 2)^2 + (y - (-3))^2 = 4^2 \Rightarrow (x - 2)^2 + (y + 3)^2 = 16$

11. The radius is 5 and the center is $(0, 0)$. Solving the equation for y results in $y = \pm\sqrt{25 - x^2}$. See Figure 11.

12. The radius is 3 and the center is $(2, 0)$. Solving the equation for y results in $y = \pm\sqrt{9 - (x - 2)^2}$.

    See Figure 12.

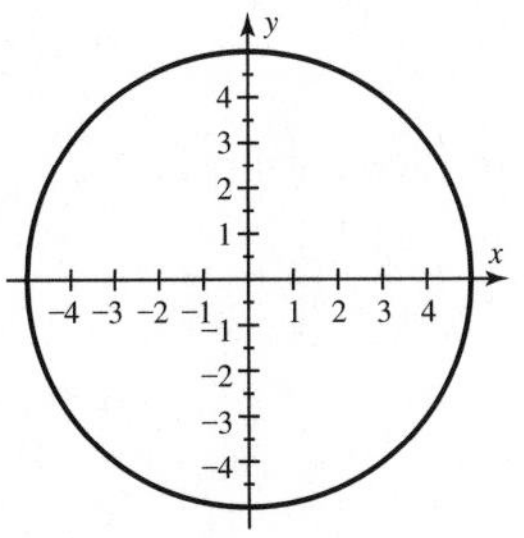

Figure 11

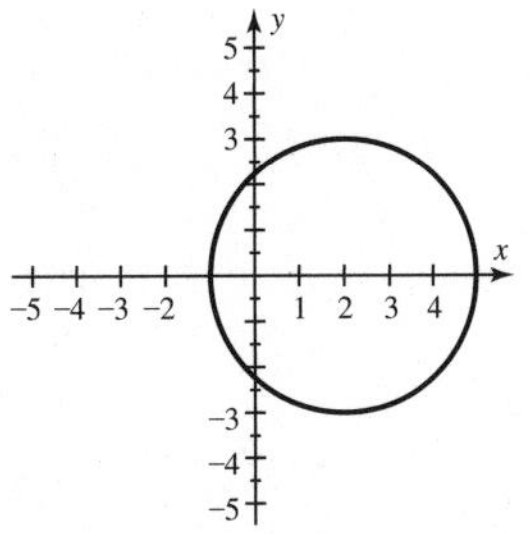

Figure 12

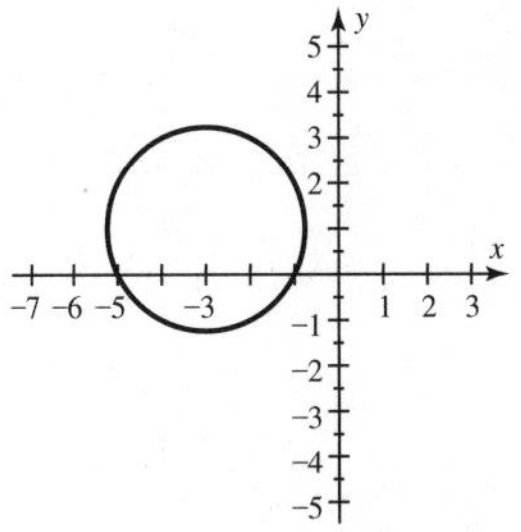

Figure 13

13. The radius is $\sqrt{5}$ and the center is $(-3, 1)$. Solving the equation for y results in $y = 1 \pm \sqrt{5 - (x + 3)^2}$.

    See Figure 13.

14. $x^2 - 2x + y^2 + 2y = 7 \Rightarrow x^2 - 2x + 1 + y^2 + 2y + 1 = 7 + 1 + 1 \Rightarrow (x - 1)^2 + (y + 1)^2 = 9$

The radius is 3 and the center is $(1, -1)$. Solving the equation for y results in $y = -1 \pm \sqrt{9 - (x - 1)^2}$.

See Figure 14.

Section 13.2

15. The ellipse has a vertical major axis with vertices $(0, \pm 5)$ and minor axis endpoints $(\pm 2, 0)$. See Figure 15.

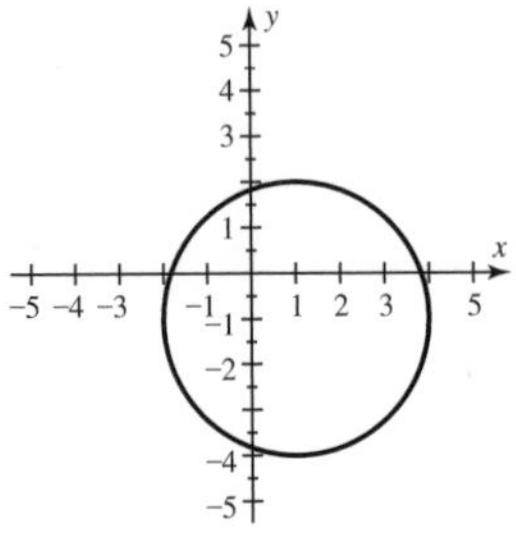

Figure 14

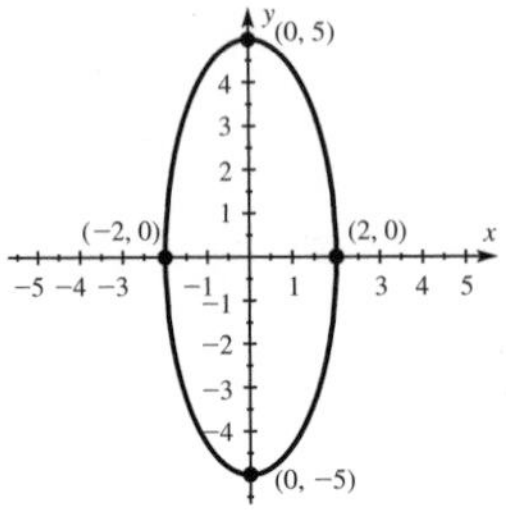

Figure 15

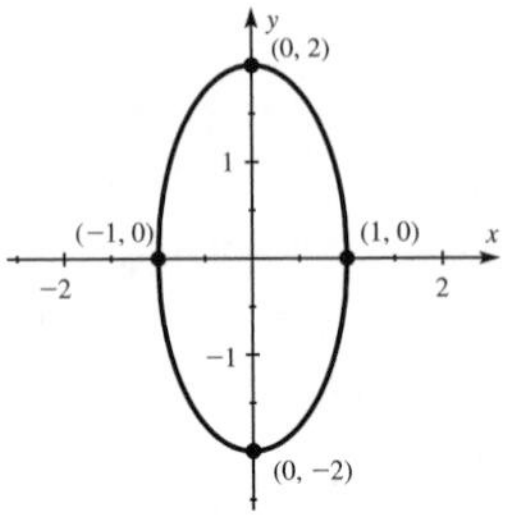

Figure 16

16. The ellipse has a vertical major axis with vertices $(0, \pm 2)$ and minor axis endpoints $(\pm 1, 0)$. See Figure 16.

17. $25x^2 + 20y^2 = 500 \Rightarrow \dfrac{25x^2}{500} + \dfrac{20y^2}{500} = 1 \Rightarrow \dfrac{x^2}{20} + \dfrac{y^2}{25} = 1$

The ellipse has a vertical major axis with vertices $(0, \pm 5)$ and minor axis endpoints $(\pm\sqrt{20}, 0)$. See Figure 17.

18. $4x^2 + 9y^2 = 36 \Rightarrow \dfrac{4x^2}{36} + \dfrac{9y^2}{36} = 1 \Rightarrow \dfrac{x^2}{9} + \dfrac{y^2}{4} = 1$

The ellipse has a horizontal major axis with vertices $(\pm 3, 0)$ and minor axis endpoints $(0, \pm 2)$. See Figure 18.

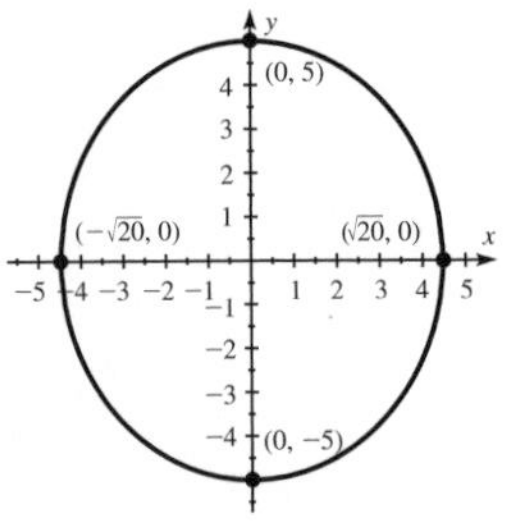

Figure 17

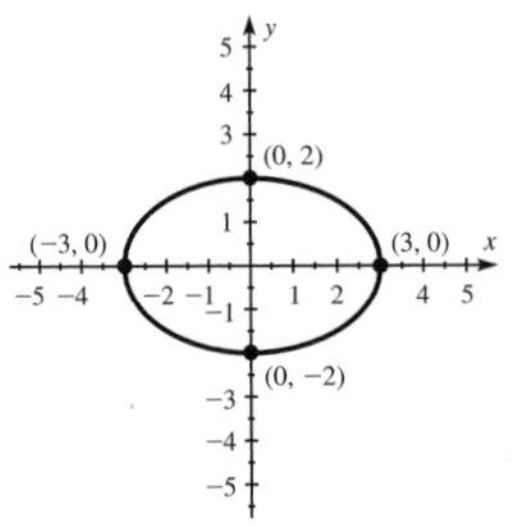

Figure 18

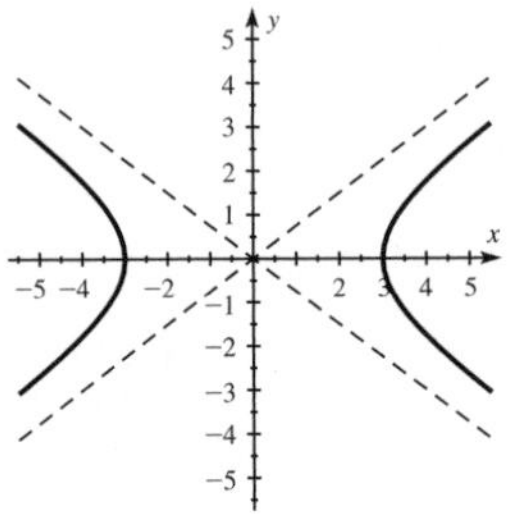

Figure 21

19. Vertical major axis with vertices $(0, \pm 4)$ and minor axis endpoints $(\pm 2, 0) \Rightarrow \dfrac{y^2}{16} + \dfrac{x^2}{4} = 1$

20. Horizontal transverse axis with vertices $(\pm 1, 0)$ and asymptotes $y = \pm 2x \Rightarrow x^2 - \dfrac{y^2}{4} = 1$

21. The hyperbola has a horizontal transverse axis with vertices $(\pm 3, 0)$ and asymptotes $y = \pm \dfrac{2}{3}x$. See Figure 21.

22. The hyperbola has a vertical transverse axis with vertices $(0, \pm 5)$ and asymptotes $y = \pm \dfrac{5}{4}x$. See Figure 22.

23. The hyperbola has a vertical transverse axis with vertices $(0, \pm 1)$ and asymptotes $y = \pm x$. See Figure 23.

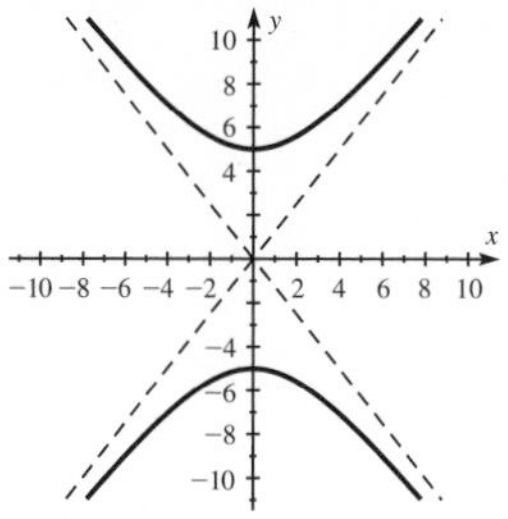

Figure 22

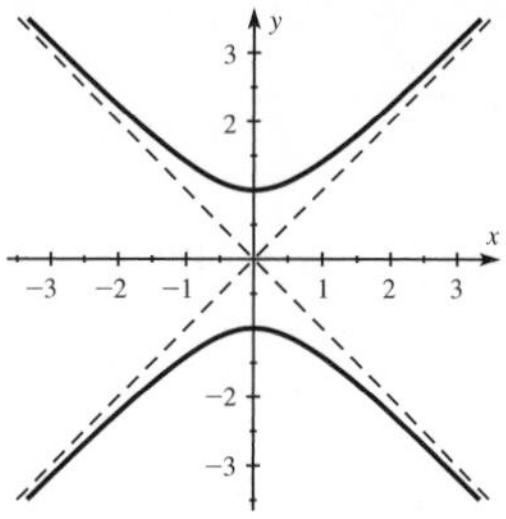

Figure 23

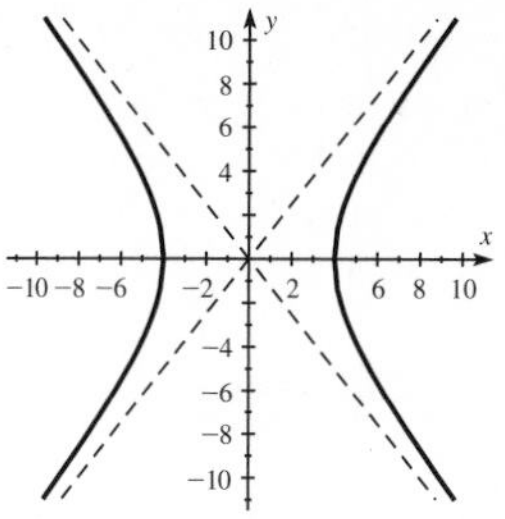

Figure 24

24. $25x^2 - 16y^2 = 400 \Rightarrow \dfrac{25x^2}{400} - \dfrac{16y^2}{400} = 1 \Rightarrow \dfrac{x^2}{16} - \dfrac{y^2}{25} = 1$

The hyperbola has a horizontal transverse axis with vertices $(\pm 4, 0)$ and asymptotes $y = \pm \dfrac{5}{4}x$. See Figure 24.

Section 13.3

25. The solutions are the intersection points (0, 3) and (3, 0). Both solutions check.

26. The solutions are the intersection points (–1, –2) and (1, 2). Both solutions check.

27. The solutions are the intersection points (0, 0) and (2, 2). Both solutions check.

28. The solutions are the intersection points (–2, –1), (–2, 1), (2, –1) and (2, 1). All four solutions check.

29. Substitute $y = x$ into the second equation.

$x^2 + (x)^2 = 32 \Rightarrow 2x^2 = 32 \Rightarrow x^2 = 16 \Rightarrow x = \pm 4$

When $x = -4$, $y = -4$. When $x = 4$, $y = 4$. The solutions are (–4, –4) and (4, 4).

30. From the first equation, $y = x - 4$. Substitute $y = x - 4$ into the second equation.

$x^2 + (x - 4)^2 = 16 \Rightarrow x^2 + x^2 - 8x + 16 = 16 \Rightarrow 2x^2 - 8x = 0 \Rightarrow 2x(x - 4) = 0 \Rightarrow x = 0$ or $x = 4$

When $x = 0$, $y = (0) - 4 = -4$. When $x = 4$, $y = (4) - 4 = 0$. The solutions are (0, –4) and (4, 0).

31. Substitute $y = x^2$ into the second equation.

$2x^2 + (x^2) = 3 \Rightarrow 3x^2 = 3 \Rightarrow x^2 = 1 \Rightarrow x = \pm 1$

When $x = -1$, $y = (-1)^2 = 1$. When $x = 1$, $y = (1)^2 = 1$. The solutions are (–1, 1) and (1, 1).

32. Substitute $y = x^2 + 1$ into the second equation.

$2x^2 - (x^2 + 1) = 3x - 3 \Rightarrow x^2 - 3x + 2 = 0 \Rightarrow (x - 1)(x - 2) = 0 \Rightarrow x = 1$ or $x = 2$

When $x = 1$, $y = (1)^2 + 1 = 2$. When $x = 2$, $y = (2)^2 + 1 = 5$. The solutions are (1, 2) and (2, 5).

33. Solve both equations for y. $2x - y = 4 \Rightarrow y = 2x - 4$ and $x^2 + y = 4 \Rightarrow y = 4 - x^2$

Graph $Y_1 = 2X - 4$ and $Y_2 = 4 - X^2$ in [–8, 8, 1] by [–25, 10, 5]. See Figures 33a & 33b.

The solutions are the intersection points (–4, –12) and (2, 0).

[–8, 8, 1] by [–25, 10, 5]

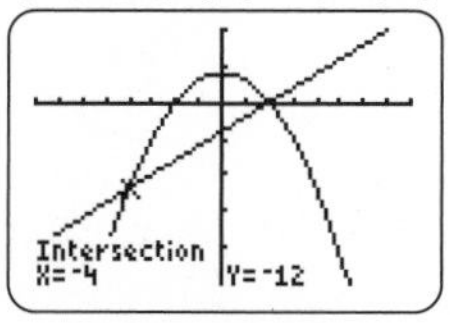

Figure 33a

[–8, 8, 1] by [–25, 10, 5]

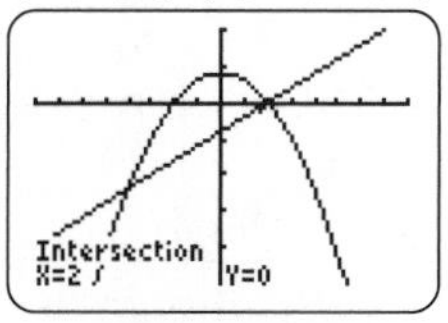

Figure 33b

34. Solve both equations for y. $x^2 + y = 4 \Rightarrow y = 4 - x^2$ and $x^2 + y^2 = 4 \Rightarrow y = \pm\sqrt{4 - x^2}$

Graph $Y_1 = 4 - X^2$, $Y_2 = \sqrt{(4 - X^2)}$ and $Y_3 = -\sqrt{(4 - X^2)}$ in [–4.7, 4.7, 1] by [–2.1, 4.1, 1].

See Figures 34a, 34b, 34c & 34d. The solutions are the intersection points (–2, 0), (–1.73, 1), (1.73, 1) and (2, 0).

[–4.7, 4.7, 1] by [–2.1, 4.1, 1]

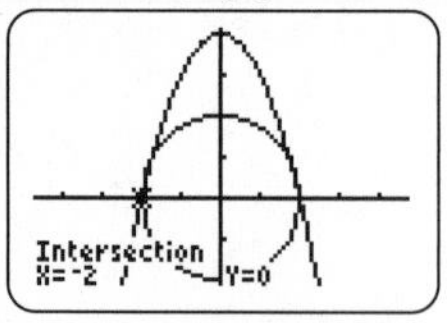

Figure 34a

[–4.7, 4.7, 1] by [–2.1, 4.1, 1]

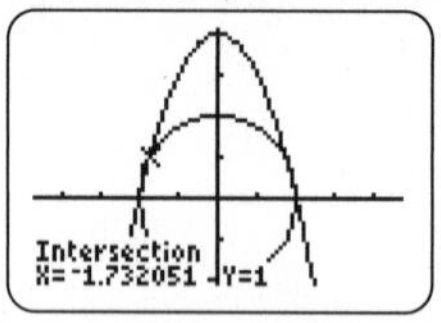

Figure 34b

[–4.7, 4.7, 1] by [–2.1, 4.1, 1]

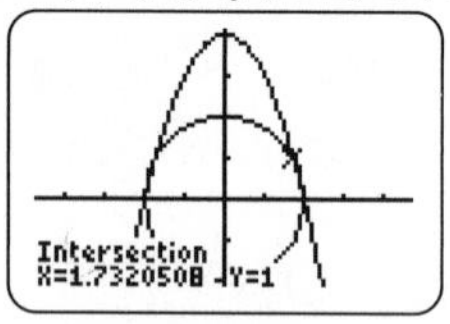

Figure 34c

[–4.7, 4.7, 1] by [–2.1, 4.1, 1]

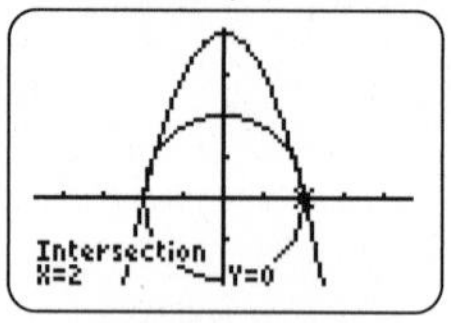

Figure 34d

35. (a) Substitute $y = x$ into the second equation.

$x^2 + 2(x) = 8 \Rightarrow x^2 + 2x - 8 = 0 \Rightarrow (x + 4)(x - 2) = 0 \Rightarrow x = -4$ or $x = 2$

When $x = -4$, $y = -4$. When $x = 2$, $y = 2$. The solutions are (–4, –4) and (2, 2).

(b) Solve the second equation for y. $x^2 + 2y = 8 \Rightarrow y = 4 - \dfrac{x^2}{2}$

Graph $Y_1 = X$ and $Y_2 = 4 - (X^2/2)$ in [–10, 10, 1] by [–10, 10, 1]. See Figures 35a & 35b.

(c) Table $Y_1 = X$ and $Y_2 = 4 - (X^2/2)$ with TblStart = –2 and ΔTbl = 1. See Figure 35c.

[–10, 10, 1] by [–10, 10, 1]

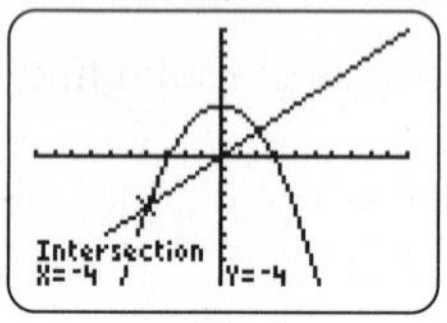

Figure 35a

[–10, 10, 1] by [–10, 10, 1]

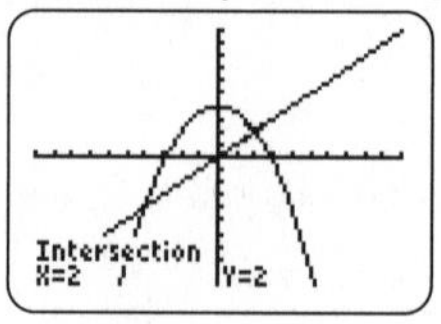

Figure 35b

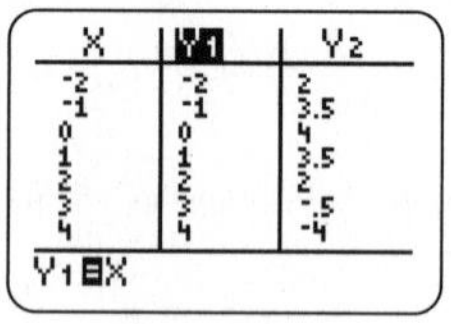

Figure 35c

36. (a) Substitute $y = x^3$ into the second equation.

$x^2 - x^3 = 0 \Rightarrow x^2(1 - x) = 0 \Rightarrow x = 0$ or $x = 1$

When $x = 0$, $y = 0^3 = 0$. When $x = 1$, $y = 1^3 = 1$. The solutions are (0, 0) and (1, 1).

(b) Solve the second equation for y. $x^2 - y = 0 \Rightarrow y = x^2$

Graph $Y_1 = X\text{^}3$ and $Y_2 = X^2$ in [–1.5, 1.5, 1] by [–1.5, 1.5, 1]. See Figures 36a & 36b.

(c) Table $Y_1 = X\text{^}3$ and $Y_2 = X^2$ with TblStart = –1 and ΔTbl = 0.5. See Figure 36c.

[–1.5, 1.5, 1] by [–1.5, 1.5, 1]

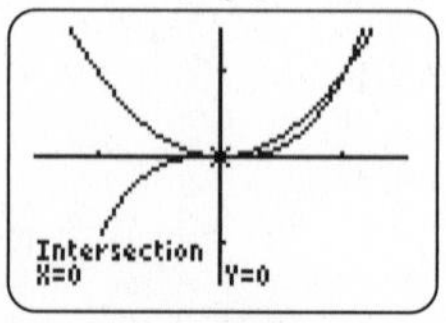

Figure 36a

[–1.5, 1.5, 1] by [–1.5, 1.5, 1]

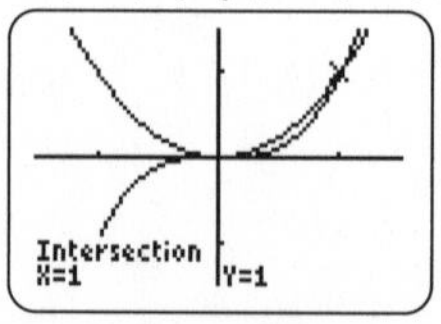

Figure 36b

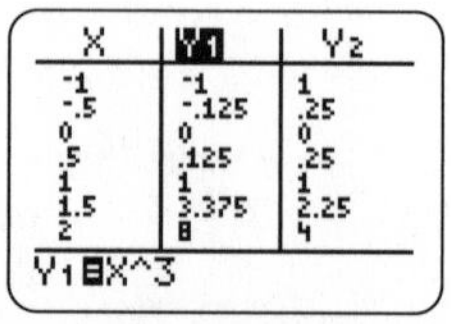

Figure 36c

37. Sketch the parabola given by $y = 2x^2$ using a solid line. Try test point (0, 2) to determine shading.

Since $2 \geq 2(0^2)$, we shade the portion of the xy-plane containing the point (0, 2). See Figure 37.

38. Sketch the line given by $y = 2x - 3$ using a dashed line. Try test point (3, 0) to determine shading.

Since $0 < 2(3) - 3$, we shade the portion of the xy-plane containing the point (3, 0). See Figure 38.

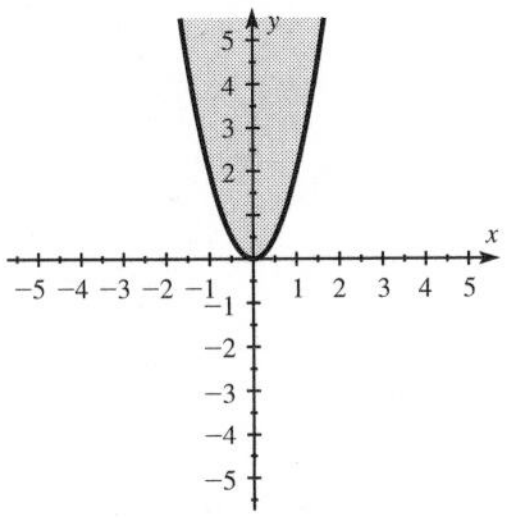

Figure 37

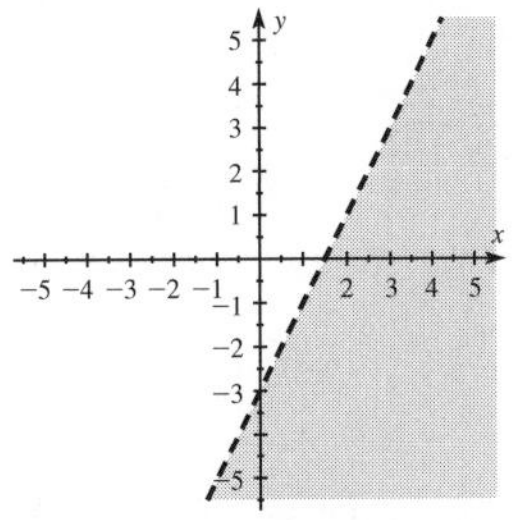

Figure 38

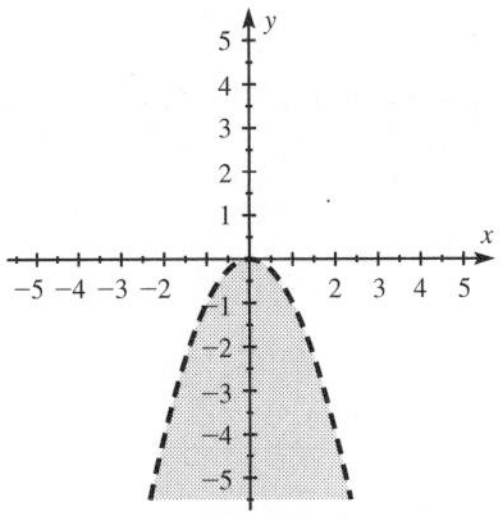

Figure 39

39. Sketch the parabola given by $y = -x^2$ using a dashed line. Try test point (0, –1) to determine shading.

Since $-1 < -(0)^2$, we shade the portion of the xy-plane containing the point (0, –1). See Figure 39.

40. Sketch the ellipse given by $\frac{x^2}{9} + \frac{y^2}{16} = 1$ using a solid line. Try test point (0, 0) to determine shading.

Since $0 + 0 \leq 1$, we shade the portion of the xy-plane containing the point (0, 0). See Figure 40.

41. Sketch the parabola given by $y = x^2 + 1$ using a solid line and the line given by $y = 2$ using a solid line.

Since the point (0, 1.5) satisfies both inequalities, we shade the portion of the xy-plane containing the point (0, 1.5).

See Figure 41.

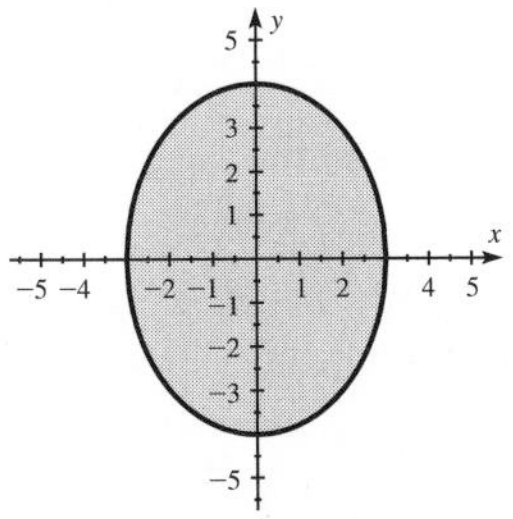

Figure 40

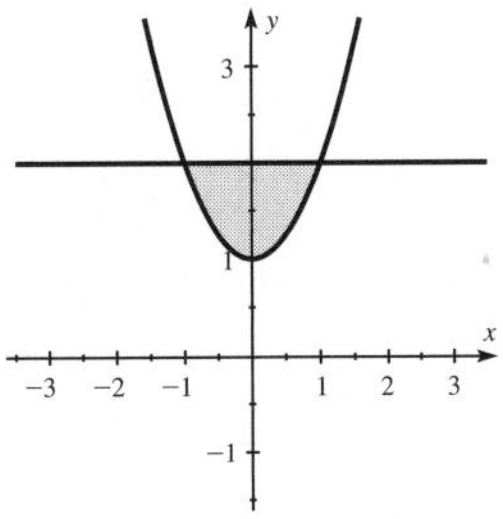

Figure 41

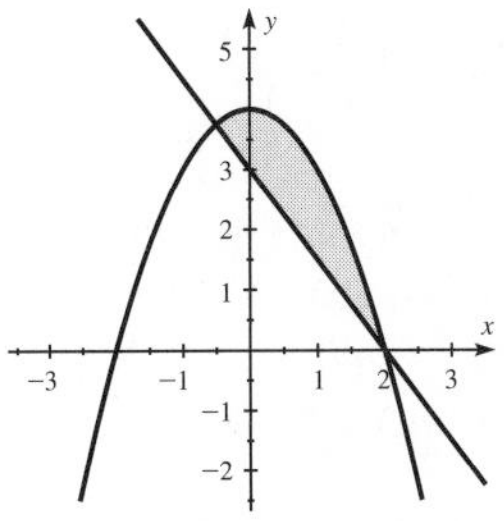

Figure 42

42. Sketch the parabola given by $y = 4 - x^2$ using a solid line and the line given by $3x + 2y = 6$ using a solid line.

Since the point (1, 2) satisfies both inequalities, we shade the portion of the xy-plane containing the point (1, 2).

See Figure 42.

43. Sketch the parabola given by $y = x^2$ using a dashed line and the parabola given by $y = 4 - x^2$ using a dashed line. Since the point (0, 2) satisfies both inequalities, we shade the portion of the xy-plane containing the point (0, 2). See Figure 43.

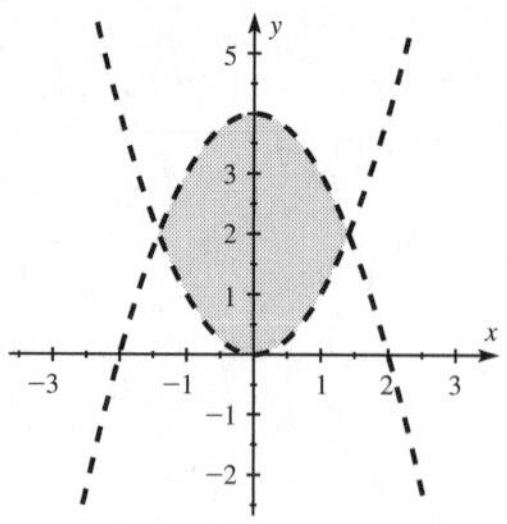

Figure 43

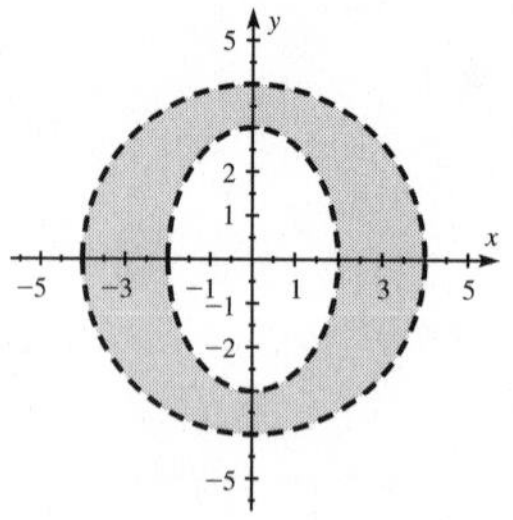

Figure 44

44. Sketch the ellipse given by $\frac{x^2}{4} + \frac{y^2}{9} = 1$ using a dashed line and the circle given by $x^2 + y^2 = 16$ using a dashed line. Since the point (3, 0) satisfies both inequalities, we shade the portion of the xy-plane containing the point (3, 0). See Figure 44.

45. A parabola with vertex (0, –2) has an equation of the form $y = a(x - 0)^2 - 2$ or $y = ax^2 - 2$. Since the parabola also passes through the point (1, –1), $-1 = a \cdot 1^2 - 2 \Rightarrow a = 1$. The equation of the parabola is $y = x^2 - 2$. Since the line passes through (0, 2) and (2, 0), its slope is $m = \frac{0 - 2}{2 - 0} = \frac{-2}{2} = -1$. The y-intercept is (0, 2). The equation of the line is $y = -x + 2$ or $y = 2 - x$. Since both the line and the parabola are solid, the system of inequalities is $y \geq x^2 - 2$ and $y \leq 2 - x$.

46. A circle of radius 2 centered at (0, 0) has the equation $x^2 + y^2 = 4$. Since the line passes through the points (0, 0) and (1, 1), its slope is $m = \frac{1 - 0}{1 - 0} = \frac{1}{1} = 1$. The y-intercept is (0, 0). The equation of the line is $y = x$. Since both the circle and the line are solid, the system of inequalities is $y \geq x$ and $x^2 + y^2 \leq 4$.

Applications

47. (a) $xy = 1000$ and $2x + 2y = 130$

(b) Solve each equation for y. $xy = 1000 \Rightarrow y = \frac{1000}{x}$ and $2x + 2y = 130 \Rightarrow y = 65 - x$

Graph $Y_1 = 1000/X$ and $Y_2 = 65 - X$ in [0, 50, 10] by [0, 50, 10]. See Figure 47.

The table has dimensions $x = 25$ inches and $y = 40$ inches.

(c) From the second equation, $y = 65 - x$. Substitute $y = 65 - x$ into the first equation.

$x(65 - x) = 1000 \Rightarrow x^2 - 65x + 1000 = 0 \Rightarrow (x - 25)(x - 40) = 0 \Rightarrow x = 25$ or $x = 40$

When $x = 25$, $y = 65 - 25 = 40$. When $x = 40$, $y = 65 - 40 = 25$. These answers are equivalent.

[0, 50, 10] by [0, 50, 10]

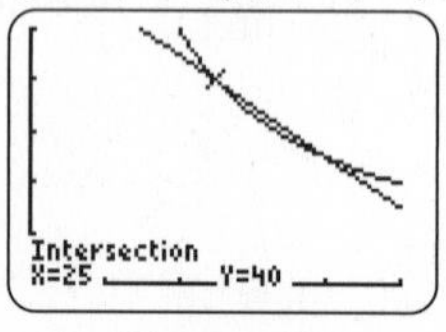

Figure 47

48. (a) $xy = 60$ and $y - x = 7$

(b) Solve each equation for y. $xy = 60 \Rightarrow y = \dfrac{60}{x}$ and $y - x = 7 \Rightarrow y = x + 7$

Graph $Y_1 = 60/X$ and $Y_2 = X + 7$ in [0, 16, 4] by [0, 16, 4]. See Figure 48.

The numbers are $x = 5$ and $y = 12$.

(c) From the second equation, $y = x + 7$. Substitute $y = x + 7$ into the first equation.

$x(x + 7) = 60 \Rightarrow x^2 + 7x - 60 = 0 \Rightarrow (x + 12)(x - 5) = 0 \Rightarrow x = -12$ or $x = 5$

When $x = -12$, $y = -12 + 7 = -5$. This does not fit the question. When $x = 5$, $y = 5 + 7 = 12$.

[0, 16, 4] by [0, 16, 4]

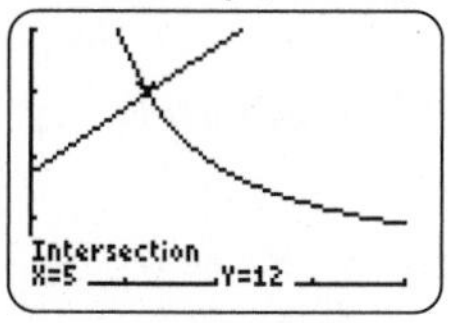

Figure 48

[0, 5, 1] by [0, 50, 10]

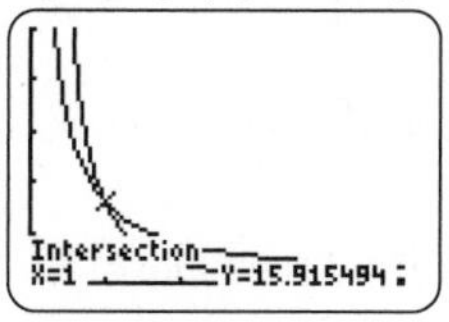

Figure 49

49. Solve each equation for h. $V = \pi r^2 h \Rightarrow h = \dfrac{V}{\pi r^2}$ and $A = 2\pi rh \Rightarrow h = \dfrac{A}{2\pi r}$

Graph $Y_1 = 50/(\pi X^2)$ and $Y_2 = 100/(2\pi X)$ in [0, 5, 1] by [0, 50, 10]. See Figure 49.

The unique answer is $r = 1$ foot and $h \approx 15.92$ feet.

50. Solve each equation for h. $V = \pi r^2 h \Rightarrow h = \dfrac{V}{\pi r^2}$ and $A = 2\pi rh + 2\pi r^2 \Rightarrow h = \dfrac{A - 2\pi r^2}{2\pi r}$

Graph $Y_1 = 35/(\pi X^2)$ and $Y_2 = (80 - 2\pi X^2)/(2\pi X)$ in [0, 4, 1] by [−5, 25, 5]. See Figures 50a & 50b.

Two solutions are possible. Either $r \approx 0.94$ inches and $h \approx 12.60$ inches or $r \approx 3.00$ inches and $h \approx 1.23$ inches.

[0, 4, 1] by [−5, 25, 5]

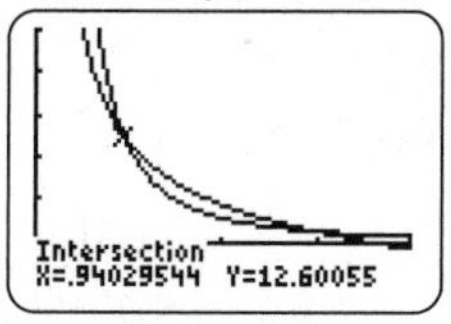

Figure 50a

[0, 4, 1] by [−5, 25, 5]

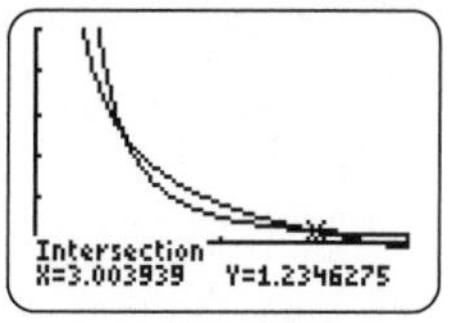

Figure 50b

[−7.5, 7.5, 1] by [−5, 5, 1]

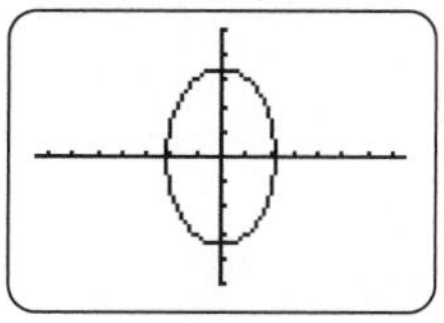

Figure 51

[−3, 3, 1] by [−2, 2, 1]

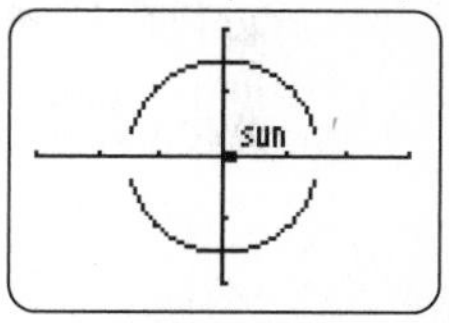

Figure 52

51. (a) $\dfrac{x^2}{5} + \dfrac{y^2}{12} = 1 \Rightarrow \dfrac{y^2}{12} = 1 - \dfrac{x^2}{5} \Rightarrow y^2 = 12\left(1 - \dfrac{x^2}{5}\right) \Rightarrow y = \pm\sqrt{12\left(1 - \dfrac{x^2}{5}\right)}$

Graph $Y_1 = \sqrt{(12(1 - X^2/5))}$ and $Y_2 = -\sqrt{(12(1 - X^2/5))}$ in [−7.5, 7.5, 1] by [−5, 5, 1]. See Figure 51.

(b) $A = \pi(\sqrt{5})(\sqrt{12}) \approx 24.33$ square units and $P = 2\pi\sqrt{\dfrac{5 + 12}{2}} \approx 18.32$ units

52. (a) $\dfrac{x^2}{1.524^2} + \dfrac{y^2}{1.517^2} = 1 \Rightarrow \dfrac{y^2}{1.517^2} = 1 - \dfrac{x^2}{1.524^2} \Rightarrow y = \pm\sqrt{1.517^2\left(1 - \dfrac{x^2}{1.524^2}\right)}$

Plot the point (0.14, 0) and Graph $Y_1 = \sqrt{(1.517^2(1 - X^2/1.524^2))}$ and $Y_2 = -\sqrt{(1.517^2(1 - X^2/1.524^2))}$ in [−3, 3, 1] by [−2, 2, 1]. See Figure 52.

(b) $P = 2\pi\sqrt{\dfrac{1.524^2 + 1.517^2}{2}} \approx 9.55$ A.U. or about 8.9×10^8 miles

$A = \pi(1.524)(1.517) \approx 7.26$ square A.U. or about 6.3×10^{16} square miles

Chapter 13 Test

1. Since $x = (y - 4)^2 - 2$, the vertex is $(-2, 4)$ and the axis of symmetry is $y = 4$. See Figure 1.

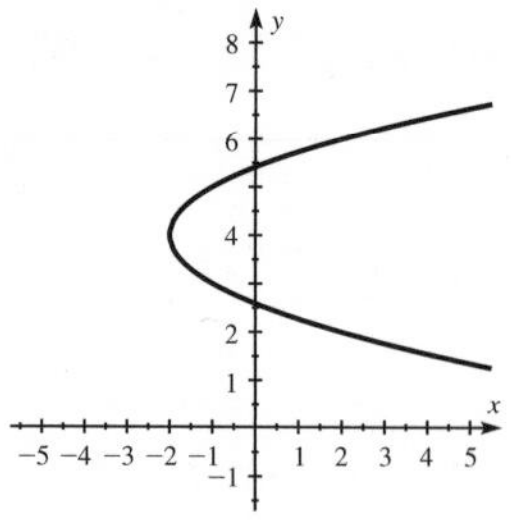

Figure 1

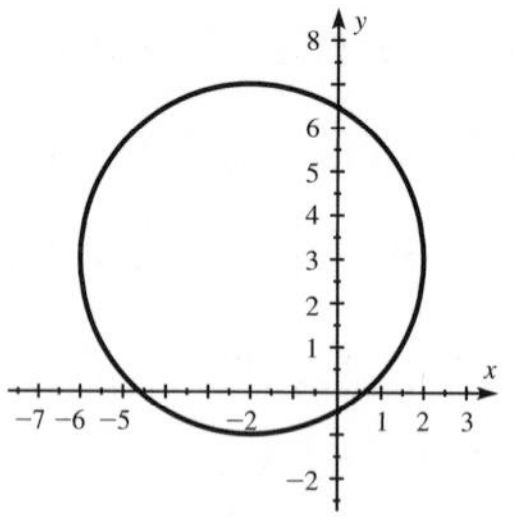

Figure 5

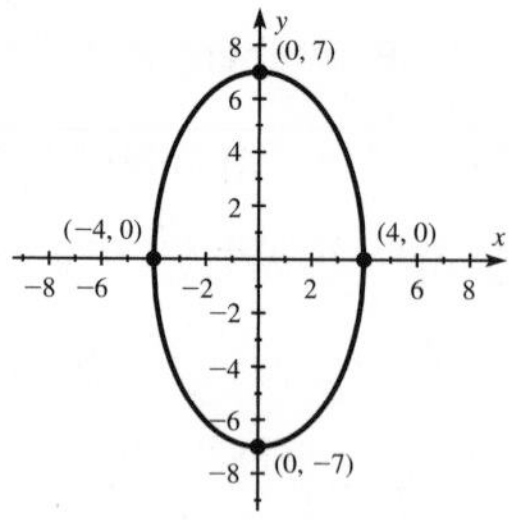

Figure 6

2. Since the parabola opens to the left and the vertex is $(1, 0)$, the equation has the form $x = a(y - 0)^2 + 1$.

   Since the parabola passes through $(0, 1)$, $0 = a(1 - 0)^2 + 1 \Rightarrow a = -1$. The equation is $x = -y^2 + 1$.

3. Since the center is $(2, -4)$ and the radius is 2, the equation is $(x - 2)^2 + (y + 4)^2 = 4$.

4. $(x - (-5))^2 + (y - 2)^2 = 10^2 \Rightarrow (x + 5)^2 + (y - 2)^2 = 100$

5. $x^2 + 4x + y^2 - 6y = 3 \Rightarrow x^2 + 4x + 4 + y^2 - 6y + 9 = 3 + 4 + 9 \Rightarrow (x + 2)^2 + (y - 3)^2 = 16$

   The radius is 4 and the center is $(-2, 3)$. Solving the equation for y results in $y = 3 \pm \sqrt{16 - (x + 2)^2}$.

   See Figure 5.

6. The ellipse has a vertical major axis with vertices $(0, \pm 7)$ and minor axis endpoints $(\pm 4, 0)$. See Figure 6.

7. Horizontal major axis with vertices $(\pm 10, 0)$ and minor axis endpoints $(0, \pm 8) \Rightarrow \dfrac{x^2}{100} + \dfrac{y^2}{64} = 1$

8. $4x^2 - 9y^2 = 36 \Rightarrow \dfrac{4x^2}{36} - \dfrac{9y^2}{36} = 1 \Rightarrow \dfrac{x^2}{9} - \dfrac{y^2}{4} = 1$

   The hyperbola has a horizontal transverse axis with vertices $(\pm 3, 0)$ and asymptotes $y = \pm \dfrac{2}{3}x$. See Figure 8.

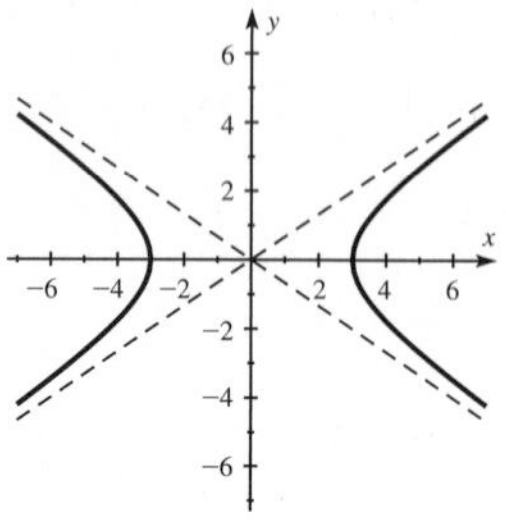

Figure 8

9. The solutions are the intersection points (0, –4) and (4, 0). Both solutions check.

10. From the first equation, $y = x - 3$. Substitute $y = x - 3$ into the second equation.

$x^2 + (x - 3)^2 = 17 \Rightarrow x^2 + x^2 - 6x + 9 = 17 \Rightarrow 2(x - 4)(x + 1) = 0 \Rightarrow x = -1$ or $x = 4$

When $x = -1$, $y = (-1) - 3 = -4$. When $x = 4$, $y = (4) - 3 = 1$ The solutions are (–1, –4) and (4, 1).

11. Solve both equations for y. $2x^2 - y = 4 \Rightarrow y = 2x^2 - 4$ and $x^2 + y = 8 \Rightarrow y = 8 - x^2$

Graph $Y_1 = 2X^2 - 4$, $Y_2 = 8 - X^2$ in [–10, 10, 1] by [–10, 10, 1]. See Figures 11a & 11b.

The solutions are the intersection points (–2, 4) and (2, 4).

[–10, 10, 1] by [–10, 10, 1]

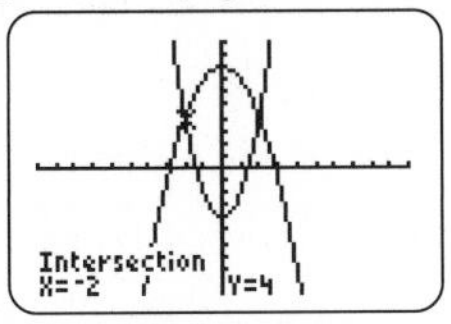

Figure 11a

[–10, 10, 1] by [–10, 10, 1]

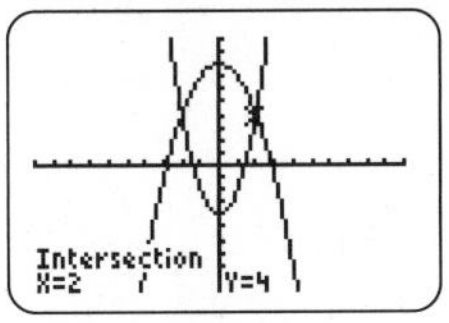

Figure 11b

12. Sketch the line given by $3x + y = 6$ using a dashed line and the circle given by $x^2 + y^2 = 25$ using a dashed line. Since the point (4, 0) satisfies both inequalities, we shade the portion of the xy-plane containing the point (4, 0). See Figure 12.

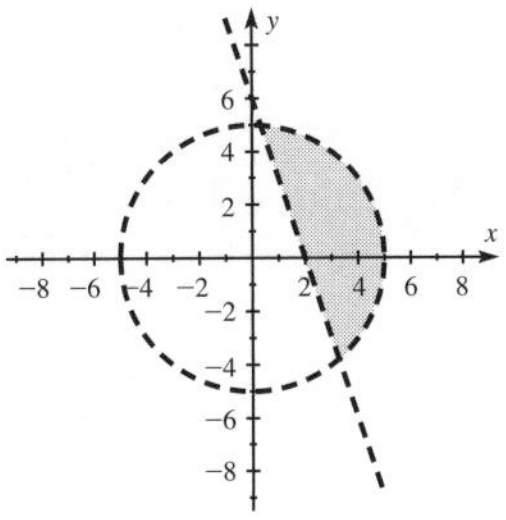

Figure 12

13. A parabola with vertex (0, –4) has an equation of the form $y = a(x - 0)^2 - 4$ or $y = ax^2 - 4$. Since the parabola also passes through the point (2, 0), $0 = a \cdot 2^2 - 4 \Rightarrow a = 1$. The equation of the parabola is $y = x^2 - 4$. The other parabola is a reflection of this parabola across the x-axis. Its equation is $y = 4 - x^2$. Since both the parabolas are solid, the system of inequalities is $y \le 4 - x^2$ and $y \ge x^2 - 4$.

14. (a) $xy = 5000$ and $2x + 2y = 300$

(b) $\dfrac{5000}{x} = 150 - x \Rightarrow 5000 = 150x - x^2 \Rightarrow x^2 - 150x + 5000 = 0 \Rightarrow (x - 50)(x - 100) = 0 \Rightarrow$

Either $x = 50$ or $x = 100$. When $x = 50$, $y = 150 - 50 = 100$. When $x = 100$, $y = 150 - 100 = 50$.

Since the width is shorter than the length, $x = 50$ and $y = 100$. The solution is 50 by 100 feet.

15. From the hint, the two equations to graph are $y = \dfrac{1183}{x^2}$ and $y = \dfrac{702 - x^2}{4x}$. Figures not shown. There are two possible solutions: Either $x \approx 22.08$ and $y \approx 2.43$ or $x \approx 7.29$ and $y \approx 22.26$. The answer is not unique.

16. (a) $\frac{x^2}{19.18^2} + \frac{y^2}{19.16^2} = 1 \Rightarrow \frac{y^2}{19.16^2} = 1 - \frac{x^2}{19.18^2} \Rightarrow y = \pm\sqrt{19.16^2\left(1 - \frac{x^2}{19.18^2}\right)}$

Plot the point (0.9, 0) and Graph $Y_1 = \sqrt{(19.16^2(1 - X^2/19.18^2))}$ and $Y_2 = -\sqrt{(19.16^2(1 - X^2/19.18^2))}$ in [–30, 30, 10] by [–20, 20, 10]. See Figure 16.

(b) The minimum distance occurs when $x = 19.18$ A.U. The distance is $19.18 - 0.9 = 18.28$ A.U. This is about 1,700,040,000 miles.

[–30, 30, 10] by [–20, 20, 10]

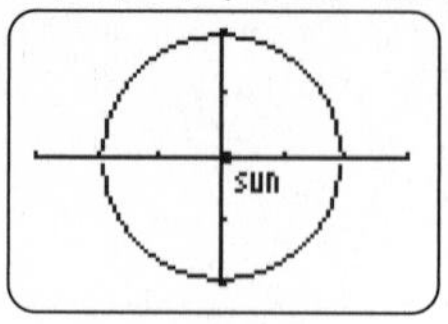

Figure 16

Chapter 13 Extended and Discovery Exercises

1. (a) $x^2 = 4y \Rightarrow x^2 = 4(1)y$. Since $p = 1$, the focus is (0, 1). See Figure 1a.

(b) $y^2 = -8x \Rightarrow y^2 = 4(-2)x$. Since $p = -2$, the focus is (–2, 0). See Figure 1b.

(c) $x = 2y^2 \Rightarrow y^2 = \frac{1}{2}x \Rightarrow y^2 = 4\left(\frac{1}{8}\right)x$. Since $p = \frac{1}{8}$, the focus is $\left(\frac{1}{8}, 0\right)$. See Figure 1c.

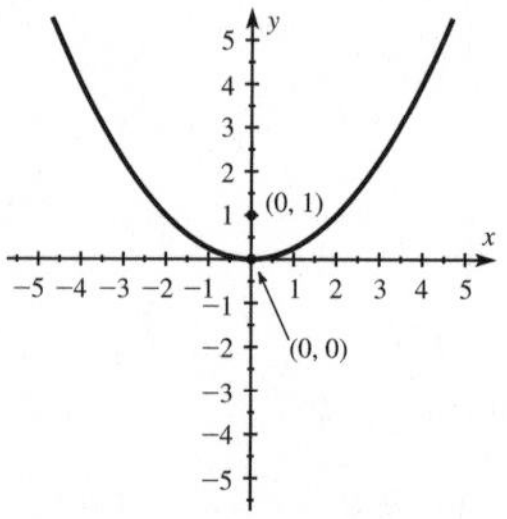

Figure 1a

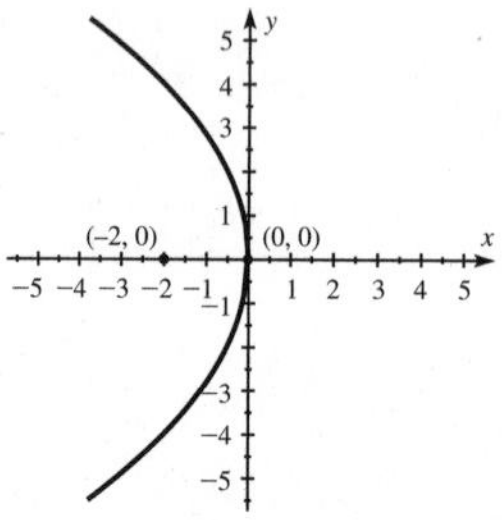

Figure 1b

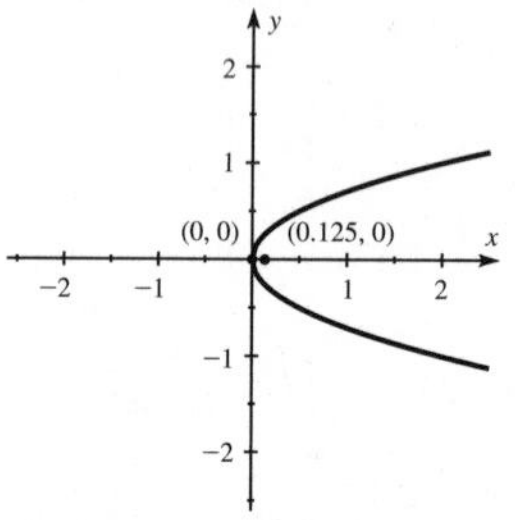

Figure 1c

2. (a) Since the vertex of the parabola is (0, 0), the cross section of the dish has an equation of the form $y = ax^2$. Since the parabola passes through (150, 44), $44 = a(150)^2 \Rightarrow 44 = 22{,}500a \Rightarrow a = \frac{44}{22{,}500} = \frac{11}{5625}$.

The equation is $y = \frac{11}{5625}x^2$.

(b) Writing this equation in the form $x^2 = 4py$ yields $x^2 = 4\left(\frac{5625}{44}\right)y$. The focus is located at $\left(0, \frac{5625}{44}\right)$.

That as, the focus is $\frac{5625}{44} \approx 127.8$ feet from the vertex.

3. (a) This is an ellipse with horizontal major axis, centered at (3, 1). See Figure 3a.

   (b) This is an ellipse with vertical major axis, centered at (–1, –2). See Figure 3b.

   (c) This is a hyperbola centered at (–1, 3). The asymptotes are $y = \pm\frac{3}{2}(x + 1) + 3$. See Figure 3c.

   (d) This is a hyperbola centered at (–1, 4). The asymptotes are $y = \pm 2(x + 1) + 4$. See Figure 3d.

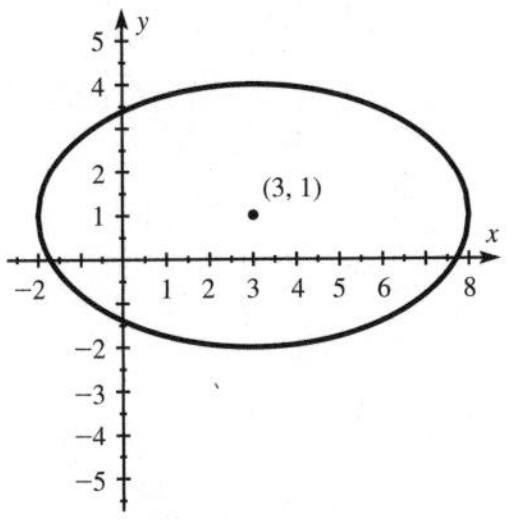

Figure 3a

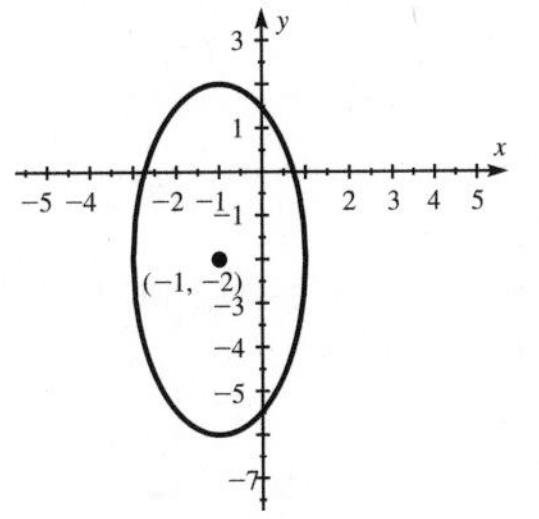

Figure 3b

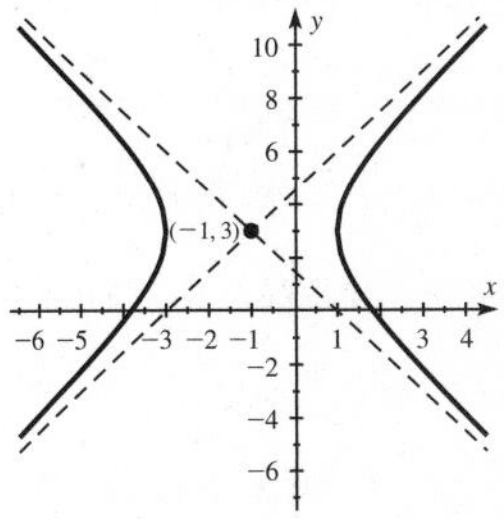

Figure 3c

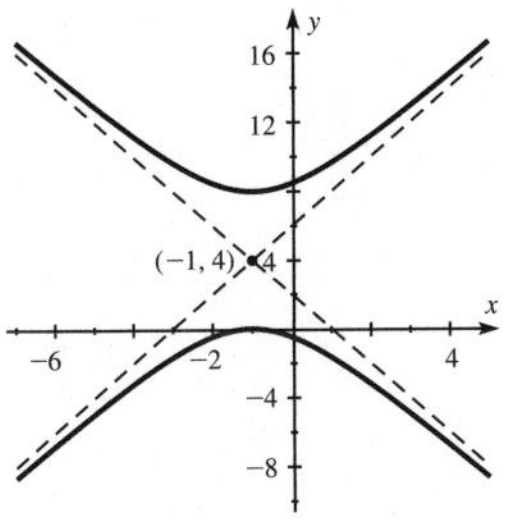

Figure 3d

4. (a) $\dfrac{(x + 3)^2}{16} + \dfrac{(y - 5)^2}{4} = 1$

   (b) $\dfrac{(y + 3)^2}{25} + \dfrac{(x - 2)^2}{9} = 1$

5. (a) $9x^2 - 18x + 4y^2 + 24y + 9 = 0 \Rightarrow 9(x^2 - 2x + 1) + 4(y^2 + 6y + 9) = -9 + 9 + 36 \Rightarrow$

   $9(x - 1)^2 + 4(y + 3)^2 = 36 \Rightarrow \dfrac{(x - 1)^2}{4} + \dfrac{(y + 3)^2}{9} = 1 \Rightarrow$ Center: (1, –3)

   (b) $25x^2 + 150x - 16y^2 + 32y - 191 = 0 \Rightarrow 25(x^2 + 6x + 9) - 16(y^2 - 2y + 1) = 191 + 225 - 16 \Rightarrow$

   $25(x + 3)^2 - 16(y - 1)^2 = 400 \Rightarrow \dfrac{(x + 3)^2}{16} - \dfrac{(y - 1)^2}{25} = 1 \Rightarrow$ Center: (–3, 1)

Critical Thinking Solutions for Chapter 13

Section 13.1.

- The circle is undefined since the radius is $\sqrt{-7} = i\sqrt{7}$.

Section 13.2

- When the nails are moved farther apart the ellipse becomes more flat (ultimately a straight line).

  When the nails are moved closer together the ellipse becomes more circular.

  When the nails come together, a circle would be formed.

- It is a circle with radius a. We can find the equation of the circle by multiplying both sides of the equation by a^2.

- Minimum distance: about 0.307 A.U. or about 28,551,000 miles

  Maximum distance: about 0.467 A.U. or about 43,431,000 miles

- The path of a comet seen at regular intervals is elliptic.

Chapter 14: Sequences and Series

14.1: Sequences

Concepts

1. 1, 2, 3, 4...

3. function; the set of natural numbers

5. 6t

7. $f(2)$

Evaluating and Representing Sequences

9. $f(1) = 1^2 = 1, f(2) = 2^2 = 4, f(3) = 3^2 = 9, f(4) = 4^2 = 16 \Rightarrow 1, 4, 9, 16$

11. $f(1) = \dfrac{1}{1+5} = \dfrac{1}{6}, f(2) = \dfrac{1}{2+5} = \dfrac{1}{7}, f(3) = \dfrac{1}{3+5} = \dfrac{1}{8}, f(4) = \dfrac{1}{4+5} = \dfrac{1}{9} \Rightarrow \dfrac{1}{6}, \dfrac{1}{7}, \dfrac{1}{8}, \dfrac{1}{9}$

13. $f(1) = 5\left(\dfrac{1}{2}\right)^1 = \dfrac{5}{2}, f(2) = 5\left(\dfrac{1}{2}\right)^2 = \dfrac{5}{4}, f(3) = 5\left(\dfrac{1}{2}\right)^3 = \dfrac{5}{8}, f(4) = 5\left(\dfrac{1}{2}\right)^4 = \dfrac{5}{16} \Rightarrow \dfrac{5}{2}, \dfrac{5}{4}, \dfrac{5}{8}, \dfrac{5}{16}$

15. $f(1) = 9, f(2) = 9, f(3) = 9, f(4) = 9 \Rightarrow 9, 9, 9, 9$

17. $a_1 = 1^3 = 1, a_2 = 2^3 = 8, a_3 = 3^3 = 27 \Rightarrow 1, 8, 27$

19. $a_1 = \dfrac{4(1)}{3+1} = 1, a_2 = \dfrac{4(2)}{3+2} = \dfrac{8}{5}, a_3 = \dfrac{4(3)}{3+3} = 2 \Rightarrow 1, \dfrac{8}{5}, 2$

21. $a_1 = 2(1)^2 + 1 - 1 = 2, a_2 = 2(2)^2 + 2 - 1 = 9, a_3 = 2(3)^2 + 3 - 1 = 20 \Rightarrow 2, 9, 20$

23. $a_1 = -2, a_2 = -2, a_3 = -2 \Rightarrow -2, -2, -2$

25. $\dfrac{1}{2}(a_1 + a_4) = \dfrac{1}{2}(10 + 4) = \dfrac{1}{2}(14) = 7$

27. The points shown are (1, 3), (2, 4), (3, 5), (4, 3) and (5, 1). The sequence is 3, 4, 5, 3, 1.

29. The points shown are (1, 6), (2, 5), (3, 4), (4, 3), (5, 2) and (6, 1). The sequence is 6, 5, 4, 3, 2, 1.

31. Numerical: See Figure 31a. Graphical: See Figure 31b.

n	1	2	3	4	5	6	7
a_n	2	3	4	5	6	7	8

Figure 31a

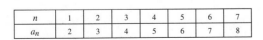

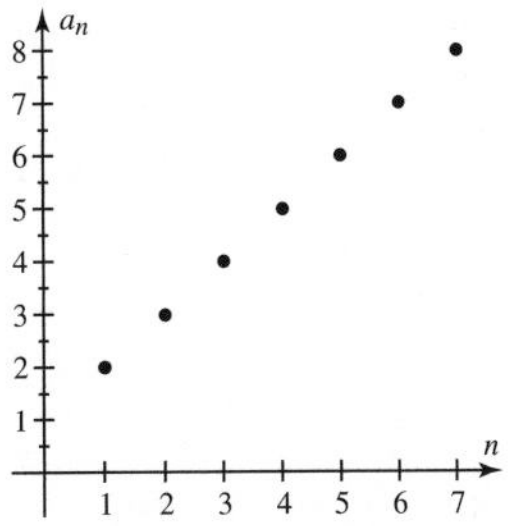

Figure 31b

33. Numerical: See Figure 33a. Graphical: See Figure 33b.

n	1	2	3	4	5	6	7
a_n	0	2	6	12	20	30	42

Figure 33a

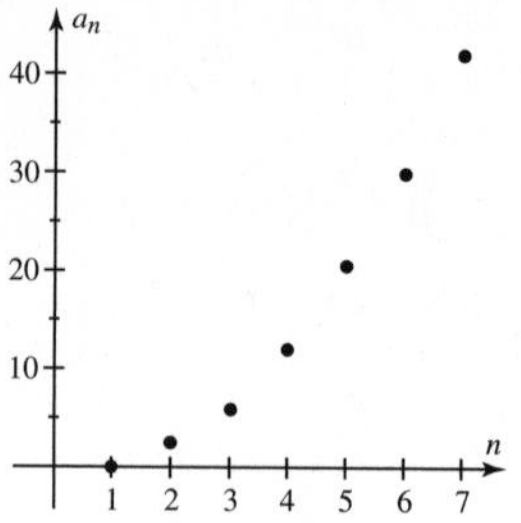

Figure 33b

35. Numerical: See Figure 35a. Graphical: See Figure 35b.

n	1	2	3	4	5	6	7
a_n	2	4	8	16	32	64	128

Figure 35a

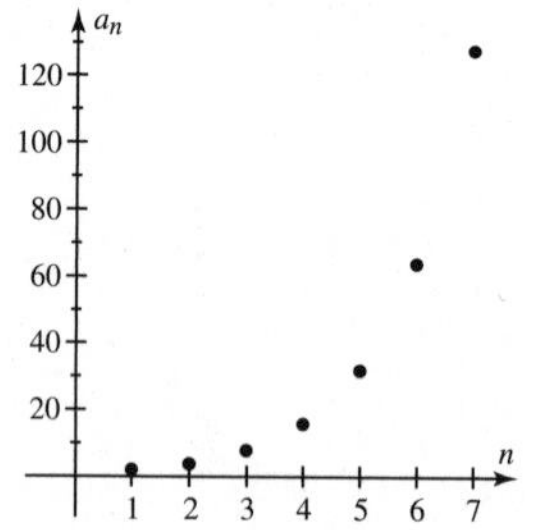

Figure 35b

Applications

37. Symbolic: $a_n = 30n$ for $n = 1, 2, 3, \ldots, 7$

Graphical: See Figure 37a. Numerical: See Figure 37b.

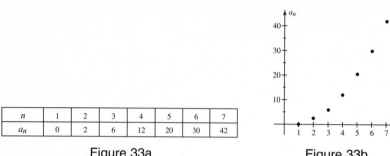

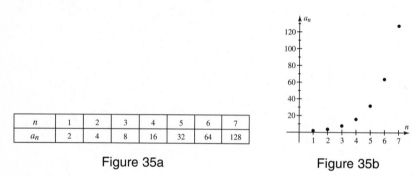

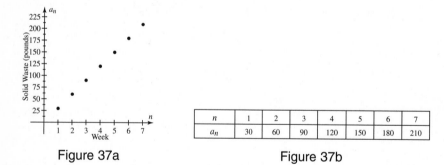

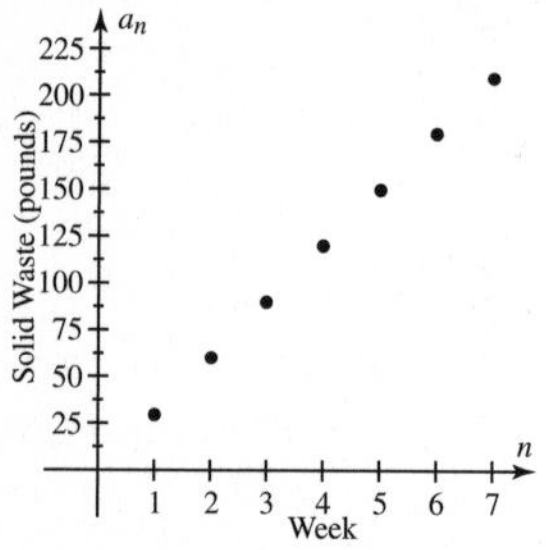

Figure 37a

n	1	2	3	4	5	6	7
a_n	30	60	90	120	150	180	210

Figure 37b

39. (a) $a_1 = 1^2 = 1, a_2 = 2^2 = 4, a_3 = 3^2 = 9, a_4 = 4^2 = 16 \Rightarrow 1, 4, 9, 16$

(b) $a_1 = 4(1) = 4, a_2 = 4(2) = 8, a_3 = 4(3) = 12, a_4 = 4(4) = 16 \Rightarrow 4, 8, 12, 16$

41. (a) After 1 year it is worth $25{,}000(0.80) = \$20{,}000$. After 2 years it is worth $20{,}000(0.80) = \$16{,}000$.

(b) $a_n = 25{,}000(0.8)^n$

(c) See Figure 41.

n	1	2	3	4	5	6	7
a_n	20,000	16,000	12,800	10,240	8192	6553.6	5242.9

Figure 41

43. (a) See Figure 43a.

(b) $a_n = 50 + 5(n - 1)$ or $a_n = 45 + 5n$

(c) $a_{23} = 50 + 5(23 - 1) = 50 + 5(22) = 50 + 110 = 160$ seats

(d) See Figure 43d.

n	1	2	3	4	5	6	7
a_n	50	55	60	65	70	75	80

Figure 43a

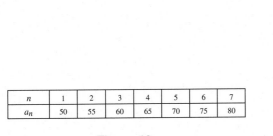

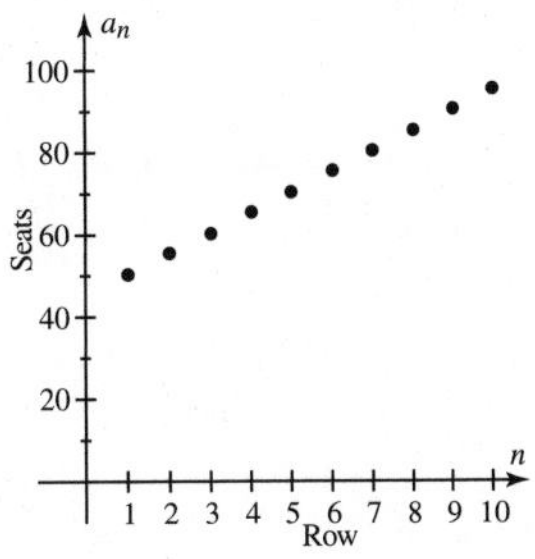

Figure 43d

14.2: Arithmetic and Geometric Sequences

Concepts

1. linear

3. $a_n = 3n + 1$; the common difference is 3. *Answers may vary.*

5. add; previous

7. 19; 4

9. $a_n = a_1(r)^{n-1}$

Arithmetic Sequences

11. Yes, the common difference is 10.

13. Yes, the common difference is –1.

15. No, there is no common difference.

17. Yes, the common difference is 3..

19. Yes, the common difference is –3.

21. Yes, the common difference is 4.

23. Yes, the common difference is 1.

25. No, there is no common difference.

27. Yes, the common difference is 2.

29. $a_n = 7 + (n - 1)(-2) \Rightarrow a_n = 7 - 2n + 2 \Rightarrow a_n = -2n + 9$

31. Note: $d = \dfrac{6 - (-2)}{2} = 4$, thus $a_n = -2 + (n - 1)(4) \Rightarrow a_n = -2 + 4n - 4 \Rightarrow a_n = 4n - 6$

33. Note: $d = \frac{8 - 16}{4} = -2$ and $a_1 = 16 - 7(-2) = 30$, thus

$$a_n = 30 + (n - 1)(-2) \Rightarrow a_n = 30 - 2n + 2 \Rightarrow a_n = -2n + 32$$

35. $a_{32} = -3 + (32 - 1)(2) = -3 + (31)(2) = -3 + 62 = 59$

37. Note: $d = 0 - (-3) = 3$, thus $a_9 = -3 + (9 - 1)(3) = -3 + (8)(3) = -3 + 24 = 21$

Geometric Sequences

39. Yes, the common ratio is 3.

41. Yes, the common ratio is 0.8.

43. No, there is no common ratio.

45. Yes, the common ratio is 2.

47. No, there is no common ratio.o.

49. Yes, the common ratio is 4.

51. Yes, the common ratio is 2.

53. No, there is no common ratio.

55. $a_n = 1.5(4)^{n-1}$

57. Note: $r = \frac{6}{-3} = -2$, thus $a_n = -3(-2)^{n-1}$

59. Note: $16 = 1 \cdot r^2 \Rightarrow r^2 = 16 \Rightarrow r = 4$ (since $r > 0$), thus $a_n = 1(4)^{n-1}$

61. $a_8 = 2(3)^{8-1} = 2(3)^7 = 4374$

63. Note: $r = \frac{3}{-1} = -3$, thus $a_6 = -1(-3)^{6-1} = -1(-3)^5 = 243$

Applications

65. (a) 3000, 6000, 9000, 12,000, 15,000; This sequence is arithmetic.

(b) $a_n = 3000n$

(c) $a_{20} = 3000(20) = 60{,}000$; When there are 20 people, the ventilation should be 60,000 cubic feet per hour.

(d) See Figure 65. The points are collinear.

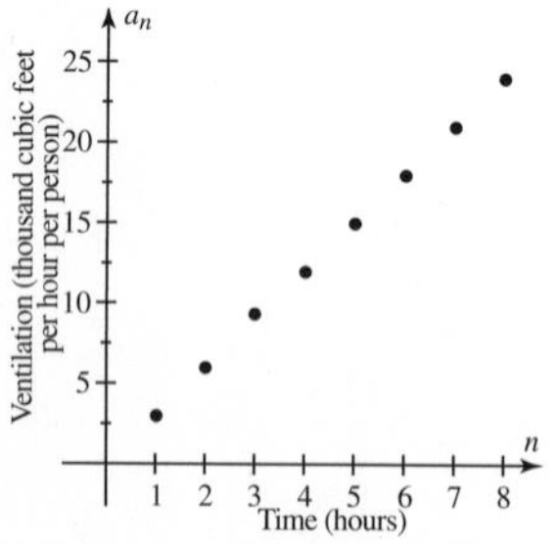

Figure 65

67. The sequence is arithmetic and the common difference is 2000.

69. (a) The sequence is geometric and the common ratio is 1.15.

(b) $a_n = 100{,}000(1.15)^{n-1}$

(c) $a_7 = 100{,}000(1.15)^{7-1} \approx 231{,}306$; During the 7th year, the home will be worth about \$231,306.

(d) See Figure 69.

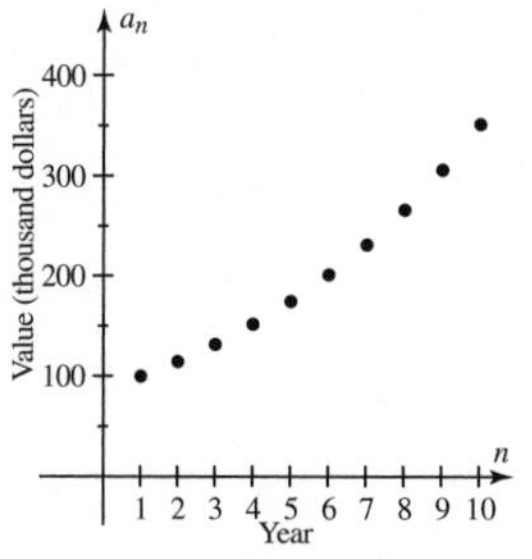

Figure 69

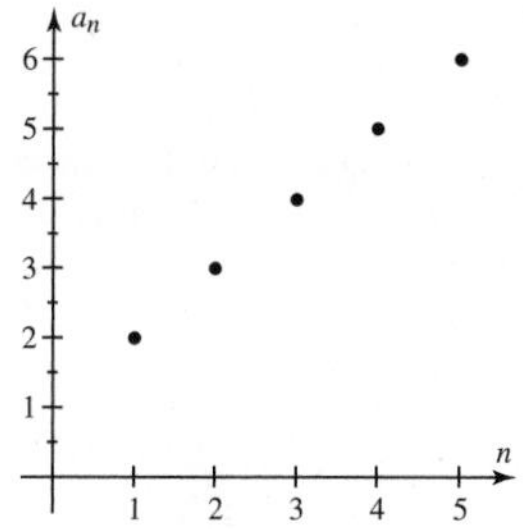

Figure 2a

n	1	2	3	4	5
a_n	2	3	4	5	6

Figure 2b

71. (a) The number of seats can be modeled by an arithmetic sequence whose common difference is 2.

(b) Since $a_1 = 40$ and $d = 2$, $a_n = 40 + 2(n - 1)$ or $a_n = 2n + 38$

(c) $a_{20} = 40 + 2(20 - 1) = 40 + 2(19) = 40 + 38 = 78$ seats

Checking Basic Concepts for Sections 14.1 & 14.2

1. $a_1 = \frac{1}{1+4} = \frac{1}{5}, a_2 = \frac{2}{2+4} = \frac{1}{3}, a_3 = \frac{3}{3+4} = \frac{3}{7}, a_4 = \frac{4}{4+4} = \frac{1}{2} \Rightarrow \frac{1}{5}, \frac{1}{3}, \frac{3}{7}, \frac{1}{2}$

2. Graphical: See Figure 2a. Numerical: See Figure 2b.

3. (a) Arithmetic. Here $d = 1 - (-2) = 3$ and $a_1 = -2$, thus $a_n = -2 + (n - 1)(3) \Rightarrow a_n = 3n - 5$

(b) Geometric. Here $r = \frac{-6}{3} = -2$ and $a_1 = 3$, thus $a_n = 3(-2)^{n-1}$

4. $a_n = 5 + (n - 1)(2) \Rightarrow a_n = 5 + 2n - 2 \Rightarrow a_n = 2n + 3$

5. $a_n = 5(2)^{n-1}$

14.3: Series

Concepts

1. series

3. arithmetic (the common difference is 2)

5. $n\left(\frac{a_1 + a_n}{2}\right)$ or $\frac{n}{2}(2a_1 + (n - 1)d)$

7. sum

9. arithmetic

Sums of Series

11. $6\left(\frac{3 + 13}{2}\right) = 6(8) = 48$

13. $40\left(\frac{1 + 40}{2}\right) = 40(21) = 840$

15. $5\left(\frac{-7 + 5}{2}\right) = 5(-1) = -5$

17. Here $r = 3$ and $n = 7$ thus $S_7 = 3\left(\frac{1 - 3^7}{1 - 3}\right) = 3\left(\frac{-2186}{-2}\right) = 3(1093) = 3279$

19. Here $r = -2$ and $n = 8$ thus $S_8 = 1\left(\frac{1 - (-2)^8}{1 - (-2)}\right) = 1\left(\frac{-255}{3}\right) = -85$

21. Here $r = 3$ and $n = 6$ thus $S_6 = 0.5\left(\frac{1 - 3^6}{1 - 3}\right) = 0.5\left(\frac{-728}{-2}\right) = 0.5(364) = 182$

23. $S_{20} = 2000\left(\frac{(1 + 0.08)^{20} - 1}{0.08}\right) \approx \$91,523.93$

25. $S_5 = 10,000\left(\frac{(1 + 0.11)^5 - 1}{0.11}\right) \approx \$65,278.01$

Summation Notation

27. $2(1) + 2(2) + 2(3) + 2(4) \Rightarrow 2 + 4 + 6 + 8 = 20$

29. $4 + 4 + 4 + 4 + 4 + 4 + 4 + 4 = 32$

31. $1^2 + 2^2 + 3^2 + 4^2 + 5^2 + 6^2 + 7^2 \Rightarrow 1 + 4 + 9 + 16 + 25 + 36 + 49 = 140$

33. $(4^2 - 4) + (5^2 - 5) \Rightarrow 12 + 20 = 32$

35. $\sum_{k=1}^{6} k^4$

37. $\sum_{k=1}^{5} \frac{1}{k^2}$

39. $\sum_{k=1}^{5} k = n\left(\frac{a_1 + a_2}{2}\right) = n\left(\frac{1 + n}{2}\right) = \frac{n(n + 1)}{2}$

Applications

41. (a) $8518 + 9921 + 10,706 + 14,035 + 14,307 + 12,249$

(b) $8518 + 9921 + 10,706 + 14,035 + 14,307 + 12,249 = 69,736$

43. (a) Each successive square has half the area of the square before it. $1, \frac{1}{2}, \frac{1}{4}, \frac{1}{8}, \frac{1}{16}$

(b) Here $r = \frac{1}{2}$ and $n = 10$ thus $S_5 = 1\left(\frac{1 - (\frac{1}{2})^{10}}{1 - (\frac{1}{2})}\right) = \left(\frac{\frac{1023}{1024}}{\frac{1}{2}}\right) = \frac{1023}{512}$

45. The sum is $14 + 13 + 12 + 11 + 10 + 9 + 8 + 7 + 6$. This is an arithmetic series with $a_1 = 14$ and $a_9 = 6$.

The sum is $S_9 = 9\left(\frac{14 + 6}{2}\right) = 9(10) = 90$ logs.

47. This is an arithmetic series with $a_1 = 35{,}000$, $n = 20$ and $d = 2000$

The sum is $S_{20} = \frac{20}{2}(2(35{,}000) + (20 - 1)(2000)) = 10(70{,}000 + 38{,}000) = 10(108{,}000) = \$1{,}080{,}000$.

49. This is an geometric sequence given by $a_n = 10(0.75)^n$. The distance it falls is $a_4 = 10(0.75)^4 \approx 3.16$ feet.

14.4: The Binomial Theorem

Concepts

1. 5

3. Row 4.

5. $4! = 1 \cdot 2 \cdot 3 \cdot 4 = 24$

7. $\frac{n!}{(n - r)!\,r!}$

Using Pascal's Triangle

9. Row 4 of Pascal's triangle is 1, 3, 3, 1. $(x + y)^3 = x^3 + 3x^2y + 3xy^2 + y^3$

11. Row 5 of Pascal's triangle is 1, 4, 6, 4, 1. $(2x + 1)^4 = (2x)^4 + 4(2x)^3(1) + 6(2x)^2(1)^2 + 4(2x)(1)^3 + (1)^4 \Rightarrow$

$(2x + 1)^4 = 16x^4 + 32x^3 + 24x^2 + 8x + 1$

13. Row 6 of Pascal's triangle is 1, 5, 10, 10, 5, 1. $(a - b)^5 = a^5 - 5a^4b + 10a^3b^2 - 10a^2b^3 + 5ab^4 - b^5$

15. Row 4 of Pascal's triangle is 1, 3, 3, 1. $(x^2 + 1)^3 = (x^2)^3 + 3(x^2)^2(1) + 3(x^2)(1)^2 + (1)^3 \Rightarrow$

$(x^2 + 1)^3 = x^6 + 3x^4 + 3x^2 + 1$

Factorials and Binomial Coefficients

17. $3! = 1 \cdot 2 \cdot 3 = 6$

19. $\frac{4!}{3!} = \frac{1 \cdot 2 \cdot 3 \cdot 4}{1 \cdot 2 \cdot 3} = 4$

21. $\frac{2!}{0!} = \frac{1 \cdot 2}{1} = 2$

23. $\frac{5!}{2!\,3!} = \frac{1 \cdot 2 \cdot 3 \cdot 4 \cdot 5}{(1 \cdot 2)(1 \cdot 2 \cdot 3)} = 2 \cdot 5 = 10$

25. ${}_5C_4 = \frac{5!}{4!\,1!} = \frac{1 \cdot 2 \cdot 3 \cdot 4 \cdot 5}{(1 \cdot 2 \cdot 3 \cdot 4)(1)} = 5$

27. ${}_6C_5 = \frac{6!}{5!\,1!} = \frac{1 \cdot 2 \cdot 3 \cdot 4 \cdot 5 \cdot 6}{(1 \cdot 2 \cdot 3 \cdot 4 \cdot 5)(1)} = 6$

29. ${}_4C_0 = \frac{4!}{0!\,4!} = \frac{1 \cdot 2 \cdot 3 \cdot 4}{(1)(1 \cdot 2 \cdot 3 \cdot 4)} = 1$

31. ${}_{12}C_7 = 792$

33. ${}_9C_5 = 126$

35. ${}_{19}C_{11} = 75{,}582$

The Binomial Theorem

37. $(m + n)^3 = ({}_3C_0)m^3 + ({}_3C_1)m^2n + ({}_3C_2)mn^2 + ({}_3C_3)n^3 \Rightarrow (m + n)^3 = m^3 + 3m^2n + 3mn^2 + n^3$

39. $(x - y)^4 = ({}_4C_0)x^4 - ({}_4C_1)x^3y + ({}_4C_2)x^2y^2 - ({}_4C_3)xy^3 + ({}_4C_4)y^4 \Rightarrow$

$(x - y)^4 = x^4 - 4x^3y + 6x^2y^2 - 4xy^3 + y^4$

41. $(2a + 1)^3 = ({}_3C_0)(2a)^3 + ({}_3C_1)(2a)^2(1) + ({}_3C_2)(2a)(1)^2 + ({}_3C_3)(1)^3 \Rightarrow (2a + 1)^3 = 8a^3 + 12a^2 + 6a + 1$

43. $(x + 2)^5 = ({}_5C_0)x^5 + ({}_5C_1)x^4(2) + ({}_5C_2)x^3(2)^2 + ({}_5C_3)x^2(2)^3 + ({}_5C_4)x(2)^4 + ({}_5C_5)(2)^5 \Rightarrow$

$(x + 2)^5 = x^5 + 10x^4 + 40x^3 + 80x^2 + 80x + 32$

45. $(3 + 2m)^4 = ({}_4C_0)(3)^4 + ({}_4C_1)(3)^3(2m) + ({}_4C_2)(3)^2(2m)^2 + ({}_4C_3)(3)(2m)^3 + ({}_4C_4)(2m)^4 \Rightarrow$

$(3 + 2m)^4 = 81 + 216m + 216m^2 + 96m^3 + 16m^4$

47. $(2x - y)^3 = ({}_3C_0)(2x)^3 - ({}_3C_1)(2x)^2y + ({}_3C_2)(2x)y^2 - ({}_3C_3)y^3 \Rightarrow (2x - y)^3 = 8x^3 - 12x^2y + 6xy^2 - y^3$

49. Here $r = 0$ and $n = 8$. The first term is $({}_8C_0)a^{8-0}b^0 = a^8$.

51. Here $r = 3$ and $n = 7$. The fourth term is $({}_7C_3)x^{7-3}y^3 = 35x^4y^3$.

53. Here $r = 0$ and $n = 9$. The first term is $({}_9C_0)(2m)^{9-0}n^0 = 512m^9$.

Checking Basic Concepts for Sections 14.3 & 14.4

1. (a) Geometric. The common ratio is $\frac{1}{2}$.

   (b) Arithmetic. The common difference is 2.

2. $12\left(\frac{4 + 48}{2}\right) = 12(26) = 312$

3. Here $r = -2$ and $n = 10$ thus $S_6 = 1\left(\frac{1 - (-2)^{10}}{1 - (-2)}\right) = 1\left(\frac{-1023}{3}\right) = -341$

4. Row 5 of Pascal's triangle is 1, 4, 6, 4, 1. $(x - y)^4 = x^4 - 4x^3y + 6x^2y^2 - 4xy^3 + y^4$

5. $(x + 2)^3 = ({}_3C_0)x^3 + ({}_3C_1)x^2(2) + ({}_3C_2)x(2)^2 + ({}_3C_3)(2)^3 \Rightarrow (x^2 - 1)^3 = x^3 + 6x^2 + 12x + 8$

Chapter 14 Review Exercises

Section 14.1

1. $f(1) = 1^3 = 1, f(2) = 2^3 = 8, f(3) = 3^3 = 27, f(4) = 4^3 = 64 \Rightarrow 1, 8, 27, 64$

2. $f(1) = 5 - 2(1) = 3, f(2) = 5 - 2(2) = 1, f(3) = 5 - 2(3) = -1, f(4) = 5 - 2(4) = -3 \Rightarrow 3, 1, -1, -3$

3. $f(1) = \frac{2(1)}{1^2 + 1} = 1, f(2) = \frac{2(2)}{2^2 + 1} = \frac{4}{5}, f(3) = \frac{2(3)}{3^2 + 1} = \frac{3}{5}, f(4) = \frac{2(4)}{4^2 + 1} = \frac{8}{17} \Rightarrow 1, \frac{4}{5}, \frac{3}{5}, \frac{8}{17}$

4. $f(1) = (-2)^1 = -2, f(2) = (-2)^2 = 4, f(3) = (-2)^3 = -8, f(4) = (-2)^4 = 16 \Rightarrow -2, 4, -8, 16$

5. The points shown are (1, –2), (2, 0), (3, 4), and (4, 2). The sequence is –2, 0, 4, 2.

6. The points shown are (1, 5), (2, 3), (3, 2), and (4, 1). The sequence is 5, 3, 2, 1.

7. Numerical: See Figure 7a. Graphical: See Figure 7b.

n	1	2	3	4	5	6	7
a_n	2	4	6	8	10	12	14

Figure 7a

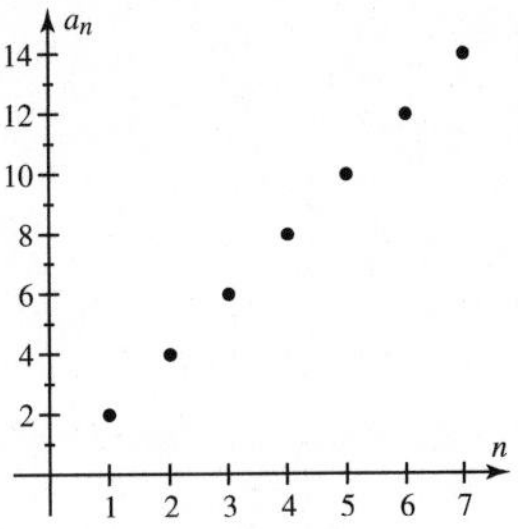

Figure 7b

8. Numerical: See Figure 8a. Graphical: See Figure 8b

n	1	2	3	4	5	6	7
a_n	−3	0	5	12	21	32	45

Figure 8a

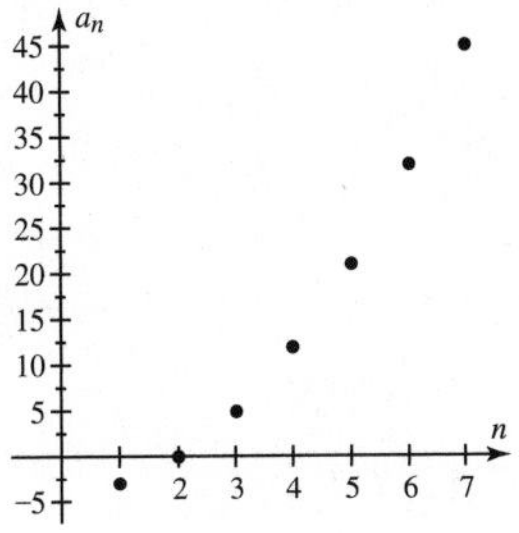

Figure 8b

9. Numerical: See Figure 9a. Graphical: See Figure 9b.

n	1	2	3	4	5	6	7
a_n	2	1	0.5	0.25	0.125	0.0625	0.0313

Figure 9a

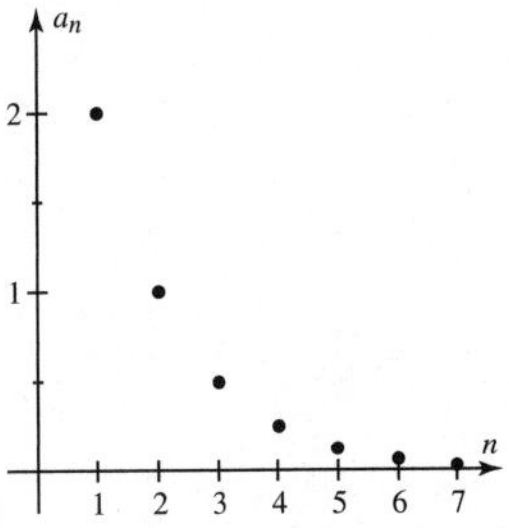

Figure 9b

10. Numerical: See Figure 10a. Graphical: See Figure 10b.

n	1	2	3	4	5	6	7
a_n	1	1.4142	1.7321	2	2.2361	2.4495	2.6458

Figure 10a

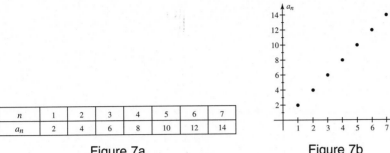

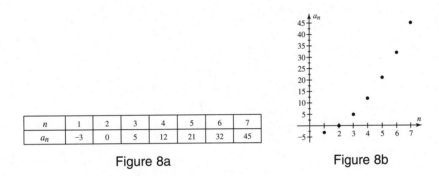

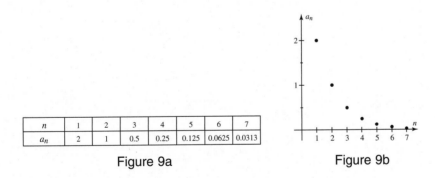

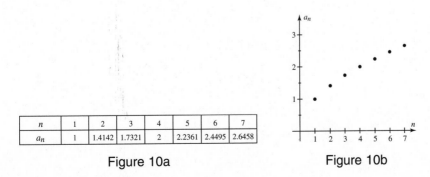

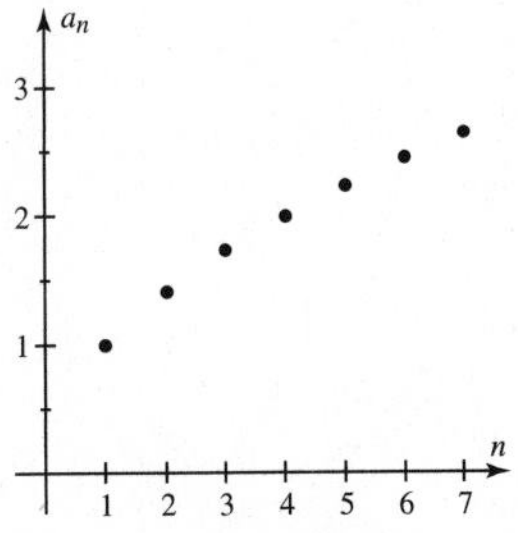

Figure 10b

Section 14.2

11. Yes, the common difference is 5.
12. No, there is no common difference.
13. No, there is no common difference.
14. Yes, the common difference is $-\frac{1}{3}$.
15. Yes, the common difference is –3.
16. No, there is no common difference.
17. Yes, the common difference is –1.
18. No, there is no common difference.
19. $a_n = -3 + (n - 1)(4) \Rightarrow a_n = -3 + 4n - 4 \Rightarrow a_n = 4n - 7$
20. Note: $d = -3 - 2 = -5$, thus $a_n = 2 + (n - 1)(-5) \Rightarrow a_n = 2 - 5n + 5 \Rightarrow a_n = -5n + 7$
21. Yes, the common ratio is 4.
22. No, there is no common ratio.
23. No, there is no common ratio.
24. Yes, the common ratio is 0.7.
25. No, there is no common ratio.
26. Yes, the common ratio is $-\frac{1}{3}$.
27. No, there is no common ratio.
28. Yes, the common ratio is 2.
29. $a_n = 5(0.9)^{n-1}$
30. Note: $r = \frac{8}{2} = 4$, thus $a_n = 2(4)^{n-1}$

Section 14.3

31. $9\left(\frac{4 + 44}{2}\right) = 9(24) = 216$
32. $5\left(\frac{4.5 + (-1.5)}{2}\right) = 5(1.5) = 7.5$
33. Here $r = -4$ and $n = 7$ thus $S_7 = 1\left(\frac{1 - (-4)^7}{1 - (-4)}\right) = \left(\frac{16{,}385}{5}\right) = 3277$
34. Here $r = \frac{1}{2}$ and $n = 9$ thus $S_9 = 1\left(\frac{1 - (\frac{1}{2})^9}{1 - (\frac{1}{2})}\right) = \left(\frac{\frac{511}{512}}{\frac{1}{2}}\right) = \frac{511}{256}$
35. $(2(1) + 1) + (2(2) + 1) + (2(3) + 1) + (2(4) + 1) + (2(5) + 1) \Rightarrow 3 + 5 + 7 + 9 + 11$
36. $\frac{1}{1 + 1} + \frac{1}{2 + 1} + \frac{1}{3 + 1} + \frac{1}{4 + 1} \Rightarrow \frac{1}{2} + \frac{1}{3} + \frac{1}{4} + \frac{1}{5}$
37. $1^3 + 2^3 + 3^3 + 4^3 \Rightarrow 1 + 8 + 27 + 64$

38. $(1-2)+(1-3)+(1-4)+(1-5)+(1-6)+(1-7) \Rightarrow -1+(-2)+(-3)+(-4)+(-5)+(-6)$

39. $\sum_{k=1}^{20} k$

40. $\sum_{k=1}^{20} \frac{1}{k}$

41. $\sum_{k=1}^{9} \frac{k}{k+1}$

42. $\sum_{k=1}^{7} k^2$

Section 14.4

43. Row 4 of Pascal's triangle is 1, 3, 3, 1. $(x+4)^3 = x^3 + 3x^2(4) + 3x(4)^2 + (4)^3 \Rightarrow$

$(x+4)^3 = x^3 + 12x^2 + 48x + 64$

44. Row 5 of Pascal's triangle is 1, 4, 6, 4, 1. $(2x+1)^4 = (2x)^4 + 4(2x)^3(1) + 6(2x)^2(1)^2 + 4(2x)(1)^3 + (1)^4 \Rightarrow$

$(2x+1)^4 = 16x^4 + 32x^3 + 24x^2 + 8x + 1$

45. Row 6 of Pascal's triangle is 1, 5, 10, 10, 5, 1. $(x-y)^5 = x^5 - 5x^4y + 10x^3y^2 - 10x^2y^3 + 5xy^4 - y^5$

46. Row 7 of Pascal's triangle is 1, 6, 15, 20, 15, 6, 1.

$(a-1)^6 = a^6 - 6a^5(1) + 15a^4(1)^2 - 20a^3(1)^3 + 15a^2(1)^4 - 6a(1)^5 + (1)^6 \Rightarrow$

$(a-1)^6 = a^6 - 6a^5 + 15a^4 - 20a^3 + 15a^2 - 6a + 1$

47. $3! = 1 \cdot 2 \cdot 3 = 6$

48. $\frac{5!}{3!2!} = \frac{1 \cdot 2 \cdot 3 \cdot 4 \cdot 5}{(1 \cdot 2 \cdot 3)(1 \cdot 2)} = 2 \cdot 5 = 10$

49. ${}_6C_3 = \frac{6!}{3!3!} = \frac{1 \cdot 2 \cdot 3 \cdot 4 \cdot 5 \cdot 6}{(1 \cdot 2 \cdot 3)(1 \cdot 2 \cdot 3)} = 2 \cdot 5 \cdot 2 = 20$

50. ${}_4C_3 = \frac{4!}{3!1!} = \frac{1 \cdot 2 \cdot 3 \cdot 4}{(1 \cdot 2 \cdot 3)(1)} = 4$

51. $(m+2)^4 = ({}_4C_0)m^4 + ({}_4C_1)m^3(2) + ({}_4C_2)m^2(2)^2 + ({}_4C_3)m(2)^3 + ({}_4C_4)(2)^4 \Rightarrow$

$(m+2)^4 = m^4 + 8m^3 + 24m^2 + 32m + 16$

52. $(a+b)^5 = ({}_5C_0)a^5 + ({}_5C_1)a^4b + ({}_5C_2)a^3b^2 + ({}_5C_3)a^2b^3 + ({}_5C_4)ab^4 + ({}_5C_5)b^5 \Rightarrow$

$(a+b)^5 = a^5 + 5a^4b + 10a^3b^2 + 10a^2b^3 + 5ab^4 + b^5$

53. $(x-3y)^4 = ({}_4C_0)x^4 - ({}_4C_1)x^3(3y) + ({}_4C_2)x^2(3y)^2 - ({}_4C_3)x(3y)^3 + ({}_4C_4)(3y)^4 \Rightarrow$

$(x-3y)^4 = x^4 - 12x^3y + 54x^2y^2 - 108xy^3 + 81y^4$

54. $(3x-2)^3 = ({}_3C_0)(3x)^3 - ({}_3C_1)(3x)^2(2) + ({}_3C_2)(3x)(2)^2 - ({}_3C_3)(2)^3 \Rightarrow (3x-2)^3 = 27x^3 - 54x^2 + 36x - 8$

Applications

55. Symbolic: $a_n = 45{,}000(1.10)$^$(n - 1)$ for $n = 1, 2, 3, \ldots, 7$. This is a geometric sequence.

Numerical: See Figure 55a. Graphical: See Figure 55b.

n	1	2	3	4	5	6	7
a_n	45,000	49,500	54,450	59,895	65,885	72,473	79,720

Figure 55a

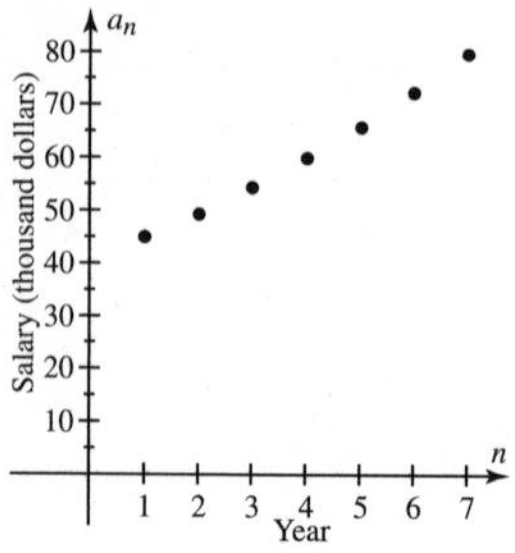

Figure 55b

56. Symbolic: $a_n = 45{,}000 + 5000(n - 1)$ for $n = 1, 2, 3, \ldots, 7$. This is an arithmetic sequence.

Numerical: See Figure 56a. Graphical: See Figure 56b

n	1	2	3	4	5	6	7
a_n	45,000	50,000	55,000	60,000	65,000	70,000	75,000

Figure 56a

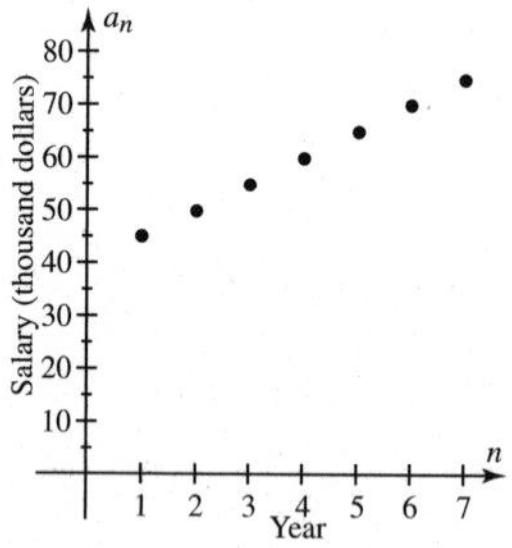

Figure 56b

57. Symbolic: $a_n = 49n$ for $n = 1, 2, 3, \ldots, 7$

Graphical: See Figure 57a. Numerical: See Figure 57b.

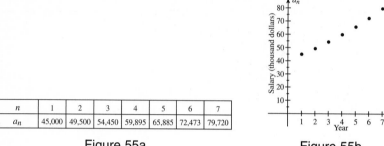

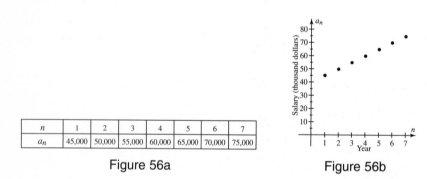

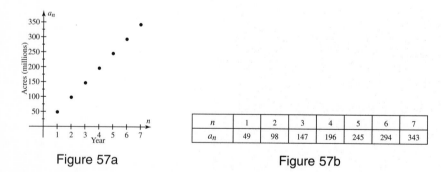

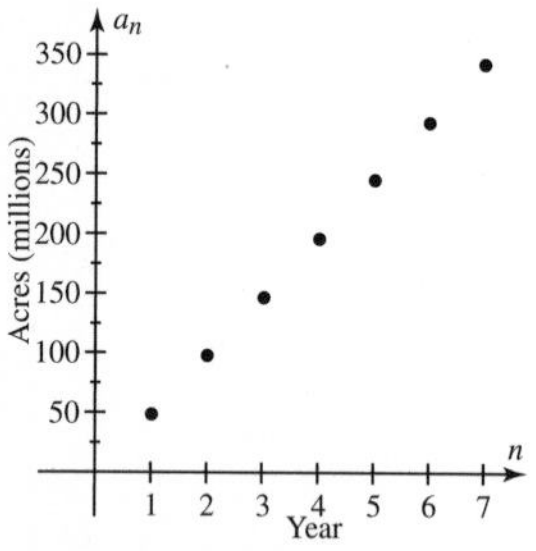

Figure 57a

n	1	2	3	4	5	6	7
a_n	49	98	147	196	245	294	343

Figure 57b

58. (a) $a_n = 1087(1.025)^{n-1}$

(b) The sequence is geometric. The common ratio is 1.025.

(c) $a_5 = 1087(1.025)^{5-1} \approx 1200$; The average mortgage payment in 2000 was about \$1200.

(d) See Figure 58.

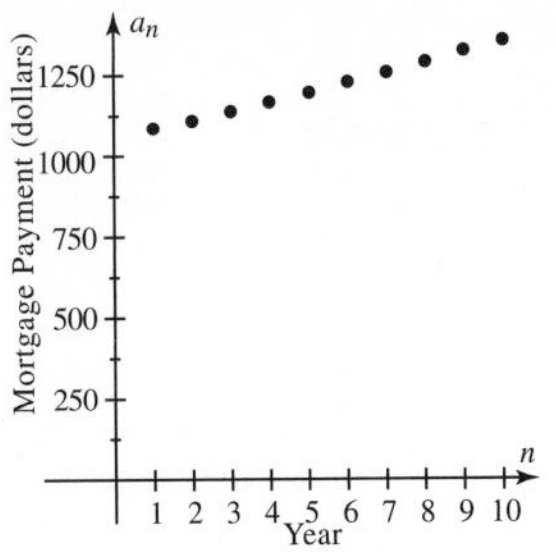

Figure 58

n	1	2	3	4	5	6	7
a_n	0	2	6	12	20	30	42

Figure 3

Chapter 14 Test

1. $f(1) = \dfrac{1^2}{1+1} = \dfrac{1}{2}, f(2) = \dfrac{2^2}{2+1} = \dfrac{4}{3}, f(3) = \dfrac{3^2}{3+1} = \dfrac{9}{4}, f(4) = \dfrac{4^2}{4+1} = \dfrac{16}{5} \Rightarrow \dfrac{1}{2}, \dfrac{4}{3}, \dfrac{9}{4}, \dfrac{16}{5}$

2. The points shown are (1, –3), (2, 2), (3, 1), (4, –2) and (5, 3). The sequence is –3, 2, 1, –2, 3.

3. See Figure 3.

4. Row 5 of Pascal's triangle is 1, 4, 6, 4, 1. $(2x-1)^4 = (2x)^4 - 4(2x)^3(1) + 6(2x)^2(1)^2 - 4(2x)(1)^3 + (1)^4 \Rightarrow$

   $(2x-1)^4 = 16x^4 - 32x^3 + 24x^2 - 8x + 1$

5. The sequence is arithmetic. The common difference is –3.

6. The sequence is geometric. The common ratio is –2.

7. $a_n = 2 + (n-1)(-3) \Rightarrow a_n = 2 - 3n + 3 \Rightarrow a_n = -3n + 5$

8. Note: $2 \cdot r^2 = 4.5 \Rightarrow r^2 = \dfrac{4.5}{2} \Rightarrow r = 1.5$, thus $a_n = 2(1.5)^{n-1}$

9. Yes, the common ratio is 2.5.

10. No, there is no common ratio.

11. $9\left(\dfrac{-1+23}{2}\right) = 9(11) = 99$

12. Here $r = -\dfrac{2}{3}$ and $n = 7$ thus $S_9 = 1\left(\dfrac{1-(-\frac{2}{3})^7}{1-(-\frac{2}{3})}\right) = \left(\dfrac{\frac{2315}{2187}}{\frac{5}{3}}\right) = \dfrac{463}{729}$

13. $3(2) + 3(3) + 3(4) + 3(5) + 3(6) + 3(7) \Rightarrow 6 + 9 + 12 + 15 + 18 + 21$

14. $\sum_{k=1}^{60} k^3$

15. $\dfrac{7!}{4!3!} = \dfrac{1 \cdot 2 \cdot 3 \cdot 4 \cdot 5 \cdot 6 \cdot 7}{(1 \cdot 2 \cdot 3 \cdot 4)(1 \cdot 2 \cdot 3)} = 5 \cdot 7 = 35$

16. ${}_5C_3 = \dfrac{5!}{3!2!} = \dfrac{1 \cdot 2 \cdot 3 \cdot 4 \cdot 5}{(1 \cdot 2 \cdot 3)(1 \cdot 2)} = 2 \cdot 5 = 10$

17. This is an arithmetic series with $a_1 = 50$ and $d = 7$, The total number of seats is

    $S_{45} = \dfrac{45}{2}(2(50) + (45-1)(7)) = 22.5(408) = 9180$ seats.

18. Symbolic: $a_n = 159{,}700(1.04)^\wedge(n - 1)$ for $n = 1, 2, 3, \ldots, 7$. This is a geometric sequence.

Numerical: See Figure 18a. Graphical: See Figure 18b.

n	1	2	3	4	5	6	7
a_n	159,700	166,088	172,732	179,641	186,826	194,299	202,071

Figure 18a

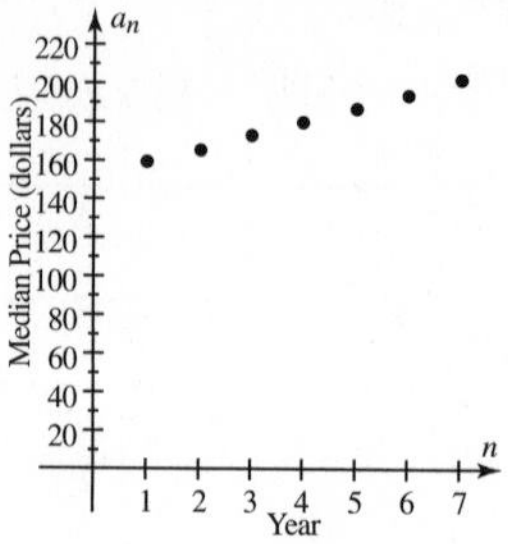

Figure 18b

19. (a) $a_n = 2000(2)^{n-1}$

(b) The sequence is geometric. The common ratio is 2.

(c) $a_6 = 2000(2)^{6-1} \approx 64{,}000$; After 30 days, there are 64,000 worms.

(d) See Figure 19.

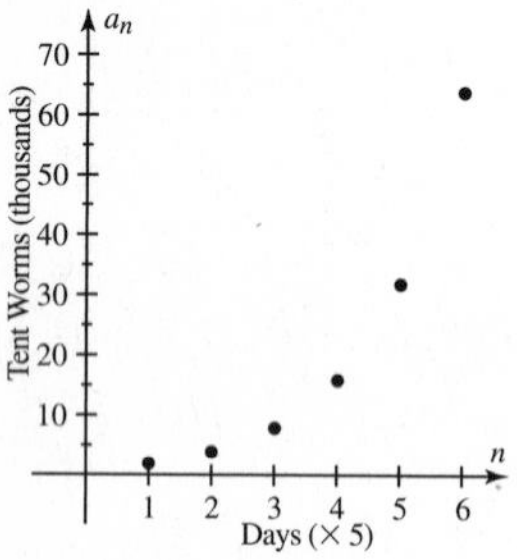

Figure 19

Chapter 14 Extended and Discovery Exercises

1. Each term of the sequence is obtained by adding the two previous terms. 1, 1, 2, 3, 5, 8, 13, 21, 34, 55, 89, 144

2. (a) Table $u(n) = 2.85u(n - 1) - 0.19(u(n - 1))^2$ with TblStart = 1 and ΔTbl = 1. See Figure 2a.

Note: be sure to set nMin = 1 and $u(n\text{Min}) = \{1\}$.

(b) Graph $u(n) = 2.85u(n - 1) - 0.19(u(n - 1))^2$ in [0, 22, 2] by [0, 11, 1]. See Figure 2b.

Note: be sure to set nMin = 1 and nMax = 20 in the WINDOW settings.

The moth population increases and then oscillates until it settles to a constant number (about 9.737 thousand).

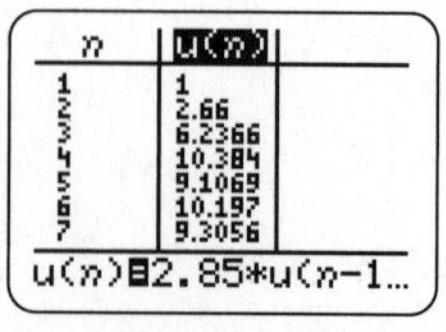

Figure 2a

[0, 22, 2] by [0, 11, 1]

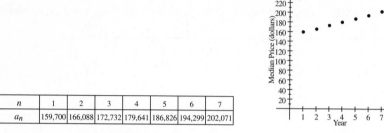

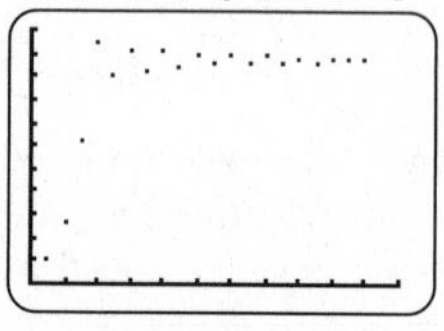

Figure 2b

3. (a) $a_4 = 0.3(2)^{4-2} + 0.4 = 0.3(2)^2 + 4 = 1.6$

The average distance between Mars and the sun is 1.6 units or about 148.8 million miles.

(b) The values are 0.4, 0.7, 1, 1.6, 2.8, 5.2, 10, 19.6, 38.8, 77.2.

The values fit very well. The relationship was proposed before the discovery of Uranus, Neptune and Pluto.

(c) If we assume that 38.8 corresponds to Pluto, then the next planet should be located at 77.2 units.

4. (a) $\pi \approx \left[90\left(\frac{1}{1^4} + \frac{1}{2^4} + \frac{1}{3^4} + \frac{1}{4^4}\right)\right]^{1/4} \approx 3.138997889$

(b) $\pi \approx 3.141590776$; This is correct to 5 decimal places.

5. (a) $S = \frac{2}{1 - (-\frac{1}{2})} = \frac{2}{\frac{3}{2}} = \frac{4}{3}$

(b) $S = \frac{1}{1 - (\frac{1}{3})} = \frac{1}{\frac{2}{3}} = \frac{3}{2}$

(c) $S = \frac{0.1}{1 - (0.1)} = \frac{0.1}{0.9} = \frac{1}{9} = 0.\overline{1}$

(d) $S = \frac{0.12}{1 - (0.01)} = \frac{0.12}{0.99} = \frac{4}{33} = 0.\overline{12}$

Chapters 1 - 14 Cumulative Review Exercises

1. The multiplication on the right side of the equation is distributed over the addition to obtain the left side of the equation.. This is a distributive property.

2. $3x - 7 = x + 3$; $3x - 7 = x + 3 \Rightarrow 2x = 10 \Rightarrow x = 5$

3. $\frac{2}{5}(x - 4) = -12 \Rightarrow x - 4 = -12\left(\frac{5}{2}\right) \Rightarrow x - 4 = -30 \Rightarrow x = -26$

4. $\frac{2}{5}z + \frac{1}{4}z > 2 - (z - 1) \Rightarrow \frac{13}{20}z > 3 - z \Rightarrow \frac{33}{20}z > 3 \Rightarrow z > 3\left(\frac{20}{33}\right) \Rightarrow z > \frac{20}{11}$

The interval is $\left(\frac{20}{11}, \infty\right)$.

5. First divide each side of $-3|t - 5| \leq -18$ by -3 to obtain $|t - 5| \geq 6$.

The solutions to $|t - 5| \geq 6$ satisfy $t \leq c$ or $t \geq d$ where c and d are the solutions to $|t - 5| = 6$.

$|t - 5| = 6$ is equivalent to $t - 5 = -6 \Rightarrow t = -1$ and $t - 5 = 6 \Rightarrow t = 11$.

The interval is $(-\infty, -1] \cup [11, \infty)$.

6. $\left|4 + \frac{2}{3}x\right| = 6 \Rightarrow 4 + \frac{2}{3}x = -6 \Rightarrow \frac{2}{3}x = -10 \Rightarrow x = -15$ or $4 + \frac{2}{3}x = 6 \Rightarrow \frac{2}{3}x = 2 \Rightarrow x = 3$

7. Begin by multiplying through by 4 to clear fractions.

$\frac{1}{4}t - (2t + 5) + 6 = \frac{t + 3}{4} \Rightarrow t - 4(2t + 5) + 4(6) = t + 3 \Rightarrow -7t + 4 = t + 3 \Rightarrow -8t = -1 \Rightarrow t = \frac{1}{8}$

8. $-3 \leq \frac{2}{3}x + 5 < 11 \Rightarrow -8 \leq \frac{2}{3}x < 6 \Rightarrow -12 \leq x < 9$. The interval is $[-12, 9)$.

9. A horizontal line has an equation of the form $y = k$ where k is the y-coordinate of a point on the line.

Thus, the equation of a horizontal line through the point (2, 3) is $y = 3$.

10. The equation is in the form $y = mx + b$ with $m = -3$ and $b = 5$. The slope is -3 and the y-intercept is 5.

11. Because the line is perpendicular to $y = -\frac{2}{3}x - 4$, the slope is the negative reciprocal of $-\frac{2}{3}$, or $\frac{3}{2}$.

A line passing through the point (1, 4) with slope $\frac{3}{2}$ has point-slope equation $y = \frac{3}{2}(x - 1) + 4$.

This equation in slope-intercept form is $y = \frac{3}{2}x + \frac{5}{2}$.

12. Because the line is parallel to $y = 2x - 7$, the slope is 2.

A line passing through the point (5, 2) with slope 2 has point-slope equation $y = 2(x - 5) + 2$.

This equation in slope-intercept form is $y = 2x - 8$.

13. Using the points $(1, -1)$ and $(0, 1)$, $m = \frac{1 - (-1)}{0 - 1} = \frac{2}{-1} = -2$. The point (0, 1) indicates that the y-intercept is $b = 1$.

The formula is $f(x) = -2x + 1$.

14. By substitution, $3(3) + (-2) = 7$ and $-2(3) - 3(-2) = 0$. However, $3(-1) + (3) \neq 7$. The solution is $(3, -2)$.

15. Multiplying the first equation by 2 and adding the two equations will eliminate the variable x.

$$\begin{array}{r} 2x - 4y = 2 \\ -2x + 7y = 4 \\ \hline 3y = 6 \end{array}$$

Thus, $y = 2$. And so $x - 2(2) = 1 \Rightarrow x = 5$. The solution is (5, 2).

16. See Figure 16.

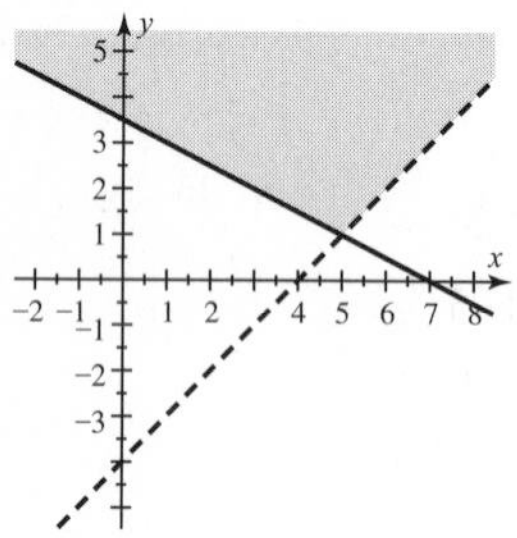

Figure 16

17. $2x^3(4x^4 - 3x^3 + 5) = 2x^3 \cdot 4x^4 - 2x^3 \cdot 3x^3 + 2x^3 \cdot 5 = 8x^7 - 6x^6 + 10x^3$

18. $(2z - 7)(3z + 4) = 2z \cdot 3z + 2z \cdot 4 - 7 \cdot 3z - 7 \cdot 4 = 6z^2 + 8z - 21z - 28 = 6z^2 - 13z - 28$

19. $\frac{x^{-2}y^3}{(3xy^{-2})^3} = \frac{x^{-2}y^3}{3^3x^3y^{-6}} = \frac{1}{27}x^{-2-3}y^{3-(-6)} = \frac{1}{27}x^{-5}y^9 = \frac{y^9}{27x^5}$

20. $\left(\frac{3b}{6a^2}\right)^{-4} = \left(\frac{6a^2}{3b}\right)^4 = \left(\frac{2a^2}{b}\right)^4 = \frac{(2a^2)^4}{b^4} = \frac{2^4(a^2)^4}{b^4} = \frac{16a^8}{b^4}$

21. $\left(\frac{1}{z^2}\right)^{-5} = \left(\frac{z^2}{1}\right)^5 = (z^2)^5 = z^{10}$

22. $\frac{8x^{-3}y^2}{4x^3y^{-1}} = \frac{8}{4}x^{-3-3}y^{2-(-1)} = 2x^{-6}y^3 = \frac{2y^3}{x^6}$

23. $4x^2 - 9y^2 = (2x)^2 - (3y)^2 = (2x - 3y)(2x + 3y)$

24. $2a^3 - a^2 + 8a - 4 = a^2(2a - 1) + 4(2a - 1) = (a^2 + 4)(2a - 1)$

25. $4x^2 - x - 3 = 0 \Rightarrow (4x + 3)(x - 1) = 0 \Rightarrow 4x + 3 = 0$ or $x - 1 = 0 \Rightarrow x = -\frac{3}{4}$ or 1

26. $x^4 - 10x^3 = -24x^2 \Rightarrow x^4 - 10x^3 + 24x^2 = 0 \Rightarrow x^2(x^2 - 10x + 24) = 0 \Rightarrow x^2(x - 4)(x - 6) = 0 \Rightarrow$

$x^2 = 0$ or $x - 4 = 0$ or $x - 6 = 0 \Rightarrow x = 0, 4, 6$

27. $\dfrac{x^2 - 7x + 10}{x^2 - 25} \cdot \dfrac{x + 5}{x + 1} = \dfrac{(x - 5)(x - 2)}{(x - 5)(x + 5)} \cdot \dfrac{x + 5}{x + 1} = \dfrac{(x - 5)(x + 5)(x - 2)}{(x - 5)(x + 5)(x + 1)} = \dfrac{x - 2}{x + 1}$

28. $\dfrac{x^2 + 7x + 12}{x^2 - 9} \div \dfrac{x^2 - 5x + 6}{(x - 3)^2} = \dfrac{(x + 4)(x + 3)}{(x - 3)(x + 3)} \cdot \dfrac{(x - 3)(x - 3)}{(x - 2)(x - 3)} = \dfrac{x + 4}{x - 2}$

29. Multiply each term by the LCD, $(x - 5)(x + 5)$.

$\dfrac{2}{x + 5} \cdot (x - 5)(x + 5) = \dfrac{-3}{x^2 - 25} \cdot (x - 5)(x + 5) + \dfrac{1}{x - 5} \cdot (x - 5)(x + 5) \Rightarrow$

$2(x - 5) = -3 + 1(x + 5) \Rightarrow 2x - 10 = x + 2 \Rightarrow x = 12$

30. Multiply each term by the LCD, $(y - 2)(x - 1)$.

$\dfrac{2y}{y^2 - 3y + 2} \cdot (y - 2)(y - 1) = \dfrac{1}{y - 2} \cdot (y - 2)(y - 1) + 2 \cdot (y - 2)(y + 1) \Rightarrow$

$2y = 1(y - 1) + 2(y^2 - 3y + 2) \Rightarrow 2y^2 - 7y + 3 = 0 \Rightarrow (2y - 1)(y - 3) = 0 \Rightarrow y = \dfrac{1}{2}$ or 3

31. $R = \dfrac{3C - 2W}{5} \Rightarrow 5R = 3C - 2W \Rightarrow 2W = 3C - 5R \Rightarrow W = \dfrac{3C - 5R}{2}$

32. Multiply the numerator and the denominator by the LCD, x^2.

$$\dfrac{\dfrac{1}{x^2} + \dfrac{2}{x}}{\dfrac{1}{x^2} - \dfrac{4}{x}} \cdot \dfrac{x^2}{x^2} = \dfrac{\dfrac{1}{x^2} \cdot x^2 + \dfrac{2}{x} \cdot x^2}{\dfrac{1}{x^2} \cdot x^2 - \dfrac{4}{x} \cdot x^2} = \dfrac{1 + 2x}{1 - 4x}$$

33. The domain is the set of x-coordinates. The range is the set of y-coordinates. $D = \{-6, -2, 0, 2\}$, $R = \{0, 1, 3, 5\}$

34. The denominator cannot equal 0. That is, $x - 8 \neq 0 \Rightarrow x \neq 8$. The domain is $\{x \mid x \neq 8\}$.

35. $$\left[\begin{array}{ccc|c} 1 & 1 & 1 & 5 \\ -2 & -1 & 1 & -10 \\ 1 & 2 & 8 & 1 \end{array}\right] \begin{array}{l} \\ R_2 + 2R_1 \rightarrow \\ R_3 - R_1 \rightarrow \end{array} \left[\begin{array}{ccc|c} 1 & 1 & 1 & 5 \\ 0 & 1 & 3 & 0 \\ 0 & 1 & 7 & -4 \end{array}\right] \begin{array}{l} R_1 - R_2 \rightarrow \\ \\ R_3 - R_2 \rightarrow \end{array} \left[\begin{array}{ccc|c} 1 & 0 & -2 & 5 \\ 0 & 1 & 3 & 0 \\ 0 & 0 & 4 & -4 \end{array}\right]$$

$$\begin{array}{l} \\ \\ (1/4)R_3 \rightarrow \end{array} \left[\begin{array}{ccc|c} 1 & 0 & -2 & 5 \\ 0 & 1 & 3 & 0 \\ 0 & 0 & 1 & -1 \end{array}\right] \begin{array}{l} R_1 + 2R_3 \rightarrow \\ R_2 - 3R_3 \rightarrow \\ \\ \end{array} \left[\begin{array}{ccc|c} 1 & 0 & 0 & 3 \\ 0 & 1 & 0 & 3 \\ 0 & 0 & 1 & -1 \end{array}\right]$$

The solution is $(3, 3, -1)$.

36. $\det A = 4(2) - 3(-3) = 8 + 9 = 17$

37. $\sqrt[3]{x^4y^4} - 2\sqrt[3]{xy} = \sqrt[3]{x^3y^3 \cdot xy} - 2\sqrt[3]{xy} = xy\sqrt[3]{xy} - 2\sqrt[3]{xy} = (xy - 2)\sqrt[3]{xy}$

38. $(4 + \sqrt{2})(4 - \sqrt{2}) = 4^2 - (\sqrt{2})^2 = 16 - 2 = 14$

39. $8(x - 3)^2 = 200 \Rightarrow (x - 3)^2 = 25 \Rightarrow x - 3 = \pm\sqrt{25} \Rightarrow x = 3 \pm 5 \Rightarrow x = -2$ or 8

40. $3\sqrt{2x + 6} = 6x \Rightarrow \sqrt{2x + 6} = 2x \Rightarrow 2x + 6 = 4x^2 \Rightarrow 4x^2 - 2x - 6 = 0 \Rightarrow 2x^2 - x - 3 = 0 \Rightarrow$

$(2x - 3)(x + 1) = 0 \Rightarrow 2x - 3 = 0$ or $x + 1 = 0 \Rightarrow x = \dfrac{3}{2}$ or -1. The answer -1 is an extraneous solution.

The only solution is $\dfrac{3}{2}$.

41. $(-3 + i)(-4 - 2i) = -3(-4) + (-3)(-2i) + i(-4) + i(-2i) = 12 + 6i - 4i - 2i^2 = 14 + 2i$

42. $\dfrac{2 - 6i}{1 + 2i} = \dfrac{2 - 6i}{1 + 2i} \cdot \dfrac{1 - 2i}{1 - 2i} = \dfrac{2 - 4i - 6i + 12i^2}{1 - 4i^2} = \dfrac{2 - 10i - 12}{1 + 4} = \dfrac{-10 - 10i}{5} = -2 - 2i$

43. The minimum y-value located on the graph is found at the vertex.

The x-coordinate of the vertex is $x = -\frac{b}{2a} = -\frac{8}{2(3)} = -\frac{4}{3}$. The y-coordinate of the vertex is

$f\left(-\frac{4}{3}\right) = 3\left(-\frac{4}{3}\right)^2 + 8\left(-\frac{4}{3}\right) + 5 = -\frac{1}{3}$. The minimum y-value located on the graph is $-\frac{1}{3}$.

44. $y = 2x^2 + 8x + 17 \Rightarrow y = 2(x^2 + 4x) + 17 \Rightarrow y = 2(x^2 + 4x + 4) + 17 - 8 \Rightarrow y = 2(x + 2)^2 + 9$

The vertex is $(-2, 9)$.

45. Using the quadratic formula, $x = \frac{4 \pm \sqrt{(-4)^2 - 4(1)(13)}}{2(1)} = \frac{4 \pm \sqrt{-36}}{2} = \frac{4 \pm 6i}{2} = 2 \pm 3i$.

46. $z^2 - 4z = 32 \Rightarrow z^2 - 4z - 32 = 0 \Rightarrow (z + 4)(z - 8) = 0 \Rightarrow z + 4 = 0$ or $z - 8 = 0 \Rightarrow z = -4, 8$

47. (a) The graph crosses the x-axis at -3 and 1. The solutions are -3, 1.

(b) Because the graph opens upward, $a > 0$.

(c) Because there are two real solutions to the equation, the discriminant is positive.

48. Solving for equality using the quadratic formula gives $x = \frac{-2 \pm \sqrt{(2)^2 - 4(1)(3)}}{2(1)} = \frac{-2 \pm \sqrt{-8}}{2}$.

Since there are no real solutions and the parabola opens upward, the parabola is above the x-axis for all values of x. The solution is $(-\infty, \infty)$.

49. (a) Because $g(-2) = 3(-2) - 2 = -8$ and $f(-8) = (-8)^2 + 1 = 65$, $(f \circ g)(-2) = f(g(-2)) = f(-8) = 65$

(b) $(g \circ f)(x) = g(f(x)) = g(x^2 + 1) = 3(x^2 + 1) - 2 = 3x^2 + 1$

50. First write the equation as $y = \frac{3x + 1}{2}$. Then interchange the x and y and solve for y.

$x = \frac{3y + 1}{2} \Rightarrow 2x = 3y + 1 \Rightarrow 2x - 1 = 3y \Rightarrow y = \frac{2x - 1}{3} \Rightarrow f^{-1}(x) = \frac{2x - 1}{3}$

51. $\ln (x^3\sqrt{y}) = \ln (x^3y^{1/2}) = \ln x^3 + \ln y^{1/2} = 3\ln x + \frac{1}{2}\ln y$

52. $2\log x - \log 4xy = \log x^2 - \log 4xy = \log \frac{x^2}{4xy} = \log \frac{x}{4y}$

53. $8\log x + 3 = 17 \Rightarrow 8\log x = 14 \Rightarrow \log x = \frac{14}{8} \Rightarrow 10^{\log x} = 10^{7/4} \Rightarrow x = 10^{7/4} \approx 56.23$

54. $4^{2x} = 5 \Rightarrow \log 4^{2x} = \log 5 \Rightarrow 2x\log 4 = \log 5 \Rightarrow 2x = \frac{\log 5}{\log 4} \Rightarrow x = \frac{\log 5}{2\log 4} \approx 0.58$

55. The graph is shown in Figure 55. The vertex is (1, 3) and the axis of symmetry is $y = 3$.

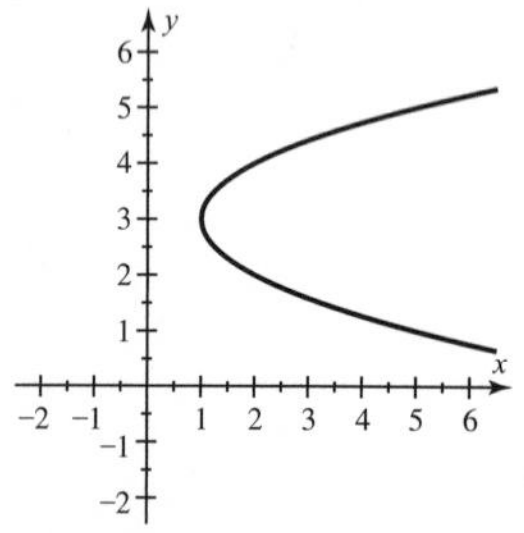

Figure 55

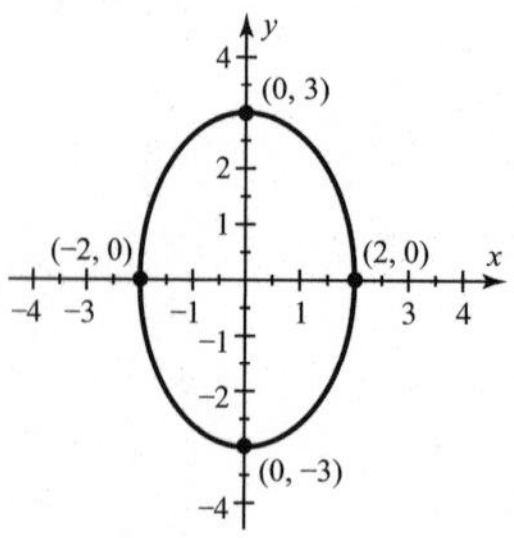

Figure 57

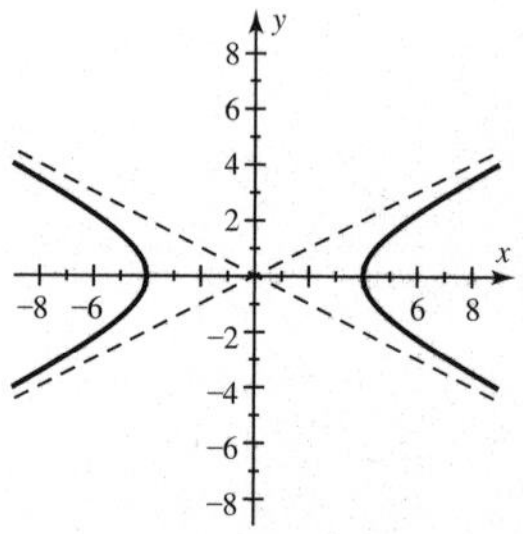

Figure 58

56. $x^2 - 6x + y^2 + 2y = -6 \Rightarrow x^2 - 6x + 9 + y^2 + 2y + 1 = -6 + 9 + 1 \Rightarrow (x - 3)^2 + (y + 1)^2 = 4$

The center is $(3, -1)$ and the radius is 2.

57. See Figure 57.

58. See Figure 58.

59. Vertical transverse axis with vertices $(0, \pm 2)$ and asymptotes $y = \pm \frac{1}{2}x \Rightarrow \frac{y^2}{4} - \frac{x^2}{16} = 1$

60. Horizontal major axis with vertices $(\pm 4, 0)$ and minor axis endpoints $(0, \pm 2) \Rightarrow \frac{x^2}{16} + \frac{y^2}{4} = 1$

61. Since the first equation is solved for y, substitute it in the second equation and solve for x.

$x^2 + 2(x^2 + 1) = 5 \Rightarrow 3x^2 + 2 = 5 \Rightarrow 3x^2 = 3 \Rightarrow x^2 = 1 \Rightarrow x = \pm 1$

When $x = -1$, $y = (-1)^2 + 1 = 2$, and when $x = 1$, $y = (1)^2 + 1 = 2$. The solutions are $(-1, 2)$ and $(1, 2)$.

62. See Figure 62.

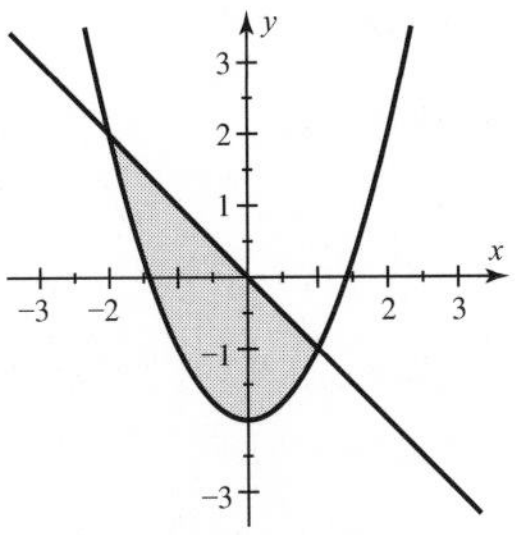

Figure 62

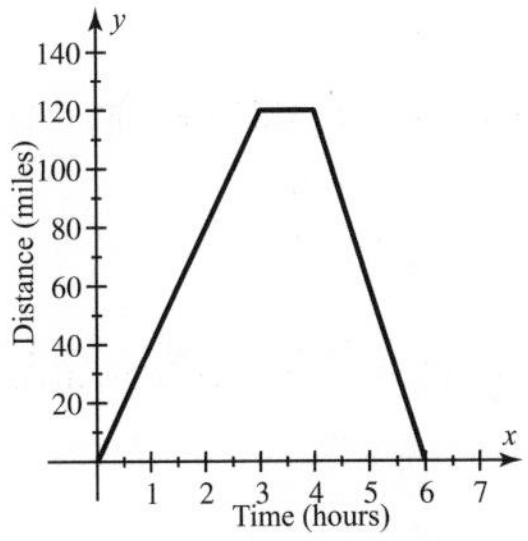

Figure 74

63. It is arithmetic because $f(n) = 5 - 2n$ defines a linear function. The common difference is -2.

64. It is geometric because $f(n) = 3(0.2)^n$ defines an exponential function. The common ratio is 0.2.

65. It is geometric because $f(n) = 7(4)^n$ defines an exponential function. The common ratio is 4.

66. It is arithmetic because $f(n) = 6n + 1$ defines a linear function. The common difference is 6.

67. Here $d = 5 - 2 = 3$, thus $a_n = 2 + (n - 1)(3) \Rightarrow a_n = 2 + 3n - 3 \Rightarrow a_n = 3n - 1$.

68. Here $r = \frac{12}{4} = 3$, thus $a_n = 4(3)^{n-1}$.

69. $9\left(\frac{3 + 35}{2}\right) = 9(19) = 171$

70. Here $r = -2$ and $n = 11$ thus $S_{11} = 1\left(\frac{1 - (-2)^{11}}{1 - (-2)}\right) = 1\left(\frac{2049}{3}\right) = 683$

71. $(2x + 3)^4 = ({}_4C_0)(2x)^4 + ({}_4C_1)(2x)^3(3) + ({}_4C_2)(2x)^2(3)^2 + ({}_4C_3)(2x)(3)^3 + ({}_4C_4)(3)^4 \Rightarrow$

$(2x + 3)^4 = 16x^4 + 96x^3 + 216x^2 + 216x + 81$

72. $(2a - 5b)^3 = ({}_3C_0)(2a)^3 - ({}_3C_1)(2a)^2(5b) + ({}_3C_2)(2a)(5b)^2 - ({}_3C_3)(5b)^3 \Rightarrow$

$(2a - 5b)^3 = 8a^3 - 60a^2b + 150ab^2 - 125b^3$

73. $r = \sqrt{\frac{14}{\pi}} \approx 2.11$ inches

74. See Figure 74.

75. (a) $f(x) = \frac{w}{2} + 0.4x \Rightarrow f(x) = \frac{170}{2} + 0.4x \Rightarrow f(x) = 0.4x + 85$

(b) $0.4(90) + \frac{w}{2} = 130 \Rightarrow 36 + \frac{w}{2} = 130 \Rightarrow \frac{w}{2} = 94 \Rightarrow w = 188$ pounds

76. Let x and y represent the speed of the airplane and the speed of the wind respectively. Then the system needed is $x - y = 360$ and $x + y = 400$. Adding the two equations will eliminate y.

$$\begin{array}{r} x - y = 360 \\ x + y = 400 \\ \hline 2x = 760 \end{array}$$

Thus, $x = 380$. And so $(380) + y = 400 \Rightarrow y = 20$.

The speed of the airplane is 380 mph and the speed of the wind is 20 mph.

77. Let x represent the width of the tent floor. Then $2x - 6$ represents the length.

$x(2x - 6) = 108 \Rightarrow 2x^2 - 6x - 108 = 0 \Rightarrow x^2 - 3x - 54 = 0 \Rightarrow (x + 6)(x - 9) = 0 \Rightarrow x = -6 \text{ or } 9$

Since the value $x = -6$ has no physical meaning, the solution is 9. The dimensions are 9 feet by 12 feet.

78. Let x represent the time required to weed the garden if they worked together. Then $\dfrac{x}{60} + \dfrac{x}{90} = 1$.

$180 \cdot \left(\dfrac{x}{60} + \dfrac{x}{90}\right) = 1 \cdot 180 \Rightarrow 3x + 2x = 480 \Rightarrow 5x = 180 \Rightarrow x = \dfrac{180}{5} = 36$ minutes

79. (a) $xy = 96$ and $3x - y = 12$

(b) Solve the second equation for y and substitute the result in the first equation. $3x - y = 12 \Rightarrow y = 3x - 12$

$x(3x - 12) = 96 \Rightarrow 3x^2 - 12x - 96 = 0 \Rightarrow x^2 - 4x - 32 = 0 \Rightarrow (x + 4)(x - 8) = 32 \Rightarrow$

$x = -4$ or $x = 8$. Since the numbers must be positive, the solution is 8. The numbers are 8 and 12.

80. Find the sum of the series $1 + 3 + 5 + \cdots + 23$. The sum is $12\left(\dfrac{1 + 23}{2}\right) = 12(12) = 144$ musicians.

Critical Thinking Solutions for Chapter 14

Section 14.1

- Each year there are r times as many female insects as there were the previous year.

Section 14.2

- No, since we can not determine the sign of r. Note that $r = \pm\sqrt[4]{\dfrac{a_5}{a_1}}$.